Tenth Anniversary Edition
Blue Book
of Gun Values™

Publisher's Note:

This book is the result of continual firearms research obtained by attending gun shows and communicating with gun dealers and collectors throughout the country. This book represents an analysis of prices for which collectible firearms have been actually selling during that period. Although every reasonable effort has been made to compile an accurate and reliable guide, gun prices may vary significantly depending upon such factors as the locality of the sale, the number of sales we were able to consider, and economic conditions. Accordingly, no representation can be made that the guns listed may be bought or sold at prices indicated, nor shall the dealer or publisher be responsible for any error made in compiling and recording such prices.

$17.95

Tenth Anniversary Edition

Blue Book
of Gun Values

By S. P. Fjestad

THE SOLID SILVER WINCHESTER
Model 1866 Rifle, Deluxe Engraved by L. D. Nimschke
and Fully Documented in the Book
L. D. NIMSCHKE FIREARMS ENGRAVER, by R. L. Wilson

The L. D. Nimschke engraved presentation *Solid Silver Winchester* on the front cover is a unique example of custom gunmaking at its most exquisite and exclusive level. Unquestionably Nimschke himself regarded this Rifle as the finest and most deluxe and significant of all his guns, in a career that spanned the second half of the 19th century. He was so proud of the masterpiece that he signed it *seven* times, including on the bottom of the frame: *L. D. NIMSCHKE ENG. N.Y.* The writer considers the Solid Silver Winchester as the most extraordinary firearm done by Nimschke in that half century of distinguished achievement.

Further, the Solid Silver Winchester — the only solid silver Winchester ever built — stands unquestionably as one of the premier guns in American history and gunmaking.

The ultimate in fine guns are those which feature a combination of history, craftsmanship and artistry, mechanical superiority and romance. The Solid Silver Winchester excels in all of these comprehensive themes.

The Rifle was custom made as a presentation from the President of Peru, Jose Balta, to the President of Bolivia, Mariano Melgarejo. The frame, forend, buttplate and carrier block are all of silver, and Nimschke's engraving record book records the job as completed in 1868 (pages 20 and 22 of the ledger, featuring several notes and prints pulled directly from parts of the rifle).

This silver is believed to have been supplied to Winchester from the rich minues of Peru.

This rifle will be featured in the writer's WINCHESTER ENGRAVING book, and in the forthcoming video production "Winchester Firearms Legends", sponsored by the Winchester Club of America and the William Benton Museum of Art, University of Connecticut.

President Jose Balta of Peru was born in 1816, and died in a military coup against his government, in 1872. He was builder of major projects, including railroads and bridges, and brought the distinguished Henry Meiggs to South America to build the world's highest railroad (Lima to La Orroya), climbing some 13,000 feet. Meiggs had built the port of San Francisco, and was responsible for construction of most of the railroads on the west coast of South America. At the time Balta ordered the Rifle, Peru was a very rich country, and one of the world's leading exporters of silver.

Balta's friend President Melgarejo was chief executive of the country which was then the world's largest exporter of silver. Melgarejo, an enthusiast of fine guns, was born in 1818, led a coup to take over Bolivia (1864) and was overthrown himself in 1870. He fled to Lima, where he was assassinated.

With the magic of the name Winchester, the distinction and artistry of the engraver Nimschke, the historical identification of the distinguished donor and recipient, the solid silver parts, the uniquely extensive signatures of the engraver, and more: The Solid Silver Winchester is worthy of the most extraordinary musuem or private collection — and is, indeed, an arms collection unto itself.

R. L. Wilson

Front and Back Cover photography by G. Allan Brown — Photographer

To order the 10th Anniversary edition of the *Blue Book of Gun Values*, clip out the coupon(s) and send in with your payment.

Toll-free ordering using your VISA or MASTERCARD is also possible. Call 1-800-877-GUNS (4867) and ask for *Blue Book of Gun Values*. Ordering is possible until March 1, 1990.

☐ YES! Please send me _____ copy(ies) of the 10th Edition of *Blue Book of Gun Values* for $17.95 per copy $2 shipping & handling ($19.95 total per book).

☐ Enclosed is my check or money order for $ _____ made out to *Blue Book of Gun Values*.

☐ Charge to my _____ VISA _____MASTERCARD
No. _____
Expiration Date _____
Signature _____
. . . or call toll-free 1-800-877-GUNS (4867) to place charge orders on VISA or MASTERCARD. MN residents call 612-853-1339.

Return to: *Blue Book Publications*
                    Attn: Subscription Dept.
                    One Appletree Square
                    Minneapolis, MN 55425

☐ YES! Please send me _____ copy(ies) of the 10th Edition of *Blue Book of Gun Values* for $17.95 per copy + $2 shipping & handling ($19.95 total per book).

☐ Enclosed is my check or money order for $ _____ made out to *Blue Book of Gun Values*.

☐ Charge to my _____ VISA _____MASTERCARD
No. _____
Expiration Date _____
Signature _____
. . . or call toll-free 1-800-877-GUNS (4867) to place charge orders on VISA or MASTERCARD. MN residents call 612-853-1339.

Return to: *Blue Book Publications*
                    Attn: Subscription Dept.
                    One Appletree Square
                    Minneapolis, MN 55425

Contents

How to Use This Book

The prices listed in this book are based on national average retail prices for both antique and modern firearms. Percentages of original condition (with corresponding prices) are listed between 10%-100% for antiques (unless rarity and age preclude upper conditions) and 60%-100% on modern firearms since condition below 60% is seldom encountered (or purchased). Consult our "Grading Criteria for Firearms" section if you have any questions as to which percentage your gun(s) represent. For your convenience the N.R.A. condition standards have been included making the conversion to percentages easier. This will especially be helpful with antiques.

For sake of simplicity the following organizational framework has been adopted throughout this publication.

1. Trademark manufacturer, brand name, or importer is listed in bold face type alphabetically, i.e.,

BROWNING, WINCHESTER, ANSCHUTZ.

2. Manufacturer information is listed directly beneath the trademark heading, i.e., MANUFACTURED IN NEW HAVEN, CT.

3. Next classification is type of gun, i.e., in alphabetical order.

PISTOLS, REVOLVERS, RIFLES, SHOTGUNS.

4. Model names appear flush left and are italics bold faced in chronological order grouped under either pistol, rifle, or shotgun subheadings, i.e.,

SINGLE ACTION ARMY, MODEL 1894, MODEL 101 O/U MAGNUM.

5. Barrel lengths, calibers, gauges and other descriptive data are further categorized adjacent to both models and sub-models in this type face. This is where most of the production data is given.

6. Variations within a model appear as sub-models and are indented and bold to differentiate them from model headings, i.e.,

PPK/S Durgarde, Mannlicher type full stock, Engraved Carbine.

7. Manufacturer and model notes appear in smaller type and should be read since they contain both important and critical, up-to-date information, i.e.,

This model was also available with No. 3 factory engraving on a very limited special order basis. Add 40% to the above values.

8. Price lines have been changed since the 6th Edition to allow the following - when the price line shown below is encountered,

Mfg.'s Sug. Retail   **$170**   **$150**   **$130**   **$115**   **$105**   **$95**   **$85**   **$80**

it automatically indicates the gun is currently manufactured and the manufacturers' retail price is shown left of the 100% column. Following are the 60-100% values. The 100% price is what you can typically expect to pay for that model in new condition with normal discounting (if any). The 98-60% remaining values represent actual selling prices in used condition - simply find the correct column and refer to the price listed.

A currently manufactured gun without a retail price published by the manufacturer/importer (becoming more common every year) will appear as follows:

No. Mfg.'s Retail   **$495 $450 $400 $350 $310 $280 $250**

Obviously, the 100% price is the national average price a consumer will pay for their gun in new condition. The same situation for a stainless steel or limited mfg./special edition firearm without retail pricing will appear as follows.

No Mfg.'s Retail   **$500 $400 $325 $265**

9. A price line with 7 values listed (represented below) indicates a

$325 $310 $290 $250 $225 $200 $175

discontinued, out of production model with values shown for 60-100% conditions. Obviously, no "Mfg.'s Sug. Retail" will appear in the left margin.

10. A 4 value price line indicates a current production gun, and

Mfg.'s Sug. Retail   **$226 $200 $175 $150**

prices are not shown in 90% or less conditon since the specimen (notice model description) is either stainless steel, a commemorative, or limited production. Because these types of firearms are almost never encountered in 90% or less condition, values for lower conditions are not listed.

To find a particular gun in this book, first look under the name of the trademark, manufacturer, importer, or brand name. Next find the correct subdivision (either pistols, revolvers, rifles, or shotguns, etc.). When applicable, antiques will appear before modern guns and are subdivided like modern weapons. Once you find the correct model or sub-model under its' respective subheading, determine the weapons' percentage of *original* condition and find the corresponding percentage column showing the price. Commemoratives will appear last under a manufacturers' heading.

Enlarged in the 10th Edition are sections on Modern Black Powder Guns, Air Rifles and Pistols, and Model Serialization breakdown of major trademarks. Four prices will be listed for both Black Powder and Air Gun Models. When using the Model Serialization section make sure your model is listed and find the serial number within the yearly range listings.

Back by popular demand is the Firearms Inventory Records section designed to give you an accurate, up-to-date record of your firearms.

Acknowledgements

It would be virtually impossible to fully acknowledge all those who have assisted me in the compilation of material for this publication. I cannot in all honesty recall many of those who have contacted me regarding information appearing in this text. So let me simply say thank you to all those who have contributed — you know who you are. To the following a special thank you.

Dr. Leonardo Antaris
(formerly Dr. Leonardo Awschalom)
Dr. David and Pat Avery
Richard Bauter of Browning
Donald Simmons of Circle Z
Ranch in Arizona
Dan Gibbons
Patrick McKune
Marty Huber of Colt's Firearms
Lt. Col. W. S. Brophy of
Marlin Firearms
Harry Akers
David Adams of Sigarms, Inc.
John Boyd of Quality Arms
Rick Kennerknecht
Steve Saul
David Noll
Dr. Kam Nassar
Keith Rolf
The late Bernard A. Lafferty
Tom Trolard
Martin Vittitow
John Woodward
Jack Stattel

Patrick Lucking
Bob Knight
A. O. Salvo
Robert Rayburn
Col. W. R. Betz of B.C.A.
Bruno Pardee of U.S.
Repeating Arms
Jack Heath of Remington Arms Co.
William Powell
Rudy Etchen
Larry DelGreco
Jim Austin of New England
Arms Co.
Richard Alexander of Interarms
Dan Sheil, Jr.
Renaud DeCrecy
Mims Reed
Peter Hoffman of
Walther Sportwaffenfabrik
LeRoy Merz
Robert White
Christine Seidel & Walter Hermann
from Mauser-Werke
Ace Collier, Jr.

and to

Carolyn Laughlin, whose patience, perseverance, and endurance were pushed beyond the gravitational pull of this planet before the computer was finally shut off. Thanks for the Herculean effort, and perhaps next year we will work only a couple of 18 hour days.

also to

Bonnie Waddell once again for dotting all my "i's" and crossing all the "t's." Thanks Bonnie for working my FAX machine overtime.

also to

Fran & Peter Mastel, our compadres on S. Padre, who provided encouragement when we needed it and helped make our low tides seem higher.

—Dedication—

The 10th Anniversary Edition of the *Blue Book of Gun Values* is dedicated to all those collectors, dealers, and other firearms enthusiasts who have chosen to share their information with me so that I, in turn, can share that knowledge with you. Where there is no knowledge you will find confusion, and where there is confusion you will find no sales in that marketplace. If this publication is reliable enough in the consumer's eyes so that gun enthusiasts will feel comfortable enough to purchase another firearm this year, I have done my job.

A Word About Pricing in this Book

Undoubtedly, the most often asked question I get during the course of a year is "Steve, how do you come up with the prices in this book?" No simple question — and no simple answer. Dealer contacts throughout the U.S., in addition to seasoned collectors provide invaluable knowledge in keeping me updated in any new price developments or trends. Some prices are "mixed" for an "average national price" due to regional price fluctuations (i.e., Kentucky flintlocks sell for more money in PA than they would in Miami).

With prices settling down since the record highs of 1980-81, more and more guns are falling in their individual price "slots", making dealer retail pricing very competitive. Also, with much more firearms information and manufacturer data available for the collector today than even 10 years ago, production rarity premiums are also more predictable than previously.

These and other factors have distilled firearms prices down to a no-fat profit stucture. Many dealers won't buy high 4-digit items like they used to at major gun shows, simply because they won't chance a big ticket, normally long turnover inventory item unless a sale has already been pre-arranged. Trading is firm in original mint condition major trademarks such as Browning, Colt's, Winchester, and others. I've talked to many collectors who feel now is the time to acquire some of those apparent "bargains" that are surfacing at gun shows currently. Whether these purchases today will keep up with the monetary appreciation afforded in the past remains to be seen - certainly a change in the inflation rate would go a long way in escalating firearms' prices.

It is important to note that prices listed for current production firearms include the manufactures suggested retail prices for 1989. They can be instantly recognized by the "Mfg. Sug. Retail" notation on the left margin of many price lines. With the advent of discount merchandising, almost all current production guns can be picked up at a sizeable discount. These discounts are reflected in the 100% column and indicate the discounted price you can typically expect to pay for a current production firearm in new condition. Because of this now common practice of "blowing out" big chunks of inventory at small profit levels, used guns in models currently produced are at or below typical dealer wholesale. Remember - all values shown represent actual retail selling prices - dealer offers when purchasing could be off 15% - 50% prices shown.

One last point regarding specific firearms pricing deserves special mention in this edition — *values for assault rifles.* Since pending federal and state legislation might drastically alter the supply of this yet-to-be-defined firearms configuration, prices could rise suddenly and dramatically. Several importers have indicated to me that their warehouses are empty and dealers are calling offering to buy remaining stock at virtually any price. If this classification will be legislated out of consumer sales, it would not surprise me to see these previous $350 - $500 guns skyrocket overnight, much like machine guns did once the BATF stopped new mfg. sales to qualified consumers. As usual, demand will control the price of the supply.

As much as I try to be more accurate every year, if you feel some price is out of line or I have omitted or misrepresented a particular model, by all means contact me and let's discuss it. Previous subscribers have been very kind in helping me with corrections of this nature in past editions. I hope your comments, observations, criticisms, and other ideas continue to come in. Most new suggestions get added to the next edition. Mistakes can happen, but they shouldn't happen twice. Direct technical and pricing correspondence to me at:

Blue Book of Gun Values
Research—Attn: S. P. Fjestad
One Appletree Square
Minneapolis, MN 55425
FAX No. 612-853-1GUN (1486)

Once again, please allow 2-4 weeks normally for a reply.

FOREWORD

As our loaded DC-10 from Lufthansa flight #430 struggles to clear the runway from Frankfurt, W. Germany after this most recent 1989 IWA Show (European firearms and sporting goods trade fair) held in Nuremburg, I am thinking that it seems only a few short years ago when the 1st edition of the *Blue Book of Gun Values* was published. I still remember staying up past 2 AM many evenings working on the 3rd edition, hand-writing the revisions/additions on many Wilson Jones 12 column notepads — hoping that the typesetter located in CA could read my handwriting. Today, looking back, it reminds me of a 15th century monk working overtime in a monastery copying documents by quill and ink on parchment.

As our plane climbs past 5,000 meters, I am once again re-affirmed in my conviction of American capitalism and those freedoms we enjoy as American citizens. After talking to most of the gun manufacturers in the world during the past 3 days, there is no question that the U.S. is the premier firearms marketplace internationally. And the reason is simple — our constitutional rights and inherant freedoms which remain therein.

This show's hot button was Assault Rifles and their recent change in status made by the our government regarding their importation status. Many citizens seem not to be concerned that this type of weapon way no longer be available to qualified buyers. After all, how many U.S. deer hunters leave for the woods each Nov. with their AK-47's and three 20-shot mag.s loaded with fresh 7.63 x 39mm ammo? Why should such a "non-sporting" arm be allowed in this "dangerous" military configuration where it seems to fall into the hands of the murderers routinely? It seems once again the weapon is more important to the serious crime than the individual who knowingly pulled the trigger.

Perhaps a study should be conducted by the Dept. of Transportation as to which type of vehicle is used most often by drunken drivers when killing other hapless drivers/pedestrians and make that model illegal to own (or import) in this country. After all, passenger vehicles kill far more Americans each year than firearms. I can't remember the last time the press blamed a Camaro or another car make for too much needless slaughter of innocent victims on our U.S. highways. Yet, in the firearms industry, the smoking gun is the culprit in manslaughter cases — not the defective individual who *chose* this intentional act of violence.

What worries me about this issue is what will be next on the list to get the axe. When will the Beretta Model 92F be re-classified as a military assault pistol and made unfit to own? My point is that once you have allowed these "peace crusaders" into the foyer of your house, sooner or later they will want your dining room, living room, bedrooms, attic, and basement. And although you will not remember having agreeing with them on the banning of one or two "non-sporting" weapons, you will be surprised when you go to the gun cabinet one day and find one remaining .177 cal. air rifle with which to do your sport shooting. I sometimes wonder what Thomas Jefferson, George Washington, or Andrew Jackson would say today if they could comment on some of the recent anti-gun legislation. Andy especially would not be pleased.

America has changed since those days, however. The urbanization of America each year is making the hunter/sportsman a little bit more of an endangered species. The manufacture of domestic firearms has slipped from 5.8 million in 1974 to 3 million in 1986. Attitudes in this country have shifted — having a PC computer in your den is now much more important than having a loaded

Nylon 66 rifle in the porch. Many boys are reaching the age of fifteen before they are allowed to own their first gun. Shooting sporting game has become much more expensive than it used to be and is certainly not as much in vogue. Hopefully, their will be enough youth who develop their shooting skills today and will use them in the future in order to carry our arms heritage far into the next century.

This year's 10th Anniversary edition was written on S. Padre Island, TX, typeset via modem transmission to Minneapolis, proofed after overnight delivery to Phoenix, AZ, corrected by FAX transmissions back to S. Padre, with final alterations being FAX'ed again back to Minneapolis. Unbelievably, the data in this 10th edition (over 5 million computer bytes) put on over 80,000 miles through telephone cables before finally being approved to go to the printer. Four short years ago, this high-tech arrangement would have been virtually impossible. I have never hesitated to implement every helpful state-of-the-art technical innovation in order to bring you, the subscriber, a more up-to-date and accurate reference work.

In closing, I would like to thank all of you once again for your support on the 10th and older editions of the *Blue Book of Gun Values*. This book has continually improved through the subscriber suggestions, corrections, and additions. I would encourage all of you to contact me if you feel there is something missing or not covered properly. This process has helped me more than any other single one thing in making this publication more accurate (even though I am behind on correspondence most of the time). Regardless, keep those cards and letters coming in. Our plane is making the final descent into O'Hare airport, and I must return my tray to it's upright position.

Steven P. Fjestad
Author — Blue Book of Gun Values

P.S. Don't forget to look at the new section in the book regarding Business listings with addresses and FAX numbers for all currently manufactured firearms. To my knowledge, no one has linked the various trademarks with with their respective manufacturer, importer, distributor, or service representative before. This section will save you time and money when trying to contact these companies.

P.S.S. I would like to thank Cold Type Setters (CTS) from Minneapolis for making these 5 million bytes of information an on-time reality in English and Viking Press of Eden Prairie, MN for making the "Webb" spin on time. Through it all, we overcame.

An Unique Concept!

The *Blue Book of Gun Values* is the only book that:

- Utilizes the professionals' grading system of percentage of original finish remaining. (Eliminates confusing descriptions such as "Good". "Excellent". "Fair".)

- Is thoroughly updated annually for up-to-date prices.

- Is based on actual selling prices. (These are the prices you can expect to pay — not artificial list prices or some "expert's" opinion.)

- Offers you personal consultation by mail on special questions you may have! (No book can cover everything.)

- Has been universally accepted by the firearms industry for reliable data including accurate pricing.

Have a question on an overlooked model or wish to consult with the *Blue Book of Gun Values*? One free written consultation is permitted involving a particular gun. Appraisals and/or additional research on 2 or more firearms will be charged at a $15.00 per gun basis. Please include a detailed description with all pertinent information about the gun(s) in question in the first letter. Good *quality* photos of the receiver, special markings, etc. would also be appreciated.

Interested in buying or selling a particular firearm(s)? Please phone or write the Blue Book of Gun Values for both availability and prices (buy and sell). All replies are treated strictly confidential.

Replies should be directed to:

Blue Book of Gun Values
Attn: Steven Fjestad - Firearms Division
One Appletree Square
Minneapolis, MN 55425
FAX NO. 612-853-1GUN (1486)

Call Toll Free 1-800-877-4867 (MN residents, please call 612-853-1339), ask for Steven P. Fjestad and if I'm not available, please leave a message. Remember, between November and March I am writing the new edition, so please have patience. I always seem to get behind during this time period.

A Word About
Blue Book Publications

On the day before Christmas Eve in 1988, the *Blue Book of Gun Values,* formerly a division of Investment Rarities, Inc. was sold to a consortium of investors — including myself. This new company is called Blue Book Publications, and while our address has remained the same, our new telephone numbers are: (612)-853-1339 for calls made within MN, 1-800-877-GUNS (4867) TOLL FREE if out-of-state, and FAX NO. (612)-853-1GUN (1867). Please refer and use these phone numbers in the future for ordering, FAXing, or any other service you might require from our new company. If I am not in or am busy, please leave a message (and have patience — I get over 5,000 phone calls annually).

Blue Book Publications will continue to published the Blue Book of Gun Values on an annual basis, maintaining the same level of quality as in previous editions. In the future, look for additional gun-related publications from Blue Book Publications — you can be assured that each new text will be uncompromising in quality and become the standard reference work on that particular subject matter. I would appreciate any new ideas you might have concerning the publication of new books.

To give you a better idea of our new company and its personnel, these photo's have been provided to give you a visual image of the voice on the phone.

Carolyn Laughlin (pictured at left) is the Blue Book Assistant Manager. Carolyn is responsible for typing each years manuscript revisions (the 10th edition required well over 600 hours of on-screen computer time). She also oversee's customer and distributor sales/service in addition to performing a multitude of other publications related activities. If Mr. Fjestad is not in or on the phone when you call, Carolyn is the person you should speak to.

Tom Stock (pictured center) is Blue Book Publication's controller. He is responsible for accounts receivable and payable, general ledger accounting, and helps in managerial decisions within the new company. Tom is not normally involved with day-to-day operations and unless you are a *Blue Book* vendor, it would be better to contact Doris, Carolyn, or Steve.

Patrick Lucking (not pictured) is the Black Powder and Airgun sections editor. Patrick revises data and prices on the Airgun and Black Powder sections annually (no small task anymore). All technical questions and Black Powder/Airgun correspondence should be directly to him per the *Blue Book* address. Patrick's goal is to someday get paid for his annual contributions.

Debra Kelly (pictured right) is responsible for the design, layout, and production of artwork and graphics involving Blue Book Publications advertizing and promotional literature. She is a seasoned veteran in the graphics field and unfortunately, specialized in 2-3 day turnarounds of Mr. Fjestad's usually somewhat great but always late ideas. You can thank Debra for the great graphics in Blue Book Publications artwork.

Doris Johnson (not pictured) is our part-time administrative assistant. Doris performs most of the day-to-day accounting procedures including individual and distributor deposits, traces lost shipments, and provides customer service in areas. Doris normally works Monday and Wednesday only and during these 2 days, she will be glad to assist you with any problems you are experiencing with shipment or payment.

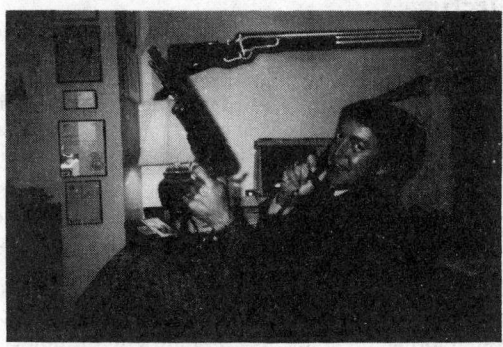

Steven Fjestad (pictured with Mr. Walker) is responsible for the text editing and overall production of each new edition. All firearms related questions and correspondence should be directed to him. Steven is usually rather busy maintaining his work load, so please have patience. Normally he is in the office between 8:30 AM-5 PM (CST) unless at a gun show or trade fair. He normally spends Jan. 1 through March 1 in a different location writing the next edition.

Introduction

How to Start Collecting

In every part of this country, there are firearms-collecting associations. You can benefit from membership/affiliation in such an association, since you can use it to meet other collectors and firearms experts who are an excellent source of information, help, guidance and invaluable education. In most major cities, there are regularly scheduled firearms shows where you can buy, sell or swap your weapons and gain insight into general prices and values. Also, at the larger national shows, you'll find many prominent and reputable dealers who usually have high-quality merchandise for sale.

I personally recommend that you attend at least one major weapons show each year. When you do, you'll be able to see everything from ultra-rare antiques to modern commemoratives. This will help you to determine where your interest lies. You can also make price comparisons. Shows are a place to meet collectors, investors and dealers from all over the nation. Once you have decided what you want to collect, we recommend you talk to everyone who could have any knowledge and provide you with information in this area. You must do the homework.

For your benefit, we've included a mini-directory of recommended reading material and reference works as well as trade publications that will further assist you in gathering the knowledge needed for your choosen area(s) of interest.

Starting Tips

My advice would be to pick out an area where knowledge or interest already exist. Expand this established base with additional knowledge. Buy the necessary books, magazines, and trade periodicals to make yourself informed as possible in the niche you've chosen. Most advanced collectors and dealers have expansive reference libraries for fast, fingertip accessibility. Don't worry about the price for reference material — one book can easily pay for itself in one gun trade. And the books themselves become investments as they go out of print and command increased prices. No one individual can know everything about every gun — reference works are a must.

Once you're "book trained" the next step is to start looking — not buying — at guns in the field you've chosen. Attend a few gun shows or visit dealers that have inventories of items you're looking for. *Don't* get side-tracked by other fascinating merchandise. Pay close attention to the coloration of blueing, crispness of metal markings (proof marks, barrel address, etc.), wood to metal fit, bore condition, and possible nonfactory alterations. In this business, the experience gained in running through your hands has no substitute. I have known people that would quote from memory every gauge, choke, barrel, stock variation available for the Model 12 Winchester, yet these same people can't spot a reblued gun. Knowing the correct factory blueing color, style of wood, and finish, production variation etc., does not come overnight. It takes experience and a well-trained eye. If in doubt about "original finish someone claims, consult a dealer or collector that does know the difference. Only after you've taken these steps are you ready to become a buyer. Anything less could result in a "long-term" investment.

Where and How to Buy and Sell Guns

This "Art" has changed drastically over the last 30 years. Dealer showrooms, gun shows, and local advertising were the only means of buying or selling guns for many years. Trading was more localized and regional price differences were more evident. Many fine weapons stayed in one locality for long periods of time. With the advent of the 5 second long distance telephone call and overnight express mail, the firearms marketplace now reaches coast to coast. International marketing is even possible where regulations permit. All this means increased merchandise exposure, more universal grading standards, and higher levels of competition in pricing firearms fairly.

Buying

It's been said that good guns are wherever you find them. Nothing could be truer. The following listing will give an idea of where to purchase collector guns —

A) Gun shows — these shows exist throughout the United States and are usually well-attended. With hundreds of showings being held yearly (check your gun shop or trade publications for dates), it is possible to take in two shows on a single weekend — locations permitting.

Their advantages include:

1. Physically inspecting potential purchases,

2. Comparing prices, against other similar items, at the same show,

3. Having a large selection from which to choose,

4. Providing unequaled opportunity to meet fellow collectors and other experts in the field to exchange information.

5. Displaying the broadest base of firearms, accessories, and memorabilia from which to develop new interests.

6. Haggle for better prices, especially for items still unsold late in the show.

7. Offer "trade-in" potential with prices established at the show — rather hard and lenghty to do by mail.

Disadvantages include:

1. A good chance of running into fakes, reblued items, and non-factory alternations or conversions. Higher prices over the last 5 years have resulted in many common models being "upgraded" to a model much rarer. Be careful on purchases where this type of activity might exist.

2. Most sales are final. Once the cash has been transformed, your inspection is over. A collector pays for his "mistakes" in this business. If a sale is contingent on a yet-to-come factory letter, part(s), or additional accessories make sure the seller includes them in his bill-of-sale. It's simply good business for both parties.

3. "Show Pressure" forcing you into decisions that have to be made in a few minutes — oftentimes with 2 other people simultaneously bargaining for the same gun.

4. Being side-tracked into other areas. Know what you want, what you want to pay for it, and don't impulse buy. Keep a level head, and stick to the areas you're familiar with. This is important with merchandise ranging from stuffed animal heads to Browning .50 calibers.

Remember — most good gun show "buys" occur during the gun shows opening hours — or the night previous to opening before the public is admitted. An apparent bargain found on Sunday afternoon sounds skeptical at best, although many dealers will "negotiate" a price very late in the show, depending on their cash flow and desire to haul a potential sale to yet another gun show. Get to the show at the opening, walk the aisles with orderly precision, avoiding back tracking, and when you find a specimen that meets *all* of your criteria *and* is on your shopping list. Buy it. Too many times I've walked back to a table ready to buy and an empty spot is all that remains. Truly good guns that are fairly priced sell fast because dealers are competing with collectors. One last item — don't interrupt an exhibitor engaged in selling (even if it's one you want). It's not in the gun circuit code of ethics. Be patient.

B Gun Shops —

Many modern gun shops have good selections of collector guns in stock. Take one gun at a time here — and make sure that gun is within your field of expertise. Sometimes dealers selling mostly new guns get items in on trade that they know very little about — including trade-ins that "aren't right". Be able to know the difference before you buy. Again, don't get sidetracked. While you are likely to get a fair deal at a gun shop — you may find an item in your field once every five years.

C) Auctions —

While not as major as gun shows or gun shops in the marketplace, auctions can be used to your advantage in buying. Large auction houses such as Christie's and Sotheby's deal in only extremely fine and rare specimens that carry big price tags. Know what you want and your monetary limit before conducting business at this level. Some auction guns are "dogs" with hidden defects that preclude their sale through reputable dealers.

Estate, household, and farm auctions can be used with some success if you know previously which guns will be sold. Frequently — no "gun" people will be in attendance and prices could be quite low. Make sure that condition is at par with your standards.

With all auctions, attend the preliminary exhibition and be sure you make a careful inspection of all guns you might bid on. Mail-order bids are sometimes an option to being at the auction. Before bids are submitted, know everything about what you're potentially purchasing.

D) Other Collectors —

Buying from other collectors is dependent on how comfortable you are with his knowledge, expertise, honesty, and previous dealings.

Serious collectors usually sell their finest guns last. Make sure the gun you're considering isn't a poor duplicate in the collection or one of his "mistakes".

Obviously, it is to a collectors advantage to sell to another collector and thereby avoid the "middleman" dealer markup. Find out if the guns were carefully chosen originally, part of an estate settlement, or other important past history. Also, big collections don't necessarily guarantee good collections. More than a few "collections" are gathered around poor quality, high quantity odds and ends.

E) Mail Order Dealer —

This area has really grown in the past 10 years. These dealers send out regular inventory listings to previous customers and much business is out-of-state.

It is to the dealers advantage to accurately grade his guns very carefully to avoid misrepresentation and eliminate customer fears in not being able to see the gun. Good mail-order dealers *always* give an inspection period. Returned guns don't make anyone happy so the dealer is always faced with selling as good a gun as possible for a competitive price. Anything less results in stagnating inventory levels.

Many of these dealers specialize in specific areas. Their specialization usually insures the buyer of good condition original guns made possible by the dealers thorough "screening" used before buying. Getting as many dealer inventory listings as possible will give you a chance to "shop" around and check prices. A dealers reputation is a big factor in this area. Deal with those you're comfortable with and will listen when you want to trade something in previously purchased.

F) Classified Ads —

Rarely anymore do good quality, collector guns show up under the "Guns for Sale" Ad in the local newspaper. The "steals" of the 60's and 70's are mostly gone. Still keep your eyes open and follow every lead. These wild goose chases can sometimes be very rewarding. An "advertised" WWII Luger for $485.00 is certainly worth buying if it turns out to be a Kreighoff. Be fast — don't hesitate when real "buys" do pop up.

G) Trade Periodicals —

Magazines such as *Shotgun News, Gun Report, The List* and others, contain thousands of private and dealer ads offering every type of firearm imaginable for sale. Some are good buys — others are out and out rip-offs. Know who you are buying from, and insist on an inspection period covering all purchases.

Selling

Certainly as many considerations confront the potential seller as the potential buyer. Different approaches must be used when selling a single gun, a few guns, or an extensive collection. Locality, modern or antique status, and proper grading all have to be studied. No standard format is applicable to every situation here.

Knowing the market and prices should be an advantage in selling. The collector is familiar with gun values, knows dealers that handle his type of guns, and has established contact with fellow collectors of similar merchandise. These potential buyers increase the liquidity base.

When selling more than one gun and similar items are involved, either the piecemeal or "sold only as a group" method should be determined first. Selling a collection intact is certainly cleaner than taking one-at-a-time. More money can be extracted selling individually — if you have the patience.

In 1981 when gold and silver were fluctuating large amounts daily, a woman called in and asked me "What's the spot price of Winchesters today?" After my initial laugh, I told her collector gun values have always been dictated by marketplace supply and demand. Just as a spot price for a Winchester will never appear in the *Wall Street Journal*, a fair market price tag on your 98% P.38 will not necessarily guarantee you instant liquidity. Lack of inflation has caused a drop in asking prices for many collector guns that are available in good supply.

When selling use the same general headings listed under buying as possibilities. Certainly an obvious place to sell a valuable gun is to the dealer who might have originally sold you the item. Since he considered it worthy of ownership previously, restocking the gun should be in his scope of interest. How much will you get? This will depend on length of ownership, any change of condition, that gun's increased market appeal (if any), and the dealers current inventory levels. Unless the funds generated in selling a gun are needed immediately, never be in a rush to sell a nice gun. Patience will reward you over panic. When that right person shows genuine interest, offer the gun professionally and stick close to your asking price — you'll probably get it.

Many major trade publications offer national exposure — and larger exposure generally means higher prices. It makes sense that 75,000 people reading *Shotgun News* will generate more interest than 300 tire-kickers at a hometown gun show. While results may take more time (3-6 weeks), the added dollars on the sale price usually justify the wait.

Trends to Be Aware of

Collecting firearms as a hobby originally started because of nostalgia over antique firearms and their place in history. Modern collectible firearms are today the fastest-growing area. If you spend time studying these modern guns, you will see there are many excellent choices to be made from Colts, Lugers, Mausers, Smith & Wessons and Winchesters. Much interest is also developing in .22-caliber pistols from antiques through modern variations. Another area showing increasing collector interest is high grade quality Damascus-barrelled shotguns.

Firearms Laws —

There are four legal classifications of firearms used by the Bureau of Alcohol, Tobacco, and Firearms of the Treasury Department.

1) Antique — Any firearm manufactured in or before 1898, and replicas that do not fire rimfire or center-fire cartridges readily available in commercial trade. Anyone can legally own an antique and no paperwork has to be completed during their purchase.

2) Modern — Firearms manufactured after 1898, excluding replica antiques, and with special regulations for class III fully automatic arms.

Any modern gun sold in the United States today must be registered if bought from a dealer. Private sales preclude this (check local and state laws).

A modern gun —

Can be shipped state to state by dealers to other dealers

May be shipped to an out-of-state dealer by a private individual

Must be registered upon sale by dealer

Is governed not only by the regulations of The Gun Control Act of 1968, but also by the appropriate local and state laws pertaining to the same

Cannot be shipped interstate to a private individual, only other licensed dealers

3) Curios and Relics — Certain specified modern firearms that can be sent interstate to licensed collectors. These include guns manufactured at least 50 years prior to the current date (not replicas thereof). Check current curio and relic listings of the BATF.

4) Class III Arms — Includes machine guns, silencers, short barreled shotguns, (under 18"), short barreled rifles, (under 16"), modern smoothbore handguns, and modern arms with a

rifled bore diameter greater than .5 inches.

The first three items may be legally owned, not withstanding federal regulations and local restrictions in a few areas. Class III items are illegal in some states. For further information, contact your local office of the BATF.

What to Collect — The Answers Depend on You

Firearms offer something for everyone. There are different-purpose firearms with many designs. Some have historical value and are quite fascinating. History has often been changed because some faction or culture had superior firearms to influence or force its culture and politics on another.

To a certain extent, there is no right or wrong area in which to collect. Pick the category you prefer and then do some studying before you make a choice and begin buying. Be sure you're comfortable with the area you ultimately decide to go with.

I would suggest that you keep your collection orderly and coherent. Collect one maker or one model in all its variations (if possible). You could also base a collection on type, such as Kentucky dueling pistols or Military automatic handguns. Collections have been based on firearms of one caliber, such as the 9mm Parabellum or .22-caliber Rim Fire. The variations are numerous, but the collection will have greater appeal if there is a visible purpose to it. This should not stop you from purchasing something outside your collection if you like it — and it is a genuine bargain.

When buying for your collection, you will be much better off if you purchase quality items. Owning only one extremely high-quality collector firearm is preferable to owning two or three lesser ones. The greatest demand and appreciation will always be with the hightest-quality pieces. Guns in poor condition may show smaller increases in value. Current production firearms and those just out of production have collector value only if in close to new condition or in the original box. The corresponding ratings shown herein would be 95%, 98% or 100%. (See section How to Use and Apply Grading System.) Commemoratives, for example, must be new (100%) or they have lost much of their collector value. If a commemorative is no more than the standard-issue firearm but with minor trim added, its chance of appreciating is about nil. At the other extreme, an antique or possibly a military firearm may be found with no remaining finish, and if there is demand because of rarity, it could be an excellent addition to a collection. The main consideration is how they are normally found and collector demand. Study my price value guidelines for a better indication of rarity and values.

A shrewd collector may look for a firearm not actively collected but with growing interest.

Antique Arms — A Very Exciting Area to Look At

Antiques span hand cannons and matchlocks to the earlier modern designs. They can be found in all states of condition and show strong appreciation even though they are expensive. High-quality Flintlock and Percussions arms, civil and military, are an excellent example of collectible antique weaponry.

In later antiques, Colts and Winchesters are the perennial favorites. Civil War period arms are very popular, as are Volcanics, Henrys, Remingtons, Smith & Wessons, Sharps, etc. Again I recommend that you spend the time thoroughly to study this book.

Modern Arms — Offering Something for Nearly Everyone

Modern arms are those manufactured after 1898. Due to this arbitrary cutoff date, there are a few later antiques which carry over to the modern category. Where this happens, I will list known accepted cutoff models or serial number information in the text.

The modern arms era brought the development of some of the most popular arms ever developed. Many are still with us today in commercial versions, often because they were adopted at one time as a military arm. In some of the more collectible later designs, we find important cutoff dates where quality designs were modified to take advantage of less expensive production. These facts will be detailed in the text while explaining their significance.

Currently, the fastest-growing collector area centers around either production arms, arms recently out of production or arms recently discontinued.

The following text will list in detail models of these, including Auto Mag, Browning, Colt, Ruger, Smith & Wesson, Winchester, etc.

Military Arms

At the end of World War II, unique firearms became available. Many were brought home as souvenirs. Since they were armed forces firearms, few survived in original condition. Military firearms provide a vast field of study, especially since many of them are directly tied to our nation's history.

Late in 1984, Federal legislation once again allowed importation of nondomestic WWI and WWII military handguns. As a result, many military Lugers (including DWM and Mauser variations), Mauser Broomhandles, Browning Hi-Powers and P.38's, have been recently imported in some quantities. Condition on most of these recent imports is 80% or lower (with pitting on some) and prices typically start in the $200 range. While many of these newer imports would make workable shooters, they have in no way lowered prices on 90% + condition specimens due to normal collector activity in top quality only military pistols. Recently imported pistols should have the importers name visibly stamped on an exterior surface. Most of these imports are 9mm.

Machine guns offer a rather elite form of military arms for the collector. Their high prices and the strict federal laws make them less appealing, however, and a Class III license has to be obtained from the BATF. In some states, they are banned by law.

What Dictates Value — A Combination of Factors

Condition, rarity, demand, special features and historical significance determine current value. All values are based on the premise that the firearm is authentic and original.

The value of a collector arm is always in relation to the condition of other examples of the same make, model and variation. Condition is the amount of over-all original finish remaining on all parts of the firearm and condition of wood, if stocked, which can run from 0 to 100%. The collector is encouraged to acquire the better examples of what is available. If you find one better than the norm and it can be purchased at a fair price, you have had a stroke of luck. Most modern arms should be in the premium class, 95% to 100%, for collector purposes and definitely for maximum appreciation.

Rarity — A Word About Its Importance to the Collector-Investor

Rarity is very much like condition in the sense that the rarer pieces are highly prized and, just as guns in the best condition, are in great demand.

Demand — Who Wants What and Why

Demand for a collector arm exists because of nostalgia, rarity, history or unusual features. Demand dictates higher prices.

Special Features

Special features can increase value. Non-standard or experimental parts, special-order options or finish can make a price difference. The most desirable of all special features is engraving and precious metal inlays.

Historical Significance

Arms are important for the roles they played in wars. Demand also exists for arms owned by famous persons. Guns owned by Western heroes and outlaws have sold for $30,000 to $50,000. The key here is authenticity and documentation. This can be in the form of factory shipping ledger entries or original signed bills of sale, etc.

Identification and Authentication

Reference books are available on almost any firearm. They offer a wealth of information and can be used to help identify through component parts, manufacturing variations, serial numbers, etc. Authentication should be done by someone knowledgeable. *See guide to reference books and recommended reading.

Restoration

Restoration occurs mainly in antiques but can be found with any poppular arms. In most cases, a restored or refinished firearm does not deserve the status of a collectible firearm. Once a firearm has been restored, it can never be returned to its original condition. Restoration of antiques is accepted by many people because of the scarcity of good original arms. Such guns should be so marked and explicitly sold as restored pieces. Unfortunately, as they pass through several owners, this information tends to be lost. Replacement or repair done with current original parts should not affect the value.

Modification and Conversion

Many collector arms have been modified for personal taste and not with the intent to defraud or produce a fake. Often, it was done before a collector demand developed. Usually, it was done to copy a much scarcer variation of the same firearm. At a recent gun show, I found offered for sale as the genuine item six of the same rare variations of a modern handgun. All were priced in the correct range, were they authentic. Each was a fake made from a more common model. Their true value was about 20% of the asking price. Upgrading can take place in most firearms but can cost the most with engraved guns. Most often a low-grade shotgun is engraved to simulate a much-scarcer, higher-grade gun.

Conversions are most common with antiques. Disagreement exists on whether it is permissible to reconvert guns such as Percussions back to their original Flintlock condition. Guns so converted should be noted as such and sold on that basis.

Dealers and Gun Prices

Although you may be concerned with wholesale-retail price breaks, such a price structure can only be applied to modern firearms — shooters you buy in the gun shop. It certainly does not apply to collectible firearms.

In the first place, practically all collectibles are out of production. That means you'll have to wait until someone decides to part with, say, a Luger he "liberated" during the war. Now the problem is: how do you find the man who wants to sell his no-longer-made Luger?

Your chances of meeting him are pretty slim — so you go to a legitimate dealer with your request. Now it's the dealer's job to find the gun you want, at a fair price — and to assure you that the Luger is original and authentic. In fact, your broker or dealer is really responsible for the Luger's meeting all criteria of collectible value.

Since the dealer has performed a valuable service for you, he naturally adds a fee to the price you eventually pay for your Luger. Without the feepaid service, you might be spending your time running around the country looking for the gun — and still end up with a "fake!"

So, although I've tried my hardest to formulate realistic prices in this guide, please remember that you may have to pay more merely because you are utilizing someone else's valuable services.

The NRA

If you own guns — or are thinking about owning guns — you face several challenges. One is your *"right* to keep and bear arms". If you're like most people, you've probably let others do the fighting for you: the National Rifle Association, your state rifle and pistol association, and the several new organizations formed to meet the threat from the gun-grabbers.

Well, the time is past when *any* gun owner — hunter to collector of expensive antiques — can sit back and ignore this threat. The anti-gun movement is professionally run, heavily financed, and supported by a majority of the news media. I strongly recommend that you become a member of the National Rifle Association. Besides being the strongest lobbying organization in America today, the NRA also offers its members firearms insurance policies, magazines and information keeping you abreast of proposed legislation changes, plus many other benefits. The United States is one of the only countries in the world that constitutionally guarantees her citizens the right to keep and bear arms. Preserving that right is the fundamental principle behind the NRA. If you want to enjoy and continue to collect firearms, join the NRA and let them help. After all, can you imagine this fascinating and rewarding hobby legislated out of existence?

If you have not joined the NRA in the past, this is the year to do so. Recent legislation against assault rifles has removed yet another classification of firearms from the law-abiding U.S. citizen. We cannot afford to lose our rights as gun owners one classification at a time. If it was not for the NRA, many battles would have already been lost to preserve this greatest of American freedoms. Giving the N.R.A. $20 is the *first* $20 firearms enthusiasts should spend annually. Without a well funded, professionally run organization to combat this threat, our individual efforts will not be enough.

To join write:

National Rifle Association
1600 Rhode Island Ave. N.W.
Washington, D.C. 20036

Yearly membership is $20.00

Grading Criteria for Firearms

The old, NRA method of firearms grading — by relying upon adjectives such as "Excellent" or "Fair" — served the firearms fraternity for a long time. Today's collectors, however, are turning away from such a subjective system. One man's "Fair" is another man's "Good!"

The leading professionals in the grading of firearms now utilize what is essentially an objective method for deciding the price range of a gun: THE PERCENTAGE OF ORIGINAL FACTORY BLUING REMAINING ON THE GUN. After looking critically at a few firearms, even the novice can soon tell whether a piece has 100%, 98%, 95%, or less bluing remaining.

Of course, factors such as "depth" and quantity of the bluing, engraving and embellishment, historical significance, and even the condition of the stock can and do affect the price. But the basic "condition" — and therefore the price — is best determined by the percentage of original bluing remaining. The key word here is "original," for if anyone other than the factory has re-blued the gun, its value as a collectors' item is greatly diminished, with the exception of rare and historical pieces that have been properly restored.

Study the drawings on these pages. Note how the bluing in certain areas of the firearm wears off first. These are usually places where the gun rubs against the holster, hand or body. We have chosen a Luger and a Winchester as examples, but the principles apply to almost any firearm.

It should be noted that the older a collectible firearm is, the smaller the percentage of original bluing one can expect to find. Some very odl and/or very rare firearms are acceptable to collectors in almost any condition! The average collector, however, will probably never have the opportunity to purchase such a specimen.

For your convenience, NRA Condition Standards are shown below. Converting from this grading system to percentages can now be done accurately.

CONVERTING TO NRA MODERN STANDARDS

When converting from NRA Modern Standards, the following rules generally apply:

Perfect — 100% with or without box. Not mint, but new.

Excellent — 95-98% (typically).

Very Good — 80-95% - all original.

Good — 60-80% - all original.

Fair — 20-60% - May not be original (shootable, not very collectible).

Poor — Under 20%.

NRA Condition Standards

MODERN CONDITIONS —

New — not previously sold at retail, in same condition as current factory production.

Perfect — in new condition in every respect.

Excellent — new condition, used but little, no noticeable marring of wood or metal, bluing perfect (except at muzzle or sharp edges).

Very Good — in perfect working condition, no appreciable wear on working surfaces, no corrosion or pitting, only minor surface dents or scratches.

Good — in safe working condition, minor wear on working surfaces, no broken parts, no corrosion or pitting that will interfere with proper functioning.

Fair — in safe working condition, but well worn, perhaps requiring replacement of minor parts or adjustments which should be indicated in advertisement, no rust, but may have corrosion pits which do not render article unsafe or inoperable.

ANTIQUE CONDITIONS —

Factory New — all original parts; 100% original finish; in perfect condition in every respect, inside and out.

Excellent — all original parts; over 80% original finish; sharp lettering, numerals and design on metal and wood; unmarred wood; fine bore.

Fine — all original parts; over 30% original finish; sharp lettering, numerals and design on metal and wood; minor marks in wood; good bore.

Very Good — all original parts; none to 30% original finish; original metal surfaces smooth with all edges sharp; clear lettering, numerals and design on metal; wood slightly scratched or bruised; bore disregarded for collectors firearms.

Good — some minor replacement parts; metal smoothly rusted or lightly pitted in places, cleaned or reblued; principal lettering, numerals and design on metal legible; wood refinished, scratched, bruised or minor cracks repaired; in good working order.

Fair — some major parts replaced; minor replacement parts may be required; metal rusted, may be lightly pitted all over, vigorously cleaned or reblued; rounded edges of metal and wood; principal lettering, numerals and design on metal partly obliterated; wood scratched, bruised, cracked or repaired where broken; in fair working order or can be easily repaired and placed in working order.

Poor — major and minor parts replaced; major replacement parts required and extensive restoration needed; metal deeply pitted; principal lettering, numerals and design obliterated, wood badly scratched, bruised, cracked or broken; mechanically inoperative, generally undesirable as a collectors firearm.

These NRA conditions have been used by the author as the guidelines for the value ranges in this work. In order to use this book correctly, the reader is urged to constantly consult these condition standards when assessing a gun before applying a value to it. They stand as the crux of the valuation matter.

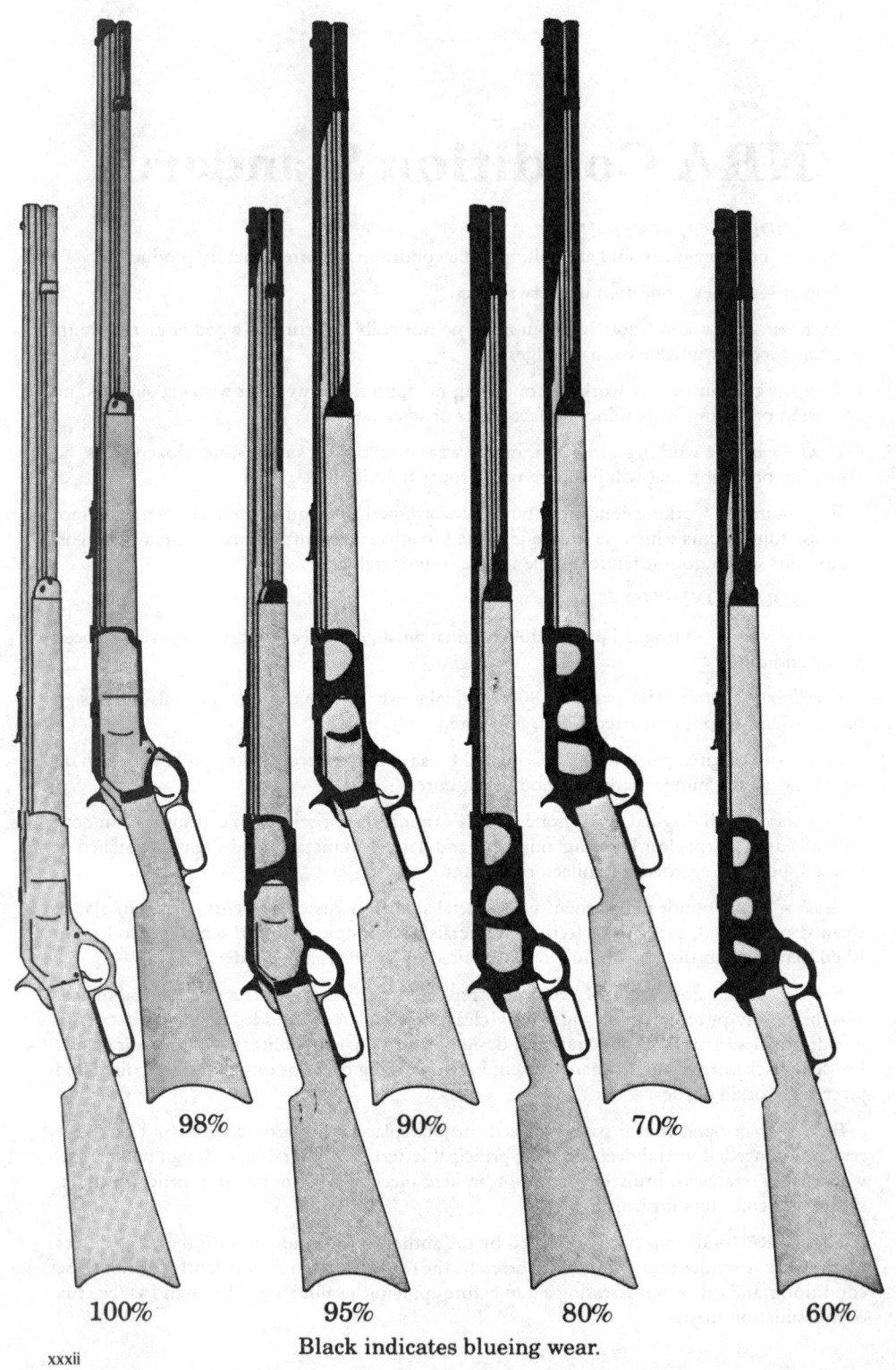

98%

90%

70%

100%

95%

80%

60%

Black indicates blueing wear.

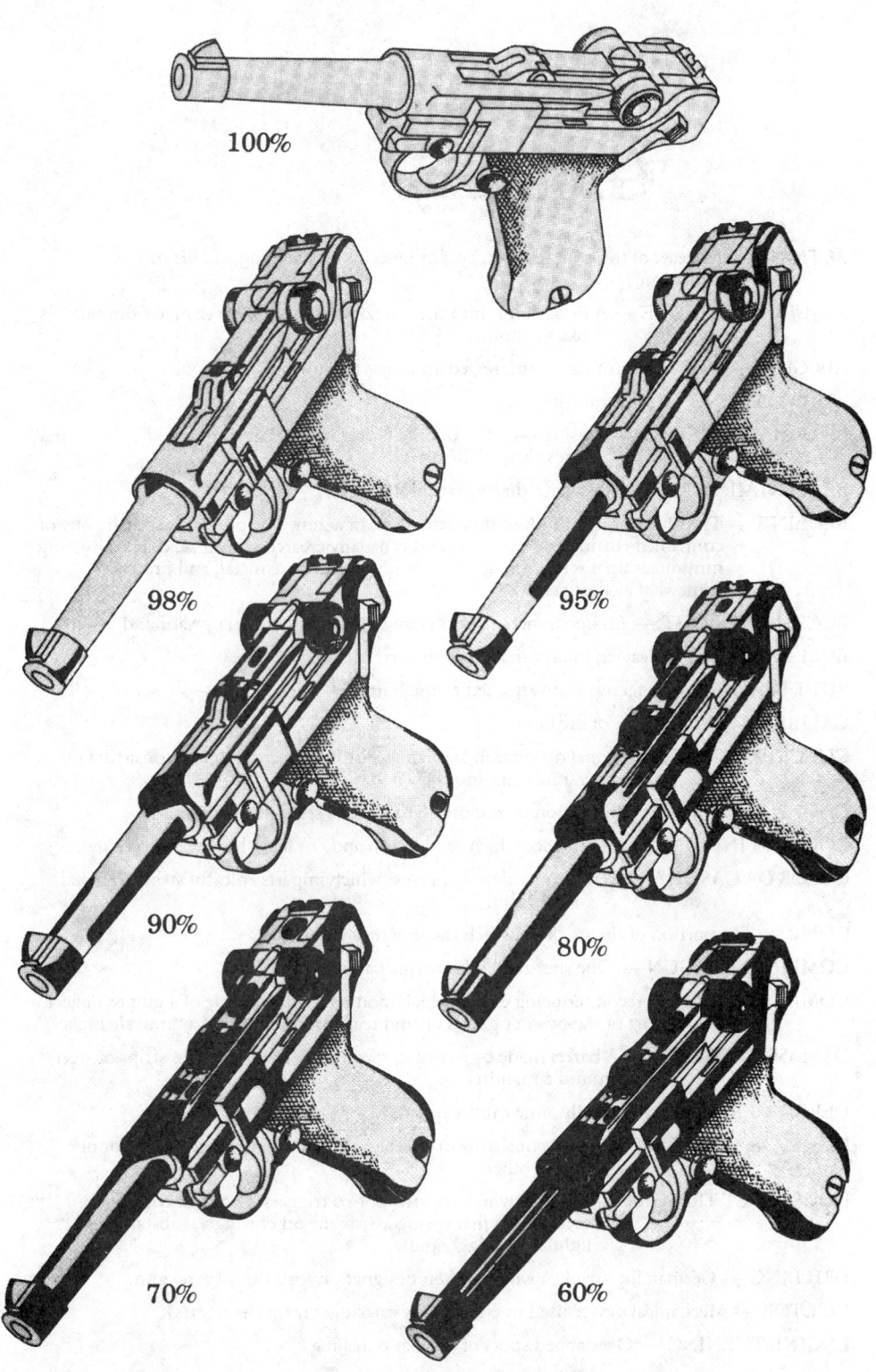

100%

98%

95%

90%

80%

70%

60%

Black indicates blueing wear.

Glossary

ACTION — The heart of the gun, receiver, bolt or breech block feeding and firearm mechanism.

ADJUSTABLE CHOKE — A device built into the muzzle of a shotgun to change from one choke to another.

AIR GUN — A gun which utilizes compressed air or gas to launch the projectile.

AUTO LOADING — See semi-automatic.

AUTOMATIC EJECTOR — A single-shot or double-barrel action that is equipped to hurl fired casses clear of the breech.

BEAVERTAIL FOREND — A wider than normal forend.

BLUEING — The blue or black finish of the metal parts of a gun. The process is actually one of controlled rusting and brushing and is usually created with an acid bath. Blueing minimizes light reflection, gives a "finish" to the bare metal, and protects somewhat against rust.

BUCKHORN SIGHT — An open, metallic rear sight with sides that curl upward and inward.

BULL BARREL — A heavier, thicker than normal barrel.

BUTT PLATE — A protective plate attached to the butt.

CALIBER — The diameter of the bore.

CHECKERING — A functional decoration applied to pistol grips and forends consisting of pointed pyramids cut into the wood.

CHOKE — The muzzle constriction on a shotgun to control spread of the shot.

COCKING INDICATOR — A device which can be seen and/or felt when a gun is cocked.

COLOR OR CASE HARDEN — A hardening process which imparts colorful swirls to metal surfaces.

COMB — The portion of the stock on which the shooter's cheek rests.

COMBINATION GUN — One shotgun and one rifle barrel.

COMPENSATOR — A recoil-reducing device which mounts on the muzzle of a gun to deflect part of the powder gasses up and rearward. Also called a "muzzle brake".

DAMASCUS BARREL — A barrel made by twisting, forming and welding thin strips of steel around a mandrel.

DERRINGER — A small, usually large-caliber pistol.

DOUBLE-BARRELLED — A gun consisting of two barrels joined either side by side or one over the other.

DOUBLE-SET TRIGGER — A device which consists of two triggers — one to cock the mechanism that spring-assists the other trigger, substantially lightening trigger pull.

DRILLING — German for "triple", which is their designation for a three-barrel gun.

EJECTOR — Mechanical device used to eject empty cartridges from chamber(s).

ENGINE TURNING — Overlapped spots of circular polishing.

ENGLISH STOCK — A very straight, slender-gripped stock.

ETCHING — A method of decorating metal gun parts.

EXTRACTOR — A device that withdraws the fired case from the chamber.

FALLING BLOCK — A single-shot action where the breech block drops straight down when the lever is pactuated.

FIT AND FINISH — Terms used to describe over-all firearm workmanship.

FLOATING BARREL — A barrel bedded to avoid contact with any point on the stock.

FLOOR PLATE — The piece which closes the bottom of the magazine body.

FOREND — The forward portion of a rifle or shotgun stock.

FREE RIFLE — A rifle designed for international-type target shooting. The only restriction on design is weight — maximum 8 kilograms (17.6 lbs.).

GAUGE — The bore diameter of a shotgun.

LAMINATED STOCK — A gunstock made of many layers of wood glued together under pressure. They are very resistant to warpage.

MAGAZINE — The container which holds cartridges under spring pressure to be fed into the gun's chamber.

MAGNUM — A modern cartridge with a higher-velocity load or heavier projectile than standard.

MANNLICHER STOCK — A full-length slender forend extending to the muzzle.

MICROMETER SIGHT — A finely adjustable target sight.

MONTE CARLO STOCK — A stock with an elevated comb used primarily for scoped rifles.

MUZZLE BRAKE — A recoil-reducing device attached to the muzzle.

OVER-UNDER — A two-barrel gun in which the barrels are stacked one on top of the other.

PARKERIZING — A matted rust-resistant oxide finish, usually gray or gray-green in color, found on military guns.

PEEP SIGHT — A rear sight consisting of a hole or aperture through which the front sight and target are aligned.

RELEASE TRIGGER — A trap shooting trigger that fires the gun when the trigger is released or pulled.

RIB — A raised sighting plane affixed to the top of a barrel.

SCHNABEL — A decorative sculptured knob at the end of a forend — usually European style.

SHORT ACTION — A rifle designed for shorter cartridges.

SIDE LOCK — A type of action, usually shotgun, when the moving parts are located on the lock plates inletted in the stock. Usually found only on high-quality guns.

SIDE PLATES — Ornamental additions to simulate a side lock gun on a boxlock.

SINGLE TRIGGER — One trigger on a double-barrel gun. It fires both barrels singly by successive pulls.

SLING SWIVELS — Metal loops affixed to the gun on which a carrying strap is attached.

TAKE DOWN — A gun which can be easily taken apart for carrying or shipping.

TANG — An extension of the receiver into the stock.

TRAP STOCK — A shotgun stock with greater length and less drop for trap shooting.

VENTILATED RIB — A sighting plane affixed along the length of a shotgun barrel with gaps or slots milled for cooling purposes.

Common Abbreviations

ACP	—	Automatic Colt Pistol	OA	—	Overall
ADJ.	—	Adjustable	OBO	—	Or Best Offer
AE	—	Automatic Ejectors	O&U	—	Over and Under
B	—	Blue	OCT.	—	Octagon
BAC	—	Browning Arms Co.	PG	—	Pistol Grip
BATF	—	Bureau of Alcohol, Tobacco,	P.O.R.	—	Price on Request
		and Firearms	RB	—	Round Barrel
BCA	—	Browning Collector's Association	REM	—	Remington
BPE	—	Black Power Express	RF	—	Rimfire
BP	—	Butt Plate	RFM	—	Rim Fire Magnum
BT	—	Beavertail	RN	—	Round Knob
CC	—	Case Colors	RR	—	Red Ramp
CF	—	Centerfire	SA	—	Single Action
CH	—	Cross Hair	SAA	—	Single Action Army
CYL	—	Cylinder	SAE	—	Selective Automatic Ejectors
DA	—	Double Action	S.G.	—	Straight Grip
DISC	—	Discontinued	SK	—	Skeet
DSL	—	Detachable Side Locks	SMG	—	Sub Machine Gun
DB	—	Double Barrel	SMLE	—	Short Magazine Lee
DST	—	Double Set Trigger			Enfield Rifle
DT	—	Double Trigger	SN	—	Serial Number
DWM	—	Deutsche Waffen and	SPEC.	—	Special
		Munitions Fabrik	SPL	—	Special
EXT	—	Extractors	S.R.C.	—	Saddle Ring Carbine
FBT	—	Full Beavertail Forearm	SS	—	Single Shot
F&M	—	Full & Modified	SST	—	Single Selective Trigger
FE	—	Fore End	S&W	—	Smith & Wesson
FFL	—	Federal Firearms License	SXS	—	Side by Side
FN	—	Fabrique Nationale	TD	—	Take Down
HB	—	Heavy Barrel	TGT.	—	Target
H&H	—	Holland & Holland	TH	—	Target Hammer
HP	—	Hollow Point	TT	—	Target Trigger
IC	—	Improved Cylinder	UMC	—	Union Metallic Cartridge Co.
LC	—	Long Colt	VG	—	Very Good
LT	—	Long Tang or Light	VR	—	Ventilated Rib
LTRK	—	Long Tang Round Knob	WBY	—	Weatherby
MAG	—	Magnum	WC	—	Wad Cutter
mag.	—	Magazine or Clip	WCF	—	Winchester Center Fire
MC	—	Monte Carlo	WFF	—	Watch For Fakes
MK	—	Mark	WIN	—	Winchester
M&P	—	Military and Police	WRA	—	Winchester Repeating Arms Co.
MR	—	Matted Rib	WRF	—	Winchester Rim Fire
N	—	Nickel	WO	—	White Outline
NIB	—	New in Box	WW	—	World War

A

A.A.

MAKER: AZANZA & ARRIZABLAGA, EIBAR, SPAIN.

Grading	100%	98%	95%	90%	80%	70%	60%

A.A.—semi-auto pistol, 7.65mm, slide marked Azanza & Arrizablaga Model 1916, A.A. in oval on frame.

	$130	$105	$85	$65	$55	$50	$45

REIMS—semi-auto pistol, 6.35mm or 7.65mm, copies of M1906 Browning, marked 1914 Model.

	$120	$100	$75	$65	$55	$50	$45

A.A.A.

MAKER: ALDAZABAL, SPAIN.

M1919—semi-auto pistol, 7.65mm.

	$110	$100	$85	$70	$65	$60	$55

A & R SALES

SOUTH EL MONTE, CA.

HANDGUN—.45 ACP semi-auto — less weight than normal Colt .45.

	$225	$205	$175	$155	$145	$135	$125

RIFLE: MARK IV SPORTER—semi-auto, .308 Winchester, M-14 action-clip fed, adj. sights.

	$295	$260	$225	$200	$175	$155	$140

A & S FAMARS

MANUFACTURED IN BRESCIA, ITALY. LIMITED IMPORTATION.

SHOTGUNS: CUSTOM MANUFACTURE

A & S Famars manufactures some of the world's finest shotguns. Values listed below are for base models with no extra embellishments or special orders.

Due to the recent devaluation of the U.S. dollar, prices may fluctuate rapidly on this trademark.

HAMMER SHOTGUN—double barrel, SxS, hammers, double triggers, various gauges. Prices usually start at $6,500 for a custom ordered gun.

Because every A & S Famars shotgun is an individual custom order, each Famars firearm must have its value ascertained on an individual appraisal basis.

SIDELOCK SHOTGUN—double barrel, sidelock SXS, hammerless, double triggers, various gauges. Prices usually start at approx. $9,000 for a custom ordered gun.

Because every A & S Famars shotgun is an individual custom order, each Famars firearm must have its value ascertained on an individual appraisal basis.

A F C

MAKER: AUGUSTE FRANCOTTE, LIEGE, BELGIUM, 1912-1914.

SEMI-AUTO PISTOL—6.35mm, 6 shot mag., frame marked "Francotte Liege".

	100%	98%	95%	90%	80%	70%	60%
	$275	$250	$220	$165	$140	$110	$85

A. J. ORDNANCE

THOMAS—.45 double action, .45 ACP, 6 shot, 3½ in. barrel, fixed sights, checkered plastic grips, delayed blowback action, each shot double action, stainless steel barrel. Discontinued.

	100%	98%	95%	90%	80%	70%	60%
	$470	$415	$385	$360	$330	$275	$220
Chrome.	$525	$470	$440	$415	$385	$330	$275

A K S

SEMI-AUTO ASSAULT RIFLE ORIGINALLY DESIGNED IN RUSSIA (1947). CURRENTLY MANUFACTURED BY SEVERAL ARSENALS IN CHINA INCLUDING NORINCO AND POLY TECHNOLOGIES, INC. ALSO MANUFACTURED IN OTHER COUNTRIES INCLUDING YUGOSLAVIA AND CZECHOSLOVAKIA. U.S.IMPORTATION BY CHINA SPORTS, INC., KENGS FIREARMS SPECIALTY, INC., B-WEST IMPORTS, AND SEVERAL OTHERS. DISTRIBUTED IN THE U.S. BY VARIOUS COMPANIES INCLUDING B-WEST IMPORTS LOCATED IN TUCSON, AZ., PTK INTERNATIONAL, INC., LOCATED IN ATLANTA, GA., FEDERAL ORDNANCE, INC. LOCATED IN SOUTH EL MONTE, CA., AMERICAN ARMS, INC. LOCATED IN NORTH KANSAS CITY, MO., AND PACIFIC INTERNATIONAL MERCHANDISING CORPORATION LOCATED IN SACRAMENTO, CA.

Also see separate listings under Norinco and Poly Technologies, Inc.

AK-47 STANDARD MILITARY RIFLE—7.62mm x 39mm (standard Russian military cal.), semi-auto Kalasnikov action, 16½ in. barrel, 5 or 30 round mag., wood stock and forearm except on folding stock model, is supplied with bayonet, sling, cleaning kit, standard military production rifle of China.

No Mfg.'s Retail	$350	$300	$250	$225	$200	$185	$165

Folding stock is available at a small additional charge.

Due to the recent controversy regarding assault rifles, this model may vary in value pending potential future legislation.

Yugoslavian/Czechoslavakian manufactured AK-47's will command a $100-$150 premium over prices listed above.

This model is also available in 5.56 NATO (.223 cal.) in limited quantities.

A M A C

SEE IVER JOHNSON SECTION IN THIS TEXT. AMAC STANDS FOR AMERICAN MILITARY ARMS CORPORATION MANUFACTURED IN JACKSONVILLE, AR.

A M T

MANUFACTURED BY ARCADIA MACHINE & TOOL LOCATED IN IRWINDALE, CA. ALSO SEE AUTO-MAG FOR DISCONTINUED MODELS.

PISTOLS: SEMI-AUTO

LIGHTNING—.22 LR, semi-auto, stainless steel only, 5 (bull only), 6½, 8½, 10½, and 12½ (disc. in 1987) in. bull or tapered barrels, adj. sights and trigger, pistol based on semi-auto Ruger action, tapered barrels. Made 1984-87.

	100%	98%	95%
	$240	$200	$150

Last Mfg.'s Sug. Retail was $289.

Grading	100%	98%	95%	90%	80%	70%	60%

This model features a frame grooved for scope mounts, Clarke trigger, Millett sights, and either Pachmayr rubber or Wayland wood grips as standard equipment.

Bull's Eye Regulation Target—similar to 6½ in. Lightning with bull barrel, except has vent rib, wooden grips, extended rear sight. Made in 1986 only.

     $350 **$285** **$220**

Last Mfg.'s Sug. Retail was $436.

AUTOMAG II—.22 Mag., stainless steel only, 3⅜, 4½, or 6 in. barrel, gas assisted action, Millett adj. sights with white outline, grooved Lexan grips, 9 shot mag. New in 1987.
 Mfg.'s Sug. Retail **$329** **$270** **$225** **$195**

BABY AUTOMAG—.22 LR, semi-auto, stainless steel only, 8½ in. vent rib barrel, Millett adj. sights, smooth walnut grips, 1,000 mfg.
     $450 **$400** **$350**

BACKUP PISTOL—.22 LR or .380 ACP cal., semi-auto action, 2½ in. barrel, stainless steel, Lexan grips, formerly TDE, 5 shot mag. in 380, 8 shot mag. in .22 LR, 18 oz. Older discontinued walnut grip models are worth a slight premium.
 Mfg.'s Sug. Retail **$243** **$200** **$165** **$135**

This model is now manufactured by Irwindale Arms, Inc. and can also be found under their own heading.

.45 ACP GOVERNMENT MODEL—.45 ACP, similar to Colt semi-auto Gov't model, stainless steel, 5 in. barrel, fixed rear sight, loaded chamber indicator, adj. trigger, wrap-around neoprene grips.
 Mfg.'s Sug. Retail **$446** **$335** **$280** **$250**

HARDBALLER—.45 ACP, similar to Colt Gold Cup Model, stainless steel, 5 in. barrel, adj. Millett rear sight, serrated rib, loaded chamber indicator, adj. trigger, wrap-around neoprene grips.
 Mfg.'s Sug. Retail **$490** **$380** **$340** **$295**

Hardballer Long Slide—same as Hardballer, except 7 in. barrel and longer slide assembly.
 Mfg.'s Sug. Retail **$524** **$410** **$360** **$310**

Note: Long slide kit is also available to convert regular Hardballer — $347 retail.

SKIPPER—same as Hardballer, except approx. 1 in. shorter slide. Discontinued in 1984.
     $395 **$330** **$295**

COMBAT SKIPPER—same as Skipper, only with fixed sights. Discontinued in 1984.
     $375 **$330** **$295**

RIFLES

LIGHTNING (25/22)—.22 LR, semi-auto based on Ruger 10-22 action, stainless steel, 25 round mag., 22 in. tapered or bull barrel, nylon pistol grip handle and forearm, folding stock with recoil pad or youth stock, fixed sights, 6 lbs. New in 1986.
 Mfg.'s Sug. Retail **$278** **$210** **$175** **$150**

Small Game Hunter (SGH)—.22 LR, same mechanical action as Lightning, except has matte black nylon stock with checkered forearm and grip, full length barrel, 10 round mag., removable recoil pad allows storage in stock, supplied with 4X scope. New in 1986.
 Mfg.'s Sug. Retail **$278** **$210** **$185** **$160**

While advertised in .22 Mag., this caliber was never manufactured.

A-SQUARE

MANUFACTURED AND DISTRIBUTED IN MADISON, IN.

A-Square also offers at extra cost fancier walnut, different wood and metal finishes, and various sights/ scope rings.

RIFLES: BOLT ACTION

Grading	100%	98%	95%	90%	80%	70%	60%

HANNIBAL GRADE—bolt action built on a P-17 Enfield receiver, various cal.'s, 22-26 in. barrel, 9 - 11¼ lbs., select walnut wood pistol grip, recoil pad. New in 1986.

Group 1—.270 Win., .30-06, and 9.3 X 62 (new in 1988) cal.'s.

Mfg.'s Sug. Retail	$1,500	$1,500	$1,300	$1,200	$1,075	$975	$900	$840

Group 2—.300 Win. Mag., .308 Norma Mag. (disc. in 1987), .338 Win. Mag., .416 Taylor (new in 1988), .458 Win. Mag., and 7mm Rem. Mag. cal.'s.

Mfg.'s Sug. Retail	$1,550	$1,550	$1,325	$1,225	$1,100	$995	$900	$840

Group 3—.300 Wby. Mag., .300 H&H (new in 1988), .340 Wby. Mag., .375 Wby. Mag., .375 H&H, .416 Hoffman, .416 Rem Mag. (new in 1989), .450 Ackley Mag., .458 Lott (new in 1989), 8mm Rem. Mag. (new in 1988), and 9.3 X 64 (new in 1988) cal.'s.

Mfg.'s Sug. Retail	$1,580	$1,580	$1,350	$1,225	$1,100	$995	$900	$840

Group 4—.338 A-Square, .375 A-Square, .378 Wby. Mag., .404 Jeffrey (new in 1988), .416 Rigby, .416 Wby. (new in 1989), .460 Short A-Square, .460 Long A-Square (disc. in 1987), .460 Wby. Mag., .495 A-Square, and .500 A-Square cal.'s.

Mfg.'s Sug. Retail	$1,600	$1,600	$1,350	$1,125	$1,100	$995	$900	$840

Above listed A-Square proprietary calibers are available in Group 4 Models only.

CAESAR GRADE—bolt action built on a Remington M-700 receiver, various cal.'s, 22-26 in. barrel, 9 - 10¾ lbs., select wood pistol grip, recoil pad. Also available in left-hand models — add $60. New in 1986.

Group 1—.270 Win. and .30-06, 9.3 X 62 (new in 1988) cal.'s.

Mfg.'s Sug. Retail	$1,620	$1,620	$1,375	$1,225	$1,100	$1,000	$900	$840

Group 2—.300 Win. Mag., .308 Norma Mag. (disc. in 1987), .338 Win. Mag., .416 Taylor (new in 1988), .458 Win. Mag., and 7mm Rem. Mag. cal.'s.

Mfg.'s Sug. Retail	$1,650	$1,650	$1,400	$1,225	$1,100	$1,000	$900	$840

Group 3—.300 Wby. Mag., .300 H&H (new in 1988), .340 Wby. Mag., .375 Wby. Mag., .375 H&H, .416 Hoffman, .416 Rem Mag. (new in 1989), .450 Ackley Mag., .458 Lott (new in 1989), 8mm Rem. Mag. (new in 1988), and 9.3 X 64 (new in 1988) cal.'s.

Mfg.'s Sug. Retail	$1,650	$1,525	$1,375	$1,200	$1,025	$925	$860	$800

A T C S A

MAKER: ARMAS DE TIRO Y CASA.

COLT POCKET PISTOL COPY—revolver, .38 cal., 6 shot.

	$155	$140	$110	$100	$90	$75	$65

SINGLE SHOT REVOLVER—target pistol.

	$195	$165	$145	$110	$100	$90	$75

AYA (AGUIRRE Y ARANZABAL)

CURRENT MANUFACTURE (LIMITED EXPORTATION) BY AYA AND PREVIOUS MANUFACTURE BY DIARM LOCATED IN EIBAR, SPAIN. LAST IMPORTED AND DISTRIBUTED BY AMERICAN ARMS, INC. LOCATED IN NORTH KANSAS CITY, MO.

Exportation of all AYA shotguns ceased in 1988. Limited manufacture of AYA shotguns is still occurring in Eibar, Spain at the original plant (non-Diarm and no U.S. exportation currently).

SHOTGUNS: O/U

AUGUSTA—12 ga. only, deluxe O/U sidelock, arabesque engraving in deep relief, select walnut. Discontinued in 1985.

	$7,500	$6,500	$5,500	$5,000	$4,000	$3,350	$2,950

Last Mfg.'s Sug. Retail was $10,000.

Grading	100%	98%	95%	90%	80%	70%	60%

CORAL "A"—12 and 16 ga., boxlock action with Kersten cross bolt, vent rib, ejectors, double triggers. Discontinued in 1985.

	$1,275	$1,050	$875	$775	$695	$625	$560

Last Mfg.'s Sug. Retail was $2,195.

CORAL "B"—same as A, except for coin-wash engraved receiver. Discontinued in 1985.

	$1,395	$1,100	$925	$820	$720	$650	$595

Last Mfg.'s Sug. Retail was $2,450.

MODEL 37 SUPER—12, 16, and 20 ga.'s, various barrel lengths and chokes, vent rib, sidelock, auto ejector, elaborate engraving, high grade wood. Merkel style action. Prices below reflect older models.

	100%	98%	95%	90%	80%	70%	60%
12 ga.	$2,600	$2,350	$2,100	$1,900	$1,700	$1,500	$1,250
16 ga.	$2,550	$2,200	$2,000	$1,700	$1,500	$1,350	$1,150
20 ga.	$3,000	$2,500	$2,000	$1,900	$1,700	$1,600	$1,475

New Model 37 Super A—game scene engraved, detachable sidelock action, nickel steel receiver. Discontinued in 1985.

	$5,000	$4,750	$4,300	$3,750	$3,250	$2,650	$2,175

Last Mfg.'s Sug. Retail was $7,300.

New Model 37 Super B—fine scroll engraved, detachable sidelock action, nickel steel receiver. Discontinued in 1985.

	$5,250	$4,750	$4,300	$3,720	$3,350	$2,650	$2,175

Last Mfg.'s Sug. Retail was $7,795.

79 "A"—12 ga. only, boxlock with double locking lugs, sel. trigger, ejectors. Discontinued in 1985.

	$1,275	$1,075	$965	$880	$790	$705	$640

Last Mfg.'s Sug. Retail was $1,595.

79 "B"—same as 79 "A", only more elaborate engraving. Discontinued in 1985.

	$1,395	$1,200	$1,085	$990	$890	$790	$695

Last Mfg.'s Sug. Retail was $1,795.

79 "C"—same as 79 "B", only more elaborate engraving, double triggers on request. Discontinued in 1985.

	$2,050	$1,825	$1,605	$1,460	$1,315	$1,165	$1,000

Last Mfg.'s Sug. Retail was $2,650.

77—12 ga. only, Merkel style O/U sidelock with Greener crossbolt, deluxe engraving-checkering. Discontinued in 1985.

	$3,100	$2,750	$2,500	$2,255	$2,030	$1,805	$1,600

Last Mfg.'s Sug. Retail was $4,100.

SHOTGUNS: SxS

U.S. importation ceased in 1988 on all AYA shotguns.

BOLERO—same as Matador, with non-selective single trigger and extractors. Discontinued in 1984.

	$440	$360	$330	$305	$275	$250	$220

IBERIA—12 and 20 ga., 3 in., boxlock, double triggers, plain walnut. Discontinued in 1984.

	$566	$440	$370	$315	$285	$255	$230

IBERIA II—12 and 16 ga., 28 in. barrels, 2¾ in. chamber only, double triggers, plain walnut. Manufactured 1984-1985 only.

	$515	$430	$370	$315	$285	$255	$230

Last Mfg.'s Sug. Retail was $570.

Grading	100%	98%	95%	90%	80%	70%	60%

MATADOR—12, 16, 20, 28, and .410 ga.'s, 26, 28, and 30 in. barrel, various chokes, Anson & Deeley boxlock, auto ejectors, beavertail forearm, SST, checkered pistol grip stock, made 1955-1963.

	$500	$450	$400	$350	$300	$275	$250

Add 20% for .410 or 28 ga.

MATADOR II—similar to Matador, with vent rib, 12 and 20 ga. only. Discontinued.

	$550	$500	$450	$400	$350	$325	$300

MATADOR III—12 and 20 ga., 3 in. chamber in 20 ga. only, boxlock, vent rib, ejectors, SST. Discontinued in 1985.

	$930	$805	$725	$650	$560	$495	$430

Last Mfg.'s Sug. Retail was $1,235.

SENIOR—12 ga. only, self-opener, engraved sidelock action, select walnut. Top-of-the-line-quality, made to special order only. Lighter up-land version also available. Disc. in 1987.

	$15,500	$12,000	$10,000	$8,000	$6,500	$5,500	$4,500

Last Mfg.'s Sug. Retail was $21,000.

NO. 1—12 or 20 ga., full sidelock action with third lever fastener, straight grip, ejectors, DT's, elaborate fine scroll engraving. Disc. in 1987.

	$2,600	$2,225	$1,950	$1,600	$1,300	$1,000	$875

Add $145 for SST.

Last Mfg.'s Sug. Retail was $3,750.

28 and .410 ga.'s—disc. in 1987.

	$2,800	$2,400	$1,995	$1,650	$1,350	$1,050	$900

Last Mfg.'s Sug. Retail was $3,895.

NO. 2—12, 16 (discontinued in 1985), 20, 28 and .410 ga.'s, 3 in. chambers, English-style sidelock, ejector, cocking indicators, DT's, third lever fastener. Disc. in 1987.

	$1,250	$1,050	$850	$700	$575	$500	$425

Add $145 for 28 or .410 ga.

Last Mfg.'s Sug. Retail was $1,650.

No. 2 — 2-barrel set—available in either 20/28 ga., or 28/.410 ga. Imported 1986-87 only.

	$1,995	$1,775	$1,600	$1,400	$1,200	$995	$850

Last Mfg.'s Sug. Retail was $2,440.

NO. 3-A—12, 16, 20, 28, and .410 ga.'s, boxlock, extractors, double triggers. Discontinued in 1985.

	$640	$540	$495	$450	$400	$375	$350

Add $25 for 28 or .410 ga.

Last Mfg.'s Sug. Retail was $850.

NO. 4-A—12, 16 (discontinued in 1985), 20, 28, and .410 ga.'s, 3 in. chambers, English-style straight stock, boxlock action, ejectors, double trigger, straight grip. Disc. in 1987.

	$600	$530	$475	$440	$410	$365	$325

Add $50 for 28 or .410 ga.

Last Mfg.'s Sug. Retail was $835.

4-A DELUXE—English-style, boxlock ejector. Stock, forearm, trigger to order. Discontinued in 1985.

	$1,700	$1,400	$1,225	$1,000	$800	$650	$525

Add 10% for 28 or .410 ga.

Last Mfg.'s Sug. Retail was $2,195.

Grading	100%	98%	95%	90%	80%	70%	60%

XXV BOXLOCK (BL)—12 and 20 ga. only, similar to 4-A Deluxe, except 25 in. barrels, Churchill rib. Discontinued in 1986.

	$995	$900	$840	$785	$740	$680	$615

Add $85 for SST.

Last Mfg.'s Sug. Retail was $1,350.

XXV SIDELOCK (SL)—12, 16, 20, 28 and .410 ga.'s, sidelock ejector, 25 in. barrels, Churchill rib. Stock, forearm, trigger to order. Discontinued in 1986.

12, 16, and 20 ga.'s

	$1,800	$1,600	$1,350	$1,175	$950	$750	$600

Last Mfg.'s Sug. Retail was $2,095.

28 and .410 ga.'s

	$1,950	$1,650	$1,400	$1,225	$1,000	$800	$650

Last Mfg.'s Sug. Retail was $2,195.

Add $85 for SST.

53-E—12, 16, and 20 ga.'s, engraved sidelock ejector, sideclips, third lock. Stock, forearm, trigger to order. Discontinued in 1986.

	$1,440	$1,195	$1,025	$925	$820	$700	$620

Add $85 for SST.

Last Mfg.'s Sug. Retail was $1,795.

56—12, 16, and 20 ga.'s, sidelock action-engraved, ejectors, sel. trigger. Discontinued in 1985.

	$4,895	$4,100	$3,700	$3,450	$3,100	$2,750	$2,500

Last Mfg.'s Sug. Retail was $5,750.

106—12, 16, and 20 ga.'s, English-style boxlock, double trigger, pistol grip, 28 in. barrels. Discontinued in 1985.

	$530	$440	$400	$360	$320	$300	$275

Last Mfg.'s Sug. Retail was $585.

107-LI—12 and 16 ga.'s, English-style boxlock, double trigger, straight grip, light English scroll engraving. Discontinued in 1985.

	$675	$560	$520	$480	$425	$400	$360

Last Mfg.'s Sug. Retail was $745.

MODEL 116—12, 16, and 20 ga.'s, 27-30 in. barrels, any choke, hand detachable H&H sidelocks, double triggers, engraved, select checkered walnut pistol grip stock. Discontinued in 1985.

	$1,000	$845	$795	$750	$675	$600	$500

Last Mfg.'s Sug. Retail was $1,125.

MODEL 117—12, 16 and 20 ga.'s, 3 in. chambers, 26-30 in. barrels, any choke, hand detachable H&H sidelocks, ejectors, SST, engraved, select checkered walnut pistol grip stock. Discontinued in 1986.

	$835	$715	$660	$620	$585	$545	$500

Last Mfg.'s Sug. Retail was $1,075.

QUAIL UNLIMITED MODEL 117—12 ga. only, 26 in. barrels choked IC/M with 3 in. chambers, upgraded wood and checkering, high gloss bluing, gold colored ST, engraved by Baron Technologies in PA, only 42 mfg. for Quail Unlimited of North America.

	$1,650	$1,400	$1,150	$975	$875	$800	$725

This model had a retail price of $1,700 but was made available to Quail Unlimited members for approx. $1,200.

Grading	100%	98%	95%	90%	80%	70%	60%

MODEL 210—12 and 16 ga.'s, boxlock, exposed hammers, double triggers, plain walnut, light engraving. Discontinued in 1985.

	100%	98%	95%	90%	80%	70%	60%
	$795	$675	$550	$475	$435	$395	$350

Last Mfg.'s Sug. Retail was $900.

711 BOXLOCK—12 ga. only, boxlock, selective trigger, ejectors, vent rib. Discontinued in 1984.

	100%	98%	95%	90%	80%	70%	60%
	$880	$680	$575	$490	$445	$395	$350

711 Sidelock—sidelock action. Manufactured in 1985 only.

	100%	98%	95%	90%	80%	70%	60%
	$995	$850	$775	$695	$625	$550	$475

Last Mfg.'s Sug. Retail was $1,250.

ABADIE

MAKER: SEVERAL BELGIAN MAKERS FOR PORTUGUESE MILITARY.

MODEL 1878 (OFFICER'S MODEL)—9.1mm, solid frame revolver, 6 shot, ejector rod, officer's issue A.

	100%	98%	95%	90%	80%	70%	60%
	$220	$195	$165	$130	$120	$110	$100

MODEL 1886 (TROOPER'S MODEL)—similar to 1878, but larger, trooper issue A.

	100%	98%	95%	90%	80%	70%	60%
	$195	$175	$160	$120	$110	$100	$90

ABBEY, GEORGE T.

UTICA, NY FROM 1845-1852. CHICAGO, IL FROM 1852-1874. PERCUSSION AND BREECHLOADING FIREARMS.

100%	98%	95%	90%	80%	70%	60%	50%	40%	30%	20%	10%

PERCUSSION RIFLE

.44 cal.—32 in. octagon barrel.

100%	98%	95%	90%	80%	70%	60%	50%	40%	30%	20%	10%
$605	$550	$470	$415	$370	$340	$305	$275	$250	$220	$195	$165

.44 cal.—octagon barrel, brass trimmed.

100%	98%	95%	90%	80%	70%	60%	50%	40%	30%	20%	10%
$770	$735	$695	$605	$550	$485	$450	$405	$365	$330	$275	$220

.44 cal.—31 in. double barrel.

100%	98%	95%	90%	80%	70%	60%	50%	40%	30%	20%	10%
$1,210	$1,100	$880	$770	$715	$650	$595	$550	$515	$475	$430	$360

.44 cal.—double barrel O/U, brass trimmed.

100%	98%	95%	90%	80%	70%	60%	50%	40%	30%	20%	10%
$1,485	$1,295	$1,130	$990	$910	$855	$770	$715	$660	$605	$495	$330

ABBEY, F.J. & COMPANY

CHICAGO, IL, 1858-1878. MUZZLE AND BREECHLOADING SHOTGUNS AND PISTOLS.

PERCUSSION RIFLE—several variations.

100%	98%	95%	90%	80%	70%	60%	50%	40%	30%	20%	10%
$605	$550	$470	$415	$360	$305	$275	$250	$210	$175	$145	$110

PERCUSSION SHOTGUN—several variations.

100%	98%	95%	90%	80%	70%	60%	50%	40%	30%	20%	10%
$800	$715	$635	$550	$470	$415	$360	$320	$285	$250	$210	$155

ACHA

MAKER: DOMINGO ACHA, SPAIN.

Grading	100%	98%	95%	90%	80%	70%	60%

MODEL 1916—semi-auto pistol, 7.76mm, 7 shot mag., 1903 Browning copy.

	100%	98%	95%	90%	80%	70%	60%
	$220	$165	$100	$85	$65	$55	$45

ATLAS—semi-auto pistol, 6.35mm, 6 shot mag., slide marked ATLAS, 1906 Browning copy.

	100%	98%	95%	90%	80%	70%	60%
	$165	$140	$125	$95	$75	$65	$50

LOOKING GLASS—semi-auto pistol, 6.35mm, 6 shot mag., blued or nickel, 1906 Browning copy, side marked "Looking Glass", many variations.

	100%	98%	95%	90%	80%	70%	60%
	$220	$165	$130	$100	$85	$70	$55

LOOKING GLASS—semi-auto pistol, 7.65mm, exposed hammer.

	100%	98%	95%	90%	80%	70%	60%
	$220	$165	$140	$105	$90	$75	$65

ACME

TRADE NAME OF DAVENPORT ARMS COMPANY SHOTGUNS, MALTBY HENLEY & CO. REVOLVERS, AND MERWIN AND HULBURT & CO. OWL HEAD REVOLVERS.

100%	98%	95%	90%	80%	70%	60%	50%	40%	30%	20%	10%

SEVEN SHOT REVOLVER—single action, .22 short rimfire.

100%	98%	95%	90%	80%	70%	60%	50%	40%	30%	20%	10%
$360	$310	$240	$185	$165	$150	$120	$110	$100	$90	$65	$55

FIVE SHOT REVOLVER—single action, .32 short rimfire.

100%	98%	95%	90%	80%	70%	60%	50%	40%	30%	20%	10%
$360	$320	$255	$200	$175	$160	$120	$110	$100	$90	$65	$55

ACME ARMS

TRADE NAME FOR CORNWALL HARDWARE CO., NY.

REVOLVERS

SEVEN SHOT—single action, .22 short rimfire.

100%	98%	95%	90%	80%	70%	60%	50%	40%	30%	20%	10%
$275	$250	$210	$185	$165	$155	$140	$125	$110	$90	$85	$75

FIVE SHOT—single action, .32 short rimfire.

100%	98%	95%	90%	80%	70%	60%	50%	40%	30%	20%	10%
$285	$255	$215	$195	$175	$165	$145	$120	$100	$90	$85	$75

SHOTGUN

SIDE-BY-SIDE—12 ga., damascus barrel.

100%	98%	95%	90%	80%	70%	60%	50%	40%	30%	20%	10%
$275	$240	$195	$165	$145	$125	$110	$95	$65	$60	$50	$45

ACME HAMMERLESS

MAKER: HOPKINS & ALLEN, FOR HULBERT BROTHERS, 1893.

REVOLVERS

FIVE SHOT—double action, top break, .32 centerfire, non-ejecting.

100%	98%	95%	90%	80%	70%	60%	50%	40%	30%	20%	10%
$145	$125	$100	$90	$80	$70	$60	$50	$40	$30	$20	$15

Also known as Forehand Model 1891, can be hammer or hammerless.

FIVE SHOT—double action, top break, .38 centerfire, non-ejecting.

100%	98%	95%	90%	80%	70%	60%	50%	40%	30%	20%	10%
$145	$125	$100	$90	$80	$70	$60	$50	$40	$30	$20	$15

Also known as Forehand Model 1891, can be hammer or hammerless.

ACTION (M.S.)

MAKER: MODESTO SANTOS, EIBAR, SPAIN.

MODEL 1915—semi-auto pistol (French Military), 7.65mm.

	100%	98%	95%	90%	80%	70%	60%
	$175	$145	$120	$85	$70	$60	$45

MODEL 1920—semi-auto pistol (action), 6.35mm.

	$195	$150	$110	$85	$65	$45	$40

ACTION ARMS LTD.

IMPORTERS AND DISTRIBUTORS LOCATED IN PHILADELPHIA, PA.

Only Action Arms Model AT88S will be listed under this heading. Uzi and Galil trademarks can be located in their respective sections.

PISTOLS

AT-88S—9mm or .41 Action Express cal., double action design patterned after CZ-75, 4.6 in. barrel, 15 shot mag. (9mm), 9 shot mag. in .41 AE, can be "cocked and locked", fixed sights, blued metal, walnut grips, 35.3 oz., mfg. in Switzerland. New in 1987.

Mfg.'s Sug. Retail	$598	$500	$415	$375	$350	$325	$295	$275

This model is also available in chrome finish at no extra charge. The AT-88S was previously designated the AT-84.

AT-88P—compact variation of the Model AT-88S, 3.7 in. barrel, 13 shot mag., 32.1 oz. New in 1989.

Mfg.'s Sug. Retail	$698	$600	$500	$425	$395	$365	$335	$300

This model is also available in chrome finish at no extra charge. The AT-88P was previously designated the AT-84P.

AT-88H—9mm or .41 Action Express cal., ultra compact variation of the Model AT-88S, 3.4 in. barrel, 10 shot mag. New in 1989.

Mfg.'s Sug. Retail	$598	$500	$415	$375	$350	$325	$295	$275

This model is also available in chrome finish at no extra charge.

RIFLES

TIMBERWOLF—.357 Mag., slide action, straight grip shotgun style stock, 18.5 in. barrel, 10 shot tube mag., integral scope base. New in 1989.

Mfg.'s Sug. Retail	$475	$415	$385	$360	$340	$320	$295	$275

ADAMS

MAKER: DEANE, ADAMS, & DEANE, LOCATED IN LONDON, ENG.

PERCUSSION REVOLVERS

100%	98%	95%	90%	80%	70%	60%	50%	40%	30%	20%	10%

MODEL 1851—double action, .38 cal., 4½ in. barrel.

$1,375	$1,265	$1,100	$990	$855	$745	$690	$605	$550	$440	$385	$330

MODEL 1851—double action, .44 cal., 6 in. barrel.

$935	$880	$800	$690	$550	$495	$440	$395	$340	$305	$275	$255

MODEL 1851—Dragoon, double action, .50 cal., 8 in. barrel.

$1,375	$1,265	$1,100	$990	$855	$715	$690	$605	$550	$385	$360	$340

ADAMS, cont.

100%	98%	95%	90%	80%	70%	60%	50%	40%	30%	20%	10%

MODEL 1851—.38 cal., cased with accessories.

100%	98%	95%	90%	80%	70%	60%	50%	40%	30%	20%	10%
$1,760	$1,595	$1,375	$1,100	$990	$910	$825	$745	$660	$605	$550	$525

MODEL 1851—.44 cal., cased with accessories.

100%	98%	95%	90%	80%	70%	60%	50%	40%	30%	20%	10%
$1,295	$1,155	$990	$880	$770	$690	$635	$550	$440	$385	$360	$330

MODEL 1851—Dragoon, .50 cal., cased with accessories.

100%	98%	95%	90%	80%	70%	60%	50%	40%	30%	20%	10%
$1,680	$1,485	$1,210	$1,185	$990	$880	$800	$715	$635	$550	$495	$470

ADAMS, JOSEPH

BIRMINGHAM, ENGLAND.

OFFICER MODEL—flintlock pistol, musket caliber .65, Brown Bess.

100%	98%	95%	90%	80%	70%	60%	50%	40%	30%	20%	10%
$2,850	$2,500	$2,250	$2,000	$1,800	$1,600	$1,400	$1,100	$900	$825	$725	$600

ADAMY, GEBRUDER

SUHL, GERMANY, 1920'S AND 1930'S.

Grading	100%	98%	95%	90%	80%	70%	60%

SHOTGUN—O/U, double trigger, engraved, cased.

Grading	100%	98%	95%	90%	80%	70%	60%
	$1,815	$1,650	$1,375	$1,155	$ 990	$ 880	$ 770

ADIRONDACK ARMS COMPANY

PLATTSBURGH, NEW YORK, 1870-1874.

Magazine loaded repeating rifle, .44 cal., brass or iron frame, later model, may also be marked A.S. Babbitt, Plattsburgh, N.Y., absorbed by Winchester in 1874, then discontinued.

This rifle was designed in 1870 and patented by Orvill M. Robinson in Upper Jay, NY. This rifle was available in .38 and .44 cal. rimfire rifles with no wooden forend and had a high cyclic rate of fire. Original models were made in Plattsburgh, NY at which time A.S. Babbitt became one of several additional partners. In 1872, Robinson was granted a patent for a second model rifle. It was similar to the 1870, except a wooden forend was added and the operating mechanism was changed considerably. Following these improvements, Mr. Oliver Winchester contacted Mr. Robinson and purchased the entire Robinson company.

100%	98%	95%	90%	80%	70%	60%	50%	40%	30%	20%	10%

EARLY MODEL—finger holds on hammer.

100%	98%	95%	90%	80%	70%	60%	50%	40%	30%	20%	10%
$2,310	$2,090	$1,760	$1,430	$1,320	$1,265	$1,210	$ 990	$ 880	$ 770	$ 660	$ 605

LATE MODEL—action worked by buttons top of receiver mid-section.

100%	98%	95%	90%	80%	70%	60%	50%	40%	30%	20%	10%
$2,200	$2,035	$1,705	$1,320	$1,210	$1,100	$ 990	$ 880	$ 770	$ 660	$ 550	$ 495

ADLER

MAKER: ENGELBRECHT & WOLFF LOCATED IN BLASII, GERMANY, 1905-1907.

Grading	100%	98%	95%	90%	80%	70%	60%

SEMI-AUTO PISTOL—7mm Adler, 8 shot mag., cocking lever on top of frame, not competitive in its price range.

Grading	100%	98%	95%	90%	80%	70%	60%
	$2,200	$1,925	$1,540	$1,045	$ 770	$ 495	$ 330

ADVANTAGE ARMS USA, INC.

PREVIOUSLY MANUFACTURED BY ADVANTAGE ARMS USA, INC. DISTRIBUTED BY WILDFIRE SPORTS, INC. LOCATED IN ST. PAUL, MN.

MODEL 422—.22 LR and Mag., 4 barrel double action derringer, rotating firing pin, 2½ in. barrel, high grade alloy frame and barrel, 4 shot, 15 oz., available in blue, nickel, or QPQ (heat treated but appears blued) finish. Add $11 for .22 Mag. Made in 1986-87 only.

		$150	$135	$115	$105	$ 95	$ 85	$ 75

Last Mfg.'s Sug. Retail was $166.
Add $6 for nickel finish.
Add $11 for QPQ finish.

AETNA

MAKER: HARRINGTON & RICHARDSON LOCATED IN WORCHESTER, MA.

Type: single action revolvers, all of the same general size and configuration, solid frame, spur trigger, so called "Suicide Specials" during their day.

100%	98%	95%	90%	80%	70%	60%	50%	40%	30%	20%	10%

AETNA NO. 2—.32 rimfire, 5 shot.

$330	$275	$215	$185	$170	$155	$145	$120	$100	$ 85	$ 75	$ 55

AETNA NO. 2½—.32 rimfire, 5 shot.

$330	$275	$215	$185	$170	$155	$145	$120	$100	$ 85	$ 75	$ 55

MODEL 1876—.22 rimfire, 7 shot.

$330	$275	$210	$195	$175	$165	$155	$130	$110	$ 95	$ 90	$ 65

MODEL 1876—.32 rimfire, 5 shot.

$330	$275	$210	$175	$165	$155	$145	$120	$105	$ 90	$ 75	$ 55

MODEL 1876—.38 rimfire, 5 shot.

$330	$275	$220	$205	$195	$175	$165	$145	$120	$105	$ 95	$ 85

AETNA ARMS COMPANY

MANUFACTURED IN NEW YORK, 1869-1883.

Single action pocket revolver, blued or nickel, birdshead grip, copy of S&W models 1-3, models marked ALLING are worth a slight premium.

SEVEN SHOT—.22 rimfire.

$250	$235	$210	$195	$175	$165	$155	$130	$110	$ 95	$ 90	$ 65

FIVE SHOT—.32 rimfire.

$230	$220	$205	$175	$165	$155	$145	$120	$105	$ 90	$ 75	$ 55

AGNER

MANUFACTURED BY SAXHOJ PRODUCTS INC. IN DENMARK. IMPORTED UNTIL 1986 BY BEEMAN ARMS, INC. LOCATED IN SANTA ROSA, CA.

AGNER, cont.

Grading	100%	98%	95%	90%	80%	70%	60%

PISTOL: SEMI-AUTO

M 80—.22 LR only, stainless steel, semi-auto target pistol, new design features unique security key safety feature, adj. French walnut grips, dry fire mechanism, 5.9 in. barrel, 2.4 lbs., 5 shot mag., limited production. Left-hand action — add $100. Imported 1981-1986.

$1,125 $1,040 $950

Last Mfg.'s Sug. Retail was $1,295.

AIR MATCH

PREVIOUSLY IMPORTED BY KENDALL INTERNATIONAL, LOCATED IN PARIS, KY.

AIR MATCH 500—.22 cal. match single shot pistol, target grips, adj. front counterweight, 10½ in. barrel. Imported 1984-86.

$695 $575 $540 $510 $475 $440 $410

Last Mfg.'s Sug. Retail was $788.

AJAX ARMY

DISTRIBUTED BY E.C. MEACHAM CO., MAKER UNKNOWN, 1880'S CIRCA.

100%	98%	95%	90%	80%	70%	60%	50%	40%	30%	20%	10%

SINGLE ACTION—.44 rimfire, spur trigger, solid frame.

| $550 | $440 | $360 | $315 | $275 | $255 | $230 | $210 | $185 | $170 | $155 | $140 |

AKRILL, E.

FRENCH, 1800'S.

FLINTLOCK RIFLE—breech loaded, .69 cal., damascus octagon barrel.

| $3,300 | $2,750 | $2,200 | $1,980 | $1,460 | $1,320 | $1,240 | $1,075 | $ 935 | $ 800 | $ 745 | $ 660 |

ALAMO RANGER

Grading	100%	98%	95%	90%	80%	70%	60%

REVOLVER—.38 cal., Spanish copy of Colt Model 1929.

$140 $120 $110 $100 $ 90 $ 85 $ 75

ALASKA

MAKER: HOOD FIREARMS COMPANY, NORWICH, CONNECTICUT, 1873-1884.

Dubbed "Suicide Specials" in their day.

REVOLVERS

100%	98%	95%	90%	80%	70%	60%	50%	40%	30%	20%	10%

SINGLE ACTION—.22 rimfire, 7 shot, spur trigger, solid frame.

| $275 | $220 | $195 | $145 | $140 | $125 | $110 | $100 | $ 90 | $ 75 | $ 70 | $ 65 |

FIVE SHOT—.32 short rimfire.

| $220 | $195 | $160 | $155 | $150 | $140 | $125 | $105 | $ 95 | $ 85 | $ 75 | $ 70 |

ALDAZABAL

MAKER: ALDAZABAL, LETURIONDO & CIA.

SEMI-AUTOMATIC PISTOL—7.65mm, 7 shot, Eibar style.

$195	$165	$110	$100	$ 90	$ 75	$ 65

ALERT

MAKER: HOOD FIREARMS COMPANY, NORWICH CONNECTICUT, 1873-1881.

These revolvers were dubbed "Suicide Specials" in their day.

REVOLVERS

100%	98%	95%	90%	80%	70%	60%	50%	40%	30%	20%	10%

SINGLE ACTION—.22 rimfire, 7 shot, spur trigger, solid frame.

100%	98%	95%	90%	80%	70%	60%	50%	40%	30%	20%	10%
$220	$195	$165	$145	$130	$125	$110	$100	$90	$75	$70	$65

FIVE SHOT—.32 short rimfire.

$170	$165	$160	$155	$150	$140	$125	$105	$95	$85	$75	$70

ALEXIA

MAKER: HOPKINS & ALLEN, NORWICH, CONNECTICUT, 1867-1915.

Also known as: Blue Jacket, Captain Jack, Chichester, Defender, Dictator, Monarch, Mountain Eagle, Hopkins & Allen, Towers Police Safety, and Universal.

Description: single action revolver, solid frame, spur trigger, inexpensive vest pocket pistol issued under numerous names for private companies, octagon barrel.

REVOLVERS

.22 RIMFIRE—7 shot.

$165	$160	$155	$145	$130	$125	$110	$100	$ 90	$ 75	$ 70	$ 65

.32 SHORT RIMFIRE—5 shot.

$170	$165	$160	$155	$150	$140	$125	$105	$ 95	$ 85	$ 75	$ 70

.38 SHORT RIMFIRE—5 shot.

$195	$180	$170	$165	$160	$145	$140	$120	$110	$100	$ 90	$ 85

.41 SHORT RIMFIRE—5 shot.

$220	$210	$205	$195	$180	$170	$160	$145	$125	$110	$100	$ 90

ALFA

MAKER: ARMERO ESPECIALISTAS REUNIDAS,LOCATED IN EIBAR, SPAIN, 1920'S.

All revolvers are marked Alfa on grips.

Grading		100%	98%	95%	90%	80%	70%	60%

EARLY MODEL—.32, .38, and .44 cal.'s, copies of S&W No. 2 by O. Hermanos.

$145	$130	$120	$110	$105	$ 95	$ 75

LATE MODEL—.22 LR, .32 S&W, and .38 S&W cal.'s, copies of Colt Police Positive and S&W Military and Police.

$160	$150	$130	$120	$110	$100	$ 90

ALKARTASUNA FABRICA DE ARMAS, S.A.

MANUFACTURED IN GUERNICA, SPAIN.

ALKARTASUNA RUBY AUTOMATIC—7.65mm, 9 shot, 3⅝ in. barrel, blue, fixed sights, checkered wood or hard rubber grips, used by French Army in WWI and WWII, made 1917-1922.

		$220	$195	$165	$110	$ 65	$ 55	$ 45

ALLEN & THURBER

Note: Ethan Allen started many plants to keep up with expanding business after 1832. Listed below is a chronological order of the firms constituting the family dynasty founded by Ethan Allen.

E. Allen — Grafton, Mass. 1832-1837

Allen & Thurber — Grafton, Mass. 1837-1842

Allen & Thurber — Norwich, Conn. 1842-1847

Allen & Thurber — Worcester, Mass. 1847-1854

Allen, Thurber, & Co. — Worcester, Mass. 1854-1856

Allen & Wheelock — Worcester, Mass. 1856-1865

E. Allen & Co. — Worcester, Mass. 1865-1871

Forehand & Wadsworth — Worcester, Mass. 1871-1890

Forehand Arms Co. — Worcester, Mass. 1890-1902

No other 19th century American firm produced a wider variety of firearms than did Ethan Allen & subsidiaries.

ALLEN FIREARMS

PREVIOUS IMPORTER LOCATED IN SANTA FE, NM IMPORTING A. UBERTI FIREARMS UNTIL EARLY IN 1987. AFTER ALLEN FIREARMS CLOSED, CIMARRON F.A. MFG. CO. LOCATED IN HOUSTON, TX PURCHASED THE REMAINING INVENTORY (IN ADDITION TO ORDERING NEW PRODUCTS UNDER THEIR NAME). UBERTI USA, INC. LOCATED IN NEW YORK, NY AND BENSON FIREARMS LOCATED IN SEATTLE, WA ARE ALSO CURRENTLY IMPORTING A. UBERTI FIREARMS AND CAN BE FOUND IN THEIR RESPECTIVE SECTIONS OF THIS TEXT.

Formerly called Western Arms — manufacturer of both modern & black powder reproduction firearms and accessories patterned after famous older models. Only modern cartridge guns will be shown in this section. Black powder guns will appear under Modern Black Powder Guns.

REVOLVERS: SINGLE ACTION

Available in either black powder or modern configured frames.

CATTLEMAN—available in .45 LC, .44-40, .38 Spl., .357 Mag., .22 LR, and .22 Mag cal.'s, 4¾, 5½, and 7½ in. barrel lengths, brass or steel backstraps and trigger guard.

		$275	$225	$190	$175	$150	$140	$125

Last Mfg.'s Sug. Retail was $289.

Also could be ordered with A, B, or C grade engraving and nickel finish.

15

Grading	100%	98%	95%	90%	80%	70%	60%

Sheriff's Model—.44-40 and .45 LC cal's., 3 in. barrel.

	$275	$225	$190	$175	$160	$150	$135

Last Mfg.'s Sug. Retail was $289.

Target Model—same as Cattleman Model, only fully adj. rear blade sight.

	$285	$230	$200	$185	$170	$150	$135

Last Mfg.'s Sug. Retail was $299.

CATTLEMAN BUNTLINE—.45 LC, .44-40, and .357 Mag. cal's, 18 in. barrel, backstrap cut for shoulder stock.

	$285	$230	$200	$185	$175	$165	$150

Last Mfg.'s Sug. Retail was $299.

BUCKHORN—.44 Mag., .44 Spl., and .44-40 cal.'s, various barrel lengths, Buntline and revolving carbine models, also available in the Buckhorn series — add approximately $60, add $30 for convertible cylinders.

	$275	$225	$205	$190	$180	$170	$160

Last Mfg.'s Sug. Retail was $299.

"OUTLAW" 1875 REMINGTON—available in .45 LC, .44-40, and .357 Mag. cal.'s, 7½ barrel. Add $40 for nickel plating.

	$240	$195	$180	$170	$155	$140	$120

Last Mfg.'s Sug. Retail was $279.

1890 REMINGTON—available in .45 LC, .44-40, and .357 Mag. cal.'s, 5½ barrel. New in 1986.

	$245	$200	$180	$170	$155	$140	$120

Last Mfg.'s Sug. Retail was $289.

PHANTOM MODEL—.357 and .44 Mag. only, 10 in. barrel for silhouette use. New in 1985.

	$315	$290	$260	$230	$215	$190	$170

Last Mfg.'s Sug. Retail was $369.

REVOLVERS: DOUBLE ACTION

INSPECTOR MODEL—.32 S&W and .38 Sp. cal.'s, 3, 4, and 6 in. barrels, double action, blued or chrome finish. New in 1985. Add $20 for target sights.

	$235	$210	$170	$145	$125	$110	$95

Last Mfg.'s Sug. Retail was $279.

TARGET PISTOLS

1871 ROLLING BLOCK TARGET PISTOL—available in .357 Mag., .22 LR, and 22 Mag. cal.'s, 9½ in. barrel. Also available in carbine model (22 in. barrel) - add $35.

	$205	$170	$150	$135	$120	$100	$90

Last Mfg.'s Sug. Retail was $229.

CARBINES AND RIFLES

CATTLEMAN REVOLVING CARBINE S.A.—available in .45 LC, .44-40, .357 Mag., and .22 LR/Mag. (convertible) cal.'s, 18 in. barrel.

	$295	$245	$225	$200	$180	$165	$150

Last Mfg.'s Sug. Retail was $339.

1875 REMINGTON CARBINE S.A.—18 in. barrel - same cal.'s as above, except .22 LR/Mag.

	$350	$290	$260	$230	$200	$175	$150

Last Mfg.'s Sug. Retail was $389.

Grading	100%	98%	95%	90%	80%	70%	60%

HENRY RIFLE OR CARBINE—.44-40 cal., brass frame, 24½ in. barrel on rifle, 22½ in. barrel on carbine.

	100%	98%	95%	90%	80%	70%	60%
	$495	$450	$415	$360	$320	$260	$220

Last Mfg.'s Sug. Retail was $569.

Could also be special ordered with grade A engraving ($250 extra), grade B engraving ($400 extra), and grade 3 engraving ($500 extra).

Henry 1 of 1,000—discontinued several years ago, premiums are slightly higher than a C engraved gun.

1866 CARBINE—.44-40, .38 Spl., .22 Mag. and .22 LR cal.'s, brass receiver, 19 in. round barrel. "Indian" model - add $40.

	100%	98%	95%	90%	80%	70%	60%
	$380	$335	$285	$260	$235	$210	$190

Last Mfg.'s Sug. Retail was $429.

1866 Trapper Carbine—.44-40 cal. only, 16 in. barrel.

	100%	98%	95%	90%	80%	70%	60%
	$380	$335	$285	$260	$235	$210	$190

Last Mfg.'s Sug. Retail was $429.

Red Cloud Commemorative carbine—same cal.'s, special engraving and brass tacks in forearm and stock.

	100%	98%	95%	90%	80%	70%	60%
	$430	$370	$310	$275	$240	$220	$200

Last Mfg.'s Sug. Retail was $469.

1866 RIFLE—brass receiver, same cal.'s as the carbine, 24¼ in. oct. barrel.

	100%	98%	95%	90%	80%	70%	60%
	$415	$355	$300	$260	$235	$210	$190

Last Mfg.'s Sug. Retail was $449.

1873 CARBINE—.44-40, .357 Mag., .22 Mag., and .22 LR cal.'s, steel receiver, 19 in. round barrel. Add $70 for nickel.

	100%	98%	95%	90%	80%	70%	60%
	$445	$400	$360	$320	$280	$240	$195

Last Mfg.'s Sug. Retail was $499.

1873 Trapper Carbine—.44-40 cal. only, 16 in. barrel.

	100%	98%	95%	90%	80%	70%	60%
	$445	$400	$360	$320	$280	$240	$195

Last Mfg.'s Sug. Retail was $499.

1873 RIFLE—casehardened receiver, same cal.'s as the carbine, 24¼ in. oct. barrel.

	100%	98%	95%	90%	80%	70%	60%
	$490	$450	$400	$360	$315	$270	$230

Last Mfg.'s Sug. Retail was $569.

SHARPS/GEMMER SPORTING RIFLE—.45-70 cal. only, copy of the famous Sharp's rifle. New in 1985.

	100%	98%	95%	90%	80%	70%	60%
	$525	$490	$410	$375	$320	$295	$270

Last Mfg.'s Sug. Retail was $599.

1979 JUSTIN CENTENNIAL COMMEMORATIVE—includes specially engraved 1866 sporting rifle and 1873 single action revolver (7½ in. barrel) with gold plated parts and inlay. Both guns are chambered for .44-40 cal. Also includes special hand signed pair of Justin boots, serial numbered belt buckle and presentation oak case. All serial numbers are matching.

Grading	100%	Issue price	Qty made

1873 1 of 1,000—.44-40 cal, special wood, only 1,000 manufactured. Discontinued in 1985.

	100%	Issue price	Qty made
	$1,350	$1,500	1,000

ALPHA ARMS INC.

PREVIOUSLY MANUFACTURED AND DISTRIBUTED IN FLOWER MOUND, TX FROM 1983-87.

Retail price included custom hard case.

Grading	100%	98%	95%	90%	80%	70%	60%

RIFLES: BOLT ACTION

Many special order options including an octagonal barrel, various finishes, and special sights were available at extra cost on the models listed below. These options, while not listed separately by price, will add value to the prices shown below.

ALPHA JAGUAR—available in most calibers from .222 Rem. through .338 Win., Mauser-type barreled action, Alphawood laminate stock, 20 to 24 in. barrel lengths, around 6 lbs. New in 1987.

Grade I Jaguar—slide safety, supplied with luggage case.

	100%	98%	95%	90%	80%	70%	60%
	$900	$800	$700	$625	$560	$500	$425

Last Mfg.'s Sug. Retail was $995.

Grade II Jaguar—similar to Grade I Jaguar, except has Douglas premium barrel.

	100%	98%	95%	90%	80%	70%	60%
	$995	$900	$800	$700	$625	$560	$500

Last Mfg.'s Sug. Retail was $1,095.

Grade III Jaguar—similar to Grade II Jaguar, except has Model 70-type 3-position safety, honed trigger and action.

	100%	98%	95%	90%	80%	70%	60%
	$1,125	$995	$900	$800	$700	$625	$560

Last Mfg.'s Sug. Retail was $1,395.

Grade IV Jaguar—similar to Grade III Jaguar, except has fully lightened action and installed swivel studs.

	100%	98%	95%	90%	80%	70%	60%
	$1,250	$1,050	$930	$825	$725	$640	$560

Last Mfg.'s Sug. Retail was $1,595.

ALPHA CUSTOM—available in most calibers from .222 Rem. through .338-284, many other calibers available on special order, 20 to 24 in. barrel lengths, limited production, right or left-hand, around 6 lbs. New in 1984.

	100%	98%	95%	90%	80%	70%	60%
	$1,525	$1,200	$975	$850	$725	$640	$560

Last Mfg.'s Sug. Retail was $1,735.

ALPHA GRAND SLAM—same general specifications as the Alpha Custom, except comes standard with laminated wood stock, fluted bolt and non-glare matte finished metal parts, right or left-hand, approx., 6½ lbs. New in 1985.

	100%	98%	95%	90%	80%	70%	60%
	$1,200	$950	$875	$750	$650	$600	$525

Last Mfg.'s Sug. Retail was $1,465.

ALPHA ALASKAN—.308 Win., .350 Rem. Mag., .358 Win., and .458 Win. cal.'s. Action is similar to Alpha Grand Slam, except barrel, receiver, bolt and safety are stainless steel, right or left-hand, approx., 6¾ - 7½ lbs. New in 1985.

	100%	98%	95%	90%	80%	70%	60%
	$1,525	$1,200	$975	$850	$725	$640	$560

Last Mfg.'s Sug. Retail was $1,735.

ALPHA BIG-FIVE—.300 H&H thru .375 H&H and .458 Win. cal.'s, action is similar to Alpha Jaguar Grade IV, except has reinforced stock and decelerator recoil pad. Made in 1987 only.

	100%	98%	95%	90%	80%	70%	60%
	$1,575	$1,250	$1,050	$895	$750	$640	$560

Last Mfg.'s Sug. Retail was $1,795.

AMERICAN ARMS

PREVIOUSLY MANUFACTURED IN GARDEN GROVE, CA.

EAGLE 380—.380 ACP only, stainless steel semi-auto, copy of Walther PPKS, 6 round mag., 3¼ in. barrel, 20 oz. Also available in black teflon finish — add $25 (discontinued in 1985).

	100%	98%	95%
	$270	$235	$215

Last Mfg.'s Sug. Retail was $289.

AMERICAN ARMS CO.

MANUFACTURED IN BOSTON, MA FROM 1870-1901. 1893 TO 1004 AT MILWAUKEE, WI. ACQUIRED BY MARLIN IN 1901.

HANDGUNS

O/U DESIGN—Wheeler Pat. Action, brass frame, spur trigger, .22 Short R.F., .32 Short R.F., .41 Short R.F.

$800	$750	$700	$650	$575	$500	$420	$360	$300	$225	$160	$110

SHOTGUNS

HAMMERLESS MODEL—12 ga., semi-hammerless.

$600	$550	$500	$450	$350	$275	$225	$175	$150	$125	$100	$ 75

WHITMORE PATENT—12 and 10 ga., hammerless, checkering, SxS. Add 10% for 10 ga. (2⅞).

$685	$625	$575	$520	$460	$400	$340	$270	$200	$150	$125	$100

SINGLESHOT—12 ga., semi-hammerless, damascus barrel.

$260	$225	$200	$175	$150	$125	$90	$70	$50	$40	$30	$20

AMERICAN ARMS, INC.

IMPORTER/MANUFACTURER/DISTRIBUTOR OF QUALITY FIREARMS INCLUDING VARIOUS SPANISH SHOTGUNS (GRULLA, INDESAL, NORICA, AND ZABALA HERMANOS) AND SEVERAL EUROPEAN PISTOLS AND RIFLES. AMERICAN ARMS ALSO MANUFACTURES SEVERAL PISTOLS IN NORTH KANSAS CITY, MO. AMERICAN ARMS IMPORTED NORICA AIRGUNS MAY BE LOCATED UNDER THE NORICA HEADING IN THE MODERN AIRGUNS SECTION IN THE BACK OF THIS PUBLICATION. HEADQUARTERED IN NORTH KANSAS CITY, MO.

American Arms also imports Franchi O/U and semi-auto shotguns which can be found under the Franchi listing in this text.

Grading	100%	98%	95%	90%	80%	70%	60%

PISTOLS

MODEL TT-9MM TOKAREV—9mm Para., semi-auto single action, 4½ in. barrel, 9 round mag., hammer block external safety, short barrel recoil, 31 oz. New in 1988.

Mfg.'s Sug. Retail	$289	$250	$230	$210	$195	$180	$170	$160

This model is patterned after the Tokarev action and is made from machined steel parts in Yugoslavia.

MODEL EP-380—.380 ACP, semi-auto double action, stainless steel, 3½ in. barrel, 7 round mag., wood checkered grips, adj. rear sight, 25 oz. New in 1988.

Mfg.'s Sug. Retail	$449	$390	$340	$275

This model is made in West Germany.

MODEL ZC-380—.380 ACP, semi-auto single action, baby Tokarev action, 3½ in. barrel, 8 round mag., black polymer grips, adj. rear sight, 26 oz. New in 1988.

Mfg.'s Sug. Retail	$289	$250	$230	$210	$195	$180	$170	$160

This model is made in Yugoslavia.

MODEL PK-22—.22 LR, semi-auto double action, 3⅓ in. barrel, 8 shot finger extension mag., black polymer grips, 22 oz. New in 1988.

Mfg.'s Sug. Retail	$199	$175	$150	$125	$110	$100	$90	$80

This model is made in North Kansas City, MO. It has patented safety features such as external hammer block and internal blocking of the firing pin until the trigger is pulled.

Grading	100%	98%	95%	90%	80%	70%	60%

MODEL PX-22—.22 LR, compact variation of the Model PK-22, 2¾ in. barrel, 7 shot finger extension mag., 15 oz. New in 1989.

Mfg.'s Sug. Retail	$189	$170	$150	$125	$110	$100	$90	$80

RIFLES

MODEL ZCY 223—.223 cal., gas operated semi-auto, standard Yugoslavian military rifle. While this model was advertised, it was never imported.

	$835	$730	$615	$500	$440	$400	$360

Last Mfg.'s Sug. Retail was $940.

MODEL ZCY 308—.308 cal., gas operated semi-auto, standard Yugoslavian military rifle. Imported in 1988 only.

	$740	$615	$500	$440	$400	$375	$350

Last Mfg.'s Sug. Retail was $825.

MODEL AKY 39—7.62 x 39mm cal., gas operated semi-auto, Teakwood fixed stock and grip, flip up Tritium night front sight and rear, Yugoslavian AK-47 military rifle. Importation began in 1988.

Mfg.'s Sug. Retail	$559	$500	$465	$415	$380	$340	$300	$270

This model is supplied with sling and cleaning kit.

Model AKF 39 Folding Stock—7.62 x 39mm cal., folding stock variation of the Model AKY-39. Importation began in 1988.

Mfg.'s Sug. Retail	$589	$520	$485	$435	$390	$340	$300	$270

MODEL AKC 47—similar to AKY 39 except does not have Tritium night sights, equipped with blade bayonet, 3 clips and cleaning kit. Importation began in 1989.

Mfg.'s Sug. Retail	$365	$325	$290	$270	$250	$225	$215	$200

Model AKF 47 Folding Stock—similar to AKF 39 except has underfolding metal stock. Importation began in 1989.

Mfg.'s Sug. Retail	$365	$325	$290	$270	$250	$225	$215	$200

EXP-64 SURVIVAL RIFLE—.22 LR, semi-auto, takedown rifle stores in oversize synthetic stock compartment, 21 in. barrel, 10 shot clip mag., open sights, receiver grooved for scope mounting, cross bolt safety, 40 in. overall length, 7 lbs. New in 1989.

Mfg.'s Sug. Retail	$165	$150	$135	$125	$115	$105	$95	$85

SM 64 TD SPORTER—.22 LR, semi-auto, takedown barrel, 21 in. barrel, checkered walnut finished hardwood stock and forend, hooded front sight and adj. rear sight, 7 lbs. New in 1989.

Mfg.'s Sug. Retail	$149	$135	$125	$115	$105	$95	$85	$75

SHOTGUNS: OVER AND UNDER

American Arms is currently importing Spanish shotguns manufactured by Zabala Hermanos, Indesal, and Grulla. American Arms imported Franchi Black Magic semi-auto and O/U shotguns will appear under the Franchi section in this text. Older Diarm models have been listed below.

LINCE—12 and 20 ga.'s, 3 in. chambers, boxlock with Greener crossbolt, various barrel lengths and chokings, available in either blue or shiny chrome finish, SST, VR, ejectors. Imported in 1986 only.

	$510	$400	$380	$360	$340	$320	$300

Add $70 for choke tubes.

Last Mfg.'s Sug. Retail was $610.

SILVER MODEL—12 and 20 ga. only, similar to Lince Model, except has brushed aluminum finished receiver, no engraving. Imported 1986-87 only.

	$495	$450	$390	$360	$330	$300	$285

Add $50 for multi-chokes.

Last Mfg.'s Sug. Retail was $545.

Grading	100%	98%	95%	90%	80%	70%	60%

SILVER I—similar to Silver Model, except also available in 28 or .410 ga. (both new in 1988), single selective trigger became standard in 1988, extractors, fixed chokes, recoil pad. New in 1987.

Mfg.'s Sug. Retail	$439	$380	$355	$330	$300	$285	$270	$255

Add $60 for 28 or .410 ga.

SILVER II—similar to Silver Model, except is supplied with choke tubes, deluxe walnut, and ejectors. New in 1987.

Mfg.'s Sug. Retail	$579	$525	$485	$440	$390	$360	$330	$300

28 and .410 ga. (fixed chokes only) are available at no extra charge.

Small Gauge Combo—includes 28 and .410 ga. barrels bored IC/M. New in 1989.

Mfg.'s Sug. Retail	$789	$675	$600	$550	$525	$495	$475	$450

STERLING/BRISTOL—12 and 20 ga.'s, 3 in. chambers, boxlock with Greener crossbolt and false side plates, various barrel lengths and choke tubes, chrome finished receiver with moderate game scene engraving, SST, VR, ejectors. New in 1986.

Mfg.'s Sug. Retail	$825	$695	$550	$495	$450	$400	$375	$350

Until 1989, this model was designated the Bristol. In 1988, the engraving pattern was changed from game scene to elaborate scroll type.

SIR—12 and 20 ga.'s, 3 in. chambers, sidelock with Greener crossbolt, various barrel lengths and chokings, chrome finished receiver with game scene engraving, ST, VR, ejectors, deluxe checkered pistol grip stock and forearm. Imported in 1986 only.

		$900	$725	$660	$610	$565	$520	$485

Add $75 for choke tubes.

Last Mfg.'s Sug. Retail was $1,090.

ROYAL—12 and 20 ga.'s, 3 in. chambers, sidelock with Greener crossbolt, various barrel lengths and chokings, chrome finished receiver with elaborate scroll engraving, ST, VR, ejectors, oil finished deluxe checkered pistol grip and forearm. Imported 1986-87 only.

		$1,595	$1,310	$1,080	$960	$850	$750	$675

Last Mfg.'s Sug. Retail was $1,730
Add $65 for choke tubes.

EXCELSIOR—12 and 20 ga.'s, 3 in. chambers, sidelock with Greener crossbolt, various barrel lengths and chokings, chrome finished receiver with elaborate deep relief engraving and multiple gold inlays, ST, VR, ejectors, oil finished deluxe checkered pistol grip and forearm. Imported 1986-87 only.

		$1,775	$1,510	$1,250	$1,100	$975	$885	$780

Add $70 for choke tubes.

Last Mfg.'s Sug. Retail was $1,925.

WATERFOWL SPECIAL—12 ga. only, Mag. chambers (3½ in. was added in 1989), 28 in. barrels with choke tubes, SST, ejectors, parkerized metal finish, matte finished stock and forearm, sling swivels, camo sling, recoil pad. New in 1987.

Mfg.'s Sug. Retail	$609	$565	$500	$460	$425	$395	$375	$350

10 ga. Waterfowl—10 ga. Mag., double triggers, extractors, matte finishes similar to 12 ga. Waterfowl, beavertail forearm. New in 1988.

Mfg.'s Sug. Retail	$829	$750	$625	$550	$495	$450	$390	$360

TURKEY SPECIAL—10 ga., 3½ in. Mag., 26 in. barrels with choke tubes, double triggers, extractors, recoil pad, non-glare metal finish, camouflage sling. New in 1988.

Mfg.'s Sug. Retail	$875	$775	$650	$575	$500	$450	$390	$360

F.S. 200—12 ga., trap or skeet model, 26 or 32 in. separated barrels only, SST, ejectors, boxlock with Greener crossbolt, black or chromed receiver, checkered walnut stock and forearm. Imported in 1986-87 only.

		$690	$560	$500	$450	$410	$375	$350

Last Mfg.'s Sug. Retail was $835.

F.S. 300—12 ga., trap or skeet model, 26, 30, or 32 in. separated barrels only, SST, ejectors, boxlock with Greener crossbolt and false side plates lightly engraved, chromed receiver, checkered walnut stock and forearm. Imported in 1986 only.

		$825	$675	$610	$555	$510	$470	$440

Last Mfg.'s Sug. Retail was $995.

Grading	100%	98%	95%	90%	80%	70%	60%

F.S. 400—12 ga., trap or skeet model, 26, 30, or 32 in. separated barrels only, ST, ejectors, sidelock with Greener crossbolt, lightly engraved chromed receiver, checkered walnut stock and forearm. Imported in 1986 only.

	$1,145	$945	$860	$800	$740	$680	$620

Last Mfg.'s Sug. Retail was $1,360.

F.S. 500—same specifications as FS 400. Importation discontinued in 1985.

	$1,175	$950	$860	$795	$730	$660	$595

Last Mfg.'s Sug. Retail was $1,360.

SHOTGUNS: SIDE-BY-SIDE

American Arms is currently importing Spanish shotguns manufactured by Zabala Hermanos and Indesal. Older discontinued Diarm models will also be shown in this section.

GENTRY/YORK—12, 20, 28, and .410 ga.'s, 3 in. chambers, boxlock, ejectors (extractors after 1986), double triggers, chromed receiver features fine scroll engraving. New in 1986.

Mfg.'s Sug. Retail	$469	$415	$360	$325	$300	$280	$260	$240

Add $30 for 28 or .410 ga.

Before 1988 this model was designated York (case coloring began in 1988).

BRITTANY—12 or 20 ga., boxlock action, 25 (20 ga.) or 27 (12 ga.) in. barrels, SST, ejectors, matted solid rib, choke tubes, engraved case colored frame, checkered walnut straight grip stock and semi-beavertail forearm, 6½ or 7 lbs. New in 1989.

Mfg.'s Sug. Retail	$649	$585	$520	$475	$435	$400	$375	$350

SHOGUN—10 ga., 3½ in. chambers, boxlock, ejectors, double triggers, chromed receiver features fine scroll engraving. Imported in 1986 only.

	$440	$350	$325	$300	$280	$260	$240

Last Mfg.'s Sug. Retail was $525.

DERBY—12, 20, 28, and .410 ga.'s, 3 in. chambers, sidelock, ejectors, double or ST trigger(s), chromed receiver features fine scroll engraving, oiled straight grip walnut stock and forearm. New in 1986.

Mfg.'s Sug. Retail	$789	$675	$550	$475	$420	$385	$350	$325

Add $35 for 28 or .410 ga.
Add $36 for ST.
Add approx. $200 for 2-barrel set (20 and 28 ga.).

Starting in 1988, this model featured a case-colored receiver.

GRULLA #2—12, 20, 28, or .410 ga., hand fitted sidelock action, 26 or 28 in. barrels, DT's, ejectors, fixed chokes, concave rib, case colored receiver with elaborate engraving, deluxe English style straight stock and splinter forearm (checkered and hand rubbed), between 5¾ - 6¼ lbs. New in 1989.

Mfg.'s Sug. Retail	$2,099	$1,895	$1,500	$1,250	$1,025	$900	$800	$700

Small Gauge Set—includes choice of 20/28 ga. or 28/.410 ga. barrel combination (26 in. fixed choke barrels). New in 1989.

Mfg.'s Sug. Retail	$2,875	$2,500	$2,100	$1,800	$1,550	$1,300	$1,150	$1,000

WATERFOWL SPECIAL—10 ga. only, 3½ in. chambers, 32 in. barrels, DT's, parkerized finish, sling swivels and camouflaged sling, extractors, fixed chokes, recoil pad. New in 1987.

Mfg.'s Sug. Retail	$609	$565	$500	$460	$425	$395	$375	$350

TURKEY SPECIAL—10 and 12 ga. only, Mag. chambers (3½ in. 12 ga. introduced in 1989), 26 in. barrels only, double triggers, parkerized finish, dull finish stock and forearm, sling swivels, recoil pad, choke tubes. New in 1987.

Mfg.'s Sug. Retail	$559	$485	$435	$395	$360	$330	$300	$285

Add $96 for 10 ga.

COMBINATION GUNS

RS COMBO—choice of .222 Rem. or .308 rifle barrel under 12 ga. barrel, engraved boxlock frame with antique silver finish, DT's, 24 in. VR barrels with shotgun choke tubes, rifle sights, grooved for scope mounting, Monte Carlo stock, 7 lbs. 14 oz. New in 1989.

Mfg.'s Sug. Retail	$749	$675	$595	$550	$495	$450	$420	$385

Grading	100%	98%	95%	90%	80%	70%	60%

SHOTGUNS: SINGLE SHOT

SINGLE SHOT MODEL—12, 20, or .410 ga., 3 in. Mag., non-exposed hammer, pistol grip stock, non-reflective finish. New in 1988.

Mfg.'s Sug. Retail	$99	$90	$80	$70	$60	$55	$50	$45

Camper Special—12, 20, or .410 ga., 3 in. Mag., folding design, 21 in. barrel, pistol grip. New in 1988.

Mfg.'s Sug. Retail	$107	$95	$80	$70	$60	$55	$50	$45

Slugger—12 or 20 ga., 24 in. Slug shotgun barrel with adj. rear sight and blade front, recoil pad. New in 1989.

Mfg.'s Sug. Retail	$115	$100	$85	$75	$65	$55	$50	$45

Youth—20 or .410 ga., 26 in. barrel, 12½ in. stock dimensions, recoil pad. New in 1989.

Mfg.'s Sug. Retail	$115	$100	$85	$75	$65	$55	$50	$45

Combo—interchangeable rifle and shotgun barrels, choice of .22 Hornet/12 ga. with 28 in. barrel or .22 LR/20 ga. with 26 in. barrel, includes fitted hard case. New in 1989.

Mfg.'s Sug. Retail	$235	$195	$165	$130	$115	$100	$90	$80

10 Ga. Model—10 ga. only, 3½ in. chambers, 26 in. multi-choke or 32 in. full fixed choke barrel, non-exposed hammer, non-reflective finish. New in 1988.

Mfg.'s Sug. Retail	$149	$135	$115	$95	$80	$70	$60	$55

Add $30 for multi-chokes (26 in. barrel).

AMERICAN BARLOCK WONDER

MANUFACTURED BY CRESCENT ARMS FOR SEARS ROEBUCK & CO.

SHOTGUNS

SIDE-BY-SIDE—various gauges, hammerless or outside hammer, damascus or steel barrels. Add 15% for steel barrels, smaller gauges.

	$240	$225	$200	$175	$140	$100	$75

SINGLE SHOT—various gauges, hammer, steel barrel. Add 35% for smaller gauges.

	$125	$115	$100	$90	$75	$60	$50

AMERICAN DERRINGER CORPORATION

MANUFACTURED AND DISTRIBUTED 1980-PRESENT IN WACO, TX.

DERRINGERS: STAINLESS STEEL

MODEL 1—available in over 40 cal.'s including .22 LR through .45-70, also 2½ in. .410 shot shell, O/U stainless steel derringer, 3 in. barrels, automatic barrel selection, "hammer block" type safety, 15 oz., spur trigger, rosewood grips. Add $25 - $150 depending on caliber. New in 1980.

Regular Cal.'s—most cal.'s between .22 LR and .38 Spl. (.22 Hornet, .223 Rem., and .30-30 are $170 extra).

Mfg.'s Sug. Retail	$200	$180	$160	$130

Larger Cal.'s—typically .41 cal. and larger (except .45 ACP — subtract $75). Add approx. $75 for Mag. cal.'s.

Mfg.'s Sug. Retail	$295	$260	$220	$180

This model can be ordered with special ser. no.'s and other custom features at additional cost(s).

Grading	100%	Issue price	Qty made

MODEL 1 TEXAS COMMEMORATIVE—.38 Spl., .44-40, or .45 LC cal.'s, similar to Model 1 except has brass frame, stainless steel barrel, and stag grips. 500 in each cal. made in 1986-87 only.

.44-40 cal.	$285	$285	500
.45 cal.	$285	$285	500
.32 Mag.	$188	$188	500
.38 Spl.	$188	$188	500

Grading	100%	98%	95%	90%	80%	70%	60%

MODEL 3—.38 Spl. only, single shot, 2½ in. barrel, 8½ oz., spur trigger, rosewood grips.
Mfg.'s Sug. Retail $115 $95 $70 $60

MODEL 4—.357 Mag. through .45 Colt cal.'s on upper barrel, 3 in. .410 shot shell lower barrel, O/U derringer combination pistol, 4¹⁄₁₀ in. barrel, rosewood grips, 16½ oz.. Add $25 for stag grips. New in 1985.
Mfg.'s Sug. Retail $338 $310 $250 $210

This model is also available on special order in either .50-70 or .50 Saunders cal. (new in 1989 - single shot only). Retail is $395.

Alaskan Survival Model—same as Model 4, only .45 - 70 cal. upper barrel.
Mfg.'s Sug. Retail $369 $335 $295 $260

MODEL 6—.45 Colt/.410 ga. O/U, 6 in. barrel, 21 oz. Add $25 for stag grips, available in high polish, satin, or gray matte finish (standard). New in 1986.
Mfg.'s Sug. Retail $338 $290 $260 $220
Add $20 for satin finish.
Add $38 for high polish finish.

MODEL 7—.22 LR, .32 S&W, .38 Spl., .38 S&W, .380 ACP, or .44 Spl. cal.'s, O/U, same basic specifications as Model 1, except ultra lightweight (7½ oz.).
Mfg.'s Sug. Retail $158 $145 $125 $105
Add $30 for .38 Spl./.22 LR cal.'s.

.44 Special Cal.—.44 Spl. cal. only.
Mfg.'s Sug. Retail $500 $445 $410 $350

MODEL 10—.45 ACP or .45 LC, O/U, 3 in. barrels, aluminum frame, matte finish, 10 oz. New in 1988.
Mfg.'s Sug. Retail $218 $190 $165 $145

MODEL 11—.38 Spl. only, same basic specifications as Model 1, matte gray finish, only 11 oz.
Mfg.'s Sug. Retail $180 $160 $145 $125

PISTOLS

.25 MAGNUM—.25 ACP, semi-auto, less than 100 manufactured.
$500 $400 $300

LM-4—see separate listing under Semmerling.

AMERICAN FIREARMS MANUFACTURING COMPANY, INC.

PREVIOUSLY MANUFACTURED IN SAN ANTONIO, TX BETWEEN 1972-1974.

AMERICAN .25 AUTOMATIC—.25 auto, 8 shot, 2¹⁄₁₀ in. barrel, smooth walnut grips, made 1966-74.

	100%	98%	95%	90%	80%	70%	60%
Stainless	$195	$180	$165				
Blue	$165	$150	$140	$120	$100	$90	$85

Grading	100%	98%	95%	90%	80%	70%	60%

AMERICAN .38 SPL.—.38 Spl., O/U configuration, approx. 3,000-4,000 mfg. between 1972-74.

	$200	$165	$135				

AMERICAN .380 AUTOMATIC—.380 auto, 8 shot, 3½ in. barrel, stainless steel, smooth walnut grips, made 1972-1974.

	$700	$500	$300				

This model is extremely rare — only 10 were manufactured. Prices hard to evaluate.

AMERICAN GUN CO.

MANUFACTURED BY CRESCENT FIREARMS CO. DISTRIBUTED BY H. & D. FOLSOM CO.

HANDGUNS

REVOLVER—.32 S&W, 5 shot, double action, top break-open action.

	$175	$160	$140	$120	$95	$65	$50

SHOTGUNS

SxS—various gauges, hammer or hammerless, damascus or steel barrels. Add 15% for steel barrels, small gauges.

	$240	$225	$200	$175	$140	$100	$75

AMERICAN HISTORICAL FOUNDATION, THE

A PRIVATE ORGANIZATION WHICH MARKETS MILITARY COMMEMORATIVES AND SUBCONTRACTS MANUFACTURERS. AHF IS LOCATED IN RICHMOND, VA.

COMMEMORATIVE ISSUES

In addition to the models listed below, AHF also marketed a .45 Auto. Armed Forces Collection and Teddy Roosevelt revolver. No information was supplied on these models, and the AHF should be contacted directly regarding further specifications/values on these special editions.

200TH CONSTITUTION REVOLVER—.44 Mag., Dan Wesson manufactured revolver with extensive 24Kt. inlays and etchings, 10 in. barrel, ivory grips, serial numbered CC001-CC950 (950 mfg.). Released in 1987.

Mfg.'s Sug. Retail $995 $995 $700 $500

SECOND AMENDMENT COMMEMORATIVE .44 MAG.—.44 Mag., 10 in. barrel, mfg. by Dan Wesson to AHF specifications, 2 different models, walnut stocks with medallions. Released in 1989.

Collector's Edition—full engraving coverage, blued frame and barrel with 24 Kt. gold plated small parts, 1,500 mfg. serial numbered 2AC 0001 - 2AC 1500.

Mfg.'s Sug. Retail $1,495 $1,495 $1,100 $800
Add $139 for walnut display case.

Deluxe Museum Edition—full engraving coverage, all metal parts 24 Kt. gold plated, 750 mfg. serial numbered 2AD 001 - 2AD 750.

Mfg.'s Sug. Retail $1,895 $1,895 $1,350 $950
Add $139 for walnut display case.

GENERAL PATTON SAA—.45 LC, 5½ in. barrel, silver plated finish with extensive scroll engraving, 2500 mfg. in 1987-88 serial numbered P0001-P2500, Ajax custom ivory-like grips, lanyard ring. Mfg. by A. Uberti in Italy.

Mfg.'s Sug. Retail $1,495 $1,495 $1,100 $800
Add $125 for walnut/glass display case.

Grading	100%	98%	95%	90%	80%	70%	60%

AMERICAN ARMED FORCES UZI—9mm, semi-auto, pistol variation, gold plated small parts and numerous 24 Kt. inlays, 1,500 mfg. in 1989, serial numbered UZI 001 - UZI 1,500, mfg. by I.M.I., includes detachable wooden stock.

Mfg.'s Sug. Retail	$2,195	$2,195	$1,500	$995			

    Add $195 for walnut/glass display case.

VIETNAM WAR COMBAT SHOTGUN—12 ga., hand engraved receiver with 24 Kt. gold plated small parts, 750 mfg. in 1989, serial numbered VN 001 - VN 750, mfg. by Savage Industries.

Mfg.'s Sug. Retail	$1,595	$1,595	$1,150	$850			

    Add $225 for walnut/glass display case.

KOREAN WAR THOMPSON RIFLE—.45 ACP, semi-auto (also in fully auto with class III license) reproduction of the famous military Thompson sub-machine gun, manufactured by Auto-Ordnance Corp., special finished high grade walnut stock, pistol grip, and forearm, multiple 24Kt. plated parts, walnut cased, 1,500 manufactured in 1985, serial numbered KW0001-KW1500. Class III — add $350.

	$1,195	$900	$725				

Last Mfg.'s Sug. Retail was $1,195.

Thompson Engraved Model—similar to above, except has full engraving coverage. Only 50 mfg.

	$2,000	$1,500	$1,000				

M1 GARAND RIFLE—.30-06 cal., reproduction of the military M1 Garand, manufactured by Springfield Armory (IL), presentation grade, various 24Kt. plated parts, high polish blue, walnut cased, released in 1984, serial numbered WW0001-WW2500, 9½ lbs.

	$1,695	$1,125	$850				

Last Mfg.'s Sug. Retail was $1,695.

VIETNAM M14 RIFLE—.308 cal., manufactured by Springfield Armory, 24Kt. gold plated metal parts, available in either a Marine Corps or Army variation, mfg. limited to 1,500 of each. Released in 1987.

Mfg.'s Sug. Retail	$1,595	$1,595	$1,175	$875			

M16 VIETNAM WAR COMMEMORATIVE—.223 cal., semi-auto version of the M16, mfg. by Colt, hand engraved, 24 Kt. gold plated small parts, medallions in stock, bipod included, 1,500 mfg. in 1988 serial numbered V 0001 - V 1500.

Mfg.'s Sug. Retail	$1,995	$1,995	$1,400	$1,000			

    Add $225 for glass display case.

AMERICAN INDUSTRIES

PLEASE REFER TO THE CALICO SECTION IN THIS TEXT.

AMERICAN INTERNATIONAL

AUSTRIA.

AMERICAN 180 AUTO CARBINE—a specialized .22 LR, designed for para military use, 177 round drum mag., 16½ in. barrel, aperture sight, high impact plastic stock.

	$660	$550	$440	$360	$330	$305	$275

    Add $550 for Laser Lok System.
    Add $125 for Extra Drum Mag. and Winder.

Note: This gun was available in a selective fire version for law enforcement only. The gun also was available with a laser assisted sighting system which, when affixed to the weapon, projects a beam to point of impact.

ANSCHUTZ

MANUFACTURED IN ULM, W. GERMANY. IMPORTED AND DISTRIBUTED
EXCLUSIVELY IN THE U.S. BY PRECISION SALES INTERNATIONAL INC. (FORMERLY
PRECISION SPORTS), WESTFIELD, MA.

PISTOLS

EXEMPLAR—.22 LR, bolt action, Match 64 left-hand action (for right-hand shooters), 10 in.
barrel, 5 shot mag., two stage trigger, adj. rear sight, receiver grooved for scope, contoured
grip and forestock are stippled, 3⅓ lbs., also available for left-hand shooters. New in 1987.

Mfg.'s Sug. Retail $395 $340 $285 $250 $225 $200 $180 $160
    Add $25 for left-hand model.

Exemplar Magnum—while advertised in 1987, the .22 Mag. was never manufactured.

Exemplar XIV—.22 LR, similar to Exemplar, except has 14 in. barrel, 4.15 lbs. New in
1988.

Mfg.'s Sug. Retail $405 $350 $290 $250 $225 $200 $180 $160

Exemplar Hornet—.22 Hornet cal., 5 shot mag., Match 54 left hand-action, 10 in.
barrel, no sights - tapped and grooved, 4.35 lbs. New in 1988.

Mfg.'s Sug. Retail $745 $650 $575 $525 $475 $415 $365 $330

RIFLES: DISCONTINUED BOLT ACTION

*Savage imported Anschutz rifles were available from 1963-1981. While some of those
models might not be listed below, refer to models of similar caliber and quality that are listed to
ascertain values.*

During the period when Savage was importing Anschutz rifles, certain models in the
Anschutz line were designated "Savage-Anschutz" for sales by Savage in the U.S.
Conversely, certain models manufactured by Savage were designated "Anschutz-Savage"
for sale by Anschutz in Europe. Some of these models did not have any modifications but
others were restocked, supplied with different sights, and had other different features from
their original counterparts. In most cases, the original model numbers were used. Some
"Anschutz-Savage" rifles have made their way into the U.S., and that explains such centerfire
calibers as .22-250, .30-06, and others. While somewhat rare, these rifles are typically based
on the Savage Model 110 action. They are not as desireable as those "Savage-Anschutz"
marked rifles utilizing the superior Anschutz action.

MARK 10 TARGET RIFLE—.22 LR cal., single shot, 26 in. heavy barrel, adj. sights, globe
front, target stock with full pistol grip, adj. palm stop, made 1963-1981.
    $350 $320 $290 $260 $230 $210 $195

MODEL 1407—.22 LR cal. "I.S.U." model, heavy barrel, no sights, discontinued.
    $375 $340 $300 $260 $230 $210 $195

MODEL 1408—.22 LR cal., heavy barrel, no sights. Discontinued. Add $150 for 1408 ED
Model.
    $375 $340 $300 $260 $230 $210 $195

MODEL 1411—.22 LR cal., prone position target model, heavy barrel, no sights.
Discontinued.
    $360 $320 $290 $260 $230 $210 $195

MODEL 1413 MATCH—.22 LR cal., adj. cheekpiece, heavy target barrel with no sights,
competition model. Discontinued.
    $550 $475 $420 $375 $325 $285 $240

MODEL 1418 MANNLICHER—.22 LR cal., hunting model, fine checkering, clip mag.
Discontinued.
    $650 $575 $500 $450 $365 $315 $275

MODEL 1418/19—.22 LR cal., sporter variation, previous importation by Savage Arms.
    $300 $260 $225 $200 $175 $150 $125

MODEL 1518 MANNLICHER—deluxe model of Model 1418.
    $700 $595 $540 $485 $430 $375 $325

Grading	100%	98%	95%	90%	80%	70%	60%

MODEL 153—.222 Rem., 24 in. barrel, folding leaf rear sight, French walnut stock, rosewood forend tip and pistol grip cap, made 1963-1981.

	$550	$475	$400	$375	$350	$300	$280

MODEL 153-S—.222 Rem., 24 in. barrel, double set triggers, otherwise, same as 153.

	$600	$525	$450	$425	$385	$330	$305

MODEL 184—.22 LR, 21½ in. barrel, Monte Carlo combination, checkered pistol grip, Schnabel forend, folding leaf sight, made 1963-1981.

	$350	$320	$290	$260	$230	$210	$195

MODEL 54 SPORTER—.22 LR, 5 shot clip, 24 in. round tapered barrel, Monte Carlo roll over combination, folding leaf sight, checkered pistol grip, made 1963-1981.

	$625	$550	$475	$425	$395	$360	$320

MODEL 54M—.22 Win. Mag., otherwise same as Sporter.

	$695	$575	$525	$475	$425	$395	$350

MODEL 141—.22 LR, 5 shot clip, 23 in. round tapered barrel, Monte Carlo stock, folding leaf sight. Discontinued.

	$345	$280	$240	$200	$180	$160	$140
Model 141M (Mag.)	$365	$300	$265	$225	$200	$180	$160

MODEL 164—.22 LR, 5 shot clip, 23 in. round tapered barrel, Monte Carlo stock, folding leaf sight, made 1963-1981.

	$345	$280	$240	$200	$180	$160	$140

MODEL 164M—same as 164, only .22 Win. Mag.

	$365	$300	$265	$225	$200	$180	$160

SPORTER RIFLES: RECENT MANUFACTURE

Prices below reflect the recent devaluation of the U.S. dollar against some foreign currencies. While the manufacturer's suggested retails have gone up considerably, prices for used specimens (98% or less original condition) have not increased proportionally, and in some cases, have changed very little.

THE KADETT—.22 LR, bolt action, 22 in. barrel, 5 shot clip mag., folding leaf rear sight, single stage trigger, grooved receiver, checkered hard-wood stock, 5½ lbs. Made in 1987 only.

	$235	$200	$180	$165	$150	$135	$120

Last Mfg.'s Sug. Retail was $265.

THE ACHIEVER—.22 LR, bolt action, 19½ in. barrel, 5 shot clip mag., folding leaf rear sight, two stage trigger, grooved receiver, stippled hard-wood stock with vented forearm and adj. length of pull, 5¼ lbs. New in 1987.

Mfg.'s Sug. Retail	$320	$270	$230	$205	$185	$165	$150	$135

MODEL 1416D CUSTOM—.22 LR, bolt action, 22½ in. barrel, 5 or 10 shot mag., Monte Carlo walnut stock, folding leaf sight.

Mfg.'s Sug. Retail	$552	$475	$400	$350	$295	$240	$225	$200

This model utilizes the Match 64 action, similar to the Anschutz Model 1403 Target.

1416DCL Classic—same specifications as 1416D Custom, except regular stock.

Mfg.'s Sug. Retail	$552	$475	$400	$350	$295	$240	$225	$200

Add $78 for left-hand action.

MODEL 1418D—.22 LR, Mannlicher full stock, skipline checkering, 19¾ in. barrel, same action as Model 1416D. Set trigger new for 1985 — add $10.

Mfg.'s Sug. Retail	$830	$740	$660	$560	$500	$425	$360	$300

MODEL 1700D/1422D CUSTOM—.22 LR, bolt action, 5 shot mag., 24 in. barrel, iron sights, weighs 7¼ lbs., heavy barrel, Monte Carlo stock with skipline checkering.

Mfg.'s Sug. Retail	$1,000	$850	$760	$650	$550	$450	$375	$335

Add $130 for Meistergrade variation (select walnut).

This model was designated 1422D until 1989 when it was changed to the Model 1700D.

This rifle employs the Anschutz Match 54 action.

Grading	100%	98%	95%	90%	80%	70%	60%

1422D Meister Grade—1422D action, features carefully selected European walnut, hand-rubbed oil finish. Disc. in 1987.

	$950	$835	$750	$650	$535	$440	$375

Last Mfg.'s Sug. Retail was $930.

1700D Featherweight—similar to Model 1700D Custom, except has McMillan fiberglass stock configured like the Custom Model, no sights, 6¼ lbs.. New in 1989.

Mfg.'s Sug. Retail	$995	$850	$760	$650	$550	$450	$375	$335

1700D/1422DCL Classic—same general specifications as 1422D Custom, except smaller diameter barrel and regular stock.

Mfg.'s Sug. Retail	$989	$840	$760	$650	$550	$450	$375	$335

Add $130 for Meistergrade variation (select walnut).

1422DCL Classic Meister Grade—1422D action, features carefully selected European walnut, hand-rubbed oil finish. Disc. in 1987.

	$875	$795	$700	$620	$510	$420	$350

Last Mfg.'s Sug. Retail was $875.

DIE MEISTERMACHER—.22 LR, similar action and specifications as Model 1422D Custom, limited edition of 25 guns, select wood, extra polish on metal parts, hand-lapped barrel, with numerous gold inlays including Olympic wreath. Made in 1985.

	$2,500	$2,000	$1,600

Last Mfg.'s Sug. Retail was $2,475. This variation sold out in late 1988.

MODEL 1700D/1432D CUSTOM—.22 Hornet, 24 in. barrel, folding leaf sight, Monte Carlo stock with skipline checkering and rosewood grip cap, 4 shot mag., 7¾ lbs. Model 1432D was disc. in 1987, and the Model 1700D was introduced in 1989.

Mfg.'s Sug. Retail	$1,130	$1,000	$850	$760	$650	$550	$450	$375

Add $130 for Meistergrade variation (select walnut).

This model was designated 1432D until 1987 and then reintroduced in 1989 as the Model 1700D.

This model comes standard with the Anschutz Match 54 action.

1700D/1432DCL Classic—same general specifications as 1432D Custom, except regular stock and 23½ (1432DCL) or 24 (1700D) in. barrel.

Mfg.'s Sug. Retail	$1,100	$975	$825	$725	$620	$500	$400	$335

Add $130 for Meistergrade variation (select walnut).

This model was designated 1432D until 1987 and then reintroduced in 1989 as the Model 1700D.

This model comes standard with the Anschutz Match 54 action.

Last Mfg.'s Sug. Retail was $849 on the Model 1432DCL.

1432D Meister Grade—1432D action, features carefully selected European walnut, hand-rubbed oil finish. Discontinued in 1986.

	$995	$850	$750	$650	$550	$475	$385

Last Mfg.'s Sug. Retail was $770.

MODEL 1433D—.22 Hornet, special order only, Match 54 target action, Mannlicher full stock, 4 round mag. Set trigger new in 1985 — add $15. Discontinued in 1986.

	$995	$840	$740	$640	$525	$425	$350

Last Mfg.'s Sug. Retail was $826.

MODEL 1516D CUSTOM—.22 Mag., otherwise the same as Model 1416D, 4 round mag.

Mfg.'s Sug. Retail	$589	$495	$400	$350	$295	$240	$225	$200

This model utilizes the Match 64 action, similar to the Anschutz Model 1403 Target.

1516DCL Classic—same specifications as 1516D Custom, except regular stock.

Mfg.'s Sug. Retail	$589	$495	$400	$350	$295	$240	$225	$200

MODEL 1518D—.22 Mag. otherwise same as Model 1418D (Mannlicher stock), 4 round mag.

Mfg.'s Sug. Retail	$847	$735	$615	$525	$440	$375	$325	$275

Add $11 for set trigger.

Grading	100%	98%	95%	90%	80%	70%	60%

MODEL 1700D/1522D CUSTOM—.22 Mag., bolt action, 5 shot mag., 24 in. barrel, iron sights, weighs 7¼ lbs., heavy barrel, Monte Carlo stock with skipline checkering.

Mfg.'s Sug. Retail	$1,029	$885	$740	$675	$550	$475	$400	$350

Add $130 for Meistergrade variation (select walnut).

This model was designated 1522D until 1989 and then reintroduced as the Model 1700D.

1522D Custom Meister Grade—1522D action, Monte Carlo stock featuring carefully selected European walnut, hand-rubbed oil finish. Discontinued in 1985.

	$995	$850	$750	$650	$575	$475	$425

Last retail price was $678.

1700D/1522DCL Classic—same general specifications as 1522D Custom, except smaller diameter barrel and regular stock.

Mfg.'s Sug. Retail	$1,015	$865	$720	$660	$540	$465	$395	$340

Add $130 for Meistergrade variation (select walnut).

This model was designated 1522DCL until 1989 and then reintroduced as the Model 1700D.

1522DCL Classic Meister Grade—1522D action, regular stock featuring carefully selected European walnut, hand-rubbed oil finish. Discontinued in 1985.

	$950	$825	$725	$625	$550	$450	$400

Last retail price was $660.

BAVARIAN 1700—.22 LR, .22 Mag., .22 Hornet, or .222 Rem. cal.'s, 24 in. barrel, clip mag., checkered European style stock with European Monte Carlo cheekpiece and schnabel forend, 7½ lbs. New in 1988.

Mfg.'s Sug. Retail	$1,000	$850	$730	$660	$525	$450	$375	$335

Add $30 for .22 Mag.

Add $130 for .22 Hornet or .222 Rem. cal.'s.

Add $130 for Meistergrade variation (select walnut).

MODEL 1700D/1532D CUSTOM—.222 Rem., otherwise same as Model 1700D/1432D Custom.

Mfg.'s Sug. Retail	$1,130	$1,000	$850	$760	$650	$550	$450	$375

Add $130 for Meistergrade variation (select walnut).

This model was designated 1532D until 1987 and then reintroduced in 1989 as the Model 1700D.

Last Mfg.'s Sug. Retail was $909 on the Model 1532D.

1532D MG Custom Meister Grade—1532D action, Monte Carlo stock featuring carefully selected European walnut, hand-rubbed oil finish. Discontinued in 1986.

	$1,075	$925	$840	$725	$600	$500	$400

Last Mfg.'s Sug. Retail was $770.

1700D/1532DCL Classic—same as Model 1700D/1532D Custom, except regular stock.

Mfg.'s Sug. Retail	$1,100	$975	$825	$725	$620	$500	$400	$335

Add $130 for Meistergrade variation (select walnut).

This model was designated 1532DCL until 1987 and then reintroduced in 1989 as the Model 1700D.

Last Mfg.'s Sug. Retail was $849 on Model 1532DCL.

RIFLES: SINGLE SHOT SILHOUETTE

MODEL 64 RIFLE—single shot, .22 LR, 26 in. round barrel, beavertail forearm, adj. single stage receiver, no sights, target stock with adj. buttplate, checkered pistol grip, made 1963-1981.

	$340	$290	$270	$240	$190	$170	$160

MODEL 64MS—.22 LR, single shot silhouette target model, 21¼ in. barrel, 8 lbs., no sights, Wundhammer swell stippled pistol grip stock, adj. trigger.

Mfg.'s Sug. Retail	$717	$640	$525	$450	$375	$350	$285	$245

Add $76 for left-hand action.

This variation employs the Model 1403 action.

Grading	100%	98%	95%	90%	80%	70%	60%

Model 64MS - FWT—similar to Model 64MS, except single stage trigger, 6¼ lbs. Disc. in 1988.

	$550	$475	$425	$350	$325	$260	$230

Last Mfg.'s Sug. Retail was $596.

MODEL 54.18MS—.22 LR, silhouette target model, 22 in. barrel, match 54 single-shot action, 8 lbs. 6 oz., walnut Wundhammer stock is stippled on pistol grip and entire forearm, no sights.

Mfg.'s Sug. Retail	$1,212	$1,050	$875	$750	$650	$550	$475	$400

Add $61 for left-hand action.

This model employs the Super Match 54 action.

Model 54.MS REP—similar to Model 54.18MS, except has repeating action, 5 shot mag., thumb hole stock with vented forestock, 7¾ lbs. New in 1989.

Mfg.'s Sug. Retail	$1,650	$1,425	$1,175	$1,000	$895	$785	$695	$600

Model 54.18MS ED—same action as Model 54.18MS, except has 19¼ in. barrel (⅞ in. diameter) with 14¼ in. extension tube, 3 removable muzzle weights. Disc. in 1988.

	$1,075	$900	$775	$675	$575	$485	$410

Last Mfg.'s Sug. Retail was $1,215.
Add $100 for left-hand action.

MATCH RIFLES: BOLT ACTION - RECENT PRODUCTION

MODEL 2000 MK—.22 LR, single shot match, 26 in. barrel, aperture sights, 7½ lbs. Disc. in 1988.

	$340	$290	$250	$210	$180	$160	$145

Last Mfg.'s Sug. Retail was $400.

MODEL 1403D—.22 LR, improved Model 645 match rifle, single shot, no sights, 8 lbs. 6 oz., adj. trigger.

Mfg.'s Sug. Retail	$700	$600	$525	$450	$360	$300	$260	$225

Add $50 for left-hand action (disc. in 1988).

MODEL 1803D—.22 LR, Match 64 action, 25½ in. target barrel, single stage adj. trigger, blond finished wood with dark stippling on pistol grip and forearm, adj. cheekpiece and buttplate, 8.6 lbs. New in 1987.

Mfg.'s Sug. Retail	$806	$700	$595	$525	$430	$365	$310	$275

Add $53 for left-hand action.

MODEL 1907 ISU—.22 LR, single shot match "I.S.U." model, 26 in. barrel, prone and position shooting, removable cheekpiece, adj. buttplate, hand stippled stock with ventilated forearm and blond wood finish, 11 lbs.

Mfg.'s Sug. Retail	$1,344	$1,175	$975	$825	$700	$595	$500	$440

Add $118 for left-hand action.

This variation was designated Model 1807 before 1989.

MODEL 1808 ED SUPER—.22 LR, single shot running target model, 32½ in. barrel, adj. stock, cheekpiece, trigger, heavy beavertail forend, 9¼ lbs., no sights, muzzle barrel weights.

Mfg.'s Sug. Retail	$1,290	$1,140	$950	$800	$695	$580	$500	$440

Add $110 for left-hand action.

MODEL 1910 SUPER MATCH II—.22 LR, single shot, 27¼ in. barrel, diopter sights, thumb hole stock is fully adj., 12 lbs., model down from 1813 (or 1913), special order only.

Mfg.'s Sug. Retail	$2,013	$1,775	$1,375	$1,050	$875	$725	$625	$550

Add $170 for left-hand action.

This variation was designated as Model 1810 before 1988.

MODEL 1911 PRONE MATCH—.22 LR, single shot match prone rifle, 27¼ in. barrel, adj. cheekpiece, buttplate, no sights.

Mfg.'s Sug. Retail	$1,576	$1,360	$1,050	$850	$725	$625	$525	$450

Add $138 for left-hand action.

This variation was designated Model 1811 before 1988.

Grading	100%	98%	95%	90%	80%	70%	60%

MODEL 1913 SUPER MATCH—.22 LR single shot, top-of-the-line match rifle, every possible refinement, international diopter sights, 27¼ in. barrel, 13.9 lbs., hand and palm rest.

Mfg.'s Sug. Retail	$2,225	$1,940	$1,400	$1,195	$975	$825	$725	$625

Add $185 for left-hand action.

This variation was designated Model 1813 before 1988.

MODEL 1827B BIATHLON—.22 LR bolt action, biathlon rifle, carries four 5 shot mag.'s in stock, special biathlon features, 21½ in. barrel, limited production.

Mfg.'s Sug. Retail	$1,744	$1,500	$1,275	$1,075	$925	$800	$700	$600

Add $119 for left-hand action.

Model 1827BT—same general specifications as Model 1827B, except has Fortner straight pull-through bolt action, 9 lbs. New in 1986.

Mfg.'s Sug. Retail	$3,498	$3,050	$2,500	$2,150	$1,895	$1,650	$1,475	$1,275

Add $270 for left-hand action.

RIFLES: SEMI-AUTO

MODEL 520/61—.22 LR, semi-auto, 24 in. barrel, 10 round mag., Monte Carlo stock, 6½ lbs. Discontinued in 1983.

	$260	$205	$185	$155	$145	$130	$120

MARK 525 SPORTER RIFLE—.22 LR, semi-auto, 24 in. barrel, 10 round mag., adj. rear sight, Monte Carlo stock, 6½ lbs. New in 1984.

Mfg.'s Sug. Retail	$435	$380	$310	$260	$220	$195	$160	$145

Mark 525 Carbine—similar to Mark 525 Rifle, except has 20 in. barrel. Disc. in 1986.

	$385	$310	$260	$220	$195	$160	$145

ANSCHUTZ SHOTGUNS

Anschutz marked O/U shotguns that were manufactured by Miroku of Japan were distributed previously in Europe. Several grades of these shotguns were manufactured and while rarely seen in the U.S., values approximate other Miroku O/U's of similar quality and features.

APACHE

MANUFACTURED BY OJANGUREN Y VIDOSA, EIBAR, SPAIN.

HANDGUN

SEMI-AUTO—6.35mm., clip fed.

	$190	$175	$160	$140	$120	$95	$75

ARMALITE INCORPORATED

COSTA MESA, CALIFORNIA.

RIFLES

AR-7 EXPLORER—semi-auto, .22 LR, 16 in. aluminum barrel with steel liner, aperture sight, gun takes down and can be stored in hollow plastic stock, gun will float, made 1959-1973, now made by Charter Arms.

	$101	$90	$80	$75	$70	$65	$60

AR-7 CUSTOM—same as above, only with custom walnut stock including cheekpiece, pistol grip. Made 1964-1970.

	$165	$140	$120	$100	$90	$80	$70

AR-180—.223 Rem. cal., semi-auto, gas operated, 18¼ in. barrel, folding stock. Manufactured by Armalite in Costa Mesa, CA, 1969-1972, Howa Machinery Ltd., Nagoya, Japan 1972 and 1973. Since 1976 the AR-180 has been made by Sterling Armament Co. Ltd., Dagenham, Essex, England. Premiums do exist for the Costa Mesa and Howa models.

	$400	$350	$310	$260	$230	$195	$180

ARMALITE INCORPORATED, cont.

SHOTGUN

AR-17—12 ga., semi-auto, 24 in. barrel, interchangeable choke tubes, gas operated, high strength aluminum barrel and receiver, plastic stock and forearm, either gold anodized or black finish. Only 2000 made between 1964-1965.

	100%	98%	95%	90%	80%	70%	60%
	$575	$460	$420	$360	$310	$260	$220

ARMES DE CHASSE

IMPORTER/DISTRIBUTOR/RETAILER LOCATED IN CHADDS FORD, PA., 19137.

Armes de Chasse also exclusively imports Chapuis (French) rifles and shotguns in addition to Zanardini (Italian) double rifles (non-exclusive). These trademarks will appear under their own headings in this text.

SHOTGUNS: SIDE-BY-SIDE

BALMORAL—12, 16, or 20 ga., boxlock with color case hardened side plates, can be chambered for 3½ in. (12 ga.), checkered English stock and splinter forearm, ST, auto safety. New in 1989.

Mfg.'s Sug. Retail	$780	$735	$625	$560	$495	$450	$420	$395

This model is mfg. in Italy in association with Dr. F. Beretta.

CHESAPEAKE—12 ga., 3½ in. chambers, designed for steel shot, boxlock action, auto ejectors, DT's, manual safety, mfg. in Italy in association with Dr. F. Beretta. New in 1989.

Mfg.'s Sug. Retail	$765	$715	$600	$540	$495	$450	$420	$395

SIMSON/SUHL

Manufactured in Suhl, East Germany. Both O/U and S X S shotguns are currently imported exclusively by Armes de Chasse located in Chadds Ford, PA.

HIGHLANDER—20 ga., boxlock action, upland game gun, extractors, DT's, manual safety, checkered English stock and splinter forearm, mfg. in Italy in association with Dr. F. Beretta. New in 1989.

Mfg.'s Sug. Retail	$675	$600	$525	$465	$430	$400	$360	$315

MODEL 70E—12, 16, or 20 ga., 2¾ and 3 in. chambers, 26¾ or 28 in. solid rib barrels, Anson & Deeley action with Greener crossbolt, ejectors, DT's, case hardened frame with light engraving. New in 1989.

Mfg.'s Sug. Retail	$812	$765	$675	$600	$500	$450	$420	$395

Models 70E, 74E, and 76E are manufactured by Simson/Suhl of E. Germany.

MODEL 74E—similar to Model 70E, except has game scene engraving and updated wood. New in 1989.

Mfg.'s Sug. Retail	$981	$925	$825	$700	$600	$500	$450	$425

MODEL 76E—similar to Model 74E, except has ornamental side plates with hunting scene engraving and other arabesques, deluxe checkered pistol grip stock and forearm. New in 1989.

Mfg.'s Sug. Retail	$1,515	$1,400	$1,195	$1,000	$895	$795	$725	$650

SHOTGUNS: O/U

The below listed Simson/Suhl O/U's are without sling swivels or cheek piece.

MODEL EJ—12 ga. only, Anson & Deeley action with double barrel hooks, DT's, ejectors, coin finished action with light engraving, checkered pistol grip stock and forearm. New in 1989.

Mfg.'s Sug. Retail	$1,000	$1,000	$725	$650	$595	$500	$450	$420

Models EJ and EU are manufactured by Simson/Suhl of E. Germany.

MODEL EU—similar to Model EJ, except has single non-selective trigger and vent rib. New in 1989.

Mfg.'s Sug. Retail	$1,200	$1,200	$875	$725	$650	$550	$500	$475

ARMINEX LTD.

PREVIOUSLY MANUFACTURED AND DISTRIBUTED IN SCOTTSDALE, AZ.

TRI-FIRE—.45 ACP, 9 mm, and .38 Super cal.'s, single action auto, interchangeable barrels allow caliber conversion. Available in 5, 6, or 7 (disc. in 1984) in. stainless barrel lengths, no grip safety, steel frame construction, ambidextrous thumb safety (on Target and Presentation only), smooth walnut grips, 38 oz. Approx. 250 mfg. between 1981-85.

	$450	$375	$325	$300	$275	$250	$225

> Add $48 if presentation cased.
> Add approx. $130/conversion unit.
>
> Last Mfg.'s Sug. Retail was $396.

Target Model—same specifications as Tri-Fire, except has 6 or 7 (discontinued in 1984) in. barrel.

	$475	$390	$335	$305	$285	$255	$230

> Last Mfg.'s Sug. Retail was $448.
>
> Quantities of this variation are very limited.

ARMINIUS

ZELLA-MEHLIS, GERMANY 1922-PRESENT. CURRENTLY IMPORTED BY FIE CORP. IN HIALEAH, FL. — SEE THE FIE SECTION FOR CURRENT PRODUCTION MODELS.

HANDGUNS: SINGLE SHOT

MODEL 1—.22 LR Target, adj. sights.

	$275	$210	$195	$165	$155	$140	$110

MODEL 2—Same as Model 1, except has set trigger.

	$340	$255	$225	$190	$170	$155	$140

HANDGUNS: REVOLVER

MODEL 3—.25 ACP, folding trigger, hammerless.

	$175	$135	$125	$105	$100	$90	$80

MODEL 8—.320 Revolver, folding trigger, hammerless.

	$175	$135	$125	$105	$100	$90	$80

MODEL 9—.32 ACP.

	$185	$140	$130	$115	$105	$95	$85

MODEL 10—.32 ACP, hammerless.

	$165	$125	$120	$100	$95	$85	$75

TARGET—.22 LR.

	$90	$70	$65	$55	$50	$45	$45

ARMS CORPORATION OF THE PHILIPPINES

MANUFACTURED IN THE PHILIPPINES. CURRENTLY IMPORTED AND DISTRIBUTED BY ARMSCOR PRECISION, LOCATED IN FOSTER CITY, CA.

REVOLVERS

MODEL M100—.22 LR, .22 Mag., or .38 Spl., double action revolver, 6 shot, 4 in. vent rib barrel, blued finish only, adj. sights, checkered hardwood grips, 33 oz. New in 1985.

	$200	$150	$125	$115	$105	$95	$85

> Formerly designated as M100TC or Special Edition. .22 LR and .22 Mag. cal.'s were discontinued in 1988.

Grading	100%	98%	95%	90%	80%	70%	60%

RIFLES

MODEL M14P—.22 LR, bolt action, 5 shot mag., 23 in. barrel, open sights, 6 lbs. New in 1986.

	$100	$75	$60	$50	$45	$40	$35

MODEL M14D—.22 LR, bolt action, similar to Model 14P, except has adj. rear sight and rear checkered mahogany stock. Made in 1987 only.

	$110	$90	$80	$70	$60	$50	$40

Last Mfg.'s Sug. Retail was $125.

MODEL M1500—.22 Mag., bolt action, 5 shot mag., 21½ in. barrel, checkered mahogany stock, open sights, 6½ lbs. New in 1986.

	$140	$115	$95	$80	$70	$65	$60

MODEL M1600—.22 LR, semi-auto, 15 shot mag., 18 in. barrel, copy of the Armalite M16, ebony stock, 5¼ lbs. New in 1986.

	$122	$90	$85	$75	$65	$60	$55

M1600R—same as M1600, except has stainless steel retractable butt stock and vent. barrel hood, 7¼ lbs. New in 1986.

	$134	$100	$90	$80	$70	$65	$60

M1600C—same as M1600, except has 20 in. barrel, fiberglass stock, barrel enclosing forearm, 7½ lbs. Made in 1986 only.

	$135	$115	$95	$85	$75	$65	$55

Last Mfg.'s Sug. Retail was $150.

M1600W—same as 1600C, except has wood stock. Made in 1986 only.

	$135	$115	$95	$85	$75	$65	$55

Last Mfg.'s Sug. Retail was $150.

M1800—.22 Hornet, bolt action, 5 shot clip mag., 23 in. barrel, checkered mahogany stock with Monte Carlo cheekpiece, 6½ lbs. Made in 1986 only.

	$155	$135	$120	$110	$100	$90	$85

Last Mfg.'s Sug. Retail was $176.

MODEL M20P—.22 LR, semi-auto, 15 shot mag., 20¾ in. barrel, open sights, 5½ lbs. New in 1986.

No Mfg.'s Retail	$94	$70	$60	$45	$40	$35	$35

MODEL M2000—same specifications as Model M20P, except has checkered mahogany stock and adj. rear sight. Made in 1986 only.

	$85	$70	$60	$50	$45	$40	$35

Last Mfg.'s Sug. Retail was $99.

MODEL MAK22 S—.22 LR, semi-auto, copy of the famous Russian Kalasnikov AK-47 rifle, 18½ in. barrel, 15 shot mag., mahogany stock and forearm, 7 lbs. New in 1986.

	$172	$135	$110	$95	$85	$80	$75

Model MAK22 F—similar to Model MAK22 S, except has metal folding stock. New in 1989.

	$200	$155	$135	$115	$95	$85	$80

SHOTGUNS

MODEL M30 D—12 ga. only, slide action, 28 or 30 in. plain barrel, 6 shot mag., all steel receiver, checkered mahogany stock and forearm, 7.3 lbs. New in 1986.

	$200	$155	$135	$115	$95	$85	$80

MODEL M30 DG—12 ga. only, law enforcement version of Model M30, 20 in. plain barrel, iron sights, 6 or 8 shot mag., about 7 lbs. Introduced in 1986. Add $5 for 8 shot mag.

	$200	$155	$135	$115	$95	$85	$80

MODEL M30 R—12 ga. only, similar to Model M30DG, except has front bead sight only, 6 or 8 shot mag. New in 1986.

	$200	$155	$135	$115	$95	$85	$80

MODEL M30 RP (COMBO)—12 ga. only, same action as M30 DG, interchangeable black pistol grip, 18¼ in. plain barrel w/front bead sight, 6¼ lbs. New in 1987.

	$200	$155	$135	$115	$95	$85	$80

ARMS RESEARCH ASSOCIATES
MANUFACTURER AND DISTRIBUTOR LOCATED IN STONE PARK, IL.

KF SYSTEM—9mm, assault carbine, 18½ in. barrel, vent barrel shroud, 20 or 36 shot mag., matte black finish, 7½ lbs., select fire-class III transferable only.
Mfg.'s Sug. Retail $379 $340 $295 $275 $250 $230 $210 $195

ARMSCORP OF AMERICA, INC.
MANUFACTURER/IMPORTER LOCATED IN BALTIMORE, MD.

PISTOLS
HI POWER—9mm, patterned after Browning design, 4⅔ in. barrel, military finish, 13 shot mag., synthetic checkered grips, spur hammer, 2 lbs. New in 1989.
Mfg.'s Sug. Retail $425 $350 $295 $275 $250 $230 $215 $200
Add $50 for hard chrome finish with combat grips.
Add $30 for round hammer.

This model is manufactured in Argentina.

Compact Detective HP—similar to Hi Power, except has 3½ in. barrel, 1.9 lbs. New in 1989.
Mfg.'s Sug. Retail $475 $380 $310 $285 $260 $240 $220 $210

SD 9—9mm, double action blowback mechanism, 3.07 in. barrel, 6 shot mag., frame is fabricated mostly of heavy gauge sheet metal stampings, chamber indicator, Israeli mfg., 1½ lbs. New in 1989.
Mfg.'s Sug. Retail $350 $295 $250 $230 $210 $195 $180 $170

This pistol has also been manufactured by Sirkus Industries - refer to their section in this text.

P 22—.22 LR, patterned after the Colt Woodsman, 4 or 6 in. barrel, 10 shot mag., checkered wooden grips. New in 1989.
Mfg.'s Sug. Retail $190 $165 $130 $115 $100 $95 $85 $75

RIFLES
M-14R—.308 cal., 20 shot mag., newly manufactured M-14 using original excellent condition forged G.I. parts including used fiberglass stock. New in 1986.
Mfg.'s Sug. Retail $799 $725 $595 $525 $465 $420 $375 $340
Add $100 for new walnut stock.

M-14 NATIONAL MATCH—.308 cal., built in accordance with A.M.T.U. MIL spec.'s, 3 different barrel weights to choose from, national match rear sight system, calibrated mag., leather sling. New in 1987.
Mfg.'s Sug. Retail $1,795 $1,550 $1,200 $975 $875 $795 $725 $650

FAL—.308 cal., Armscorp forged receiver, 21 in. Argentinian rebuilt barrel, manufactured to military spec.'s, supplied with one military 20 round mag., tangent rear sight, 10 lbs. New in 1987.
Mfg.'s Sug. Retail $875 $740 $600 $540 $465 $420 $375 $340
Subtract $55 if without flash hider.
Add $75 for heavy barrel with bipod (14 lbs.).
Add $400 (retail) for .22 LR conversion kit.

This model is guaranteed to shoot within 2.5 MOA with match ammunition.

FAL Bush Model—similar to FAL, except has 18 in. barrel with flash suppressor, 9¾ lbs. New in 1989.
Mfg.'s Sug. Retail $900 $760 $625 $550 $465 $420 $375 $340

FAL Para Model—similar to FAL Bush Model, except has metal folding stock, leaf rear sight. New in 1989.
Mfg.'s Sug. Retail $930 $775 $635 $550 $465 $420 $375 $340

FAL Factory Rebuilt—factory (Argentine) rebuilt FAL without flash suppressor in excellent condition with Armscorp forged receiver, 9 lbs. 10 oz.
Mfg.'s Sug. Retail $675 $625 $560 $520 $450 $400 $360 $320

Grading	100%	98%	95%	90%	80%	70%	60%

M36 ISRAELI SNIPER RIFLE

.308 cal., gas operated semi-auto, Bullpup configuration, 22 in. free floating barrel, Armscorp M14 receiver, 20 shot mag., includes suppressor and bipod, 10 lbs. Civilian offering in 1989.

Mfg.'s Sug. Retail	$3,000	$2,900	$2,500	$2,275	$2,050	$1,900	$1,775	$1,600

EXPERT MODEL—.22 LR, semi-auto, 20.9 in. barrel, 10 shot mag., wood stock with one - screw takedown, iron sights with grooved receiver, 5.1 lbs. New in 1989.

Mfg.'s Sug. Retail	$220	$195	$150	$125	$115	$105	$95	$85

ARMSPORT

CURRENT IMPORTERS AND DISTRIBUTORS FROM MIAMI, FL. SPECIALIZING IN EUROPEAN MANUFACTURERS.

Armsport also imports black powder firearms. They are listed in the Black Powder section of this book.

COMBINATION GUNS

2781 AND 2782—12 ga./.222 cal., O/U turkey gun, blued receiver. Model 2782 has chrome receiver. Model 2782 was imported in 1985 only. Model 2782 new in 1985.

Mfg.'s Sug. Retail	$750	$650	$550	$495	$440	$395	$350	$300

Last Mfg.'s Sug. Retail on Model 2781 was $650.

2783—similar to Model 2782, except is deluxe model with lateral rib. Imported 1986-1988.

	$1,350	$1,075	$925	$820	$750	$680	$600

Last Mfg.'s Sug. Retail was $1,600.

2784—same action as Model 2783, except is chambered for .243 W. Imported 1986-1988.

	$1,350	$1,075	$925	$820	$750	$680	$600

Last Mfg.'s Sug. Retail was $1,600.

2785—same action as Model 2783, except is chambered for .270 W. Imported 1986-1988.

	$1,350	$1,075	$925	$820	$750	$680	$600

Last Mfg.'s Sug. Retail was $1,600.

2786—20 ga./.222 cal., O/U turkey gun, otherwise same specifications as Model 2783. Made in 1986 only.

	$1,350	$1,075	$925	$820	$750	$680	$600

Last Mfg.'s Sug. Retail was $1,350.

2787—same as Model 2786, except is chambered for .243 W. Made in 1986 only.

	$1,350	$1,075	$925	$820	$750	$680	$600

Last Mfg.'s Sug. Retail was $1,350.

2788—same as Model 2786, except is chambered for .270 W. Made in 1986 only.

	$1,350	$1,075	$925	$820	$750	$680	$600

Last Mfg.'s Sug. Retail was $1,350.

4043—12, 16, 20 ga./rifle O/U combination gun, choice of caliber, select walnut, 23½ in. barrels, relief engraved. Discontinued in 1983.

	$1,675	$1,260	$1,090	$925	$840	$755	$670

4651—Tikka deluxe O/U shotgun/rifle, exposed hammers, combo. 12 ga./.222. 12 ga. is chambered for 3 in. shells. Discontinued in 1984.

	$750	$565	$490	$415	$375	$340	$300

4690—Tikka deluxe O/U shotgun/rifle, hammerless, combo 12 ga./.222. 12 ga. is chambered for 3 in. shells. Discontinued in 1984.

	$1,095	$820	$750	$700	$650	$575	$500

Grading	100%	98%	95%	90%	80%	70%	60%

RIFLES: BOLT-ACTION

2801—.30-06 cal., 24 in. barrel, iron sights, checkered walnut stock and forearm. Imported in 1986 only.

	$725	$600	$495	$430	$380	$335	$285

Last Mfg.'s Sug. Retail was $895.

2802—same as Model 2801, except chambered for .308 cal.

	$725	$600	$495	$430	$380	$335	$285

Last Mfg.'s Sug. Retail was $895.

2803—same as Model 2801, except chambered for .270 Win. cal.

	$725	$600	$495	$430	$380	$335	$285

Last Mfg.'s Sug. Retail was $895.

2804—same as Model 2801, except chambered for .243 Win. cal.

	$725	$600	$495	$430	$380	$335	$285

Last Mfg.'s Sug. Retail was $895.

2805—same as Model 2801, except chambered for 7mm Rem. Mag.

	$725	$600	$495	$430	$380	$335	$285

Last Mfg.'s Sug. Retail was $895.

2806—same as Model 2801, except chambered for .300 Win. Mag.

	$725	$600	$495	$430	$380	$335	$285

4601, 4603, 4605, & 4606—Tikka deluxe, .30-06 cal., bolt-action. Model 4603 is .270 Win. Model 4605 is 7mm Rem. Model 4606 is 300 Win. Mag. Discontinued in 1984.

	$725	$545	$450	$380	$340	$295	$260

4602, 4604, & 4607—Tikka deluxe .308 Win. bolt-action. Model 4604 is .243 Win. Model 4607 .222 Rem. Discontinued in 1983.

	$675	$510	$450	$420	$390	$350	$310

RIFLES: DOUBLE & COMBINATION

4020—Express set O/U double rifle with ejectors plus an extra set of O/U shotgun barrels. Discontinued in 1986.

	$3,850	$3,300	$2,860	$2,420	$2,200	$1,980	$1,760

Last Mfg.'s Sug. Retail was $4,400.

4021—same combination as Model 4020, except rifle has extractors. Discontinued in 1986.

	$3,400	$2,910	$2,520	$2,135	$1,940	$1,745	$1,550

Last Mfg.'s Sug. Retail was $3,875.

4022—Express O/U rifle only with ejectors, choice of calibers. Discontinued in 1986.

	$3,450	$2,945	$2,555	$2,160	$1,965	$1,770	$1,570

Last Mfg.'s Sug. Retail was $3,925.

4023—same as Model 4022, except has extractors. Discontinued in 1986.

	$2,925	$2,515	$2,180	$1,845	$1,675	$1,510	$1,340

Last Mfg.'s Sug. Retail was $3,350.

4010—Emperor SxS, double rifle with extra set of 20 ga. barrels and forearm. Completely hand made and finished using the best materials and craftsmen, choice of caliber, leather fitted case. Discontinued in 1983.

	$16,300	$12,225	$10,595	$8,965	$8,150	$7,335	$6,520

4011—same as Model 4010, except rifle only, 9.3 x 74R cal. Discontinued in 1984.

	$12,750	$9,565	$8,290	$7,015	$6,375	$5,740	$5,100

4012—Emperor "One-of-a-Kind" SxS rifle/shotgun set. Special engraving finishing per individual customer order, choice of gauges, calibers. Leather fitted case. Rare. Discontinued in 1983.

	$26,000	$19,500	$16,900	$14,300	$13,000	$11,700	$10,400

4013—same as Model 4012, but SxS double rifle only. Discontinued in 1983.

	$22,850	$17,140	$14,855	$12,570	$11,425	$10,285	$9,140

Grading	100%	98%	95%	90%	80%	70%	60%

RIFLES: LEVER-ACTION

4500 & 4501—.44-40 cal., deluxe copy of Winchester Model 1873 Rifle, engraved. Model 4501 is .357 Mag. Model 4500 (.44-40) discontinued in 1984. Model 4501 (.357 Mag.) discontinued in 1986.

	$1,135	$975	$845	$715	$650	$585	$520

Last Mfg.'s Sug. Retail was $1,296.

4502 & 4503—.44-40 cal., deluxe copy of Winchester Model 1873 Carbine, engraved. Model 4503 is .357 Mag.. Model 4502 (.44-40) discontinued in 1984. Model 4503 (.357 Mag.) discontinued in 1986.

	$960	$825	$715	$605	$550	$495	$440

Last Mfg.'s Sug. Retail was $1,095.

4504—.357 Mag., standard copy of Winchester Model 1873 carbine. Discontinued in 1986.

	$555	$470	$410	$345	$315	$285	$250

Last Mfg.'s Sug. Retail was $625.

RIFLES: SEMI-AUTO

2785 & 2786—.22 LR cal., semi-auto, 10 shot mag.. Model 2786 is military type with 15 round mag. Imported in 1985 only.

	$150	$125	$100	$90	$80	$70	$60

Last Mfg.'s Sug. Retail was $170.

SHOTGUNS: O/U

The below models designated by -3 suffixes indicate 1988 models.

2528—12 ga., 3 in. Mag., 28 in. barrels, single trigger with auto ejectors. Discontinued in 1983.

	$595	$450	$390	$330	$300	$270	$240

2626—20 ga., 3 in. Mag., 26 in. barrels, single trigger with auto ejectors. Discontinued in 1983.

	$595	$450	$390	$330	$300	$270	$240

2697 & 2698—10 ga., 3½ in. Mag., similar to Models 2699 & 2700 except have 3 screw in choke tubes, Model 2698 has 31½ barrels. New in 1989.

Mfg.'s Sug. Retail	$995	$815	$650	$575	$520	$495	$475	$450

2699/2700C & 2700—10 ga., 3½ in. Mag., 27 (2699 - new in 1989), 28 (2700C), or 32 (2700) in. barrels with 12mm vent rib, extractors, DT's. New in 1986.

Mfg.'s Sug. Retail	$915	$750	$625	$550	$475	$430	$395	$370

2700B—similar to Model 2700, except has deluxe walnut (32 in. barrels only). Made in 1987 only.

	$660	$575	$480	$430	$395	$370	$350

Last Mfg.'s Sug. Retail was $795.

2701 & 2703—12 and 20 ga., 3 in. Mag., 26 and 28 in. barrels, double triggers, extractors. Discontinued in 1985, and reintroduced in 1989.

Mfg.'s Sug. Retail	$485	$420	$360	$295	$265	$230	$200	$185

2702-3 & 2704-3—1988 designations for Models 2701 & 2703. Model 2702-3 is 12 ga. Model 2704-3 is 20 ga. Imported in 1988 only.

	$425	$365	$295	$260	$220	$200	$185

Last Mfg.'s Sug. Retail was $490.

2705—.410 ga., double triggers, 26 in. barrels, bored I & M, extractors. Importation began in 1986.

Mfg.'s Sug. Retail	$595	$495	$395	$350	$300	$275	$235	$200

2706—12 ga. only, law enforcement model, 20 in. barrels, double triggers, extractors. Imported in 1986 only.

	$330	$280	$260	$240	$220	$200	$185

Last Mfg.'s Sug. Retail was $375.

2708-3—12 ga. only, slug gun, 20 in. barrels, double triggers, extractors. Importation began in 1986.

Mfg.'s Sug. Retail	$510	$440	$370	$300	$260	$240	$220	$200

Grading	100%	98%	95%	90%	80%	70%	60%

2711, 2713-3, 2721, & 2723—12 and 20 ga., 3 in. Mag., 26 and 28 in. barrels, extractors. Models 2721 and 2723 have ejectors and were discontinued in 1985.

Mfg.'s Sug. Retail	$535	$445	$385	$340	$310	$275	$250	$230

Add 25% with ejectors.

Last Mfg.'s Sug. Retail was $375 on Models 2721/2723.

2717-3, 2719-3, & 2720—12 and 20 ga., 3 in. Mag., 26 and 28 in. barrels. Models 2719 and 2720 are 20 ga. and .410 ga. respectively. New in 1986. Models 2717-3 and 2719-3 were discontinued in 1988.

Mfg.'s Sug. Retail	$650	$530	$425	$365	$325	$300	$280	$260

Last Mfg.'s Sug. Retail was $550 on Models 2717-3 & 2719-3.

2712, 2714-3, 2722, & 2724—12 and 20 ga., 3 in. Mag., 26 and 28 in. barrels. Models 2712 and 2722 are 12 ga., engraved with 12mm vent rib. Models 2722 and 2724 have ejectors. Importation of Models 2712, 2722, and 2724 were discontinued in 1986. Model 2714-3 was discontinued in 1988.

	$500	$395	$350	$300	$275	$235	$200

Last Mfg.'s Sug. Retail was $395 on Models 2712/2722/2724.

Last Mfg.'s Sug. Retail was $615 on Model 2714-3.

2715-3 & 2716-3—12 ga. only, 28 in. barrels with 3 choke tubes, auto ejectors, single trigger. Imported in 1988 only.

	$575	$465	$400	$350	$295	$265	$245

Last Mfg.'s Sug. Retail was $680.

2718, 2733, & 2735—12 and 20 ga., 3 in. Mag., 26 and 28 in. barrels, SST, extractors. Models 2733/2735 have deluxe Boss actions. Model 2718 was discontinued in 1985.

Mfg.'s Sug. Retail	$575	$515	$450	$385	$330	$295	$265	$245

Last Mfg.'s Sug. Retail was $390 on Model 2718.

2734 & 2736—12 (2734) or 20 (2736) ga., similar to Models 2733 and 2735, except has 3 choke tubes.

Mfg.'s Sug. Retail	$610	$530	$440	$400	$350	$295	$265	$245

2746 & 2747—12 ga., 3½ in. chambers, 27 (2746) or 31 (2747) in. barrels with wide rib and 3 choke tubes, auto extractors, Boss type action. New in 1989.

Mfg.'s Sug. Retail	$650	$565	$495	$460	$430	$400	$380	$365

Add $10 for 31 in. barrels.

2726, 2728, 2741/2, & 2743/4—12 and 20 ga., 3 in. Mag., 26 and 28 in. barrels, SST, ejectors. Models 2741 and 2743 have deluxe Boss actions. Models 2726 & 2728 were discontinued in 1985.

Mfg.'s Sug. Retail	$620	$535	$450	$410	$360	$300	$275	$250

Add $40 for 3 choke tubes (Models 2742 & 2744).

Last Mfg.'s Sug. Retail on Models 2726 & 2728 was $440.

2727-3 & 2729-3—1986 designations for Models 2726 & 2728 respectively. -3 suffixes indicate 1988 designations. Importation disc. in 1988.

	$550	$450	$385	$330	$295	$265	$245

Last Mfg.'s Sug. Retail was $615.

2730—12 ga., skeet gun, 27 in. barrel, has six interchangeable chokes, Boss-type action.

Mfg.'s Sug. Retail	$730	$595	$525	$470	$425	$395	$370	$350

2731—same as Model 2730, except is 20 ga. and has 26 in. barrels.

Mfg.'s Sug. Retail	$730	$600	$550	$485	$450	$425	$395	$375

4014—Emperor Grade SxS. Individually fitted per customer H&H type action, engraved, fitted leather case, choice of gauge, barrel lengths, etc. Completely hand finished.

Emperor Grade models are discontinued. Limited availability.

	$9,175	$6,885	$5,965	$5,050	$4,590	$4,130	$3,670

Grading	100%	98%	95%	90%	80%	70%	60%

4015—Emperor "One-of-a-Kind" SxS. Similar to Model 4014, except that every part of the gun is made per customer order. Specifications including style of engraving, dimensions, wood configuration, special requests, etc. No expense spared. Discontinued in 1984.

	$18,000	$13,500	$11,700	$9,900	$9,000	$8,100	$7,200

4016—Emperor SxS with outside hammers, fitted leather case, extensively engraved, any gauge. Discontinued in 1983.

	$4,550	$3,415	$2,960	$2,505	$2,275	$2,050	$1,820

4017—Emperor "One-of-a-Kind" SxS with outside hammers. Flexibility of options is similar to Model 4015. Discontinued in 1984.

	$12,750	$9,565	$8,290	$7,015	$6,375	$5,740	$5,100

4030 & 4031—12 ga. SxS, Holland-style detachable locks, English walnut, ejectors, engraved. Model 4031 is 20 ga. — discontinued in 1983.

	$3,950	$2,965	$2,570	$2,175	$1,975	$1,780	$1,580

4032 & 4033—12 ga. Premier Mono Trap Gun, 32 in. barrel, ejector. Model 4033 is same, except for 34 in. barrel. Discontinued in 1986.

	$1,810	$1,560	$1,350	$1,145	$1,040	$935	$830

Last Mfg.'s Sug. Retail was $2,075.

4034 & 4035—12 ga. Premier Mono Trap Set, 32 in. single, 30 in. O/U. Model 4035 is same, except has 34 in. single, 32 in. O/U. Discontinued in 1986.

	$2,565	$2,215	$1,920	$1,625	$1,475	$1,330	$1,180

Last Mfg.'s Sug. Retail was $2,950.

4040—12 ga. Slug Special SxS, 23 in. barrels. Discontinued in 1984.

	$1,325	$995	$865	$730	$665	$600	$530

4046 & 4047—12 ga. trap gun, 34 in. barrel, extra trigger mechanism. Model 4047 is 32 in. Discontinued in 1986.

	$2,860	$2,460	$2,100	$1,850	$1,700	$1,500	$1,300

Last Mfg.'s Sug. Retail was $3,275.

4050—Pigeon Grade O/U, 12 ga., engraved. Discontinued in 1986.

	$2,375	$2,025	$1,755	$1,485	$1,350	$1,215	$1,080

Last Mfg.'s Sug. Retail was $2,700.

4055 & 4056—Premier Skeet 12 ga., selective trigger, ejectors, engraved, select wood. Model 4056 is 20 ga. — discontinued in 1983.

	$2,000	$1,500	$1,300	$1,100	$1,000	$900	$800

4061 & 4062—.410 ga. SxS, single trigger, selective ejectors. Model 4062 is 28 ga. — discontinued in 1983.

	$995	$750	$650	$550	$500	$450	$400

4063 & 4064—.410 ga. O/U, single trigger, selective ejectors. Model 4064 is 28 ga. Discontinued in 1983.

	$995	$750	$650	$550	$500	$450	$400

SHOTGUNS: REPEATING

2755—12 ga., 7 shot, Atis mfg., black anodized receiver, 24 or 28 in. barrel with VR. Made in 1985-87 only.

	$335	$260	$225	$195	$180	$160	$145

Last Mfg.'s Sug. Retail was $395.

2755A—same as Model 2755, except has 30 in. barrel. Made in 1986-87 only.

	$335	$260	$225	$195	$180	$160	$145

2756—12 ga., 28 in. VR barrel, 3 interchangeable chokes. Made in 1986-87 only.

	$390	$335	$280	$230	$205	$190	$175

Last Mfg.'s Sug. Retail was $465.

2756A—same as Model 2756, except has 30 in. vent rib barrel. Made in 1986-87 only.

	$390	$335	$280	$230	$205	$190	$175

Last Mfg.'s Sug. Retail was $465.

Grading	100%	98%	95%	90%	80%	70%	60%

2757—12 ga. only, law enforcement model, 20 in. barrel, black receiver. Made in 1986-87 only.

	$310	$250	$205	$190	$175	$155	$140

Last Mfg.'s Sug. Retail was $375.

2766, 2767, & 2768—12 ga., Fabarms mfg., 25 in. barrel. Model 2768 has 20 in. barrel. Imported in 1985 only.

	$260	$220	$200	$180	$160	$140	$120

Last Mfg.'s Sug. Retail was $300.

SHOTGUNS: SEMI-AUTO

2751—12 ga., 3 in. Mag., semi-auto, Atis mfg., black anodized receiver, 28 in. barrel. Made in 1985-87 only.

	$430	$340	$310	$285	$255	$230	$200

Last Mfg.'s Sug. Retail was $575.

2751A—same as Model 2751, except has 30 in. full choke barrel. Made in 1986-87 only.

	$430	$340	$310	$285	$255	$230	$200

Last Mfg.'s Sug. Retail was $575.

2752—same action as Model 2751, except chrome receiver and engraving. Made in 1986-87 only.

	$440	$345	$310	$285	$255	$230	$200

Last Mfg.'s Sug. Retail was $600.

2752A—same as Model 2752, except has 30 in. barrel. Made in 1986-87 only.

	$440	$345	$310	$285	$255	$230	$200

Last Mfg.'s Sug. Retail was $600.

2753—same action as Model 2751, except has 28 in. barrel with 3 interchangeable chokes. Made in 1986-87 only.

	$460	$355	$315	$285	$255	$230	$200

Last Mfg.'s Sug. Retail was $650.

2753A—same as Model 2753, except has chrome receiver and engraving. Made in 1986-87 only.

	$470	$365	$320	$285	$255	$230	$200

Last Mfg.'s Sug. Retail was $675.

2761 & 2762—12 ga., black or chrome receiver, Fabarms made, engraved action, 27 in. barrel. Add $75 for interchangeable choke tubes. Imported during 1985 only.

	$410	$360	$315	$295	$270	$245	$215

Last Mfg.'s Sug. Retail was $475.

SHOTGUNS: SINGLE AND SIDE-BY-SIDE

1033—10 ga. SxS, 3½ in. Mag., 32 in. full and full chokes. Discontinued in 1985.

	$395	$340	$315	$275	$250	$225	$200

Last Mfg.'s Sug. Retail was $450.

1050-1—1986 designation for the Model 1051. -1 suffix designates 1988 importation only.

	$485	$375	$310	$250	$230	$210	$200

Last Mfg.'s Sug. Retail was $595.

1051 & 1052—12 ga. SxS, 3 in. Mag., 28 in. mod. & full chokes. Model 1052 is 20 ga., 3 in. Mag., 26 in. Imp. & Mod. Discontinued in 1985.

	$330	$280	$260	$240	$225	$205	$180

Last Mfg.'s Sug. Retail was $375.

1053-1—1986 designation for the Model 1052. -1 suffix designates 1988 importation only.

	$485	$375	$310	$250	$230	$210	$200

Last Mfg.'s Sug. Retail was $595.

Grading	100%	98%	95%	90%	80%	70%	60%

1055 & 1057—28 and .410 ga. SxS, 3 in. Mag., 26 in. barrel, Imp. and Mod. chokes. Model 1057 is 28 ga., 3 in. Mag., 26 in. Imp. & Mod. Discontinued in 1985.

	100%	98%	95%	90%	80%	70%	60%
	$330	$280	$260	$240	$225	$205	$180

Last Mfg.'s Sug. Retail was $375.

Model 1057 was redesignated 1055 in 1985 and Model 1055 was changed to 1054.

1054-1 & 1055-1—.410 (1054) or .28 (1055) ga. -1 suffix designates 1988 importation only.

	$485	$375	$310	$250	$230	$210	$200

Last Mfg.'s Sug. Retail was $595.

1101, 1102, 1103, & 1104—12 ga., folding single barrel w/vent rib. Model 1102 is 20 ga. Model 1103 is .410 ga. Model 1104 is 28 ga. Discontinued in 1985.

	$125	$105	$90	$75	$70	$65	$60

Last Mfg.'s Sug. Retail was $140.

1107 & 1108—12 ga., folding single barrel 19 in., pistol grip. Model 1108 is 20 ga. Discontinued in 1983.

	$135	$105	$95	$85	$75	$70	$65

1125, 1126, & 1127—12 or 20 ga., single barrel, 3 in. chamber, bottom lever opening, Model 1127 is 20 ga. New in 1987.

Mfg.'s Sug. Retail	$110	$95	$80	$60	$50	$45	$40	$35

1128—.410 ga., otherwise similar to Models 1125/1126/1127.

Mfg.'s Sug. Retail	$110	$95	$80	$60	$50	$45	$40	$35

1212 & 1213—12 ga., SxS, outside hammers, engraved action, 20 in. barrels. Model 1213 is 20 ga. — discontinued in 1983.

	$450	$340	$295	$250	$225	$205	$180

1225—12 ga. only, O/U configuration, folding action, top lever break. Made in 1986-87 only.

	$275	$235	$200	$185	$170	$165	$150

Last Mfg.'s Sug. Retail was $345.

1226—20 ga. only, O/U configuration, folding action, top lever break. Made in 1986-87 only.

	$275	$235	$200	$185	$170	$165	$150

Last Mfg.'s Sug. Retail was $345.

SHOTGUNS: TRI-BARREL

MODEL 2900—12 ga., 3 barrel with F & M 28 in. barrels over IC. Made in 1986-87 only.

	$1,050	$895	$770	$670	$595	$525	$460

Last Mfg.'s Sug. Retail was $1,450.

ARRIETA, S.L.

MANUFACTURED IN ELGOIBAR, SPAIN. CURRENTLY IMPORTED AND DISTRIBUTED BY MORTON'S LIMITED LOCATED IN LEXINGTON, KY.

Prices could differ from values shown below because of the fluctuating U.S. dollar.

SHOTGUNS: DISCONTINUED SxS

Values listed below are for 12 or 16 ga. Add 10% for either 20, 28 or .410 ga. Also add 10% for matched pair.

490 EDER—12, 16, or 20 ga., boxlock, double triggers, extractors, light engraving. Discontinued in 1986.

	$475	$405	$350	$300	$270	$245	$220

Last Mfg.'s Sug. Retail was $540.

500 TITAN—12, 16, or 20 ga., Purdey type action with H&H pattern double safety sidelocks, satin receiver engraved, double triggers, extractors. Discontinued in 1986.

	$575	$495	$430	$365	$330	$300	$265

Last Mfg.'s Sug. Retail was $660.

Grading	100%	98%	95%	90%	80%	70%	60%

501 PALOMERA—12, 16, or 20 ga., same action as 500, fine border engraving, blued or casehardened action. Discontinued in 1986.

	100%	98%	95%	90%	80%	70%	60%
	$680	$570	$495	$420	$380	$345	$305

Last Mfg.'s Sug. Retail was $760.

505 ALASKA—12, 16, or 20 ga., same action as 501, blued action extensively engraved. Discontinued in 1986.

	100%	98%	95%	90%	80%	70%	60%
	$750	$645	$560	$475	$430	$390	$345

Last Mfg.'s Sug. Retail was $860.

SHOTGUNS: CURRENT SxS

All Arrieta shotguns have frames scaled to individual guages. Various special options are available by custom order, and a few are listed below.

ADD THE FOLLOWING AMOUNTS FOR CURRENTLY MANUFACTURED SHOTGUNS.
Add 10% for small gauges (20, 28, or .410).
Add approx. $600-$800 for single trigger depending on action.
Add 10% for matched pair.
Add 10% for rounded action on standard models.
Extra barrels are priced from $900-$1,500/set depending on model.

510 MONTANA—12, 16, or 20 ga., H&H-type sidelocks, all inner parts gold-plated.

	100%	98%	95%	90%	80%	70%	60%
Mfg.'s Sug. Retail	$2,175	$2,175	$1,600	$1,300	$1,000	$800	$675	$615

550 FIELD—12, 16, or 20 ga., best hand fitted double safety Holland-type sidelocks, hand detachable, blue finish, moderate engraving.

	100%	98%	95%	90%	80%	70%	60%
Mfg.'s Sug. Retail	$2,175	$2,175	$1,600	$1,300	$1,000	$800	$675	$615

557 STANDARD—12, 16, or 20 ga., Demi-Bloc steel barrels, detachable engraved sidelocks, double triggers, ejectors.

	100%	98%	95%	90%	80%	70%	60%
Mfg.'s Sug. Retail	$2,550	$2,550	$1,800	$1,425	$1,100	$900	$750	$640

558 PATRIA—12, 16, or 20 ga., same as 557, except frame, tangs, and sidelocks 100% engraved.

	100%	98%	95%	90%	80%	70%	60%
Mfg.'s Sug. Retail	$2,625	$2,625	$1,850	$1,425	$1,100	$900	$750	$640

560 CUMBRE—12, 16, or 20 ga., same as 558, except is more elaborately engraved.

	100%	98%	95%	90%	80%	70%	60%
Mfg.'s Sug. Retail	$2,795	$2,795	$1,975	$1,500	$1,175	$925	$750	$640

570 LIEJA—12, 16, or 20 ga., same as 560, except has non-detachable sidelocks.

	100%	98%	95%	90%	80%	70%	60%
Mfg.'s Sug. Retail	$3,000	$3,000	$2,175	$1,625	$1,275	$1,025	$850	$750

575 SPORT—12, 16, or 20 ga., same as 560, except is more elaborately engraved.

	100%	98%	95%	90%	80%	70%	60%
Mfg.'s Sug. Retail	$3,025	$3,025	$2,175	$1,625	$1,275	$1,025	$850	$750

578 VICTORIA—12, 16, or 20 ga., same as 570 except is fine English scrollwork engraved.

	100%	98%	95%	90%	80%	70%	60%
Mfg.'s Sug. Retail	$3,330	$3,330	$2,375	$1,750	$1,375	$1,100	$925	$850

585 LIRIA—12, 16, or 20 ga., same as 575, except has profuse engraving.

	100%	98%	95%	90%	80%	70%	60%
Mfg.'s Sug. Retail	$3,770	$3,770	$2,575	$2,100	$1,800	$1,500	$1,225	$1,025

588 CIMA—similar to M585 Liria, except has more engraving.

	100%	98%	95%	90%	80%	70%	60%
Mfg.'s Sug. Retail	$3,850	$3,850	$2,600	$2,150	$1,825	$1,525	$1,225	$1,025

590 REGINA—12, 16, or 20 ga., same as 570, except has more profuse engraving.

	100%	98%	95%	90%	80%	70%	60%
Mfg.'s Sug. Retail	$4,000	$4,000	$2,700	$2,225	$1,900	$1,600	$1,275	$1,050

595 PRINCIPE—all gauges, sidelock action, relief engraved hunting scenes, ejectors, DT's.

	100%	98%	95%	90%	80%	70%	60%
Mfg.'s Sug. Retail	$6,070	$6,070	$4,300	$3,750	$3,300	$2,875	$2,475	$2,000

600 IMPERIAL—12, 16, or 20 ga., top-of-the-line self-opening action, very ornate engraving throughout.

	100%	98%	95%	90%	80%	70%	60%
Mfg.'s Sug. Retail	$5,320	$5,320	$3,800	$3,500	$3,100	$2,750	$2,400	$1,950

600-1 IMPERIAL—12, 16, or 20 ga., similar to 600 Imperial, except has light border engraving around sidelocks, tangs, trigger guard. Importation disc. in 1988.

	100%	98%	95%	90%	80%	70%	60%
	$4,600	$3,825	$3,500	$3,175	$2,835	$2,460	$2,000

Last Mfg.'s Sug. Retail was $5,380.

Grading	100%	98%	95%	90%	80%	70%	60%

601 TIRO—all gauges, sidelock action with nickle plating, ejectors, SST, self-opening action, border engraving.

Mfg.'s Sug. Retail $6,280 $6,280 $4,400 $3,750 $3,350 $3,000 $2,600 $2,200

801—all gauges, Holland-style detachable sidelocks, self-opening action, ejectors, coin-wash finish, finest Churchill style engraving.

Mfg.'s Sug. Retail $8,995 $8,995 $6,600 $5,500 $4,950 $4,500 $4,000 $3,450

Model's 801 through 875 are also available with self-opening actions as an option — add $800.

802—12, 16, or 20 ga., similar to 801 only non-detachable sidelocks, finest Holland-style engraving.

Mfg.'s Sug. Retail $8,995 $8,995 $6,600 $5,500 $4,950 $4,500 $4,000 $3,450

803—all gauges, similar to 801, finest Purdey-style engraving.

Mfg.'s Sug. Retail $6,050 $6,050 $4,100 $3,650 $3,300 $2,900 $2,550 $2,150

863 (DUNN'S FINE GRADE)—all gauges, sidelock, special model for American upland hunter, level rib, scroll engraved, this model sold exclusively through Dunn's (mfg.'s suggested retail price is $1,995).

Add 10% for 20, 28, or .410 ga.

This model has been redesignated the Model 900.

871—all gauges, rounded frame sidelock action with Demi-Block barrels, scroll engraved, ejectors, DT's.

Mfg.'s Sug. Retail $4,260 $4,260 $3,000 $2,500 $2,100 $1,700 $1,450 $1,275

872—all gauges, rounded frame sidelock action with Demi-Block barrels, elaborate scroll engraving with third lever fastener.

Mfg.'s Sug. Retail $10,430 $10,430 $8,000 $6,900 $5,800 $5,100 $4,400 $3,600

873—all gauges, sidelock action with Demi-Block barrels, game scene engraving, ejectors, SST.

Mfg.'s Sug. Retail $6,290 $6,290 $4,400 $3,750 $3,350 $3,000 $2,600 $2,200

874—all gauges, sidelock action with Demi-Block barrels, action is gold line engraved.

Mfg.'s Sug. Retail $7,730 $7,730 $5,650 $4,400 $3,750 $3,350 $3,000 $2,600

875—all gauges, top-of-the-line quality, built to individual customer spec.'s only, elaborate engraving with gold. inlays.

Mfg.'s Sug. Retail $13,875 $13,875 $10,000 $8,600 $7,700 $6,800 $5,900 $4,950

SHOTGUNS: 900 SERIES

The 900 series is made exculsively for Morton's Limited and replaces the 600 and 800 series guns in 1988.

Add $1,950 retail for self-opening action on the 900 series.

900—all gauges, sidelock, Purdey style scroll engraving, sold exclusively through Dunn's/Jaeger Inc.

Mfg.'s Sug. Retail $1,995 $1,995 $1,600 $1,300 $1,000 $800 $675 $615

This model is sold by Dunn's and is designated the Fine Grade.

901—all gauges, sidelock, Churchill style engraving, best quality.

Mfg.'s Sug. Retail $7,850 $7,850 $5,700 $4,400 $3,750 $3,350 $3,000 $2,600

902—all gauges, sidelock, Holland & Holland style engraving, best quality.

Mfg.'s Sug. Retail $7,850 $7,850 $5,700 $4,400 $3,750 $3,350 $3,000 $2,600

903—all gauges, sidelock, Purdey style engraving, best quality.

Mfg.'s Sug. Retail $4,940 $4,495 $3,675 $3,050 $2,550 $2,155 $1,825 $1,655

This model is sold through Dunn's located in Grand Junction, TN and is designated the Best Grade.

904—all gauges, sidelock, rounded frame, scroll engraving, best quality.

Mfg.'s Sug. Retail $7,850 $7,850 $5,700 $4,400 $3,750 $3,350 $3,000 $2,600

905—all gauges, sidelock, scroll engraving with game scenes cameos.

Mfg.'s Sug. Retail $8,325 $8,325 $5,900 $4,500 $3,800 $3,400 $3,000 $2,600

Grading	100%	98%	95%	90%	80%	70%	60%

906—all gauges, sidelock, border engraving, special field gun available for either lead or steel shot.

Mfg.'s Sug. Retail	$2,450	$2,450	$1,700	$1,375	$1,050	$850	$675	$615

907—all gauges, sidelock, Purdey style engraving, special field gun available for either lead or steel shot.

Mfg.'s Sug. Retail	$4,000	$4,000	$2,700	$2,225	$1,900	$1,600	$1,275	$1,050

908—all gauges, sidelock, Purdey style engraving.

Mfg.'s Sug. Retail	$4,020	$4,020	$2,700	$2,225	$1,900	$1,600	$1,275	$1,050

909—all gauges, sidelock, round frame, large scroll engraving.

Mfg.'s Sug. Retail	$4,500	$4,500	$3,000	$2,500	$2,100	$1,775	$1,550	$1,300

ARRIZABLAGA

MANUFACTURED IN EIBAR, SPAIN. CURRENTLY IMPORTED AND DISTRIBUTED BY MORTON'S LIMITED LOCATED IN LEXINGTON, KY.

ADD THE FOLLOWING AMOUNTS ON ARRIZABLAGA SHOTGUNS:

All Arrizablaga shotguns have self-opening (assisted) actions.

Add 5% for matched pair.

Add $2,630 (retail) for extra barrels.

Add $430 for 28 ga.

Add $1,095 for .410 ga.

Add $1,050 for single trigger.

Add $225 for pistol grip stock.

HEAVY SCROLL MODEL—12, 16, or 20 ga., sidelock action, elaborate engraving, deluxe oil finished stock and forearm.

Mfg.'s Sug. Retail	$8,735	$8,735	$6,200	$5,400	$4,750	$4,300	$3,850	$3,325

ENGLISH SCROLL MODEL—12, 16, or 20 ga., sidelock action, English scroll engraving, deluxe oil finished walnut stock and forearm.

Mfg.'s Sug. Retail	$9,200	$9,200	$6,500	$5,650	$4,950	$4,500	$4,000	$3,450

SPECIAL MODEL—12, 16, or 20 ga., sidelock top of the line model, best quality wood and engraving.

Mfg.'s Sug. Retail	$13,780	$13,780	$9,000	$8,200	$7,400	$6,600	$5,900	$4,950

ASTRA

MANUFACTURED BY UNCETA Y CIA., GUERNICA, SPAIN. CURRENTLY IMPORTED BY INTERARMS LOCATED IN ALEXANDRIA, VA.

PISTOLS: CURRENT MANUFACTURE

CONSTABLE—double action, .22 LR (10 shot), .32 auto (8 shot — discontinued 1984), .380 ACP (7 shot), exposed hammer, 3½ in. barrel, fixed sight, 28 or 40 (.380 ACP) oz., blue or chrome, plastic grips, made 1965-present.

Mfg.'s Sug. Retail	$365	$300	$245	$210	$180	$165	$150	$135

Subtract $15 for .380 ACP cal.

Add $10 for chrome finish or wood grips.

Constable Stainless—.380 ACP only, stainless version of the Constable. Made in 1986 only.

	$300	$260	$240	$220	$200	$175	$150

Last Mfg.'s Sug. Retail was $345.

Constable Sport—same as Constable, except has 6 in. barrel, blue finish only, 35 oz. Made in 1986-87 only.

	$285	$230	$200	$180	$165	$150	$135

Last Mfg.'s Sug. Retail was $330.

Grading	100%	98%	95%	90%	80%	70%	60%

Blue Engraved Constable—blue engraved. Importation discontinued in 1987.

		$340	$295	$250			

Add $20 for .22 LR or checkered wood grips.

Last Mfg.'s Sug. Retail was $375.

Chrome Engraved Constable—chrome engraved. Importation discontinued in 1987.

		$350	$295	$250			

Add $20 for .22 LR or checkered wood grips.

Last Mfg.'s Sug. Retail was $390.

CONSTABLE A-60—.380 ACP, double action, 3½ in. barrel, 13 shot mag., ambidextrous safety, adj. rear sight, blue finish only. New in 1986.

Mfg.'s Sug. Retail	$435	$370	$310	$270	$245	$220	$185	$160

MODEL A-80—double action, semi-auto, 9mm, .38 Super (disc.) or .45 ACP cal.'s, 15 shot mag. (9 for .45 ACP), 3¾ in. barrel. Made 1982-present.

Mfg.'s Sug. Retail	$425	$370	$320	$285	$265	$240	$210	$185

Add $35 for chrome finish (disc.).

MODEL A-90—1986 designation for Model A-80, 9mm or .45 ACP only, blue only, 36 or 40 oz. New in 1986.

Mfg.'s Sug. Retail	$500	$400	$340	$295	$265	$245	$225	$200

MODEL 4000 FALCON—.22 LR, .32 ACP, .380 ACP cal.'s, 4 in. barrel, fixed sights, blue, plastic grips, exposed hammer, made 1956-1986.

	$400	$350	$300	$260	$235	$200	$150

Add 50% for .22 cal.

Add 100% for engraved M-4000.

Last Mfg.'s Sug. Retail was $340.

PISTOLS: DISCONTINUED

MODEL 1911—.25 ACP or .32 ACP, semi-auto, may have external or internal hammer.

	$220	$165	$155	$135	$125	$110	$100

MODEL 1915/1916—.32 ACP semi-auto.

	$240	$180	$170	$145	$135	$120	$110

Note: Models 1915/1916 were later referred to as Model 100.

CAMPO GIRO 1913—made 1913.

	$800	$700	$600	$550	$500	$450	$400

CAMPO GIRO 1913-16—made 1913-16.

	$495	$435	$390	$355	$295	$255	$220

MODEL 200 FIRECAT AUTOMATIC PISTOL—.25 auto, 2¼ in. barrel, 6 shot, blue, plastic grips, made 1920-present, U.S. importation stopped by GCA 68.

Add 50% for engraved M-200.

	$240	$190	$165	$145	$125	$110	$100

MODEL 300—.32 ACP or .380, semi-auto.

Add 20% if Nazi-proofed. Add 100% for engraved M-300.

	$350	$300	$270	$240	$210	$180	$150

MODEL 400 AUTOMATIC PISTOL—9mm Bayard long, 9 shot, 6 in. barrel, blue, fixed sights, plastic grips, made 1921-1945.

	$300	$265	$230	$200	$170	$135	$100

Add 200% for Navy variation.

Approx. serial range of Nazi accepted specimens (no markings) is S/N 92,851 - 98,850. These will bring a premium.

MODEL 600 MOD. AUTOMATIC—9mm Luger, 8 shot, 5¼ in. barrel, blue, fixed sights, wood or plastic grips, made 1944-1945.

	$250	$225	$200	$175	$155	$140	$130

Add a 20% + premium for Nazi Waffenamt proofing (approx. serial range 1 - 10,500).

Grading	100%	98%	95%	90%	80%	70%	60%

MODEL 700 SPECIAL—.32 ACP semi-auto.

	$500	$465	$425	$350	$275	$215	$170

MODEL 800 CONDOR AUTOMATIC—same as 600, except has exposed hammer, 9mm, made 1958-1965.

	$1,200	$1,000	$800	$650	$550	$450	$350

MODEL 900—7.63 Mauser cal., Broomhandle copy, parts non-interchangeable with Mauser. Made from 1928-1936.

	$2,000	$1,800	$1,300	$850	$700	$525	$425

Add $400 for matching detachable stock.
Add 50% for early Bolo grip variation.
Add 25% for specimens with Japanese characters.

MODEL 902—7.63 Mauser cal., semi-auto, similar to 900 except 20 shot mag.

	$6,500	$5,000	$4,250	$3,000	$2,500	$2,100	$1,700

Add $700 for original "booted" stock.
Deduct 50% for selective fire version.

MACHINE PISTOLS—class III, transferrable only, 10 or 20 shot detachable mag., several variations.

	$1,800	$1,500	$1,200	$1,000	$800	$675	$535

MODEL 3000 POCKET AUTOMATIC—.32 auto and .380 auto, 4 in. barrel, fixed sights, blue, plastic grips, made 1947-1956. Add 100% for engraved M3000.

	$325	$280	$240	$210	$180	$150	$120

MODEL 1000—semi-auto, .32 ACP.

	$560	$420	$365	$310	$280	$255	$225

MODEL 2000 CUB—.22 short and .25 auto cal.'s, 2¼ in. barrel, fixed sights, blue, plastic grips, also chrome finish, made 1954-present, U.S. importation stopped by GCA 68. Astra also made 2000 Cubs for Colt called Jr. Model see Colt section.

	$200	$170	$140	$115	$95	$85	$75

Add 50% for engraved M-2000.

MODEL 2000 CAMPER—same as Cub, .22 short only, with 4 in. barrel, made 1955-1960.

	$300	$250	$200	$160	$125	$90	$70

ASTRA CADIX DOUBLE ACTION REVOLVER—.22 LR, 9 shot, .38 Spl., 5 shot, 4 or 6 in. barrel, adj. sights, blue, plastic grips, made 1960-1968.

	$165	$155	$140	$120	$110	$85	$55

REVOLVERS

.357 D/A REVOLVER—.357 Mag., 6 shot, 3, 4, 6 or 8½ in. barrel (add $10), adj. sights, blue, checkered wood grips, made 1972-1988.

	$250	$215	$185	$170	$155	$140	$125

Last Mfg.'s Sug. Retail was $295.

Stainless steel.—4 in. barrel only. Disc. in 1987.

	$285	$245	$205				

Last Mfg.'s Sug. Retail was $330.

.44/.45 CAL. D/A REVOLVER—.41 Mag. (discontinued in 1985), .44 Mag. and .45 ACP (disc. in 1987), 6 shot, 6 or 8½ in. (.44 Mag. only) barrels. Made 1980-87.

	$280	$235	$210	$190	$180	$170	$160

Last Mfg.'s Sug. Retail was $315.

Stainless steel—.44 Mag. only, 6 in. barrel only.

Mfg.'s Sug. Retail	$450	$370	$300	$265			

CONVERTIBLE REVOLVER—9mm with extra .357 Mag. cylinder, 6 shot, 3 in. barrel, blue only, checkered walnut grips. Made 1986 - present.

Mfg.'s Sug. Retail	$395	$335	$275	$250	$225	$200	$180	$160

Grading	100%	98%	95%	90%	80%	70%	60%

TERMINATOR—.44 Mag. or .44 Spl. (disc.) cal., 6 shot, adj. rear sight, Roberts rubber grips, 2¾ in. shrouded barrel only.

Blue finish

Mfg.'s Sug. Retail	$250	$230	$190	$180	$170	$160	$150	$140

Stainless steel

Mfg.'s Sug. Retail	$275	$250	$230	$190

This model is distributed by Sile Distributors, Inc. located in New York, NY. Remaining quanities of stainless steel are limited.

AUSTRALIAN AUTOMATIC ARMS PTY. LTD.

MANUFACTURED IN TASMANIA, AUSTRALIA. CURRENTLY IMPORTED AND DISTRIBUTED BY NORTH AMERICAN SALES INTERNATIONAL, INC. (NASI) LOCATED IN MIDLAND, TX.

SAR—.223 cal., semi-auto assault rifle, 16¼ or 20 in. (new in 1989) barrel, 5 or 20 shot M-16 style mag., fiberglass stock and forearm, 7½ lbs. New in 1986.

Mfg.'s Sug. Retail	$663	$625	$550	$510	$465	$410	$370	$335

Add $25 for 20 in. barrel.

Also available in fully auto version (AR) — same values as shown above.

SAC—.223 cal., semi-auto assault carbine, 10½ in. barrel, 20 shot mag., fiberglass stock and forearm, 6.9 lbs. New in 1986.

This model is available to class III dealers and law enforcement agencies only — values can be obtained by contacting North American Sales International, Inc.

SAP—.223 cal., semi-auto assault pistol, 10½ in. barrel, 20 shot mag., fiberglass stock and forearm, 5.9 lbs. New in 1986.

Mfg.'s Sug. Retail	$650	$615	$550	$475	$430	$380	$340	$295

Also available in fully automatic version (MP) — same values as shown above.

SP—.223 cal., semi-auto, sporting configuration, 16¼ or 20 in. barrel, wood stock and forearm, 5 or 20 shot M-16 style mag., 7.5 lbs. New in 1989.

Mfg.'s Sug. Retail	$712	$650	$615	$550	$475	$430	$380	$340

Add $23 for 20 in. barrel.

AUTO MAG

Short recoil rotary bolt system made entirely of stainless steel. Most pistols were sold in .44 AMP cal. although .357 AMP was also a popular factory option. Several other calibers and variations were marketed through Lee Jurras including exotics like the .44 Condor (16 in. barrel and scoped - one of a kind). Also, a .30 cal. Cougar with 12 in. barrel and highly polished metal was a one of a kind item. Other limited Jurras variations include The Custom 100 Series, The Grizzly, The Backpacker, and Metallic Silhouette. Other manufacturers logo's include Auto Mag Corp., TDE, High Standard, and AMT. A unique handgun, the Auto Mag has never been a commercial success due to high manufacturing costs and functioning problems. Initial reaction to Dirty Harry's use of this weapon in the movie "Sudden Impact" made prices escalate considerably, but most values appear to have stablized since 1986. Be aware of fakes - especially of the XP variety (re-serialized, re-stamped, location of markings,etc.). Also, the ease of barrel swapping should be considered when deciding a potential purchase.

Grading	100%	98%	95%	90%	80%	70%	60%

Serial number ranges for the various models are as follows: Pasadena mfg. - A0000 through A03300. TDE North Hollywood - mostly A03400 through A05015 although some were marked with very low ser. no.'s. TDE El Monte mfg. - A05016 through A08300. High Standard guns were originally marked with "H" prefix serial numbers (only 132 made), after which they carried standard "A0" prefix serial numbers. The "H" prefix guns remain a collectors item and command a 25% premium over values listed below. TDE/OMC marked pistols - B00001 through B00370 are known as the "B" series or solid bolt models (only 370 manufactured). This "B" series also commands collector premiums. AMT manufactured the last two lots of Auto Mags; the first was the "C" series and was basically the same as the "B" except that only 50 guns were fabricated. The last Auto Mags made by AMT were appropriately serial numbered LAST 1 through LAST 50. These guns had the reputation of being the poorest quality but do carry collector premiums. One interesting variation is the North Hollywood "two-line" model. Also, the first .357 cal. pistols manufactured did not have the words AUTO MAG appearing on the gun. These too are collectors items.

LESS THAN 10,000 AUTO MAGS WERE PRODUCED BY ALL MANUFACTURERS.

In addition to the above calibers, a very few non-factory .22 and .25 cal. prototypes were fabricated by Kent Lomont in addition to several engraved models. These specimens will usually demand a premium over the values listed below. Also, some barrels and pistols were made in Covina, CA.

ORIGINAL PASADENA—.44 AMP only, 6½ in. VR barrel.
$1,875 $1,600 $1,500

TDE NORTH HOLLYWOOD
.44 AMP—6½ in. VR barrel.
$1,875 $1,600 $1,500

.357 AMP—two line address.
$1,900 $1,700 $1,600

TDE EL MONTE
.44 AMP—6½ VR, 8, or 10 in. tapered barrel.
$1,750 $1,550 $1,450

.357 AMP—6½ VR, 8, or 10 in. tapered barrel.
$1,550 $1,450 $1,300

HIGH STANDARD—"H" prefixed serial numbers.
$2,100 $1,900 $1,675

TDE/OMC "B" SERIES—6½ VR or 10 in. barrel.
$1,850 $1,700 $1,600

AMT "C" SERIES—6½ VR or 10 in. barrel.
$1,950 $1,800 $1,650

Add 50% + for L.E. Jurras custom models.
Add 10% for Jurras Lion marked models.

Lee Jurras added his Lion's head logo (from 1977 on) on TDE manufactured guns.
Add $500 for shoulder stock.

Note: guns were cased (plastic attache style) with accessories. Original Auto-Mag ammo (mfg. by CDM in Mexico) is currently selling for approx. $75 a box.

AUTO-ORDNANCE CORP.
MANUFACTURED AND DISTRIBUTED IN WEST HURLEY, NY.

Auto-Ordnance Corp. manufactures an exact reproduction of the original 1927 Thompson machine gun. They are currently available in semi-auto only since production ceased on fully automatic variations in 1986 (mfg. 1975-1986).

Grading	100%	98%	95%	90%	80%	70%	60%

SEMI-AUTO CARBINE

1927 A1 STANDARD—.45 ACP, 16 in. plain barrel, solid steel construction, standard military sight, walnut stock and horizontal forearm. Discontinued in 1986.

	100%	98%	95%	90%	80%	70%	60%
	$570	$490	$430	$360	$315	$290	$270

Last Mfg.'s Sug. Retail was $575.

1927 A1 DELUXE—.45 ACP, 16 in. finned barrel, solid steel construction, adj. rear sight, walnut stock and hand grips.

	100%	98%	95%	90%	80%	70%	60%
Mfg.'s Sug. Retail	$716	$600	$515	$440	$370	$320	$295	$275

Add $140 (retail) for 50 shot drum Mag. on this model and other 1927 variations. Also add $113 (retail) for Thompson hard case (violin type).

THOMPSON M1—.45 ACP, combat model, side-cocking lever, flat black finish. New in 1986.

	100%	98%	95%	90%	80%	70%	60%
Mfg.'s Sug. Retail	$625	$535	$470	$420	$350	$310	$285	$265

1927 A1C LIGHTWEIGHT—.45 ACP, same as 1927 A-1 Deluxe, except made of a lightweight alloy. 20% weight reduction. New in 1984.

	100%	98%	95%	90%	80%	70%	60%
Mfg.'s Sug. Retail	$632	$545	$480	$425	$350	$310	$285	$265

1927 A5 PISTOL/CARBINE—.45 ACP, 13 in. finned barrel, alloy construction, overall length 26 in., 30 round mag.

	100%	98%	95%	90%	80%	70%	60%
Mfg.'s Sug. Retail	$623	$535	$470	$415	$340	$300	$275	$260

1927 A3 22 CAL.—.22 LR, 16 in. finned barrel, alloy steel construction, walnut stock and hand grips.

	100%	98%	95%	90%	80%	70%	60%
Mfg.'s Sug. Retail	$488	$425	$365	$320	$285	$260	$230	$200

PISTOLS

1911 A1 SEMI-AUTO—.38 Super, 9mm Luger or .45 ACP cal. Copy of the original Colt Gov't Model, blue only.

	100%	98%	95%	90%	80%	70%	60%
Mfg.'s Sug. Retail	$349	$300	$265	$245	$235	$225	$215	$200

Add $37 for .38 Super or 9mm.

ZG-51 "Pit Bull"—.45 ACP only, compact variation of the 1911 A1, 3½ in. barrel, 7 round mag., 36 oz. New in 1988.

	100%	98%	95%	90%	80%	70%	60%
Mfg.'s Sug. Retail	$386	$325	$280	$250	$235	$225	$215	$200

AUTO — POINTER

MANUFACTURED BY YAMAMOTO CO. FORMERLY IMPORTED BY SLOANS.

SEMI-AUTO SHOTGUN—12 or 20 ga., gas operated. Discontinued.

	100%	98%	95%	90%	80%	70%	60%
	$320	$240	$225	$195	$180	$160	$145

NOTES

B

BSA GUNS LIMITED

BIRMINGHAM SMALL ARMS, LOCATED IN BIRMINGHAM, ENGLAND.
MANUFACTURED 1861-1987 IN ENGLAND. IMPORTED UNTIL 1985 BY PRECISION
SPORTS, ITHACA, NY AND 1986 BY BSA GUNS LTD., LOCATED IN GRAND PRAIRIE, TX.
CURRENTLY, BSA RIFLES ARE IN THE PROCESS OF MOVING MANUFACTURE TO
KARACHI, PAKISTAN AND ARE IMPORTED AND DISTRIBUTED BY SAMCO GLOBAL
ARMS, INC., LOCATED IN MIAMI, FL.

Samco also imports various military surplus bolt action rifles including Hakim, Lee Enfield,
Loewe, Mauser, Steyr, and others. In addition to these imports, Samco also sells sporterized
variations of the above trademarks and these can be found under the Samco section in this
text.

RIFLES: RECENT IMPORTATION

Grading	100%	98%	95%	90%	80%	70%	60%

CF-2 ACTION—.222 R., .22-250, .243 Win., 6.5 x 55mm, 7 x 57, 7 x 64mm, 7mm Rem.
Mag., .270 Win., .308 Win., .30-06, .300 Win. Mag. cal.'s, bolt action, barrel length 23-26
in., 7½-8 lbs. CF-2 nomenclature designates an action rather than a model. CF-2 actioned
models are listed below. Add $70 for double set trigger option on the below listed models.
Limited quanities of English mfg. models remain.

Sporter/Classic—same cal.'s as above, checkered oil finished walnut stock. New in
1986.

Mfg.'s Sug. Retail	$360	$315	$260	$240	$225	$210	$195	$180

Sporter Model features Monte Carlo stock, rosewood capped forearm and pistol grip stock,
and swivels.

Classic Varminter—available in .222R-.243 W. cal.'s only, heavy barrel, matte finish,
with swivels. Imported in 1986 only.

	$300	$260	$240	$225	$210	$190	$175

Last Mfg.'s Sug. Retail was $345.

Heavy Barrel Model—.222R, .22-250, and .243W cal.'s only, around 9 lbs., no sights.

Mfg.'s Sug. Retail	$410	$375	$300	$260	$240	$225	$210	$180

Carbine Model—20 in. barrel. Discontinued in 1985.

	$350	$325	$295	$270	$250	$225	$200

Last Mfg.'s Sug. Retail was $480.

Stutzen Rifle—Mannlicher style full length stock, same general specifications as
Sporter/Classic, 20½ in. barrel. Not available in 7mm Rem. Mag. or .300 Win. Mag cal.'s.

Mfg.'s Sug. Retail	$385	$350	$295	$260	$240	$225	$210	$180

Regal Custom—similar to Sporter Model, except has deluxe walnut and extra
checkering, ebony forend cap, choice of engraving, and stock finishes. Imported in 1986
only.

	$875	$795	$685	$590	$550	$500	$450

Last Mfg.'s Sug. Retail was $950.

CFT TARGET RIFLE—7.62mm, single shot, bolt action, aperture front and rear sights,
26½ in. barrel, 11 lbs. Disc. in 1987.

	$675	$590	$550	$500	$450	$400	$360

Last Mfg.'s Sug. Retail was $780.

Grading	100%	98%	95%	90%	80%	70%	60%

RIFLES: DISCONTINUED, SINGLE SHOT

NO. 12 MARTINI—.22 LR, 29 in. barrel, target sights, straight stock, pre-WWII.

	$360	$275	$250	$210	$175	$155	$130

MODEL 15—same as 12, except pistol grip stock, better grade target sights, pre-WWII.

	$385	$305	$275	$240	$200	$175	$155

CENTURION MATCH RIFLE—same as 15, except Centurion guarantee — 1½ in. grouping at 100 yards, 24 in. barrel, pre-WWII.

	$440	$385	$330	$275	$240	$220	$175

MATCH 12/15—similar to 15, except made after WWII.

	$385	$305	$275	$240	$200	$175	$155

MODEL 12/15—heavy barrel.

	$415	$330	$305	$270	$230	$195	$165

MODEL 13—lighter version of 12.

	$340	$265	$235	$200	$165	$150	$125

MODEL 13 SPORTER—same as 13, except has sport sights.

	$330	$240	$220	$175	$155	$140	$120
.22 Hornet.	$385	$305	$275	$240	$200	$175	$155

MARTINI INTERNATIONAL MATCH—.22 LR, 29 in. heavy barrel, international sights, made 1950-1953.

	$415	$360	$320	$275	$255	$230	$200

INTERNATIONAL LIGHT—26 in. lightweight barrel.

	$415	$360	$320	$275	$255	$230	$200

INTERNATIONAL MKII—improved trigger, ejectors and stock design, made 1953-1959.

	$425	$375	$340	$315	$285	$255	$220

INTERNATIONAL MKIII—longer action, floating barrel, made 1959-1967.

	$495	$430	$385	$360	$330	$305	$265

INTERNATIONAL ISU—modeled to meet ISU standards, 28 in. barrel, made 1968-discontinued.

	$495	$430	$385	$360	$330	$305	$265

INTERNATIONAL MARK V—same as ISU, but heavier barrel, made 1976-discontinued.

	$525	$460	$430	$375	$350	$330	$305

RIFLES: DISCONTINUED, BOLT ACTION

MAJESTIC FEATHERWEIGHT DELUXE—.243, .270, .308, and .30-06 cal.'s, bolt action, 22 in. barrel, folding sight, checkered European style stock, made 1959-1965.

	$330	$250	$220	$195	$180	$165	$145
.458 Mag.	$445	$375	$305	$275	$220	$210	$200

MAJESTIC DELUXE—.222, .22 Hornet, .243, 7 x 57, .308, and .30-06 cal.'s, heavier barrel.

	$330	$250	$220	$195	$180	$165	$145

MONARCH DELUXE—same as Majestic Deluxe, but American design stock, made 1965-1974.

	$350	$275	$250	$220	$195	$180	$165

MONARCH DELUXE VARMINT—same as Monarch Deluxe, except .222 and .243 cal.'s, 24 in. heavy barrel. Discontinued.

	$370	$305	$275	$250	$210	$195	$180

MARTINI ISU MATCH .22—single shot, bolt action, .22 cal. only, similar to CFT Model. Add $100 for Mk. V.H.B. Model. Discontinued in 1985.

	$825	$700	$600	$530	$475	$435	$400

Last Mfg.'s Sug. Retail was $1,000.

BAFORD ARMS, INC.

MANUFACTURED BY BAFORD ARMS, INC. LOCATED IN BRISTOL, TN. DISTRIBUTED BY C.L. REEDY & ASSOCIATES, INC. LOCATED IN MELBOURNE, FL.

MODEL 35 FIRE POWER—9mm Para., semi-auto single action, patterned after the Browning Hi-Power, total stainless steel construction, 4¾ in. barrel, combat hammer and safety, Pachmayr grips, removable barrel bushing, Millett Mk. II sights, 14 shot mag., 32 oz. New in late 1988.

Mfg.'s Sug. Retail	$495	$495	$395	$325			

THUNDER DERRINGER—.44 Spl./.410 shotshell, single shot, tip out action, 3 in. barrel, blued steel finish, spur trigger, wood grips. New in 1988.

Mfg.'s Sug. Retail	$130	$130	$110	$95	$90	$85	$80	$75

Add $90 for interchangable barrel kit.

Interchangeable pistol barrels are chambered in various calibers between .22 Short and 9mm Para. There are two types: one fits flush while the other facilitates a scope mounting.

BAIKAL

MANUFACTURED IN THE U.S.S.R. NOT IMPORTED INTO THE U.S. CURRENTLY.

Baikal shotguns cannot be directly imported into the U.S. In recent years, however, a few O/U's have been seen for sale and have no doubt been "imported" into this country one at a time. Quality is in the intermediate level and collector interest is not particularly great. Most O/U shotguns fall into the $400 - $1,000 range if quality is at par with other more famous trademarks. The most commonly encountered Baikal models are the 650, 650E, and the 750 series. The MC series represent their top-of-the-line models (No.'s 5, 6, 7, 8, 109, 110, 111) and retailed from $1,500 (MC-5) to $5,850 (MC-111) when offered in 1983. Currently, collector interest is not sufficient to support the older retail prices and demand is very limited.

BAILONS GUNMAKERS LIMITED

MANUFACTURED AND DISTRIBUTED IN BIRMINGHAM, ENGLAND. LIMITED EXPORTATION INTO THE U.S.

Bailons also makes to special order, both boxlock and sidelock shotguns in most popular gauges. Prices are subject to negotiation and dependant upon the amount and type of engraving specified as well as quality of the wood.

HUNTING RIFLE—various cal.'s, modified Mauser bolt action, 24 in. barrel, set triggers, sights, engraving, and types of finishes are at optional cost, prices below reflect standard rifle with no options. New in 1986.

Mfg.'s Sug. Retail	$1,850	$1,675	$1,475	$1,350	$1,200	$1,075	$900	$795

BAKER GUN & FORGING CO.

BATAVIA, NEW YORK. 1889-1933.

SHOTGUNS

Note: Original damascus guns in 80% or better condition with bright case colors will approach the values of steel barrel counterparts.

BATAVIA SPECIAL—12, 16, and 20 ga.'s, 26, 28, 30, and 32 in. barrels, any standard choke, checkered pistol grip stock, sidelock, extractors.

	$385	$305	$275	$260	$250	$220	$200

BATAVIA LEADER—same as Special, except has deluxe finish.

	$440	$360	$335	$305	$285	$265	$220
Auto ejectors	$525	$440	$415	$385	$370	$330	$305

BLACK BEAUTY SPECIAL—same as Leader, except has engraved, select wood.

	$745	$650	$615	$590	$550	$525	$495
Auto ejectors	$855	$760	$725	$700	$660	$635	$605

Grading	100%	98%	95%	90%	80%	70%	60%

BATAVIA EJECTOR—same as Leader, but finer finish.

	100%	98%	95%	90%	80%	70%	60%
	$880	$770	$745	$715	$690	$660	$635
Damascus barrels	$440	$330	$305	$275	$250	$220	$165

BAKER S GRADE—same as Leader, but finer finish, better grade wood.

	100%	98%	95%	90%	80%	70%	60%
	$880	$775	$745	$715	$690	$650	$635
Auto ejectors	$1,100	$990	$965	$935	$910	$880	$745

BAKER R GRADE—same as Leader, except scroll and game scene engraved, Krupp barrels, fancy wood.

	100%	98%	95%	90%	80%	70%	60%
	$1,100	$990	$965	$935	$910	$880	$745
Auto ejectors	$1,320	$1,210	$1,155	$1,100	$1,075	$1,045	$965
Damascus barrel	$550	$415	$385	$360	$330	$275	$230

PARAGON GRADE—custom order only to customer specifications.

	100%	98%	95%	90%	80%	70%	60%
	$1,650	$1,430	$1,320	$1,210	$1,155	$1,045	$770
Auto ejectors	$1,815	$1,595	$1,485	$1,375	$1,210	$1,100	$990

EXPERT GRADE—auto ejectors standard, overall finer grade wood and engraving.

	100%	98%	95%	90%	80%	70%	60%
	$2,500	$2,100	$1,850	$1,500	$1,250	$1,000	$750

DELUXE GRADE—best quality.

	100%	98%	95%	90%	80%	70%	60%
	$3,750	$3,250	$2,950	$2,650	$2,300	$2,000	$1,600

Single trigger — add $200.

Damascus barrels—also known as Early Paragon Grade, if 50% or less condition subtract 50% or more. If 90% or better prices will be the same as for damascus L.C. Smith guns.

BARRETT FIREARMS MANUFACTURING, INC.

MANUFACTURED AND DISTRIBUTED IN MURFREESBORO, TN.

MODEL 82 RIFLE—.50 Browning machine gun cartridge, semi-auto recoil operation, 33-37 in. barrel, 11 round mag., 2,850 FPS muzzle velocity, 35 lbs., scope sight only, parkerized finish. Made in 1985-87.

	$4,000	$3,450	$2,975	$2,500	$2,250	$2,000	$1,800

Last Mfg.'s Sug. Retail for consumers was $3,180 in 1985.

This model has undergone design changes since initial production.

MODEL 82A1—.50 BMG, current military configuration, variant of the original Model 82, available to civilians, supplied with Leupold M3 Ultra 10X scope, back-up iron sights also included, 2 mags., and fitted hard case, 33 in. barrel, 11 shot mag., 32.5 lbs.

Mfg.'s Sug. Retail	$5,795	$5,795	$4,500	$3,750	$3,150	$2,650	$2,200	$2,000

Subtract $800 if without Leupold M3 scope and extra mag.

BAR-STO

PREVIOUS MANUFACTURER OF SEMI-AUTO PISTOLS.

BAR-STO .25 ACP—.25 ACP, patterned after the Baby Browning, brushed stainless steel finish, walnut grips, approx. 250 manufactured in the 1974 circa.

	$195	$165	$125

BAUER FIREARMS CORPORATION

PREVIOUSLY MANUFACTURED IN FRASER, MI.

BAUER .25 AUTOMATIC—.25 auto, 2½ in. barrel, 6 shot, fixed sights, checkered walnut or pearlite grips, made 1972-1984.

	$150	$130	$110

Note: These guns are identical to the Baby Browning, except stainless steel.

Grading	100%	98%	95%	90%	80%	70%	60%

THE RABBIT—combination gun, all metal construction, .22 cal. and .410 ga., O/U configuration. Made 1982-1984.

	100%	98%	95%	90%	80%	70%	60%
	$125	$100	$90	$80	$70	$60	$50

BAYARD

MAKER: ANCIENS ETABLISSEMENTS PIEPER, HERSTAL, BELGIUM.

Even though Bayard Models 1908, both 1923's, and 1930 were manufactured only by Anciens Etablissements Pieper of Herstal, Belgium these pistols are listed under this heading as they are most commonly referred to by this trademark designation.

.25 and .380 cal.'s are more rare than the .32's and will command a 20% + premium above values listed below unless indicated differently.

MODEL 1908 POCKET AUTOMATIC—.25 auto, .32 auto, .380 auto, 6 shot, 2¼ in. barrel, fixed sights, blue, hard rubber grips.

	$220	$195	$165	$100	$85	$70	$55

MODEL 1923 POCKET AUTOMATIC—.25 auto, 2½ in. barrel, blue, fixed sights, checkered hard rubber grips.

	$220	$195	$140	$100	$85	$70	$55

BAYARD 1923 POCKET AUTOMATIC—.32 auto, .380 auto, 6 shot, 3⁵⁄₁₆in. barrel, fixed sights, blue, checkered hard rubber grips.

	$220	$165	$140	$130	$120	$110	$100

Add 50% for .380 cal.

BAYARD 1930 POCKET AUTOMATIC—slight modification of 1923.

	$220	$165	$140	$130	$120	$110	$100

BEEMAN PRECISION ARMS, INC.

IMPORTER AND DISTRIBUTOR LOCATED IN SANTA ROSA, CA.

Beeman is a large importer, specializing in high quality European rifles and pistols mostly. Trademarks currently being distributed in the U.S. are manufacturers: Agner (discontinued in 1986), Erma (discontinued in 1985), FAS, Fabarm, Feinwerkbau, Korth, Krico, Unique, and Weihrauch. These trademarks will appear under their respective alphabetical headings. Air rifles, pistols, and/or black powder firearms will appear under those headings in the back of the book.

Below listed firearms are manufactured to Beeman specifications, and are therefore listed under the Beeman Heading.

PISTOLS: SEMI-AUTO

BEEMAN MP-08—.380 ACP, Luger type toggle action, 3½ in. barrel, 6 shot mag., blue, 1.4 lbs., made 1968-present.

Mfg.'s Sug. Retail	$390	$335	$275	$240	$185	$145	$115	$95

In 1988, Beeman took over importation of this model in .380 ACP cal. only with new Luger style checkered walnut grips and 3½ in. barrel. Previous variations had plastic grips.

BEEMAN P-08—.22 LR, Luger type toggle action, 8 shot mag., 3.8 in. barrel, blue, checkered walnut grips, 1.9 lbs., made 1969-present.

Mfg.'s Sug. Retail	$390	$335	$275	$240	$185	$145	$115	$95

PISTOLS: SINGLE SHOT

SP STANDARD—.22 LR cal., sidelever action, 8, 10, 12, or 15 in. barrel, adj. sights and walnut grips, single shot. Add $10 and $30 for 12 in. and 15 in. barrel respectively. Made in W. Germany. Imported in 1985-86 only.

	$230	$200	$180	$170	$160	$150	$140

Last Mfg.'s Sug. Retail was $250.

SP DELUXE—similar to SP Standard, except has forearm, about 3½ lbs. Add $10 and $30 for 12 in. and 15 in. barrel respectively. Made in W. Germany. Imported in 1985-86 only.

	$260	$220	$200	$185	$170	$155	$145

Last Mfg.'s Sug. Retail was $300.

BEHOLLA PISTOL

BECKER & HOLLANDER, SUHL, GERMANY.

BEHOLLA POCKET AUTOMATIC—.32 auto, 7 shot, 2.9 in. barrel, blue, serrated wood or rubber grips, made 1915-1920, from 1920-1925 the same gun was made by Stenda-Werke.

$225	$170	$150	$135	$120	$100	$90

BENELLI

MANUFACTURED IN ITALY. SHOTGUNS CURRENTLY IMPORTED BY HECKLER AND KOCH, INC. LOCATED IN CHANTILLY, VA. HANDGUNS CURRENTLY IMPORTED BY SILE DISTRIBUTORS, INC., LOCATED IN NEW YORK, NY.

PISTOLS

MODEL B-76—9mm Luger, selective double action, all steel, 4¼ in. barrel, 8 round mag., 34 oz.

Mfg.'s Sug. Retail	$428	$395	$340	$295	$245	$225	$210	$190

MODEL B-76S TARGET—9mm, similar to B-76 except has 5½ barrel, target grips, and adj. rear sights.

Mfg.'s Sug. Retail	$595	$475	$425	$395	$350	$325	$300	$280

MODEL B-77—.32 ACP, selective double action, all steel, 4¼ in. barrel, 8 round mag.

Mfg.'s Sug. Retail	$399	$275	$245	$225	$200	$180	$170	$160

MODEL B-80—.30 Luger, selective double action, all steel, 4¼ in. barrel, 8 round mag., 34 oz.

Mfg.'s Sug. Retail	$385	$275	$245	$225	$200	$180	$170	$160

MODEL B-80S TARGET—similar to B-80, except has 5½ barrel, target grips, and adj. rear sights.

Mfg.'s Sug. Retail	$572	$395	$350	$325	$295	$275	$250	$225

MODEL MP3S—.32 Smith & Wesson Long Wad Cutter, target variation with 5½ in. barrel, target grips, and adj. rear sights.

Mfg.'s Sug. Retail	$572	$395	$350	$325	$295	$275	$250	$225

SHOTGUNS: SEMI-AUTO

MODEL SL-121V—12 ga., mechanically like SL-123V, various barrel lengths, black receiver finish, 3 in. Mag.— no extra charge. Discontinued in 1985.

	$340	$300	$270	$245	$215	$190	$175

Last Mfg.'s Sug. Retail was $397.

MODEL SL-121 SLUG—12 ga., mechanically like SL-123V, only 21¹⁄₁₆ in. cylinder bore barrel, approx. 7 lbs. 3 oz. Discontinued in 1985.

	$375	$325	$295	$270	$245	$225	$200

Last Mfg.'s Sug. Retail was $434.

MODEL SL123V AND DELUXE—12 ga. fast "3rd generation" action, lower receiver Ergal special aluminum alloy, various chokes, approx. 6 lbs. 13 oz. Discontinued in 1985.

	$395	$350	$320	$295	$265	$240	$220

Last Mfg.'s Sug. Retail was $464.

MODEL 123V SPECIAL TRAP AND SKEET—12 ga., choice of engraving and frame finish .32 in. barrel, approx. 7 lbs. 10 oz. Skeet model — add $115. Discontinued in 1985.

	$490	$440	$395	$360	$330	$300	$280

Last Mfg.'s Sug. Retail was $584.

MODEL SL201—20 ga., 26 in. barrel bored imp. mod., approx. 5 lbs. 10 oz. Discontinued in 1985.

	$350	$300	$270	$240	$220	$200	$180

Last Mfg.'s Sug. Retail was $399.

Grading	100%	98%	95%	90%	80%	70%	60%

M1 SUPER 90—12 ga. only, 3 in. Mag., semi-auto, incorporates improvements on the Benelli action, including rotating Montefeltro bolt system, 19¾ in. cyl. bore barrel with iron sights, 7 shot mag., fiberglass stock and forearm, 7¼ lbs. New in 1986. Imported exclusively by H&K.

Mfg.'s Sug. Retail	$606	$535	$395	$350	$310	$295	$270	$240

Add $36 for pistol grip stock.

M1 SUPER 90 FIELD—similar to M1 Super 90, except has 26 or 28 in. vent rib barrel and 3-shot plug, includes 3 screw in choke tubes.

Mfg.'s Sug. Retail	$648	$550	$425	$370	$330	$295	$275	$260

MONTEFELTRO SUPER 90 STANDARD HUNTER—12 ga. only, 3 in. chamber, 26 or 28 in. VR barrel with 3 choke tubes, matte black metal finish, checkered walnut stock and forearm with choice of high gloss or satin finish, 5 round mag., 7¼ lbs. New in 1988.

Mfg.'s Sug. Retail	$675	$575	$440	$370	$330	$295	$275	$260

Add $59 for left-hand action.

Montefeltro Turkey Gun—similar to Montefeltro Standard Hunter except has 24 in. VR barrel with 3 choke tubes, satin finish wood only, 7 lbs. New in 1989.

Mfg.'s Sug. Retail	$675	$575	$440	$370	$330	$295	$275	$260

Montefeltro Uplander—similar to Montefeltro Turkey Gun except has 21 in. VR barrel with 3 choke tubes, satin finish wood only, 7 lbs. New in 1989.

Mfg.'s Sug. Retail	$675	$575	$440	$370	$330	$295	$275	$260

BLACK EAGLE—12 ga., Montefeltro action, similar to Montefeltro Super 90 Standard Hunter except has black synthetic stock and forearm, 21, 24, or 26 in. VR barrel with 3 choke tubes, right hand only. New in 1989.

Mfg.'s Sug. Retail	$795	$700	$600	$475	$395	$340	$300	$275

M3 SUPER 90—12 ga. only, defense configuration incorporating convertible (fingertip activated) pump or semi-auto action, 19¾ in. cyl. bore barrel with rifle sights, polymer stock has integral pistol grip, 7½ lbs. New in 1989.

Mfg.'s Sug. Retail	$801	$715	$600	$475	$395	$340	$300	$275

SPECIAL 80 SKEET—12 ga. only, skeet variation, limited availability.

Mfg.'s Sug. Retail	$531	$450	$350	$315	$275	$250	$225	$195

BENSON FIREARMS LTD.

MANUFACTURED BY ALDO UBERTI IN ITALY. PREVIOUSLY IMPORTED AND DISTRIBUTED FROM 1987-1989 BY BENSON FIREARMS LTD. LOCATED IN SEATTLE, WA. BENSON FIREARMS LTD. COMBINED WITH A. UBERTI USA INC. IN EARLY 1989.

Benson Firearms can be differentiated from other A. Uberti imports by the "Benson Firearms Seattle, WA" barrel marking. Many of the models listed below are similar to those models imported by Allen Firearms (disc. in 1987) and A. Uberti USA, Inc., (current importer).

REVOLVERS: SINGLE ACTION

Can be ordered with either black powder or modern configured frames.

CATTLEMAN—available in .45 LC, .44-40, .38 Spl., .357 Mag., .22 LR, and .22 Mag cal.'s, 4¾, 5½, and 7½ in. barrel lengths, brass or steel backstraps and trigger guard. Disc. in 1989.

		$325	$235	$190	$175	$160	$150	$135

Add $30 for steel backstrap.
Add $64 for stainless steel construction (Disc. in 1987).

Last Mfg.'s Sug. Retail was $359.

Sheriff's Model—.44-40 and .45 LC cal.'s, 3 in. barrel, brass backstrap. Disc. in 1989.

		$250	$210	$190	$175	$160	$150	$135

Add $24 for steel backstrap.

Last Mfg.'s Sug. Retail was $295.

Grading	100%	98%	95%	90%	80%	70%	60%

Target Model—same as Cattleman Model, only fully adj. rear blade sight, brass backstrap. Disc. in 1989.

	$345	$240	$200	$185	$170	$150	$135

Add $26 for steel backstrap.
Add $60 for stainless steel construction (Disc. in 1987).

Last Mfg.'s Sug. Retail was $389.

CATTLEMAN BUNTLINE—.45 LC and .357 Mag. cal.'s, 18 in. barrel, brass backstrap cut for shoulder stock. Disc. in 1989.

	$350	$250	$210	$185	$175	$165	$150

Add $30 for target sights.
Add $30 for steel backstrap.

Last Mfg.'s Sug. Retail was $395.

BUCKHORN—.44 Mag., .44 Spl., and .44-40 cal.'s, various barrel lengths, brass backstap, Buntline and revolving carbine models, also available in the Buckhorn series — add approximately $66, add $30 for convertible cylinders. Disc. in 1989.

	$310	$210	$205	$190	$180	$170	$160

Add $30 for steel backstrap.
Add $36 for target sights.

Last Mfg.'s Sug. Retail was $369.

1873 STALLION—.22 LR/.22 Mag. convertible, 4¾, 5½, or 6½ in. barrel, case hardened frame. Disc. in 1989.

	$315	$210	$195	$170	$155	$140	$120

Add $27 for steel backstrap and trigger guard.
Add $26 for target sights.
Add $50 for stainless steel.

Last Mfg.'s Sug. Retail was $389.

"OUTLAW" 1875 REMINGTON—available in .45 LC, .44-40, and .357 Mag. cal.'s, 7½ in.barrel. Disc. in 1989.

	$325	$225	$195	$170	$155	$140	$120

Add $43 for nickel plating.

Last Mfg.'s Sug. Retail was $369.

1890 REMINGTON—available in .45 LC, .44-40, and .357 Mag. cal.'s, 5½ in. barrel. New in 1986. Disc. in 1989.

	$340	$220	$190	$175	$155	$140	$120

Add $43 for nickel plating.

Last Mfg.'s Sug. Retail was $385.

PHANTOM MODEL—.357 and .44 Mag. only, 10 in. barrel for silhouette use. New in 1985. Disc. in 1989.

	$490	$395	$325	$290	$260	$230	$215

Last Mfg.'s Sug. Retail was $559.

REVOLVERS: DOUBLE ACTION

INSPECTOR MODEL—.32 S&W and .38 Sp. cal.'s, 3, 4, and 6 in. barrels, double action, blued or chrome finish. New in 1985. Disc. in 1989.

	$400	$295	$245	$210	$170	$145	$125

Add $40 for target sights.
Add $30 for chrome plating.

Last Mfg.'s Sug. Retail was $445.

TARGET PISTOLS

1871 ROLLING BLOCK TARGET PISTOL—available in .357 Mag., .22 LR, .22 Mag., and .22 Hornet cal.'s, 9½ in. barrel. Also available in carbine model (22 in. barrel) — add $54. Disc. in 1989.

	$275	$205	$175	$150	$135	$120	$100

Last Mfg.'s Sug. Retail was $315.

Grading	100%	98%	95%	90%	80%	70%	60%

CARBINES AND RIFLES

CATTLEMAN REVOLVING CARBINE S.A.—available in .45 LC, .44-40, .357 Mag., and .22 LR/Mag. (convertible) cal.'s, 18 in. barrel, fixed sights. Disc. in 1989.

	$425	$285	$230	$200	$185	$180	$175

Add $40 for target sights.

Last Mfg.'s Sug. Retail was $475.

1875 REMINGTON CARBINE S.A.—18 in. barrel — same cal.'s as above, except .22 LR/Mag. Disc. in 1989.

	$440	$285	$230	$200	$230	$185	$175

Add $80 for nickel plating.

Last Mfg.'s Sug. Retail was $540.

HENRY RIFLE OR CARBINE—.44-40 cal., brass frame, 24½ in. barrel on rifle, 22½ in. barrel on carbine. Disc. in 1989.

	$750	$580	$490	$415	$360	$320	$260

Can also be special ordered with grade A engraving ($234 extra), grade B engraving ($412 extra), and grade 3 engraving ($635 extra).

Last Mfg.'s Sug. Retail was $875.

Henry 1 of 1,000—discontinued several years ago, premiums are slightly higher than a C engraved gun.

1866 CARBINE—.44-40, .38 Spl., .22 Mag. and .22 LR cal.'s, brass receiver, 19 in. round barrel. "Indian" model — add $80. Disc. in 1989.

	$565	$420	$340	$285	$260	$235	$210

Last Mfg.'s Sug. Retail was $649.

1866 Trapper Carbine—.22 LR, .38 Spl., or .44-40 cal., 16 in. barrel. Disc. in 1989.

	$565	$420	$340	$285	$260	$235	$210

Last Mfg.'s Sug. Retail was $649.

Red Cloud Commemorative Carbine—same cal.'s, special engraving and brass tacks in forearm and stock. Disc. in 1989.

	$650	$475	$385	$310	$275	$240	$220

Last Mfg.'s Sug. Retail was $729.

1866 RIFLE—brass receiver, same cal.'s as the carbine, 24¼ in. oct. barrel. Disc. in 1989.

	$610	$445	$370	$300	$260	$235	$210

Add $61 for "Indian" model (19 in. barrel).

Last Mfg.'s Sug. Retail was $689.

1873 CARBINE—.44-40, .357 Mag., .22 Mag., and .22 LR cal.'s, steel receiver, 19 in. round barrel. Add $120 for nickel finish. Disc. in 1989.

	$675	$525	$450	$395	$360	$320	$280

Last Mfg.'s Sug. Retail was $795.

1873 Trapper Carbine—.44-40 cal. only, 16 in. barrel. Disc. in 1989.

	$675	$525	$450	$395	$360	$320	$280

Last Mfg.'s Sug. Retail was $795.

1873 RIFLE—case hardened receiver, same cal.'s as the carbine, 24¼ in. oct. barrel. Disc. in 1989.

	$725	$535	$460	$400	$360	$320	$280

Last Mfg.'s Sug. Retail was $855.

BERETTA, DR. FRANCO

MANUFACTURED IN BRESCIA, ITALY. DISTRIBUTED EXCLUSIVELY THROUGH DOUBLE M SHOOTING SPORTS, GUILFORD, CT.

BLACK DIAMOND SHOTGUNS: OVER AND UNDER

Retail values listed below reflect 1988 prices as no new information was forwarded to this writer by publication release.

Black Diamond target guns are imported exclusively by Double M Shooting Sports.

Grading	100%	98%	95%	90%	80%	70%	60%

FIELD MODEL—12, 16, 20, 28, and .410 ga.'s, variety of chokes, coin finish receiver.

Mfg.'s Sug. Retail	$960	$720	$630	$570	$510	$455	$430	$410

GRADE ONE—12, 16, 20, 28, and .410 ga.'s, variety of chokes, coin finish receiver with acid etched engraving, French walnut. Trap or skeet model also available, except in 16 ga.

Mfg.'s Sug. Retail	$1,440	$1,020	$900	$810	$720	$630	$570	$525

GRADE TWO—12, 16, 20, 28, and .410 ga.'s, variety of chokes, coin finish receiver with moderate engraving, French walnut. Trap or skeet model also available, except in 16 ga.

Mfg.'s Sug. Retail	$2,040	$1,475	$1,320	$1,200	$1,080	$930	$815	$750

GRADE THREE—12, 16, 20, 28, and .410 ga.'s, variety of chokes, coin finish receiver with scrollwork engraving, French walnut. Trap or skeet model also available, except in 16 ga.

Mfg.'s Sug. Retail	$3,000	$2,100	$1,920	$1,775	$1,560	$1,410	$1,200	$1,035

GRADE FOUR—12, 16, 20, 28, and .410 ga.'s, variety of chokes, coin finish receiver with elaborate engraving, French walnut. Trap or skeet model also available, except in 16 ga.

Mfg.'s Sug. Retail	$3,960	$2,760	$2,520	$2,280	$2,100	$1,920	$1,740	$1,560

SKEET SET—includes 12, 20, 28, and .410 barrels, available in Grades One through Four. Multiply above individual values by 275% to obtain correct prices on 4 barrel skeet sets.

SHOTGUNS: CURRENT MANUFACTURE

The models listed below were imported and distributed by Excam located in Hialeah, FL until 1988.

GAMMA STANDARD O & U—12, 16, and 20 ga.'s, 26 and 28 in. barrels, coin finish receiver with extensive engraving, Italian walnut. Add $83 with single trigger and ejectors. Imported 1984-1988.

	$400	$360	$330	$300	$275	$260	$240

Last Mfg.'s Sug. Retail was $445.

Gamma Standard—with interchangeable choke tubes. Importation disc. in 1988.

	$580	$515	$475	$430	$395	$360	$335

Last Mfg.'s Sug. Retail was $630.

GAMMA DELUXE O & U—12, 16, and 20 ga.'s, 26 and 28 in. barrels, coin finish receiver with extensive engraving, Italian walnut. Add $84 with single trigger and ejectors. Imported 1984-1988.

	$445	$405	$370	$350	$325	$300	$275

Last Mfg.'s Sug. Retail was $480.

Gamma Deluxe—with interchangeable choke tubes. Importation disc. in 1988.

	$635	$570	$530	$490	$450	$420	$390

Last Mfg.'s Sug. Retail was $685.

GAMMA TARGET O & U—12 ga. only, SST, ejectors, Wundhammer swell pistol grip, English walnut stock and beavertail forearm. Imported 1986-1988.

	$550	$505	$455	$410	$370	$350	$325

Last Mfg.'s Sug. Retail was $595.

ALPHA TWO STANDARD O & U—12, 16, and 20 ga.'s, 26 and 28 in. barrels, coin finish receiver with extensive engraving, Italian walnut. Add $76 with single trigger and ejectors. Imported 1984-1988.

	$360	$330	$300	$275	$250	$230	$210

Last Mfg.'s Sug. Retail was $395.

ALPHA TWO DELUXE O & U—12, 16, and 20 ga.'s, 26 and 28 in. barrels, coin finish receiver with extensive engraving, sling swivels, Italian walnut. Add $75 with single trigger and ejectors, $80 for interchangeable choke tubes (discontinued in 1985). Imported 1984-1988.

	$395	$355	$330	$300	$275	$250	$230

Last Mfg.'s Sug. Retail was $435.

Grading	100%	98%	95%	90%	80%	70%	60%

AMERICA STANDARD O & U—.410 ga. only, 26 and 28 in. barrels, coin finish receiver with extensive engraving, Italian walnut. Deluxe model — add $85. Imported 1984-1988.

	$305	$280	$265	$240	$215	$205	$190

Last Mfg.'s Sug. Retail was $335.

EUROPA O & U—.410 ga. only, 26 in. barrels, coin finish receiver with some engraving, Italian walnut. Deluxe model — add $95 (discontinued in 1985). Imported 1984-1988.

	$275	$250	$235	$220	$210	$200	$185

Last Mfg.'s Sug. Retail was $295.

FRANCIA STANDARD SXS—.410 ga. only, double triggers, extractors, checkered walnut. Imported 1986-1988. Add $19 for Deluxe Model.

	$235	$220	$210	$200	$185	$175	$160

Last Mfg.'s Sug. Retail was $255.

ALPHA THREE STANDARD SXS—12, 16, and 20 ga.'s, 26 and 28 in. barrels, coin finish receiver with extensive engraving, Italian walnut. Single trigger — add $25 (discontinued in 1985), ejectors — add $100. Imported 1984-1988.

	$390	$355	$325	$300	$275	$250	$235

Last Mfg.'s Sug. Retail was $425.

BETA THREE SINGLE BARREL—single barrel field gun, available in 12, 16, 20, 24, 28, 32, and .410 ga.'s, vent rib, chrome finish receiver. Imported 1985-1988.

	$155	$145	$140	$130	$125	$120	$115

Last Mfg.'s Sug. Retail was $190.

BERETTA, PIETRO

MANUFACTURED IN BRESCIA, ITALY 1680-PRESENT AND ACCOKEEK, MD 1983 TO DATE. U.S. HEADQUARTERS IN ACCOKEEK, MD HAS BEEN IMPORTING BERETTA EXCLUSIVELY SINCE 1980. 1970-1977 MANUFACTURE WAS IMPORTED EXCLUSIVELY BY GARCIA.

Note: On January 15, 1985, the U.S. government announced that Beretta would be sole manufacturer of the new 9mm double action military handgun. This prestigious and large military contract was initially manufactured in Italy and now is manufactured in Beretta's Accokeek, Maryland plant.

PISTOLS: DISCONTINUED, SEMI-AUTO

MODEL 1910—.25 ACP cal., single action, 7 shot, fixed sights, wood grips, mfg. 1910-1934.

	$300	$275	$250	$195	$165	$145	$110

MODEL 1915—.32 ACP, 8 shot, 3.3 in. barrel, fixed sights, blue, wood grips, made 1915-1919.

	$300	$305	$275	$250	$195	$165	$110

MODEL 1915—9mm Glisenti, second variation - larger version, made 1915.

	$400	$385	$330	$275	$220	$195	$140

9mm Para. is not interchangeable and potentially dangerous if interchanged with 9mm Glisenti.

MODEL 1923—9mm, 8 shot, 4 in. barrel, fixed sights, steel grips, made 1923-1935.

	$500	$425	$350	$300	$250	$200	$150

Add 25% for slotted rear grip strap.

MODEL 1934—.380 ACP (9mm Kurz), 3⅜ in. barrel, fixed sights, blue, plastic grips, Italy's service weapon in WWII, military models have poorer finish, made 1934-1959.

	$290	$275	$250	$195	$165	$140	$110
Commercial model	$290	$330	$275	$220	$195	$165	$140

MODEL 1935—.32 ACP, 3½ in. barrel, fixed sights, blue, plastic grips, the wartime model had poor finish, made 1935-1959.

	$250	$225	$200	$180	$160	$140	$120
Commercial model	$275	$250	$215	$185	$165	$145	$125

Grading	100%	98%	95%	90%	80%	70%	60%

MODEL 318—.25 ACP, 2½ in. barrel, fixed sights, blue, plastic grips, made 1934-1939.

	$275	$250	$220	$195	$165	$140	$110

MODEL 418—.25 ACP, fixed sights.

	$220	$190	$170	$145	$125	$110	$100

MODEL 420—.25 ACP, chrome finish, small coverage engraving.

	$350	$300	$260	$230	$200	$175	$160

MODEL 421—.25 ACP, gold plated, elaborate engraving.

	$475	$430	$400	$360	$320	$280	$230

PISTOLS: POST WWII

100% values on below listed models assume NIB condition.

MODEL 948—.22 LR, 3½ or 6 in. barrel, fixed sights, hammer.

	$175	$150	$125	$100	$75	$60	$50

MODEL 949 OLYMPIC TARGET—.22 S or LR, 8¾ in. barrel, target sights, adj. barrel weights, blue, muzzle brake, checkered wood grips with thumbrest, made 1959-1964.

	$660	$550	$495	$385	$305	$250	$195

MODEL 950CC MINX M2—.22 short, hinged 2⅜ in. barrel, fixed sights, blue, plastic grips, made 1955-disc.

	$135	$115	$105	$95	$85	$75	$70

MODEL 950CC SPECIAL MINX M4—same as M2, with 4 in. barrel.

	$135	$115	$105	$95	$85	$75	$70

MODEL 950B JETFIRE—same as M2, in .25 ACP.

	$135	$115	$105	$95	$85	$75	$70

MODEL 951 BRIGADIER—9mm, 4½ in. barrel, fixed sights, blue, plastic grips, current Italian service pistol, made 1952-present. "Brigadier" or "Israeli" — add $350.

	$250	$215	$195	$175	$150	$130	$115

MODEL 20—.25 ACP, double action, alloy frame, 9 shot, 2½ in. barrel, 10.9 oz., plastic or walnut grips. Discontinued in 1985.

	$160	$140	$125	$115	$95	$85	$75

Last Mfg.'s Sug. Retail was $214.

MODEL 70 PUMA OR COUGAR—.32 ACP or .380 ACP cal.'s, 3½ in. barrel, fixed sights, blue, plastic grips, .32 Puma alloy frame, .380 Cougar steel frame. Discontinued.

	$200	$180	$165	$150	$130	$110	$90

MODEL 70T—same as 70, .32 ACP, target sights. Discontinued.

	$275	$250	$220	$195	$165	$150	$140

MODEL 70S—.22 LR or .380 ACP cal.'s, single action, 3½ in. barrel, 9 shot, blued finish, plastic grips, weight .22 cal. — 18 oz., .380 ACP — 23 oz., steel frame, .22 LR has adj. rear sight. Discontinued in 1985.

	$240	$210	$185	$170	$155	$140	$125

Last Mfg.'s Sug. Retail was $295.

MODEL 71 JAGUAR—alloy frame, .22 LR version of 70. Discontinued.

	$220	$195	$180	$160	$150	$140	$110

MODEL 72 JAGUAR—same as 71, with 6 in. barrel. Discontinued.

	$220	$195	$180	$160	$150	$140	$110

MODEL 76P-76W TARGET PISTOL—.22 LR, single action, 11 shot, steel frame, 6 in. barrel, adj. sights, blued finish, thumbrest plastic grips (76-P). Discontinued in 1985. Add $40 for thumbrest wood grips(Model 76-W).

	$345	$300	$275	$245	$220	$195	$170

Last Mfg.'s Sug. Retail was $395.

MODEL 81P-81W—.32 ACP, double action, 13 shot, 3.8 in. barrel, fixed sights, blue, wood grips (W Suffix) — add $20. Nickel finish — add $90, imported 1976-1984.

	$300	$250	$225	$195	$175	$155	$135

Grading	100%	98%	95%	90%	80%	70%	60%

MODEL 82W—.32 ACP, double action, more compact than Model 81, 10 shot, walnut grips, 17 oz. Nickel finish — add $75. Importation discontinued in 1984.

| | $300 | $250 | $225 | $195 | $175 | $155 | $135 |

MODEL 84W-EL—same as Model 84 only specially engraved, select walnut grips. Presentation case. Discontinued in 1984.

| | $1,025 | $770 | $720 | $615 | $565 | $520 | $460 |

MODEL 86P-86W—.380 ACP only, double-action, tip-up 4⅓ in. barrel, 8 shot mag., plastic or walnut grips, 23 oz. Add $80 for walnut grips (86-W). This model was advertised, but never released.

1986 advertised Mfg.'s Sug. Retail was $480.

MODEL 90 DOUBLE ACTION AUTOMATIC—.32 ACP, 3⅝ in. barrel, fixed sights, blue, plastic grips, made 1969-1983.

| | $275 | $195 | $175 | $155 | $130 | $110 | $95 |

MODEL 92—same general specifications as current Model 92SB, originally made 1976 until discontinued.

| | $400 | $350 | $315 | $280 | $255 | $240 | $220 |

Early production Model 92's had a frame mounted safety and mag. release button at base of pistol grip in addition to a serial number suffix. The Model 92's design evolved from the Beretta Model 951. Military contracts have normally specified steel frame fabrication.

Model 92S—same as Model 92, second model. Discontinued.

| | $375 | $325 | $260 | $230 | $200 | $180 | $165 |

MODEL 92SB-P—9mm Luger, double action, 16 shot, 4.92 in. barrel, fixed sights, alloy frame, high-polish blued finish, plastic grips (Model 92SB-P), 34½ oz., made 1980-1985.

| | $475 | $425 | $385 | $345 | $310 | $285 | $260 |

Last Mfg.'s Sug. Retail was $600.

Model 92SB-W—same as above, only with wooden grips. Discontinued in 1985.

| | $495 | $430 | $390 | $355 | $330 | $290 | $260 |

Last Mfg.'s Sug. Retail was $620.

MODEL 92SB-P COMPACT—same as Model 92SB, except has 4.3 in. barrel, 14 shot, 31 oz., plastic grips (Model 92SB-P). Add $60 for nickel finish. Discontinued in 1985.

| | $475 | $425 | $385 | $345 | $310 | $285 | $260 |

Last Mfg.'s Sug. Retail was $620.

Model 92SB-W Compact—same as above only with wooden grips. Discontinued in 1985.

| | $495 | $430 | $390 | $355 | $335 | $300 | $280 |

Last Mfg.'s Sug. Retail was $635.

MODEL 100—.32 ACP, fixed sights. Discontinued.

| | $250 | $220 | $195 | $165 | $150 | $140 | $130 |

MODEL 101—same as 70T, in .22 LR. Discontinued.

| | $250 | $220 | $195 | $165 | $150 | $140 | $130 |

PISTOLS: SEMI-AUTO, RECENT MANUFACTURE

MODEL 21-W—.22 LR or .25 ACP, double action, alloy frame, 7 shot mag. (.22 LR) or 8 shot mag. (.25 ACP), 2½ in. barrel, walnut grips, 12.3 oz.

| *Mfg.'s Sug. Retail* | $205 | $185 | $155 | $140 | $130 | $115 | $95 | $85 |

Add $18 for nickel finish.
Add $32 for engraving.

MODEL 71—.22 LR, single action, 8 shot, 6 in. barrel, plastic grips with thumbrest, finger extension mag. Imported in 1987 only.

| | $190 | $160 | $140 | $130 | $115 | $95 | $85 |

Last Mfg.'s Sug. Retail was $215.

Grading	100%	98%	95%	90%	80%	70%	60%

MODEL 84P-84W—.380 ACP, double action, alloy frame, 3.82 in. barrel, 14 shot, 22½ oz. Model 84-P has plastic grips.

Mfg.'s Sug. Retail	$467	$380	$330	$300	$270	$240	$210	$190

Add $66 for nickel finish.

Add $26 for wooden grips (Model 84-W).

MODEL 85P-85W—same general specifications as the Model 84, except 8 shot, 22 oz., walnut grips only.

Mfg.'s Sug. Retail	$413	$340	$300	$270	$240	$210	$190	$175

Add $67 for nickel finish.

Add $27 for wooden grips (Model 85-W).

MODEL 87—.22 LR, double action semi-auto, 7 shot mag., 3.82 or 6 in. target barrel with counterweight, wood grips, 20 oz. (3.82 in. barrel). Importation began in 1986.

Mfg.'s Sug. Retail	$447	$365	$320	$280	$245	$210	$190	$175

Add $13 for target barrel (single action only).

MODEL 89—.22 LR, single action target semi-auto, matte black finish on metal parts, 10 shot mag., anatomical wood grips, adj. sights. Importation began in 1988.

Mfg.'s Sug. Retail	$620	$500	$450	$395	$350	$300	$275	$250

MODEL 92F—9mm Luger, official U.S. military variation of 92 Series, 4.9 in. barrel, alloy frame, 15 shot mag., chamber loaded indicator, non-glare military finish, squared off trigger guard to facilitate two-hand shooting, extended mag. base. Model 92F-P has plastic grips. Model 92F-W has wooden grips. New in 1984.

Mfg.'s Sug. Retail	$600	$550	$440	$410	$375	$335	$300	$275

Plastic grips are currently more desireable than wood, even though wood adds $27 to the retail price.

The U.S. military in 1985 announced this model to replace the Colt .45 as the standard government issue sidearm. This contract with Beretta involves over 315,000 Model 92SB-F's being manufactured for U.S. military consumption over the next three years. Because of the emphasis on military production, commercial models have been limited to date and sometimes command premiums over the values listed above. The Model 92F and Model 92F Compact (reintroduced in 1989) are the only variations available for commercial sale currently. Actual delivery of commercial Model 92's began in January of 1986.

MODEL 92F COMPACT—similar to Model 92F, except has 4.3 in. barrel and 13 shot mag. While temporarily suspended in 1986, production was resumed in 1989.

Mfg.'s Sug. Retail	$620	$565	$450	$415	$375	$335	$300	$275

MODEL 950 BS—.22 short or .25 ACP cal.'s, single action, alloy frame, 8 shot (.25 cal. only) or 6 shot mag., tip-up 2½ and 4 in. (.22 only) barrel, plastic grips, thumb safety, 8-10 oz.

Mfg.'s Sug. Retail	$153	$135	$120	$110	$100	$90	$80	$70

Add $27 for nickel finish.

Add $67 for engraved variation.

Model 950 EL—same general specifications as Model 950 BS, only with wooden grips and gold plated parts. Importation disc. in 1988.

	$190	$175	$150	$140	$130	$115	$105

Last Mfg.'s Sug. Retail was $210.

RIFLES: BOLT-ACTION, RECENT MANUFACTURE

MODEL 500 CUSTOM—.222 Rem., .223 Rem., .243 Win., .270 Win., .30-06, or .308 Win. cal., 3 action length, 24 in. barrel, iron sights, checkered walnut stock with recoil pad. Importation was resumed in 1988 only.

	$595	$530	$450	$395	$350	$315	$275

Last Mfg.'s Sug. Retail was $725.

Model 500S—same as Model 500, except is equipped with iron sights. Imported in 1986 only.

	$615	$560	$460	$400	$350	$315	$275

Last Mfg.'s Sug. Retail was $700.

Grading	100%	98%	95%	90%	80%	70%	60%

Model 500 DL—same specifications as Model 500, only better walnut and light engraving. Disc. in 1986.

	100%	98%	95%	90%	80%	70%	60%
	$1,395	$1,260	$1,000	$875	$795	$725	$650

Last Mfg.'s Sug. Retail was $1,595.

Model 500 DLS—same as Model 500 DL, except is equipped with iron sights. Imported in 1986 only.

	$1,420	$1,285	$1,020	$875	$795	$725	$650

Last Mfg.'s Sug. Retail was $1,625.

Model 500 EELL—same specifications as Model 500 DL, only select walnut and more engraving. Disc. in 1986.

	$1,550	$1,260	$1,150	$1,000	$875	$800	$725

Last Mfg.'s Sug. Retail was $1,745.

Model 500 EELLS—same as Model 500 EELL, except is equipped with iron sights. Imported in 1986 only.

	$1,575	$1,425	$1,200	$1,120	$875	$800	$725

Last Mfg.'s Sug. Retail was $1,785.

MODEL 501—available in either .243 or .308 Win. cal.'s., medium bolt action, 6 shot, 23 in. barrel, no sights, checkered walnut stock. Disc. in 1986.

	$595	$530	$465	$395	$350	$315	$275

Last Mfg.'s Sug. Retail was $665.

Model 501 S—same as Model 501, except is equipped with iron sights. Imported in 1986 only.

	$615	$560	$460	$400	$350	$315	$275

Last Mfg.'s Sug. Retail was $700.

Model 501 DL—same specifications as Model 501, only better walnut and light engraving. Disc. in 1986.

	$1,395	$1,260	$1,000	$875	$795	$725	$650

Last Mfg.'s Sug. Retail was $1,575.

Model 501 DLS—same as Model 501 DL, except is equipped with iron sights. Imported in 1986 only.

	$1,420	$1,285	$1,020	$875	$795	$725	$650

Last Mfg.'s Sug. Retail was $1,625.

Model 501 EELL—same specifications as Model 501 DL, only select walnut and more engraving. Disc. in 1986.

	$1,550	$1,260	$1,150	$1,000	$875	$800	$725

Last Mfg.'s Sug. Retail was $1,745.

Model 501 EELLS—same as Model 501 EELL, except is equipped with iron sights. Imported in 1986 only.

	$1,575	$1,425	$1,200	$1,120	$875	$800	$725

Last Mfg.'s Sug. Retail was $1,785.

MODEL 502—available in either .30-06, .270 and 7mm Rem. Mag. cal.'s., long bolt action, 5 or 6 shot, 24 in. barrel, no sights, checkered walnut stock. Disc. in 1986.

	$625	$565	$490	$440	$395	$360	$330

Last Mfg.'s Sug. Retail was $710.

Model 502 S—same as Model 502, except is equipped with iron sights. Imported in 1986 only.

	$650	$595	$525	$460	$395	$360	$330

Last Mfg.'s Sug. Retail was $745.

Model 502 DL—same specifications as Model 502, only better walnut and light engraving. Also available in .375 H&H Mag. Disc. in 1986.

	$1,495	$1,310	$1,175	$1,025	$900	$775	$695

Last Mfg.'s Sug. Retail was $1,640.

Grading	100%	98%	95%	90%	80%	70%	60%

Model 502 DLS—same as Model 502, except is equipped with iron sights. Imported in 1986 only.

	$1,410	$1,325	$1,175	$1,025	$900	$775	$695

Last Mfg.'s Sug. Retail was $1,660.

Model 502 EELL—same specifications as Model 502 DL, only select walnut and more engraving. Also available in .375 H&H Mag. Disc. in 1986.

	$1,575	$1,425	$1,200	$1,120	$875	$800	$725

Last Mfg.'s Sug. Retail was $1,785.

Model 502 EELLS—same as Model 502 EELL, except is equipped with iron sights. Imported in 1986 only.

	$1,575	$1,425	$1,200	$1,120	$875	$800	$725

Last Mfg.'s Sug. Retail was $1,785.

RIFLES: CURRENT MANUFACTURE

AR 70—.222 or .223 cal., semi-auto assault rifle, 5, 8 or 30 round mag.'s, Diopter sights, epoxy finish, 17.72 in. barrel, 8.3 lbs.

Mfg.'s Sug. Retail	$1,065	$850	$695	$575	$475	$420	$360	$310

SSO EXPRESS O/U—.375 H&H and .458 Win. Mag. cal.'s, sidelock action, case hardened receiver, double triggers, 23 in. barrels, auto ejectors, 11 lbs., cased.

Mfg.'s Sug. Retail	$17,533	$12,500	$9,500	$8,250	$6,950	$6,100	$5,600	$4,875

Add $425 for claw mounts.

Older specimens (not custom ordered within the last 2 years) could have values considerably lower than those listed above.

SSO5 EXPRESS O/U—similar to SSO Express except has more elaborate engraving and better walnut.

Mfg.'s Sug. Retail	$19,600	$14,250	$11,750	$8,750	$7,500	$6,750	$6,100	$5,600

Older specimens (not custom ordered within the last 2 years) could have values considerably lower than those listed above.

MODEL S689 O/U—9.3 x 74R and .30-06 cal.'s, boxlock action, nickel (discontinued in 1985) or case hardened (new in 1986) finished receiver, double triggers, 23 in. barrels, auto ejectors, 7.7 lbs.

Mfg.'s Sug. Retail	$4,907	$3,700	$2,600	$2,200	$1,850	$1,550	$1,275	$1,050

Add $1,200 for scope and claw mounts.

SHOTGUNS: OVER & UNDER, DISCONTINUED

BL-1—12 ga., 26, 28, and 30 in. barrels, various chokes, boxlock, extractors, double triggers, checkered pistol grip stock, made 1968-1973.

	$385	$330	$275	$220	$190	$175	$160

BL-2—same as BL-1, with single selective trigger, more engraving.

	$420	$385	$360	$305	$265	$225	$185

BL-2 Stake-Out—riot configuration with 18 in. barrels, DT.

	$385	$330	$275	$220	$190	$175	$160

BL-2/S—same as BL-2, with vent rib and speed trigger, made 1974-1976.

	$440	$385	$330	$305	$265	$225	$185

BL-3—O/U, same as BL-2, with more engraving, vent rib and ejectors, also available in 20 ga., made 1968-1976.

	$595	$550	$525	$470	$440	$385	$350

BL-3 SKEET

	$660	$605	$580	$525	$470	$415	$370

BL-3 TRAP

	$580	$520	$495	$450	$415	$375	$335

BL-4—deluxe version of BL-3, more engraving, better wood.

	$695	$650	$595	$550	$495	$450	$395

BL-4 SKEET

	$745	$690	$635	$550	$495	$450	$395

Grading	100%	98%	95%	90%	80%	70%	60%

BL-4 TRAP

	100%	98%	95%	90%	80%	70%	60%
	$675	$625	$580	$525	$475	$425	$360

BL-5—higher grade version of BL-4.

	$910	$855	$800	$715	$650	$575	$475

BL-5 SKEET

	$960	$910	$855	$760	$675	$600	$500

BL-5 TRAP

	$850	$820	$775	$695	$595	$525	$430

BL-6—auto ejectors, sidelock, elaborate engraving.

	$1,250	$1,100	$990	$935	$850	$765	$680

BL-6 SKEET

	$1,295	$1,100	$990	$935	$850	$765	$680

BL-6 TRAP

	$1,100	$950	$885	$810	$755	$670	$580

MODEL S55B—12 and 20 ga., O/U, 26, 28, or 30 in. barrels, various chokes, boxlock, extractors, selective trigger, checkered pistol grip stock. Discontinued.

	$550	$495	$440	$385	$330	$300	$280

MODEL S56 E—same as S55B, with engraved receiver and auto ejectors. Discontinued.

	$605	$555	$515	$460	$415	$365	$330

MODEL S58 SKEET—same as S56E, with 26 in. Bohler steel barrels, skeet bore, wide vent rib, skeet.

	$770	$695	$630	$550	$495	$445	$395

MODEL S58 TRAP—same as S58 Skeet, with 30 in. barrels, imp. mod. and full choke, Monte Carlo stock with pad.

	$700	$625	$550	$495	$450	$410	$365

SILVER SNIPE—12 and 20 ga., 26, 28, and 30 in. barrels, boxlock, extractors, trigger optional, checkered pistol grip stock, made 1955-1967.

	$415	$370	$330	$295	$265	$230	$210

SST—with vent. rib and single selective trigger.

	$550	$495	$440	$415	$360	$330	$295

Add 25% for ejectors.

GOLDEN SNIPE—same as Silver Snipe, with auto ejectors and vent. rib standard.

	$660	$605	$550	$525	$470	$430	$385

SST—with single selective trigger.

	$715	$660	$605	$580	$525	$465	$410

MODEL 57 E—higher quality version of Golden Snipe, made 1955-1967.

	$825	$770	$660	$635	$550	$495	$450

SST—with single selective trigger.

	$880	$825	$715	$690	$605	$540	$495

ASEL MODEL—12 and 20 ga., 26, 28, or 30 in. barrels, various chokes, single trigger, checkered pistol grip stock, auto ejectors, made 1947-1964.

	$1,340	$1,100	$990	$880	$800	$720	$650

GRADE 100—12 ga., 26, 28, and 30 in. barrels, any choke, sidelock, double trigger, auto ejectors, checkered pistol grip or straight stock.

	$1,820	$1,550	$1,300	$1,100	$900	$775	$695

MODEL 200—same as 100, with chrome lined bores and action parts, higher quality engraving.

	$2,310	$2,000	$1,870	$1,650	$1,375	$1,100	$875

MODEL 680—competition trap and skeet model, .12 ga. only, boxlock, various chokes. Mono-trap model available. Silver finish receiver, hand engraved, premium walnut. 2 barrel set — add $62. Discontinued.

	$1,215	$1,030	$870	$790	$715	$635	$550

Grading	100%	98%	95%	90%	80%	70%	60%

SHOTGUNS: OVER & UNDER, RECENT MANUFACTURE

MODEL 682 SKEET—competition skeet model, 12, 20, 28 (disc. in 1988), or .410 ga. (disc. in 1988), 26 (12 ga. only) or 28 in. barrels, boxlock, skeet chokes, silver finish receiver, hand engraved, premium walnut, cased. New in 1984.

Mfg.'s Sug. Retail	$2,073	$1,700	$1,500	$1,250	$1,050	$950	$895	$800

Model 682 Sporting—similar specifications to Model 682, 28 or 30 (new in 1989) in. VR barrels, except over-field stock dimensions and hand engraved silver finished receiver. Multichokes are standard.

Mfg.'s Sug. Retail	$2,153	$1,750	$1,525	$1,275	$1,050	$950	$895	$800

This variation has been specifically designed for sporting clay target shooting.

Model 682 Deluxe—same as Model 682, except deluxe walnut and elaborate engraving. Discontinued in 1986.

	$2,650	$2,300	$2,100	$1,850	$1,600	$1,400	$1,200

Last Mfg.'s Sug. Retail was $3,000.

Model 682 2-Barrel Skeet Set—12 ga. only, two barrel set bored for skeet and sporting play competition. Imported in 1988 only.

	$4,950	$4,200	$3,675	$3,175	$2,850	$2,500	$2,175

Last Mfg.'s Sug. Retail was $6,650.

Model 682 4-Ga. Skeet Set—four barrel skeet set comes with interchangeable barrels (28 in.) in 12, 20, 28, and 410 ga.'s. New in 1985.

Mfg.'s Sug. Retail	$4,913	$4,150	$3,675	$3,175	$2,850	$2,500	$2,175	$1,900

MODEL 682 TRAP—12 ga. only, competition trap model, silver or Bruniton finish (matte black), 30 or 32 in. barrels, adj. trigger, supplied with case. New in 1985.

Mfg.'s Sug. Retail	$2,053	$1,695	$1,500	$1,250	$1,050	$950	$895	$800

Add $67 for multi-chokes.

This model is designated the Model 682 X if with Bruniton matte black finish.

Model 682 Mono—single under-barrel trap model, high post vent rib, 32 or 34 in. barrel. No extra charge for multi-chokes. Imported 1985-1988.

	$1,530	$1,400	$1,200	$1,025	$925	$875	$775

Last Mfg.'s Sug. Retail was $1,890.

Model 682 Top Single—12 ga. only, single over-barrel trap model, 32 or 34 in. barrel. New in 1986.

Mfg.'s Sug. Retail	$2,187	$1,675	$1,475	$1,250	$1,025	$925	$875	$775

Subtract $75 if without multi-chokes.

Multi-chokes became standard in 1989.

Model 682 Combo—12 ga. only, supplied with mono under or upper single barrel and O/U barrel sets. Otherwise same specifications as Model 682 Trap. Cased.

Mfg.'s Sug. Retail	$2,827	$2,250	$2,000	$1,725	$1,525	$1,375	$1,200	$1,000

Subtract $54 if without multi-chokes.

MODEL SUPER SPORT—12 ga. only, 28 or 30 in. VR barrels with multi-chokes, similar to Model 682 Sporting. New in 1989.

Mfg.'s Sug. Retail	$2,287	$1,995	$1,725	$1,500	$1,250	$1,050	$950	$875

MODEL 685—12 and 20 ga. 2¾ or 3 in. chambers, matte chromed receiver, extractors, single trigger. Discontinued in 1986.

	$650	$575	$495	$450	$400	$360	$320

Last Mfg.'s Sug. Retail was $875.

MODEL 686 FIELD—12, 20, and 28 ga., field model, boxlock action, various barrels/chokes, ejectors, single trigger, engraved silver finished receiver, special walnut, pistol or straight grip stock. Multi-chokes disc. in 1987.

Mfg.'s Sug. Retail	$1,147	$950	$775	$650	$575	$525	$460	$415

Add $110 for multi-chokes.

Grading	100%	98%	95%	90%	80%	70%	60%

Model 686 Sporting—12 ga. only, deluxe checkered walnut stock and forearm with over-field dimensions, 28 in. barrels only, multi-chokes standard. New in 1987.

Mfg.'s Sug. Retail	$1,653	$1,360	$1,200	$1,025	$925	$875	$775	$695

This variation has been specifically designed for sporting clay target shooting.

Model 686 Onyx—12 or 20 ga., 3 in. chambers, boxlock action, 26 or 28 in. barrels with multi-chokes, matte finish on metal parts, single trigger, ejectors. New in 1988.

Mfg.'s Sug. Retail	$1,167	$1,000	$850	$740	$685	$635	$575	$525

This model is also available with a straight grip English stock at no extra charge.

Model 686 Combo—same as Model 686 Field, except is supplied with 1 set each of 20 ga. (28 in.) and 28 ga. (26 in.) barrels. Introduced in 1986.

Mfg.'s Sug. Retail	$1,713	$1,425	$1,250	$1,100	$950	$875	$820	$775

MODEL 687 L FIELD—12 and 20 (discontinued in 1985) ga.'s, boxlock, various barrels/chokes, ejectors, floral engraved nickel finished receiver, select walnut, fitted case.

Mfg.'s Sug. Retail	$1,573	$1,225	$995	$825	$700	$635	$575	$525

Subtract $100 without multi-chokes.

Model 687 Sporting Clays—12 or 20 ga. only, deluxe checkered walnut stock and forearm with over-field dimensions, 28 in. barrels only, multi-chokes standard. New in 1987.

Mfg.'s Sug. Retail	$2,173	$1,925	$1,695	$1,500	$1,250	$1,050	$950	$875

This variation has been specifically designed for sporting clay target shooting.

Model 687 Golden Onyx Field—12 or 20 ga., 3 in. chambers, similar to Model 686 Onyx, except has more engraving, better walnut, and several gold inlays. Introduced in 1988.

Mfg.'s Sug. Retail	$1,800	$1,375	$1,075	$875	$775	$685	$635	$575

MODEL 687 EL FIELD—same general specifications as Model 687L Field, except available in 20 ga. also, 2¾ or 3 in. chambers, boxlock with sideplates, better walnut, and more engraving.

Mfg.'s Sug. Retail	$2,607	$2,250	$1,975	$1,725	$1,500	$1,350	$1,150	$1,000

MODEL 687 EELL FIELD—12, 20, or 28 ga., same general specifications as Model 687EL, except has extra select walnut, game scene engraving, 3 in. chambers and gold plated trigger, multi-chokes introduced in 1988.

Mfg.'s Sug. Retail	$3,767	$3,175	$2,650	$2,300	$1,950	$1,725	$1,500	$1,250

Add $53 for multi-chokes (except 28 ga.).

This model is also available with a straight grip English stock at no extra charge (20 ga. - fixed chokes only).

Model 687 EELL Sporting Clays—12 or 20 ga. only, deluxe checkered walnut stock and forearm with over-field dimensions, 28 in. barrels only, multi-chokes standard. New in 1987.

Mfg.'s Sug. Retail	$3,600	$3,150	$2,650	$2,300	$1,925	$1,725	$1,500	$1,250

This variation has been specifically designed for sporting clay target shooting.

Model 687 EELL Top Single Trap—12 ga. only, single over-barrel trap model, 32 or 34 in. barrel. New in 1988.

Mfg.'s Sug. Retail	$3,800	$3,200	$2,700	$2,300	$1,925	$1,725	$1,500	$1,250

Available with either full fixed choke or with multi-chokes at $53 extra.

Model 687 EELL Top Trap Combo—12 ga. only, supplied with 30 or 32 in. O/U barrels and a mono trap upper barrel, multi-chokes standard. New in 1988.

Mfg.'s Sug. Retail	$4,833	$4,200	$3,775	$3,395	$3,000	$2,775	$2,550	$2,250

Add $54 for multi-chokes.

Model 687 EELL Mono Trap Combo—12 ga. only, supplied with 30 or 32 in. O/U barrels and a mono trap bottom barrel. Imported 1986-1988.

	$4,175	$3,725	$3,395	$3,000	$2,775	$2,550	$2,250

Add $140 for multi-chokes.

Last Mfg.'s Sug. Retail was $4,900.

Model 687 EELL 4-Ga. Skeet Set—four ga. skeet set, cased. New in 1988.

Mfg.'s Sug. Retail	$6,767	$5,400	$4,675	$3,925	$3,395	$3,000	$2,700	$2,450

Grading	100%	98%	95%	90%	80%	70%	60%

SHOTGUNS: CUSTOM SERIES, OVER AND UNDER

"SO" SERIES O/U SHOTGUNS—12 ga., 26-30 in. barrels, sidelock, any chokes, vent rib, auto ejectors, SST, checkered stock in various configurations (field, skeet, or trap), grades differ in wood, engraving, and finish, cased, made 1948-present.

	100%	98%	95%	90%	80%	70%	60%
SO-2 (discontinued)	$4,900	$4,200	$3,500	$2,850	$2,200	$1,900	$1,750

SO-3—2nd grade of the SO series. Disc. in 1987.

	$7,850	$6,800	$5,980	$5,475	$4,450	$3,875	$3,400

Last Mfg.'s Sug. Retail was $8,250.

SO-3 EL—grade-up from SO-3 with better wood and engraving. Discontinued in 1985.

	$8,250	$6,900	$6,000	$5,500	$4,450	$3,900	$3,500

Last Mfg.'s Sug. Retail was $8,100.

SO-3 EELL—best quality model, custom specifications, choice of engraving motifs. Disc. in 1987.

	$8,995	$7,975	$6,700	$5,750	$5,000	$4,500	$3,950

Add $1,375/set of O/U barrels.

Last Mfg.'s Sug. Retail was $11,625.

SO-4—12 ga., sidelock, available in field, skeet, or trap configurations, custon spec.'s, fluorescent sights, wide rib, cased. Disc. in 1987.

	$8,350	$7,000	$6,100	$5,500	$4,500	$4,000	$3,500

Add $2,300 for extra set of O/U barrels.

Last Mfg.'s Sug. Retail was $8,700.

SO-5—best quality O/U, extensively engraved, top quality checkered walnut stock (semi-pistol grip) and forearm, available in either Trap, Skeet, or Sporting configurations.

Mfg.'s Sug. Retail	$13,693	$10,000	$8,500	$7,800	$6,750	$5,950	$5,200	$4,500

Add $3,933 for extra set of barrels.
Add $3,327 for Trap Combo set.
Add $733 for SST.

Older specimens (not custom ordered within the last 2 years) could have values considerably lower than those listed above.

SO-5 EELL—next to top-of-the-line model, available in either Trap, Skeet, or Sporting configurations, custom built to customer dimensions. Importation disc. in 1988.

	$15,950	$12,250	$10,500	$8,500	$7,800	$6,750	$5,950

Last Mfg.'s Sug. Retail was $21,750.

Older specimens (not custom ordered within the last 2 years) could have values considerably lower than those listed above.

SO-6—best quality O/U, extensively engraved, top quality checkered walnut stock (semi-pistol grip) and forearm, field dimensions, built to customer specifications.

Mfg.'s Sug. Retail	$15,480	$11,250	$8,750	$7,850	$6,750	$5,950	$5,200	$4,500

Add $4,000 for extra set of barrels.
Add $733 for SST.

Older specimens (not custom ordered within the last 2 years) could have values considerably lower than those listed above.

SO-6 EELL—current top-of-the-line model, field dimensions, custom built to customer specifications.

Mfg.'s Sug. Retail	$23,973	$17,300	$12,750	$11,000	$8,500	$7,800	$6,750	$5,950

Older specimens (not custom ordered within the last 2 years) could have values considerably lower than those listed above.

SHOTGUNS: SIDE-BY-SIDE, DISCONTINUED

MODEL 409 PB—12, 16, 20, and 28 ga.'s, 27, 28, and 30 in. barrels, various chokes, double triggers, plain extractors, checkered pistol grip stock, made 1934-1964.

	$770	$660	$605	$550	$495	$440	$385

Grading	100%	98%	95%	90%	80%	70%	60%

MODEL 410 E—higher quality, auto ejector version of 409PB.

	$880	$770	$715	$660	$605	$550	$495

MODEL 410—same as 410 E, except 10 ga. Mag., 32 in. barrel, full choke, heavier construction, made 1934. Discontinued.

	$990	$880	$825	$770	$715	$660	$550

MODEL 411 E—same as 409 PB, with false sideplates and finer finishing, made 1934-1964.

	$1,210	$1,100	$1,045	$990	$880	$825	$770

MODEL 424-426—12 and 20 ga. (Model 426 only), 26 and 28 in. barrels, various chokes, boxlock, extractors, double triggers, light engraving, checkered straight stock. Model 426 — add $115.

	$900	$715	$660	$635	$550	$495	$415

MODEL 426 E—same as 424, with auto ejectors, SST, select wood and more intricate engraving, silver pigeon inlay. Discontinued in 1983.

	$1,115	$935	$880	$855	$770	$715	$635

MODEL 625—12 and 20 ga., 26-30 in. barrels, various chokes, boxlock, extractors, double triggers, light engraving, checkered straight stock. Imported 1984-1986.

	$795	$745	$660	$580	$530	$485	$440

Last Mfg.'s Sug. Retail was $835.

MODEL GR-2—12 and 20 ga.'s, 26 and 28 in. barrels, various chokes, boxlock, extractors, double triggers, checkered pistol grip stock, made 1968-1976.

	$660	$605	$550	$495	$385	$330	$275

MODEL GR-3—same as GR-2, with select wood and more engraving, made 1968-1976.

	$770	$715	$660	$605	$495	$440	$385

MODEL GR-4—same as GR-3, with auto ejectors, made 1968-1976.

	$880	$825	$770	$715	$605	$550	$495

SILVER HAWK—12 ga. Mag. & 10 ga. Mag. with double triggers and extractors. Add $100 for 10 ga. Discontinued in 1967.

	$495	$380	$325	$275	$250	$225	$200

SILVER HAWK FEATHERWEIGHT—12, 16, 20, and 28 ga.'s, 26-32 in. barrels, high solid rib, various chokes, double triggers, checkered pistol grip stock, beavertail forearm. Discontinued in 1967.

	$495	$440	$415	$385	$360	$330	$275
Single trigger.	$550	$495	$440	$415	$385	$360	$330

SO-6 DOUBLE BARREL—same general specifications and embellishments as the SO series O/U guns, but s x s, made 1948-1982.

	$5,900	$5,500	$5,280	$5,060	$4,840	$4,400	$3,850

SO-7 DOUBLE BARREL—top of the line s x s, finest quality wood, more elaborate engraving. Discontinued.

	$8,250	$7,700	$7,150	$6,600	$6,050	$5,500	$4,620

Model 627 EL Sport—same as Model 627 EL Field, except 12 ga. only, knurled rib, sporting clays dimensions. Importation disc. in 1988.

	$1,800	$1,625	$1,500	$1,300	$1,100	$925	$795

Last Mfg.'s Sug. Retail was $1,995.

SHOTGUNS: SIDE-BY-SIDE, RECENT MANUFACTURE

MODEL 626 FIELD—12 and 20 (disc. in 1987) ga., 2¾ in. chambers, 26 and 28 in. barrels, various chokes, boxlock, ejectors, single trigger, moderate engraving, pistol grip or straight checkered stock. Imported 1984-1988.

	$895	$800	$740	$685	$595	$540	$490

Last Mfg.'s Sug. Retail was $995.

MODEL 626 ONYX—12 or 20 ga., 3 in. chambers, 26 in. VR barrels with multi-chokes, matte finished metal parts, select checkered walnut stock and form. New in 1988.

Mfg.'s Sug. Retail	$1,533	$1,195	$995	$850	$750	$685	$595	$540

Grading	100%	98%	95%	90%	80%	70%	60%

MODEL 627 EL FIELD—12 and 20 (disc. in 1987) ga., 2¾ in. chambers, 26 and 28 in. barrels, various chokes, boxlock, ejectors, single trigger, extensive engraving, pistol grip or straight checkered stock, cased. New in 1985.

Mfg.'s Sug. Retail $2,600 $2,150 $1,800 $1,600 $1,300 $1,100 $925 $795
Add $55 for multi-chokes and 3 in. chambers.

MODEL 627 EELL—12 and 20 (disc. in 1987) ga., 2¾ in. chambers, 26 and 28 in. barrels, various chokes, boxlock, ejectors, single trigger, elaborate engraving, pistol grip or straight checkered stock, cased. New in 1985.

Mfg.'s Sug. Retail $4,453 $3,700 $3,100 $2,550 $2,100 $1,750 $1,600 $1,450

Multi-chokes are not an option on this model.

SHOTGUNS: CUSTOM SERIES, SIDE-BY-SIDE

MODEL 451 SERIES—12 ga., totally hand-made, sidelock action, ejectors, scroll engraving. Custom made to order with fitted luggage case, various grades have increasing embellishments in EL Models.

Model 451—disc. in 1987.

$6,000 $5,200 $4,875 $4,600 $4,300 $3,995 $3,600

Last Mfg.'s Sug. Retail was $12,375.

Model 451 E—12 ga. only, double triggers, specifications furnished by individual customer. New in 1989.

Mfg.'s Sug. Retail $20,467 $14,650 $10,950 $9,750 $8,500 $7,800 $6,750 $5,800
Add $4,000 for extra set of barrels.
Add $787 for SST.

Older specimens (not custom ordered within the last 2 years) could have values considerably lower than those listed above.

Model 451 EL—discontinued in 1984.

$6,450 $5,400 $4,875 $4,600 $4,300 $4,000 $3,600

Model 451 EELL—previous top-of-the-line model, choice of engraving motifs per customer specifications. Disc. in 1987, reintroduced in 1989.

Mfg.'s Sug. Retail $24,367 $17,500 $12,950 $11,000 $8,500 $7,800 $6,750 $5,950

Last Mfg.'s Sug. Retail in 1987 was $14,925.

Older specimens (not custom ordered within the last 2 years) could have values considerably lower than those listed above.

SHOTGUNS: SINGLE BARREL, DISCONTINUED

MARK II TRAP—12 ga., 32 or 34 in. wide vent rib, full choke, boxlock with auto ejector, Monte Carlo stock, recoil pad, made 1972-1976.

$660 $605 $580 $550 $495 $440 $385

MODEL FS-1 SINGLE BARREL—12, 16, 20, 28, and .410 ga.'s, 26 and 28 in. barrels, full choke, checkered semi-pistol grip, under lever break open, folds to length of barrel (also known as Companion).

$225 $200 $175 $125 $100 $85 $65

TR-1 TRAP—12 ga., 32 in. full choke barrel, under lever break open, Monte Carlo pistol grip stock with pad, engraved, made 1968-1971.

$275 $250 $220 $195 $140 $110 $100

TR-2 TRAP—same as TR-1, with high rib, made 1969-1973.

$290 $260 $230 $205 $150 $120 $110

MODEL 412—12, 20, 28, or .410 ga., monobloc construction, folding action, sling swivels, checkered walnut stock and forearm, 5 lbs. Importation disc. in 1988.

$190 $170 $125 $100 $85 $70 $60

Last Mfg.'s Sug. Retail was $215.

Grading	100%	98%	95%	90%	80%	70%	60%

SHOTGUNS: SLIDE ACTION, DISCONTINUED

MODEL SL-2—12 ga., 26, 28, and 30 in. barrels, various chokes, vent rib, checkered pistol, grip stock, made 1968-1971.

	$300	$275	$250	$220	$195	$165	$140

SILVER PIGEON—12 ga., various chokes, light engraving.

	$250	$200	$175	$160	$150	$140	$130

GOLD PIGEON—12 ga., various chokes, vent rib, engraved. Also deluxe models — add $200.

	$450	$375	$310	$275	$240	$215	$195

RUBY PIGEON—12 ga., various chokes, vent rib, elaborately engraved, special deluxe walnut.

	$575	$450	$395	$350	$295	$260	$230

SHOTGUNS: SEMI-AUTO, DISCONTINUED

SILVER LARK—12 ga., various chokes.

	$295	$260	$240	$220	$200	$185	$170

GOLD LARK—12 ga., vent rib, light scroll engraving, select walnut.

	$450	$375	$320	$260	$230	$210	$195

RUBY LARK—12 ga., vent rib, heavy engraving, deluxe walnut.

	$635	$550	$475	$395	$350	$295	$260

MODEL AL-1—12 and 20 ga., semi-auto gas operated, 26, 28, and 30 in. plain barrel, various chokes, checkered pistol grip stock, made 1971-1973.

	$385	$360	$330	$305	$250	$195	$165

MODEL AL-2—12 and 20 ga., 26, 28, and 30 in. barrels, vent rib, various chokes, gas operated, checkered pistol grip stock, made 1968-1975.

	$330	$305	$275	$250	$220	$195	$165

MODEL AL-2 SKEET—same as AL-2, with 26 in. wide rib skeet bored barrel, made 1969-1975.

	$395	$360	$320	$275	$220	$200	$185

MODEL AL-2 TRAP—same as AL-2, with 30 in. full choke barrel, wide rib, Monte Carlo stock, with recoil pad, made 1969-1975.

	$375	$345	$315	$285	$250	$195	$165

MODEL AL-2 MAGNUM—12 ga., 28 and 30 in. mod. or full choke, 3 in. chambers, made 1973-1975.

	$415	$385	$330	$275	$250	$230	$210

MODEL AL-3—continuation of the AL-2 series, made 1975-1976.

Field grade	$395	$360	$330	$260	$240	$220	$190
Magnum grade	$425	$385	$330	$275	$250	$230	$210
Skeet grade	$400	$360	$330	$260	$240	$220	$190
Trap grade	$385	$350	$295	$250	$225	$210	$185

MODEL AL-3 DELUXE TRAP—same as AL-3, with fully engraved receiver, premium grade wood, made 1975-1976.

	$770	$715	$660	$605	$550	$495	$440

MODEL 301—continuation of the AL-3 series, scroll engraved receiver, made 1977-1982.

Field grade	$395	$360	$330	$260	$240	$220	$190
Magnum grade	$425	$385	$330	$275	$250	$230	$210
Skeet grade	$400	$360	$330	$260	$240	$220	$190
Trap grade	$385	$350	$295	$250	$225	$210	$185

MODEL 301 SLUG GUN—22 in. barrel, with sights. Discontinued.

	$395	$360	$330	$305	$265	$230	$190

SHOTGUNS: SEMI-AUTO, RECENT MANUFACTURE

MODEL 1200 FIELD—12 ga., inertia recoil system, 28 in. VR barrels with multi-chokes, checkered European walnut stock and forearm (pre-1989), matte black polymer stock and forearm (starting in 1989), recoil pad, 4 shot mag., approx. 8 lbs., importation began in 1984.

Mfg.'s Sug. Retail	$580	$475	$415	$350	$295	$250	$225	$200

Grading	100%	98%	95%	90%	80%	70%	60%

Model 1200 Magnum—12 ga., 3 in. chamber, 28 in. VR barrel with multi-chokes (2), matte black polymer stock and forearm. New in 1989.

Mfg.'s Sug. Retail	$580	$475	$435	$365	$310	$260	$230	$200

Model 1200 Riot—12 ga. only, 20 in. cyl. bore barrel with iron sights, extended mag. New in 1989.

Mfg.'s Sug. Retail	$580	$475	$415	$350	$295	$250	$225	$200

MODEL 302—12 and 20 ga.'s, self-compensating gas operation semi-auto, designed for both 2¾ and 3 in. shells, available with interchangeable chokes, slug barrel, trap and skeet models(disc.), VR, mag. cut-off. Made 1982-1987. This model was superseded by the Model 303.

	$395	$365	$340	$310	$280	$255	$225

Add $30 for multi-choke set.

Last Mfg.'s Sug. Retail was $480.

Model 302 Super Lusso—same specifications as Model A302, but includes hand engraved receiver, many gold plated parts, and stock and forearm made from presentation grade walnut. Disc. in 1986.

	$2,150	$1,950	$1,750	$1,550	$1,300	$1,050	$895

Last Mfg.'s Sug. Retail was $2,500.

MODEL A-303—12 and 20 ga.'s, 2¾ or 3 in. chambers, same gas operation as the Model 302, 26, 28, 30, or 32 in. VR barrel, high-strength alloy receiver, select wood with beavertail forearm, multi-chokes became standard in 1987.

Mfg.'s Sug. Retail	$653	$525	$425	$375	$335	$300	$270	$240

Subtract $60 without multi-chokes.

Model A-303 Upland—12 ga. only, 24 in. VR barrel with multi-chokes, English style stock. New in 1989.

Mfg.'s Sug. Retail	$680	$550	$450	$395	$350	$300	$270	$240

Model A-303 Sporting—12 ga. only, 2¾ in. chambers, sporting clay dimensions, 28 in. VR barrel with multi-chokes. New in 1988.

Mfg.'s Sug. Retail	$733	$575	$475	$425	$365	$310	$280	$250

Model A-303 Skeet—12 or 20 ga., 26 in. VR barrel with fixed skeet choking.

Mfg.'s Sug. Retail	$673	$540	$440	$375	$335	$300	$270	$240

Model A-303 Trap—12 ga. only, 30 or 32 in. VR barrel with fixed choking or multi-chokes.

Mfg.'s Sug. Retail	$673	$540	$370	$330	$300	$270	$240	$225

Add $54 for multi-chokes (with Monte Carlo stock).

Model A-303 Slug—12 or 20 ga., 3 in. chamber (12 ga. only), 22 in. cylinder bore barrel, iron sights.

Mfg.'s Sug. Retail	$680	$550	$425	$360	$325	$295	$265	$240

Model A-303 Youth—20 ga. only, 3 in. chamber, 24 in. VR barrel with multi-chokes. New in 1988.

Mfg.'s Sug. Retail	$733	$585	$425	$375	$330	$300	$270	$240

COMMEMORATIVES

MODEL A-303 DUCKS UNLIMITED—12 or 20 ga., D.U. serialization, 5,500 mfg. in 12 ga. 1986-87, 3,500 mfg. in 20 ga. 1987-88.

12 ga.	$575	$450	$350
20 ga.	$675	$475	$375

These D.U. Models had no retail pricing from Beretta. Rather, they were auctioned off at D.U. dinners, and as a result, prices could vary substantially from region to region.

MODEL 687 O/U SHOTGUN TERCENTENNIAL—12 ga., comes with S.S.T. and ejectors. Limited production, only 300 manufactured.

	$3,400	$2,600	$2,300

MODEL 84 PISTOL TERCENTENNIAL—commemorative, only 300 manufactured. Fully engraved with gold inlays. Presentation case. Only 100 imported to U.S.

	$2,300	$1,750	$1,550

BERGMANN

MANUFACTURED IN GAGGENAU, GERMANY 1892-1944. RE-ESTABLISHED IN 1931
UNDER BERGMANN ERBEN.

PISTOLS: SEMI-AUTO

Prices established are for original guns with matching parts.

MODEL 1894 (ANTIQUE)—5mm or 8mm. Extremely rare. 5mm — add 50%.

$4,500	$3,750	$3,350	$2,860	$2,550	$2,200	$1,900	$1,600	$1,250	$995	$925	$850

MODEL 1896-NO. 2—5mm, smaller type frame.

$2,100	$1,900	$1,600	$1,300	$1,100	$895	$715	$660	$610	$565	$515	$450

MODEL 1896-NO. 3—6.5mm - 80mm barrel.

$2,200	$1,950	$1,650	$1,350	$1,125	$925	$750	$700	$665	$630	$600	$565

MODEL 1896-NO. 4—8mm, military contract.

$2,275	$2,000	$1,650	$1,350	$1,125	$925	$750	$700	$665	$630	$600	$565

MODEL 1897-NO. 5—7.8mm, commercial manufacture.

$2,600	$2,275	$2,000	$1,650	$1,350	$1,125	$925	$750	$700	$665	$630	$600

MODEL 2—.25 cal., small frame. Model 2A — add $100.

$300	$285	$260	$240	$215	$180	$160	$135	$115	$95	$80	$65

MODEL 3—.25 cal., small frame. Model 3A — add $100.

$300	$285	$260	$240	$215	$180	$160	$135	$115	$95	$80	$65

ERBEN—Models I, II, and Special, .25 Cal. except Special .32 Cal.

$335	$300	$285	$260	$240	$215	$180	$160	$135	$115	$95	$80

BERGMANN-BAYARD PISTOLS

Even though the below listed Bergmann-Bayard models were manufactured only by Anciens Etablissements Pieper of Herstal, Belgium these pistols are listed under this heading as they are most commonly referred to by this trademark designation.

MODEL 1908—9mm Bergmann, identified by a mounted knight on the left magazine housing and is without finger cuts at base of magazine housing.

$1,500	$1,250	$1,000	$750	$600	$500	$400	$360	$335	$310	$285	$260

Add 25% if backstrap is slotted for shoulder stock.
Add $2,500 for excellent original leather/wood shoulder stock.

MODEL 1910 STANDARD COMMERCIAL—9mm Bergmann, mechanically similar to Model 1908 except does not have finger cuts in bottom of magazine housing, circular grooves are present on each side of magazine base.

$1,100	$900	$700	$600	$500	$400	$350	$315	$280	$265	$245	$225

MODEL 1910 SPANISH CONTRACT—9mm Bergmann, total contract was for 3,000 pistols, can be identified from standard commercial pistols by the Spanish military acceptance stamp struck on the receiver.

$1,350	$1,100	$900	$750	$600	$450	$350	$315	$280	$265	$245	$225

MODEL 1910 DANISH GOVERNMENT CONTRACT—9mm Bergmann, Trolit grips were used for the original conversion, followed later by wood replacements, total contract was for 4,840 pistols with delivery made 1911-1914.

$1,250	$1,000	$850	$700	$575	$450	$350	$315	$280	$265	$245	$225

Deduct 20% if converted and overstamped M.1910/21.

This variation can be identified from the usual commercial pistols by the Danish proof mark on the left receiver side and Danish inventory number on right side of receiver.

MODEL 1910/21 TOJHUS—9mm Bergmann, these pistols are marked "Haerens Tojhus" and are numbered from 1-900, original grips were black Trolit, replacement grips are either all smooth or with checkered circles above and below grip screw.

$1,250	$1,000	$850	$700	$575	$450	$350	$315	$280	$265	$245	$225

This contract was manufactured by the Danish Royal Arsenal located in Copenhagen.

MODEL 1910/21 RUSTKAMMER—9mm Bergmann, pistols are marked "Haerens Rustkammer", and numbered 901-2204, grip replacements are the same as noted for Haerens Tojhus.

$1,100	$900	$700	$600	$500	$400	$350	$315	$280	$265	$245	$225

This contract was manufactured by the Danish Royal Arsenal located in Copenhagen.

BERNARDELLI, VINCENZO

MANUFACTURED SINCE 1721 IN BRESCIA, ITALY. PISTOLS AND SHOTGUNS/COMBO GUNS UNDER $1,500 ARE CURRENTLY IMPORTED BY MAGNUM RESEARCH, INC. LOCATED IN MINNEAPOLIS, MN. SHOTGUNS OVER $1,500 ARE CURRENTLY IMPORTED BY ASPEN OUTFITTING CO. LOCATED IN ASPEN, CO. LONG ARMS WERE PREVIOUSLY IMPORTED AND DISTRIBUTED IN THE U.S. BY QUALITY ARMS INC. LOCATED IN HOUSTON, TX, AND ARMES DE CHASSE LOCATED IN CHADDS FORD, PA.

PISTOLS: SEMI-AUTO, DISCONTINUED

VEST POCKET MODEL—.25 auto, 2⅛ in. barrel, fixed sights, blue, bakelite grips, made 1945-1948.

	100%	98%	95%	90%	80%	70%	60%
	$250	$195	$165	$140	$110	$90	$65

BABY SEMI-AUTO—.22 S or L, 2⅛ in. barrel, fixed sights, blue, bakelite grips, made 1949-1968.

	$250	$175	$150	$130	$100	$90	$80

SPORTER MODEL—.22 LR, 6, 8, and 10 in. barrels, target sights, blue, wood grips, made 1949-1968.

	$305	$275	$220	$165	$140	$110	$85

MODEL 60—.22 LR, .32 auto, .380 auto cal.'s, 3½ in. barrel, fixed sights, blue, bakelite grips, made 1959-present.

	$220	$195	$180	$165	$155	$135	$120

MODEL 68—.22 short and .22 LR cal.'s, vest pocket model, 6 shot, bakelite grips, 8½ oz.

	$140	$120	$110	$100	$90	$80	$70

PISTOLS: SEMI-AUTO, RECENT MFG.

Prices could differ from values shown below because of the fluctuating U.S. dollar.

MODEL 80—.22 LR and .380 auto cal.'s, 3½ in. barrel, adj. sights, blue, thumbrest plastic grips, imported 1968-1988.

	$185	$160	$150	$140	$130	$115	$100

Add $5 for .380 ACP.

Note: This model was produced to conform to import regulations of GCA 1968. Importation of this model was discontinued in 1988.

MODEL USA—.22 LR, .32 (disc.), and .380 cal.'s, semi-auto, single action, steel frame, chamber indicator, adj. sights, target bakelite grips, 7 shot (.380 ACP) or 10 shot (.22 LR) mag.

Mfg.'s Sug. Retail	$289	$265	$240	$220	$195	$175	$150	$130

This model has the same technical specifications as the Model 60.

MODEL AMR—.22 LR, .32 (disc.), and .380 cal.'s, similar action to USA Model except has 6 in. barrel and adj. rear sight.

Mfg.'s Sug. Retail	$309	$290	$245	$225	$195	$175	$150	$130

MODEL 90 SPORT TARGET—same as 80, only .32 ACP and .22 LR, with 6 in. barrel, imported 1968-1988.

	$210	$185	$170	$155	$140	$120	$110

Last Mfg.'s Sug. Retail was $245.

MODEL 69 TARGET—.22 LR, target semi-auto, single action, 5.9 in. heavy barrel, 10 shot mag., wrap-around checkered wooden grips, 38 oz.

Mfg.'s Sug. Retail	$459	$420	$360	$320	$285	$240	$200	$185

This model was previously designated Model 100.

MODEL 100 TARGET—.22 LR, 5.9 in. barrel, adj. sight, blue, checkered wood, thumbrest grips, cased, imported 1968-1988.

	$395	$325	$295	$260	$225	$190	$175

Last Mfg.'s Sug. Retail was $360.

Grading	100%	98%	95%	90%	80%	70%	60%

MODEL P010 TARGET—.22 LR, single action, 5.9 in. barrel, adj. sights and trigger, matte black finish, large anatomic walnut stippled grips with thumbrest, 10 shot mag., 40.5 oz. New in 1989.

Mfg.'s Sug. Retail	$519	$475	$395	$350	$320	$285	$260	$240

Add $59 for wooden case.

MODEL P018—7.65mm (disc. in 1988) or 9mm Luger, double action, semi-auto, steel construction, 4⅞ in. barrel, 36 oz., 16 shot mag., plastic (standard) or walnut checkered grips. Imported 1985-present.

Mfg.'s Sug. Retail	$499	$450	$385	$340	$300	$275	$250	$230

Add $40 for walnut grips.

Add $49 for carrying case w/combination lock (standard until 1989).

P018 COMPACT—similar to Model P018 except has 4 in. barrel and 14 shot mag., approx. 2 lbs. New in 1989.

Mfg.'s Sug. Retail	$519	$465	$395	$345	$300	$275	$250	$230

SHOTGUNS: SIDE-BY-SIDE, DISCONTINUED

MODEL 110—12 ga., trap or skeet model, separated barrels, high post rib.

	$2,000	$1,500	$1,300	$1,100	$1,000	$900	$800

MODEL 110 EXTRA—same as Model 110, except engraved.

	$3,021	$2,265	$1,970	$1,665	$1,510	$1,360	$1,210

S. UBERTO 1 GAMECOCK—12, 16, 20, and 28 ga.'s, 25¾ in. imp. cyl. and mod., 27½ in. full and mod., hammerless, boxlock, extractors, two triggers, English style stock, checkered.

	$853	$635	$605	$550	$495	$440	$415

Add 20% for ejectors.

SHOTGUNS: SIDE-BY-SIDE, CURRENT MFG.

Prices could differ from values shown below because of the fluctuating U.S. dollar.

Bernardelli shotguns are manufactured with straight grip, English-style stocks with pistol grip available as a special order. Importation of Bernardelli shotguns has been inconsistent in the past and current dealer inventories of older merchandise might be priced less than similar models currently imported.

Models 112E, S. Uberto 1, 190, 190MC, 190 Combination Gun, and the 220 are currently being imported by Magnum Research, Inc. located in Minneapolis, MN starting in 1989. The balance of the Bernardelli shotgun line is imported by Aspen Outfitting Co. located in Aspen, CO. Magnum Research imported models reflect 1989 pricing while the balance of currently manufactured shotguns imported by Aspen Outfitting Co. have 1988 retail prices that have gone up approximately 20% (1989 retail pricing was not forwarded to this writer by publication release).

BRESCIA HAMMER DOUBLE BARREL—12, 16, and 20 ga.'s, 25¾, 27½ and 29½ in. mod. and full, 12 ga., 25½ in. imp. cyl. and mod., sidelock, extractors, two triggers, straight English stock, splinter forearm, checkered.

Mfg.'s Sug. Retail	$1,838	$650	$550	$450	$425	$395	$375	$350

Sudden drop in values reflects desirability factor in today's marketplace.

ITALIA HAMMER DOUBLE BARREL—same as Brescia, except higher grade engraving and wood.

Mfg.'s Sug. Retail	$2,062	$995	$850	$735	$650	$600	$550	$475

Sudden drop in values reflects desirability factor in today's marketplace.

ITALIA EXTRA—hammer double, 12, 16, and 20 ga.'s. Top-of-the-line hammer model.

Mfg.'s Sug. Retail	$4,891	$2,750	$2,200	$1,650	$1,375	$1,050	$800	$600

Sudden drop in values reflects desirability factor in today's marketplace.

MODEL 112E—12 ga., Anson & Deeley action, light engraving.

Mfg.'s Sug. Retail	$1,092	$995	$850	$775	$695	$625	$550	$495

Grading	100%	98%	95%	90%	80%	70%	60%

S. UBERTO 1—12, 16, 20, and 28 ga.'s, Anson & Deeley action, Purdey locks, light engraving, case hardened receiver, double triggers, extractors.

Mfg.'s Sug. Retail	$1,173	$1,050	$900	$800	$700	$625	$550	$495

Add $75 for single trigger.

S. Uberto 1E—same as S. Uberto 1, except with ejectors.

Mfg.'s Sug. Retail	$1,632	$1,395	$1,075	$925	$850	$740	$650	$565

Add $75 for single trigger.

S. UBERTO 2—12, 16, 20, and 28 ga.'s, Anson & Deeley action, Purdey locks, light scroll engraving, silver finished receiver, double triggers, extractors.

Mfg.'s Sug. Retail	$1,594	$1,360	$1,075	$925	$820	$720	$650	$540

Add $75 for single trigger.

S. Uberto 2E—same as S. Uberto 2, except with ejectors.

Mfg.'s Sug. Retail	$1,679	$1,425	$1,095	$935	$860	$750	$665	$575

Add $75 for single trigger.

S. UBERTO F.S.—12, 16, 20, and 28 ga.'s, Purdey locks, relief engraved with hunting scenes on silver finished receiver, double triggers, extractors.

Mfg.'s Sug. Retail	$1,749	$1,455	$1,120	$945	$870	$760	$670	$580

Add $75 for single trigger.

S. Uberto F.S.E.—same as S. Uberto F.S., except with ejectors.

Mfg.'s Sug. Retail	$1,832	$1,495	$1,150	$970	$895	$780	$690	$595

Add $75 for single trigger.

ROMA 3—same as S. Uberto, double triggers, extractors, false sideplates, casehardened receiver.

Mfg.'s Sug. Retail	$1,628	$1,395	$1,075	$925	$850	$740	$650	$565

Add $75 for single trigger.

Roma 3E—same as Roma 3, except with ejectors.

Mfg.'s Sug. Retail	$1,713	$1,435	$1,110	$950	$865	$745	$655	$570

Add $75 for single trigger.

ROMA 4—more deluxe model than Roma 3, false sideplates, scroll engraved, silver finished receiver.

Mfg.'s Sug. Retail	$1,769	$1,475	$1,140	$955	$870	$750	$660	$575

Add $75 for single trigger.

Roma 4E—same as Roma 4, except with ejectors.

Mfg.'s Sug. Retail	$1,852	$1,495	$1,150	$970	$895	$780	$690	$595

Add $75 for single trigger.

ROMA 6—12, 16, 20, and 28 ga.'s, fully engraved sideplates, Purdey locks, silver finish receiver, single trigger, finely figured English walnut.

Mfg.'s Sug. Retail	$1,992	$1,560	$1,195	$1,000	$930	$800	$710	$620

Roma 6E—same as Roma 6, except with ejectors.

Mfg.'s Sug. Retail	$2,075	$1,600	$1,220	$1,015	$945	$810	$720	$630

ELIO—12 ga. only, lightweight, extractors, fine English style scroll engraving on silver finish receiver.

Mfg.'s Sug. Retail	$1,601	$1,375	$1,025	$880	$730	$675	$600	$540

Elio E—same as Elio, except with ejectors.

Mfg.'s Sug. Retail	$1,230	$1,050	$895	$745	$695	$610	$545	$450

SLUG GUN—12 ga. only, 23¾ in. barrels, Anson & Deeley action, Purdey locks, lightly engraved, silver finish receiver.

Mfg.'s Sug. Retail	$1,699	$1,420	$1,085	$920	$800	$715	$640	$560

SLUG DELUXE—12 ga. only, 23¾ in. barrels, sideplates, with extensive engraving featuring hunting scenes, cheekpiece, ejectors, silver finished receiver.

Mfg.'s Sug. Retail	$2,187	$1,855	$1,425	$1,225	$1,000	$895	$750	$650

HEMINGWAY—12 ga. only, boxlock action, coin finished receiver with game scene engraving, 23½ in. barrels, DT's, deluxe checkered walnut stock and forearm, 6¼ lbs.

Mfg.'s Sug. Retail	$1,838	$1,495	$1,150	$970	$895	$780	$690	$595

Add $75 for single trigger.

Grading	100%	98%	95%	90%	80%	70%	60%

120 COMBO—combination gun, 12 ga. over choice of 12 cal.'s, deluxe checkered walnut stock and forearm, iron sights, double triggers, vent recoil pad, coin washed receiver with light engraving.

Mfg.'s Sug. Retail	$2,411	$1,950	$1,585	$1,300	$1,050	$850	$760	$650

Add $130 for extra set of shotgun barrels.

LAS PALOMAS PIGEON—12 ga. live pigeon gun, single trigger, special dimensions for live pigeon shooting.

Mfg.'s Sug. Retail	$3,775	$3,200	$2,495	$2,200	$1,900	$1,750	$1,625	$1,500

HOLLAND V.B. LISCIO—12 ga. only, Holland type sidelocks, light engraving, silver finish receiver, single trigger, ejectors, select walnut.

Mfg.'s Sug. Retail	$6,000	$5,775	$4,800	$3,900	$3,350	$2,850	$2,450	$2,100

HOLLAND V.B. INCISO—12 ga. only, H&H sidelock action, Purdey locks, various barrel lengths, single trigger, ejectors, straight or pistol grip stock, 100% engraved on coin finished receiver.

Mfg.'s Sug. Retail	$6,995	$6,750	$5,650	$4,850	$4,200	$3,700	$3,300	$2,850

HOLLAND V.B. LUSSO—12 ga. only, H&H sidelock action, Purdey locks, various barrel lengths, single trigger, ejectors, straight or pistol grip stock, same features as Holland V.B. Inciso, only extra select wood and game scene engraving.

Mfg.'s Sug. Retail	$8,750	$7,950	$6,850	$5,950	$5,200	$4,500	$3,995	$3,550

HOLLAND V.B. EXTRA—20 ga. only, H&H style action, any barrel length and choke, double triggers, auto ejectors, straight or pistol grip stock, 100% engraved on coin finished receiver. Prices are completely dependent upon individual customer specifications.

Mfg.'s Sug. Retail	$15,500	$13,750	$9,995	$8,750	$7,500	$6,500	$5,250	$4,400

Older specimens (not custom ordered within the last 2 years) could have values considerably lower than those listed above.

HOLLAND V.B. GOLD—top-of-the-line model, made to individual order. Very limited production and ultra-rare.

Mfg.'s Sug. Retail	$34,500	$31,000	$22,000	$17,500	$13,000	$11,500	$10,000	$8,500

Older specimens (not custom ordered within the last 2 years) could have values considerably lower than those listed above.

SHOTGUNS: OVER & UNDER, CURRENT MANUFACTURE

MODEL 115—12 ga. only, inclined plane lockings, blued receiver, single trigger, ejectors.

Mfg.'s Sug. Retail	$1,915	$1,770	$1,425	$1,225	$1,000	$895	$750	$650

Model 115S—same as 115, except moderate engraving.

Mfg.'s Sug. Retail	$2,500	$2,175	$1,950	$1,745	$1,500	$1,250	$1,025	$950

Model 115L—same as 115S, except extensive scroll engraving on silver finish receiver.

Mfg.'s Sug. Retail	$3,170	$2,650	$2,400	$2,050	$1,750	$1,450	$1,200	$1,050

Model 115E—sideplate, boxlock action, ejector, bulino game scene engraving.

Mfg.'s Sug. Retail	$5,200	$4,800	$4,125	$3,750	$3,100	$2,650	$2,200	$1,850

MODEL 115 TRAP—12 ga. only, same specifications as Model 115, except trap dimensions.

Mfg.'s Sug. Retail	$2,160	$1,915	$1,770	$1,425	$1,225	$1,000	$895	$750

Model 115S Trap—same specifications as 115 Trap, except light engraving.

Mfg.'s Sug. Retail	$2,710	$2,375	$2,000	$1,500	$1,275	$1,040	$935	$850

Model 115E Trap—same specifications as 115S Trap, except with extensively engraved sideplates.

Mfg.'s Sug. Retail	$5,250	$4,750	$4,200	$3,675	$3,100	$2,800	$2,400	$1,950

MODEL 190—12 ga, SST, ejectors, engraved silver receiver, select checkered walnut stock and forearm. New in 1986.

Mfg.'s Sug. Retail	$1,053	$925	$800	$700	$600	$525	$475	$450

Model 190 MC—similar to Model 190 except has Monte Carlo stock. Importation began in 1989.

Mfg.'s Sug. Retail	$1,155	$1,000	$825	$700	$600	$525	$475	$450

Model 190 Special—12 ga. only, similar to Model 190, except has better walnut and engraving. New in 1988.

Mfg.'s Sug. Retail	$1,350	$1,275	$975	$895	$800	$700	$600	$525

Grading	100%	98%	95%	90%	80%	70%	60%

MODEL 190 COMBO GUN—combination rifle/shotgun chambered for 12, 16, or 20 ga. under .243, .30-06, or .308 cal., boxlock action, DT's. Importation began in 1989.

Mfg.'s Sug. Retail	$1,320	$1,250	$1,000	$895	$800	$700	$600	$525

MODEL 200 LIGHTWEIGHT—12 ga. only, silver gray finished receiver with game scene engraving. New in 1988.

Mfg.'s Sug. Retail	$1,150	$1,050	$875	$800	$700	$600	$525	$475

MODEL 220—12 ga. only, silver gray finished receiver with engraving. New in 1988.

Mfg.'s Sug. Retail	$1,213	$1,100	$975	$895	$800	$700	$600	$525

ORIONE—12 ga., double Purdey lock, vent rib, case hardened receiver, double triggers, extractors.

Mfg.'s Sug. Retail	$1,380	$1,150	$995	$850	$750	$640	$555	$495

ORIONE S—same as Orione, except ejectors, engraved nickel finish receiver.

Mfg.'s Sug. Retail	$1,425	$1,175	$1,025	$860	$760	$650	$560	$510

ORIONE L—same as Orione S, single trigger, finer engraving, English or pistol type select walnut stock.

Mfg.'s Sug. Retail	$1,550	$1,285	$1,125	$950	$840	$750	$650	$550

ORIONE E—top-of-the-line, deep relief engraving.

Mfg.'s Sug. Retail	$1,660	$1,375	$1,200	$1,020	$900	$820	$710	$650

SHOTGUNS: SEMI-AUTO

MODEL 9MM FLOBERT—9mm rimfire shot cartridge, 24.4 in. barrel, 3 shot mag., steel receiver, walnut stock and forearm with sling and swivels, 5 lbs. 3 oz.

Mfg.'s Sug. Retail	$225	$190	$160	$145	$130	$115	$105	$95

SHOTGUNS: FOLDING MODELS

SINGLE BARREL—12, 16, 20, 24, 28, 32 or .410 ga., gun folds in half. Current manufacture, but available in Europe only.

Mfg.'s Sug. Retail	$295	$245	$190	$175	$150	$135	$125	$115

DOUBLE BARREL—12 and 16 ga., gun folds in half, double triggers. Current manufacture, but available in Europe only.

Mfg.'s Sug. Retail	$675	$570	$430	$370	$315	$285	$260	$230

BERSA

CURRENTLY IMPORTED AND DISTRIBUTED EXCLUSIVELY BY EAGLE IMPORTS, INC., LOCATED IN OCEAN, NEW JERSEY. PREVIOUSLY IMPORTED AND DISTRIBUTED BEFORE 1988 BY ROCK ISLAND ARMORY LOCATED IN GENESEO, IL AND OUTDOOR SPORTS HEADQUARTERS, INC. LOCATED IN DAYTON, OH.

MODEL 223—.22 LR, single action semi-auto, 10 shot mag., 3½ in. barrel, squared off trigger guard, nylon grips, blued action. Importation disc. in 1988.

	$200	$170	$150	$125	$115	$105	$95

Last Mfg.'s Sug. Retail was $239.

MODEL 23—.22 LR, double action semi-auto, 10 shot mag., 3½ in. barrel, walnut grips, 24½ oz. New in 1988.

Mfg.'s Sug. Retail	$264	$220	$180	$150	$125	$115	$105	$95

Add $25 for satin nickel finish.

MODEL 224—similar to Model 223, except has 4 in. barrel. Imported in 1987-1988 only.

	$200	$170	$150	$125	$115	$105	$95

Last Mfg.'s Sug. Retail was $239.

MODEL 225—similar to Model 223, except has 5 in. barrel and 10 shot mag. Discontinued in 1986.

	$155	$135	$125	$115	$105	$95	$85

Last Mfg.'s Sug. Retail was $170.

Grading	100%	98%	95%	90%	80%	70%	60%

MODEL 226—similar to Model 225, except has 6 in. barrel. Importation disc. in 1988.

	100%	98%	95%	90%	80%	70%	60%
	$200	$170	$150	$125	$115	$105	$95

Last Mfg.'s Sug. Retail was $239.

MODEL 323—.32 ACP, single action semi-auto, 8 shot mag., thumbrest plastic grips, 25 oz. Discontinued in 1986.

	100%	98%	95%	90%	80%	70%	60%
	$105	$95	$85	$75	$65	$55	$45

Last Mfg.'s Sug. Retail was $125.

MODEL 383—.380 ACP, single action semi-auto, 3½ in. barrel, blued finish, nylon grips, 7 shot mag. Importation disc. in 1988.

	100%	98%	95%	90%	80%	70%	60%
	$170	$150	$135	$120	$105	$90	$75

Last Mfg.'s Sug. Retail was $188.

MODEL 383—.380 ACP, double action semi-auto, 3½ in. barrel, blued finish, custom wood grips, 7 shot mag. Importation disc. in 1988.

	100%	98%	95%	90%	80%	70%	60%
	$200	$170	$150	$125	$115	$105	$95

Last Mfg.'s Sug. Retail was $239.

MODEL 83—.380 ACP, double action semi-auto, 3½ in. barrel, blued finish, custom walnut grips, 7 shot mag., 24½ oz. New in 1988.

Mfg.'s Sug. Retail	$264	$220	$180	$150	$125	$115	$105	$95

Add $25 for satin nickel finish.

MODEL 85—.380 ACP, similar specifications to Model 83 except has 13 shot mag., 30½ oz. New in 1988.

Mfg.'s Sug. Retail	$349	$300	$270	$245	$220	$195	$170	$150

Add $17 for satin nickel finish.

BERTUZZI

MANUFACTURED IN BRESCIA, ITALY. IMPORTED AND DISTRIBUTED BY NEW ENGLAND ARMS CO. LOCATED IN KITTERY POINT, ME.

SHOTGUNS: S X S

MODEL ORIONE—12 ga., scalloped Anson & Deeley boxlock action, beavertail forearm, single trigger, auto ejector. This model is available on special order only — contact the distributor listed above for availability, prices, and options. Prices start at $3,500.

BEST QUALITY SIDELOCK—various gauges, best quality sidelock model with extensive engraving. Prices start at $7,500.

HAMMER GUN—all gauges, upper tang safety, double triggers, fine quality engraving. Prices start at $3,500 and approach $5,000 with ejectors and single trigger. The self-cocking mechanism is popular in this model and prices can vary between $6,500-$15,000.

SHOTGUNS: O/U

ZEUS—12 ga., sidelock, auto ejector, deluxe engraving, deluxe wood checkering, SST. This model is available on special order only — contact the distributor listed above for availability, prices, and options. Prices generally range from $8,500-$10,000.

ZEUS EXTRA LUSSO—12 ga., sidelock, auto ejector, deluxe wood, deluxe checkering and engraving, SST. This model is available on special order only — contact the distributor listed above for availability, prices, and options. Prices generally range from $10,000-$15,000.

BIGHORN RIFLE CO.

PREVIOUSLY MANUFACTURED IN OREM, UT.

BIGHORN RIFLE—Mauser action, choice of calibers, custom made bolt-action of high quality, interchangeable barrels (gun is supplied with 2 barrels), adj. trigger, deluxe walnut stock, many custom options. Made in 1984 only.

	100%	98%	95%	90%	80%	70%	60%
	$2,100	$1,800	$1,600	$1,400	$1,200	$1,000	$850

BIGHORN PISTOL—.22 LR, bolt action design, research is underway to gather more information concerning this model.

BINGHAM, LTD.

MANUFACTURED 1976-1985 IN NORCROSS, GA.

RIFLES

PPS 50—.22 LR only, blowback action, 50 round drum mag., standard model has Beechwood stock. Add $20 for deluxe model with walnut stock. Duramil model has chrome finish and walnut stock — add $30. Discontinued in 1985.

	$195	$160	$145	$135	$125	$110	$100

This model was styled after the Soviet WWII Model PPSH Sub Machine Gun.

Last Mfg.'s Sug. Retail was $230.

AK-22—.22 LR only, blowback action, styled after AK 47, 15 round mag. standard, 29 round mag. available. Standard model has Beechwood stock. Deluxe model has walnut stock — add $20. Discontinued in 1985.

	$195	$160	$145	$135	$125	$110	$100

Last Mfg.'s Sug. Retail was $230.

BANTAM—.22 LR and 22 Mag., bolt action single shot, 18½ in. barrel. Discontinued in 1985.

	$110	$90	$75	$65	$55	$45	$40

Last Mfg.'s Sug. Retail was $120.

FG-9—9mm only, blowback action, semi-auto assault carbine, 20½ in. barrel. New design for 1984. While advertised this model was never manufactured.

BITTNER

MANUFACTURED BY GUSTAV BITTNER LOCATED IN VIEPRTY, BOHEMIA, (AUSTRIA, HUNGARY).

Grading	80%	70%	60%	50%	40%	30%	20%	10%

BITTNER MODEL 1893—7.7mm Bittner cal., pistol with hand activated repeater mechanism, box magazine, checkered grips, limited manufacture in 1893 circa.

	$3,100	$2,600	$2,300	$2,000	$1,650	$1,325	$990	$750

BLASER

MANUFACTURED BY BLASER JAGDWAFFEN GmbH IN W. GERMANY. CURRENTLY IMPORTED AND DISTRIBUTED IN THE U.S. BY AUTUMN SALES INC. LOCATED IN FORT WORTH, TX.

Grading	100%	98%	95%	90%	80%	70%	60%

Prices could differ from values shown below because of the fluctuating U.S. dollar.

MODEL R-84—available in 14 cal.'s between .22-250 and .375 H&H, 23 or 24 in. barrel. short bolt action with 60 degree rotation, checkered walnut stock and forearm, approx. 7 lbs. Introduced in 1988.

Mfg.'s Sug. Retail	$1,595	$1,595	$1,295	$1,100	$1,000	$900	$825	$750

Add $50 for left-hand action.

Add $545 per interchangeable barrel.

Grading	100%	98%	95%	90%	80%	70%	60%

ULTIMATE BOLT ACTION—.22-250, .243, .25-06, .270, .308, .30-06, 7 x 57, 7 x 64, .264 Win. Mag., 7mm Rem. Mag., 300 Win. Mag., .338 Win. Mag., and .375 H&H cal.'s, unique bolt action design with 60 degree bolt throw, interchangeable barrel capability, 3 locking lugs, safety lever cocks and uncocks the firing pin spring, exposed hammer, aluminum receiver, 22 or 24 in. barrel, single set trigger, silver finished receiver has light engraving, select checkered walnut stock and forearm, 6¾ lbs. Extra interchangeable barrels are $545 each, extra bolt heads are $175 each. New in 1985.

Mfg.'s Sug. Retail	**$1,495**	**$1,495**	**$1,150**	**$975**	**$925**	**$825**	**$750**	**$675**

All models are available in left-hand version at no extra charge.

ULTIMATE: SPECIAL ORDER

All of the below listed models may be ordered with a butt stock cartridge trap — add $250-$500 depending on model. Special order guns require 3 to 9 months to hand fabricate.

Ultimate Deluxe—same as Ultimate, except better wood and game scene engraving.

Mfg.'s Sug. Retail	**$1,595**	**$1,595**	**$1,200**	**$1,000**	**$950**	**$850**	**$775**	**$700**

Ultimate Deluxe Carbine—.243 Win. and .308 Win. cal.'s only, 19½ in. barrel with full length forearm. New in 1986.

Mfg.'s Sug. Retail	**$1,800**	**$1,800**	**$1,400**	**$1,150**	**$1,000**	**$900**	**$825**	**$750**

Ultimate Super Deluxe—similar to Ultimate Deluxe, except features better wood and game scene engraving. New in 1986.

Mfg.'s Sug. Retail	**$4,030**	**$4,030**	**$3,300**	**$2,950**	**$2,600**	**$2,300**	**$2,100**	**$1,850**

Ultimate Exclusive—similar to Ultimate Super Deluxe, except features better wood and game scene engraving. New in 1986.

Mfg.'s Sug. Retail	**$5,655**	**$5,655**	**$4,750**	**$4,300**	**$2,975**	**$2,600**	**$2,275**	**$1,975**

Add $700 per interchangeable barrel.

Ultimate Super Exclusive—similar to Ultimate Exclusive, except features better wood and game scene engraving. New in 1986.

Mfg.'s Sug. Retail	**$8,905**	**$8,905**	**$7,700**	**$6,800**	**$5,900**	**$5,000**	**$4,500**	**$3,950**

Add $950 per interchangeable barrel.

Ultimate Royal—best quality Ultimate, featuring Bavarian cheekpiece and checkering/carving on stock and forearm, elaborate game scene engraving, gold plated hammer. New in 1986.

Mfg.'s Sug. Retail	**$11,500**	**$11,500**	**$9,000**	**$7,500**	**$6,750**	**$6,000**	**$5,375**	**$4,600**

Add $1,200 per interchangeable barrel.

MODEL K77 A SINGLE SHOT—available in 11 cal.'s between .22-250 and .300 Weatherby Mag., break open action, 23 or 24 in. barrel, 3 piece take down, upper tang safety, checkered walnut stock and forearm, engraved silver finished receiver, sling swivels, 5½ lbs. Importation began in 1988.

Mfg.'s Sug. Retail	**$2,280**	**$2,025**	**$1,700**	**$1,475**	**$1,300**	**$1,100**	**$925**	**$800**

Add $50 for Mag. calibers.
Add $730-$778 per interchangeable barrel.

BORCHARDT

MANUFACTURED IN GERMANY FROM 1894 - 1897

PISTOL: SEMI-AUTO

These prices are established with matching parts and original finish guns.

MODEL 1893—7.65mm, with accessories, cased. Subtract 40% if uncased.

Ludwig Loewe manufacture—serial numbered 1-1104.

	$9,995	**$7,950**	**$6,250**	**$4,995**	**$4,200**	**$3,750**	**$3,000**

DWM Manufacture—starting approx. 1895, serial numbered 1105-3000.

	$8,500	**$6,500**	**$5,250**	**$4,400**	**$4,000**	**$3,400**	**$2,850**

BOSS & COMPANY

MANUFACTURED IN LONDON, ENGLAND. 1832 TO DATE.

Boss is one of the world's finest shotguns. It has always been custom built to customer specifications. Less than 10,000 have been manufactured to date. We will list the basic models with approximate values, but should the opportunity for purchase or sale arise, competent appraisals should be secured.

SHOTGUNS

BOSS SIDE-BY-SIDE—all gauges, barrel lengths and chokes to specifications, bar-action sidelock, checkered stock, pistol or straight grip stock, standard with either double or non-selective single trigger.

	100%	98%	95%	90%	80%	70%	60%
	$15,000	$13,000	$12,000	$10,000	$9,000	$8,000	$7,000

    20 gauge — add 20%.
    28 gauge — add 40%.
    .410 gauge — add 60% + .
    SST — add $1,000. Patented "3 pull" system.
    Add 10% for opening assist.
    Add appropriate price ($500 on up) if properly cased.

BOSS O/U—all ga.'s, barrel lengths and chokes to specifications, shell-framed sidelock, auto ejectors, SST, stock to specifications.

	100%	98%	95%	90%	80%	70%	60%
	$19,000	$15,870	$13,800	$12,000	$10,300	$9,000	$7,800

    20 gauge — add 30%.
    28 gauge — add 65%.
    .410 gauge — add 75% + .
    SST — add $1,000. Patented "3 pull" system.
    Add 10% for opening assist.
    Add appropriate price ($500 on up) if properly cased.

Note: above values represent base gun only. Any additional engraving and/or special orders will add considerably to the above prices.

BOSWELL, CHARLES

PREVIOUSLY MANUFACTURED IN LONDON, ENGLAND. IN 1988 CHARLES BOSWELL WAS PURCHASED BY U.S. INTERESTS AND CAPE HORN OUTFITTERS LOCATED IN CHARLOTTE, NC HAS BEEN RETAINED TO SELL AND MANUFACTURE THE BOSWELL GUNS IN THE US. IN ADDITION TO AQUIRING THEIR ENTIRE INVENTORY OF ENGLISH MANUFACTURED FIREARMS, CAPE HORN OUTFITTERS ALSO INTENDS TO FABRICATE NEW SHOTGUNS AND DOUBLE RIFLES IN THE U.S. USING THE BEST MATERIALS INCLUDING ENGLISH LOCK MECHANISMS AND WILL RETAIN THE CHARLES BOSWELL CO. TRADEMARK. EVERY GUN WILL BE CUSTOM ORDERED TO AN INDIVIDUAL CLIENT'S REQUIREMENTS/SPECIFICATIONS. PREVIOUSLY IMPORTED BY SAXON ARMS, LTD., LOCATED IN CLEARWATER, FL.

SHOTGUNS: SIDE-BY-SIDE

Older guns will be marked Malin & Boswell while newer specimens will be marked Malin only.

BOXLOCK SXS—made to individual order, choice of game scene engraving, Anson & Deeley boxlock actions, select European hybrid walnut, double triggers, leather cased, currently mfg. While each shotgun is priced per individual special order, the below listed prices represent standard features and embellishments.

Best Quality
Mfg.'s Sug. Retail

	100%	98%	95%	90%	80%	70%	60%
	$8,500	$8,500	$6,500	$5,650	$4,800	$4,200	$3,750	$3,250

Deluxe Grade—game scene engraved.
Mfg.'s Sug. Retail

	100%	98%	95%	90%	80%	70%	60%
	$9,500	$9,500	$7,250	$6,000	$5,000	$4,400	$3,750	$3,250

    Add $1,500 for smaller gauges.

Grading	100%	98%	95%	90%	80%	70%	60%

SIDELOCK SXS—made to individual order, choice of game scene engraving, H&H sidelock action, select European hybrid walnut, double triggers, leather cased, currently mfg. While each shotgun is priced per individual special order, the below listed values represent standard features and embellishments.

Mfg.'s Sug. Retail	$17,500	$17,500	$15,000	$12,750	$10,000	$9,000	$8,500	$7,750

Add $4,000 for smaller gauges except .410 — add $5,000.

DOUBLE RIFLES

BOXLOCK SXS RIFLE—made to individual order, .300 Express, .375 H&H, and .458 Win. Mag. cal.'s, choice of game scene engraving, Anson & Deeley boxlock actions, select European hybrid walnut, double triggers, leather cased.

Mfg.'s Sug. Retail	$40,000	$40,000	$31,500	$25,000	$21,000	$17,500	$16,500	$15,000

.600 Nitro Express

Mfg.'s Sug. Retail	$50,000	$50,000	$38,500	$32,500	$28,000	$22,000	$20,000	$17,500

SIDELOCK SXS RIFLE—made to individual order, .300 Express, .375 H&H, and .458 Win. Mag. cal.'s, choice of game scene engraving, H&H sidelock action, select European hybrid walnut, double triggers, leather cased.

Mfg.'s Sug. Retail	$55,000	$55,000	$42,000	$35,000	$31,000	$25,000	$21,500	$18,750

.600 Nitro Express

Mfg.'s Sug. Retail	$65,000	$65,000	$49,500	$40,000	$37,500	$31,000	$27,000	$23,000

BREDA, ERNESTO

MANUFACTURED IN MILAN, ITALY. LIMITED IMPORTATION BY DIANA IMPORTS CO., LOCATED IN SAN FRANCISCO, CA.

SHOTGUNS: SEMI-AUTO

GOLD SERIES SEMI-AUTO—12 ga. semi-auto, 2¾ in., 25 and 27 in. barrels, gas operated. Current model has interchangeable choke tubes, vent rib is standard. $26 for choke tubes (each).

Antares Standard—all steel construction

Mfg.'s Sug. Retail	$495	$440	$375	$340	$310	$285	$260	$240

Argus—lightweight standard, weighs only 6.6 lbs.

Mfg.'s Sug. Retail	$510	$450	$380	$340	$310	$285	$260	$240

Aries—Magnum, 3 in. chambers, 7.9 lbs.

Mfg.'s Sug. Retail	$525	$460	$395	$350	$320	$295	$270	$250

STANDARD—12 ga., semi-auto, 2¾ in., 25 and 27 in. barrels, recoil operated, lightly engraved. Current model has interchangeable choke tubes. Add $35 for vent rib, $20 for choke tubes (each). Discontinued.

	$300	$275	$255	$230	$215	$200	$180

GRADE 1—12 ga., same as standard, except with fancier wood and engraving.

	$575	$530	$485	$440	$410	$380	$350

GRADE 2—12 ga., exceeds Grade 1 on embellishments.

	$685	$620	$560	$500	$460	$420	$375

GRADE 3—12 ga., top-of-the-line semi-auto.

	$850	$790	$700	$640	$590	$540	$480

MAGNUM MODEL—12 ga. only, chambered for 3 in. shells. Add $20 for vent rib.

	$470	$415	$380	$350	$315	$290	$265

ALTAIR SPECIAL—12 ga. semi-auto, 2¾ in., 25 and 27 in. barrels, gas operated, alloy construction. Current model has interchangeable choke tubes, vent rib is standard. $26 for choke tubes (each). Choice of blued or chromed receiver.

Mfg.'s Sug. Retail	$495	$440	$375	$340	$310	$285	$260	$240

SHOTGUNS: OVER AND UNDER

VEGA SPECIAL—12 ga. only, boxlock action, 26 and 28 in. barrels, single trigger, ejectors, blue only.

Mfg.'s Sug. Retail	$650	$575	$495	$460	$440	$400	$375	$350

Grading	100%	98%	95%	90%	80%	70%	60%

VEGA SPECIAL TRAP—12 ga. only, boxlock action, triggers and locks designed for competition shooting, 30 and 32 in. barrels, single trigger, ejectors, blue only.

Mfg.'s Sug. Retail	$1,114	$885	$820	$760	$720	$675	$635	$575

SIRIO STANDARD—12 ga. only, boxlock action, 26 and 28 in. barrels, single trigger, ejectors, blue only, action extensively engraved. Also available in skeet model (28 in. barrels).

Mfg.'s Sug. Retail	$2,225	$2,000	$1,850	$1,630	$1,480	$1,320	$1,200	$1,050

SHOTGUNS: SIDE-BY-SIDE

ANDROMEDA SPECIAL—12 ga. only, single trigger, ejectors, select checkered walnut, satin finish receiver with elaborate engraving.

Mfg.'s Sug. Retail	$685	$640	$550	$480	$420	$365	$300	$250

BREN

MANUFACTURED 1983-86 BY DORNAUS & DIXON ENT., INC., LOCATED IN HUNTINGTON BEACH, CA.

Note: the Bren 10 shoots a Norma factory loaded 10mm auto. cartridge. Ballistically, it is very close to a .41 Mag. Bren pistols also have unique power seal rifling, with five lands and grooves.

Since the discontinuance of the Bren pistol in 1986, collector interest has accelerated, driving prices up substantially. Some of this interest has been created by its appearance in both movies and television, much like the S & W Model 29 and Auto Mag exposure in the past. Values below reflect the current, short term interest in these models.

ORIGINAL BREN 10 MAGAZINES ARE CURRENTLY SELLING FOR $150-$175 IF NEW.

100% VALUES IN THIS SECTION ASSUME NIB CONDITION. SUBTRACT 10% WITHOUT BOX/MANUAL.

BREN 10 STANDARD MODEL—10mm only, semi-auto selective double action design, brushed satin finish, 5 in. barrel, 11 shot, stainless steel frame. Manufactured 1984-86.

$1,200 $995 $725

Last Mfg.'s Sug. Retail was $500.

BREN 10 POCKET MODEL—10mm only, semi-auto selective double action design, stainless frame, compact version of the full-size Bren 10, 4 in. barrel, 28 oz., 9 shot. Manufactured 1984-86.

$1,275 $1,000 $750

Last Mfg.'s Sug. Retail was $600.

BREN 10 MILITARY/POLICE MODEL—10mm only, identical to standard model, except has matte black finish. Manufactured 1984-86.

$1,250 $995 $725

Last Mfg.'s Sug. Retail was $550.

BREN 10 SPECIAL FORCES MODEL—10mm only, commercial version of the military pistol submitted to the U.S. gov't. Model D has dark finish. Model L has light finish. Discontinued in 1986.

$1,350 $1,075 $800

Last Mfg.'s Sug. Retail was $600.

BREN 10 DUAL-MASTER PRESENTATION MODEL—10mm and .45 ACP, supplied with extra slide and barrel to accommodate the .45 ACP, same Mag. for both cal.'s, extra fine finish, with wood presentation case. Discontinued in 1986.

$1,650 $1,255 $850

Last Mfg.'s Sug. Retail was $800.

Grading	100%	98%	95%	90%	80%	70%	60%

BREN 10 INITIAL COMMEMORATIVE—10mm only, 2,000 annnounced mfg.(exact amount unknown), 22Kt. gold plated detailing, laser engraved stocks, special presentation chest. Discontinued in 1986.

$2,750 $2,000 $1,600

Last Mfg.'s Sug. Retail was $2,000.

MARKSMAN MODEL—.45 ACP, 250 mfg. for a retail shop in Chicago called "The Marksman", action similar to Bren 10 Standard Model.

$1,100 $850 $600

BRETTON

MANUFACTURED IN SAINT-ETIENNE, FRANCE. DISTRIBUTED BY MANDALL SHOOTING SUPPLIES, LOCATED IN SCOTTSDALE, AZ AND QUALITY ARMS, INC., LOCATED IN HOUSTON, TX.

SHOTGUNS: OVER AND UNDER

Bretton also has introduced a Fair Play Model which has a pivot break open action similar to most O/U's. This model to date has had limited U.S. importation. All Bretton shotguns are extremely lightweight and well balaced because of their unique design (permitting total disasembly including barrels) and use of lightweight materials.

BABY STANDARD—12 and 20 ga. only, sliding breech action allows barrels to move straight forward, double triggers, side opening lever, blued action and barrels, recoil pad, checkered walnut stock and forearm.

Mfg.'s Sug. Retail	$795	$750	$625	$575	$475	$430	$395	$360

Available from Mandall Shooting Supply only.

DELUXE GRADE—12, 16, and 20 ga.'s, action same as Baby Standard, engraved coin finished receiver, deluxe checkered walnut stock and forearm, extremely lightweight, 4.8 lbs.

Mfg.'s Sug. Retail	$995	$895	$750	$675	$600	$550	$500	$460

Available from Quality Arms, Inc. only.

BRNO ARMS

MANUFACTURED IN BRNO & UHERSKI BROD, CZECHOSLOVAKIA. CURRENTLY IMPORTED AND DISTRIBUTED BY T.D.ARMS LOCATED IN NEW BALTIMORE, MI. PREVIOUSLY IMPORTED BY SAKI INTERNATIONAL LOCATED IN ROCKY RIVER, OH AND ON A LIMITED BASIS BY PRAGOTRADE HEADQUARTERED IN REXDALE, ONTARIO - CANADA.

PISTOLS

CZ-70—7.65mm, double-action, similar to Walther PP, 1 lb. 9 oz., 8 shot mag. Discontinued.

	$995	$895	$750	$625	$500	$400	$325

Very few of this model were imported.

CZ-75—9mm Parabellum, Poldi steel, selective double-action, thumb safety, 4¾ in. barrel, 35 oz., 15 shot mag. Available in either baked enamel finish, matted blue finish, or high polished blue finish.

Mfg.'s Sug. Retail	$699	$500	$395	$360	$335	$310	$285	$260

Walnut grips — add $35.

Earlier variations of this model (imported by Pragotrade from Canada) with high polish finish will sell in the $650-$950 + range as they are relatively rare and desireable compared to recent U.S. importation.

CZ-765—.32 ACP, double action, 8 shot, 25 oz., similar to CZ-70. Imported in 1986 only.

	$375	$335	$295	$270	$250	$220	$190

Last Mfg.'s Sug. Retail was $425.

Grading	100%	98%	95%	90%	80%	70%	60%

CZ-83—7.65mm (.32 ACP) or .380 ACP (new in 1986) cal.'s, modern design, 15 shot mag., mfg. began in 1985.

| | $595 | $540 | $475 | $415 | $350 | $295 | $250 |

This model has had very limited importation. 1986 retail was $415.

PAV—.22 LR, single shot, 9¾ in. barrel, all steel construction. Imported in 1986 only.

| | $95 | $85 | $75 | $65 | $60 | $55 | $50 |

Last Mfg.'s Sug. Retail was $105.

DRULOV 70—.22 cal., single shot. Add $30 for set trigger. Discontinued in 1986.

| | $105 | $95 | $85 | $75 | $70 | $65 | $60 |

Last Mfg.'s Sug. Retail was $115.

DRULOV 75—.22 cal., single shot with set trigger & micrometer sights. Also available in left-hand.

| *Mfg.'s Sug. Retail* | $345 | $300 | $250 | $215 | $185 | $155 | $140 | $120 |

DRULOV 78—.22 cal., similar to Drulov 75. Imported in 1986 only.

| | $275 | $240 | $200 | $175 | $150 | $130 | $110 |

Last Mfg.'s Sug. Retail was $180.

RIFLES: BOLT ACTION

HORNET SPORTER—miniature Mauser action, .22 Hornet, 23 in. barrel, 3-leaf express sight, double set trigger, checkered pistol grip stock, also called Z-B Mauser. Discontinued.

| | $875 | $700 | $600 | $470 | $385 | $305 | $220 |

MODEL 21H—6.5 x 57, 7 x 57, and 8 x 57 cal.'s, 20½ in. barrel, double set trigger, 2-leaf sight, checkered pistol grip stock. Discontinued.

| | $850 | $675 | $575 | $470 | $385 | $305 | $220 |

MODEL 22F—same as 21H, with full length stock. Discontinued.

| | $1,050 | $900 | $700 | $525 | $440 | $360 | $275 |

MODEL I—.22 LR, 22¾ in. barrel, 3-leaf sight, plain pistol grip stock. Discontinued.

| | $595 | $540 | $485 | $405 | $375 | $320 | $265 |

MODEL II—same as Model I, with checkered deluxe walnut stock. Discontinued.

| | $635 | $570 | $515 | $430 | $405 | $350 | $295 |

MODEL V—same as Model II.

| | $635 | $570 | $515 | $430 | $405 | $350 | $295 |

MODEL ZKM-452—.22 LR, bolt-action, 5 or 10 round mag., 25 in. barrel, 6 lbs. 10 oz., w/ beechwood stock. Importation discontinued in 1986.

| | $210 | $175 | $160 | $140 | $120 | $105 | $90 |

Last Mfg.'s Sug. Retail was $239.

MODEL ZKM-452D—same as ZKM-452 only with walnut Monte Carlo stock.

| *Mfg.'s Sug. Retail* | $399 | $350 | $295 | $260 | $230 | $195 | $170 | $150 |

ZKB 680 (FOX II)—.22 Hornet or .222 Rem. (discontinued) cal.'s, 23½ in. barrel, 5 shot mag., 5 lbs. 12 oz., set triggers.

| *Mfg.'s Sug. Retail* | $499 | $445 | $380 | $340 | $295 | $255 | $230 | $200 |

ZKK 600—.30-06, .270 Win., 7 x 57, 7 x 64mm cal.'s, improved Mauser type action, 23½ in. barrel. Add $20 for Monte Carlo stock.

| *Mfg.'s Sug. Retail* | $599 | $530 | $430 | $395 | $360 | $330 | $300 | $275 |

ZKK 601—.243 Win. and .308 Win. cal.'s, otherwise same as ZKK 600. Add $20 for Monte Carlo stock (standard for 1987).

| *Mfg.'s Sug. Retail* | $599 | $530 | $430 | $395 | $360 | $330 | $300 | $275 |

ZKK 602—.8 x 68mm, .375 H&H, .416 Rigby, and .458 Win. Mag. cal.'s, otherwise same as ZKK 600. Add $60 for Monte Carlo stock.

| *Mfg.'s Sug. Retail* | $689 | $575 | $475 | $425 | $375 | $340 | $310 | $280 |

Grading	100%	98%	95%	90%	80%	70%	60%

RIFLES: SEMI-AUTO

CZ-511—.22 LR, semi-auto, select walnut stock, adj. sights. Discontinued in 1986.

	$280	$250	$230	$215	$200	$190	$180

Last Mfg.'s Sug. Retail was $310.

MODEL 581—.22 LR, semi-auto, select walnut stock, adj. sights, 5 shot mag. Discontinued.

	$600	$540	$495	$440	$395	$350	$295

RIFLES: O/U

SUPER EXPRESS—O/U rifle, 71x 65R, 9.3 x 74R, .375 H&H, and .458 Win. Mag. cal.'s, sidelock action with Kersten breech crossbolt, engraved, about 9 lbs. Add $185 for 9.3 x 74R cal. Add $195 for .375 H&H and .458 Win. Mag. (discontinued) cal.'s.

Mfg.'s Sug. Retail	$3,900	$3,350	$2,875	$2,300	$1,875	$1,600	$1,375	$1,200

This model may be ordered with 6 different types of engraving options. They are: Grade I — add $2,060, Grade II — add $1,030, Grade III — add $1,545, Grade IV — add $1,030, Grade V — add $620, Grade VI — add $660.

SHOTGUNS/COMBINATIONS GUNS: O/U
ZH-SERIES

ZH series over and unders are unique in that they permit 8 different interchangeable barrels including rifle and shotgun sets, interrupter on double trigger, blued action, engraved, diamond checkered walnut. Add $25 for Monte Carlo stock, $45 for set triggers.

ZH-300—12 ga. only, double triggers with rear trigger doubling as single trigger. New in 1986.

Mfg.'s Sug. Retail	$599	$530	$430	$395	$360	$330	$300	$275

ZH-301—12 ga. field, 27½ in. barrels. Discontinued in 1986.

	$570	$505	$460	$435	$410	$390	$370

Last Mfg.'s Sug. Retail was $605.

ZH-302—12 ga., skeet model, 26 in. barrels. Discontinued in 1986.

	$575	$510	$465	$440	$415	$395	$375

Last Mfg.'s Sug. Retail was $615.

ZH-303—12 ga., trap model, 30 in. barrels. Discontinued in 1986.

	$575	$510	$465	$440	$415	$395	$375

Last Mfg.'s Sug. Retail was $615.

ZH-304—7 x 57R mm x 12 ga., combination rifle/shotgun. Discontinued in 1986.

	$640	$570	$500	$450	$410	$380	$350

Last Mfg.'s Sug. Retail was $685.

ZH-305—5.6 x 52R mm x 12 ga., combination rifle/shotgun. Discontinued.

	$685	$640	$585	$520	$460	$415	$360

ZH-306—5.6 x 50mm Mag. x 12 ga., combination rifle/shotgun. Discontinued.

	$685	$640	$585	$520	$460	$415	$360

ZH-321—16 ga. field, 27 in. barrels. Discontinued in 1986.

	$570	$505	$460	$435	$410	$390	$370

Last Mfg.'s Sug. Retail was $605.

ZH-324—7 x 57R mm x 16 ga., combination rifle/shotgun. Discontinued in 1986.

	$640	$570	$530	$495	$475	$450	$420

Last Mfg.'s Sug. Retail was $685.

300 COMBO SET—300 style engraving and features, equipped with 8 interchangeable barrels that include various O/U configurations including shotgun/shotgun and shotgun/rifle configurations in various ga.'s and cal.'s. New in 1986.

Mfg.'s Sug. Retail	$3,500	$3,000	$2,675	$2,150	$1,700	$1,500	$1,300	$1,100

500—12 ga. only, ejectors, field tubes, acid etched engraving. New in 1986.

Mfg.'s Sug. Retail	$629	$545	$450	$400	$365	$330	$300	$275

Grading	100%	98%	95%	90%	80%	70%	60%

Model 500 Combo Set—shotgun/rifle set comprised of 4 barrels including 12 ga. over barrels with choice of 5.6 x 52R, 7 x 57R, 7 x 65R mm's, or 12 ga. under barrels (in either field, skeet, or trap chokings), sling swivels, set trigger on rifle/shotgun combo, chemically engraved, about 7½ lbs. New in 1987.

Mfg.'s Sug. Retail	$2,169	$1,920	$1,625	$1,400	$1,200	$1,075	$950	$825

This model is available in limited quanitity.

CZ-581—12 ga., boxlock with Greener crossbolt, Poldi steel action, 28 in. barrels, vent rib, sel. ejectors, sling swivels. Add $30 for single trigger.

Mfg.'s Sug. Retail	$649	$525	$440	$400	$370	$355	$340	$320

CZ-584—12 ga. and 7 x 57R mm rifle/shotgun combination , .222 Rem. and .308 Win. cal.'s also available, 24½ in. barrels, ejectors. Discontinued in 1986.

	$920	$820	$750	$700	$650	$600	$550

Last Mfg.'s Sug. Retail was $999.

SUPER SERIES—available in 12 ga. field, skeet, and trap configuration as well as combination shotgun/rifle in 12 ga. x 7 x 57R or 7 x 65R cal.'s. Add $70 for single trigger or trap and skeet model. Add $700 for extra set of 12 ga. field barrels.

Mfg.'s Sug. Retail	$899	$800	$700	$640	$590	$550	$515	$475

A hand engraved model is also available at $2,000 retail.

Super Combo—3 barrel set including 12 ga., 7 x 57R mm, and 7 x 65R mm barrels. New in 1987.

Mfg.'s Sug. Retail	$2,169	$1,925	$1,640	$1,425	$1,250	$1,100	$1,000	$925

SHOTGUNS: SIDE-BY-SIDE

ZP-49—12 ga. only, ejectors, double triggers, true sidelock, Purdey-type top bolt, cocking indicators, walnut stock, swivels. Imported in 1986 only.

	$590	$520	$470	$430	$395	$365	$335

Last Mfg.'s Sug. Retail was $650.

ZP-149—similar to ZP-49, except plain receiver. Add $20 for engraving. New in 1986.

Mfg.'s Sug. Retail	$589	$535	$460	$420	$385	$350	$320	$290

ZP-349—12 ga. only, extractors, double triggers, true sidelock, Purdey-type top bolt, cocking indicators, walnut stock with cheekpiece, beavertail forearm, swivels, 7.3 lbs. Add $20 for engraving. Imported in 1986 only.

	$450	$390	$360	$325	$300	$270	$250

Last Mfg.'s Sug. Retail was $520.

BRONCO

ECHAVE Y ARIZMENDI, EIBAR, SPAIN.

MODEL 1918 POCKET AUTOMATIC—7.65mm, 6 shot, 2½ in. barrel, fixed sights, blue, hard rubber grips, made 1918-1925.

	$175	$150	$100	$80	$70	$60	$50

VEST POCKET AUTOMATIC—6.35mm, small frame. Discontinued.

	$160	$125	$110	$95	$80	$60	$40

BROWN PRECISION INC.

MANUFACTURER LOCATED IN LOS MOLINOS, CA.

Brown Precision Inc. manufactures primarily rifles using Remington or Winchester actions and restocks them using a combination of Kevlar and Graphite (wrinkle finish) to save weight. Stock colors are green, brown, gray, black, camo brown, camo grown, or camo gray.

Grading	100%	98%	95%	90%	80%	70%	60%

STANDARD HIGH COUNTRY BOLT ACTION RIFLE—Rem. Model 700 BDL action, .243, .25-06, .270, 7mm Mag., .308, and .30-06 cal.'s, 22 in. standard barrel, no sights, Kevlar stock, swivels and pad, made 1975 - present.

Mfg.'s Sug. Retail	$986	$940	$850	$700	$600	$525	$440	$400

Add $170 for desert camo stock w/22 in. factory recontoured barrel.

Add $660 for gray wrinkle camo stock, LH action, stainless barrel, and Leupold 2.5X scope.

Custom High Country—similar to High Country, except has ADL action and 20 in. stainless steel barrel and electroless nickel black wrinkle finish, 5 lbs. 11 oz.

Mfg.'s Sug. Retail	$1,059	$995	$900	$750	$650	$575	$500	$450

Add $113 for brown wrinkle camo stock and 24 in. factory barrel.

Add $840 for green wrinkle complete camo rifle w/4X Leupold compact scope.

Add $27 for left-hand action (700 BDL only).

MODEL 7 SUPER LIGHT—.243 cal., Model 7 action, 18 in. factory barrel, no sights, 5 lbs. 4 oz.

Mfg.'s Sug. Retail	$1,059	$995	$900	$750	$650	$575	$500	$450

LAW ENFORCEMENT SELECTIVE TARGET—.308 cal., Model 700 Varmint action with 20 in. factory barrel, O.D. green camouflage, with Conetrol rings, and Zeiss scope, 8 lbs. 14 oz.

Mfg.'s Sug. Retail	$1,059	$995	$900	$750	$650	$575	$500	$450

OPEN COUNTRY VARMINT RIFLE—uses Rem. VS hardware that is tuned and precision bedded. New in 1989.

Mfg.'s Sug. Retail	$1,086	$1,000	$900	$750	$650	$575	$500	$450

PRO-HUNTER—.375 H & H or .458 Win. Mag. cal., Model 7 ADL action, 20 or 22 in. stainless steel barrel, claw extractor conversion, dull electroless nickel, blue, or teflon finish, express sights, synthetic stock (four different colors), 6 lbs. 7 oz. New in 1988.

Mfg.'s Sug. Retail	$1,798	$1,798	$1,575	$1,425	$1,250	$1,100	$1,000	$925

Add $100 for left-hand action.

BROWN PRECISION WINCHESTER 70—.270 or .30-06 cal., 22 in. featherweight barrel, camo stock in four colors with black recoil pad, 6¼ lbs. New in 1989.

Mfg.'s Sug. Retail	$599	$599	$525	$465	$420	$385	$325	$300

Add $20 for 7mm Rem. Mag. (24 in. sporter barrel).

BLASER BOLT ACTION RIFLE—standard Camex Blaser cal.'s and action, fiberglass stock and nickel plated barrel.

Mfg.'s Sug. Retail	$1,395	$1,395	$1,150	$995	$875	$750	$675	$600

BROWNING ARMS

ESTABLISHED CIRCA 1880 IN OGDEN, UT. HEADQUARTERS (NOT MANUFACTURING) CURRENTLY LOCATED IN MORGAN, UT. MANUFACTURED BY F.N. IN HERSTAL AND LIEGE, BELGIUM: ALSO SINCE 1976 BY MIROKU IN JAPAN AND SALT LAKE CITY, UT.

The Browning section in this text has been arranged in the following order—PISTOLS, RIFLES, SHOTGUNS: SEMI-AUTO, SHOTGUNS: O/U, OTHER SHOTGUNS, LIMITED EDITIONS-COMMEMORATIVES.

The Browning firm, first known as J.M. Browning & Bro., was established in Ogden, Utah about 1880. Later known as Browning Brothers and Browning Arms Company (BAC), the firm actually manufactured only one gun — the Model 1878 Single Shot which was John M.'s first patent. Winchester bought the production and distribution rights to this gun in 1883, bringing it out as the Winchester M1885. From that time until 1900 Mr. Browning sold Winchester the exclusive rights to 31 rifles and 13 shotguns, of which Winchester produced only 7 rifles (M1885SS: the lever actions M1886, 1892, 1894 and 1895: and the slide action .22's M1890 and 1906) and 3 shotguns (M1887, M1893 and M1897). The other models were bought from Browning simply to keep them out of the hands of other arms makers.

Grading	100%	98%	95%	90%	80%	70%	60%

John M. Browning, perhaps the greatest firearms inventor the world has ever known, was directly responsible for an estimated 80 separate firearms that evolved from his 128 patents. During his most prolific period from 1894 to 1910, Browning sold the rights to his rifles, semi-auto pistols, shotguns and machine guns to Winchester, Remington, Colt's and Stevens in this country and to Fabrique Nationale for sale outside the U.S. Every Colt and FN semi-auto pistol is based on a Browning patent. In 1902 Browning broke off relations with Winchester when the company refused to negotiate a royalty arrangement for his new semi-auto shotgun(A-5). Browning took the prototype to FN where it became the most commercially successful of all his inventions. FN has produced 6 automatic pistols, 3 rifles and 2 shotguns designed by John M. Browning and is still a major producer of arms sold by Browning in the U.S. and by FN distributors world wide.

Our American military was armed for many years with Browning designed weaponry, not the least of which is the venerable "Old Slabside" 1911 Gov't Model .45 ACP. Today, the firm that bears the Browning name still stands at the forefront with the other makers of fine sporting weapons.

Note: Between 1966-1971 Browning used a salt-curing process to speed the drying time needed for their walnut stock blanks. Unfortunately, the salt would be released from the wood and oxidize the metal surface(s) after a period of time. These guns, including Safari and high grade rifles (including BAR's), superposed shotguns, and T-bolt models should be examined carefully around the edges of the wood for signs of freckling and rust. Discount guns that show evidence of salt corrosion 10-30%, depending on how bad rusting has occurred. Check screws and wood under buttplate as well.

Editor's Note: It is important to note the differences in values of Browning weapons manufactured in Belgium by F.N. and those made recently in Japan by Miroku. We feel that these values are somewhat higher because of collector interest in Browning guns made in Belgium and not as the result of any inferiority of the quality of Browning guns made anywhere else.

BROWNING SERIALIZATION

IN ADDITION TO THE BROWNING SERIALIZATION LISTED IN THE BACK OF THIS TEXT, THE FOLLOWING CODES WILL DETERMINE THE YEAR AND ORIGIN OF THOSE GUNS MADE FROM 1975 TO DATE. THE 2 LETTERS IN THE MIDDLE OF THE SERIAL NUMBER ARE THE CODE DESIGNATIONS FOR YEAR OF MANUFACTURE. THEY REPRESENT THE FOLLOWING: RV - 1975, RT - 1976, RR - 1977, RP - 1978, RN - 1979, PM - 1980, PZ - 1981, PY - 1982, PX - 1983, PW - 1984, PV - 1985, PT -1986, PR - 1987, PP - 1988, PN - 1989. SINCE MOST BROWNINGS USE A 3-DIGIT MODEL IDENTIFICATION CODE (APPEARING FIRST ON EUROPEAN OR U.S. MFG. GUNS AND LAST ON JAPANESE MFG.), BOTH WHERE AND WHEN THE SPECIMEN WAS MADE CAN EASILY BE DETERMINED (i.e. SER. NO. 611RP2785 WOULD BE A MODEL B-2000 MADE IN EITHER BELGIUM OR PORTUGAL IN 1978 WITH 2785 BEING THE SER. NO.— SER. NO. 1479PX368 INDICATIES A BSS 20 GA. MFG. IN JAPAN IN 1983 WITH SER. NO. 1479).

AS A FINAL NOTE: MOST POST-WAR BROWNINGS ARE COLLECTIBLE ONLY IF IN 95% OR BETTER CONDITION AS MOST MODELS HAVE RELATIVELY HIGH MFG. AND ARE NOT THAT OLD. CONDITION UNDER 95% IS NORMALLY VERY SHOOTABLE, BUT NOT AS COLLECTIBLE AND VALUES FOR 95% OR LESS CONDITION COULD BE LOWER THAN SHOWN IN SOME AREAS.

MOST 100% VALUES IN THIS SECTION ASSUME N.I.B. CONDITION. SUBTRACT 10% WITHOUT BOX/MANUAL. ALSO, ALL ADD ONS OR DEDUCTIONS IN THIS SECTION REFLECT RETAIL PRICING WITHOUT ANY DISCOUNTING.

PISTOLS: SEMI-AUTO, F.N. PRODUCTION UNLESS OTHERWISE NOTED

MODEL 1900-FN—7.65mm cal., first Belgium Browning, 4 in. barrel. Made 1899-1910. 724,500 manufactured.

	100%	98%	95%	90%	80%	70%	60%
	$325	$300	$275	$250	$225	$195	$150

Add 30% for early pistols with "pistol logo" grips.

Grading	100%	98%	95%	90%	80%	70%	60%

MODEL 1903-FN—9mm Browning Long cartridge, 5 in. barrel. Made 1903-1939. 58,400 produced.

	$450	$400	$350	$300	$260	$220	$180

This variation was also manufactured with a detachable shoulder stock — this accessory is rare and can add as much as 400% to values listed above.

MODEL 1903-SWEDISH CONTRACT—9mm cal., manufactured by Husqvarna and Swedish Arsenal (so marked), many were imported into U.S. and converted to .380 ACP from original Browning 9mm Long. Deduct 25% for .380 ACP conversion.

	$300	$260	$230	$200	$180	$150	$125

MODEL 1905-FN (VEST POCKET)—6.35mm (.25 ACP), dubbed "Vest Pocket" model, manufactured by Fabrique Nationale, Herstal, Belgium. Made 1906-1959. 1,086,133 produced. Nickel finish — add 10%.

First Variation—no slide lock/safety lever.

	$375	$325	$300	$280	$225	$195	$150

Add 10% for nickel finish.

Second Variation—post 1908, with slide lock/safety lever.

	$325	$300	$275	$250	$225	$195	$150

Add 10% for nickel finish.

MODEL 1910-FN—7.65mm (.32 ACP) and Browning 9mm short (.380 ACP) 4 in. barrel. FN manufacture. Made 1912-1980. 701,266 produced. Add 25% for Browning import .32 ACP.

	$325	$300	$275	$250	$225	$195	$150

Add 20% if BAC marked and .380 ACP.
Add 30% for BAC marked and 7.65 mm.

BAC marked pistols were imported 1954-1968.

MODEL 1922 OR 10/22 FN—7.65mm or .380 ACP cal.'s, modified Model 1910 with 4½ in. barrel, longer grip frame and mag., made for commercial sale as well as military contracts. Several hundred thousand made by Nazis during the occupation of Liege, Belgium 1940-1944. Manufactured between 1912-1959.

	$240	$215	$195	$175	$150	$125	$110

Add 10% for .380 ACP or Waffenampt proofing.
Add 20% for foreign contracts.

The Model 10/22 and M1922 are the same pistol. The Model 1910 was modified by FN technicians for sale to Serbian arm forces in 1923. Also sold to France, Holland, Yugoslavia, and other countries. Also made by the German military 1940-1944.

FN "BABY" MODEL—6.35mm (.25 ACP) cal., lighter, smaller modification of Browning Model 1905 Vest Pocket .25, has no grip safety or slide lock, imported under BAC trademark from 1954-1970 in standard blue finish, lightweight nickel and engraved Renaissance models, manufactured 1931-1983. Total production is over 510,000.

FN Marked—slide marked Fabrique Nationale, blued finish standard.

	$395	$350	$310	$280	$245	$225	$200

BAC Marked—slide marked Browning Arms Co., blued finish standard.

	$300	$265	$225	$195	$180	$165	$150

Lightweight model—nickel frame, with pearl grips.

	$395	$350	$310	$280	$245	$225	$200

Renaissance model—engraved, satin grey finish.

	$875	$760	$600

FN/BROWNING MODEL 10/71—4½ in. barrel, modified version of Model 1922 (10/22) in .380 ACP cal. with target sights and grips in addition to incorporating a magazine finger tip extension designed to comply with GCA of 1968. Sold in U.S. by BAC 1970-1974 as the "Standard .380", still manufactured by FN as Model 125.

	$375	$295	$250	$220	$205	$190	$160

This model is also referred to as the Model 1955.

Renaissance or Gold Line model

	$995	$850	$775

Grading	100%	98%	95%	90%	80%	70%	60%

MODEL 1935 HI-POWER—9mm, 13 shot mag. 4⅝ in. barrel, Browning's last pistol design, millions made 1927 to date in variations for commercial, military, and police use in over 68 countries, first imported under BAC trademark in 1954.

Please refer to the Fabrique Nationale section of this book for pre-1954 variations (including WWII and earlier commercial models).

HI-POWER: POST-1954 MFG.—9mm, same as FN model 1935, has BAC slide marking, 13 shot mag., 4⅝ in. barrel, polished blue finish, checkered walnut stocks, fixed sights, molded grips were introduced in 1986. Made 1954-present.

Fixed sights

Mfg.'s Sug. Retail	$473	$425	$360	$325	$300	$280	$260	$240

Subtract $20 for molded grips.

This model has been produced with both a spur (discontinued) or round (current mfg.) hammer configuration. The round cone hammer variation is more desireable but does not necessarily command a higher value.

Adj. sights

Mfg.'s Sug. Retail	$518	$465	$390	$350	$325	$300	$280	$255

Matte Blue—non-glare matte finish, ambidextrous safety, fixed sights only. New in 1985.

Mfg.'s Sug. Retail	$437	$395	$335	$300	$280	$260	$240	$225

Nickel/Silver Chrome finish—discontinued in 1985.

$485	$430	$405	$380	$360	$340	$315

Last Mfg.'s Sug. Retail was $525.

.30 Luger Hi-Power—.30 Luger cal., mfg. for European sales in 1986-87 (most are marked F.N. on slide), approximately 1,500 imported in late 1986-89, similar specifications as 9mm model.

$435	$385	$345	$295	$265	$225	$200

A few specimens have been noted with B.A.C. slide markings and are more desirable than F.N. marked pistols.

GP Competition—9mm, competition model with 6 in. barrel, detent adj. rear sight, rubber wrap-around grips, front counterweight, improved barrel bushing, decreased trigger pull, approx. 36½ oz.

$625	$550	$475	$425	$395	$350	$325

The original GP Competition came in a black plastic case w/accesories and are more desirable than later imported specimens which were computer serial numbered and came in a styrafoam box. Above prices are for older models — deduct 10% if newer model (computer serial numbered).

Tangent rear sight model—manufactured from 1965-1978. Adj. rear sight to 500 meters. A total of approximately 7,000 were imported by Browning Arms Co. A variation with grip strap slotted to accommodate a shoulder stock was also available from Browning on special order; approx. 250 were imported. This variation will command a premium; beware of fakes, however (carefully examine slot milling).

$700	$600	$525	$440	$400	$370	$340

Add $150 for original slotted rear grip strap.

This variation is worth a slight premium if with "T" ser. no. prefix (mfg. 1964-1969).

BCA EDITION HI-POWER—limited edition made specifically for the Browning Collectors Association.

$700	$500	$400

RENAISSANCE HI-POWER—extensive scroll engraving on gray silver receiver, synthetic pearl grips, gold plated trigger. Discontinued in 1980. Add 5% for adj. sights.

Round Hammer	$1,250	$900	$725
Spur Hammer/adj. sights	$1,050	$860	$700
Spur Hammer/fixed sights	$975	$825	$650

CASED RENAISSANCE SET—one each .25 auto, .380 auto, and Hi-Power Renaissance models in walnut case, made 1955-1969.

$3,400	$2,750	$2,100

Grading	100%	98%	95%	90%	80%	70%	60%

CENTENNIAL MODEL HI-POWER—same as fixed sight Hi-Power, chrome plated with inscription "Browning Centennial/1878-1978", engraved on side, cased, 3,500 produced in 1978. Issue price — $500.

	$600	$500	$425				

LOUIS XVI MODEL—9mm, engraved throughout in leaf scroll patterns, satin finish, checkered grips, walnut case. Discontinued in 1984. Add 5% for adj. sights.

	$1,000	$850	$750				

9 MM CLASSIC SERIES - PISTOL—9mm, Hi-Power action, less than 2,500 manufactured in Classic model and under 350 manufactured in Gold Classic. Both editions feature multiple engraved scenes, and a special silver grey finish, presentation grips, cased. Manufactured 1984-86.

	$850	$675	$495				

Last Mfg.'s Sug. Retail was $1,000.

Gold Classic—5 gold inlays, select walnut grips are both checkered and carved. Manufactured 1984-86.

	$1,800	$1,450	$1,150				

Last Mfg.'s Sug. Retail was $2,000.

HI-POWER DOUBLE ACTION—this model was first listed in the Browning catalog in 1985 but was never manufactured. The proposed 1985 retail price was $494.

BDA-380—.380 ACP, double action, 14 shot, $3^{13}/_{16}$ in. barrel, fixed sights, smooth walnut grips, 23 oz., introduced 1982-current production, manufactured by Beretta.

Mfg.'s Sug. Retail	$453	$350	$310	$265	$240	$220	$200	$180

Nickel finish

Mfg.'s Sug. Retail	$478	$380	$320	$275	$250	$225	$205	$185

BDA MODEL—9mm (9 shot) — 2,740 manufactured, .38 Super — 752 manufactured, .45 ACP (7 shot), manufactured from 1977-1979 by Sig-Sauer of W. Germany (same as Sig-Sauer 220).

	100%	98%	95%	90%	80%	70%	60%
9mm.	$495	$450	$400	$340	$300	$260	$220
.38 Super	$650	$575	$495	$450	$390	$350	$320
.45 ACP	$495	$440	$380	$320	$280	$260	$220

NOMAD MODEL—.22 LR, 10 shot, 4½ and 6¾ in. barrels, steel frame, adj. sights, blued finish, black plastic grips, made 1962-1974 by FN.

	$295	$250	$200	$180	$165	$150	$135

CHALLENGER MODEL—.22 LR, 10 shot, 4½ and 6¾ in. barrels, steel frame, adj. sights, checkered wrap-around walnut grips, gold plated trigger, made 1962-1975 by FN.

	$360	$285	$225	$195	$180	$165	$150

Renaissance—engraved satin nickel finish.

	$1,000	$795	$600				

Gold Line—blued finish, gold lining on perimeter of frame surfaces.

	$1,350	$1,100	$850				

CHALLENGER II—.22 cal., Salt Lake City mfg., 6¾ in. barrel, alloy frame, 38 oz., plastic impregnated hardwood grips. Made 1975-1982.

	$260	$180	$170	$145	$135	$120	$110

CHALLENGER III—.22 cal., Salt Lake City mfg., 5½ in. bull barrel, 35 oz., 11 shot, alloy frame, adj. sights, manufactured 1982-1985.

	$220	$190	$170	$145	$135	$120	$110

Last Mfg.'s Retail was $240.

CHALLENGER III SPORTER—same as Challenger III, except 6¾ in. round barrel, 29 oz., wide trigger. Manufactured 1982-85.

	$220	$190	$170	$145	$135	$120	$110

Last Mfg.'s Sug. Retail was $240.

BUCK MARK .22—.22 LR, 11 shot, 5½ in. bull barrel, composite grips with skipline checkering, adj. sights, matte blued finish. New in 1985.

Mfg.'s Sug. Retail	$208	$170	$150	$130	$120	$110	$100	$90

Grading	100%	98%	95%	90%	80%	70%	60%

Buck Mark Plus—similar to Buck Mark, except has uncheckered wooden grips. New in 1987.

Mfg.'s Sug. Retail	$253	$210	$170	$145	$135	$120	$110	$100

Buck Mark Silhouette—silhouette variation of the Buck Mark, 9⅞ in. bull barrel, hooded target sights, laminated wood stocks and forearm, matte blue, 53 oz. New in 1987.

Mfg.'s Sug. Retail	$353	$295	$255	$220	$195	$170	$150	$135

Buck Mark Varmint—same action as Buck Mark, 9⅞ in. bull barrel with ramp and full length scope base, laminated wood grips, optional detachable forearm, matte blue, 48 oz. New in 1987.

Mfg.'s Sug. Retail	$319	$255	$225	$195	$175	$155	$135	$120

MEDALIST TARGET MODEL—.22 LR, 6¾ in. barrel, vent rib, adj. target sights and barrel weights (3 supplied), blued finish, target walnut grips with thumbrest, dry-fire mechanism, 46 oz., cased, made 1962-1975 by FN.

	100%	98%	95%	90%	80%	70%	60%
	$575	$495	$440	$400	$375	$325	$300
Gold Line (407 mfg. in 1963)	$1,650	$1,200	$875				
Renaissance Model	$2,150	$1,850	$1,400				
BCA Edition Engraved (22 mfg.)	$2,350	$1,900	$1,400				
BCA Edition Non-engraved (38)	$1,250	$950	$600				

Note: without case and accessories — deduct 15%.

INTERNATIONAL MEDALIST—early model manufactured 1971 and 1974, 5.9 in. barrel, only 681 made with BAC markings and blued finish. Currently manufactured by FN in the parkerized international configuration.

	100%	98%	95%	90%	80%	70%	60%
	$595	$525	$460	$400	$350	$300	$275
Early Model	$650	$615	$550	$425	$360	$330	$280

RIFLES: SINGLE SHOT

MODEL 1878—.38 Long (rare), .40-72, and .45-70 cal.'s, J.M. Browning's first patent, fewer than 600 made by Browning Brothers in Ogden, Utah between 1878-1883, various stocks with and without pistol grips, full and half length, with or without ramrod, several receiver configurations, a very few were made in the deluxe model, seldom found in unused condition.

	100%	98%	95%	90%	80%	70%	60%
	$5,000	$4,250	$3,650	$3,075	$2,700	$2,300	$1,850

Add 10% for ramrod model with pistol grip and checkered stock.

MODEL 78—.22-250, 6mm, .243, .25-06, 7mm Mag., .30-06, and .45-70 cal.'s, 24 or 26 in. round or octagon barrel, lever activated falling block, no sights except .45-70, checkered walnut stock, approx. 24,000 made 1973-1982.

	100%	98%	95%	90%	80%	70%	60%
	$425	$350	$320	$295	$275	$265	$250
.45-70 cal.	$470	$375	$325	$300	$275	$265	$250

MODEL 1885—.22-250, .223R., .270 Win., .30-06, 7mm Rem. Mag., and .45-70 cal.'s, falling block action, sear safety, 28 in. octagonal barrel, adj. trigger, no sights, checkered walnut stock and forearm, gold trigger, 8¾ lbs. Introduced in 1985.

Mfg.'s Sug. Retail	$700	$550	$475	$400	$360	$330	$295	$275

Only very limited quanities of this model will be available initially.

RIFLES: SEMI-AUTO .22 LR

GRADES I - III—.22 LR or .22 short, takedown design, 11 shot (16 for .22 short) tube mag. in buttstock, 19¼ in. barrel in LR, 22¼ in. barrel in short (rare), checkered pistol grip stock, semi-beavertail forearm, stock has hole machined halfway to allow partial filling of tube mag., 4¾ lbs., adj. folding rear sight, grades differ in finish, amount of engraving, and grade of wood, made 1914-1976 by FN, 1976-present by Miroku in Japan.

Grade I — FN

	100%	98%	95%	90%	80%	70%	60%
	$375	$300	$250	$220	$165	$150	$140

Add 10-15% for "shorts only" or thumb wheel rear sight older models if in 95% or better condition.

FN Grade I's have a lightly engraved blued steel receiver, checkered walnut, blued trigger, and a variety of rear sights.

Grading	100%	98%	95%	90%	80%	70%	60%

Grade I — Miroku
Mfg.'s Sug. Retail — $329 / $260 / $220 / $190 / $165 / $150 / $135 / $115

Miroku manufactured .22's can be determined by year of manufacture in the following manner: RV suffix — 1975, RT — 1976, RR — 1977, RP — 1978, RN — 1979, PM — 1980, PZ — 1981, PY — 1982, PX — 1983, PW — 1984, PV — 1985, PT — 1986, PR — 1987, PP — 1988, PN — 1989.

Grade II — FN

$695 / $500 / $400 / $360 / $325 / $295 / $260

FN Grade II's have gray chromed receiver, deluxe wood with finer checkering, gold plated trigger, and engraving depicting two squirrels and two prairie dogs. Signed or unsigned by engraver.

Grade II — Miroku—discontinued in 1984.

$425 / $350 / $295 / $225 / $200 / $180 / $160

Grade III — FN

$1,300 / $975 / $855 / $825 / $770 / $715 / $605

FN Grade III's have coin finish or gray chromed receiver, extra deluxe walnut with skipline checkering, gold plated trigger, and more elaborate game scene engraving usually featuring a dog flushing ducks or upland game. Signed or unsigned by engraver. A few were also special ordered with blued finish and special engraving — these command an extra premium.

Grade III — Miroku—discontinued in 1983.

$750 / $650 / $540 / $495 / $450 / $400 / $360

Grade VI — Miroku—game scene engraved with gold inlays, choice of blued or grayed receiver, deluxe walnut. New in 1987.
Mfg.'s Sug. Retail — $675 / $575 / $485 / $400 / $360 / $325 / $295 / $260

BAR-22—.22 LR, 20¼ in. barrel, 15 shot tube mag., folding leaf sight, high polish alloy receiver, checkered pistol grip stock, 5 lbs. 13 oz., made 1977-1985 by Miroku.

$215 / $185 / $165 / $150 / $135 / $120 / $105

Last Mfg.'s Sug. Retail was $245.

BAR-22 GRADE II—engraved model of BAR-22 featuring game scenes on silver greyed alloy receiver, select French walnut. Discontinued in 1985.

$305 / $265 / $245 / $210 / $195 / $175 / $160

Last Mfg.'s Sug. Retail was $350.

RIFLES: BAR HIGH POWER

BROWNING PATENT 1900 HIGH POWER—.35 Rem. only, manufactured by FN from 1910-1931, only 4,913 made in standard and deluxe grades, similar to Remington Model 8 auto-loading rifle.

$650 / $575 / $495 / $440 / $385 / $340 / $300

Deluxe model—with checkered walnut stock and adj. sights on solid rib barrel.

$750 / $650 / $550 / $525 / $470 / $440 / $415

BAR AUTO RIFLE—.243, .270, .308, and .30-06 cal.'s available in standard model, Mag. cal.'s include 7mm Rem., 300 Win., and .338 Mag., gas operated, blued receiver, 22 or 24 (Mag. only) in. barrel, folding leaf sight, walnut stock. Grades differ in engraving, finish, and grade of wood, 7 lbs. 6 oz., made 1967-present.

Note: .338's were limited production, mostly seen in the deluxe grade 2 only. During the last year of .338 production, several were delivered in a grade 1 by FN. Although being rarer than the grade 2, it is not as desirable. The following prices are on the Portugese assembled guns, manufactured by FN, and are so stamped on the barrel.

Add 10% for FN manufactured BAR's.
Add 25% for .338 Win. Mag. cal.

Grade I—current manufacture, no engraving, blued finish.
Mfg.'s Sug. Retail — $595 / $510 / $440 / $395 / $350 / $325 / $300 / $280
Subtract $15 without sights.

Ordering this gun without sights became an option in 1988.

Grading	100%	98%	95%	90%	80%	70%	60%

Grade I Magnum—current manufacture, no engraving, with recoil pad, 8 lbs. 6 oz.

Mfg.'s Sug. Retail	$645	$555	$485	$425	$375	$350	$330	$310

Subtract $16 without sights.

Ordering this gun without sights became an option in 1988.

Grade II—blued receiver, engraved with big game heads, manufactured 1967-1974.

	$725	$625	$550	$525	$470	$440	$415

Grade II Magnum—magnum version of Grade II, manufactured 1967-1974.

	$795	$675	$595	$550	$510	$460	$430

Grade III—features elk and sheep game scenes etched on greyed steel receiver, select checkered stock and forearm. Discontinued in 1984.

	$895	$795	$660	$620	$580	$560	$540

Grade III Magnum—magnum version of Grade III. Discontinued in 1984.

	$925	$800	$700	$660	$620	$595	$580

Grade IV—engraved satin finish greyed receiver depicts big game animal scenes and trigger guard, carved boarders on checkering.

	$1,350	$1,150	$1,000	$900	$825	$750	$675

Last Mfg.'s Sug. Retail on this model was $1,670.

Grade IV Magnum—magnum version of Grade IV. Discontinued in 1984.

	$1,495	$1,225	$1,050	$950	$850	$775	$700

Last Mfg.'s Sug. Retail on this model was $1,720.

Grade V—more elaborate engraving than Grade IV, with gold inlays. Manufactured 1971-1974.

	$3,250	$2,600	$2,100	$1,750	$1,600	$1,450	$1,250

Grade V Magnum—magnum version of Grade V.

	$3,450	$2,800	$2,200	$1,900	$1,700	$1,595	$1,485

BAR NORTH AMERICAN DEER RIFLE ISSUE—.30-06 cal. only, BAR style action with silver grey finish and engraved action, 600 total production, walnut cased with accessories. Discontinued in 1983 but modest inventories remain at the factory.

Mfg.'s Sug. Retail	$3,550	$2,800	$2,200	$1,700

RIFLES: FAL

The following semi-auto FAL's were imported by BAC in limited numbers. Current production FAL's can be found under the Fabrique Nationale heading.

FAL G SERIES STANDARD—7.62mm, assault rifle, wood butt stock, wood or nylon forearm, milled receiver.

	$3,200	$2,850	$2,300	$1,950	$1,650	$1,350	$1,040

G Series Heavy Barrel—wood furniture, milled receiver with special bipod.

	$6,000	$5,250	$4,700	$4,160	$3,600	$3,100	$2,650

G Series Lightweight—lightweight variation of the FAL.

	$4,000	$3,500	$3,000	$2,500	$2,100	$1,875	$1,600

The Lightweight Model had the trigger frame, magazine, and return spring tube made out of aluminum.

Browning Arms Co. Import—milled receiver, wood or nylon furniture.

	$2,400	$2,000	$1,700	$1,550	$1,400	$1,275	$1,150

CAL Prototype—originally imported in 1980, prototype to the current FN FNC, at first declared illegal but later given amnesty, only 20 imported.

	$6,000	$5,250	$4,700	$4,160	$3,600	$3,100	$2,650

G series FAL's were imported between 1959-1962 by Browning Arms Co. This rifle was declared illegal by the GCA of 1968 and was exempted 5 years later. Total numbers exempted are: Standard model-1822, Heavy Barrel model-21, Paratrooper model-5.

Grading	100%	98%	95%	90%	80%	70%	60%

RIFLES: LEVER ACTION

BL-22 GRADE I—.22 S, L, and LR, 20 in. barrel, short throw lever, folding leaf sight, 5 lbs., exposed hammer, Western style stock and forearm, made 1970-present by Miroku.

Mfg.'s Sug. Retail	$287	$230	$200	$175	$150	$125	$110	$100

BL-22 Grade II—same general specifications as BL-22, except scroll engraved blue receiver and checkered select walnut.

Mfg.'s Sug. Retail	$327	$270	$230	$195	$165	$140	$125	$115

MODEL 65 LIMITED EDITION—.218 Bee, patterned after the Winchester Model 65, round tapered 24 in. barrel, open sights (hooded front), blued metal finish, 7 shot tube mag., uncheckered pistol grip stock and semi-beavertail forearm, metal buttplate, 6¾ lbs. 3,500 total mfg. for Grade I in 1989 only.

Grade I

Mfg.'s Sug. Retail	$550	$550	$465	$425

High Grade—grayed receiver (and lever) with scroll engraving and gold plated animals, gold plated trigger, deluxe checkered walnut stock and semi-beavertail forearm. 1,500 total mfg. in 1989.

Mfg.'s Sug. Retail	$850	$850	$775	$700

MODEL 71 CARBINE—.348 Win., reproduction of the Winchester Model 71 carbine, 20 in. barrel, open sights, 4 shot mag., 8 lbs. New in 1987.

Grade I—uncheckered satin finished walnut stock and forearm, 4,000 manufactured in 1986-87 only.

	$595	$475	$410	$365	$340	$320	$300

Last Mfg.'s Sug. Retail was $600.

High Grade—deluxe checkered walnut stock and forearm with high gloss finish, scroll engraved-gray receiver with gold inlays and trigger, 3,000 manufactured in 1986-87 only.

	$895	$735	$660

Last Mfg.'s Sug. Retail was $980.

MODEL 71 RIFLE—.348 Win. reproduction of the Winchester Model 71 rifle, 24 in. barrel, open sights, 4 shot mag., 8 lbs. 2 oz. Made in 1986-87 only.

Grade I—uncheckered satin finished walnut stock and forearm, 3,000 manufactured in 1986-87 only.

	$595	$475	$410	$365	$340	$320	$300

Last Mfg.'s Sug. Retail was $600.

High Grade—deluxe checkered walnut stock and forearm with high gloss finish, scroll engraved-gray receiver with gold inlays and trigger, 3,000 manufactured in 1986-87 only.

	$895	$735	$660

Last Mfg.'s Sug. Retail was $980.

MODEL 81 BLR—.22-250, .222R., .223R., .243, .257 Roberts, .308 Win., .358 Win., and 7mm-08 Rem. cal.'s, rotary bolt locking lugs, 20 in. barrel, 4 shot detachable mag., adj. sight, checkered stock, recoil pad, 1971 mfg. in Belgium, 1972-present by Miroku. No sights became an option in 1988.

Mfg.'s Sug. Retail	$473	$380	$325	$285	$250	$220	$195	$165

Add 15% + for Belgium mfg. (1971 only).
Subtract $15 without sights.

This model was also manufactured by TRW in Cleveland, OH for a very limited production in .243 and .308 cal.'s. While they are rare, they are not widely collected and premiums currently do not exist.

MODEL 1886 GRADE I—.45-70 Gov't. only, patterned after the Winchester Model 1886, blued receiver, 26 in. octagon barrel, full mag., crescent buttplate, open sights, 7,000 manufactured in 1986 only.

	$775	$600	$475

Last Mfg.'s Sug. Retail was $578.

Grading	100%	98%	95%	90%	80%	70%	60%

Model 1886 High Grade—same general specifications as Model 1886, except has checkered high grade walnut stock and forearm, greyed steel receiver, with game scene engraving including elk and American Bison, gold accenting with "1 of 3,000" engraved on top of barrel. 3,000 manufactured in 1986 only.

	$995	$800	$650				

Last Mfg.'s Sug. Retail was $935.

Model 1886 Montana Centennial—similar to Model 1886 High Grade, 2,000 manufactured in 1986 only to commemorate Montana Centennial.

	$925	$775	$625				

Last Mfg.'s Sug. Retail was $935.

B-92 CARBINE—.357 Mag. and .44 Rem. Mag. cal.'s, 20 in. barrel, patterned after the Winchester Model 92, 11 round mag. (tubular), blued finish. Discontinued in 1986.

	$290	$245	$225	$200	$175	$160	$150

Last Mfg.'s Sug. Retail was $342.

B-92 Centennial—.44 Mag., limited quantities.

	$395	$325	$275				

Last Mfg.'s Sug. Retail was $295.

MODEL 1895 GRADE I—.30/40 Krag or .30-06 cal. only, patterned after the Winchester Model 1895, blued receiver, 24 in. barrel, 4 round mag.(box type), select walnut, rear buckhorn sight, 8 lbs., made 1 year only — 1984.

	100%	98%	95%	90%	80%	70%	60%
.30/40 Krag	$550	$475	$375	$325	$300	$280	$260
.30-06	$650	$525	$400	$350	$325	$300	$280

Production totaled 6,000 in the .30-06 cal. and 2,000 in .30/40 Krag for this model.

Model 1895 High Grade—same general specifications as Model 1895, except gold plated game scenes on satin finish receiver, gold trigger, and finely checkered select French walnut.

	$995	$895	$795				

Production totaled 1,000 in the .30-06 cal. and 1,000 in .30/40 Krag for this model.

RIFLES: BOLT ACTION

A-BOLT HUNTER MODEL—.25-06, .270, .30-06, 7mm Mag., .300 and .338 Win. Mag. cal.'s, short action available in .22-250, 243 W., 257 Roberts, .284 Win. (new in 1989), 7mm-08 Rem., 308W, and .375 H&H (new in 1988) cal.'s, matte blue finish, 3 lug rotary bolt locking, 22 (short action only), 24 in. (disc. in 1987), or 26 in. barrel (new in 1988 — long action Mag. cal.'s only),60 degree bolt throw, adj. trigger, hidden detachable mag., no sights, checkered pistol grip. New in 1985 by Miroku.

Mfg.'s Sug. Retail	$455	$355	$320	$285	$265	$240	$225	$210

Add $58 for open sights.

Medallion Model—same A-Bolt specifications, except has rosewood pistol grip and forend caps, better walnut stock, and high lustre bluing, no sights.

Mfg.'s Sug. Retail	$528	$425	$365	$325	$290	$265	$250	$235

Add $23 for left-hand action.
Add $90 for .375 H&H cal. (open sights only).

Micro Medallion Model—.22-250, .243 Win., .257 Roberts, .308 Win., or 7mm-08 Rem. cal.'s, scaled down variation of the A-Bolt Hunter Model, 20 in. barrel, short action, 13⁵⁄₁₆ in. length of pull, 3 round mag., no sights. Introduced in 1988.

Mfg.'s Sug. Retail	$528	$425	$365	$325	$290	$265	$250	$235

Gold Medallion Model—.270 Win., .30-06, and 7mm Rem. Mag. cal.'s, similar to Medallion Model, except has extra select walnut stock with continental style cheekpiece, gold lettering and light engraving, no sights. New in 1988.

Mfg.'s Sug. Retail	$690	$580	$500	$425	$360	$330	$300	$265

Stainless Stalker—.270 Win., .30-06, and 7mm Rem. Mag. cal.'s, action and barrel are stainless steel, wood stock has painted weather resistant, dull finish, no sights. New in 1987.

Mfg.'s Sug. Retail	$579	$525	$415	$350				

Grading	100%	98%	95%	90%	80%	70%	60%

Camo Stalker—.270 Win., .30-06, and 7mm Rem. Mag. cal.'s, laminated black and green wood stock, matte finish on metal parts, no sights. New in 1987.

Mfg.'s Sug. Retail	$483	$400	$340	$310	$285	$250	$230	$215

Composite Stalker—.270 Win., .30-06, and 7mm Rem. Mag. cal.'s, CamoWood stock (various color wood laminations), matte non-glare metal finish. New in 1988.

Mfg.'s Sug. Retail	$455	$385	$320	$295	$270	$240	$225	$210

A-BOLT BIGHORN SHEEP ISSUE—.270 Win. only, 22 in. barrel, high grade walnut stock with gloss finish and skipline checkering, deep relief engraving on receiver barrel, floorplate, and trigger guard, two 24Kt. inlays depicting bighorn sheep. 600 manufactured in 1986-87 only.

	$1,000	$800	$625

Last Mfg.'s Sug. Retail was $1,365.

A-BOLT PRONGHORN ISSUE—.243 Win., presentation grade walnut with skipline checkering and pearl borders, receiver and barrel engraving, multiple gold inlays on receiver top and floor plate, 500 manufactured in 1987 only.

Mfg.'s Sug. Retail	$1,302	$995	$800	$625

A-BOLT GRADE I .22 LR/MAG.—.22 LR or .22 Mag. (new in 1989), 60 degree bolt throw, 22 in. barrel, checkered walnut stock and forearm, 5 shot mag., adj. trigger, available with or without open sights, 5 lbs. 9 oz. New in 1986.

.22 LR cal.

Mfg.'s Sug. Retail	$340	$270	$225	$190	$175	$160	$145	$130

Add $10 for open sights.

A 15 shot mag. is also available for this model at $15 retail.

.22 Win. Mag. cal.

Mfg.'s Sug. Retail	$390	$310	$255	$210	$190	$175	$160	$150

Add $10 for open sights.

GOLD MEDALLION .22 A-BOLT—similar to A-Bolt, except has high grade select walnut stock checkered 22 lines per inch, rosewood pistol and forend cap, high gloss finish, gold filled lettering and moderate engraving, solid recoil pad. New in 1988.

Mfg.'s Sug. Retail	$450	$385	$330	$295	$265	$240	$225	$210

MODEL BBR—.25-06, .270, .30-06, 7mm Mag., .300 and .338 Win. Mag. cal.'s, short action available in .22-250, 243 W., 257 Roberts, 7mm-08 Rem., and 308 Win. cal.'s, 24 in. barrel, 60 degree throw, fluted bolt, adj. trigger, hidden detachable mag., no sights, checkered pistol grip, Monte Carlo stock, made 1978-1984 by Miroku.

	$470	$360	$330	$305	$250	$220	$200

Some rare production calibers will add premiums to the values listed above (i.e., add 50% for .243 Win. cal.).

BBR LIGHTNING GOLD RIFLE ISSUE (ELK)—7mm Rem. Mag., bolt action rifle, 1,000 manufactured, deeply blued receiver which has multiple animals gold inlaid, high grade walnut stock and forearm feature skipline checkering. Discontinued in 1986.

	$1,195	$950	$795

Last Mfg.'s Sug. Retail was $1,395.

T-BOLT T-1—.22 LR, straight pull bolt-action, 5 shot mag., 22 in. barrel, adj. rear sight, 5½ lbs., plain pistol grip stock, made 1965-1974 by FN.

	$300	$255	$210	$180	$160	$140	$120

An aperture rear sight was standard for the first nine years of production.

T-BOLT T-2—same as T-1, only with select checkered walnut stock (lacquer finished), 24 in. barrel, 6 lbs.

	$395	$350	$295	$240	$200	$180	$160

Add $100 for aperture rear sight.

Late production T-2—features oil finished stock, plastic front sight, and Browning computerized serialization.

	$300	$255	$210	$180	$160	$140	$120

Grading	100%	98%	95%	90%	80%	70%	60%

HIGH-POWER BOLT ACTION MODEL—.222 R. (Sako action), .22-250 (Sako action), .243 Win., .257 Roberts, .264 Win. Mag., .270, .284 Win. (Sako action), .30-06, .308 Win., 7mm Mag., .300 Win. Mag., .308 Norma Mag., .300 H&H, .338 Mag., .375 H&H, and .458 Win. Mag. cal.'s, standard Mauser type action with either short or long (more desireable) extractor, 22 or 24 in. (heavy available) barrel, folding leaf sight (except on .222 R. and .22-250), checkered pistol grip stock, made 1959-1974 by FN.

The .243 and .308 Win. cal.'s were built on the small ring Mauser action prior to using the Sako medium action. The .222 Rem. Mag. was also furnished less the rear sight.

Note: Grades differ in engraving, finish, checkering, and grade of wood. It should be noted that the salt wood problem is more common in these high powered models. Guns should be checked carefully for rust below wood surfaces.

Safari Grade—basic model with blued finish.

	100%	98%	95%	90%	80%	70%	60%
Standard cal.'s	$795	$675	$550	$450	$400	$350	$325
Mag. cal.'s	$900	$750	$650	$595	$525	$450	$400
.257 Roberts	$1,295	$1,050	$825	$700	$600	$525	$450
.284 Win.	$1,550	$1,200	$950	$800	$700	$600	$500
.308 Norma Mag.	$1,350	$1,100	$850	$700	$600	$525	$450
.338 Win. Mag.	$1,050	$850	$735	$650	$595	$525	$450
.375 H&H	$1,200	$1,000	$800	$700	$600	$525	$450
.458 Win. Mag.	$1,195	$1,100	$900	$700	$600	$525	$450

Deduct 10%-15% for short extractor.
Add 20% for pencil barrel.

Between 1963 and 1974, Browning also offered short and medium barrelled actions in the Safari, Medallion and Olympian Grades. These models have Sako barrelled actions and were stocked by FN. Medium weight barrels could also be ordered.

Safari Grade - Short Sako Action—short action, .222 Rem. or .222 Rem. Mag. cal.

	100%	98%	95%	90%	80%	70%	60%
	$800	$675	$550	$450	$400	$350	$325

Safari Grade - Medium Sako Action—medium action, .22-250, .243, .284 or .308 cal.

	100%	98%	95%	90%	80%	70%	60%
	$800	$675	$550	$450	$400	$350	$325

Medallion Grade—features select figured walnut with skipline checkering, rosewood grip and forearm caps, blue/black lustre bluing, receiver and barrel portion scroll engraved, ram's head engraved on floor plate.

	100%	98%	95%	90%	80%	70%	60%
	$1,450	$1,195	$1,000	$925	$830	$700	$575

Add 10%-50% for rare calibers.
Add 20% for pencil barrel.
Add 15% for long extractor.

This model was also available with a Sako short or long action - cal.'s are the same as listed for the Sako Safari.

Olympian Grade—top-of-the-line model featuring highly figured walnut stock that is both checkered and carved. Receiver, floor plate, and trigger guard are chrome plated in a satin finish that have deep relief animal scenes engraved, as well as deep scroll work on other metal parts.

	100%	98%	95%	90%	80%	70%	60%
	$2,250	$2,000	$1,875	$1,700	$1,550	$1,350	$1,175

Add 10%-50% for rare calibers (.22-250 and .284 are the rarest).
Add 20% for pencil barrel.
Add 15% for long extractor.

This model was also available with a Sako short or long action - cal.'s are the same as listed for the Sako Safari.

RIFLES: SLIDE ACTION

BPR-22-MAGNUM—.22 Mag., short-stroke action, 20¼ in. barrel, 11 round tube mag., made 1977-1982.

	100%	98%	95%	90%	80%	70%	60%
	$270	$195	$170	$160	$140	$130	$100

BPR-22 Grade II—same as BPR-22, only engraved action, select walnut.

	100%	98%	95%	90%	80%	70%	60%
	$380	$295	$265	$250	$230	$200	$150

BROWNING ARMS, cont.

TROMBONE MODEL—.22 LR only, slide action with tube mag., fixed sights, takedown, 24 in. barrel, hammerless, similar to Win. Model 61, with either F.N. or U.S. (rare) barrel address.

FN Barrel Address

$550	$475	$395	$350	$295	$260	$225

BAC Barrel Markings

$650	$540	$460	$410	$345	$295	$250

Over 150,000 "Trombones" were made by FN from 1922-1974. About 3,200 were imported by BAC in late 1960's. Very rare with factory engraving.

BCA GRADE III FN TROMBONE—only 60 manufactured for the Browning Collectors Association in 1985-86, silver engraved frame with deluxe walnut.

$2,295	$1,995	$1,600

RIFLES: OVER AND UNDER

EXPRESS RIFLE—.270 Win. or .30-06 cal.'s, superposed style action. 24 in. barrels, auto ejectors, Fleur-de-lis engraving, single trigger, folding leaf rear sight, 6 lbs. 14 oz., cased. Discontinued in 1986.

$1,995	$1,750	$1,600	$1,475	$1,300	$1,100	$900

Last Mfg.'s Sug. Retail was $3,125.

SHOTGUNS: DISCONTINUED SEMI-AUTO

BROWNING CHOKES AND THEIR CODES (ON REAR LEFT-SIDE OF BARREL)

* designates full choke (F).

*- designates improved modified choke (IM).

** designates modified choke (M).

**- designates improved cylinder choke (IC).

**$ designates skeet (SK).

*** designates cylinder bore (CYL).

AUTO-5 STANDARD - 1903-1939 MANUFACTURE—12 or 16 ga.(introduced in U.S. in 1923), 26-32 in. barrel, recoil operated, various chokes, checkered pistol grip stock, made 1903-1939 by FN, grades differ in engraving, inlays, and grade of wood. Approx. ser. range 1-229,000 (12ga.), 1-128,000 (16 ga.).

	100%	98%	95%	90%	80%	70%	60%
Grade 1	$475	$425	$375	$325	$285	$250	$200
Solid matte rib	$575	$495	$425	$375	$325	$275	$250
With vent rib	$695	$500	$450	$400	$350	$300	$250
Grade 2.(disc.1940)	$1,250	$1,000	$875	$750	$625	$550	$495
Solid matte rib	$1,450	$1,150	$1,000	$875	$750	$625	$575
With vent rib	$1,625	$1,300	$1,200	$1,000	$850	$750	$650
Grade 3.(disc. 1940)	$2,500	$2,200	$1,975	$1,775	$1,500	$1,250	$995
Solid matte rib	$2,700	$2,400	$2,100	$1,850	$1,650	$1,375	$1,100
With vent rib	$2,950	$2,550	$2,250	$2,000	$1,775	$1,500	$1,225
Grade 4.(disc. 1940)	$3,995	$3,655	$3,300	$2,995	$2,550	$2,050	$1,600
Solid matte rib	$4,150	$3,885	$3,450	$3,175	$2,700	$2,200	$1,800
With vent rib	$4,350	$4,000	$3,650	$3,150	$2,750	$2,300	$1,975

Pre-WWII 16 ga. A-5's are chambered for 2$\frac{9}{16}$ in. shells. These shotguns are considerably less desirable than 16 ga. A-5's chambered for 2¾ in. modern shotshells. Since some guns have been modified to 2¾ in., careful inspection is advised before purchasing or shooting.

"AMERICAN BROWNING" AUTO-5—12, 16, and 20 ga.'s, Remington-produced model of the Auto 5, very similar to the Remington Model 11, except with Browning logo, mag. cut-off, and different engraving, over 45,000 manufactured in 12 ga., over 25,000 in 16 ga., and 20,000 in 20 ga., stocks have Remington style round knob pistol grips with black plastic caps. Manufactured 1940-1942 and ser. numbered approx. 229,000-346,000 (12 ga.) with "B" prefix.

$395	$345	$295	$225	$200	$185	$170

Add 10% for vent rib and/or 20 ga.

Grading	100%	98%	95%	90%	80%	70%	60%

AUTO-5 STANDARDWEIGHT—12 or 16 ga., recoil operation, 26-32 in. barrels, standard production gun between 1952-1969, various chokes, checkered walnut stock and forearm, synthetic Browning marked buttplate, lacquer (until approx. 1966) or polyurethane finish, buttstock has either round knob pistol grip (1952-1976) or flat knob (introduced in 1967), watch for cracked forearms on all A-5's (due to barrel recoil), between 7⅓-8 lbs.

Plain barrel	$435	$395	$360	$325	$295	$270	$240
Matted Rib	$475	$410	$370	$330	$300	$275	$245
Vent Rib	$525	$440	$395	$350	$315	$295	$260

Add 10% for N.I.B. condition.

Barrel addresses appeared as follows: 1952-1958 "St. Louis, Missouri", 1959-1968 "St. Louis, Missouri and Montreal P.Q.", 1969-1975 "Morgan, Utah and Montreal, P.Q.". Make sure barrel address circa matches year of mfg (see listings in the back of this text). Standardweight models had H or M prefixes.

SHOTGUNS: RECENT MANUFACTURE

NOTE: Barrels are not interchangeable between older Belgium models and recent shotguns manufactured by Miroku in Japan.

NOTE: The use of steel shot is recommended in those recent models manufactured in Japan - NOT in the older Belgium variations.

AUTO-5 LIGHTWEIGHT—12 and 20 ga.'s, recoil operated, 26, 28, and 30 in. barrels, various chokes, scroll engraved receiver, checkered pistol grip stock, approx. 10 oz. lighter than Standardweight, made 1952-1976 by FN, made 1976-present by Miroku in Japan. Over 2,750,000 A-5's were manufactured by FN in all configurations between 1902-1976.

FN model	$450	$400	$375	$325	$295	$270	$240
FN-vent rib	$550	$460	$410	$370	$330	$295	$260

Add 10% for N.I.B. condition.

Light 12 Miroku—12 ga. only, now standard with vent rib (1986).

Mfg.'s Sug. Retail	$685	$555	$435	$400	$350	$300	$280	$260

Subtract $40 without Invector chokes.

Light 20 Miroku—20 ga. only, 2¾ in. chamber, similar to original Belgium Light 20, VR, Invector choke standard. New in 1987.

Mfg.'s Sug. Retail	$685	$555	$445	$420	$380	$340	$300	$270

AUTO-5 MAGNUM—12 and 20 ga.'s, 3 in. chamber, 26, 28, 30, and 32 in. barrels, various chokes, vent rib, similar to Standard, made 1958-1976 by FN, made 1976-present by Miroku.

FN model.	$550	$450	$400	$350	$320	$260	$240
FN, vent rib.	$650	$575	$525	$480	$430	$340	$315

Add 10% for N.I.B. condition.
Add 15% for 20 ga. with VR if NIB.

Between 1976-1985 approx. 2,000 Belgian 12 ga. A-5 Mag.'s were imported into the U.S. These late models can be differentiated by serialization — also, slight premiums may be asked. The 20 ga. Mag. was not introduced until 1967.

A-5 Mag. Miroku—12 or 20 ga., VR barrel.

Mfg.'s Sug. Retail	$707	$595	$490	$425	$385	$350	$325	$290

Subtract $40 without Invector chokes.

AUTO-5 BUCK SPECIAL—same as Standard only with 24 in. barrel, slug bore, adj. sight, made 1958-1976 by FN, made 1976-1984 and 1989 again by Miroku. Between 1985-1988, Buck Special barrels were available at extra cost.

FN model	$550	$460	$410	$370	$330	$295	$240

Miroku model

Mfg.'s Sug. Retail	$685	$555	$445	$395	$360	$320	$290	$240

Add $22 for Buck Special on 3 in. Mag. receiver.

Grading	100%	98%	95%	90%	80%	70%	60%

AUTO-5 SKEET—same as Standard Light only with 26 or 28 in. skeet bored, vent rib barrel, pre-1976 by FN, 1976-1983 by Miroku.

FN model	$450	$400	$375	$325	$295	$270	$240
FN model, vent rib	$550	$460	$410	$335	$320	$295	$270

Standard Miroku

	$460	$420	$380	$340	$300	$270	$250

AUTO-5 TRAP MODEL—same as Standard, 12 ga. only, 30 in. full vent rib barrel, 8½ lbs., made by FN until 1971.

	$535	$460	$410	$335	$320	$295	$270

AUTO-5 SWEET 16—similar to Standardweight Model, except 16 ga.(2¾ in. chamber) only and approx. 10 oz. lighter, gold plated trigger, made 1953-1976 by Fabrique Nationale.

Plain Barrel

	$500	$395	$350	$295	$250	$220	$195

Solid Matte Rib

	$660	$525	$450	$350	$275	$250	$225

Vent Rib

	$795	$695	$600	$525	$450	$375	$325

Sweet 16 Miroku—16 ga. only, similar to original Belgium Sweet 16, VR, invector choke standard. New in 1987 — limited mfg.

Mfg.'s Sug. Retail	$685	$575	$450	$430	$390	$350	$310	$275

AUTO-5 2-MILLIONTH COMMEMORATIVE—12 ga., 2,500 made, 1971-74 mfg., special walnut, engraving, high-luster bluing, cased with Browning book. Issue price — $550-$700.

	$1,195	$900	$750

A-5 CLASSIC SERIES SHOTGUN—12 ga., 5,000 manufactured in Classic model, 500 manufactured in Gold Classic. Both editions feature game scenes, John M. Browning's profile, and other inscriptions, special silver grey finished receiver. Introduced in 1984.

Classic Model—no inlays. Factory inventories were depleted in 1987.

$895	$750	$600

Last Mfg.'s Sug. Retail was $1,260.

Gold Classic Model—features 5 inlays depicting duck hunting scenes.

Mfg.'s Sug. Retail	$6,500	$4,750	$3,995	$3,250

A-5 DU 50TH ANNIVERSARY—12 ga. only, 5,500 manufactured in 1987 only for Ducks Unlimited chapters throughout North America. Prices will fluctuate greatly from chapter to chapter as these guns were auctioned to the highest bidder. Receiver is specially engraved and has "Fiftieth year" depicted on right side of receiver, deluxe checkered stock and forearm, high gloss bluing. Reports on guns having been resold recently indicate price ranges from $1,250 - $1,800.

A-5 DU Sweet Sixteen—16 ga. only, companion 1988-89 DU auction gun, 5500 manufactured in 1988 only. Early indications show a limited amount of resales occuring in the $1,300 - $1,500 range.

DOUBLE AUTOMATIC SHOTGUN—short recoil action, 12 ga. only, 2 shot, 26, 28, and 30 in. barrel, various chokes, checkered pistol grip stock, blued steel receiver, made 1952-1971.

	$435	$400	$350	$300	$260	$220	$195
w/vent rib	$550	$495	$420	$375	$325	$295	$245

TWELVETTE DOUBLE AUTO—similar to Double Auto, except hiduminum (aircraft alloy) frame and color anodized in blue, silver, brown, green, and black, about 7 lbs. without rib, approx. 67,000 (all variations) made 1952-1971.

	$450	$400	$350	$295	$250	$220	$200
w/vent rib	$575	$495	$425	$395	$340	$280	$250

For dark red, royal blue, brown, or gold colored receivers — add 10% (rare).

Grading	100%	98%	95%	90%	80%	70%	60%

TWENTYWEIGHT DOUBLE AUTO—similar to Twelvette, but ¾ pound lighter, 26½ in. barrel only, made 1952-1971.

	100%	98%	95%	90%	80%	70%	60%
	$475	$400	$350	$285	$235	$220	$200
w/vent rib	$625	$525	$450	$400	$350	$295	$260

B/2000 STANDARD—12 and 20 ga.'s, 26, 28, or 30 in. barrel, various chokes, vent rib, gas operated, checkered pistol grip stock, Belgium manufactured but assembled in Portugal, approx. 115,000 imported into the U.S. between 1974-1983.

	100%	98%	95%	90%	80%	70%	60%
	$395	$360	$340	$320	$295	$275	$220

B/2000 MAGNUM—same as B/2000 Auto Shotgun, with 3 in. chambers, recoil pad, vent rib.

	100%	98%	95%	90%	80%	70%	60%
	$420	$380	$360	$330	$305	$285	$230

B/2000 SKEET—same as Standard, with 26 in. skeet bored barrel, floating vent rib, skeet stock, pad.

	100%	98%	95%	90%	80%	70%	60%
	$400	$350	$330	$310	$285	$260	$210

B/2000 TRAP—same as Standard, with 30 in. full choke, floating rib, Monte Carlo trap stock.

	100%	98%	95%	90%	80%	70%	60%
	$400	$350	$330	$310	$285	$260	$210

B/2000 BUCK SPECIAL—12 and 20 ga.'s, barrel sights on 24 in. barrel.

	100%	98%	95%	90%	80%	70%	60%
	$410	$360	$340	$320	$295	$270	$220

1976 CANADIAN OLYMPICS B2000—12 ga., 100 manufactured in 1976 for Canadian sales only, high polish blue with multiple gold inlays including Olympic crest, 30 in. barrel, cased. Issue price was $1,295.

	100%	98%	95%
	$1,395	$995	$695

MODEL B-80—12 and 20 ga.'s, 3 in. capability by changing barrel, gas operation, 4 shot, hunting models use choice of steel or aluminum receiver, anodized aluminum was used in the Superlight (12 ga. made in 1984 only), 6 to 8 lbs. 1 oz. Buck special discontinued in 1984. Components manufactured by Beretta of Italy and finished and assembled FN's plant in Portugal. Made 1981-late 1988. Invector choke standard in 1985.

	100%	98%	95%	90%	80%	70%	60%
	$450	$375	$325	$295	$275	$250	$230

Last Mfg.'s Sug. Retail was $562.

Steel frames were reintroduced into production again in 1988.

Model B-80 Upland Special—12 and 20 ga.'s, 2¾ in. chamber, 22 in. vent. rib barrel, straight grip stock, invector chokes. Mfg. 1986-1988.

	100%	98%	95%	90%	80%	70%	60%
	$475	$390	$340	$305	$280	$260	$240

Last Mfg.'s Sug. Retail was $562.

MODEL B 80 DU COMMEMORATIVE—Manufactured for American DU Chapters (The Plains and others), price fluctuates greatly as collector support is sometimes limited. Unless new, this models' values approximate those of the regular Model B-80. If NIB, values recently have been in the $700-$995 range.

A-500—12 ga. only, gas operation self adjusting for any load, 3 in. chamber, 26, 28, or 30 in. invector choked barrel with vent rib, checkered walnut stock and forearm with recoil pad, rotary bolt lock-up, magazine cut off, high polished blue, light engraving, approx. 7 lbs. 5 oz. New in 1987.

	100%	98%	95%	90%	80%	70%	60%
Mfg.'s Sug. Retail	$560	$465	$390	$345	$305	$280	$260	$240

SHOTGUNS: OVER AND UNDER

SUPERPOSED SHOTGUN: 1931-1976 MANUFACTURE—12, 20, 28, and .410 ga.'s, 26½, 28, 30, and 32 in. barrels, various chokes, boxlock, auto ejectors, SST or DT, checkered pistol grip stock, made 1931-1940 and 1949-1976 by FN, grades differ in amount of engraving, inlay, general quality of workmanship and wood. Currently, shorter barrel (26½ in.) superposed models are bringing a small premium over a 30 in. F & M model. Prices below assume vent rib models, earlier matted rib guns will be 5-10% less, depending on condition.

NOTE: The use of steel shot is NOT recommended in the older Superposed Series manufactured in Belgium.

Grading	100%	98%	95%	90%	80%	70%	60%

BROWNING CHOKES AND THEIR CODES (ON BARREL)

* designates full choke (F).

*- designates improved modified choke (IM).

** designates modified choke (M).

**- designates improved cylinder choke (IC).

**$ designates skeet (SK).

*** designates cylinder bore (CYL).

    Add 15%-20% for 20 ga.

    Add 20%-40% for 28 or .410 ga.

    Deduct 25% for early DT models.

Skeet Models—avail. in every ga. and grade; no price change.

Trap Models—available in every grade, 12 ga. only; deduct 5-10%.

Trap Model w/Broadway—vent rib is ⅝ in. wide; deduct 10-15%.

Grade I Standard

	100%	98%	95%	90%	80%	70%	60%
Grade I Standard	$1,275	$1,000	$925	$840	$775	$650	$550
Grade I Lightning	$1,350	$1,050	$975	$870	$810	$690	$600
Grade I Magnum	$1,500	$1,250	$995	$920	$840	$740	$650

The Grade I has a blued steel frame with hand engraved scroll and rosette patterns, checkered walnut stock and forearm. Grade I Standard was discontinued in 1973. Lightning Model was discontinued in 1976.

Pigeon Grade

	100%	98%	95%	90%	80%	70%	60%
Pigeon Grade	$2,250	$2,050	$1,950	$1,815	$1,650	$1,570	$1,485

Also designated Grade II temporarily after WWII and renamed Pigeon in 1960. This grade featured a silver grey receiver with 2 flying pigeons surrounded by fine scroll engraving on each side of the frame. The receiver bottom and tangs also exhibit fine scroll work. The Pigeon Grade was discontinued in 1974.

Grade III—12 and 20 ga.'s, satin finished receiver with game scene engraving featuring pheasants and fighting cocks on receiver, receiver bottom has a retriever and pheasant. Discontinued in 1960.

	100%	98%	95%	90%	80%	70%	60%
	$2,400	$2,150	$2,000	$1,815	$1,650	$1,570	$1,485

Pointer Grade

	100%	98%	95%	90%	80%	70%	60%
Pointer Grade	$2,850	$2,450	$2,050	$1,850	$1,700	$1,625	$1,500

Also designated Grade III, manufactured post-war only until renamed Pointer in early 1960. Features engraved silver grey receiver with a Pointer depicted on each frame side, select walnut. Discontinued in 1966.

Grade IV—limited manufacture between 1950-1955, engraving usually featured a fox and bird scene.

	100%	98%	95%	90%	80%	70%	60%
	$3,150	$2,700	$2,450	$2,125	$1,875	$1,750	$1,650

Diana Grade

	100%	98%	95%	90%	80%	70%	60%
Diana Grade	$3,300	$2,800	$2,500	$2,150	$1,900	$1,800	$1,700

Also designated Grade V in post-war manufacture until renamed Diana in 1960. Pre-WWII Grade V's featured more delicate scroll engraving with deer adorning the right side and wild bore shown on the left. Post-WWII guns exhibit deep relief engraving with duck and pheasant game scenes on each frame side, select checkered walnut stock and forearm. Discontinued in 1976.

Midas Grade

	100%	98%	95%	90%	80%	70%	60%
Midas Grade	$4,450	$3,850	$3,400	$3,000	$2,700	$2,500	$2,300

Also designated Grade VI during post-war manufacture until renamed Midas in 1960. Pre-WWII Midas Grades featured an inlaid pigeon with outstretched wings on blued frame sides and bottom plus trigger guard. This earlier Midas also exhibited multiple gold escutcheons and gold lining. Post-war models feature deep relief scroll engraving with gold inlaid ducks and pheasants on frame sides and a grouse on the bottom. Ejector trip rods, ejector hammers and firing pins are also 18Kt. gold plated. Finest checkered walnut. Discontinued in 1976.

Grading	100%	98%	95%	90%	80%	70%	60%

Grade VI

	$5,500	$4,500	$4,000	$3,500	$3,200	$3,000	$2,600

Offered from 1955-1960 only. Elaborate deep relief scroll engraved with multiple gold inlays.

SUPERPOSED WITH EXTRA BARREL(S) OR SUPER-TUBES

Could be ordered from the factory in the following combinations: 12 or 20 ga. with one extra set of barrels in same ga. 12 ga. with one extra set in 20 ga. 12 or 20 ga. with two extra barrel sets of same ga. 20 ga. with one extra set in either 28 or .410 ga. 20 ga. with both 28 and .410 ga. barrel sets. 28 ga. with extra set of .410 barrels. Super-Tubes were adaptable on 12 ga. guns only; came from the factory cased with accessories, 16½ in. long, factory installation.

Extra barrel set(s) — add 40-50% of the guns' value for each extra set.

Super-Tubes — available for 12 ga. only, single ga. — add $250.

Super-Tube Set — 3 ga. set (20, 28 and .410 ga.'s) — add $600.

Exposition/Exhibition Model

This specially manufactured Superposed saw limited production from the late 60's through 1976. This model had its own serial range (usually 3 digit) with a "C" prefix. Grades A through G ranged from fairly simple scroll designs without gold inlays up to extremely ornate designs featuring multi-colored gold inlaid game figures. Most of these guns were produced by FN for display purposes, potential production models, or potential engraving standardization. Many of these Exhibition/Exposition superposed models were consigned to Browning Arms Co. during the 1970's because of the depressed market conditions of that time. Prices are determined by the embellishments and engraving per individual gun (A Grade being the lowest, G Grade with gold being the highest). Prices usually start at around $5,000, while a G Grade with extensive gold inlays could reach 5 digits.

BICENTENNIAL SUPERPOSED SUPERLIGHT SHOTGUN—specially
engraved limited edition Model, 51 produced — one for each state and Washington, D.C. Left side has U.S. Flag, bald eagle and state emblem inlaid in gold. Right side has gold inlaid hunter and turkey. Blued receiver, extra fancy checkered English stock, Schnabel forend, velvet lined wood case. Made 1976 by FN.

	$14,000	$10,000	$8,750

WATERFOWL SUPERPOSED SHOTGUN SERIES—12 ga., 500 made of each
issue. Gold inlays with extensive engraving, lightning action, 28 in. barrels, walnut cased, factory is almost sold out of the Pintail and Black Duck Issues.

1981 Mallard Issue

	$4,500	$3,995	$3,250

Last Mfg.'s Sug. Retail was $7,000. This issue is sold out.

1982 Pintail Issue

Mfg.'s Sug. Retail	$8,800	$4,650	$4,100	$3,300

1983 Black Duck Issue

Mfg.'s Sug. Retail	$8,800	$4,750	$4,100	$3,300

OVER/UNDER CLASSIC SERIES SHOTGUN—20 ga. only, 26 in. barrels, less
than 2,500 manufactured in Classic model and under 350 manufactured in Gold Classic. Both editions feature multiple engraved scenes and a special silver grey finish. Select American walnut featuring oil finish. Available in 1986 only.

	$1,750	$1,500	$1,200

Last Mfg.'s Sug. Retail was $2,000.

Gold Classic—8 gold inlays, select walnut forearm and stock are both checkered and carved. Available in 1986 only.

	$4,750	$3,950	$3,150

Last Mfg.'s Sug. Retail was $6,000.

SUPERPOSED SUPERLIGHT—12 and 20 ga.'s, 26½ in. solid or VR barrels, lightened
slimmer firearm and straight grip stock, made 1967-1976 by FN.

	100%	98%	95%	90%	80%	70%	60%
12 gauge	$1,600	$1,395	$1,225	$1,110	$1,025	$925	$800
20 gauge	$1,995	$1,750	$1,575	$1,350	$1,250	$1,000	$850

For Pigeon, Diana, and Midas grade Superlight 12 ga. models use previous values on standard model high-grades and add approximately 25% (plus gauge premiums) except for Pointer - add 40%.

There is also a Quail Unlimited limited edition in the Superlight series. Values are somewhat higher but difficult to ascertain because so few are bought and sold each year.

Grading	100%	98%	95%	90%	80%	70%	60%

SUPERPOSED SHOTGUN: 1983-86 MANUFACTURE—12 and 20 ga.'s. In 1983, Browning announced renewed production of the famous Belgium "Superposed" O/U in Grade I only. Available in Lightning or Superlight models, 3 in. chambers in Lightning 20 ga., 26½ or 28 in. barrels. Belgium manufactured from 1983-86.

Grade I—limited availability.

	100%	98%	95%	90%	80%	70%	60%
	$1,595	$1,300	$1,100	$975	$850	$725	$595

Last Mfg.'s Sug. Retail was $1,995.

SUPERPOSED CONTINENTAL—20 ga. O/U shotgun w/extra set of .30-06 O/U rifle barrels. Shotgun barrels are 26½ in., rifle barrels are 24 in., SST, ejectors, elaborate scroll engraved receiver, special oil finish walnut, cased. 500 mfg. Discontinued in 1986.

	100%	98%	95%	90%	80%	70%	60%
	$3,150	$2,550	$2,150	$1,950	$1,600	$1,250	$1,000

Last Mfg.'s Sug. Retail was $4,375.

SUPERPOSED PRESENTATION MODELS (P1-P4)—custom made versions of the Lightning Field, Super Light, Trap, and Skeet guns, specifications the same as Standard models, with differences in finish, engraving and inlay(s), and grade of wood and checkering. These guns were introduced by FN in 1977 and were discontinued after 1984. Add $1,775 for extra set of barrels, add $3,600 for 2 sets of extra barrels.

P Series Trap — deduct 10% from values listed below.

P Series Broadway Trap — deduct 15-20% from values listed below.

P Series Skeet 12 and 20 ga. — add 5-10% to values listed below.

Since P Series Superposed were discontinued in 1985, collector interest will undoubtedly increase and prices might be increased somewhat. BAC has no remaining inventory of this model. Interestingly, the P series models are rarer than most of the pre-1976 high grade Superposed models.

Add 20% for 20 ga.

Add 30% for 28 ga.

Add 40% for .410 ga.

Presentation 1—silver grey or blued receiver, oak leaf and fine scroll engraved, choice of 6 different animal scenes.

	100%	98%	95%	90%	80%	70%	60%
	$2,650	$2,250	$1,995	$1,750	$1,500	$1,250	$1,000

Presentation 1 w/gold inlays—same as Presentation 1, only with gold inlays.

	100%	98%	95%	90%	80%	70%	60%
	$3,150	$2,700	$2,300	$2,000	$1,825	$1,700	$1,500

Presentation 2—silver grey or blued receiver, high relief engraving, choice of 3 different sets of game scenes.

	100%	98%	95%	90%	80%	70%	60%
	$2,995	$2,450	$2,100	$1,850	$1,725	$1,600	$1,400

Presentation 2 w/gold inlays—same as Presentation 2, only with gold inlays.

	100%	98%	95%	90%	80%	70%	60%
	$3,475	$3,150	$2,700	$2,300	$2,000	$1,825	$1,700

Presentation 3—silver grey or blued receiver, more elaborate high relief engraving with choice of partridges, mallards or geese depicted on frame sides in 18Kt. gold.

	100%	98%	95%	90%	80%	70%	60%
	$4,950	$4,100	$3,600	$3,200	$2,875	$2,300	$2,000

Presentation 4—features engraved side plates in either silver grey or blued finish, engraved game scenes include waterfowl on right frame side, 5 pheasants on left frame side, 2 quail on receiver bottom, and a retriever's head on trigger guard. Extra figure walnut stock and forearm.

	100%	98%	95%	90%	80%	70%	60%
	$5,480	$4,385	$3,900	$3,600	$3,300	$3,000	$2,750

Presentation 4 w/gold inlays—same as Presentation 4, only with game scenes inlaid in 18Kt. gold.

	100%	98%	95%	90%	80%	70%	60%
	$6,580	$5,265	$4,750	$4,250	$3,800	$3,500	$3,200

P SERIES SUPERLIGHT—available in various configurations including multi-barrel sets. Typically, add 20-25% onto the values listed for the regular P series as shown above. Also add 20-40% for the 28 ga. and .410 ga. respectively.

LIEGE O/U—12 ga., 26½, 28 or 30 in. barrels, various chokes, boxlock, auto ejectors, non-selective single trigger, vent rib, checkered pistol grip stock, approx. 10,000 made 1973-1975 by FN.

	100%	98%	95%	90%	80%	70%	60%
	$700	$600	$550	$500	$425	$400	$375

This model is also known as the B 26.

Grading	100%	98%	95%	90%	80%	70%	60%

B 27—F.N. manufactured modified B 26, recently imported into the U.S., same action as Liege (B 26), blued or satin finished receiver with light engraving, no BAC markings.

Standard Game—28 in. barrels, $\frac{9}{32}$ in. vent rib, pistol grip stock, Schnabel forearm, SST, blued receiver, choking M/F only.

	$775	$675	$600	$550	$475	$425	$400

Also available in Skeet model with gold "Browning" logo on blued receiver. Prices are the same.

Deluxe Game (Grade II)—same as Standard Grade, except has 30 in. barrels, better wood and English scroll engraved satin finished receiver, choking M/F only.

	$875	$725	$625	$575	$510	$475	$445

Grand Deluxe Game—28 in. IC/IM & M/F choked barrels, game scene engraved, signed by the engraver, 90% receiver coverage.

	$1,100	$850	$775	$700	$640	$580	$520

This model was also available in a Trap configuration — values are about the same as above.

Deluxe Skeet—same as Deluxe, except is designed for skeet shooting.

	$850	$725	$625	$575	$510	$475	$445

International Skeet is also available at same price; hand fit pistol grip with stippling and International Type recoil pad.

Deluxe Trap—same as Deluxe, except is configured for trap shooting.

	$750	$650	$560	$530	$500	$475	$445

City of Liege Commemorative—limited edition of 250 units manufactured to commemorate the 1,000th anniversary of the city of Liege, cased. Only 29 imported into the U.S.

	$1,125	$975	$910	$850	$775	$700	$600

ST-100—12 ga., Belgian mfg., O/U trap configuration with separated barrels and adj. point of impact, manufactured 1979-1983 for European sale mostly, floating VR, ST, deluxe checkered walnut stock and forearm, non-B.A.C. model.

	$2,250	$1,950	$1,700	$1,400	$1,200	$975	$825

SUPERPOSED HIGH GRADES: 1985-88 MANUFACTURE

Browning, in 1985, resumed production of the Superposed in Pigeon, Pointer, Diana, and Midas grades. They were available in 12 and 20 ga. only, in either a Lightning or Superlight configuration. These higher grades were custom ordered from the factory with delivery ranging from 6-12 months. Custom options could be ordered on each grade with corresponding prices being higher than shown below. Engraving patterns on these various grades will nearly duplicate those styles manufactured before 1976. Skeet and Trap models were not available. Discontinued in late 1986 because the devaluation of the U.S. dollar created prices which were uncompetitive with the values of pre-1976 Superposed shotguns.

In 1987, Browning announced that the Pigeon, Pointer, Diana, and Midas grades would be sold exclusively through Browning specialty dealers, and would be imported on a very limited, custom order basis only.

Pigeon Grade

Mfg.'s Sug. Retail	$3,850	$2,900	$2,250	$1,950	$1,800	$1,650	$1,525	$1,450

Pointer Grade

Mfg.'s Sug. Retail	$4,750	$3,450	$2,300	$2,100	$1,850	$1,725	$1,625	$1,500

Diana Grade

Mfg.'s Sug. Retail	$5,650	$4,350	$2,950	$2,500	$2,150	$1,900	$1,800	$1,600

Midas Grade

Mfg.'s Sug. Retail	$7,000	$5,500	$3,950	$3,425	$3,000	$2,700	$2,500	$2,200

B-125—12 or 20 ga. only, retains all the features of the original Superposed, parts are subcontracted worldwide to decrease production costs, less ornate engraving styles (Belgian engraving — choice of 3) or customer preferences. Prices available by quotation from select, authorized Browning dealers or B.A.C. directly. Introduced in 1988.

Grading	100%	98%	95%	90%	80%	70%	60%

SHOTGUNS: CITORI SERIES O/U

All Citori shotguns may be used with steel shot.

CITORI HUNTING—12, 20, 28 and .410 ga.'s, 26, 28, and 30 in. barrels, various chokes, boxlock, auto ejectors, SST, vent rib, checkered pistol grip stock, grades differ in amount of engraving, finish, and wood, made 1973-present by Miroku.

Citori Grade I

Mfg.'s Sug. Retail	$985	$725	$615	$555	$475	$425	$395	$350

Subtract $40 without Invector chokes.
Subtract $10 for 28 or .410 ga.

Invector chokes became standard on this model in 1988.

Citori Upland Special—12, 16 (new in 1989), and 20 ga.'s, checkered straight grip stock, 24 in. barrels, Invector chokes standard. New in 1984.

Mfg.'s Sug. Retail	$1,005	$750	$625	$575	$495	$450	$425	$395

Citori Grade II—12, 20, 28, and .410 ga.'s. Discontinued in 1983.

	$995	$810	$740	$685	$610	$570	$540

Citori Grade III—12, 20, 28, and .410 ga.'s, greyed steel with engraved game scenes, Invector chokes standard. New in 1985.

Mfg.'s Sug. Retail	$1,385	$1,100	$925	$800	$700	$625	$585	$550

Add $140 (retail) for .410 or 28 ga.

Citori Grade V—12, 20, 28, and .410 ga.'s, extensive deep relief engraving with game scenes on satin grey receiver. Discontinued in 1984.

	$1,425	$1,265	$1,100	$990	$880	$795	$695

Citori Grade VI—12, 20, 28, and .410 ga.'s, blued or grayed receiver with extensive engraving including 8 gold inlays.

Mfg.'s Sug. Retail	$1,995	$1,550	$1,275	$1,100	$1,000	$895	$795	$695

Add $130 for 28 or .410 ga.'s.

CITORI O/U SPORTER—same as Citori Field, only with 26 in. barrels, various chokes, straight grip stock, Schnabel forearm. Discontinued 1983. Add $30 for 28 and .410 ga.'s.

	$875	$740	$600	$550	$495	$440	$385

Sporter Grade II—12, 20, 28, and .410 ga.'s.

	$1,130	$1,075	$1,020	$965	$880	$770	$715

Sporter Grade V—12, 20, 28, and .410 ga.'s.

	$1,500	$1,395	$1,225	$1,100	$990	$880	$825

CITORI LIGHTNING—12, 16, 20, 28, and .410 ga.'s, (3½ in. 12 ga. was introduced in 1989), 26, 28, and 30 in. barrels, Invector chokes standard in 12, 16, and 20 ga.'s, boxlock, auto ejectors, SST, vent rib, checkered round knob pistol grip stock and slimmer forearm, grades differ in amount of engraving, finish, and quality of wood. Introduced in 1988.

Grade I

Mfg.'s Sug. Retail	$995	$735	$625	$555	$475	$425	$395	$350

Subtract $10 for 28 or .410 ga.

Grade III—12, 16, 20, 28, and .410 ga.'s, greyed steel receiver with engraved game scenes, Invector chokes standard. New in 1988.

Mfg.'s Sug. Retail	$1,400	$1,125	$925	$800	$700	$625	$585	$550

Add $135 for 28 or .410 ga.

Grade VI—12, 16, 20, 28, and .410 ga.'s, blued or greyed receiver with extensive engraving including 8 gold inlays.

Mfg.'s Sug. Retail	$2,025	$1,575	$1,300	$1,100	$1,000	$895	$795	$695

Add $125 for 28 or .410 ga.

SPORTING CLAYS GTI MODEL—12 ga. only, 28 or 30 in. barrel with 13 mm vent. rib and barrels, red lettering on receiver, checkered stock and semi-beavertail forearm, approx. 8 lbs. New in 1989.

Mfg.'s Sug. Retail	$1,125	$975	$775	$625	$575	$525	$495	$450

Grading	100%	98%	95%	90%	80%	70%	60%

Special Sporting Model—target dimensions, high post tapered rib, 28, 30, or 32 in. barrels, full pistol grip with palm swell, approx. 8 lbs. 3 oz. New in 1989.

Mfg.'s Sug. Retail	$1,100	$950	$760	$625	$575	$525	$495	$450

Add $625 for 2 barrel set (28 and 30 in. barrels).

Lightning Sporting Clays—features rounded pistol grip, Lightning style forearm, high or low post vent. rib, "Lightning Sporting Clays Edition" inscribed and gold-filled on receiver, 30 in. barrels. New in 1989.

Mfg.'s Sug. Retail	$1,050	$925	$740	$620	$575	$525	$495	$450

Add $50 for high-post rib.

CITORI SKEET—12, 20, 28, and .410 ga.'s, same action as Citori Field, only with high post target rib (standard in 1985), 26 and 28 in. skeet barrels, recoil pad.

Mfg.'s Sug. Retail	$1,055	$900	$740	$625	$550	$495	$440	$385

Add $35 for Invector chokes.
Add $10 for 28 or .410 ga.

Grade II—12, 20, 28, and .410 ga.'s, high rib. Discontinued in 1983.

	$1,000	$850	$800	$740	$690	$650	$600

Grade III—12, 20, 28, and .410 ga.'s, Invector chokes only. New in 1986.

Mfg.'s Sug. Retail	$1,525	$1,200	$1,000	$830	$715	$625	$550	$495

Grade V—12, 20, 28, and .410 ga.'s, high rib. Discontinued in 1984.

	$1,495	$1,265	$1,100	$990	$880	$795	$650

Grade VI—Skeet gauges, choice of blue or grey finished receiver with gold inlays, deluxe walnut.

Mfg.'s Sug. Retail	$2,125	$1,695	$1,450	$1,250	$1,100	$960	$875	$825

CITORI 3 GAUGE SKEET SET—12 ga. only, comes with 1 removable forearm and 3 sets of barrels consisting of 20, 28 and .410 ga.'s, cased. New in 1987.

Grade I—with high post target rib.

Mfg.'s Sug. Retail	$2,460	$2,125	$1,850	$1,650	$1,450	$1,275	$1,050	$975

Grade III—with high post target rib.

Mfg.'s Sug. Retail	$2,835	$2,300	$1,975	$1,750	$1,525	$1,395	$1,250	$1,125

Grade VI—with high post target rib.

Mfg.'s Sug. Retail	$3,465	$2,950	$2,400	$2,050	$1,875	$1,700	$1,675	$1,495

CITORI 4 GAUGE SKEET SET—12 ga. only, comes with 1 removable forearm and 4 sets of barrels consisting of 12, 20, 28 and .410 ga.'s, cased. New in 1985.

Grade I—with high post target rib.

Mfg.'s Sug. Retail	$3,530	$2,900	$2,350	$1,925	$1,695	$1,500	$1,400	$1,295

Grade III—with high post target rib.

Mfg.'s Sug. Retail	$4,025	$3,250	$2,600	$2,150	$1,950	$1,800	$1,675	$1,500

Grade VI—with high post target rib.

Mfg.'s Sug. Retail	$4,515	$3,550	$2,995	$2,550	$2,300	$2,000	$1,850	$1,700

CITORI TRAP—same as Standard Citori, with 12 ga., 30 and 32 in. barrels, trap chokes, Monte Carlo stock, recoil pad. Invector chokes became standard in 1988.

Mfg.'s Sug. Retail	$1,105	$925	$750	$600	$525	$440	$415	$360

Subtract $45 without Invector chokes or high rib.

Plus Trap—features adj. rib and stock, back-bored barrel, available mid-1989.

Mfg.'s Sug. Retail	$1,500	$1,200	$1,000	$830	$715	$625	$550	$495

Add $50 for ported barrels.

Grade II—high post rib. Discontinued in 1983.

	$1,000	$850	$800	$740	$690	$650	$600

Grade III—12 ga. only, high post rib. New in 1986.

Mfg.'s Sug. Retail	$1,525	$1,225	$995	$850	$715	$625	$550	$495

Grade V—high post rib. Discontinued in 1984.

	$1,395	$1,125	$990	$880	$795	$710	$620

Grading	100%	98%	95%	90%	80%	70%	60%

Grade VI—12 ga. only, Invector chokes became standard in 1985.

Mfg.'s Sug. Retail $2,125 $1,695 $1,400 $1,225 $1,100 $960 $875 $825

Trap Combination Set—Grade I only, 32 in. O/U and 34 in. single barrel, cased. Discontinued.

$1,185 $1,100 $1,045 $990 $910 $855 $800

CITORI SUPERLIGHT—12, 20, 28, and .410 ga.'s, 2¾ in. chambers except for .410, English stock, 6 lbs. 9 oz., oil finish, Invector chokes became standard in 1988, manufactured in 1983-present.

Grade I

Mfg.'s Sug. Retail $1,005 $775 $640 $575 $495 $450 $425 $395
Subtract $36 without Invector chokes.
Subtract $30 for 28 or .410 ga.

Grade III—same gauges as Grade I, Invector chokes standard on 12, 16, and 20 ga.'s. New in 1986.

Mfg.'s Sug. Retail $1,410 $1,150 $950 $800 $700 $625 $585 $550
Add $115 for 28 or .410 ga.

Grade V—sideplate available. Discontinued in 1984.

$1,425 $1,265 $1,100 $990 $880 $795 $695

Grade VI—Invector chokes standard, except not available on 28 and .410 ga.'s.

Mfg.'s Sug. Retail $2,035 $1,625 $1,425 $1,100 $1,000 $895 $795 $695
Add $90 for 28 or .410 ga.

SHOTGUNS: SINGLE BARREL

BT-99 COMPETITION TRAP GUN—12 ga., 32 or 34 in. vent. rib barrel, mod., imp. mod., or full choke, boxlock, auto ejector, checkered pistol grip stock, beavertail forearm, made 1971-present by Miroku. Invector chokes became standard in 1986, and values below assume Invector choking.

Mfg.'s Sug. Retail $1,005 $815 $675 $540 $460 $400 $360 $330
Subtract $24 without Invector chokes.

BT-99 Plus—same action as BT-99 except has adj. rib to control point of impact and new recoil reduction system that reduces felt recoil by 50%, stock has adj. comb and buttplate (recoil pad), back bored barrel, Invector chokes, 8¾ lbs. New in 1989.

Mfg.'s Sug. Retail $1,520 $1,295 $1,050 $900 $775 $675 $595 $550
Add $50 for ported barrel.

BT-99 2 Barrel Set—discontinued in 1983.

$1,030 $880 $825 $750 $700 $650 $600

BT-99 Pigeon Grade—satin grey receiver with deep relief, engraved pigeons in fleur-de-lis background. Discontinued in 1984.

$1,200 $900 $800 $700 $600 $525 $440

RECOILLESS SINGLE BARREL TRAP—12 ga., special bolt-action design that eliminates 70% of felt recoil, 27 or 30 in. vent. rib Invector barrel, rib adjusts for 3 points of impact, stock has adj. pull (2 sizes) and comb height, about 8½ lbs. Late 1989 delivery.

Prices have not been established on this model at this writing.

SHOTGUNS: DISCONTINUED, SIDE-BY-SIDE

BSS MODEL—12 and 20 ga.'s, 26, 28, or 30 in. barrels, various chokes, boxlock, auto ejectors, checkered pistol grip stock, beavertail forearm, selective single trigger, made 1971-1988 by Miroku.

$550 $495 $450 $400 $365 $330 $300
Add 10%-15% for 20 ga.

Last Mfg.'s Sug. Retail was $775.

Early guns had a single non-selective trigger (silver plated) — subtract 10%.

Grade II—satin greyed steel receiver featuring an engraved pheasant, duck, quail and dogs. Discontinued in 1983.

$1,025 $925 $800 $700 $600 $525 $450

Grading	100%	98%	95%	90%	80%	70%	60%

Sporter Model—has straight grip stock and slim forearm, oil finish, 26 or 28 in. barrels. Disc. in 1988.

	$595	$550	$495	$450	$395	$360	$320

Add 10%-15% for 20 ga.

Last Mfg.'s Sug. Retail was $775.

BSS SIDELOCK—12 and 20 ga.'s, engraved sidelock action in satin grey finish, ST, 26 or 28 in. barrels, English select walnut stock, splinter forend, manufactured 1983-1988 in Korea.

	$1,795	$1,295	$1,125	$975	$825	$750	$675

Last Mfg.'s Sug. Retail was $2,000

SHOTGUNS: SLIDE ACTION

BPS MODEL—10 (new in 1988), 12, or 20 ga., gauges are chambered for Mag. ammo. Invector option (standard for 1985) allows 6 screw-in choke tubes to be interchanged, bottom ejection, double action bars, thumb safety, 5 shot capacity, vent rib, all steel receiver. Manufactured by Miroku 1977-to-date.

Hunting Model—12 or 20 ga., 3 in. chambers

Mfg.'s Sug. Retail	$434	$350	$295	$250	$225	$200	$185	$175

Magnum Model (Hunting & Stalker)—10 or 12 ga., 3½ in. chamber, 12 ga. 3½ in. new in 1989, 28 (12 only) or 30 in. barrel with Invector chokes and vent. rib, 4 shot mag., 8¾ (12 ga.) or 9½ (10 ga.) lbs.

Mfg.'s Sug. Retail	$509	$450	$395	$360	$330	$310	$290	$275

Stalker Model—12 ga. only, all metal parts have a dull matte finish, non-glare black stippled stock and forearm. New in 1987.

Mfg.'s Sug. Retail	$434	$350	$295	$250	$225	$200	$185	$175

Upland Special—12 and 20 ga.'s, 22 in. barrel, straight grip stock with Schnabel forearm, 6½ - 7½ lbs. New in 1985.

Mfg.'s Sug. Retail	$434	$350	$295	$250	$225	$200	$185	$175

Youth and Ladies Model—20 ga. only, 22 in. vent rib barrel, straight grip shortened stock, 6¾ lbs. New in 1986.

Mfg.'s Sug. Retail	$434	$350	$295	$250	$225	$200	$185	$175

Buck Special—12 or 20 (disc. in 1984) ga., 3 in. chamber, 24 in. barrel with Invector chokes, iron sights. Reintroduced in 1988.

Mfg.'s Sug. Retail	$440	$360	$300	$250	$225	$200	$185	$175

Trap Model—12 ga., 30 in. barrel. Discontinued in 1984 but trap barrel only is available in 1985.

	$360	$300	$270	$230	$210	$190	$170

Wild Turkey Federation Commemorative—only 500 manufactured. Discontinued.

	$495	$395	$325

Pacific Edition DU—limited mfg., DU serialization, cased.

	$595	$475	$350

The Coastal DU—limited mfg., DU serialization, cased.

	$595	$475	$350

Waterfowl Deluxe—12 ga. Mag., gold trigger and etching, invector chokes, limited mfg.

	$625	$525	$450

MODEL 12 GRADE I—20 ga. only, 2¾ in. chamber only, reproduction of the famous Winchester Model 12 with slight design improvements, 26 in. VR barrel bored modified, 5 round mag., high post floating rib, walnut stock and forearm with semi-gloss finish, take down, 7 lbs. 1 oz. New in 1988.

Mfg.'s Sug. Retail	$735	$735	$665	$575	$475	$425	$380	$350

Browning Arms Company is limiting manufacture to 8,500 Grade I Model 12's. In the upcoming years, Browning is also reintroducing the 28 ga. Model 12 as well as the Model 42 (.410 ga.).

Grading	100%	98%	95%	90%	80%	70%	60%

Model 12 Grade V—similar specifications to Grade I, except has select walnut checkered 22 lines per inch with high gloss finish, extensive game scene engraving including multiple gold inlays. New in 1988.

Mfg.'s Sug. Retail	**$1,187**	**$1,187**	**$975**	**$825**	**$735**	**$650**	**$560**	**$525**

Browning Arms Company is limiting manufacture to 4,000 Grade V Model 12's.

LIMITED EDITION SETS INCLUDING BLACK POWDER

BICENTENNIAL 1876-1976 SET—.45-70 Model 78 rifle with specially engraved receiver, silver finish, fancy wood, cased, with engraved knife and medallion, 1,000 sets produced in 1976. Issue price — $1,500.

$1,495 **$875** **$600**

CASED RENAISSANCE SET—one each .25 auto, .380 auto, and Hi-Power Renaissance models in walnut case, made 1955-1969.

$3,400 **$2,750** **$2,100**

JONATHAN BROWNING MOUNTAIN RIFLE—50 cal., percussion, 30 in. octagon barrel, single set trigger, engraved lock plate, select walnut stock, cased with medallion, 1,000 produced in 1978. Issue price — $650.

$650 **$500** **$440**

MOUNTAIN RIFLE—same as Jonathan Browning Mountain Rifle, without Centennial embellishments, not cased. Also in .45 and .54 cal.'s.

$225 **$200** **$170** **$150** **$135** **$125** **$110**

CENTENNIAL O/U RIFLE/SHOTGUN—superposed 20 ga. action fitted with .30-06, 24 in. barrels, folding leaf sight, 26½ in. mod. and full, 20 ga. barrels, auto ejectors, SST, elaborately engraved, gold inlaid, high grade checkered walnut stock, deluxe walnut case, 500 produced to commemorate Browning Centennial — 1878-1978.

$3,150 **$2,550** **$2,150** **$1,950** **$1,600** **$1,250** **$1,000**

CENTENNIAL SET—complete Browning set made in 1978, included various models and other accessories.

$4,750 **$2,700** **$1,995**

BRUCHET

MANUFACTURED IN SAINT ETIENNE. DISTRIBUTED EXCLUSIVELY SINCE 1982 BY WES GILPIN LOCATED IN DALLAS, TX.

Paul Bruchet has been manufacturing his shotguns patterned after the Darne action since 1981, following his tenure at Darne as line foreman until 1979 (at which time the Darne plant closed). The new Bruchet Models are designated "A" or "B". All shotguns are totally hand made with approximately 50 guns being produced each year.

MODEL A—12, 16, 20, 28, or .410 ga., small key opening, ejectors, double triggers only, basically 4 variations (1, 1A, 2, and 2A), wide assortment of customer specified special orders.

Retail values are as follows: Model 1A starts at under $2,000, the Model 2 starts at $3,000, and the Model 2A starts at $3,500. Each additional grade represents more embellishments and better grade of walnut. Magnum chambers can be ordered at a small surcharge. Importation began in 1982.

MODEL B—12, 16, 20, 28, or .410 ga., large key opening, self-opening (assisted) action, ejectors, double triggers only, basically special ordered to individual customer specifications.

Retail values are as follows: Model B starts at $5,800 and includes deluxe carrying case. Each additional upgrade represents more embellishments and a better grade of walnut. Magnum chambers can be ordered at a small surcharge. Importation began in 1982.

BUDISCHOWSKY

MANUFACTURED IN MT. CLEMENS, MI.

PISTOLS: SEMI-AUTO

TP-70—.22 LR, double action, 2½ in. barrel, stainless steel, fixed sights, plastic grips, made 1973-1977.

	$440	$385	$330

TP-70—.25 ACP, same as .22 LR, except for caliber, made 1973-1977.

	$330	$275	$220

Note: In 1977, Norton Arms marketed this pistol. Quality of workmanship is not on a par with the early Budischowsky and values are approximately 35% less.

SEMI-AUTO PISTOL—.223 cal., 11⅝ in. barrel, 20 or 30 round mag., fixed sights, a novel designed assault-type pistol.

	$470	$415	$385	$360	$305	$250	$220

ASSAULT RIFLE—.223 cal., semi-auto, 18 in. barrel, wooden para-military stock.

	$505	$440	$415	$385	$330	$275	$250

ASSAULT RIFLE FOLDING STOCK

	$525	$470	$440	$415	$360	$305	$275

BUSHMASTER FIREARMS INC.

ORIGINALLY MANUFACTURED BY GWINN ARMS CO., WINSTON-SALEM, N.C. 1972-1974. CURRENTLY MANUFACTURED AND DISTRIBUTED BY BUSHMASTER FIREARMS INC. LOCATED IN NORTH WINDHAM, ME. 1974-TO DATE.

BUSHMASTER PISTOL—.223 Rem., semi-auto., top bolt (older models with aluminum receivers) or side bolt (current mfg.) operation, steel frame (current mfg.), 11½ in. barrel, parkerized finish, adj. sights, wood stock, 5¼ lbs..

Mfg.'s Sug. Retail	$375	$350	$280	$250	$225	$180	$140	$120

Add $40 for electroless nickel finish (disc. in 1988).

This model uses a 30 shot M-16 mag. and the AK-47 gas system.

BUSHMASTER RIFLE—.223 Rem., semi-auto., top bolt (older models with aluminum receivers) or side bolt (current mfg.) operation, steel frame (current mfg.), 18½ in. barrel, parkerized finish, adj. sights, wood stock, 6¼ lbs., base values are for folding stock model.

Mfg.'s Sug. Retail	$350	$295	$260	$230	$200	$180	$140	$120

Add $40 for electroless nickel finish (disc. in 1988).

Add $65 for fixed rock maple wood stock.

This model uses a 30 shot M-16 mag. and the AK-47 gas system.

Rifle Combination System—includes rifle with both metal folding stock and wood stock with pistol grip.

Mfg.'s Sug. Retail	$450	$400	$370	$330	$310	$275	$235	$200

C

CETME

Grading	100%	98%	95%	90%	80%	70%	60%

AUTOLOADING RIFLE—.308 cal., 17¾ in. barrel, gas operated, roller cam action, similar to HK-91 in appearance, wood military style stock, aperture rear sight.

	$715	$660	$605	$550	$440	$385	$330

C Z

PREVIOUSLY MANUFACTURED IN STRAKONICE, CZECHOSLOVAKIA. 1921 TO APPROX. 1958.

PISTOLS: SEMI-AUTO

"DUO" POCKET AUTOMATIC—.25 auto, 6 shot, 2⅛ in. barrel, fixed sights, blue or nickel, plastic grips, made 1926-present (current Z pistol by Brno).

	$200	$185	$170	$150	$125	$100	$75

Add 40% for WWII years.

This model was manufactured by Dushek and is the same as the Z pistol equivalent by Brno.

CZ 22—.380 cal., derived from Mauser Nickle Pistol and manufactured under license from Mauser. Mfg. in 1923 only.

	$400	$350	$320	$300	$275	$235	$200

CZ 24—.380 cal., same design as CZ 22 except there is no gap between trigger and frame, also small detail differences. Mfg. in 1925-1941 (approx.).

	$350	$320	$290	$260	$230	$195	$150

VZ 27—.32 auto, 8 shot, 3⅞ in. barrel, fixed sights, plastic grips, made 1927-1951.

	$200	$185	$170	$150	$145	$125	$90

Add 150% for Nazi police or Navy marked.

Commercial variations are rarer than Waffenampt marked specimens. Pre-war commercial models (serial numbered below 20,000) are rare (both commercial and Waffenampt proofed) — add 100% to prices listed above.

Post-WWII commercial variations are currently averaging approx. $250 if in 95% + condition while reworks (very common) are averaging just under $200.

VZ 38 DOUBLE ACTION AUTOMATIC—.380 auto, 9 shot, double action only, 4⅝ in. barrel, fixed sights, blue, plastic grips, made 1938-1939.

	$300	$240	$200	$170	$155	$140	$125

For Waffenampt proofed — add 50%.

Changed to Model 39T after 1939.

MODEL 1945 DOUBLE ACTION AUTOMATIC—.25 auto, 8 shot, 2½ in. barrel, fixed sights, blue, plastic grips. Double action only. Manufactured between 1945-1952.

	$200	$175	$165	$150	$140	$130	$120

NEW MODEL .006 DOUBLE ACTION AUTOMATIC—.32 auto, 8 shot, 3⅜ in. barrel, fixed sight, blue, plastic grips, called VZ-50 in Czechoslovakia, used by National Police.

	$500	$425	$350	$300	$265	$230	$190

CZ HANDGUNS: CURRENT MFG.

Note: modern commercial CZ handguns are located in the Brno section of this book.

Grading	100%	98%	95%	90%	80%	70%	60%

RIFLES: MILITARY

G 33-40—8mm, manufactured between 1940-42, most have been sporterized.

	100%	98%	95%	90%	80%	70%	60%
	$350	$295	$260	$230	$200	$175	$150

This model is Brno mfg., not CZ.

CZ RIFLES: CURRENT MFG.

Note: modern commercial Czeskoslovenska rifles are located in the Brno section of this book.

CABANAS

MANUFACTURED BY INDUSTRIAS CABANAS, S.A. IN AGUILAS, MEXICO. DISTRIBUTED AND RETAILED BY MANDALL SHOOTING SUPPLIES INC. LOCATED IN SCOTTSDALE, AZ.

.22 BLANK POWERED RIFLE—shoots oversize .177 pellets/BB's powered by .22 blanks, 1,150 fps, single shot bolt action operation, iron sights, models vary in barrel lengths, stock configurations, etc.

	100%	98%	95%	90%	80%	70%	60%
Mini-82 Youth Rifle *Mfg.'s Sug. Retail*	$70	$70	$65	$55	$50	$45	$40	$35
R-83 Larger Youth *Mfg.'s Sug. Retail*	$80	$80	$75	$65	$55	$45	$40	$35
Safari *Mfg.'s Sug. Retail*	$100	$100	$90	$80	$70	$60	$50	$40
Varmint *Mfg.'s Sug. Retail*	$110	$110	$100	$90	$80	$70	$60	$50
Espronceda 1V *Mfg.'s Sug. Retail*	$120	$120	$110	$100	$90	$80	$70	$60
Leyre *Mfg.'s Sug. Retail*	$135	$135	$120	$110	$100	$90	$80	$70

Master—top-of-the-line model, 19⅔ in. barrel, adj. iron sights.

	100%	98%	95%	90%	80%	70%	60%
Mfg.'s Sug. Retail	$150	$150	$135	$120	$110	$100	$90	$80

Blanks (6mm) and BB's (4.5mm) are available at $3.50 for 50 of each.

CABELA'S INC.

SPORTING GOODS DEALER LOCATED IN SIDNEY, NB.

SHOTGUNS: SIDE BY SIDE

HEMINGWAY MODEL—mfg. for Cabela's by V. Bernardelli located in Italy, ST, ejectors.

Mfg.'s Sug. Retail	$975	$925	$775	$700	$640	$575	$525	$465

AYA GRADE II CUSTOM—mfg. for Cabela's by AYA located in Eibar, Spain, ST, ejectors, similar to AYA Model II with Model 53 engraving and trim. Discontinued and sold out.

	$1,295	$1,150	$895	$775	$700	$640	$575

CALICO

MANUFACTURED AND DISTRIBUTED BY CALICO IN BAKERSFIELD, CA.

A complete line of accessories is available for all Calico rifles and pistols.

CARBINES

M-100—.22 LR, semi-auto carbine, assault configuration with folding buttstock, 100 round helical feed mag., alloy frame, ambidextrous safety, 16.1 shrouded barrel with flash suppressor/muzzle brake, 4.2 lbs. empty. New in 1986.

Mfg.'s Sug. Retail	$300	$260	$230	$210	$190	$175	$160	$150

Grading	100%	98%	95%	90%	80%	70%	60%

M-105 SPORTER—similar to M-100 except has walnut distinctively styled buttstock and forend, 4¾ lbs. empty. New in 1989.

Mfg.'s Sug. Retail	$319	$275	$240	$220	$195	$175	$160	$150

MODEL M-900—9mm Para., retarded blowback action, assault configuration with folding buttstock, cast aluminum receiver with stainless steel bolt, static cocking handle, 16 in. barrel, fixed rear sight with adj. post front, 50 (standard) or 100 shot helical feed mag., ambidextrous safety, black polymer pistol grip and forend, 3.7 lbs. empty. New in 1989.

Mfg.'s Sug. Retail	$459	$395	$340	$320	$300	$285	$270	$255

SEMI-AUTO PISTOLS

M-110—.22 LR, same action as M-100 Carbine, 6 in. barrel with muzzle brake, 100 round helical feed mag., includes notched rear sight and adj. windage front sight, 10½ in. sight radius, ambidextrous safety, pistol grip storage compartment, 2.21 lbs. empty. New in 1989.

Mfg.'s Sug. Retail	$250	$225	$200	$180	$165	$150	$140	$130

M-950—9mm Para., same operating mechanism as the M-900 Carbine, 6 in. barrel, 50 (standard) or 100 shot helical feed mag., 2¼ lbs. empty. New in 1989.

Mfg.'s Sug. Retail	$443	$385	$340	$320	$300	$285	$270	$255

Many accessories are also available for this model.

CAMEX-BLASER USA, INC.

PREVIOUS IMPORTER/DISTRIBUTOR OF BLASER JAGWAFFEN GmbH RIFLES.

Previously imported Camex-Blaser rifles can be located in the Blaser section in this text.

CARTRIDGE FIREARMS

UNKNOWN MAKER.

Many models of pistols, rifles, and shotguns — antique and modern. Many poor quality copies in addition to a few high quality, nicely engraved guns. Most of these firearms that are average quality, trade in the $100-$300 area. Engraved models can add as much as 150%. High mfg.

CASARTELLI, CARLO

MANUFACTURED IN BRESCIA, ITALY. IMPORTED AND DISTRIBUTED BY NEW ENGLAND ARMS CO. LOCATED IN KITTERY POINT, ME.

Casartelli rifles and shotguns are mostly available through special order only. Details can be obtained by writing the above importer/distributor.

RIFLES

AFRICA MODEL — BOLT ACTION—various heavy and Mag. cal.'s, action is square B ridge type Mauser, takedown, limited production.

Mfg.'s Sug. Retail	$8,750	$8,750	$7,250	$5,600	$5,150	$4,700	$4,275	$3,850

SAFARI MODEL — BOLT ACTION—standard cal.'s, regular Mauser action, limited production.

Mfg.'s Sug. Retail	$6,750	$6,350	$4,700	$4,275	$3,850	$3,300	$2,825	$2,400

KENYA — DOUBLE RIFLE—most standard and Mag. cal.'s, sidelock action, elaborate game scene and/or scroll engraving, limited production.

Mfg.'s Sug. Retail	$29,500	$29,500	$21,750	$18,000	$15,750	$13,000	$11,000	$8,950

SHOTGUNS

SIDELOCK MODEL—various ga.'s, elaborate game scene and/or scroll engraving, limited production.

Mfg.'s Sug. Retail	$14,500	$12,950	$9,950	$8,600	$7,400	$6,100	$5,000	$4,150

CASPIAN ARMS LTD.

CURRENTLY MANUFACTURED AND DISTRIBUTED IN HARDWICK, VT.

Caspian Arms is currently manufacturing both steel and stainless steel high quality frames and related small parts for the Colt Government Model 1911-A1. For more information, Caspian Arms can be contacted directly.

GOVERNMENT MODEL—.45 ACP, similar to Colt Model 1911, available in either stainless steel or regular steel, specifications similar to Colt Model 1911, extra slides also available in .38 Super or 9mm, checkered walnut grips, high profile sights, adj. trigger. Manufacture began in 1986.

Mfg.'s Sug. Retail	$550	$550	$485	$425	$390	$365	$345	$325

This model is being manufactured on a very limited basis.

Vietnam Commemorative—.45 ACP, total production is 1,000, hand engraved by J.J. Adams, nickel plated, branch service medallion installed in grips. Manufacture began in 1986.

Mfg.'s Sug. Retail	$1,200	$1,200	$995	$795

Add $350 for gold plating.
Add $200 for serial numbers below RVN100.

This Vietnam Commemorative is also available in 24Kt. gold hand inlay edition for $14,000 — very limited production.

MODEL 110—.38 Super (limited) or .45 ACP, similar to Colt Model 1911, stainless steel barrel, extended safety, adj. National Match trigger, Combat Commander hammer, Bo-Mar low mount sights, beavertail grip safety, throated and polished feed ramp, hand fitted slide, tuned extractor, checkered front strap and trigger guard, hand checkered stocks, chrome receiver with matte blue slide. Introduced in mid-1988.

Mfg.'s Sug. Retail	$899	$899	$800	$740	$675	$600	$550	$495

This model is also available in .38 Super with limited availability.

CENTURY GUN DISTRIBUTING, INC.

MANUFACTURED BY CENTURY MANUFACTURING, INC. LOCATED IN GREENFIELD, IN. DISTRIBUTED BY CENTURY GUN DISTRIBUTING INC., ALSO LOCATED IN GREENFIELD, IN.

REVOLVERS

MODEL 100—.30-30 (new in '87), .375 Win. (new in '86) and .444 Marlin (new in '86), .45-70, or .50-70 Gov't (new in '87) cal., single action 6 shot, manganese bronze frame, steel cylinder, 6½, 8, 10, 12, 14, or 14⅞ in. round barrel, crossbolt safety with unique hammer safety, adj. sights, walnut grips, less than 600 have been manufactured since 1976. Values below are for .45-70 cal. Other calibers are priced from $1,600 on up.

Mfg.'s Sug. Retail	$750	$685	$585	$495	$450	$410	$375	$350

This model was originally made in Evansville, IN and production was halted at ser. no. 524. The second series is being made in Greenfield, IN with limited production resuming in 1986. Earlier handmade "Evansville" Model 100's (disc.) are currently selling for between $2,000-$3,000, depending on the region.

CENTURY INTERNATIONAL ARMS, INC.

IMPORTERS AND DISTRIBUTORS LOCATED IN ST. ALBANS, VT.

Century Arms imports a variety of used military rifles and pistols, including various Mauser rifle contract models, French Lebels and MAS models, Mannlichers, F.N. Model 49's, Lee Enfields, Hakims, Mosin-Nagants, Egyptian Rashid's, Chinese SKS-56's, arsenal refinished M-1 carbines/Garands and various WWI and WWII used military pistols (including Mauser Broomhandles, French PA 35's, and a few Lugers). Because most of these items range in the $95-$200 price range, individual listings are not listed in this text. Most of these models are in good to like new condition overall. In addition, surplus and currently manufactured ammunitions are available at very competitive prices. Generally these models offer good values to the shooter and a few are collectible.

Grading	100%	98%	95%	90%	80%	70%	60%

CENTURION—.300 Win. Mag., .303 British, and 7mm Rem. Mag. cal.'s, P-14 action with sporterized stock and 24 in. barrel, checkered beechwood stock, tapped and drilled for scope mounts. New in 1987.

	$210	$165	$140	$130	$120	$110	$100

MAS 36 SPORTER—7.5mm, Mas 36 action with shorter barrel, military stock has been sporterized, reblued metal, positive safety.

	$135	$115	$95	$85	$80	$75	$70

SWEDISH CONTRACT M38—6.5 X 55mm, Swedish Mauser M38 with new Monte Carlo stock, 24 in. barrel, 5 shot fixed mag.

	$190	$150	$135	$125	$115	$105	$95

INFIELD SPORTER NO. 4—.303 British, new checkered stock with Monte Carlo cheekpiece, 25.2 in. barrel, 10 shot detach. mag.

	$165	$135	$125	$115	$105	$95	$90

JUNGLE SPORTER NO. 5—.303 British, 20.5 in.barrel with flash eliminator, new checkered Monte Carlo stock and forearm, detach. mag.

	$190	$150	$135	$125	$115	$105	$95

MAS .223—.223 cal., civilian version of the FAMAS 5.56mm assault rifle, made by Giat in France, switchable ejection port, rubber covered cheekpiece, bullpup configuration, protected sights, with bipod, 20 shot mag. New in 1986.

	$1,095	$900	$800	$725	$660	$600	$550

M-1 GARAND—.30-06, 24 in. barrel, arsenal repaired stocks, good to very good condition.

	$350	$275	$250	$235	$215	$200	$190

CHAMPLIN FIREARMS

ENID, OK.

BOLT ACTION RIFLE—standard, all calibers, round or octagon barrel, adj. trigger. 1966-discontinued.

	$5,400	$4,100	$3,575	$2,860	$2,640	$2,200	$1,650

  Rib and express sights — add $165.
  Deluxe wood — add $150-450.
  Deluxe checkering — add $70 for 26 lines/in.

CHAPUIS

MANUFACTURED IN FRANCE. CURRENTLY IMPORTED BY ARMES DE CHASSE LOCATED IN CHADDS FORD, PA 19317.

Chapuis rifles and shotguns are manufactured on a limited basis. Most of their emphasis is on high quality double rifles and shotguns. For further information regarding this respected French trademark, please contact the importer listed above. The below listed models are imported exclusively by Armes de Chasse.

RG EXPRESS MODEL 89—7 X 65R, 8 X 57JRS, 9.3 X 74R, or .375 H&H, double rifle, sidelock, full line of options are available. Importation began in 1989.

Mfg.'s Sug. Retail	$6,500	$6,500	$5,500	$4,775	$4,100	$3,575	$2,860	$2,640

RG PROGRESS—12, 16, 20 ga. or rifled slug, rifled barrel option available as well as combination guns. Importation began in 1989.

Mfg.'s Sug. Retail	$2,500	$2,500	$2,100	$1,800	$1,600	$1,400	$1,200	$995

CHARLIN ARMS

PREVIOUSLY MANUFACTURED IN FRANCE.

Charlin Arms previously made shotguns which were patterned after Darne firearms. Typically, they are very high quality and values seem to approximate the Darne guns. Once you have determined the comparable model in Darne, please refer to the Darne section in this book.

CHARLES DALY
SEE DALY, CHARLES.

CHARTER ARMS
MANUFACTURED AND DISTRIBUTED IN STRATFORD, CT.

REVOLVERS: DOUBLE ACTION

All Charter Arms revolvers have a hammer block safety system, 8 groove rifling, unbreakable beryllium copper firing pin, triple safety features, no sideplate, steel frames, and lifetime warranty to the original owner.

BONNIE & CLYDE SET—.32 H&R Mag. (Bonnie) and .38 Spl. (Clyde), matched pair, 6 shot, 2½ in. fully shrouded barrel, wood laminate grips (color coordinated), blued finish, pistols individually marked Bonnie or Clyde on barrels, supplied with gun rugs. New in 1989.

No Mfg.'s Retail	$535	$395	$360	$330	$295	$260	$240

PATHFINDER—.22 LR or .22 Mag., 6 shot, 2, 3, and 6 (discontinued in 1985) in. barrels, round butt, adj. sights, walnut grips, wide trigger and spur hammer.

No Mfg.'s Retail	$225	$165	$150	$140	$130	$120	$110

Pathfinder — Square Butt—.22 LR and 22 Mag., 6 in. barrel, square butt, otherwise same as Pathfinder.

No Mfg.'s Retail	$230	$175	$145	$130	$120	$105	$90

Pathfinder Stainless—stainless variation, .22 LR and Mag., 3 in. barrel.

No Mfg.'s Retail	$290	$225	$190	$175

UNDERCOVER—.32 S&W and .38 Spl. cal.'s, 5 shot in .38 Spl., 6 shot in .32 S&W, 2 and 3 in. barrels, wide trigger and spur hammer, fixed sights, .38 Spl. can also be ordered with pocket hammer.

No Mfg.'s Retail	$216	$155	$145	$135	$125	$115	$100

Undercover Stainless—2 in. barrel only.

No Mfg.'s Retail	$273	$195	$180	$165

UNDERCOVERETTE—same as Undercover, in .32 S&W long, 6 shot, 2 in. barrel, blue. Discontinued.

	$155	$140	$110	$100	$90	$70	$55

BULLDOG—.44 Spl., 5 shot, 2½ or 3 (disc. in 1988) in. barrels, wide trigger and spur or pocket hammer, checkered bulldog grips (walnut or neoprene).

No Mfg.'s Retail	$232	$160	$145	$130	$120	$110	$105

Bulldog Stainless—2½ in. bull or 3 in. regular barrel.

No Mfg.'s Retail	$286	$205	$180	$160

Target Bulldog—.357 Mag. or .44 Spl. cal., 5 shot, 4 in. shrouded barrel, adj. sights, square butt only, blued finish. Mfg. in 1986-1988.

	$195	$180	$165	$150	$130	$115	$100

Subtract $10 for .357 Mag. cal.

Last Mfg.'s Sug. Retail was $255.

Target Bulldog Stainless—9mm Federal, .357 Mag. or .44 Spl. cal., 5 shot, 5½ in. shrouded VR barrel, adj. sights, square butt target grips only, matte finished, 28 oz. New in 1989.

No Mfg.'s Retail	$375	$265	$235	$200

BULLDOG PUG—.44 Spl., 5 shot, 2½ in. shrouded barrel, walnut or neoprene grips. New in 1986.

No Mfg.'s Retail	$250	$185	$160	$145	$130	$115	$100

Bulldog Pug Stainless—2½ in. shrouded barrel. New in 1987.

No Mfg.'s Retail	$300	$210	$175	$160

Grading	100%	98%	95%	90%	80%	70%	60%

BULLDOG TRACKER—.357 Mag. (.38 Spl.), 5 shot, 2½, 4, and 6 in. bull barrels, adj. sights, blue only, checkered bulldog grips, square butt on 4 or 6 in. barrel only. Discontinued in 1986 - reintroduced in 1989.

No Mfg.'s Retail	$250	$185	$160	$145	$130	$115	$100

POLICE BULLDOG—.32 H&R Mag., .38 Spl. or .44 Spl. cal., 5 or 6 shot, fixed sights, blue only, 3½ or 4 in. barrel, Neoprene grips or square butt (.44 Spl. only).

No Mfg.'s Retail	$234	$175	$145	$130	$120	$110	$105

.44 Special is 5 shot.

Stainless Police Bulldog—.32 Mag., .357 Mag. (new in 1989), .38 Spl. (disc. in 1988) or .44 Spl. (new in 1989), 5 shot, square butt, 3½ (.44 Spl. only) or 4 in. regular or bull barrel. New in 1987.

No Mfg.'s Retail	$287	$205	$180	$160			

Add $20 for .357 Mag. or .44 Special cal.

Neoprene grips are standard on these models except for the .357 Mag. (square butt).

POLICE UNDERCOVER—.32 H&R Mag. or .38 Spl. cal., 6 shot, spur or pocket hammer, 2 in. shrouded barrel, checkered walnut grips, fixed sights, blue only.

No Mfg.'s Retail	$250	$185	$160	$145	$130	$115	$100

Stainless Police Undercover

No Mfg.'s Retail	$280	$205	$180	$160			

OFF DUTY—.38 Spl., 5 shot, 2 in. barrel, fixed sights, blue only, matte black finish.

No Mfg.'s Retail	$184	$125	$115	$105	$100	$95	$90

Stainless Off Duty

No Mfg.'s Retail	$240	$185	$160	$145			

PIT BULL—9mm Federal, .357 Mag., or .38 Spl. cal., 5 shot, 2½, 3½, or 4 in. full shroud barrel, Neoprene grips, approx. 26 oz. New in 1989.

No Mfg.'s Retail	$286	$205	$180	$160	$140	$125	$115

Stainless Pit Bull—2½ or 3½ in. shrouded barrel.

No Mfg.'s Retail	$312	$225	$190	$165			

PISTOLS: SEMI-AUTO

MODEL 40—.22 LR only, double action semi-auto., 3.3 in. barrel, 8 shot mag., 21½ oz., fixed sights, stainless steel. Manufactured 1984-86.

	$265	$240	$220				

Last Mfg.'s Sug. Retail was $319.

MODEL 79K—.32 and .380 ACP cal.'s, double action semi-auto., 3.6 in. barrel, 7 shot mag., 24½ oz., fixed sights, stainless steel. Manufactured 1984-86.

	$325	$300	$280				

Last Mfg.'s Sug. Retail was $390.

EXPLORER II & S II PISTOL—.22 LR, semi-auto survival pistol, barrel unscrews, 8 shot mag., black, gold (discontinued), silvertone, or camouflage finish, 6, 8, or 10 in. barrels, simulated walnut grips. Discontinued in 1986.

	$90	$80	$70	$60	$55	$50	$45

Last Mfg.'s Sug. Retail was $109.

This model uses a modified AR-7 action.

TARGET PISTOLS

MODEL 42T (COMPETITION II TARGET)—.22 LR only, single action, 5.9 in. barrel, target model with checkered walnut grips, adj. sights, blue finish only. Made 1984-1985 only.

	$490	$450	$395	$350	$300	$260	$220

Last Mfg.'s Sug. Retail was $599.

RIFLES

AR-7 EXPLORER RIFLE—.22 LR cal., takedown, barreled action stores in cycolac stock, 8 shot mag., adj. sights, 16 in. barrel. Black finish on AR-7, silvertone on AR-7S. Camouflage finish new in 1986 (AR-7C).

No Mfg.'s Retail	$146	$115	$100	$85	$75	$65	$55

CHINESE FIREARMS

MOST CHINESE FIREARMS FOR U.S. EXPORT ARE CURRENTLY BEING MANUFACTURED BY TWO COMPANIES: POLY TECHNOLOGIES, INC. AND NORINCO. POLY TECHNOLOGIES, INC. IS CURRENTLY BEING IMPORTED BY KENG'S FIREARMS SPECIALTY LOCATED IN RIVERDALE, GA AND IS DISTRIBUTED BY PTK INTERNATIONAL, INC. IN ATLANTA, GA. NORINCO IS IMPORTED AND DISTRIBUTED BY CHINA SPORTS, INC. LOCATED IN DALLAS, TX. PLEASE REFER TO THE POLY TECHNOLOGIES, INC. AND NORINCO SECTIONS IN THIS TEXT TO FIND OUT MORE ABOUT THESE FIREARMS. IN ADDITION TO THESE TWO TRADEMARKS, OTHER CHINESE MODELS HAVE BEEN MANUFACTURED UNDER VARIOUS SUBCONTRACTS WITH THE CHINESE ARSENALS. THESE GUNS (TYPICALLY AKS COPIES) ARE GENERALLY UNMARKED AND QUALITY CAN VARY GREATLY.

CHIPMUNK MANUFACTURING INC.

MANUFACTURED AND DISTRIBUTED IN MEDFORD, OR.

CHIPMUNK SINGLE SHOT RIFLE—.22 LR or .22 Mag. (disc. 1987) cal., manually cocked single shot, 16⅛ in. barrel, iron sights (adj. aperture rear), 30 in. overall length, 2½ lbs.

Mfg.'s Sug. Retail	$130	$105	$85	$70	$60	$50	$45	$40

Deluxe Rifle—similar to standard rifle, except has deluxe hand checkered walnut. New in 1987.

Mfg.'s Sug. Retail	$180	$140	$110	$85	$70	$60	$50	$45

SILHOUETTE PISTOL—.22 LR, bolt action design with 14⅞ in. barrel, iron sights, rear grip walnut stock. New in 1987.

Mfg.'s Sug. Retail	$150	$125	$95	$80	$70	$60	$50	$45

CHURCHILL, E.J., (GUNMAKERS) LTD.

PREVIOUSLY MANUFACTURED IN LONDON, ENGLAND. THE COMPANY UNDERWENT VARIOUS TRADING FORMS UNTIL CHURCHILL, ATKIN, GRANT & LANG LTD. CLOSED IN 1981. CURRENTLY, E.J. CHURCHILL SIDE BY SIDE SHOTGUNS ARE MANUFACTURED IN SURREY, ENGLAND AND WHILE THEY ARE NOT IMPORTED INTO THE U.S., THESE MODELS ARE SHOWN WITH U.S. PRICES IF PURCHASED IN ENGLAND. PRICES ARE SUBJECT TO FLUCTUATING U.S. DOLLAR.

Churchill Guns are among the world's finest with many custom features. We will list both discontinued and current models and approximate values, but strongly urge competent appraisal if purchase or sale is contemplated.

Prices could differ from values shown below because of the fluctuating U.S. dollar.

SHOTGUNS AND RIFLES

All below models were built or finished to customer specifications pertaining to choking, chambers, barrel lengths, stock measurements, weight, engraving patterns. Standardized patterns did exist, however, for each model. The "XXV" designation referred to the 25 in. barrel length which was a Churchill specialty and was also a registered trademark.

PREMIER QUALITY SXS—all ga.'s, best quality, easy opening or standard opening, 25, 28, 30, and 32 in. barrels, any choke, sidelock, auto ejectors, standard with double triggers, engraved, checkered, straight or pistol grip stock. Also manufactured in some double rifles. Discontinued.

	$17,000	$15,000	$12,000	$10,000	$9,000	$7,500	$6,500

20 ga. — add 20%.
28 ga. — add 40%.
SST — add $1,000.
16 ga. — deduct 10%.
Double rifle — add 35%.

Premier Grade—12 ga. only, sidelock, assisted opening, limited current mfg.

Mfg.'s Sug. Retail	$18,750	$16,000	$14,000	$12,000	$10,000	$9,000	$7,500	$6,500

Grading	100%	98%	95%	90%	80%	70%	60%

IMPERIAL SXS—all ga.'s, most barrel lengths, second quality sidelock model, ejectors, mostly standard opening, a few made as easy opening. Also manufactured in some double rifles. Discontinued.

	100%	98%	95%	90%	80%	70%	60%
	$13,500	$11,500	$9,500	$7,500	$6,500	$5,250	$4,000

    20 ga. — add 20%.
    28 ga. — add 40%.
    SST — add $1,000.
    16 ga. — deduct 10%.
    Double rifle — add 35%.

Imperial Grade—12 and 20 ga.'s, second quality sidelock model, ejectors, standard opening, limited current mfg.

	100%	98%	95%	90%	80%	70%	60%
Mfg.'s Sug. Retail	$14,250	$12,000	$9,950	$7,700	$6,600	$5,600	$4,500	$3,500

FIELD MODEL—12 ga. only, most barrel lengths, third quality sidelock model. Discontinued.

	100%	98%	95%	90%	80%	70%	60%
	$9,000	$8,000	$7,000	$6,000	$5,000	$4,500	$3,500

    20 ga. — add 20%.
    28 ga. — add 40%.
    SST — add $1,000.
    16 ga. — deduct 10%.

HERCULES MODEL—all ga.'s, 25-30 in. barrels, best quality boxlock model, ejectors, easy opening or standard opening. Also made in some double rifles in .22 Hornet and similar cal.'s.

	100%	98%	95%	90%	80%	70%	60%
	$9,000	$8,000	$7,000	$6,000	$5,000	$4,500	$3,500

    20 ga. — add 20%.
    28 ga. — add 40%.
    SST — add $1,000.
    16 ga. — deduct 10%.
    Double rifle — add 35%.

UTILITY MODEL—mostly 12 ga., 25-30 in. barrels, second quality boxlock model, ejectors, checkered straight or pistol grip stock. Discontinued.

	100%	98%	95%	90%	80%	70%	60%
	$6,250	$4,500	$3,500	$3,000	$2,500	$2,000	$1,800

    20 ga. — add 20%.
    28 ga. — add 40%.
    .410. — add 60%.
    SST — add $500.
    16 ga. — deduct 10%.

CROWN MODEL—12, 16, 20, and .410 (rare) ga.'s, third quality boxlock model, various barrel lengths. Discontinued.

	100%	98%	95%	90%	80%	70%	60%
	$4,500	$3,500	$3,000	$2,500	$2,000	$1,600	$1,200

    20 ga. — add 20%.
    28 ga. — add 40%.
    .410 — add 60%.
    SST — add $500.
    16 ga. — deduct 10%.

REGAL—12, 16, 20, 28, and .410 ga.'s, second quality boxlock model introduced after WWII, released after Utility Model was discontinued. Premium for 28 and .410 ga.'s.

	100%	98%	95%	90%	80%	70%	60%
	$6,000	$4,300	$3,750	$3,100	$2,500	$2,000	$1,800

    20 ga. — add 20%.
    28 ga. — add 40%.
    .410 ga. — add 60%.
    SST — add $500.
    16 ga. — deduct 10%.

Regal Grade—12, 20, 28, and .410 ga.'s, best quality boxlock model, ejectors, standard opening, limited current production.

	100%	98%	95%	90%	80%	70%	60%
Mfg.'s Sug. Retail	$5,625	$4,800	$4,000	$3,500	$3,000	$2,500	$2,000	$1,800

Grading	100%	98%	95%	90%	80%	70%	60%

PREMIER QUALITY O/U—12, 16, and 20 ga.'s, same barrel and bore as Premier Double, engraved, sidelock, auto ejectors, checkered pistol grip or straight stock. Discontinued.

	100%	98%	95%	90%	80%	70%	60%
	$17,000	$15,000	$12,000	$10,000	$9,000	$7,500	$6,500

20 ga. — add 20%.
28 ga. — add 40%.
SST — add $1,000.
Vent rib — add $500.
16 ga. — deduct 10%.

RIFLES

"ONE OF ONE THOUSAND RIFLE"—Mauser type bolt action, .270, 7mm Rem. Mag., .308, .30-06, .300 Win. Mag., .375 H&H Mag., and .458 Win. Mag. cal.'s, 5 shot standard, 3 shot mag. Magnum, 24 in. barrel, classic French walnut stock, swivel recoil pad with trap, trap pistol grip cap, made in 1973 for Interarms 20th Anniversary, limited, 100 produced.

	100%	98%	95%	90%	80%	70%	60%
	$1,400	$1,250	$1,000	$900	$750	$700	$600

CHURCHILL

CURRENTLY DISTRIBUTED BY ELLETT BROTHERS LOCATED IN CHAPIN, SC. PREVIOUSLY IMPORTED (UNTIL 1988) BY KASSNAR IMPORTS, INC. LOCATED IN HARRISBURG, PA. NOT AFFILIATED WITH E.J. CHURCHILL GUNMAKERS, LTD.

In late 1988 the Churchill trademark was sold to Ellett Brothers located in Chapin, SC.

RIFLES

HIGHLANDER—.25-06 Rem., .243 Win., .270 Win., .308 Win., .30-06, 7mm Rem. Mag., or .300 Win. Mag. cal., bolt action, 22 in. barrel, thumb safety, no sights, 3 or 4 shot mag., checkered walnut stock, 7½ lbs.

Mfg.'s Sug. Retail	$460	$395	$350	$330	$300	$270	$240	$215

Add $30 for iron sights (disc).

REGENT—same cal.'s as Highlander, deluxe checkered walnut with Monte Carlo comb and cheekpiece. Last imported by Kassner in 1988.

	$555	$455	$385	$340	$300	$280	$260

Add $30 for iron sights.

Last Mfg.'s Sug. Retail was $610.

ROTARY 22—.22 LR, beginners rifle, bolt hold-open device, adj. rear sight, 10 shot rotary mag. Importation began in 1989.

Mfg.'s Sug. Retail	$130	$120	$105	$95	$85	$75	$65	$55

SHOTGUNS

WINDSOR I SXS—10 (disc. in 1988), 12, 16, 20, 28, and .410 ga.'s, double barrel, 23-32 in. barrels, Anson and Deeley boxlock, antique silver finish receiver with fine scroll engraving, extractors, double triggers, checkered pistol grip and forend.

Mfg.'s Sug. Retail	$653	$550	$465	$450	$385	$300	$250	$230

Add $150 for 10 ga.
Add $55 for 28 or .410 ga.
Add $30 for Flyweight Models (25 in. barrels - disc. in 1988).

WINDSOR II SXS—12 and 20 ga.'s, double barrel, 26-30 in. barrels, Anson and Deeley boxlock, antique silver finish receiver with fine scroll engraving, ejectors, double triggers, checkered pistol grip and forend. Add $100 for 10 ga. (disc.). Importation disc. in 1987.

	$595	$485	$415	$350	$315	$270	$240

Last Mfg.'s Sug. Retail was $638.

Grading	100%	98%	95%	90%	80%	70%	60%

WINDSOR VI SXS—12 and 20 (disc.) ga.'s, double barrel, 25 and 28 in. barrels, sidelock, antique silver finish receiver with fine scroll engraving, ejectors, double triggers, checkered pistol grip and forend. Disc. in 1987.

	$840	$700	$600	$550	$510	$460	$420

Last Mfg.'s Sug. Retail was $900.

ROYAL SXS—available in 12, 20, 28, or .410 ga., DT's, extractors, checkered walnut stock and forearm, case hardened receiver, new in late 1988.

Mfg.'s Sug. Retail	$540	$485	$405	$370	$310	$275	$250	$230

Add $20 for 28 ga.
Add $74 for .410 ga.

MONARCH O/U—12, 20, 28, or .410 ga., 25, 26 or 28 in. vent rib barrels, SST, extractors, boxlock action, DT, checkered European walnut stock and forearm, 6½-7½ lbs.

Mfg.'s Sug. Retail	$529	$460	$370	$340	$300	$250	$230	$210

Add $67 for .410 ga. with 26 in. barrels.
Deduct $40 without SST.
Deduct $33 for 28 ga.

WINDSOR III O/U—12, 20, or .410 ga. (disc.), double barrel, 27 or 30 in. barrels, double bottom lock, antique silver finish receiver with fine scroll engraving, extractors, SST, vent rib, checkered pistol grip and forend.

Mfg.'s Sug. Retail	$625	$550	$495	$450	$380	$340	$300	$280

Add $140 for Flyweight Model or choke tubes (disc.).
Add $75 for .410 ga.

WINDSOR IV O/U—12, 20, 28, or .410 ga., double barrel, 26-30 in. barrels, double bottom lock, antique silver finish receiver with fine scroll engraving, ejectors, SST, vent rib, checkered pistol grip and forend. Interchangeable chokes became standard in 1989.

Mfg.'s Sug. Retail	$852	$725	$640	$530	$470	$430	$395	$360

Deduct $52 for 28 or .410 ga.
Deduct $100 if without choke tubes.

REGENT V O/U—12 and 20 ga.'s, double barrel, 27 in. barrels, double bottom locks with fully engraved side plates, antique silver finish receiver with extra fine scroll engraving, ejectors, single trigger, vent rib, checkered pistol grip and forend. Interchangeable choke tubes standard. Discontinued in 1986.

	$750	$630	$560	$520	$460	$420	$385

Last Mfg.'s Sug. Retail was $850.

REGENT VII O/U—12 and 20 ga.'s, double barrel, 27 in. barrels, double bottom lock, antique silver finish receiver with extra fine scroll engraving, ejectors, single trigger, vent rib, checkered pistol grip and forend. Interchangeable choke tubes standard.

Mfg.'s Sug. Retail	$1,100	$895	$795	$700	$620	$560	$510	$470

REGENT TRAP AND SKEET O/U—12 and 20 ga.'s, double barrel, 26 and 30 in. barrels, double bottom lock, antique silver finish receiver with sideplates engraved in fine scroll, ejectors, SST, vent rib, checkered pistol grip and forend.

Mfg.'s Sug. Retail	$963	$795	$650	$575	$540	$485	$440	$390

Add $40 for trap variation.

REGENT GRADE O/U SHOTGUN RIFLE COMBINATION—12 ga. over either .222 Rem., .223, .243 Win. (disc.), .270 Win., .30-06, or .308 Win. cal., double barrel, 25 in. barrels, double bottom lock, antique silver finish receiver with extra fine scroll engraving, ejectors, single trigger, vent rib, checkered pistol grip and forend.

Mfg.'s Sug. Retail	$927	$800	$700	$635	$560	$510	$475	$440

WINDSOR GRADE SEMI-AUTO—12 ga. only, 26, 28, and 30 in. barrels, gas operation, anodized alloy receiver, vent rib, checkered pistol grip and forend, 7½ lbs. Deluxe model includes polished receiver with etching.

	$380	$320	$300	$275	$250	$225	$200

Last Mfg.'s Sug. Retail was $420.
Add $35 for choke tubes.
Add $55 for Deluxe model.

Grading	100%	98%	95%	90%	80%	70%	60%

REGENT GRADE SEMI-AUTO—12 ga. only, 26, 28, and 30 in. barrels, gas operation, anodized alloy receiver, vent. rib, checkered pistol grip and forend, 7½ lbs. Deluxe model includes polished receiver with etching. Discontinued in 1986.

Add $35 for choke tubes.
Add $55 for Deluxe model.

	100%	98%	95%	90%	80%	70%	60%
	$440	$365	$340	$320	$300	$285	$270

Last Mfg.'s Sug. Retail was $495.

WINDSOR GRADE SLIDE ACTION—12 ga. only, 26, 27, 28, and 30 in. barrels, double slides, anodized alloy receiver, vent rib, checkered pistol grip and forend, 7½ lbs. Discontinued in 1986.

	100%	98%	95%	90%	80%	70%	60%
	$385	$330	$310	$275	$250	$225	$200

Last Mfg.'s Sug. Retail was $430.

CIMARRON F.A. MFG. CO.

IMPORTER/DISTRIBUTOR/RETAILER LOCATED IN HOUSTON, TX. CURRENTLY IMPORTING ALDO UBERTI MODERN AND BLACK POWDER FIREARMS. BLACK POWDER REPRODUCTIONS CAN BE LOCATED IN THE BLACK POWDER SECTION UNDER CIMARRON ARMS IN THE BACK OF THIS TEXT. PREVIOUSLY NAMED OLD-WEST GUNS CO.

REVOLVERS & CARBINES: SINGLE ACTION REPRODUCTIONS

The Cimarron Arms reproduction of the 1873 Colt Peacemaker is available in two configurations listed below. These pistols are extremely accurate reproductions of the original Colt SAA and are marked (and machined) the same as the originals including serial numbers on frames, backstrap, trigger guard, and cylinder. Frames are radiused and cylinders are beveled. Frames are blued or case hardened, stocks are walnut - choice of 4¾, 5½, or 7½ in. barrel. All Cimarron SAA's are barrel marked - CIMARRON F.A. MFG. Co. HOUSTON, TX. U.S.A.

The "Old Model" configuration has the older style black powder frame, screw in cylinder pin retainer, and circular "bullseye" ejector head.

The Standard Model includes the post-1890 style frame with spring loaded cross-pin cylinder retainer and "half-moon" ejector head.

Both the Old Model and Standard Model are available in the authentic old style "charcoal blue" finish (sometimes referred to as fire-bluing).

Add $20 for Charcoal Blue finish on models listed below.
Add $90 for nickel finish on models listed below.
Add $280 for "A" style engraving (30% coverage) on SAA's listed below.
Add $425 for "B" style engraving (50% coverage) on SAA's listed below.
Add $750 for "C" style engraving (100% coverage) on SAA's listed below.
Add $825 for "Texas Cattlebrands" engraving pattern.

CATTLEMAN SA & VARIATIONS—available in .45 LC, .44-40, .38 Spl., .357 Mag., .22 LR, and .22 Mag cal.'s, 4¾, 5½, and 7½ in. barrel lengths, brass or steel backstraps and trigger guard.

Standard or Old Model (Cattleman)

Mfg.'s Sug. Retail	$389	$345	$275	$250	$220	$195	$175	$160

Add $10 for .357 Mag. cal.

Sheriff's Model—.44-40 and .45 LC cal.'s, 3 in. barrel, brass or steel backstrap and trigger guard.

Mfg.'s Sug. Retail	$389	$345	$275	$250	$220	$195	$175	$160

Target Model—similar to Cattleman Model except has fully adj. target rear sight, brass or steel backstrap.

Mfg.'s Sug. Retail	$399	$355	$280	$255	$220	$195	$175	$160

Add $40 for .357 Mag. cal.

This variation is available in the Standard Model configuration only and with standard finish.

Grading	100%	98%	95%	90%	80%	70%	60%

CATTLEMAN BUNTLINE—.45 LC, .44-40, and .357 Mag. cal.'s, 18 in. barrel, brass or steel backstrap cut for shoulder stock.

Mfg.'s Sug. Retail	$399	$355	$280	$255	$220	$195	$175	$160

Add $10 for target sights.

BUNTLINE CARBINE—similar cal.'s to Cattleman Buntline except also includes .22 LR/.22 Mag. (convertible cylinders), 18 in. barrel, includes non-detachable shoulder stock with brass hardware and finger extension trigger guard.

Mfg.'s Sug. Retail	$399	$355	$280	$255	$220	$195	$175	$160

Add $20 for target sights.

Add $20 for .22 LR/.22 Mag. combo.

BUCKHORN—.44 Mag. or .44 Spl., reinforced variation of the Cattleman designed for more powerful cartridges, 4¾, 6 or 7½ in. barrel, brass or steel backstap.

Mfg.'s Sug. Retail	$415	$365	$285	$260	$220	$195	$175	$160

Buckhorn Convertible Model—includes .44 Mag./.44-40 cylinders, 4¾, 6 or 7½ in. barrel.

Mfg.'s Sug. Retail	$427	$375	$295	$265	$220	$195	$175	$160

Add $12 for target sights.

Buckhorn Target Model—.44 Mag. or .44 Spl. cal., 4¾, 6 or 7½ in. barrel, adj. rear sight.

Mfg.'s Sug. Retail	$407	$365	$280	$255	$220	$195	$175	$160

Buckhorn Buntline—.44 Mag., .44 Spl., or .44-40 cal., 18 in. barrel, fixed or target sights.

Mfg.'s Sug. Retail	$419	$370	$285	$265	$220	$195	$175	$160

Add $30 for target sights.

Buckhorn Carbine—.44 Mag., .44 Spl., or .44-40 cal., 18 in. barrel, includes non-detachable shoulder stock with brass hardware and lanyard ring.

Mfg.'s Sug. Retail	$429	$375	$290	$265	$220	$195	$175	$160

Add $30 for target sights.

SPECIAL EDITION SAA'S

U.S. CAVALRY MODEL—authentic reproduction of original Colt military cavalry contract, 7½ in. barrel, marked U.S. on lower left frame, one piece walnut grips with military cartouche.

Mfg.'s Sug. Retail	$459	$400	$330	$300	$280	$260	$240	$220

U.S. ARTILLERY MODEL—Renaldo A. Carr 1895 U.S. Artillery Model Commemorative, limited mfg.

Mfg.'s Sug. Retail	$459	$400	$330	$300	$280	$260	$240	$220

7TH CAVALRY CASED SET—U.S. Cavalry Model in case with accessories.

Mfg.'s Sug. Retail	$715	$650	$600	$550	$500	$460	$420	$385

JUDGE ROY BEAN COMMEMORATIVE—mfg. to commemorate Judge Roy Bean's Texas cattlebrand.

Mfg.'s Sug. Retail	$2,000	$1,750	$1,400	$1,175	$995	$875	$750	$625

REMINGTON REPRODUCTIONS

"OUTLAW" 1875 REMINGTON—available in .45 LC, .44-40, and .357 Mag. cal.'s, 7½ barrel.

Mfg.'s Sug. Retail	$340	$315	$245	$200	$170	$155	$140	$120

Add $60 for nickel plating.

Model 1875 Carbine—same cal.'s as Outlaw 1875, 18 in. barrel, includes non-detachable shoulder stock with brass hardware and lanyard ring.

Mfg.'s Sug. Retail	$449	$405	$340	$300	$265	$230	$200	$180

1890 REMINGTON—available in .45 LC, .44-40, and .357 Mag. cal.'s, 5½ barrel.

Mfg.'s Sug. Retail	$347	$320	$250	$210	$175	$160	$145	$125

Grading	100%	98%	95%	90%	80%	70%	60%

1871 ROLLING BLOCK TARGET PISTOL—available in .357 Mag., .22 LR, or .22 Mag. cal., 9½ in. barrel.

Mfg.'s Sug. Retail	$299	$265	$205	$180	$160	$140	$125	$110

1871 Rolling Block Baby Carbine—same cal.'s as Target Pistol, has 22 in. barrel and walnut stock and forearm, brass trigger guard and buttplate.

Mfg.'s Sug. Retail	$339	$310	$245	$205	$170	$155	$140	$120

ROLLING BLOCK SPORTING RIFLE—.45-70 cal., 30 in. barrel, walnut stock and forearm. New in 1989.

Mfg.'s Sug. Retail	$625	$565	$430	$395	$350	$320	$300	$275

Deluxe Rolling Block Sporting Rifle—similar to standard model, except has select wood.

Mfg.'s Sug. Retail	$725	$640	$485	$450	$375	$340	$320	$295

REVOLVERS: DOUBLE ACTION

INSPECTOR MODEL—.38 Sp. cal., 3, 4, or 6 in. barrel, double action, blued or chrome finish.

Mfg.'s Sug. Retail	$389	$345	$275	$250	$220	$195	$175	$160

Add $20 for target sights.
Add $20 for chrome plating.

RIFLES: WINCHESTER REPRODUCTIONS

Add $20 for Charcoal Blue finish for below listed models.

HENRY RIFLE/CARBINE—.44-40 cal., brass frame, 24½ in. barrel on rifle, 22½ in. barrel on carbine.

Mfg.'s Sug. Retail	$725	$650	$525	$465	$415	$360	$325	$295

Subtract $30 for Carbine Model.

Can also be special ordered with Grade A engraving ($325 extra), Grade B engraving ($575 extra), and Grade C engraving ($750 extra).

1866 SPORTING RIFLE—.22 LR, .22 Mag., .38 Spl., or .44-40 cal., brass receiver, 24 in. octagon barrel.

Mfg.'s Sug. Retail	$579	$495	$400	$350	$320	$275	$240	$200

1866 YELLOWBOY CARBINE—same cal.'s as 1866 Sporting Rifle, 19 in. round barrel with 2 bands, saddle ring, uncheckered walnut stock and forearm.

Mfg.'s Sug. Retail	$575	$490	$400	$350	$320	$275	$240	$200

1866 Trapper Carbine—.44-40 cal., 16 in. round barrel.

Mfg.'s Sug. Retail	$575	$490	$400	$350	$320	$275	$240	$200

1866 Yellowboy Indian Carbine—.22 LR, .22 Mag., .38 Spl., or .44-40 cal., 19 in. round barrel.

Mfg.'s Sug. Retail	$649	$575	$475	$400	$350	$300	$260	$220

This model has a photo engraved brass frame and has brass tacks in stock and forearm.

Red Cloud Commemorative Carbine—same cal.'s as Yellowboy Indian Carbine, includes special engraving representing Oglalla Indian tribe symbols, brass tacks in forearm and stock.

Mfg.'s Sug. Retail	$649	$575	$475	$400	$350	$300	$260	$220

1873 SPORTING RIFLE—.22 LR, .22 Mag., .357 Mag., .44-40, or .45 LC cal., 24½ in. octagon barrel, case hardened reciever, full mag., iron sights.

Mfg.'s Sug. Retail	$695	$625	$500	$450	$425	$395	$370	$345

1873 Carbine—.22 LR, .22 Mag., .357 Mag., .44-40, or 45 LC cal., blued steel receiver, saddle ring, 19 in. round barrel.

Mfg.'s Sug. Retail	$649	$575	$475	$400	$350	$300	$260	$220

Add $90 for nickel plating.

1873 Trapper Carbine—.44-40 cal. only, 16 in. barrel, blue finish only.

Mfg.'s Sug. Retail	$649	$575	$475	$400	$350	$300	$260	$220

CLASSIC DOUBLES

MANUFACTURED IN TOCHIGI CITY, JAPAN. IMPORTED AND DISTRIBUTED BY
CLASSIC DOUBLES INTERNATIONAL, INC. LOCATED IN ST. LOUIS, MO.

In late 1987, Winchester/Olin discontinued importation of their Japanese shotgun models
(Models 101 and 23). At that point, Classic Doubles International, Inc. became the sole importer
of these shotguns. There have been very few changes made during this changeover of importation.
However, the new Classic Double shotguns (Models 101 and 201) do not have the Winchester
trademark or definitive Winchester proofmark stamped on the barrels. The Model 201 is a new
model designation.

AT THIS WRITING, THE FIREARMS FACILITY AT TOCHIGI CITY, JAPAN IS TEMPORARILY
CLOSED. HOWEVER, THERE IS A GOOD SUPPLY OF MOST OF THE BELOW LISTED
MODELS.

SHOTGUNS: O/U - MODEL 101

All newly imported Classic Doubles have an interchangeable choke tube system compatible
with the older Winchester manufatctured models. Prices listed include a luggage style
carrying case.

CLASSIC FIELD GRADE I—12 or 20 ga., 3 in. chambers, vent rib, 25½ or 28 in. vent.
barrels with choke tubes, blued receiver with moderate scroll engraving, ejectors, checkered
pistol grip or English stock and forearm, 6¼ - 7 lbs.

Mfg.'s Sug. Retail **$1,905 $1,700 $1,400 $1,250 $1,100 $1,000 $900 $825**

WATERFOWL MODEL—12 ga. only, 3 in. chambers, 30 in. barrels with vent rib and
choke tubes, matte blued receiver with moderate engraving, low gloss walnut stock with
vent recoil pad, 7 ¾ lbs.

Mfg.'s Sug. Retail **$1,520 $1,375 $1,150 $995 $895 $800 $700 $600**

CLASSIC SPORTER—12 ga. only, made for Sporting Clays competition, 28 or 30 in. vent
barrels and rib with choke tubes, quick detachable stock system, border engraved coin
finished receiver with non-reflective matte surface on top frame and lever, checkered walnut
stock and forearm, 7¾ lbs.

Mfg.'s Sug. Retail **$1,980 $1,775 $1,500 $1,295 $1,150 $1,000 $900 $825**
Add $965 for extra barrel.

CLASSIC FIELD GRADE II—12, 20, 28 and .410 ga.'s, 28 in. choke tube vent. barrels
and rib, deluxe walnut with round knob pistol grip stock and forearm with fine fleur-de-lis
checkering, coin finished receiver (different sizes) with game scene engraving featuring
hunting motifs on receiver sides and bottom, .410 ga. bored M/F only, 6¼ - 7lbs.

Mfg.'s Sug. Retail **$2,190 $1,950 $1,675 $1,425 $1,245 $1,100 $1,000 $900**

the .410 and 28 ga.'s are more desireable in this model.

CLASSIC FIELD GRADE II TWO BARREL SET—12 and 20 ga. barrels, both with
Winchokes, 26 in. barrels - 20 ga., 28 in. barrels - 12 ga., coin finished receiver with game
scene engraving and borders, 6½ (20 ga.) or 7 (12 ga.) lbs.

Mfg.'s Sug. Retail **$3,420 $2,995 $2,500 $2,100 $1,825 $1,550 $1,375 $1,200**

TARGET GUNS

CLASSIC TRAP SINGLE—12 ga. only, over single 32 or 34 in. barrel with vent. rib and
choke tubes, blued receiver with light engraving, choice of Monte Carlo or regular stock,
recoil pad, 8½ lbs.

Mfg.'s Sug. Retail **$2,070 $1,750 $1,425 $1,250 $1,100 $1,000 $900 $825**

CLASSIC TRAP O/U—12 ga. only, 30 or 32 in. vent. barrels and rib with choke tubes,
finish and engraving similar to Classic Trap Single, choice of Monte Carlo or standard
stock with recoil pad, 8¾ or 9 lbs.

Mfg.'s Sug. Retail **$1,905 $1,700 $1,300 $1,125 $1,000 $900 $825 $750**

CLASSIC TRAP COMBO—includes one set of O/U barrels (30 or 32 in.) and one over
single barrel (32 or 34 in.), choke tubes, choice of Monte Carlo or standard stock, 8¾ or 9
lbs.

Mfg.'s Sug. Retail **$2,825 $2,575 $2,125 $1,875 $1,600 $1,475 $1,300 $1,175**

Grading	100%	98%	95%	90%	80%	70%	60%

CLASSIC SKEET—12 or 20 ga., 27½ in. vent. barrels and rib, choke tubes on 12 ga. only, smaller ga.'s are bored SK/Sk, similar metal finish to Classic Trap models, 7¼ or 7¾ lbs.

Mfg.'s Sug. Retail	$1,905	$1,700	$1,450	$1,275	$1,125	$1,000	$900	$825

Classic Skeet 4 ga. Set—similar to Classic Skeet except has 4 barrels (12, 20, 28, and .410 ga.), 12 ga. has choke tubes, smaller ga.'s are bored SK/SK.

Mfg.'s Sug. Retail	$4,765	$4,300	$3,900	$3,500	$3,100	$2,875	$2,600	$2,400

SHOTGUNS: SIDE BY SIDE

MODEL 201 CLASSIC—12 or 20 ga., 3 in. chambers, forged steel monoblock with improved lug design, 26 in. choke tube barrels with vent. rib, high lustre bluing, no engraving, SST, ejectors, premium walnut stock and beavertail forearm with fancy checkering pattern, solid red rubber recoil pad, 6¾ - 7 lbs.

Mfg.'s Sug. Retail	$2,190	$1,900	$1,650	$1,450	$1,275	$995	$875	$775

Add $120 for 20 ga.

The 12 ga. can be ordered with choke tubes at no extra charge.

Model 201 Classic Small Bore Set—28 and .410 ga. two barrel set, similar to Model 201 Classic except has smaller frame and overall dimensions, 28 in. VR barrels only bored IC/M on 28 ga. and M/F on .410 ga., 6 or 6½ lbs

Mfg.'s Sug. Retail	$3,675	$3,295	$2,650	$2,250	$1,900	$1,700	$1,550	$1,400

CLERKE PRODUCTS

SANTA MONICA, CA.

HI-WALL—single shot rifle, falling block replica of Winchester 1885 High Wall, lever operated, case hardened receiver, 26 in. barrel, available in most modern calibers, no sights, checkered walnut pistol grip stock, Schnabel forearm, made 1972-1974.

	$250	$225	$185	$175	$150	$140	$125

DELUXE HI-WALL—same as Hi-Wall, except half octagon barrel, select wood and recoil pad.

	$300	$275	$235	$210	$180	$160	$145

CLIFTON ARMS

MANUFACTURER AND RETAILER OF CUSTOM RIFLES LOCATED IN GRAND PRAIRIE, TX. CLIFTON ARMS MOSTLY SPECIALIZES IN COMPOSITE STOCKS (WITH OR WITHOUT INTEGRAL, RETRACTABLE BIPOD).

Clifton Arms mostly manufactures composite, hand laminated stocks that are modeled after the Dakota 76 rifle. However, custom rifles can be ordered by contacting the company and specifying the type of action, caliber, barrel and stock configuration and or color. Price quotations vary per individual, special ordered rifle.

COBRAY INDUSTRIES

SEE LISTING UNDER S.W.D. IN THE S SECTION OF THIS TEXT.

COGSWELL & HARRISON, LIMITED

LONDON, ENGLAND. 1770 TO DATE.

SHOTGUNS

REGENCY—12, 16, or 20 ga., double barrel, 26, 28, or 30 in. barrels, any choke combination, hammerless Anson & Deeley system, boxlock, double triggers, auto ejectors, straight English stock, made 1970-present.

Mfg.'s Sug. Retail	$3,200	$2,750	$2,500	$2,250	$2,000	$1,800	$1,600	$1,375

Grading	100%	98%	95%	90%	80%	70%	60%

AMBASSADOR MODEL—double barrel, same gauges and barrels as Regency, boxlock with false sideplates, auto ejectors, double triggers, engraved game scene or scroll rose motif, English stock.

Mfg.'s Sug. Retail	$4,000	$3,650	$3,100	$2,850	$2,700	$2,500	$2,250	$1,995

MARKOR—12, 16, or 20 ga., double barrel, 27½ or 30 in. barrel and choke, boxlock, double trigger, English stock. Discontinued.

	$1,500	$1,350	$1,200	$1,000	$950	$825	$700
Auto ejectors	$1,750	$1,500	$1,350	$1,200	$1,100	$900	$700

HUNTIC MODEL—12, 16, or 20 ga., double barrel, 25, 27, or 30 in. barrels, any choke, sidelock, auto ejectors, English style stock. Discontinued.

	$3,500	$3,200	$3,000	$2,800	$2,500	$2,175	$1,850

SST — add $400.

AVANT TOUT SERIES—12, 16, and 20 ga., double barrel, 25, 27½, or 30 in. barrels, boxlock, false sideplates, straight English stock, auto ejectors, series discontinued.

REX OR AVANT TOUT III—no sideplates.

	$1,800	$1,650	$1,500	$1,350	$1,200	$1,075	$895

SANDHURST OR AVANT TOUT II

	$2,500	$2,300	$2,150	$2,000	$1,750	$1,500	$1,225

KONOR OR AVANT TOUT I

	$2,850	$2,700	$2,500	$2,250	$2,000	$1,775	$1,500

SST — add $400.
20 ga. — add 20%.
16 ga. — deduct 10%.

BEST QUALITY—12, 16, and 20 ga.'s, double barrel, 25, 26, 28, or 30 in. barrels, any choke, hand detachable sidelock, auto ejectors, double triggers standard, English stock.

Primic Model—discontinued.

	$5,750	$4,650	$4,150	$3,650	$3,050	$2,500	$1,950

Victor Model

Mfg.'s Sug. Retail	$10,000	$8,600	$6,250	$5,000	$4,350	$3,740	$3,000	$2,375

SST — add $400.
20 ga. — add 20%.
16 ga. — deduct 10%.

Note: Degree of engraving and grade of wood are the basic differences among models.

COLT'S FIREARMS

CURRENTLY MANUFACTURED IN HARTFORD, CT.

Manufactured from 1836-1841 in Paterson, NJ; 1847 to 1848 in Whitneyville, CT; 1854 to 1864 in London, England; and from 1848 to date in Hartford, CT. Colt Firearms became a division of Colt Industries in 1964.

PERCUSSION REVOLVERS

Prices shown for percussion Colt's are for guns only. Original cased guns with accessories will bring a healthy premium over non-cased models. Be very careful when buying an "original" cased gun, as many fake cases have shown up in recent years.

Grading	80%	70%	60%	50%	40%	30%	20%	10%

Prices shown on the following pages for extremely rare Colt's firearms might not include values in the 90% or greater condition column. Prices are very hard to establish since these excellent to mint specimens are seldomly seen or sold.

Grading	80%	70%	60%	50%	40%	30%	20%	10%

POCKET MODEL PATERSON—the "Baby Paterson", .28 and .31 cal., 5 shot, 2½ in. to 4¾ in. barrels, blued metal with walnut varnished grips, serial range 1-500, marked Patent Arms M'g Co., Paterson, N.J., Colt's Pt., made 1837-1838.

Without loading lever

	$11,000	$9,900	$8,250	$6,050	$4,400	$3,300	$3,025	$2,750

Factory modified—with loading lever.

	$12,100	$11,000	$9,350	$7,150	$5,500	$4,400	$4,125	$3,850

POCKET MODEL PATERSON—.31 and .34 cal., 2½ in. to 4¾ in. octagon barrels, larger gauge than the "Baby" model, serial range 1-800, blued metal with walnut varnished grips, made 1837-1840.

Without loading lever

	$11,000	$9,900	$8,250	$6,050	$4,400	$3,850	$3,300	$3,025

With loading lever

	$13,200	$12,100	$10,450	$8,250	$6,600	$5,500	$5,225	$4,950

BELT MODEL PATERSON—.31 and .34 cal., 5 shot, 4-6 in. barrels, can be found with Pocket Model straight grip or flared grip, blued metal with walnut varnished stocks, same may have case hardened hammer, marked with the Paterson, N.J. address.

Straight grip—without loading levers.

	$13,200	$12,100	$9,900	$8,800	$6,600	$4,400	$3,850	$3,025

Flared grip—without loading lever.

	$11,000	$9,900	$8,800	$7,700	$5,500	$3,850	$3,300	$2,750

Note: Add 10% to premium pieces with loading lever.

TEXAS PATERSON—.36 cal., 4-12 in. octagon barrels, 7½ and 9 in. barrels are most common, serial range 1-1000, blued metal with case hardened hammer and frame and walnut varnished grips, this model has the greatest collector appeal of the Patersons, stagecoach holdup scene rolled on cylinder and flared grip style.

Without loading lever

	$27,500	$24,200	$22,000	$17,600	$13,200	$9,900	$8,250	$7,700

With loading lever

	$33,000	$29,700	$27,500	$24,200	$17,600	$13,200	$9,900	$8,800

Note: Authentic martially marked models have considerable added value and should be appraised individually.

WALKER COLT—.44 cal., 6 shot, 9 in. round and octagon barrel, designed for military use, blued metal, case hardened frame, lever, hammer, brass trigger guard, cylinder unfinished with Texas Ranger and Indian battle scene, all numbered in companies A, B, C, D, and E, one piece walnut grips, with inspectors marks, all inspector's marks well worn, as are revolvers, top of barrel marked, "ADDRESS SAM COLT NEW YORK CITY", made 1847.

Military model

	$49,000	$42,500	$37,500	$33,500	$31,000	$28,500	$26,000	$24,000

Civilian model—serial numbered from 1001-1100.

	$45,000	$41,000	$36,500	$32,500	$30,500	$27,000	$25,000	$23,000

WHITNEYVILLE HARTFORD DRAGOON—.44 cal., 6 shot, 7½ in. octagon and round barrel, some of the left-over Walker parts were used in Dragoons, blued metal with casehardened frame, lever, hammer, brass trigger guard and steel cylinder bears Texas Ranger and Indian battle scene.

Rear frame cut out for grips

	$45,000	$40,500	$36,500	$32,900	$29,500	$26,500	$23,000	$21,400

Straight rear frame

	$42,500	$38,250	$34,500	$31,000	$27,800	$26,000	$23,400	$21,000

FIRST MODEL DRAGOON—.44 cal., 6 shot, 7½ in. round and octagon barrel, blued metal with case hardened frame, lever, hammer, brass grip straps, silvered straps for civilian market, serial range numbered after Hartford Dragoon, 1341 to around 8000, made 1848-1850.

Grading	80%	70%	60%	50%	40%	30%	20%	10%

Military model

| | $9,900 | $8,800 | $7,150 | $6,050 | $4,950 | $4,235 | $2,750 | $1,100 |

Civilian model

| | $8,800 | $7,700 | $6,050 | $4,950 | $3,850 | $3,575 | $2,200 | $880 |

FLUCK MODEL DRAGOON—basically a First Model Dragoon, with 7½ in. altered Walker barrels and fully martially marked, should be extensively checked over, used to replace defective Walkers, made 1848.

| | $9,900 | $8,800 | $7,150 | $6,050 | $4,950 | $4,125 | $2,420 | $1,870 |

SECOND MODEL DRAGOON—.44 cal., 6 shot, 7½ in. round and octagon barrel, serial range following the First Model Dragoon 8000-10,700, made 1850-1851.

Military model

| | $8,800 | $7,700 | $6,600 | $5,500 | $4,400 | $3,630 | $2,200 | $1,100 |

Civilian model

| | $6,600 | $5,500 | $4,400 | $4,125 | $3,850 | $3,300 | $2,200 | $1,100 |

New Hampshire or Massachusetts

| | $8,800 | $7,700 | $6,600 | $5,500 | $4,400 | $3,850 | $2,750 | $1,650 |

THIRD MODEL DRAGOON—.44 cal., 6 shot, 7½ in. round or octagon barrel, same basic features as earlier models, but with round trigger guard and rectangular cylinder slots, serial range approximately 10,200-19,600, some overlapping of numbers, with approximately 10,500 produced from 1851-1861.

Third model Dragoon

| | $4,400 | $4,125 | $3,850 | $3,300 | $2,750 | $2,475 | $2,200 | $1,650 |

Martially marked U.S.

| | $4,950 | $4,400 | $4,125 | $3,850 | $3,300 | $2,750 | $2,420 | $1,980 |

Third model—8 in. barrel.

| | $8,800 | $7,150 | $6,050 | $5,500 | $5,225 | $4,950 | $3,850 | $3,300 |

First and second variation—shoulder stock model.

| | $8,800 | $7,150 | $6,050 | $5,280 | $4,950 | $4,675 | $4,125 | $3,300 |

C.L. Dragoon

| | $6,600 | $5,500 | $4,950 | $4,400 | $4,125 | $3,850 | $3,025 | $2,750 |

ENGLISH HARTFORD DRAGOON—basically a Third Model Dragoon, assembled at Colt's London factory, with unique serial range 1-700, some were assembled from earlier parts inventories, easy to spot with British proofs of crown over V and crown over GP, the blue was of the English type, many were engraved.

English Hartford Dragoon—not engraved.

| | $5,500 | $4,950 | $4,400 | $3,850 | $3,300 | $3,025 | $1,980 | $1,100 |

1848 BABY DRAGOONS—.31 cal., 5 shot, 3, 4, 5, and 6 in. octagon barrels, most without loading lever, serial range 1-15,500, a scaled down version of the .44 caliber Dragoons, early ones with Texas Ranger scene and later ones with the holdup scene.

Type I—left hand barrel stamping, Texas Ranger and Indian scene, serial range 1-about 150.

| | $3,630 | $3,025 | $2,475 | $1,980 | $1,650 | $1,320 | $990 | $825 |

Type II—with Texas Ranger and Indian scene, 11,600 serial range, without loading lever.

| | $2,365 | $1,925 | $1,650 | $1,430 | $1,210 | $990 | $770 | $605 |

Type III—with Stagecoach scene and oval cylinder slots, serial range 10,400-12,000.

| | $2,365 | $1,925 | $1,650 | $1,430 | $1,210 | $990 | $770 | $605 |

Type IV—with Stagecoach holdup scene, rectangle cylinder slots, serial range 11,000-12,500.

| | $2,640 | $2,310 | $1,925 | $1,595 | $1,320 | $1,045 | $825 | $660 |

Type V—with Stagecoach holdup scene, rectangle cylinder slots and loading lever, serial range 11,600-15,500.

| | $2,915 | $2,475 | $2,090 | $1,760 | $1,485 | $1,210 | $935 | $770 |

Grading	80%	70%	60%	50%	40%	30%	20%	10%

1849 POCKET MODEL—.31 cal., 5 or 6 shot, 3, 4, 5, and 6 in. octagon barrels, most with loading levers, blued metal with case hardened frame, lever and hammer, grip straps of brass (silver plated), or steel (silver plated or blued), serial range 12,000 to 340,000, made 1850-1873.

First Type—4, 5, and 6 in. barrel, loading lever and small or large brass trigger guard.

	$1,705	$1,320	$990	$770	$605	$550	$495	$350

Second Type—4, 5, and 6 in. barrel, loading lever and steel grip straps.

	$1,815	$1,540	$1,255	$990	$770	$605	$440	$350

Wells Fargo Model—3 in. barrel, without loading lever and with small round trigger guard.

	$2,310	$1,925	$1,595	$1,320	$1,045	$825	$605	$500

1849 POCKET MODEL—London pistols were of the same general configuration, but of better finish, serial range 1-11,000, made 1853-1857.

Early Type—serial numbered under 1000, with small trigger guard and brass grip straps.

	$2,035	$1,595	$1,265	$1,045	$880	$715	$605	$500

Late Type—oval trigger guard and steel grip straps.

	$1,705	$1,320	$990	$770	$650	$575	$500	$450

1851 NAVY—.36 cal., 6 shot, 7½ in. octagon barrel and loading lever, blued metal with casehardened frame, lever and hammer, one piece walnut finished grips, cylinder scene of Texas Navy battle with Mexico, serial range 1-highest recorded number was 215,348, three barrel addresses 1-74,000 (ADDRESS SAM COLT, HARTFORD, CT.), 74,000-101,000 (ADDRESS SAM COLT, HARTFORD, CT.) 101,000-215,348 (ADDRESS COL. SAM COLT, NEW YORK, U.S. AMERICA), made 1850-1873.

First Model—square back trigger guard, bottom wedge screw, serial range 1-1,250.

	$6,750	$5,500	$4,350	$3,650	$2,900	$2,440	$1,850	$1,320

Second Model—square back trigger guard, top wedge screw, serial range 1,250-4,000.

	$3,360	$2,775	$2,375	$1,980	$1,650	$1,320	$1,120	$925

Third Model—small round brass trigger guard, serial range 4,200-85,000.

	$2,310	$1,980	$1,650	$1,450	$1,200	$980	$860	$725

Fourth Model—large round brass trigger guard, serial range 85,000-215,348.

	$2,250	$1,915	$1,585	$1,385	$1,125	$925	$800	$660

Iron Gripstrap Model—most often seen in fourth model.

	$2,995	$2,575	$2,100	$1,715	$1,385	$1,190	$925	$790

Martially Marked U.S. Navies—brass or iron gripstrap.

	$3,300	$3,000	$2,640	$1,900	$1,580	$1,320	$1,100	$895

Cut for shoulder stock—first and second type (like third model Dragoon).

	$5,100	$4,750	$4,350	$3,960	$3,300	$2,640	$2,310	$1,980

Third Type—four screw frame.

	$4,620	$3,960	$3,300	$2,500	$2,175	$1,915	$1,650	$1,320

51 NAVY LONDON MODEL—basically the same gun as the Hartford piece with London barrel address, with British proof marks in serial range 1-42,000, made 1853-1857.

Early First Model—serial range below 2000, brass grip straps and small trigger guard.

	$3,300	$2,750	$2,200	$1,320	$1,100	$935	$825	$660

Late Second Model—balance of production, large round trigger guard, steel grip straps, all London parts.

	$2,035	$1,650	$1,320	$1,100	$935	$825	$660	$550

1860 MODEL ARMY—.44 cal., 6 shot, 7½ and 8 in. round barrels with loading lever, blued metal with case hardened frame, lever and hammer, one piece walnut grips, normally blued steel back strap and brass trigger guard, barrel markings were (ADDRESS SAM COLT, HARTFORD, CT.) on early productions and (ADDRESS COL. SAM COLT, NEW YORK, U.S. AMERICA) on balance, serial range 1-about 200,500, Texas Navy scene on round cylinder model, made 1860-1873.

Grading	80%	70%	60%	50%	40%	30%	20%	10%

1860 MODEL ARMY—Fluted Cylinder Model, full length cylinder flutes and no cylinder scene, 7½ or 8 in. barrel, grips of Navy (very rare) or Army size, usually 4 screw frames.

	$3,150	$2,900	$2,530	$2,200	$2,025	$1,895	$1,750	$1,575

ROUND CYLINDER MODEL—roll engraved Texas Navy scene, some with early Hartford address, Army grips, four screw frame to about 50,000 range, most were sold to the U.S. Government and will be martially marked.

	$3,700	$3,150	$2,600	$2,000	$1,350	$975	$605	$550

CIVILIAN MODEL—same general configurations as Round Cylinder Model, but with 3 screw frame, no shoulder stock cuts and better blue finish than military pieces, late New York barrel address.

	$3,850	$3,330	$2,725	$2,120	$1,450	$1,075	$700	$575

1861 MODEL NAVY—.36 cal., 6 shot, 7½ in. round barrel with loading lever, blued metal with case hardened frame, lever and hammer, silver plated brass grip straps, the barrel address was (ADDRESS COL. SAM COLT, NEW YORK, U.S. AMERICA), serial range 1 - 38,843, cylinder scene of Texas Navy and MEXICO BATTLE, MADE 1861-1873.

Regular production model

	$3,025	$2,365	$1,870	$1,430	$1,265	$990	$770	$550

Martially Marked Navies—will bear the U.S. stamp and inspector's marks, those marked U.S.N. on butt were of a 650 piece order for the Navy.

	$4,750	$4,125	$3,465	$2,750	$2,310	$1,925	$1,430	$990

London Mark Navy—with (ADDRESS COL. COLT, LONDON), for barrel address.

	$3,975	$3,520	$3,025	$2,585	$2,200	$2,090	$1,705	$1,320

Shoulder Stock Cut Navy—4 screw frames in serial range 11,000-14,000, made for third style stock (see Dragoon stocks).

	$5,375	$4,895	$4,400	$3,905	$3,465	$3,025	$2,420	$1,925

Fluted Cylinder Navy—in serial range 1-100, with fluted cylinder and without rolled cylinder scene.

	$9,750	$8,900	$8,800	$7,150	$6,050	$4,950	$3,850	$3,025

1862 POLICE MODEL—.36 cal., 4½, 5½, and 6½ in. barrels, 5 shot, semi-fluted cylinder, last design of the Colt Percussion Pistols, mostly seen with brass trigger guards and grip straps, streamlined design, mfg. 1861-1873.

	$3,025	$2,365	$1,870	$1,430	$1,265	$990	$770	$550

DERRINGERS

100%	98%	95%	90%	80%	70%	60%	50%	40%	30%	20%	10%

FIRST MODEL DERRINGER—.41 rimfire, single shot, 2½ in. barrel, scroll engraving standard, blued, nickel, or silver plated barrel, downward pivoting barrel, no grips, serial numbered 1-6,500, manufactured approximately 1870-1890.

$850	$820	$750	$675	$600	$540	$495	$440	$395	$340	$295	$250

SECOND MODEL DERRINGER—.41 rimfire or centerfire, single shot, 2½ in. barrel, scroll engraving standard, blued, nickel, or silver plated barrel, downward pivoting barrel, checkered and varnished walnut grips, "No 2" marked on top of barrel, serial numbered 1-9,000, manufactured approximately 1870-1890.

$550	$520	$480	$440	$395	$360	$330	$295	$260	$220	$180	$140

.41 Centerfire — add 100%.

THIRD MODEL DERRINGER (THUER MODEL)—.41 rimfire and centerfire, single shot, side pivoting 2½ in. barrel, varnished walnut grips, blued barrels, bronze frames were either nickel or silver plated, engraving optional, Colt-barrel address, spur trigger, serial numbered approx. 1-47,000, manufactured approximately 1875-1910.

$400	$360	$320	$275	$240	$210	$180	$150	$125	$100	$80	$60

.41 centerfire is worth an additional 30% and early models are worth considerably more.

Grading	100%	98%	95%	90%	80%	70%	60%

FOURTH MODEL DERRINGER—.22 Short, single shot similar in appearance to the 3rd Model, 2½ in. barrel, approx. 112,000 mfg. between 1959-1963 with either D or N suffix. A few were put in books, picture frames, penholders, bookends, etc. (these will command premiums).

				$100	$85	$65	

LORD DERRINGER—.22 short only, side pivoting Thuer action, gold plated with black chrome barrel and walnut grips, manufactured approximately 1959-1963 by Colt, cased.

				$100	$85	$65	

LADY DERRINGER—.22 short only, side pivoting Thuer action, full gold plated finish with pearlite grips, manufactured approximately 1959-1963 by Colt, cased.

				$100	$85	$65	

LORD & LADY CASED SET—one each of the Lord & Lady derringers or combinations, consecutive serial numbers.

			$250	$175	$125		

LADY CASED SET—cased pair of Lady Derringers.

			$250	$175	$125		

LORD CASED SET—cased pair of Lord Derringers.

			$250	$175	$125		

POCKET PISTOLS

100%	98%	95%	90%	80%	70%	60%	50%	40%	30%	20%	10%

CLOVERLEAF HOUSE PISTOL—.41 short or long rimfire, cloverleaf configured 4 shot cylinder, spur trigger, 1½ or 3 in. barrel, approx. 7,500 mfg. in ser. no. range 1-8,300 during 1871-1876.

$850	$820	$750	$675	$600	$540	$495	$440	$395	$340	$295	$250

This model is sometimes referred to as the Jim Fisk model as he was murdered by Edward Stokes with a Cloverleaf.

5-shot Cloverleaf—similar to 4-shot model, except has round 5-shot cylinder and 2⅞ barrel only, approx. 2,500 mfg. in ser. no. range 6,160-9,950 during 1871-1876.

$995	$925	$850	$775	$695	$620	$550	$495	$440	$395	$340	$295

OPEN TOP REVOLVER (OLD LINE)—.22 short or long rimfire, 2⅜ or 2⅞ in. barrel, without topstrap on frame, with or without integral ejector, blued or nickel plated, varnished walnut grips, approx. 114,200 mfg. 1871-1877.

$450	$400	$350	$325	$300	$280	$255	$230	$200	$175	$150	$125

NEW LINE REVOLVER AND VARIATIONS

1st Model—.22, .30, .32, .38, or .41 cal. rim and centerfire, mfg. 1873-1876, 7 (.22 cal. only) or 5 shot, short cylinder flutes, cylinder stop slots cut on exterior of cylinder, 1¾, 2¼, or 4 in. barrel, full nickel or blue/case hardened finish, spur trigger, many thousands mfg. 1873-1876.

$400	$350	$300	$275	$250	$225	$200	$185	$170	$160	$145	$120

2nd Model—similar to 1st Model, except has longer cylinder flutes and cylinder stop slots are on the back of cylinder, may or may not have loading gate, mfg. 1876-1884.

$400	$350	$300	$275	$250	$225	$200	$185	$170	$160	$145	$120

Caliber rarity on both models from highest mfg. to lowest is: .22, .32, .30, .41, and .38.

NEW HOUSE MODEL—.38 or .41 cal. centerfire, 5 shot, 2¼ in. barrel, spur trigger, checkered hard rubber grips, approx. 4,000 mfg. 1880-1886 starting at ser. no. 10,300.

$1,000	$925	$850	$775	$695	$620	$550	$495	$440	$395	$325	$260

NEW POLICE MODEL—.32, .38, or .41 cal. centerfire, 5 shot, 2¼, 4½, 5, or 6 in. barrel, spur trigger, with or without ejector, stamped or etched "NEW POLICE" on barrel, approx. 4,000 mfg. 1882-1886.

$850	$820	$750	$675	$600	$540	$495	$440	$395	$340	$295	$250

Grading	80%	70%	60%	50%	40%	30%	20%	10%

PERCUSSION CONVERSIONS

Research is currently underway to categorize the many variations (including Thuer) that exist on Percussion revolvers which were converted for centerfire capability. Over 46,000 conversions were made on the following models listed in order of highest mfg. to lowest: 1862 Police and Pocket Navy, Model 1860 Army Richards, Thuer's patent conversions, Model 1851 Navy, Model 1861 Navy, Model 1860 Army Richards-Mason. Out of these, the Models 1862 Police and Pocket Navy accounted for slightly over 50%. Be wary of "2nd" generation alterations. Prices generally are in the $650-$2,000 + range with rarer variations selling for considerably more.

"OPEN TOP" REVOLVERS

1871-72 OPEN TOP MODEL RIMFIRE—.44 cal. rimfire, 6 shot, 7½ in. barrel, without frame topstrap, blued metal with casehardened hammer, serial range 1-approximately 7000, barrel address (ADDRESS COL. SAM COLT, NEW YORK, U.S. AMERICA), forerunner of the single action Army, quite desirable, made 1871-1872.

Regular Production Model—7½ in. barrel, New York address, Army grips.

	$8,000	$6,950	$5,750	$4,400	$3,025	$1,925	$1,650	$1,100

Regular Production—with Navy grips.

	$8,500	$7,400	$6,150	$4,950	$3,300	$2,200	$1,925	$1,650

Late Production—with address (COLT PT. F. A. MANUFACTURING CO., HARTFORD, CT., U.S.A.).

	$6,400	$5,200	$4,500	$3,850	$2,475	$1,540	$1,375	$1,045

Note: Models with 8 in. barrel of COLTS/PATENT frame markings have added value.

REVOLVERS: SINGLE ACTION ARMY — 1873-1940 MFG.(SER. NO.'S 1 - 357,000)

Note: The Colt SAA was produced in over 30 Calibers with just about any special order feature or combination of special orders available directly from the factory. All of these special orders act independently and interdependently to determine a correct value for a particular Colt SAA. Single action Colt's rank at the top for revolver collectors. When contemplating a purchase in the 4 digit plus price range, several professional opinions should be secured. Caliber rarities make a major difference in pricing single actions.

It is advisable to procure a factory letter when buying or selling older or recently manufactured Colt Single Action's (hence guaranteeing authenticity and value credibility). These watermarked letters are available by writing Colt Industries in Hartford, CT, with a charge of $35 per serial number - if Colt cannot provide you with proper documentation after conducting research, they will refund you $10. Include your name and address, Colt model name, serial number, and check to: COLT HISTORIAN, P.O. BOX 1868, HARTFORD, CT 06101. Please allow adequate time for proper response.

Values shown below are for guns without special order features. Factory engraving, ivory grips, very rare special order barrel lengths, and special finishes would add considerably to the values shown below. One final word on single action Colts: Black Powder Colts (pre 182,000 serial range) should be scrutinized carefully for restamped serial numbers on various parts. This makes a major difference in pricing the SAA, as a true, original collector's gun differs greatly in value from a restamped "parts gun". .44-40 and .45 cal.'s in the pre 182,000 serial range will bring premiums over other calibers, especially in shorter barrel lengths. The .44-40 caliber is very collectible since this ammunition at inception was interchangeable with the most popular rifle/carbine of its circa - the Winchester Model 1873.

EARLY MODEL SAA—serial range 1-100, with frame pinched to make rear sight, .45 cal., 7½ in. barrel, made 1813.

	$9,950	$9,200	$8,500	$7,525	$6,875	$6,250	$5,275	$3,900

EARLY MARTIAL MARKED SAA—serial range to 24,000, .45 cal., 7½ in. barrel, U.S. marked.

	$7,900	$6,600	$5,275	$4,600	$3,750	$2,900	$2,450	$2,175

Grading	80%	70%	60%	50%	40%	30%	20%	10%

.44 RIMFIRE SAA—mostly in .44 Henry rimfire, 7½ in. barrel, serial numbered in own range 1-1863, mfg. 1875-1880, most specimens were shipped to Mexico and saw hard use, rare in any original condition.

	80%	70%	60%	50%	40%	30%	20%	10%
	$8,000	$7,000	$6,000	$4,950	$3,700	$2,600	$2,100	$1,500

This variation is one of the most frequently faked Colt revolvers — be careful (and get a receipt).

SINGLE ACTION ARMY (SAA)—single action, 6 shot revolver, over 30 calibers, 3 in. (Sheriff's model), 4¾, 5½, 7½, and 12 in. (Buntline model) barrels. Blue, nickel, or case hardened frame, walnut or hard rubber grips, total production 357,000, made 1873-1940.

SAA'S WITH SERIAL NUMBERS BEFORE 182,000 ARE ANTIQUES AND ARE GENERALLY MORE COLLECTIBLE THAN POST-1898 SAA'S. VALUES FOR BOTH PERIODS OF MANUFACTURE IN THE 10%-80% CONDITION RANGE ARE SIMILAR — POST-1898 SAA REVOLVERS IN 80%-100% CONDITION WILL AVERAGE 10%-25% LOWER IN VALUE THAN ANTIQUE MANUFACTURE.

100%	98%	95%	90%	80%	70%	60%	50%	40%	30%	20%	10%

.45 cal.

100%	98%	95%	90%	80%	70%	60%	50%	40%	30%	20%	10%
$4,500	$3,850	$3,100	$2,600	$2,100	$1,820	$1,500	$1,225	$995	$785	$715	$660

.44-40 cal.—roll-die "Colt Frontier Six Shooter" marking on left side of barrel.

$5,000	$4,175	$3,350	$2,800	$2,300	$1,995	$1,640	$1,350	$1,125	$935	$825	$715

Colt changed from the etched barrel marking to a roll die in approx. 1881.

.41 cal.

$4,175	$3,450	$2,850	$2,500	$2,175	$1,710	$1,400	$1,000	$900	$700	$640	$550

.38-40 cal.

$3,850	$3,100	$2,500	$2,200	$1,900	$1,545	$1,100	$825	$770	$660	$605	$550

.32-20 cal.

$3,675	$2,900	$2,250	$1,850	$1,520	$1,275	$1,050	$825	$770	$660	$605	$550

.22 cal.

$10,000	$8,750	$7,175	$6,600	$5,500	$4,400	$3,300	$2,750	$2,425	$2,050	$1,780	$1,400

SAA IN .38 SPECIAL CAL.—only 82 made, plus 7 in. target version, pre-War.

$3,700	$3,450	$2,875	$2,300	$1,725	$1,265	$920	$850	$780	$720	$680	$630

CAVALRY MODEL SAA—.45 Colt, 7½ in. barrel, marked U.S. on left lower frame. With one piece walnut grips, military cartouche.

			$3,500	$3,000	$2,500	$2,000	$1,900	$1,800	$1,700	$1,600

ARTILLERY MODEL SAA—.45 Colt, 5½ in. barrel, marked U.S. on left lower frame. With one piece walnut grips, military cartouche. These guns are the original artillery model Colts returned to the factory or Springfield Armory. Barrels were shortened to 5½ in. and the guns were refinished and reissued to the military. Very seldom do the serial numbered parts on these guns match. A factory letter on this model will designate factory refurbishing.

			$3,000	$2,750	$2,550	$2,200	$1,800	$1,500	$1,250	$995

ETCHED BARREL .44-40 SAA—Colt Frontier, "Colt Frontier Six Shooter" acid etched into barrel instead of stamped, 21,000-65,000 ser. no. range.

$8,600	$7,800	$6,000	$5,760	$5,000	$4,400	$3,600	$3,000	$2,400	$2,000	$1,750	$1,500

This variation was only produced from 1876-1881. Watch for fake, replaced, or re-etched barrels.

SHERIFF'S MODEL SAA—3 or 4 in. barrel, without ejector rod. Watch For Fakes.

$10,750	$9,600	$8,400	$7,200	$5,760	$4,500	$3,600	$3,000	$2,400	$2,000	$1,900	$1,800

Fakes can be detected on this model by re-welded frames.

FLAT-TOP TARGET SAA—various calibers from .22 to .476 Eley, approximately 925 produced, 1888-1896.

$12,200	$11,000	$9,900	$8,800	$8,250	$7,700	$6,600	$6,050	$5,500	$4,950	$4,400	$3,850

Note: Different calibers command lower prices than shown for .476 Eley; qualified appraisal should be secured.

100%	98%	95%	90%	80%	70%	60%	50%	40%	30%	20%	10%

BISLEY MODEL SAA—differs from single action Army by hump backed grip frame and raked hammer, approximately 44,350 produced, 1894-1915.

.32-20 cal.

100%	98%	95%	90%	80%	70%	60%	50%	40%	30%	20%	10%
$3,000	$2,600	$2,100	$1,900	$1,300	$1,100	$895	$715	$660	$610	$550	$475

.38-40 cal.

100%	98%	95%	90%	80%	70%	60%	50%	40%	30%	20%	10%
$3,200	$2,750	$2,350	$2,100	$1,600	$1,300	$1,050	$825	$720	$650	$595	$525

.41 cal.

100%	98%	95%	90%	80%	70%	60%	50%	40%	30%	20%	10%
$3,450	$2,950	$2,500	$2,250	$1,775	$1,450	$1,250	$925	$795	$725	$650	$625

.44-40 cal.

100%	98%	95%	90%	80%	70%	60%	50%	40%	30%	20%	10%
$3,750	$3,350	$2,860	$2,550	$2,200	$1,900	$1,600	$1,250	$995	$925	$850	$750

.45 cal.

100%	98%	95%	90%	80%	70%	60%	50%	40%	30%	20%	10%
$3,600	$3,300	$2,700	$2,400	$2,150	$1,850	$1,500	$1,150	$880	$825	$770	$695

.455 Eley—manufactured for the international revolver contests held in Bisley, England.

100%	98%	95%	90%	80%	70%	60%	50%	40%	30%	20%	10%
$5,200	$4,650	$4,100	$3,650	$2,950	$2,650	$2,350	$1,950	$1,700	$1,400	$1,175	$995

BISLEY TARGET FLAT-TOP—flat top frame, removable target sights, 976 produced, 1894-1913.

Values are 150% greater than respective Standard Bisley Models.

POST-WAR 1ST GENERATION SAA—approx. 860 manufactured in various configurations after 1945. These specimens in 98% + condition will approximate values on the pre-war models. Ser. no. range 357,000-357,860.

2ND GENERATION SINGLE ACTION ARMY: 1956-1975 MFG.

Popular demand brought back the Single Action Army in 1956 with minor modifications, most not noticeable except to experts. Serial numbers began at 0001SA and continue to 73,000SA before the "New Model" was introduced in 1976 (ser. no. 80000 SA). Premiums are paid for rare production variances if NIB condition. Prices stated assume 7½ barrel length. It should be noted that many "premium niches" exist in this model as collectors are establishing premiums paid for rarer production variances (the interrelation of barrel length, caliber, frame type, finish quality, year of manufacture, and other special features).

The order of desirability on standard 2nd generation SAA'S is as follows: 4¾ barrels are the most desirable, followed by 5¾ in., and then 7½ in. Caliber desirability is as follows: .44-40 has the most demand followed by .44 Spl., .45, .38 Spl., and then .357 Mag. It follows that desirable calibers found with desirable barrel lengths will command healthy premiums — especially if production was unusually low in a particular combination. Reference books specifically on the post-war SAA are a must when determining the rarity factors (or if they exist) on these multiple production combinations. Buntlines, Sheriff's models, and special orders through the Custom Gun Shop are in a class by themselves and have to be evaluated one at a time.

It is advisable to procure a factory letter when buying or selling older or recently manufactured Colt Single Action's (hence guaranteeing authenticity and value credibility). These watermarked letters are available by writing Colt Industries in Hartford, CT, with a charge of $35 per serial number - if Colt cannot provide you with proper documentation after conducting research, they will refund you $10. Include your name and address, Colt model name, serial number, and check to: COLT HISTORIAN, P.O. BOX 1868, HARTFORD, CT 06101. Please allow adequate time for proper response.

Grading	100%	98%	95%	90%	80%	70%	60%

SINGLE ACTION ARMY—SA suffix, .357 Mag., .38 Special, .44 Special., and .45 LC cal.'s, 3 (Sheriff's Model), 4¾, 5½, 7½, and 12 in. (Buntline) barrel lengths, all blue, blue/case hardened, or nickel finishes, hard rubber stocks (standard until 1970).

	100%	98%	95%	90%	80%	70%	60%
.357 Mag.	$675	$600	$550	$525	$500	$475	$450
.38 Spl.	$850	$775	$700	$650	$615	$575	$550
.44 Spl.	$800	$750	$675	$635	$590	$575	$550
.45 LC	$800	$750	$675	$635	$590	$575	$550

100% assumes NIB condition for this model.

   Add 20-25% for 4¾ in. barrel.

   Add 10-15% for nickel finish.

   Add $200 + for original ivory grips.

Earlier 2nd generations with the Rampant Colt grips (serial numbered under 50,000 approximately) are a little more desirable than those SAA's with Eagle grips (serial numbered over 50,000 approximately).

Early 2nd generation SAA's in 98% + original condition with the black box (pre-1965) will command a premium over values listed above. "Stagecoach" boxes were used approx. 1965-1973 and are not quite as desirable as the one-piece black box. Original "Stagecoach" boxes in excellent condition are currently selling for approx. $50.

Factory Engraved 2nd Generation SAA's—since approximately only 350 SAA's were factory engraved (with almost 90% being in .45 LC cal.), accurate pricing with this degree of rarity factor is difficult to ascertain with any degree of accuracy. Prices overall will be at least 50% higher than their 3rd generation engraved counterparts.

Factory engraved 2nd generation SAA's are at least 10 times rarer than 3rd generation engraved pistols.

Sheriff's Model—SM suffix, .45 cal., 3 in. barrel, case-hardened finish, many custom options were ordered in this variation, approx. 500 mfg. 1960-1975.

	100%	98%	95%	90%	80%	70%	60%
	$1,200	$950	$800	$750	$695	$625	$550

   Add 20% for nickel finish.

   Add $200 for ivory grips.

Buntline Special—.45 Colt only, 12 in. barrel, case hardened frame, hard rubber (rarer) or walnut grips. Over 3,900 mfg. between 1957-1975.

	100%	98%	95%	90%	80%	70%	60%
	$795	$675	$635	$600	$575	$550	$525

   Add 50% for nickel finish (rare).

NEW FRONTIER—"NF" suffix, flat-top frame, adj. rear sight, .357 Mag., .38 Spl. (rare), .44 Spl., or .45 cal., 4¾ (rare), 5½ (rare) or 7½ (common) in. barrel, uncheckered walnut grips, case-hardened frame, over 4,200 mfg. 1961-1975.

	100%	98%	95%	90%	80%	70%	60%
	$650	$600	$575	$550	$525	$500	$475

Nickel or full-blue finish is very rare in this model.

New Frontier Buntline Special—.45 Colt only, 12 in. barrel, flat-top frame, adj. rear sight. Approx. 70 mfg. 1962-1967.

	100%	98%	95%	90%	80%	70%	60%
	$1,350	$1,100	$950	$850	$725	$600	$500

3RD GENERATION SINGLE ACTION ARMY: 1976-1981 MFG.

Values below assume 7½ in. barrel (most frequently encountered barrel length).

The order of desirability on standard 3nd generation SAA'S is as follows: 4¾ barrels are the most desirable, followed by 5¾ in., and then 7½ in. Caliber desirability is as follows: .44-40 has the most demand followed by .44 Spl., .45 LC, .38 Spl., and then .357 Mag. It follows that desirable calibers found with desirable barrel lengths will command healthy premiums — especially if production was unusually low in a particular combination. Reference books specifically on the post-war SAA are a must when determining the rarity factors(or if they exist) on these multiple production combinations. Buntlines, Sheriff's models, and special orders through the Custom Gun Shop are in a class by themselves and have to be evaluated one at a time.

Grading	100%	98%	95%	90%	80%	70%	60%

SINGLE ACTION ARMY—.38 Spl., .357 Mag., .44 Spl., .44-40, or .45 cal., 3 (Sheriff's Model), 4¾, 5½, 7½, or 12 in. (Buntline) barrel lengths, all blue, blue/case hardened, or nickel finishes, walnut or rubber stocks.

3rd model production began in 1976 with ser. no. 80000SA and reached no. 99999SA in 1978. At this point the SA suffix changed to a prefix (beginning with SA01001).

It is advisable to procure a factory letter when buying or selling older or recently manufactured Colt Single Action's (hence guaranteeing authenticity and value credibility). These watermarked letters are available by writing Colt Industries in Hartford, CT, with a charge of $35 per serial number - if Colt cannot provide you with proper documentation after conducting research, they will refund you $10. Include your name and address, Colt model name, serial number, and check to: COLT HISTORIAN, P.O. BOX 1868, HARTFORD, CT 06101. Please allow adequate time for proper response.

Standard Model

	100%	98%	95%	90%	80%	70%	60%
.357 Mag.	$500	$480	$460	$440	$420	$410	$400
.44 Spl.	$675	$625	$600	$580	$560	$540	$525
.44-40	$850	$800	$750	$700	$650	$600	$550
.44-40 Black Powder Frame	$950	$875	$825	$750	$700	$650	$600
.45 LC	$675	$635	$595	$575	$550	$525	$500

100% assumes NIB condition for this model.
Add 5% for 5¾ in. barrel.
Add 25%-30% for 4¾ in. barrel.
Add $200 for ivory grips.

While nickel finish was originally an extra cost option (and therefore rarer today), current values for nickel finished 3rd generation SAA's are approximately the same as for the standard blued finish.

FACTORY ENGRAVED 3RD GENERATION SAA'S

3rd generation factory engraved SAA's were produced in much greater numbers than their 2nd generation counterparts. As a result, pricing is also more predictable - especially on .45 LC cal. Since over 80% of all engraved 3rd generation SAA's are in .45 LC, values listed below represent this caliber. Engraved specimens encountered in other calibers (especially .44-40, approx. 2% of engraved production) will be considerably more expensive. Most specimens encountered are in 7½ in. barrel length. Pistols with 4¾ (most desirable) or 5½ in. barrels will add additional premiums.

SAA Class A Engraved—with class A engraving (25% coverage on gun).

	100%	98%	95%	90%	80%	70%	60%
	$1,125	$975	$875	$800	$725	$650	$575

Add 10% for nickel finish.

SAA Class B Engraved—with class B engraving (50% coverage on gun).

	100%	98%	95%	90%	80%	70%	60%
	$1,300	$1,130	$1,050	$975	$880	$760	$650

Add 10% for nickel finish.

SAA Class C Engraved—with class C engraving (75% coverage on gun).

	100%	98%	95%	90%	80%	70%	60%
	$1,575	$1,295	$1,125	$1,025	$925	$825	$725

Add 10% for nickel finish.

SAA Class D Engraved—with class D engraving (100% coverage on gun).

	100%	98%	95%	90%	80%	70%	60%
	$1,900	$1,625	$1,300	$1,125	$995	$875	$795

Add 10% for nickel finish.

Sheriff's Model—.44-40 or .45 cal., 3 in. barrel, case hardened finish, many custom options were ordered in this variation.

	100%	98%	95%	90%	80%	70%	60%
	$725	$675	$650	$625	$600	$575	$550

Add 10% for nickel finish.
Add $200 for ivory grips.

This model was also available with two cylinders (.45 LC & .45 ACP or .44 Spl. & .44-40) — add $200. The .45 LC/.45 ACP is perhaps more desirable.

Grading	100%	98%	95%	90%	80%	70%	60%

Buntline Special—.45 Colt only, 12 in. barrel, case hardened frame.

	$700	$650	$625	$600	$575	$535	$500

Add 10% for nickel finish.

NEW FRONTIER—"NF" suffix, flat-top frame, adj. rear sight, .44 Spl., .44-40 (rare), or .45 cal.'s, 4¾ (rare), 5½ (rare) or 7½ (common) in. barrel, uncheckered walnut grips, case hardened frame, mfg. 1978-1981.

	$475	$440	$425	$410	$395	$380	$365

3rd generation NF serialization can be differentiated from 2nd by 5 digits (starting with 0) followed by the NF suffix. 2nd generation guns had 4 digit numbers.

For factory engraved New Frontier Models, refer to above SAA engraved listing and subtract 25%.

New Frontier Buntline Special—.45 Colt only, 12 in. barrel, flat-top frame, adj. rear sight. Rare.

	$600	$560	$540	$520	$500	$485	$460

SINGLE ACTION ARMY: CURRENT MANUFACTURE (1982-89)

STANDARD SINGLE ACTION ARMY—.44-40 or .45 cal., 3 (special order only), 4 (disc. in 1988), 4¾, 5 (disc. in 1987), 5½, 7½ or 10 (special order only) in. barrel, blue, royal blue, or nickel finish, blackpowder frame, 3 line patent date, custom order only.

Values below are for base gun only with blued finish and no engraving or other embellishments. A SAA custom order MUST EXCEED $1,095 RETAIL for Colt to accept the order.

Mfg.'s Sug. Retail	$837	$775	$695	$650	$600	$550	$500	$475

Add $121 for nickel finish.

Most collector interest in recently manufactured SAA's is for either mint or NIB specimens.

CUSTOM ORDER SAA'S—the Colt Custom Shop will perform additional work (special orders including engraving, custom stocks, non-standard barrel lengths, gold or silver plating, and other custom features) if the individual work order totals over $1,095 retail. Quotations are supplied at $15/each for these special order guns. Please contact the Colt Custom Gun Shop for this written estimate regarding these custom built SAA's. The listings below represent some of the special order prices (retail) which may be ordered individually.

Mfg.'s Sug. Retail	$1,095	$995	$550	$495	$450	$425	$395	$360

This retail price already assumes $258 of additional special orders listed below.

Add $199 for royal blue finish.
Add $226 for mirror brite finish.
Add $367 for gold or silver plating.
Add $105 for consecutive serial numbers (pair).
Add $576 for individual unique serial number.

CLASS "A" ENGRAVING (¼ METAL COVERAGE) — ADD $880.
CLASS "B" ENGRAVING (½ METAL COVERAGE) — ADD $1,173.
CLASS "C" ENGRAVING (¾ METAL COVERAGE) — ADD $1,466.
CLASS "D" ENGRAVING (FULL METAL COVERAGE) — ADD $1,759.
ADD AN ADDITIONAL 13% (APPROX.) FOR BUNTLINE ENGRAVING.

SCOUT MODEL SAA

SCOUT SAA—.22 LR cal., blue finish only with case colored frame (discontinued in 1985), blue frame became standard later in production, 4¾, 6, or 7½ in. barrel. Discontinued in 1986.

	$195	$180	$165	$150	$140	$130	$120

Last Mfg.'s Sug. Retail was $181.

Grading	100%	98%	95%	90%	80%	70%	60%

NEW FRONTIER SCOUT, BUNTLINE SCOUT—.22 LR and .22 WRF interchangeable cylinders, 4¼, 4¾ or 9½ in. barrel (Buntline), alloy frame, made 1958-1972. Add $15 for nickel finish or interchangable cylinder.

		$225	$190	$170	$150	$140	$130	$120

Add 50% for Buntline Model.

This model can be denoted by a "P" suffix (mfg. 1962-1970) or "G" suffix (mfg. 1970-1978).

PEACEMAKER SCOUT—.22 LR or .22 Mag. cal., color case hardened steel frame, 4¾, 6, or 7½ (Buntline) barrel, black composition grips, mfg. 1970-1977.

		$250	$215	$190	$170	$155	$140	$130

This model can be differentiated by either a "G" or "L" prefix on the serial number.

PISTOLS: SEMI-AUTO

Until several years ago, the Single Action Army revolver commanded the most attention among Colt handgun collectors. Since 1987, Colt Semi-Auto's have been in tremendous demand and have out-accelerated every other area of Colt collecting. Because condition and originality play such a key role in determining Colt Semi-Auto prices, many variations have had their values pushed upward to the point where it is difficult to accurately determine a realistic price - especially on those models in 98% original condition or better. As a result, 95% through 100% values in this section are meant to be used only as a guideline. I recently heard of a mint Model 1900 U.S. marked that sold for close to $10,000. Four years ago I doubt whether the same specimen would have brought $1,500. As always, the hardest prices to ascertain when firearms market conditions are bullish are the 98-100% values.

MODEL 1900—.38 ACP, 6 in. barrel, blue, fixed sights, plain walnut grips, sharp spur hammer, sight safety, made 1900-1903. Add 100% for USN marked, 80% for US marked with inspector initials.

		$3,000	$2,350	$1,400	$675	$585	$500	$440

This model is serial numbered approximately between 1-3,000.

MODEL 1902 SPORTING—.38 ACP, 6 in. barrel, blue, fixed sights, checkered hard rubber grips, no safety, round back hammer, made 1902-1908.

		$2,500	$1,750	$800	$550	$475	$430	$375

This model is serial numbered approximately 3,001 on up.

MODEL 1902 MILITARY—.38 ACP, 6 in. barrel, blue, similar to 1902 Sporting, hammer changed to spur type in 1908, made 1902-1929. Add 10% for front slide serrations.

		$2,500	$1,750	$800	$660	$550	$375	$320

MODEL 1902 MILITARY-U.S. ARMY MARKED—similar specifications to 1902 Military, only serial number range 15,001-15,200.

		$6,500	$4,750	$2,500	$2,000	$1,500	$1,000	$750

MODEL 1903 POCKET (38 ACP)—.38 ACP, 4½ in. barrel, wood blue, similar to 1902 Sporting, but 4½ in. barrel, 7½ in. overall, made 1903-1929.

		$925	$725	$550	$400	$300	$225	$150

Add 10% for early round hammer.

MODEL 1903 POCKET (32 ACP)—.32 ACP, 4 in. barrel, wood blue, checkered hard rubber grips, hammerless, slide lock and grip safety, barrel lock bushing, made 1903-1940.

		$600	$475	$395	$325	$275	$230	$200

Add 20% for first model (Type I) with barrel bushing, mfg. 1903-1911.

Type 2 - 32 ACP's still retain their barrel bushing but have a 3¾ in. barrel and were made from 1908-1910.

Type 3 - 32 ACP's do not have a barrel bushing and were made from 1910-1926.

Type 4 - 32 ACP's have the added magazine safety (of which there are both the commercial and "U.S. Property" variations).

Add $100 for nickel finish (mostly w/pearl grips).

Model 1903 Parkerized—U.S. property.

		$750	$625	$475	$375	$320	$270	$235

Grading	100%	98%	95%	90%	80%	70%	60%

MODEL 1905 MILITARY—.45 ACP, 5 in. barrel, blue fixed sights, checkered walnut stocks, similar to 1902 .38 ACP, made 1905-1911. Add 100% for 1907 U.S. Contract Model. Add 200% for early model (serial No. 1-201) that has shoulder stock.

	$2,150	$1,375	$785	$660	$550	$495	$440

MODEL 1908 POCKET (MODEL M 380 ACP)—.380 ACP, first issue, 3¾ in. barrel only, same as Pocket Model .32 ACP (32 ACP), except chambered for .380 ACP, made 1908-1940.

	$625	$500	$425	$350	$300	$250	$225

Type 2 - 380 ACP's with barrel bushing and were made from 1908-1910 (6,251 mfg.) — add 25%.

Type 3 - 380 ACP's do not have a barrel bushing and were made from 1910-1926.

Type 4 - 380 ACP's have the added magazine safety (of which there are both the commercial and "U.S. Property" variations).

   Add $100 for nickel finish (mostly w/pearl grips).

Model 1908 Parkerized—U.S. property.

	$900	$750	$550	$475	$400	$350	$300

POCKET MODEL-HAMMERLESS—.25 ACP, 2 in. barrel, fixed sights, checkered hard rubber grips on early models, walnut on later, magazine disconnect added on guns made after 1916, made 1908-1941.

	100%	98%	95%	90%	80%	70%	60%
Blue finish	$395	$325	$275	$260	$240	$200	$155
Nickel finish	$450	$350	$295	$250	$220	$165	$130

100% values assume NIB condition. Deduct 15% if without cardboard box.

.45 ACP TO .22 LR CONVERSION UNIT—consists of slide assembly, barrel, bushing, floating chamber ejector, recoil spring and guide, magazine and slide stop, made 1938-present. Add 100% for pre-war manufacture ("U"-prefix serial on slide). Over 5,000 mfg. in all variations.

	100%	98%	95%	90%	80%	70%	60%
Adj. sight	$260	$210	$175	$150	$140	$120	$100
Fixed sight	$235	$190	$160	$140	$120	$110	$100

.22 LR TO .45 ACP CONVERSION UNIT—converted service Ace .22 to .45 ACP, made 1938-1942. Very rare — 112 mfg.

	$1,000	$800	$700	$600	$500	$400	$350

These units are serial numbered on top of slide.

JUNIOR POCKET MODEL—2¼ in. barrel, blue, checkered walnut grips, made by Astra in Spain from 1958-1968.

	100%	98%	95%	90%	80%	70%	60%
.22 short	$300	$275	$250	$210	$180	$160	$140
.25 ACP	$250	$225	$200	$180	$150	$140	$130

SUPER .38 AUTOMATIC PISTOL—identical to Gov't Model .45, except chambered for .38 Super automatic, made 1928-1970.

	100%	98%	95%	90%	80%	70%	60%
Pre-War	$1,700	$1,350	$1,050	$925	$825	$725	$650
Post-War	$495	$450	$395	$350	$325	$300	$280

Pre-war variations are serialized below 34,450.

SUPER MATCH .38—same as Super .38, but hand honed action, match grade barrel, made 1935-1941. Examine carefully for fakes.

	100%	98%	95%	90%	80%	70%	60%
Fixed sights	$2,700	$2,250	$1,800	$1,700	$1,200	$1,000	$800
Adjustable sights	$2,300	$1,800	$1,600	$1,500	$1,025	$875	$750

SUPER MATCH .38 MS—.38 Super cal., 1961 mfg., serial numbered 101 MS - 855 MS, 754 total manufactured, same configuration as the .38 Midrange.

	$2,200	$1,800	$1,675	$1,495	$1,375	$1,175	$1,000

Grading	100%	98%	95%	90%	80%	70%	60%

GOVERNMENT MODEL 1911 .45ACP SEMI-AUTO & VARIATIONS

MODEL 1911—.45 ACP, 5 in. barrel, fixed sights, flat main spring housing, polished blue finish only (commercial and original military), checkered walnut grips. Colt licensed other companies to manufacture under government contracts, made 1912-1925.

MOST M1911 VARIATIONS LISTED BELOW ARE NOT AS COLLECTIBLE IF UNDER 60% ORIGINAL CONDITION. HOWEVER, THEY ARE STILL VERY DESIRABLE AS SHOOTERS AND VALUES (IF IN ORIGINAL CONDITION) WILL APPROXIMATE THE 60% PRICES IF IN GOOD MECHANICAL CONDITION.

Add 20% for 4-digit ser. no., 40% for 3-digit, 60% + for 2-digit.

Colt Model 1911's are enjoying high demand as of this writing and prices have increased the most in the 95%-100% condition factors. Be careful on the 98% + condition specimens, especially the rarer variations. Some collectors are now requiring a potential high-dollar Model 1911 to pass the X-ray test (detects welding and other metalurgical alterations) before purchasing.

COLT COMMERCIAL—initially "C" preceding serial number, approx. ser. no range C1-C130,000. Watch for fakes.

	100%	98%	95%	90%	80%	70%	60%
1912-1914	$1,300	$1,000	$800	$670	$575	$425	$400
1914-1925	$1,100	$900	$725	$625	$525	$375	$340

approx. 130,000 mfg. between 1912-1925.

COLT MILITARY—right side of slide marked "MODEL OF 1911 U.S. ARMY", blue finish only (not parkerized unless reworked).

	100%	98%	95%	90%	80%	70%	60%
1912-1913	$1,500	$1,050	$775	$650	$475	$425	$385
1914-1925	$1,100	$900	$700	$580	$530	$400	$360

Over 2,550,000 M1911 pistols were ordered during WWI by U.S. Government but approx. 650,000 were mfg. between 1911-1925. This variation with a parkerized finish will indicate post-WWI reworking, usually marked with an arsenal code (ie. AA-AUGUSTA ARSENAL, SA-SPRINGFIELD ARESENAL, etc.). These reworks do not have the same values as original, unaltered specimens and prices generally are in the $295-$425 range.

NORTH AMERICAN ARMS COMPANY—less than 100 manufactured in Quebec, Ontario during 1918 only, blued finish. Be very wary of fakes as this variation is perhaps the most desirable Colt semi-auto.

100%	98%	95%	90%	80%	70%	60%
$9,750	$8,350	$7,500	$6,250	$5,350	$4,200	$2,750

REMINGTON - UMC—over 21,500 mfg. in 1918 only, blued finish.

100%	98%	95%	90%	80%	70%	60%
$1,250	$950	$750	$670	$550	$450	$350

SPRINGFIELD ARMORY—approx. 30,000 manufactured between 1914-1915, blued finish.

100%	98%	95%	90%	80%	70%	60%
$1,150	$825	$750	$675	$550	$450	$350

U.S. NAVY—over 31,000 mfg. between 1911-1914 in defined serial ranges, blued finish. Marked "MODEL OF 1911 U.S. NAVY" on right slide side.

100%	98%	95%	90%	80%	70%	60%
$1,500	$1,100	$900	$800	$755	$675	$600

U.S. MARINE CORPS.—approx. 13,500 mfg. between 1911-1913 and 1916-1918 in defined serial ranges, blued finish, right side of slide slide marked "MODEL OF 1911 U.S.M.C.".

100%	98%	95%	90%	80%	70%	60%
$1,500	$1,100	$900	$800	$755	$675	$600

WWI BRITISH SERIES—serialized W10001-W21000, marked "CALIBRE 455", blued finish, proofed with broad arrow British Ordnance punch, mfg. 1915-1916.

100%	98%	95%	90%	80%	70%	60%
$1,450	$935	$825	$700	$600	$520	$445

Add 25% for variations with either Navy or Marine markings. Many WWI British-series M1911's were exported back to the U.S. following WWI and were converted to .45 ACP. Usually, a "5" has been crossed-out of the original cal. designation. These reworks are not as collectible and prices range from $350-$500.

BRITISH RAF REWORK—this variation is the WWI British series re-issued to RAF officers in the early 1920's, blued finish, differentiated by hand-stamped "RAF" or "R.A.F." on left side of frame.

100%	98%	95%	90%	80%	70%	60%
$1,250	$935	$880	$825	$725	$635	$550

Grading	100%	98%	95%	90%	80%	70%	60%

A.J. SAVAGE MUNITIONS CO.—mfg. slides only, blued finish, marked in middle on left side of slide with flaming ordnance bomb with "S" in center.

	$1,650	$1,200	$1,000	$850	$750	$675	$600

NORWEGIAN 1912 11.25MM—approx. 300 mfg. with "C" prefix in 1913-14 only, usually encounterd in 90% or less condition.

	$1,300	$950	$850	$775	$685	$605	$525

NORWEGIAN 1914 11.25MM—This model has a distinctive extended slide release, approx. 20,000 mfg. between 1919-1932.

	$1,075	$825	$725	$625	$550	$500	$450

Add 50% for Waffenamt Nazi mfg. — specimens were made in 1945 only.

ARGENTINE CONTRACT—mfg. 1917-1925, ser. no.'s are in C110,000-130,000 range, slide marked "Pistola Automatica Sistema Colt, Calilbre 11,25 mm, Modelo 1916", usually marked with Argentine seal.

	$925	$700	$600	$540	$475	$410	$350

RUSSIAN CONTRACT—approx. 14,500 mfg. with frame marked "ANGLO ZAKAZIVAT", blued finish, made 1915-1916, seldomly encountered — watch for fakes.

	$2,450	$1,825	$1,575	$1,350	$1,200	$1,100	$1,000

GOVERNMENT MODEL 1911A1 .45 ACP & VARIATIONS

MODEL 1911 A1—.45 ACP, blue or parkerized, checkered walnut grips, plastic on later military guns, checkered arched mainspring housing and longer grip safety spur. As in the Model 1911, Colt licensed other companies to produce under gov't contract during WWII, made 1925-1970.

Inspect carefully for arsenal reworks (so marked by proofing, normally on left side of frame above or behind trigger), and reparkerizing.

MOST M1911 A1 VARIATIONS LISTED BELOW ARE NOT AS COLLECTIBLE IF UNDER 60% ORIGINAL CONDITION. HOWEVER, THEY ARE STILL VERY DESIRABLE AS SHOOTERS AND VALUES (IF IN ORIGINAL CONDITION) WILL APPROXIMATE THE 60% PRICES IF IN GOOD MECHANICAL CONDITION.

Add 20% for 4-digit ser. no., 40% for 3-digit, 60% + for 2-digit.

PRE-WWII COLT COMMERCIAL—"C" preceding serial number, mfg. 1925-1942. Approx. ser. no. range C130,000-C215,000.

	$1,150	$950	$750	$620	$575	$495	$400

1946-1969 COLT COMMERCIAL—"C" prefix until 1950 when changed to "C" suffix, approx. 196,000 manufactured 1946-1970.

	$525	$450	$395	$360	$340	$320	$295

Add 30% for "C" prefix models after ser. no. 221,000.

COLT MILITARY—approx. 1,627,000 mfg. between 1924-1945, ser. no.'s 700,000 - on up, add 20% for SA marked post-WWII National Match, right side of frame marked "M1911A1 U.S. ARMY".

	$550	$475	$425	$350	$315	$295	$275

On early 1911 A1 military models with bright blue finish — add 100% if condition is 98% or better.

1968-1969 BB TRANSITIONAL

	$695	$600	$550	$495	$425	$375	$325

ITHACA—approx. 441,557 mfg. 1943-1945 in Ithaca, NY, ser. no. ranges 1,208,670 - 1,279,675, 1,141,430 - 1,471,430, 1,743,845 - 1,890,500, 2,075,100 - 2,134,400, and 2,619,000 - 2,693,615. Parkerized finish.

	$550	$465	$420	$375	$340	$320	$295

UNION SWITCH AND SIGNAL—approx. 55,100 mfg. 1943 only in Swissvale, PA, ser. no. range 958,101 - 1,088,725. Parkerized finish.

	$975	$825	$650	$525	$420	$360	$295

Grading	100%	98%	95%	90%	80%	70%	60%

REMINGTON RAND—approx. 948,905 mfg. 1943-1945 in Syracuse, NY, ser. no. ranges 1,279,700 - 1,441,431, 1,890,500 - 2,075,100, 2,134,400 - 2,244,800, and 2,380,000 - 2,619,000. Parkerized finish.

	$550	$465	$420	$375	$340	$320	$295

SINGER MFG. CO.—500 mfg. 1942 in Elizabeth, NJ, ser. no. range S800,001 - S800,500. Parkerized finish.

	$8,950	$7,500	$6,850	$6,125	$5,700	$5,175	$4,750

The Singer 1911A1 variation is one of the most sought after Colt models. In recent years, values have increased significantly and as a result, many fakes have emerged. Most specimens are now recognized by ser. no. and be very cautious when contemplating a purchase. Some collectors unsure of authenticity are now requiring X-ray testing to determine originality (slide restampings, ser. no. changes, etc.).

MEXICAN CONTRACT—mfg. approx. 1921-1927 with "C" prefix ser. no.'s, frames marked "EJERCITO MEXICANO", most surviving examples show much use.

	$925	$810	$740	$660	$560	$450	$375

BRAZILIAN

	$825	$700	$635	$605	$550	$495	$440

ARGENTINE CONTRACT—mfg. 1927-early 30's, ser. no.'s are in low C140,000 range, slide marked "EJERCITO ARGENTINO COLT.CAL.45 MOD.1927" checkered walnut grips.

This variation has recently been imported again.

	$495	$430	$385	$350	$325	$295	$270

In 1927, the Argentina Arsenal began manufacturing the Model 1911A1. The slide marking is two lines and reads "EJERCITO ARGENTINO SYST.COLT.CAL. 11.25 mm MOD.1927". Values will approximate those shown above.

ACE MODELS: PRE-WWII

COMMERCIAL ACE—.22 LR, similar to Government .45 ACP, but in .22LR cal., 4¾ in. barrel, blue, adj. sights, checkered walnut grips, almost 11,000 mfg. (ser. no. range 1-10,935) 1931-1941 and 1947.

	$1,500	$1,275	$900	$750	$600	$450	$400

SERVICE MODEL ACE—.22 LR, 5 in. barrel, blue or parkerized finish, same as .45 ACP National Match except for caliber, has floating chamber to simulate .45 ACP recoil, limited mfg. 1935-1945.

	$1,650	$1,300	$1,050	$825	$600	$520	$450

This variation is marked "SERVICE MODEL" on left frame, serial numbers have "SM" suffix and have ranges to approx. 13,800.

PRE-WWII NATIONAL MATCH MODELS

NATIONAL MATCH—.45 ACP, same as Government Model, except has hand honed action, match grade barrel, blue, made 1933-1941 within ser. no. range C164,800 - C215,000.

Fixed sights

	$1,400	$1,175	$950	$695	$525	$500	$440

Adj. sights

	$1,500	$1,250	$995	$750	$585	$540	$495

DRAKE CUSTOM NATIONAL MATCH

	$935	$880	$855	$825	$770	$715	$635

GOVERNMENT NATIONAL MATCH REWORKS—assembled by government armorers, all parts marked "NM", blued finish.

	$850	$775	$700	$640	$585	$510	$450

These pistols were made specifically for the U.S. shooting team.

Grading	100%	98%	95%	90%	80%	70%	60%

POST-WWII NATIONAL MATCH MODELS

GOLD CUP NATIONAL MATCH—.45 ACP, match grade barrel, new design bushing, flat mainspring housing, long adj. stop trigger, hand fitted slide with enlarged ejection port, adj. target sights, gold medallions in grips, "NM" suffix, made 1957-1970.

	$625	$550	$475	$450	$405	$380	$350

Note: This model was the first National Match Model manufactured following WW II.

GOLD CUP MKIII NATIONAL MATCH—.38 Spl., same as Gold Cup National Match, except chambered for .38 Spl., mid-range wadcutter, made 1961-1974.

	$635	$580	$550	$495	$470	$440	$385

MKIV/SERIES 70 GOLD CUP NATIONAL MATCH—.45 ACP, flat mainspring housing, accurizer barrel and bushing, adj. trigger, target hammer, solid rib, Colt Elliason sight, made 1970-1983.

	$560	$415	$385	$360	$330	$305	$275

MKIV/SERIES 70 GOLD CUP 75TH ANNIVERSARY NATIONAL MATCH—same as Gold Cup except for commemorative aspect for Camp Perry, 1978, 200 made; add 100% to standard Mark IV/Series 70 Gold Cup prices.

GOLD CUP MKIV SERIES 80 NATIONAL MATCH—.45 ACP, 5 in. barrel, 7 shot mag., 39 oz., Colt-Elliason adj. rear sight, wide grooved adj. target trigger, under cut front sight, flat mainspring housing, critical internal parts are hand honed, manufactured 1983-present.

Mfg.'s Sug. Retail	$766	$625	$515	$450	$400	$380	$350	$325

Stainless Gold Cup National Match—similar to Gold Cup, only manufactured from stainless steel, matte finish, released late in 1986.

Mfg.'s Sug. Retail	$822	$665	$545	$465

Add $55 for bright stainless steel finish (high polish).

PISTOLS: SEMI-AUTO, RECENT MANUFACTURE

The prices listed below are for original factory finished guns with no extra engraving. The listings below show 1989 factory engraving costs. These prices should be added to the cost of each engraved production gun to determine the correct value.

MODEL'S MUSTANG, .380 ACP GOVERNMENT, DETECTIVE SPECIAL, AND DIAMONDBACK

  CLASS "A" ENGRAVING (¼ METAL COVERAGE) — ADD $587.
  CLASS "B" ENGRAVING (½ METAL COVERAGE) — ADD $793.
  CLASS "C" ENGRAVING (¾ METAL COVERAGE) — ADD $1,026.
  CLASS "D" ENGRAVING (FULL METAL COVERAGE) — ADD $1,203.

MODEL'S .45 ACP GOLD CUP, GOVERNMENT MODEL, OFFICER'S ACP, PYTHON, COMBAT COMMANDER, KING COBRA, TROOPER MKV, LAWMAN MKV, AND DELTA ELITE.

  CLASS "A" ENGRAVING (¼ METAL COVERAGE) — ADD $734.
  CLASS "B" ENGRAVING (½ METAL COVERAGE) — ADD $997.
  CLASS "C" ENGRAVING (¾ METAL COVERAGE) — ADD $1,231.
  CLASS "D" ENGRAVING (FULL METAL COVERAGE) — ADD $1,495.

SPECIAL ENGRAVING—Also available: inlays, seals, custom grips, lettering, prices quoted on request.

MKIV/SERIES 70 GOVERNMENT MODEL—.45 ACP, .38 Super, 9mm, or 9mm Steyr, 5 in. barrel, checkered walnut grips/medallion. A slight premium might be asked for the Series 70 models if NIB. Series 70 models were mfg. 1970-1983 and were serial numbered with with "70G" prefixes 1970-1976, "G70" suffixes 1976-1980, and "70B" prefixes 1981-1983.

	100%	98%	95%	90%	80%	70%	60%
Blue finish	$435	$385	$350	$325	$300	$275	$250
Nickel finish	$465	$410	$370	$340	$315	$285	$260

9mm Steyr was made for European exportation only. However, a few specimens have found their way into the United States. Prices for NIB specimens usually start in the $750 + range.

Grading	100%	98%	95%	90%	80%	70%	60%

Conversion Unit—converts .45 ACP to .22 LR

	100%	98%	95%	90%	80%	70%	60%
	$250	$230	$210	$190	$170	$155	$140

Post-War Ace Service Model—.22 LR, similar specifications to previous Pre-WWII manufacture, "SM" prefix, approx. 30,000 mfg. between 1978-1982.

	$525	$450	$415	$380	$360	$340	$325

MKIV/SERIES 80 GOVERNMENT MODEL—.45 ACP, .38 Super and 9mm, single action, 5 in. barrel, 7 shot mag. in .45, approx. 38 oz., action has new firing pin safety, checkered walnut grips with medallion. Production started in 1983 with ser. no. FG01000.

Blue Finish

Mfg.'s Sug. Retail	$594	$490	$440	$360	$335	$315	$295	$275

Add $4 for 9mm or .38 Super cal.

Nickel Finish—available in .45 ACP (disc. in 1986) and .38 Super (disc. in 1987) cal.'s.

	$515	$465	$380	$350	$315	$285	$260

Last Mfg.'s Sug. Retail was $600.

Satin Nickel/Blue—is supplied with Colt-Pachmayr grips. Disc. in 1986.

	$500	$445	$370	$345	$310	$280	$255

Last Mfg.'s Sug. Retail was $557.

Stainless Steel

Mfg.'s Sug. Retail	$629	$525	$470	$425			

Bright Stainless Steel—high polish stainless finish. New in 1986.

Mfg.'s Sug. Retail	$692	$580	$500	$450			

Conversion Unit—converts .45 ACP to .22 LR (Series 70 and 80) or 9mm (Series 80 only). Disc. in 1987.

	$270	$244	$210	$190	$170	$155	$140

Last Mfg.'s Sug. Retail was $305.

.380 SERIES 80 GOVERNMENT MODEL—.380 ACP only, single action, 3¼ in. barrel, 7 shot mag., fixed sights, composition stocks, 21¾ oz. New in 1985.

Blue Finish

Mfg.'s Sug. Retail	$384	$310	$280	$235	$215	$200	$190	$180

Nickel Finish—bright polish nickel finish with white composite grips.

Mfg.'s Sug. Retail	$427	$360	$310	$270	$240	$220	$210	$200

Coltguard Finish—employs a high strength electroless matte nickel finish. New in 1986.

Mfg.'s Sug. Retail	$406	$325	$300	$260	$235	$210	$200	$185

Stainless Steel—new in 1989.

Mfg.'s Sug. Retail	$409	$335	$310	$270			

MUSTANG—similar to .380 Series Gov't., except has 2¾ in. barrel, 5 shot mag., blue finish only, 18½ oz. New in 1986.

Mfg.'s Sug. Retail	$384	$310	$280	$235	$215	$200	$190	$180

Nickel finish—bright polish nickel finish with white composite grips. New in 1987.

Mfg.'s Sug. Retail	$427	$360	$315	$270	$240	$220	$210	$200

Coltguard finish—employs a high strength electroless matte nickel finish. New in 1987.

Mfg.'s Sug. Retail	$406	$330	$300	$260	$235	$210	$200	$185

MUSTANG PLUS II—.380 ACP only, 2¾ in. barrel, blued finish, black composition grips, 7 shot mag., 20 oz. New in 1988.

Mfg.'s Sug. Retail	$384	$310	$280	$235	$215	$200	$190	$180

This model has the full grip length of the .380 Government Model.

MUSTANG POCKET LITE—similar to Mustang, except has aluminum alloy receiver, blue only, black composite grips, 12½ oz. Introduced in 1987.

Mfg.'s Sug. Retail	$384	$310	$280	$235	$215	$200	$190	$180

Grading	100%	98%	95%	90%	80%	70%	60%

MKIV/SERIES 80 GOLD CUP NATIONAL MATCH—.45 ACP, flat mainspring housing, accurizer barrel and bushing, adj. trigger, target hammer, solid rib, Colt-Elliason sight, made 1983-present.

Mfg.'s Sug. Retail	$766	$625	$515	$450	$400	$380	$350	$325

Stainless Gold Cup National Match—similar to Gold Cup, only manufactured from stainless steel, matte finish, released late in 1986.

Mfg.'s Sug. Retail	$822	$665	$545	$465

Add $55 for bright stainless steel finish (high polish).

Combat Elite—similar to Gold Cup, only with Colt-Pachmayr wrap around rubber grips, beveled magazine well, stainless steel receiver with carbon steel slide, and 3 dot fixed sighting system.

Mfg.'s Sug. Retail	$724	$615	$570	$450	$400	$360	$330	$300

LIGHTWEIGHT COMBAT COMMANDER—.45 ACP, 4¼ in. barrel, same as Government Model, except shorter and lighter alloy frame, 27½ oz., round spur hammer, made 1951-present, fixed sights. Add 10% for .38 Super and 9mm (discontinued cal.'s).

Mfg.'s Sug. Retail	$594	$495	$440	$395	$350	$300	$265	$240

COMBAT COMMANDER—same as Lightweight, except steel frame, .45 ACP, .38 Super, and 9mm.

Blued Finish

Mfg.'s Sug. Retail	$594	$495	$440	$395	$350	$300	$265	$240

Add $4 for 9mm or .38 Super cal.

Satin Nickel—disc. in 1986.

	$495	$450	$410	$365	$310	$275	$250

Last Mfg.'s Sug. Retail was $550.

OFFICER'S ACP—.45 ACP only, 3½ in. barrel, 34 oz., 6 shot mag., short version of the Government Model. New in 1985.

Blued Finish

Mfg.'s Sug. Retail	$594	$495	$440	$395	$350	$300	$265	$240

Matte Blued Finish

Mfg.'s Sug. Retail	$577	$485	$430	$365	$300	$260	$230	$200

Officers Stainless Steel—matte stainless steel finish. New in 1986.

Mfg.'s Sug. Retail	$629	$525	$465	$400

Add $63 for bright stainless steel finish (high polish - new in 1987).

Officers Lightweight—similar to Officers ACP, except has alloy frame and weighs 24 oz. New in 1986.

Mfg.'s Sug. Retail	$594	$495	$435	$390	$350	$300	$265	$240

Officers Satin Nickel—discontinued in 1985.

	$470	$410	$370	$320	$280	$260	$235

Last Mfg.'s Sug. Retail was $513.

DELTA ELITE—10mm Norma, 5 in. barrel, black neoprene grips, high profile 3 dot sights, blue finish, 7 shot mag., 38 oz. Introduced in 1987.

Mfg.'s Sug. Retail	$658	$590	$495	$445	$380	$350	$330	$310

Stainless Steel—matte stainless steel finish, new in 1989.

Mfg.'s Sug. Retail	$700	$600	$540	$465

Add $63 for brite stainless steel finish (Ultimate).

DELTA GOLD CUP—10mm Norma, target variation, includes adj. rear sight and trigger (serrated also), wrap around combat grips, new in 1989.

At this writing, prices have yet to be published on this model.

PISTOLS: SEMI-AUTO .22 CAL.

Note: All 100% Woodsmans with the original serial numbered box, test target, instruction folder, hang tag, and screw driver command a 10-25% premium, depending on the model's rarity. Note add ons at the end of some models for specific premium percentages.

Over 690,000 Woodsmans with variations were manufactured between 1915-1977.

Grading	100%	98%	95%	90%	80%	70%	60%

PRE-WOODSMAN—.22 LR, 6½ in. barrel, made 1915-1927, production totaled about 54,000.

	$700	$550	$450	$375	$300	$250	$225

This model was manufactured to use standard velocity ammunition only (not high speed). Colt did offer a conversion kit for high velocity ammo after the transition.

Woodsmans mfg. between 1915-1922 had a lightweight pencil barrel (approx. serial range 1-31,000). The medium barrel was introduced approx. 1922 and was retained until the 90,000 serial range (approx. mfg. 1922-1934).

WOODSMAN 1ST SERIES—.22 LR, 10 shot Mag., blue only, bottom mag. release, checkered wood grips, marked "The Woodsman" on receiver, adj. sights, mfg. from 1927-1947, total production was approx. 112,000.

Note: guns made prior to 1932 were designed for standard velocity .22 LR ammunition only. The new style main spring housing, designed for high velocity ammunition, began appearing at approx. ser. no. 80,000 and was completely phased in by approx. ser. no. 85,000. Later guns, INCLUDING ALL PISTOLS MADE AFTER WWII, were designed for high velocity ammunition.

Between 1934 and 1947 a tapered barrel was standard production (approx. ser. range 90,000-187,423).

Sport Model—4½ in. barrel, this model was introduced in 1933.

	$750	$595	$525	$450	$375	$325	$300

Approx. serial range on this variation is 86,105 - 187,423.

Target Model—6½ in. barrel.

	$600	$535	$475	$400	$325	$275	$250

Note: Colt discontinued the 1st Model series in 1947. These guns are quite different from the 2nd Model series started in 1948.

WOODSMAN 1ST SERIES MATCH TARGET—.22 LR only, 6½ in. heavy barrel, commonly called "Bullseye" Match Target, mfg. 1938-1944, production totaled around 16,000. Difficult to find in mint condition.

	$1,400	$1,150	$925	$750	$575	$475	$400

WOODSMAN 2ND SERIES—.22 LR only, slide stop and hold open, push button mag. release on this model is located on the left side of frame behind the trigger guard, Coltwood plastic grips (mfg. 1948-1950) or brown plastic grips (mfg. 1950-1955), mfg. between 1948-1955, total production on all 2nd Series was approx. 146,000.

Sport Model—4½ in. barrel.

	$500	$425	$350	$300	$250	$225	$200

Target Model—6 in. barrel.

	$400	$350	$300	$250	$225	$200	$175

Match Target Model—4½ in. heavy barrel. This variation will command a premium over the 6 in. barrel.

	$695	$550	$495	$425	$395	$370	$335

Match Target Model—6 in. heavy barrel.

	$595	$500	$410	$370	$335	$295	$275

WOODSMAN 3RD SERIES—.22 LR only, slide stop and hold open, mfg. between 1955-1977, black plastic grips (mfg. 1955-1960) or walnut grips (1960-1977), 3rd Series can be differentiated from 2nd Series by their bottom mag. release.

Sport Model—4½ in. barrel.

	$395	$365	$335	$300	$275	$225	$200

Grading	100%	98%	95%	90%	80%	70%	60%

Target Model—6 in. barrel.

	100%	98%	95%	90%	80%	70%	60%
	$350	$300	$275	$250	$225	$200	$175

Match Target Model—4½ in. heavy barrel.

	$550	$460	$400	$375	$350	$325	$295

Match Target Model—6 in. heavy barrel.

	$500	$460	$400	$375	$350	$325	$295

CHALLENGER MODEL—similar to Woodsman 2rd Series, only with fixed sights, without hold open, and bottom mag. release, 4½ and 6 in. barrels, mfg. between 1950-1955 with total production reaching approximately 77,000.

	$350	$300	$275	$250	$225	$210	$180

HUNTSMAN MODEL—.22 LR only, fixed sights and no hold open, 4½ and 6 in. barrels, black plastic grips to 1960 - walnut grips after 1960, mfg. between 1955-1977 with total production reaching over 100,000.

	$300	$280	$260	$240	$220	$200	$180

The Huntsman is very similar to the Challenger Model, except is built on a 3rd series frame.

TARGETSMAN MODEL—similar to the Huntsman, except has adj. rear sight and thumbrest on left grip, 6 in. barrel only, approx. 65,000 mfg. 1959-1977.

	$350	$300	$280	$260	$240	$220	$200

REVOLVERS: DOUBLE ACTION

100%	98%	95%	90%	80%	70%	60%	50%	40%	30%	20%	10%

MODEL 1877 LIGHTNING—.38 Colt and .32 Colt (very rare), 2, 2½, 3½, 4½, and 6 in. barrels without ejector. 4½, 5, 6, 7, and 7½ in. barrels with ejector, 6 shot double action, long cylinder fluting, blued finish with case hardened frame and hammer, full nickel plating also available, made from 1877-1910. Over 166,000 mfg.

100%	98%	95%	90%	80%	70%	60%	50%	40%	30%	20%	10%
$1,100	$895	$800	$740	$660	$575	$495	$425	$340	$265	$185	$130

MODEL 1877 THUNDERER—.41 Colt cal. only, otherwise same general specifications as Model 1877 Lightning.

$1,250	$975	$860	$795	$695	$600	$510	$430	$350	$275	$195	$140

MODEL 1878 FRONTIER—.32-20 WCF, .38-40 WCF, .44-40 WCF, .45 Colt, and .450-.455-.476 Eley cal.'s, 3½ and 4 in. barrels without ejector, 4¾, 5½, and 7½ in. with ejector. 6 in. is 1902 U.S. Revolver. 6 shot cylinder with long flutes, pinched frame, removable trigger guard, early guns have checked walnut stocks, later guns have hard black rubber. Made 1878-1905. Over 51,000 made.

$1,350	$1,000	$875	$800	$700	$600	$510	$430	$350	$275	$200	$150

MODEL 1889 "NAVY"—.38 short and long Colt, and .41 short and long Colt, 3, 4½, and 6 in. barrel, wood or rubber grips, blue or nickel finish, the first solid frame, swing out cylinder (counter-clockwise rotation) Colt produced, approx. 28,000 made 1889-1894, 1st 5,000 were ordered by U.S. Navy - hence name.

Blue finish

$850	$795	$675	$500	$425	$330	$295	$265	$245	$225	$205	$190

Nickel finish

$995	$850	$700	$525	$450	$330	$295	$265	$245	$225	$205	$190

MODEL 1892 "NEW ARMY & NAVY" (2ND ISSUE)—similar to 1889 Navy, but double cylinder notches, double locking bolt, and shorter flutes, square cyl. release thumb catch, .38 Special added in 1904, .32-30 added in 1905, mfg. 1892-1907. Add $100 for U.S.N. markings.

$375	$330	$295	$265	$245	$225	$205	$190	$175	$160	$150	$140

This model also had sub-variations that included Models 1894, 1895, 1896, 1901, & 1903. Values will approximate those shown above.

OFFICER'S MODEL TARGET FIRST ISSUE—.38 Spl., 6 in. barrel, adj. sights, blue, made 1904-1908.

$500	$450	$400	$365	$335	$305	$275	$245	$215	$180	$155	$135

100%	98%	95%	90%	80%	70%	60%	50%	40%	30%	20%	10%

OFFICER'S MODEL TARGET SECOND ISSUE—.22 LR, .32 Police Positive, and .38 Spl., 4, 4½, 5, 6, and 7½ in. barrels, 7½ in. barrel in .38 Spl. only, adj. sights, checkered walnut grips, made 1908-1940.

| $450 | $400 | $365 | $335 | $305 | $275 | $245 | $215 | $180 | $160 | $140 | $125 |

Add $75 for .22 LR cal.

MODEL 1905 MARINE CORPS—same as New Navy Second Issue, except has a round butt, in .38 short, long, and special, only 6 in. barrel, made 1905-1909 in approx. ser. no. range 10,000-10,925, about 925 mfg.

| $745 | $660 | $595 | $520 | $480 | $440 | $395 | $360 | $330 | $295 | $260 | $225 |

ARMY SPECIAL MODEL—.32-20, .38 (various), and .41 Colt, 4, 4½, 5, and 6 in. barrels, hard rubber grips, fixed sights, rounded cylinder release thumb catch, has heavier frame than New Navy, approx. ser. no. range 291,000-540,000, mfg. 1908-1927.

Blue finish

| $330 | $295 | $265 | $245 | $225 | $205 | $190 | $175 | $160 | $150 | $140 | $120 |

Nickel finish

| $385 | $330 | $295 | $265 | $245 | $225 | $205 | $190 | $175 | $160 | $145 | $125 |

NEW SERVICE MODEL—.38 Spl., .357 Mag., .38-40, .44-40, .44 Russian, .44 Spl., .45 ACP, .45 Colt, .450 Eley, .455 Eley, and .476 Eley, 4, 5, and 6 in. barrels in .38 Spl., 4½, 5½, and 7½ in. barrel in all others, blue or nickel finish, walnut stock, made 1898-1942. Rare cal.'s (Eley cal.'s and .44 Russian) will command premiums over values listed below.

Commercial

| $650 | $595 | $540 | $485 | $445 | $400 | $365 | $335 | $310 | $285 | $265 | $245 |

Magnum

| $495 | $450 | $400 | $375 | $345 | $325 | $305 | $290 | $275 | $260 | $250 | $240 |

1917 Army

| $550 | $520 | $485 | $460 | $405 | $360 | $335 | $310 | $285 | $260 | $245 | $225 |

New Service Target—similar to New Service Model, except hand honed action and adj. sights, 7½ in. barrel only, square butt, blue only, made 1900-1940.

| $725 | $645 | $580 | $520 | $480 | $440 | $395 | $360 | $330 | $295 | $260 | $225 |

Shooting Master—various cal.'s from 38 Spl. through .45 LC, 6 in. barrel, checkered walnut grips with Colt Medallion, machined grip straps, trigger, hammer, and ejector rod head, round butt, approx. ser. no. range 333,000 - 350,000.

| $875 | $775 | $675 | $595 | $520 | $480 | $440 | $395 | $360 | $330 | $295 | $260 |

The Shooting Master could be ordered with a square butt after 1933.

OFFICIAL POLICE—.32-20 (discontinued 1942), .41 long (discontinued 1930), .38 Spl., and .22 LR (introduced 1930), 6 shot, square butt, 4, 5, and 6 in. barrels, 2 in. barrel in .38 Spl., checkered walnut grips, fixed sights, made 1927-1969.

Blue finish

| $330 | $295 | $265 | $245 | $225 | $205 | $190 | $175 | $160 | $150 | $140 | $120 |

Nickel finish

| $385 | $330 | $295 | $265 | $245 | $225 | $205 | $190 | $175 | $160 | $150 | $140 |

Add 15% for .22 LR cal.

Marshall Model—.38 Special, 2 or 4 in. barrel, round butt, differentiated by "M" suffix and "COLT MARSHALL" on barrel, about 2,500 mfg. 1954-1956 in approx. ser. no. range 833350-M through 845320-M.

| $495 | $450 | $400 | $365 | $335 | $305 | $275 | $245 | $215 | $180 | $160 | $140 |

Commando Model—.38 Special, 2 in. (rare), 4 in. (common), or 6 in. (rare) barrel, parkerized finish, about 50,000 mfg. between 1942-1945, 32 oz., marked "COLT COMMANDO" on barrel.

| $295 | $265 | $245 | $225 | $205 | $190 | $175 | $160 | $150 | $140 | $120 | $105 |

OFFICIAL POLICE MKIII—.38 Spl., 4, 5, and 6 in. barrels, made 1969-1975.

Blue finish

| $165 | $155 | $145 | $135 | $125 | $115 | $105 | $100 | $95 | $90 | $85 | $80 |

Nickel finish

| $195 | $185 | $175 | $165 | $155 | $145 | $135 | $125 | $115 | $105 | $100 | $95 |

100%	98%	95%	90%	80%	70%	60%	50%	40%	30%	20%	10%

METROPOLITAN MKIII—.38 Spl., similar to Official Police, except heavier and 4 in. heavy barrel only, blue finish, mfg. 1969-1972.

| $165 | $155 | $145 | $135 | $125 | $115 | $105 | $100 | $95 | $90 | $85 | $80 |

OFFICER'S MODEL SPECIAL—.22 LR and .38 Spl., 6 in. barrel, blue, similar to Second Issue, only heavier non-tapered barrel, new style hammer and "Coltmaster Sight", checkered plastic grips, made 1949-1953.

| $350 | $315 | $290 | $265 | $245 | $225 | $205 | $190 | $175 | $160 | $150 | $140 |

Add $75 for .22 LR cal.

OFFICER'S MODEL MATCH—.22 LR, .22 Mag, or .38 Spl., 6 in. barrel, tapered heavy barrel, wide spur hammer, Accro sight, large target grips (walnut), made 1953-1970.

| $450 | $400 | $365 | $335 | $305 | $275 | $245 | $215 | $180 | $160 | $140 | $125 |

Add $75 for .22 LR cal.
Add 100% for .22 Mag. cal.

NEW POCKET—.32 short and long Colt, 2½, 3½, and 6 in. barrel, rubber grips, made 1895-1905.

Blue finish

| $300 | $265 | $245 | $225 | $205 | $190 | $175 | $160 | $150 | $140 | $120 | $105 |

Nickel finish

| $330 | $295 | $265 | $245 | $225 | $205 | $190 | $175 | $160 | $150 | $140 | $120 |

POCKET POSITIVE—same as New Pocket, except has positive lock feature, also chambered for .32 Colt, .32 S&W, and .32 Colt New Police, made 1905-1940.

Blue finish

| $330 | $295 | $265 | $245 | $225 | $205 | $190 | $175 | $160 | $150 | $140 | $120 |

Nickel finish

| $365 | $325 | $295 | $265 | $245 | $225 | $205 | $190 | $175 | $160 | $150 | $140 |

NEW POLICE—.32 Colt and .32 Colt New Police, 2½, 4, and 6 in. barrels, fixed sights, same frame as New Pocket, except larger grips, rubber grips, made 1896-1905.

Blue finish

| $265 | $240 | $220 | $200 | $185 | $175 | $160 | $150 | $140 | $120 | $110 | $100 |

Nickel finish

| $275 | $245 | $225 | $205 | $190 | $175 | $160 | $150 | $140 | $120 | $110 | $100 |

NEW POLICE TARGET—6 in. barrel, blue.

| $365 | $325 | $295 | $265 | $245 | $225 | $205 | $190 | $175 | $160 | $150 | $140 |

POLICE POSITIVE—.32 Colt, .32 New Police, .38 New Police, and .38 S&W, 2½ in. (.32 only), 4, 5, and 6 in. barrels, improved "positive lock" version of the New Police, walnut or rubber grips, made 1905-1947.

Blue finish

| $330 | $295 | $265 | $245 | $225 | $205 | $190 | $175 | $160 | $150 | $140 | $120 |

Nickel finish

| $385 | $335 | $295 | $265 | $245 | $225 | $205 | $190 | $175 | $160 | $150 | $140 |

POLICE POSITIVE TARGET MODEL—.22 LR, .22 WRF, .32 Colt, and .32 New Police, 6 in. barrel, blue, adj. sight, checkered walnut grips, made 1905-1940.

| $550 | $520 | $480 | $440 | $395 | $360 | $330 | $295 | $260 | $220 | $180 | $140 |

POLICE POSITIVE SPECIAL—.32-20, .32 New Police, .38 New Police, and .38 Spl., 4, 5, and 6 in. barrels, fixed sights, frame longer to permit longer cylinder, wood, rubber, or plastic grips, made 1907-1973.

| $300 | $265 | $245 | $225 | $205 | $190 | $175 | $160 | $150 | $140 | $120 | $105 |

CAMP PERRY MODEL—.22 LR, 8 in. (rare) and 10 in., Officer's Model frame modified to accept a flat single shot chamber. The model name was stamped on the left side of the chamber, the only single shot Colt on a revolver frame. 2,488 mfg. between 1926-1941.

| $1,150 | $975 | $915 | $860 | $810 | $750 | $685 | $620 | $540 | $460 | $395 | $340 |

COLT'S FIREARMS, cont.

100%	98%	95%	90%	80%	70%	60%	50%	40%	30%	20%	10%

BANKER'S SPECIAL—2 in. barrel, blue, rounded butt, made 1926-1940.

.38 cal.

$500	$460	$410	$375	$335	$305	$275	$245	$215	$180	$160	$140

.22 cal.

$775	$665	$595	$525	$480	$440	$395	$360	$330	$295	$260	$225

COURIER—.22 S, L, & LR, .32 New Police, double action, 6 shot, 3 in. barrel. Discontinued after a limited production in 1956. Add 10% for 22 cal.

$850	$795	$725	$650	$575	$500	$425	$385	$335	$305	$275	$245

AIRCREWMAN SPECIAL—.38 Spl., double action, aluminum frame, 2 in. barrel, 11 oz., fixed sights, checkered walnut grips, mfg. 1951 mostly.

$750	$695	$640	$580	$520	$480	$440	$400	$370	$345	$325	$295

Approx. 1,200 mfg. within ser. no. range 2,900LW - 7,775LW. Original U.S. or A.F. will command large premiums.

BORDER PATROL—.38 Spl., double action, 6 shot, 4 in. heavy barrel, 400 mfg. during 1952 only in 610,000 ser. no. range.

$700	$625	$565	$535	$460	$400	$365	$335	$305	$275	$245	$215

DETECTIVE SPECIAL—.38 Spl., .32 New Police, and .38 New Police, 2 in. barrel, blue, wood or plastic grips, made 1926-1972.

$365	$325	$295	$265	$245	$225	$205	$190	$175	$160	$140	$125

COBRA (ROUND BUTT)—first issue, 2 in. barrel, blue, same as Detective Special, only alloy frame.

$310	$285	$260	$240	$220	$200	$185	$170	$160	$150	$140	$120

COBRA (SQUARE BUTT)—blue, same as Cobra Round Butt, only 4 in. barrel, square butt, made 1951-1973.

$340	$295	$265	$245	$225	$205	$190	$175	$160	$150	$140	$120

AGENT FIRST ISSUE—.38 Spl., same as Cobra first issue, except shorter grip frame, made 1955-1973.

$275	$245	$225	$205	$190	$175	$160	$150	$140	$120	$110	$100

AGENT L.W.—.38 Spl., same as First Issue, except shrouded ejector rod, alloy frame, matte finish since 1982. Made 1973-86.

$225	$205	$190	$175	$160	$150	$140	$130	$120	$115	$110	$100

Last Mfg.'s Sug. Retail was $260.

COBRA SECOND ISSUE—.38 Spl., same as Cobra first issue, except shrouded ejector rod, made 1973-1981.

$300	$265	$245	$225	$205	$190	$175	$160	$150	$140	$120	$105

DETECTIVE SPECIAL SECOND ISSUE—.38 Spl., same as first issue, shrouded ejector rod, 2 and 3 in. barrels, fixed sights, wrap-around wood grips, made 1973-86. Add $50 for nickel.

$340	$300	$265	$245	$225	$205	$190	$175	$160	$150	$140	$120

Last Mfg.'s Sug. Retail was $429.

Also available with class A engraving - add $590 if in 98% condition or better.

COMMANDO SPECIAL—.38 Spl., steel frame, shrouded ejector rod, 2 in. barrel, matte parkerized finish, rubber grips. Manufactured 1984-86.

$230	$205	$190	$175	$160	$150	$140	$130	$120	$110	$100	$95

Last Mfg.'s Sug. Retail was $260.

POLICE POSITIVE SECOND ISSUE—same as Detective Special Second Issue, except 4 in. barrel, .38 Spl.

$240	$210	$195	$175	$160	$150	$140	$130	$120	$115	$110	$105

DIAMONDBACK—.22 LR and .38 Spl., 2½ (very rare in .22 LR), 4, or 6 in. VR barrel, adj. sights, steel frame, checkered walnut grips, made 1966-86. Add $55 for nickel finish.

$395	$335	$295	$265	$245	$225	$205	$190	$175	$160	$150	$140

Last Mfg.'s Sug. Retail was $461.

Note: Approximately 2,200 Diamondbacks were made with 6 in. barrels and nickel finish in .22 cal. - made 1979. Add additional $150 for 100% specimens.

	100%	98%	95%	90%	80%	70%	60%	50%	40%	30%	20%	10%

VIPER MODEL—.38 Spl., alloy frame, 4 in. barrel, made 1977-1984.

	100%	98%	95%	90%	80%	70%	60%	50%	40%	30%	20%	10%
	$225	$205	$190	$175	$160	$150	$140	$130	$120	$110	$105	$100

COLT .357 MAG—4 in. or 6 in. barrel, heavy frame, Accro sight, blue, checkered walnut grips. Later guns marked Trooper, made 1953-1961.

Standard hammer

$330	$300	$285	$270	$260	$250	$240	$230	$220	$210	$200	$190

Wide hammer w/target grips

$385	$335	$300	$285	$265	$255	$245	$235	$225	$215	$205	$195

TROOPER—.38 Spl., 4 in. barrel, blue, quick draw ramp front sight, adj. rear sight, checkered walnut grips, made 1953-1969.

Standard hammer

$240	$220	$210	$200	$190	$180	$170	$165	$160	$155	$150	$145

Wide hammer and target grips

$275	$245	$225	$210	$200	$190	$180	$170	$165	$160	$155	$150

Grading	100%	98%	95%	90%	80%	70%	60%

TROOPER MK III—.22 LR, .22 Mag., and .357 Mag. cal.'s, 4, 6, or 8 in. barrel, adj. sights, walnut target grips, made 1969-1983.

Blue finish	$319	$255	$190	$180	$170	$160	$150
Nickel finish	$339	$270	$200	$190	$180	$170	$160

LAWMAN MK III—.357 Mag., 2 in. and 4 in. barrel, shrouded ejector rod for 2 in. barrel, fixed sights, checkered walnut grips, made 1969-1983.

Blue finish	$288	$230	$190	$180	$170	$160	$150
Nickel finish	$307	$245	$200	$190	$180	$170	$160

TROOPER MK V—.357 Mag., 4 and 6 in. barrel, adj. sights, walnut target grips, improved version of Mark III action, vent rib barrel, redesigned in 1980. Discontinued in 1986.

Blue finish

$320	$290	$250	$215	$185	$170	$160

Last Mfg.'s Sug. Retail was $362.

Nickel finish

$345	$315	$285	$235	$200	$185	$170

Last Mfg.'s Sug. Retail was $396.

LAWMAN MK V—.357 Mag., 2 and 4 in. barrel, shrouded ejector rod for 2 in. barrel, fixed sights, checkered walnut grips, improved version of MK III action. Manufactured in 1984 and 1985 only.

Blue finish

$285	$250	$200	$175	$160	$150	$140

Last Mfg.'s Sug. Retail was $309.

Nickel finish

$300	$265	$225	$200	$180	$170	$160

Last Mfg.'s Sug. Retail was $328.

PEACEKEEPER—.357 Mag. only, 4 or 6 in. barrel, matte blue finish, rubber combat grips, adj. rear sight, about 42 oz. Mfg. 1985-1987.

$290	$255	$235	$205	$195	$180	$165

Last Mfg.'s Sug. Retail was $330.

BOA—.357 Mag., deep blue polish, full length ejector shroud with Mark V action, 1,200 manufactured in 4 and 6 in. barrel lengths. Entire production run was purchased by Lew Horton Distributing Co., Inc. located in Southboro, MA. Manufactured in 1985 only.

$460	$420	$395	$375	$350	$325	$295

Last Mfg.'s Sug. Retail was $525.

Grading	100%	98%	95%	90%	80%	70%	60%

KING COBRA—.357 Mag., blued metal, black neoprene round butt grips, 4 or 6 in. solid rib barrel only, outline sights, approx. 42 oz. (4 in. barrel). New in 1988.

Mfg.'s Sug. Retail	$409	$340	$300	$260	$235	$210	$200	$185

KING COBRA STAINLESS—.357 Mag., stainless steel construction, black neoprene round butt grips, 2 (disc. in 1987), 2½ (new in 1988), 4, or 6 in. solid rib barrel, outline sights, approx. 36 oz. (2½ in. barrel). New in late 1987.

Mfg.'s Sug. Retail	$435	$380	$330	$280

King Cobra Bright Stainless—similar to King Cobra, except for bright stainless steel, 4 or 6 in. barrel only. New in 1988.

Mfg.'s Sug. Retail	$472	$410	$365	$325

PYTHON—.357 Mag., 2½, 3 (disc.), 4, 6, or 8 in. barrel with vent rib, royal blue finish, full shrouded ejector rod, checkered walnut grips. Made 1955-present.

Blue finish

Mfg.'s Sug. Retail	$730	$525	$385	$350	$325	$300	$275	$250

Early 4 and 6 in. Pythons without letter prefix before ser. no. will bring a small premium if in 100% condition or N.I.B., as well as the discontinued 3 in. barrel.

Also available with Class A, B, C, or D engraving — prices are the same as the .45 ACP Government Models listed previously under the Pistols: Semi-Auto, Recent Manufacture.

Nickel finish—discontinued in 1985.

	$595	$450	$350	$325	$300	$275	$250

Last Mfg.'s Sug. Retail was $693.

Stainless Steel Python—stainless steel construction, matte finish, neoprene combat stocks, 2½, 4, 6 or 8 (new in 1989) in. barrel. Introduced 1983.

Mfg.'s Sug. Retail	$836	$645	$590	$535

The 6 in. barrel includes neoprene target stocks.

Ultimate Stainless Steel Model—deluxe, highly polished stainless model. New in 1985.

Mfg.'s Sug. Retail	$860	$680	$600	$540

PYTHON HUNTER—.357 Mag., 8 in. barrel, includes EER Leupold 2X scope, Halliburton aluminum case and accessories, mfg. in 1981 only.

	$995	$895	$830	$760	$700	$650	$595

Last Mfg.'s Sug. Retail was $995.

PYTHON .38 SPECIAL—8 in. barrel, blued. Discontinued.

	$450	$425	$375	$350	$325	$300	$275

RIFLES: DISCONTINUED

Grading	80%	70%	60%	50%	40%	30%	20%	10%

FIRST MODEL RING LEVER—.34, .36, .38, .40, and .44, 8 or 10 shot revolving cylinder, 32 in. octagon barrel, walnut stock, no forend, 200 produced, Percussion, made 1837-1838.

Standard Model

	$10,450	$9,350	$8,250	$7,150	$6,050	$5,500	$4,950	$3,850

Altered Model—attached loading lever.

	$11,000	$9,900	$8,800	$7,700	$6,600	$6,050	$5,500	$4,400

SECOND MODEL RING LEVER—same as First Model, without top strap over cylinder, .44 caliber only, Percussion, 5000 produced, 1838-1841.

Standard Model

	$10,450	$9,350	$8,250	$7,150	$6,050	$5,500	$4,950	$3,850

Altered Model

	$11,000	$9,900	$8,800	$7,700	$6,600	$6,050	$5,500	$4,400

Grading	80%	70%	60%	50%	40%	30%	20%	10%

MODEL 1839 CARBINE—.525 smooth bore, 6 shot cylinder, 24 in. barrel, exposed hammer for cocking, blued, walnut stock, Percussion, approximately 950 produced, 1838-1841.

Standard Model

	$7,700	$6,600	$5,500	$4,950	$4,400	$4,235	$3,960	$3,520

Early Model—no loading lever.

	$13,200	$12,100	$10,450	$9,350	$8,250	$7,260	$6,600	$5,500

MODEL 1855 REVOLVING—.36, .44, and .56 cal., various barrel lengths and stock styles, 5 or 6 shot cylinder, blued with walnut butt stock, no forend, percussion, made 1856-1864.

½ Stock Sporter—24, 27, and 30 in. barrel, approximately 1500 produced.

	$3,080	$2,860	$2,640	$2,200	$1,925	$1,650	$1,430	$1,210

Full Stock Sporter—21, 24, 27, 30, and 31 in. barrel, approximately 2000 produced.

	$3,740	$3,520	$3,300	$2,970	$2,420	$1,925	$1,760	$1,540

Military Model, U.S.—marked, 21-37 in. barrel, 9310 produced.

	$5,280	$4,950	$4,400	$3,850	$3,300	$2,750	$2,420	$1,980

.36 Caliber Carbine Model—15, 18, and 21 in. barrel, 4400 produced.

	$6,050	$5,500	$4,400	$3,300	$2,475	$1,925	$1,650	$1,430

.56 Caliber Artillery Carbine—24 in. barrel.

	$7,150	$6,050	$4,950	$3,850	$3,300	$2,860	$2,475	$2,200

Shotgun Model—.60 and .75 cal., smooth bore, 27, 30, 33, and 36 in. barrels, 1100 produced.

	$3,850	$3,300	$3,025	$2,750	$2,200	$1,870	$1,650	$1,375

100%	98%	95%	90%	80%	70%	60%	50%	40%	30%	20%	10%

MODEL 1861 MUSKET—.58 cal., Percussion, muzzle loader, 40 in. barrel, with 3 bands, metal parts, white walnut stock, 75,000 produced, 1861-1865.

$1,320	$1,100	$990	$880	$825	$770	$715	$605	$495	$330	$295	$275

COLT-BURGESS LEVER ACTION—.44-40 cal., 25½ in. barrel, 15 shot tube mag., blue with case hardened lever and hammer, walnut stock, 6400 produced, 1883-1885.

$1,650	$1,540	$1,320	$1,100	$935	$770	$660	$605	$550	$470	$415	$385

COLT-BURGESS CARBINE—same as Rifle, with 20 in. barrel.

$2,200	$1,980	$1,760	$1,375	$1,265	$1,100	$990	$880	$825	$715	$605	$550

COLT-BURGESS BABY CARBINE—same as Carbine, with lightened frame.

$2,750	$2,420	$2,200	$1,650	$1,430	$1,320	$1,155	$1,045	$935	$880	$825	$715

LIGHTNING SLIDE ACTION—small frame, .22 cal., 24 in. barrel, open sights, walnut straight stock, round or octagon barrel, 90,000 produced, 1887-1904.

$935	$880	$770	$605	$440	$330	$305	$275	$220	$200	$175	$150

LIGHTNING SLIDE ACTION—medium frame, same as small frame, in .32-20, .38-40, and .44-40, with larger frame.

$1,265	$1,100	$990	$825	$605	$495	$415	$305	$275	$220	$195	$165

LIGHTNING CARBINE MEDIUM FRAME—same as Rifle, with 20 in. barrel.

$1,870	$1,760	$1,540	$1,320	$935	$825	$715	$605	$525	$440	$415	$330

LIGHTNING BABY CARBINE MEDIUM FRAME—lightened version of Carbine.

$4,400	$3,850	$3,300	$2,750	$1,650	$990	$880	$770	$660	$550	$525	$440

LIGHTNING SLIDE ACTION—large frame, .38-56 - .50-95, express, large version of previously described Lightnings, 6500 produced, 1887-1894.

$2,200	$1,980	$1,760	$1,430	$1,265	$1,100	$880	$660	$550	$495	$440	$330

LIGHTNING CARBINE LARGE FRAME—22 in. barrel.

$3,300	$3,025	$2,750	$2,200	$1,925	$1,650	$1,485	$1,100	$990	$880	$715	$550

BABY CARBINE LARGE FRAME—lightened version.

$8,250	$7,700	$6,600	$4,950	$4,125	$3,575	$3,080	$2,750	$2,420	$2,200	$1,925	$1,650

Note: .50-95 express will bring premium of 20%.

Grading	100%	98%	95%	90%	80%	70%	60%

DOUBLE RIFLE SXS—Various cal.'s in the .45 range, hammers, very limited production between 1878-1880. Most guns were owned by friends of Caldwell Colt — Sam Colt's son, the original designer. Colt Double Rifles are extremely rare and desirable, and should be examined carefully. Prices start in the $5,000 range and go up in proportion to the gun's original finish, estimated 40 or less mfg.

.22 CAL RIFLES

COLTEER 1-22—.22 LR and Mag., single shot bolt action, 20 or 20 in. round barrel, adj. rear sight, plain walnut stock, approx. 50,000 made 1957-1966.

	$250	$215	$175	$140	$110	$95	$80

STAGECOACH—.22LR, semi-auto, 16½ in. barrel, 13 shot mag. deluxe walnut, saddle ring w/leather thong, roll-engraved hold-up scene, over 25,000 mfg. 1965-mid 70's.

	$300	$250	$215	$175	$140	$110	$90

COURIER—similar to Colteer semi-auto, except pistol-grip stock and enlarged forearm, mfg. 1970-mid 70's.

	$250	$215	$175	$140	$110	$95	$80

COLTEER—.22 LR, similar to Stagecoach, except 19 3/8 in. barrel, 15 shot mag., no engraving and plain walnut, over 25,000 mfg. 1965-mid 70's.

	$250	$215	$175	$140	$110	$95	$80

BOLT ACTION CENTERFIRE RIFLES

COLT "57"—.243 or .30-06 cal., FN Mauser action, mfg. by Jefferson Mfg. Co. in N. Haven, CT during 1957, approx. 5,000 mfg starting at ser. no. 1, checkered American Monte Carlo walnut stock, wrap-around front sight.

	$500	$430	$390	$340	$300	$265	$230

This model was also available in a deluxe version with deluxe hand checkered walnut stock — add 15%.

COLTSMAN STANDARD RIFLE—.243 Win., .30-06, .300 Mag., and .308 cal.'s, mfg. by Kodiak, Mauser or Sako-action, 22 in. or 24 in.(.300 Mag.), 5 or 6 shot mag., approx. 10,000 (both models) mfg. 1958-1966.

	$450	$395	$350	$300	$265	$230	$210

COLTSMAN CUSTOM RIFLE—deluxe variation including deluxe walnut with skipline checkering and rosewood forearm cap.

	$675	$575	$495	$430	$390	$340	$300

COLT SAUER RIFLE (STANDARD ACTION)—non-rotating bolt action, manufactured in Germany by J. P. Sauer & Son, .25-06, .270 Win. and .30-06, 24 in. barrel, 4 round mag., no sights, checkered walnut stock with rosewood forend tip and pistol grip cap, recoil pad. Discontinued in 1985.

	$950	$750	$700	$660	$620	$575	$500

Last Mfg.'s Sug. Retail was $1,257.

COLT SAUER SHORT ACTION—same as the standard except in .22-250, .243 Win. and .308 Win. Discontinued in 1985.

	$900	$600	$575	$550	$525	$485	$430

Last Mfg.'s Sug. Retail was $1,257.

COLT SAUER MAGNUM—same as the standard except in 7mm Rem. Mag., 300 Win. Mag., and 300 Weatherby Mag. Discontinued in 1985.

	$1,100	$900	$795	$720	$660	$600	$545

Last Mfg.'s Sug. Retail was $1,300.

COLT SAUER GRAND ALASKAN—heavier version in .375 H&H Mag., adj. sights.

	$1,295	$1,100	$995	$900	$820	$740	$690

COLT SAUER GRAND AFRICAN—.458 Win. Mag., 4 round capacity, 9 lb. 12 oz. Discontinued in 1985.

	$1,350	$1,100	$995	$900	$820	$740	$690

Last Mfg.'s Sug. Retail was $1,400.

Grading	100%	98%	95%	90%	80%	70%	60%

DRILLINGS

COLT SAUER DRILLING—12 ga./.30-06 or .243 Combo gun, 25 in. barrels, engraved, 8 lbs. Discontinued in 1985.

	100%	98%	95%	90%	80%	70%	60%
	$3,350	$2,750	$2,400	$2,100	$1,800	$1,500	$1,250

Last Mfg.'s Sug. Retail was $4,228.

RIFLES: SINGLE SHOT CENTERFIRE

COLT-SHARPS RIFLE—.17 Bee, .22-250, .243, .25-06, 7mm Rem. Mag., .30-06, or .375 H&H cal.'s, Sharps falling block action, high-gloss bluing, deluxe checkered walnut stock and forearm, mfg. 1970-1977.

	100%	98%	95%	90%	80%	70%	60%
	$2,295	$1,950	$1,650	$1,200	$1,000	$800	$650

RIFLES: CURRENT MANUFACTURE

AR - 15A2 GOV'T MODEL RIFLE (INCLUDING EARLIER SPORTER VARIATIONS)—semi-auto version of the M-16 rifle with forward bolt assist, 5.56mm (.223), gas operated, 20 in. barrel, straight line black nylon stock, aperture rear, post front sight, 7 lbs. 8 oz., 20 and 30 round box mag.

Mfg.'s Sug. Retail	$816	$595	$520	$470	$420	$380	$335	$275

Subtract $70 for older field-style rear sight assembly (pre-1987).

In 1987, Colt replaced the AR-15A2 Sporter II Rifle with the AR-15A2 Gov't Model. This new model has the 800 meter rear sighting system housed in the receivers carrying handle (similar to the M-16 A2).

Colt has scheduled this model to be finished in a Z-Coat green tiger-stripe camouflage and will be available later in 1988. Accessories include a camouflage canvas carrying case, a nylon sling, and a cleaning kit. Prices on this model have yet to be established.

AR - 15A2 H-BAR—similar to AR-15A2 Gov't Model Rifle, except has heavy barrel, 8 lbs. New in 1986.

Mfg.'s Sug. Retail	$870	$745	$650	$575	$520	$460	$410	$355

AR - 15A2 Delta H-Bar—similar to AR-15A2 H-Bar, except has 3-9X rubber armored variable scope, removable cheek piece, adj. scope mount, and leather sling. Cased. New in 1987.

Mfg.'s Sug. Retail	$1,360	$1,360	$995	$900	$820	$740	$690	$640

AR - 15A2 Sporter II—standard 20 in. barrel, rear sight adj. for windage only, 7½ lbs.

Mfg.'s Sug. Retail	$740	$550	$500	$450	$400	$370	$330	$275

AR - 15A2 CARBINE—similar to older AR-15A2 Sporter II Rifle, except has collapsible buttstock, field sights, 16 in. barrel, 5 lbs. 13 oz., shortened forearm. Disc. in 1988.

	$575	$500	$450	$400	$370	$330	$275

Last Mfg.'s Sug. Retail was $770.

AR - 15A2 GOV'T MODEL CARBINE—similar to AR-15A2 Gov't Model Rifle, except has collapsible buttstock, 800 meter adj. rear sight, 16 in. barrel, 5 lbs. 13 oz., shortened forearm. New in 1988.

Mfg.'s Sug. Retail	$836	$695	$630	$530	$470	$430	$390	$340

AR-15 9mm Carbine—same as 5.56mm Carbine, except 9mm with 20 shot Mag., 6 lbs. 5 oz. Made in 1985-86 only.

	$595	$550	$515	$470	$430	$390	$340

Last Mfg.'s Sug. Retail was $696.

AR - 15 SCOPE (4X) AND MOUNTS

Mfg.'s Sug. Retail	$262	$210	$175	$160

SHOTGUNS: DISCONTINUED

Strong, original case colors and vivid damascus barrel patterning will make the difference when determining values on the Models 1878 and 1883. Remember, these are black powder shotguns.

100%	98%	95%	90%	80%	70%	60%	50%	40%	30%	20%	10%

MODEL 1878 HAMMER SHOTGUN SXS—10 and 12 ga., 28-32 in. blued or browned damascus barrels, double triggers, sideplates, case hardened breech, non-automatic ejectors, semi-pistol grip stock, 22,683 mfg. between 1878-1889. Many of these guns were ordered with special features - these original guns command premiums above the prices listed below.

100%	98%	95%	90%	80%	70%	60%	50%	40%	30%	20%	10%
$3,350	$2,995	$2,675	$2,200	$1,925	$1,650	$1,485	$1,100	$990	$880	$715	$550

MODEL 1883 HAMMERLESS SXS—8, 10 and 12 ga., 28-32 in. barrels, many deluxe custom orders occur in this model. Mfg. from 1883-1895. Approx. serial range is No. 1-3,050 and 4,055-8,365. Seldom encountered in mint condition.

100%	98%	95%	90%	80%	70%	60%	50%	40%	30%	20%	10%
$3,750	$3,350	$2,995	$2,675	$2,200	$1,925	$1,650	$1,485	$1,100	$990	$880	$715

This model was generally a custom order gun with no standard grades being designated. Quality was extremely high, and the high cost of manufacture is a large reason why the gun never sold in large numbers commercially. The Model 1883 was discontinued after only 12 years of manufacture(it was one of the most expensive shotguns during its day). Values above assume moderate engraving and above average walnut.

Grading	100%	98%	95%	90%	80%	70%	60%

STANDARD AUTO SHOTGUN—12 or 20 ga. (also available in Mag.'s), mfg. by Franchi of Italy, aluminum frame, 26, 28, 30, or 32 in. plain or VR barrel, almost 5,300 mfg. (both models) 1962-1966.

		100%	98%	95%	90%	80%	70%	60%
		$375	$350	$325	$295	$260	$230	$200

Add $50 for VR barrel.

CUSTOM AUTO SHOTGUN—similar to Standard Model, except deluxe walnut, hand engraved receiver, mfg. 1962-1966.

		100%	98%	95%	90%	80%	70%	60%
		$475	$425	$375	$350	$325	$295	$260

COLTSMAN PUMP SHOTGUN—12, 16, or 20 ga., Franchi frame assembled by both Kodiak and Montgomery Wards, 26 or 28 in. plain barrel, aluminum frame, approx. 2,000 mfg. 1961-1965.

		100%	98%	95%	90%	80%	70%	60%
		$325	$295	$260	$230	$200	$180	$165

COLT COMMEMORATIVES & LIMITED PRODUCTION

As a reminder on commemoratives, I would like to repeat a few facts, especially for the beginning collector, applicable to all manufacturers of commemoratives. Commemoratives are current production guns designed as a reproduction of an historically famous gun model, or as a tie-in with historically famous persons or events. They are generally of very excellent quality and often embellished with select woods and finishes such as silver, nickel, or gold plating. Obviously, they are manufactured to be instant collectibles and to be pleasing to the eye. As with firearms in general, not all commemorative models have achieved collector status, although most enjoy an active market. Consecutive-numbered pairs as well as collections based on the same serial number will bring a premium. Remember that handguns usually are in some type of wood presentation case, and that rifles may be cased or in packaging with graphics styled to the particular theme of the collectible. The original factory packaging and papers should always accompany the firearm as they are necessary to realize full value at the time of sale. All commemorative firearms should be absolutely new, unfired, as issued since any obvious use or wear removes it from collector status and lowers its value significantly. A fired gun with obvious wear or without its original packaging can lose as much as 50% of its normal value.

In recent years, commemoratives in general have experienced poor liquidity and an overall reduction of prices. Commemorative production in some trademarks has totalled well over 250,000 units, and some collectors are weighing the "limited production" factor on each model before paying a premium over the standard production model of that particular commemorative. The following values reflect maximum purchase prices made in various areas of the U.S. In some regions it is possible to purchase an SAA commemorative made in substantial quantity for almost no premium over a standard production SAA. Because of this, prices could fluctuate over 25% depending on the geographic location of purchase or sale.

Grading	100%	Issue price	Qty made

A FINAL NOTE ON COMMEMORATIVES: AS A RULE, WHAT DETERMINES THE BOTTOM OF THE MARKET IN COMMEMMORATIVES IS THE TOP OF THE MARKET FOR THEIR STANDARD MODEL PRODUCTION RELATIVES. A PROBLEM WITH LIMITED EDITIONS IS THAT OVER THE YEARS OF OWNERSHIP, MOST OF THE ORIGINAL AMOUNT MANUFACTURED STAYS IN THE SAME N.I.B. CONDITION. THUS, IF SUPPLY ALWAYS IS CONSTANT AND IN ONE CONDITION, DEMAND HAS TO INCREASE BEFORE PRICE APPRECIATION CAN OCCUR. TAKING INTO CONSIDERATION THE INFLATION FACTOR DURING THE PAST 2 DECADES, MANY OLDER, HIGH MANUFACTURE COMMEMORATIVES/LIMITED EDITIONS HAVE NOT PERFORMED VERY WELL AS INVESTMENTS. YET, OTHERS HAVE. AFTER 26 YEARS OF SPECIAL EDITION PRODUCTION, MANY MODELS' PERFORMANCE RECORD CAN BE ACCURATELY ANALYZED AND ANY APPRECIATION (OR DEPRECIATION) CAN BE COMPARED AGAINST OTHER PURCHASES OF EQUAL VINTAGE. YOU BE THE JUDGE.

1961 GENESEO, ILLINOIS 125TH ANNIVERSARY DERRINGER

	$450	$28	104

1961 SHERIFF'S MODEL—blue and case hardened.

	$1,450	$130	478

1961 SHERIFF'S MODEL—nickel.

	$3,250	$140	25

1961 125TH ANNIVERSARY MODEL SAA

	$595	$150	7,390

1961 KANSAS STATEHOOD SCOUT

	$275	$75	6,201

1961 PONY EXPRESS CENTENNIAL SCOUT

	$425	$80	1,007

1961 CIVIL WAR CENTENNIAL PISTOL

	$75	$33	24,114

1962 ROCK ISLAND ARSENAL CENTENNIAL SCOUT

	$175	$39	550

1962 COLUMBUS, OHIO SESQUICENTENNIAL SCOUT

	$525	$100	200

1962 FORT FINDLAY, OHIO SESQUICENTENNIAL SCOUT

	$525	$90	110

1962 FORT FINDLAY CASE PAIR—.22 LR - .22 Mag.

	$2,500	$185	20

1962 NEW MEXICO GOLDEN ANNIVERSARY SCOUT

	$325	$80	1,000

1962 FORT MCPHERSON, NEBRASKA CENTENNIAL DERRINGER

	$295	$29	300

1962 WEST VIRGINIA STATEHOOD CENTENNIAL SCOUT

	$295	$75	3,452

1963 WEST VIRGINIA STATEHOOD CENTENNIAL SAA .45

	$795	$150	600

1963 ARIZONA TERRITORIAL CENTENNIAL SCOUT

	$295	$75	5,355

1963 ARIZONA TERRITORIAL CENTENNIAL SAA .45

	$795	$150	1,280

1963 CAROLINA CHARTER TERCENTENARY SCOUT

	$395	$75	300

1963 CAROLINA CHARTER TERCENTENARY 22/45 COMBO

	$995	$240	251

1963 H. COOK "1 TO 100" 22/45 COMBO

	$1,050	$275	100

Grading	100%	Issue price	Qty made
1963 FORT STEPHENSON, OHIO SESQUICENTENNIAL SCOUT			
	$525	$75	200
1963 BATTLE OF GETTYSBURG CENTENNIAL SCOUT			
	$295	$90	1,019
1963 IDAHO TERRITORIAL CENTENNIAL SCOUT			
	$350	$75	902
1963 GEN. JOHN HUNT MORGAN INDIANA RAID SCOUT			
	$650	$75	100
1964 CHERRY'S SPORTING GOODS 35TH ANNIVERSARY 22/45 COMBO			
	$1,450	$275	100
1964 NEVADA STATEHOOD CENTENNIAL SCOUT			
	$275	$75	3,984
1964 NEVADA STATEHOOD CENTENNIAL SAA .45			
	$750	$150	1,688
1964 NEVADA STATEHOOD CENTENNIAL 22/45 COMBO			
	$1,050	$240	189
1964 NEVADA ST. CENT. 22/45 COMBO W/EXTRA ENGR. CYL.'S			
	$1,125	$350	577
1964 NEVADA "BATTLE BORN" SCOUT			
	$295	$85	981
1964 NEVADA "BATTLE BORN" SAA .45			
	$1,195	$175	80
1964 NEVADA "BATTLE BORN" 22/45 COMBO			
	$2,450	$265	20
1964 MONTANA TERRITORIAL CENTENNIAL SCOUT			
	$295	$75	2,300
1964 MONTANA TERRITORIAL CENTENNIAL SAA .45			
	$795	$150	851
1964 WYOMING DIAMOND JUBILEE SCOUT			
	$295	$75	2,357
1964 GENERAL HOOD CENTENNIAL SCOUT			
	$295	$75	1,503
1964 NEW JERSEY TERCENTENARY SCOUT			
	$275	$75	1,001
1964 NEW JERSEY TERCENTENARY SAA .45			
	$850	$150	250
1964 ST. LOUIS BICENTENNIAL SCOUT			
	$295	$75	802
1964 ST. LOUIS BICENTENNIAL SAA .45			
	$795	$150	200
1964 ST. LOUIS BICENTENNIAL 22/45 COMBO			
	$1,095	$240	250
1964 CALIFORNIA GOLD RUSH SCOUT			
	$350	$80	500
1964 PONY EXPRESS PRESENTATION SAA .45			
	$950	$250	1,004
1964 CHAMIZAL TREATY SCOUT			
	$295	$85	450
1964 CHAMIZAL TREATY SAA .45			
	$1,150	$170	50

Grading	100%	Issue price	Qty made
1964 CHAMIZAL TREATY 22/45 COMBO			
	$1,895	$280	50
1964 COL. SAM COLT SESQUICENTENNIAL PRESENTATION SAA .45			
	$895	$225	4,750
1964 COL. SAM COLT SESQUICENTENNIAL DELUXE PRES. SAA .45			
	$1,950	$500	200
1964 COL. SAM COLT SESQUICENTENNIAL SPEC. DELUXE PRES. SAA .45			
	$2,950	$1,000	50
1964 WYATT EARP BUNTLINE SAA .45			
	$1,750	$250	150
1965 OREGON TRAIL SCOUT			
	$275	$75	1,995
1965 JOAQUIN MURIETTA 22/45 COMBO			
	$1,450	$350	100
1965 FORTY-NINER MINER SCOUT			
	$295	$85	500
1965 OLD FT. DES MOINES RECONSTRUCTION SCOUT			
	$350	$90	700
1965 OLD FT. DES MOINES RECONSTRUCTION SAA .45			
	$850	$170	100
1965 OLD FT. DES MOINES RECONSTRUCTION 22/45 COMBO			
	$1,250	$290	100
1965 APPOMATTOX CENTENNIAL SCOUT			
	$275	$75	1,001
1965 APPOMATTOX CENTENNIAL SAA .45			
	$795	$150	250
1965 APPOMATTOX CENTENNIAL 22/45 COMBO			
	$1,075	$240	250
1965 GENERAL MEADE CAMPAIGN SCOUT			
	$295	$75	1,197
1965 ST. AUGUSTINE QUADRACENTENNIAL SCOUT			
	$325	$85	500
1965 KANSAS COWTOWN SERIES—Wichita Scout.			
	$295	$85	500
1966 KANSAS COWTOWN SERIES—Dodge City Scout.			
	$295	$85	500
1966 COLORADO GOLD RUSH SCOUT			
	$295	$85	1,350
1966 OKLAHOMA TERRITORY SCOUT			
	$295	$85	1,343
1966 DAKOTA TERRITORY SCOUT			
	$295	$85	1,000
1966 GENERAL MEADE SAA .45			
	$895	$165	200
1966 ABERCROMBIE & FITCH "TRAILBLAZER"—New York.			
	$1,950	$275	200
1966 KANSAS COWTOWN SERIES—Abilene Scout.			
	$295	$95	500
1966 INDIANA SESQUICENTENNIAL SCOUT			
	$275	$85	1,500

Grading	100%	Issue price	Qty made
1966 PONY EXPRESS .45 SAA 4-SQUARE SET (4 GUNS)			
	$3,850	$1,400	
1966 CALIFORNIA GOLD RUSH SAA .45			
	$1,095	$175	130
1966 ABERCROMBIE & FITCH "TRAILBLAZER"—Chicago.			
	$1,950	$275	100
1966 ABERCROMBIE & FITCH "TRAILBLAZER"—San Francisco.			
	$1,950	$275	100
1967 LAWMAN SERIES—Bat Masterson Scout.			
	$325	$90	3,000
1967 LAWMAN SERIES—Bat Masterson SAA .45.			
	$850	$180	500
1967 ALAMO SCOUT			
	$295	$85	4,250
1967 ALAMO SAA .45			
	$795	$165	750
1967 ALAMO 22/45 COMBO			
	$1,095	$265	250
1967 KANSAS COWTOWN SERIES—Coffeyville Scout.			
	$295	$95	500
1967 KANSAS TRAIL SERIES—Chisolm Trail Scout.			
	$275	$100	500
1967 WORLD WAR I SERIES—Chateau Thierry .45 Auto.			
	$550	$200	7,400
1967 WORLD WAR I SERIES—Chateau Thierry Deluxe.			
	$1,375	$500	75
1967 WORLD WAR I SERIES—Chateau Thierry Spec. Deluxe.			
	$2,250	$1,000	25
1968 NEBRASKA CENTENNIAL SCOUT			
	$275	$100	7,001
1968 KANSAS TRAIL SERIES—Pawnee Trail Scout.			
	$275	$110	501
1968 WORLD WAR I SERIES—Belleau Wood.			
	$550	$200	7,400
1968 WWI SERIES—Belleau Wood Deluxe.			
	$1,350	$500	75
1968 W W I SERIES—Belleau Wood Special Deluxe.			
	$2,250	$1,000	25
1968 LAWMAN SERIES—Pat Garrett Scout.			
	$325	$110	3,000
1968 LAWMAN SERIES—Pat Garrett .45 SAA.			
	$850	$220	500
1969 GEN. NATHAN BEDFORM FORREST SCOUT			
	$295	$110	3,000
1969 KANSAS TRAIL SERIES—Santa Fe Trail Scout.			
	$275	$120	501
1969 WWI SERIES—Battle of 2nd Marne .45 Auto.			
	$550	$220	7,400
1969 WWI SERIES—Battle of 2nd Marne Deluxe.			
	$1,450	$500	75
1969 WWI SERIES—Battle of 2nd Marne Spec. Deluxe.			
	$2,250	$1,000	25

Grading	100%	Issue price	Qty made

1969 ALABAMA SESQUICENTENNIAL SCOUT

	$295	$110	3,001

1969 ALABAMA SESQUICENTENNIAL .45 SAA

	$15,000	1	

1969 GOLDEN SPIKE SCOUT

	$295	$135	11,000

1969 KANSAS TRAIL SERIES—Shawnee Trail Scout.

	$275	$120	501

1969 WWI SERIES—Meuse-Argonne .45 Auto.

	$550	$220	7,400

1969 WWI SERIES—Meuse-Argonne .45 Deluxe.

	$1,450	$500	75

1969 WWI SERIES—Meuse-Argonne Spec. Deluxe.

	$2,250	$1,000	25

1969 ARKANSAS TERRITORIAL SESQUICENTENNIAL SCOUT

	$225	$110	3,500

1969 LAWMAN SERIES—.45 SAA Wild Bill Hickock.

	$850	$220	500

1969 LAWMAN SERIES—Wild Bill Hickock Scout.

	$325	$117	3,000

1969 CALIFORNIA BICENTENNIAL SCOUT

	$275	$135	5,000

1970 KANSAS FORT SERIES—Ft. Learned Scout.

	$275	$120	500

1970 WWII SERIES—European Theatre.

	$550	$250	11,500

1970 WWII SERIES—Pacific Theatre.

	$550	$250	11,500

Note: A complete set of the WWI and WWII Series standard grade models (6 guns) with matching serial numbers in NIB condition is currently selling in the $3,300 range.

1970 TEXAS RANGER SAA .45

	$1,450	$650	1,000

1970 KANSAS FORTS—Ft. Hays Scout.

	$295	$130	500

1970 MARINE SESQUICENTENNIAL SCOUT

	$275	$120	3,000

1970 MISSOURI SESQUICENTENNIAL SCOUT

	$275	$125	3,000

1970 MISSOURI SESQUICENTENNIAL .45 SAA

	$695	$220	900

1970 KANSAS FORTS—Ft. Riley Scout.

	$275	$130	500

1970 LAWMAN SERIES—Wyatt Earp Scout.

	$395	$125	3,000

1970 LAWMAN SERIES—Wyatt Earp .45 SAA.

	$1,350	$395	500

1971 NRA CENTENNIAL .45 SAA

	$695	$250	5,000

1971 NRA CENTENNIAL .357 SAA

	$695	$250	5,000

1971 NRA CENTENNIAL GOLD CUP .45

	$595	$250	2,500

Grading	100%	Issue price	Qty made
1971 1851 NAVY—U.S. Grant.			
	$595	$250	4,750
1971 1851 NAVY—Robert E. Lee.			
	$595	$250	4,750
1971 1851 NAVY—Lee-Grant Set.			
	$1,350	$500	250
1971 KANSAS SERIES—Ft. Scott Scout.			
	$295	$130	500
1973 FLORIDA TERRITORY SEQUICENTENNIAL SCOUT			
	$275	$125	2,001
1973 ARIZONA RANGER SCOUT			
	$295	$135	3,001
1974 PEACEMAKER CENTENNIAL .45			
	$750	$300	1,500
1974 PEACEMAKER CENTENNIAL 44.40			
	$795	$300	1,500
1974 PEACEMAKER CENT. CASED PAIR			
	$1,650	$625	500
USS TEXAS BATTLESHIP SPECIAL EDITION (1975)—.45 ACP, Model 1911A1 with special embillishments, nickel finish, this model is not a factory commemorative.			
	$1,000	unknown	500
1976 U.S. BICENTENNIAL SET			
	$1,950	$1,695	1,776
1977 2ND AMENDMENT .22			
	$325	$195	3,020
1977 U.S. CAVALRY 200TH ANNIVERSARY SET			
	$995	$995	3,000
1978 STATEHOOD 3RD MODEL DRAGOON			
	$12,500	$12,500	52
1979 NED BUNTLINE .45 SAA			
	$725	$895	3,000
OHIO PRESIDENT'S SPECIAL EDITION (1979)—.45 ACP, Model 1911A1 with special Ohio embellishments, this is not a factory commemorative.			
	$895	unknown	250
1979 TOMBSTONE CENTENNIAL .45 AUTO			
	$695	$550	300
1980 DRUG ENFORCEMENT AGENCY(DEA) .45 AUTO			
	$1,100	$550	910
1980 OLYMPICS ACE MODEL SPECIAL EDITION			
	$1,250	$1,000	200
1980 HERITAGE-WALKER .44 PERCUSSION			
	$1,475	$1,475	1,847
1981 "JOHN M. BROWNING" .45 AUTO			
	$875	$1,100	3,000
1982 JOHN WAYNE SAA STANDARD			
	$1,300	$2,995	3,100
1982 JOHN WAYNE SAA DELUXE			
	$7,500	$10,000	500
1982 JOHN WAYNE SAA PRESENTATION			
	$15,750	$20,000	100

Note: Each grade of the above John Wayne commemoratives has its own serial number range.

Grading	100%	Issue price	Qty made

1983 BUFFALO BILL WILD WEST SHOW CENTENNIAL SAA .45

	$1,350	$1,350	500

1983 "ARMORY MODEL" SAA .45 ACP—this model had limited production, and

should not be confused as being a commemorative. So called because was shipped with extra .45 long Colt cylinder and the "Colt Armory Edition" book by E. Grant, presentation cased.

	$1,125	$1,125	500

Armory model commemoratives available with class A engraving — $2,062, B engraving — $2,375, C engraving — $2,690, D engraving — $3,000. 20 total available.

1984 1ST EDITION GOV'T MODEL .380 ACP

	$425	$425	1,000

Serial range RC00000-01000.

1984 JOHN WAYNE "DUKE" FRONTIER .22

	$450	$475	1,000

1984 COLT/WINCHESTER SET—1 ea. of the Model 1894 Winchester carbine and

Colt Peacemaker, serial numbered 1WC-4440WC, .44-40 cal., elaborate gold etching, cased. Pistol became available for sale individually in 1986 - see individual listing below for values.

Please refer to 1984 Winchester/Colt Set in the Winchester Commemorative section in this text.

WINCHESTER/COLT SAA—.44-40 cal., 7½ in. barrel, gold etching, this

commemorative was originally made as part of the 1984 Winchester/Colt rifle-pistol set but now can be purchased individually. Originally manufactured in 1984.

	$750	N/A	4,000 (sets)

1984 USA EDITION SAA—.44-40 cal., 7½ in. barrel, old style black powder frame,

bullseye ejector rod head, 3 line patent date, high polished blue with gold line engraving. 100 guns total mfg. — 1 for each state and its capitol.

	$3,995	$4,995	100

1984 KIT CARSON .22 NEW FRONTIER—6 in. barrel, color case hardened frame,

gold artwork, serial numbered KCC0001-KCC1000, cased.

	$550	$550	1,000

1984 SECOND EDITION GOV'T MODEL .380 ACP

	$495	$525	1,000

Serial range 00000-01000RC.

1984 OFFICER'S COMMENCEMENT ISSUE—Officer's ACP with Marine Corps

emblem, rosewood grips, silver plated oak leaf scroll, cased.

	$650	$700	1,000

1984 THEODORE ROOSEVELT COMMEMORATIVE SAA—.44-40 cal., 7½

in. barrel, black powder frame, case colored receiver, factory "B" hand engraving, ivory stocks, cased.

	$1,495	$1,695	500

1984 NORTH AMERICAN OILMEN SAA BUNTLINE—.45 Long Colt, 12 in.

barrel, non-fluted cylinder, elaborate gold etching, ebony grips with ivory inlays, stand-up glass case, ser. no.'s 1-100 manufactured for Canada, 101-200 for the U.S.

	$3,900	$3,900	200

1986 150th ANNIVERSARY SAA—.45 Long Colt, 10 in. barrel, 50% engraved, royal

blue finish, Goncalo Alves smooth grips, 150th anniversary logo in stocks, cherrywood case. 1,000 manufactured in 1986 only.

	$1,450	$1,595	1,000

1986 150th ANNIVERSARY ENGRAVING SAMPLER SAA—various cal.'s, 4

different engraving styles on metal surfaces, 75% coverage, ivory grips, signed by the engraver, available with either blue or nickel finish. Add $120 for nickel. New in 1986.

	$1,550	$1,613	unknown

Grading	100%	Issue price	Qty made

1986 150th ANNIVERSARY ENGRAVING SAMPLER .45 M1911 A1—.45 ACP, 4 different engraving styles on metal surfaces, 75% coverage, ivory grips, signed by the engraver, available with either blue or nickel finish. Add $60 for nickel. New in 1986.

	$1,095	$1,155	unknown

1986 TEXAS 150th SESQUICENTENNIAL SAA—.45 cal., Sheriff's model, 4 in. barrel, gold etching, smooth ivory grips, French fit oak presentation case. Made in 1986 only.

	$895	$1,836	unknown

100% price reflects recent distribution closeout.

1986 MUSTANG FIRST EDITION—.380 ACP, 1,000 manufactured serialized MU00001-MU01000 (the first thousand of production), rosewood stocks, walnut presentation case. Made in 1986 only.

	$450	$475	1,000

OFFICER'S ACP HEIRLOOM EDITION—.45 ACP, personalized with individual's choice for serial number (ie. John Smith 1), mirror brite bluing, jeweled barrel, hammer, and trigger, ivory grips, with historical letter and mahogany case. New in 1986.

	$1,643	$1,575	open

1986 DOUBLE DIAMOND SET—set is comprised of a Python Ultimate .357 Mag. revolver and Officer's Model .45 ACP, both guns in stainless steel, smooth rosewood grips, presentation cased. 1,000 sets manufactured in 1986 only, serial numbered 1-1,000 (matched).

	$1,575	$1,575	1,000

COMBAT ELITE CUSTOM EDITION—.45 ACP, with ambidextrous thumb safety, wide grip safety, hand honed action, and carrying case, ser. numbered CG00001 - CG00500. Made in 1987.

	$900	$900	500

SNAKE EYES LIMITED EDITION—includes two Python revolvers (2½ in. barrels), one finished in brite stainless steel and the other in royal blue finish, grips are ivory like with scrimshaw "snake eyes" dice on left side and royal flush poker hand on right, includes chips and playing cards, 500 sets only of consecutive serial numbers. New in 1989.

	$3,500	$2,950	500

DELTA H-BAR RIFLE—AR-15 A2 H-Bar rifle selectively chosen and equipped with 3 x 9 variable power rubber armored scope, leather sling, shoulder stock cheekpiece, cased. 1987 manufacture.

	$1,360	$1,360	open

12TH MAN-'SPIRIT OF AGGIELAND'—.45 ACP, manufactured to commemorate Texas A & M University, serial numbered TAM001-TAM999, 24Kt gold plating including wreaths on left frame and inscription on right, cherrywood glass top presentation case, includes personalized class graduation inscription. Available in 1987 only.

	$950	$950	999

KLAY-COLT 1851 NAVY—.36 cal., cased reproduction of the 3rd Model 1851 Navy, special fabrication insuring old world quality, charcoal bluing, heat treated screws and accessories, cased. 1986 introduction.

Standard Edition—no engraving.

	$1,850	$1,850	150

Engraved Edition—choice of engraving.

	$3,150	$3,150	50

Optional engraving patterns with or without gold inlays available at extra cost.

COMMANDO ARMS

MANUFACTURED PREVIOUSLY IN KNOXVILLE, TN.

Commando Arms became the new name for Volunteer Enterprises in the late '70's.

Grading	100%	98%	95%	90%	80%	70%	60%

MARK 45—.45 ACP, carbine styled after the Thompson sub-machine gun, 16½ in. barrel.

	$350	$315	$280	$225	$195	$175	$160

CONNECTICUT VALLEY ARMS, INC.
MANUFACTURED AND DISTRIBUTED IN NORCROSS, GA.

CVA manufactures mostly percussion/flintlock/finished and kit guns in either rifle or shotgun configurations. Black powder firearms can be found in the back of this text.

SHOTGUNS

TRAPPER—12 ga. only, single shot trap configuration, multi-choke barrel. New in 1988.

Mfg.'s Sug. Retail	$228	$195	$170	$155	$145	$135	$125	$115

BRITTANY II SXS—.410 ga. only, double triggers, extractors, manufacture began in 1988.

Mfg.'s Sug. Retail	$168	$145	$135	$125	$115	$105	$100	$95

CONTENTO/VENTURA
PREVIOUSLY IMPORTED BY VENTURA IMPORTS IN SEAL BEACH, CA. VENTURA ALSO IMPORTED BERTUZZI AND PIOTTI.

SHOTGUNS

CONTENTO O/U—12 ga., 32 in. barrels, boxlock, optional screw in choke tubes, high vent rib, SST, auto ejectors, hand checkered Monte Carlo trap stock.

	$1,045	$990	$935	$880	$770	$690	$635

MK 2—2 barrel, O/U, with extra single barrel.

	$1,375	$1,320	$1,265	$1,210	$1,100	$1,020	$965

MK 2—leather cased, combination set.

	$1,705	$1,650	$1,595	$1,540	$1,430	$1,350	$1,295

MK 3—engraved, O/U.

	$1,650	$1,570	$1,485	$1,375	$1,295	$1,185	$1,100

MK 3—2 barrel, O/U, with extra single barrel.

	$2,200	$2,035	$1,925	$1,815	$1,650	$1,595	$1,515

MK 3—leather cased, combination set.

	$2,750	$2,420	$2,200	$2,090	$1,955	$1,815	$1,760

MODEL 51 SXS—12, 16, 20, 28, and .410 ga.'s, 26-32 in. barrels, various chokes, extractors, boxlock, double triggers, checkered straight stock.

	$385	$360	$330	$305	$250	$220	$165
Auto ejectors	$495	$440	$385	$360	$305	$275	$220

MODEL 52 SXS—10 ga., double triggers only, otherwise similar to 51.

	$525	$495	$470	$415	$360	$305	$250

MODEL 53 SXS—deluxe version of 51, scalloped frame, auto ejectors.

	$470	$440	$415	$385	$330	$275	$220
SST	$605	$550	$525	$495	$440	$385	$330

MODEL 61 SXS—12 and 20 ga.'s, 26, 27, 28, and 30 in. barrels, H&H sidelocks, various chokes, floral engraved, hand detachable locks, cocking indicators, select walnut pistol grip stock, auto ejectors.

	$880	$825	$770	$745	$690	$605	$550
SST	$1,020	$965	$910	$855	$800	$715	$660

MODEL 65 SXS—same as 61, with elaborate engraving and quality hand finishing.

	$1,100	$1,045	$990	$965	$880	$825	$770

CONTINENTAL ARMS CORPORATION

MADE IN BELGIUM.

DOUBLE RIFLE—.270, .303, .30-40, .348, .30-06, .375 H&H, .400 Jeffreys, .465, .475, .500, and .600, Nitro Express cal.'s, 24 or 26 in. barrels, Anson & Deeley boxlock system, double triggers, checkered stock.

	100%	98%	95%	90%	80%	70%	60%
	$5,500	$4,620	$3,850	$3,300	$2,970	$2,750	$2,420

COONAN ARMS, INC.

MANUFACTURED AND DISTRIBUTED IN ST. PAUL, MN.

COONAN .357 MAG. MODEL B—.357 Mag. only, stainless steel and alloy construction, single action, semi-auto, design based on the Colt Model 1911, 7 shot mag., 5 in. barrel, 42 oz., smooth walnut grips. New in 1983.

Mfg.'s Sug. Retail $680 $660 $530 $425

     Add $40 for 6 in. barrel (new in 1989).

     Add $118 for adj. rear sight.

     Add $130 for BoMar sight.

This model can be differentiated from the Model A in that it has an extended grip safety lever, linkless barrel system, trigger bar slot is enclosed, and recontoured rear grip strap. This model became standard in 1985.

A .38 Spl. conversion kit became available in 1986 — add $40.

COONAN .357 MAG. MODEL A—original model without above listed improvements, special order only, limited supply.

Mfg.'s Sug. Retail $625 $625 $525 $425

This variation will also shoot .38 + P loads. Limited supply has created premiums for this model.

Model A's are denoted by serialization under 2,000.

COMP I—IPSC competition variation with 2 chamber compensator, fixed sights, standard finish, stippled grip strap. New in 1989.

Mfg.'s Sug. Retail $1,350 $1,250 $1,100 $995

     Comp I Deluxe—similar to Comp I except has adj. sights, checkered grip straps, jeweled small parts, blued stainless steel slide. New in 1989.

     Mfg.'s Sug. Retail $1,650 $1,525 $1,395 $1,200

COSMI, AMERICO & FIGLIO

MANUFACTURED IN TORRETTI, ITALY. IMPORTED AND DISTRIBUTED BY NEW ENGLAND ARMS LOCATED IN KITTERY POINT, ME.

SEMI-AUTO MODEL—12 or 20 ga., semi-auto, unique action has cartridge loading from back of stock, 8 shot mag., VR barrel, pivoting break-open action, custom order gun only with dimensions specified by individual customer.

Standard Grade

Mfg.'s Sug. Retail $4,000 $4,000 $3,300 $2,970 $2,650 $2,320 $1,995

Deluxe Grade

Mfg.'s Sug. Retail $5,000 $4,500 $4,000 $3,500 $2,970 $2,650 $2,320

Above values represent base models without additional engraving, better walnut, etc.

CRESCENT FIRE ARMS COMPANY

MANUFACTURED 1888-1893 IN NORWICH, CT. SOLD TO H&D FOLSOM IN 1893 AND BECAME A DIVISION OF STEVENS ARMS & TOOL IN 1926.

Values below assume standard models with double triggers, extractors, original finish, and 100% working order. Sidelock actions were also available and will command premiums from prices listed below. Shotguns with exposed hammers can equal their hammerless counterparts if condition is 80% or better.

SXS SHOTGUN

12 ga.

	100%	98%	95%	90%	80%	70%	60%
	$195	$175	$150	$125	$100	$85	$65

16 ga.

	$195	$175	$150	$125	$100	$85	$65

20 ga.

	$295	$265	$230	$200	$170	$150	$125

28 ga.

	$375	$325	$280	$250	$200	$150	$100

.410 ga.

	$400	$350	$300	$250	$200	$150	$100

Inexpensive, but hard to duplicate at today's prices. Later bought out by Folsom and became maker of "house" guns for various companies.

CUSTOM GUN GUILD

MANUFACTURED IN DORAVILLE, GA.

WOOD'S MODEL IV SINGLE SHOT—Various cal.'s, custom manufactured, falling block type single shot, lightweight, only 5½ lbs. Manufactured in 1984 only.

	100%	98%	95%	90%	80%	70%	60%
	$2,975	$2,500	$2,250	$2,000	$1,850	$1,700	$1,050

D

D W M

DEUTSCHE WAFFEN AND MUNITIONS FABRIKEN. BERLIN, GERMANY 1900-1930.

Grading	100%	98%	95%	90%	80%	70%	60%

POCKET AUTOMATIC—7.65mm, 3½ in. barrel, blue, hard rubber grips, made 1921-1931.

	100%	98%	95%	90%	80%	70%	60%
	$700	$630	$580	$500	$420	$380	$330

DAEWOO

MANUFACTURED IN KOREA. PREVIOUSLY IMPORTED BY STOEGER INDUSTRIES OF HACKENSACK, NJ.

MAX II (K2)—5.56 cal. (.223), assault rifle, 18 in. barrel, gas operated rotating bolt, folding fiberglass stock, interchangeable mag.'s with the Colt M16, 7 lbs. Importation discontinued in 1986.

	$495	$425	$375	$350	$325	$295	$270

Last Mfg.'s Sug. Retail was $609.

MAX I (K1A1)—similar to above, except has retractable stock. Importation discontinued in 1986.

	$475	$395	$375	$350	$325	$295	$270

Last Mfg.'s Sug. Retail was $592.

DAISY

MANUFACTURER LOCATED IN ROGERS, AR. ALSO SEE DAISY SECTION UNDER MODERN AIR RIFLES & PISTOLS.

RIFLES: DISCONTINUED

V/L STANDARD RIFLE—single shot, .22 V/L, a caseless air ignited cartridge, 18 in. barrel, plastic stock, 19,000 produced, 1968-1969.

	$110	$90	$75	$65	$55	$45	$30

V/L PRESENTATION—same as Standard, but walnut stock, 4,000 produced.

	$165	$130	$110	$90	$70	$55	$45

V/L PRESENTATION KIT—comes with case, gun cradles, 300 rounds of ammo, and a gold plate on the butt with owner's name and serial number of gun.

	$275	$165	$130	$110	$90	$70	$55

Note: The Daisy .22 V/L is the only commercial caseless ammo system. It was discontinued because the BATF ruled that the gun constituted a firearm, and since Daisy is federally licensed to manufacture air weapons only, the factory decided to discontinue manufacture.

LEGACY RIFLES: CURRENT MFG.

All Legacy models have removable adj. triggers, takedown barrels, and an adj. rear sight. Weight is between 6½ - 7 lbs.

MODELS 2201/2211/2221—.22 LR cal., single shot, bolt action, models vary in features, prices range from $80-$130. New in 1988.

Model 2201 has copolymer stock with adj. butt plate. Model 2211 has walnut finished hardwood stock. Model 2221 was disc. in 1988.

Grading	100%	98%	95%	90%	80%	70%	60%

MODELS 2202/2212/2222—.22 LR cal., bolt action repeater, 10 round rotary mag., models vary in features, prices range from $90-$135. New in 1988.

Model 2202 has copolymer stock with adj. butt plate, 10 shot rotary mag. Model 2212 has a walnut finished hardwood stock. Model 2222 was disc. in 1988.

MODELS 2203/2213—.22 LR cal., semi-auto, 7 shot clip mag., models vary in features, prices range from $95-$140. New in 1988.

Model 2203 has copolymer stock with adj. butt plate. Model 2213 has American hardwood stock.

DAKIN GUN CO.

SAN FRANCISCO, CA. 1960'S.

SHOTGUNS

MODEL 100 SXS—12 and 20 ga.'s, boxlock, engraved, double trigger.

	$340	$255	$240	$205	$190	$170	$155

MODEL 147 SXS—12 and 20 ga.'s, boxlock, engraved, vent rib, double trigger.

	$385	$290	$270	$235	$215	$195	$175

MODEL 160 SXS—12 and 20 ga.'s, boxlock, single trigger, ejectors, vent rib.

	$460	$345	$300	$255	$230	$210	$185

MODEL 215 SXS—12 and 20 ga.'s, sidelock, heavy engraving, special walnut, single trigger, ejectors, vent rib.

	$960	$720	$625	$530	$480	$435	$385

MODEL 170 O&U—12, 16, and 20 ga.'s, boxlock, light engraving, double triggers, vent rib.

	$485	$365	$325	$270	$245	$220	$195

DAKOTA ARMS INC.

MANUFACTURED AND DISTRIBUTED IN STURGIS, SD.

DAKOTA 76 CLASSIC GRADE—.257 Roberts, .270, .280 Rem., .30-06, 7mm Rem. Mag., .338, .300 Win. Mag., .375 H&H, or .458 Win. Mag. cal., custom frame incorporating many Win. Model 70 features, 23 in. barrel, Mauser type extractor, checkered deluxe walnut stock, 7½ lbs. Left-hand action available at no extra charge. New in 1987.

Mfg.'s Sug. Retail	$1,950	$1,875	$1,550	$1,375	$1,150	$990	$880	$770

This Model is also available with a composite stock at no extra charge.

Short Action Classic Grade—same cal.'s as Alpine Grade, 21 in. barrel, short action receiver similar to Alpine Grade, right or left hand action. New in 1989.

Mfg.'s Sug. Retail	$1,850	$1,775	$1,450	$1,300	$1,075	$925	$800	$700

Other calibers are available on a special order basis.

SAFARI GRADE—.300 Win. Mag., .338, 7mm Rem. Mag., .375 H&H, .416 Hoffman, or .458 Win. Mag. cal.'s, 23 in. barrel, one-piece drop trigger guard assembly with hinged floor plate, checkered walnut stock with ebony forearm tip. Left-hand action available at no extra charge. New in 1987.

Mfg.'s Sug. Retail	$2,850	$2,650	$2,375	$2,150	$1,850	$1,600	$1,350	$1,050

Subtract $400 (retail) if ordered with composite stock.

.416 RIGBY AFRICAN GRADE—.416 Rigby, 4 shot mag., select wood with cross bolts in the stock, other features similar to Safari Grade Model, "R" prefix on serial number. New in 1989.

Mfg.'s Sug. Retail	$3,500	$3,300	$2,925	$2,600	$2,300	$1,950	$1,675	$1,400

ALPINE GRADE—.22-250, .243, 6mm Rem., 250-3,000, 7mm/08, .308, or .358 cal., short action variation of the Classic Grade, lighter weight model featuring a blind 4 shot mag., slimmer stock and barrel, serial numbered with a "K" prefix, 6½ lbs. New in 1989.

Mfg.'s Sug. Retail	$1,850	$1,775	$1,450	$1,300	$1,075	$925	$800	$700

Other calibers are available on a special order basis.

DAKOTA SINGLE ACTION REVOLVERS

MANUFACTURED IN EUROPE, IMPORTED AND DISTRIBUTED BY E.M.F. CO., INC. LOCATED IN SANTA ANA, CA.

Note: Other firearms imported by E.M.F. Co., Inc. will be found in the E section of this book.

Values listed below are for revolvers with brass backstrap and trigger guard — add $40 for steel backstrap and trigger guard option.

SINGLE ACTION ARMY & FRONTIER—.22 LR-.45 LC cal.'s, copy of the Colt S.A.A., 4⅝, 5½, and 7½ in. barrels, blue finish, case hardened frame, 1-piece walnut grips, solid brass backstrap and trigger guard.

Mfg.'s Sug. Retail	$480	$300	$225	$165	$150	$135	$125	$110

Add $100 for nickel finish.

Add $60 for convertible cylinders.

Target Model—.357 Mag., .44-40, and .45 LC cal.'s, 5½ or 7½ in. barrel, case hardened frame, brass backstrap. New in 1987.

Mfg.'s Sug. Retail	$500	$325	$240	$185	$150	$140	$130	$120

Buntline Model—12 in. barrel, .357, .44-40, and .45 LC cal.'s, blue only.

Mfg.'s Sug. Retail	$520	$300	$250	$175	$160	$150	$140	$130

Buckhorn Model—16¼ in. barrel, otherwise same as Buntline. Importation disc. in 1987.

$295	$250	$180	$170	$160	$150	$140

Last Mfg.'s Sug. Retail was $495.

Engraved Model—.32-20, .357, .38-40, .44-40, and .45 cal.'s, 4¾, 5½ or 7½ in. barrel.

Mfg.'s Sug. Retail	$600	$435	$335	$310	$285	$260	$230	$200

Add $90 for nickel finish.

Sheriff's Model—.357, .44-40, and .45 cal.'s, 3½ in. barrel only.

Mfg.'s Sug. Retail	$520	$300	$250	$175	$150	$140	$130	$120

U.S. Army SAA—variety of cal.'s, premium quality construction. Discontinued in 1985.

$300	$205	$180	$165	$155	$145	$135

Last Mfg.'s Sug. Retail was $395.

Convertible Model—available with .22 LR/.22 Mag., .32-20/.32 H & R Mag., .357 Mag./9mm, or .44-40/.44 Spl., .45 LC/.45 ACP double cylinders. New in 1986.

Mfg.'s Sug. Retail	$580	$380	$310	$260	$220	$195	$170	$150

Fast Draw Model—.22 LR, .22 Mag., .32-20, .32 H & R Mag., .357 Mag., .38-40, 9mm, .44 Spl., .44-40, .45 ACP, and .45 LC cal.'s, case hardened frame, 4⅝ in. barrel.

Mfg.'s Sug. Retail	$480	$300	$225	$165	$150	$135	$125	$110

Bisley Model—.22 LR, .22 Mag., .32-20, .32 H & R Mag., .38-40, .357 Mag., 9mm, .44 Spl., .44-40, .45 ACP, and .45 LC cal.'s, 4⅝, 5½, 7½ in. barrel lengths. New in 1986.

Mfg.'s Sug. Retail	$540	$325	$275	$190	$170	$160	$150	$140

Add $100 for nickel finish.

Engraved Bisley—.32-20, .38-40, .357 Mag., .44-40, and .45 LC cal.'s, 4⅝, 5½ or 7½ in. barrel, action engraved throughout. New in 1987.

Mfg.'s Sug. Retail	$700	$385	$320	$220	$200	$180	$160	$145

Add $100 for nickel finish.

U.S. Army Commemorative—.45 cal., 7½ in. barrel, serial numbered 1-500, blue finish, case hardened frame, steel backstrap and trigger guard, 1-piece walnut grips. Importation disc. in 1987.

$350	$265	$185	$170	$160	$150	$135

Last Mfg.'s Sug. Retail was $495.

DAKOTA PREMIER—.45 LC, black powder frame, initial mfg. was with 4⅝ or 5½ in. barrel, steel backstrap and trigger guard. New in 1987.

Mfg.'s Sug. Retail	$520	$375	$295	$250	$190	$170	$160	$150

This model will be available in other calibers and barrel lengths in the future.

DALY, CHARLES
MANUFACTURED BY B.C. MIROKU, JAPAN.

SHOTGUNS

In the early sixties, C. Daly guns were manufactured by the firm of B.C. Miroku in Tokyo, Japan. This Japanese gun manufacturing company has produced guns for many companies, Browning being the current biggest customer. Miroku guns are high quality with excellent fit and finish. Many of them are highly engraved and are fine examples of the gunmaker's art. Charles Daly Miroku Guns are becoming quite collectible in some areas. Their production ceased in 1976.

O/U SHOTGUN—12, 20, 28, and .410 ga.'s, 26, 28, and 30 in. vent rib barrels, various chokes, boxlock, auto ejectors, selective single trigger, select walnut checkered pistol grip stock, superior and diamond grade trap have Monte Carlo stocks, the grades differ in amount of engraving and wood, made 1963-1976 by Miroku.

   Add 10% for 20 ga. on models listed below.
   Add 30% for 28 ga. on models listed below.
   Add 40% for .410 ga. on models listed below.

VENTURE GRADE

	$550	$495	$470	$440	$415	$360	$305

VENTURE SKEET—26 in. skeet and skeet.

	$575	$525	$495	$470	$440	$385	$330

VENTURE TRAP—30 in. imp. mode. and full.

	$530	$495	$470	$415	$360	$330	$300

FIELD GRADE—12 and 20 ga.'s, field gun.

	$625	$550	$525	$500	$450	$400	$375

SUPERIOR GRADE

	$725	$660	$635	$605	$550	$495	$440

SUPERIOR TRAP

	$640	$590	$550	$500	$460	$425	$390

This model had an optional selective ejection system enabling the shooter to deactivate the ejectors.

DIAMOND GRADE FIELD

	$1,070	$990	$935	$880	$770	$715	$660

DIAMOND GRADE SKEET

	$1,095	$990	$910	$800	$745	$690	$635

DIAMOND GRADE TRAP

	$925	$885	$800	$740	$685	$620	$560

WIDE RIB DIAMOND GRADE FLAT-TOP TRAP

	$960	$920	$840	$815	$760	$700	$640

DIAMOND REGENT GRADE—mostly 12 ga., extensive frame engraving with gold inlays, rare.

	$2,000	$1,700	$1,425	$1,275	$1,100	$990	$880

EMPIRE DOUBLE BARREL SHOTGUN—12, 16, and 20 ga.'s, 26, 28, and 30 in. barrels, various chokes, boxlock, extractors, single trigger, checkered pistol grip stock, made 1968-1971.

	$545	$495	$470	$415	$360	$305	$250
Vent rib	$595	$535	$500	$450	$400	$350	$300

SUPERIOR GRADE SINGLE BARREL TRAP—12 ga., 32 or 34 in. vent rib, full choke barrel, auto ejector, Monte Carlo stock with recoil pad, made 1968-1976.

	$550	$525	$495	$440	$385	$330	$305

1974 WILDLIFE COMMEMORATIVE—duck scene engraved, Diamond grade, Trap, or Skeet, limited to 500 guns, made 1974.

	$1,650	$1,430	$1,320	$1,100	$990	$880	$770

DALY, CHARLES: 1976 TO PRESENT

CURRENTLY IMPORTED BY OUTDOOR SPORTS HEADQUARTERS LOCATED IN
DAYTON, OH. ITALIAN MANUFACTURED.

Note: The Charles Daly "Noramatic" shotguns were produced in 1968 by Breda in Italy.
Current production shotguns have been manufactured in Italy since 1976 by Breda in Milan.

NORAMATIC LIGHTWEIGHT SHOTGUN—12 ga., 26 and 28 in. barrel, various
chokes, available with quick choke interchangeable tubes, checkered pistol grip stock, same
as the Breda shotgun, made 1968 only.

	100%	98%	95%	90%	80%	70%	60%
	$305	$275	$250	$220	$195	$165	$140

Add $25 for vent rib.
Add $15 for quick choke.

NORAMATIC SUPER LIGHTWEIGHT—12 and 20 ga.'s, same as Lightweight,
except approx. ½ lb. lighter.

	100%	98%	95%	90%	80%	70%	60%
	$330	$305	$275	$250	$220	$195	$165

Add $25 for vent rib.
Add $15 for quick choke.

NORAMATIC MAGNUM—same as Lightweight, with 3 in. 12 or 20 ga. chambers, 28 or
30 in. vent rib barrel, full choke.

	100%	98%	95%	90%	80%	70%	60%
	$330	$305	$275	$250	$220	$195	$165

NORAMATIC TRAP—same as Lightweight, with 30 in. full vent rib barrel, Monte Carlo
stock.

	100%	98%	95%	90%	80%	70%	60%
	$360	$330	$305	$275	$250	$220	$195

PRESENTATION O/U—12 and 20 ga.'s, with choke tubes, Purdey double underlug
locking action with decorative engraved sideplates, French walnut, single trigger, ejectors.
Discontinued in 1986.

	100%	98%	95%	90%	80%	70%	60%
	$995	$840	$750	$670	$615	$560	$520

Last Mfg.'s Sug. Retail was $1,165.

CHARLES DALY LUXE O/U—12 or 20 ga., box lock with self adj. crossbolt, 26 or 28
chrome lined VR barrels with internal choke tubes, SST, ejectors, antique silver finish on
receiver, deluxe hand checkered walnut stock and forearm. New in 1989.

Mfg.'s Sug. Retail	$650	$575	$500	$460	$425	$400	$375	$350

This model is mfg. by Indesul of Spain.

CHARLES DALY FIELD—similar to Luxe Grade except has fixed chokes, extractors,
machine stock checkering, and blued receiver. New in 1989.

Mfg.'s Sug. Retail	$450	$395	$370	$340	$315	$285	$260	$230

DIAMOND O/U FIELD—12 and 20 ga. (discontinued in 1986) Mag.'s, with choke tubes.
Same action as Presentation model without sideplates, engraved, select walnut, single
trigger, ejectors. Available only in "Trap" and "Skeet" models for 1989.

	100%	98%	95%	90%	80%	70%	60%
	$695	$600	$550	$510	$460	$420	$380

Last Mfg.'s Sug. Retail was $895.

Diamond O/U Trap or Skeet—12 ga. only, 26 or 30 in. barrels only.

Mfg.'s Sug. Retail	$1,050	$850	$700	$550	$500	$475	$450	$425

Deduct $50 for Skeet Model.

SUPERIOR II O/U—12 and 20 ga.'s, various chokes, boxlock action, single trigger, ejectors,
engraved. Disc. in 1988.

	100%	98%	95%	90%	80%	70%	60%
	$675	$575	$475	$425	$395	$375	$350

Add $35 for 12 ga. Mag. Disc. in 1987.

Last Mfg.'s Sug. Retail was $875.

FIELD III O/U—12 and 20 ga.'s, various chokes, boxlock action, single trigger.

Mfg.'s Sug. Retail	$450	$395	$370	$340	$315	$285	$260	$230

SUPERIOR SXS—12 and 20 ga.'s, boxlock action, various chokes, single trigger.
Discontinued in 1985.

	100%	98%	95%	90%	80%	70%	60%
	$550	$470	$405	$345	$315	$280	$250

Last Mfg.'s Sug. Retail was $624.

Grading	100%	98%	95%	90%	80%	70%	60%

CHARLES DALY AUTOMATIC—12 ga., 2¾ or 3 in. chambers, gas operation, alloy frame, pistol grip (high gloss) or English stock, vent rib, 5 shot mag. Also available as slug gun with iron sights. Invector chokes became standard in 1986.

Mfg.'s Sug. Retail	$365	$320	$275	$235	$205	$190	$170	$150

Add $15 for oil finished English stock.

MULTI-XII—12 ga. only, 3 in. chamber, 27 in. vent rib multichoke barrel, self adjusting gas operation, deluxe checkered walnut stock with recoil pad and forearm. Imported in 1987 only.

$425	$360	$320	$285	$250	$225	$195

Last Mfg.'s Sug. Retail was $498.

DALY, CHARLES: PRUSSIAN MANUFACTURE

Charles Daly was an importer whose goal was to give the U.S. shotgun consumer a European manufactured gun of similar quality to the premier American shotguns of the circa. In that behalf, he had various European firms fabricate shotguns with American shooting features and preferences. Many "Prussian" Daly's were built by various firms in Suhl, Germany. Importation ceased prior to WWII. These Prussian Charles Daly's utilized the finest materials and best workmanship of their time.

SHOTGUNS

EMPIRE O&U—12, 16, and 20 ga.'s, various barrel lengths, Anson & Deeley boxlock, ejectors and double triggers, fine engraving, deluxe walnut. Discontinued 1933.

$4,000	$3,400	$2,740	$2,380	$2,010	$1,825	$1,645

DIAMOND O&U—same as Empire model, only finer workmanship and materials.

$5,000	$4,300	$3,475	$3,000	$2,600	$2,300	$2,000

SUPERIOR SXS—10, 12, 20, 28, and .410 ga.'s, Anson & Deeley boxlock, various barrel lengths, ejectors (except superior model). Discontinued 1933.

$1,050	$790	$690	$580	$525	$475	$420

EMPIRE SXS—same as Superior, only more engraving and better wood.

$2,300	$1,725	$1,495	$1,265	$1,150	$1,035	$920

DIAMOND SXS—like Empire model, only more elaborate.

$4,000	$3,300	$2,700	$2,300	$1,900	$1,645	$1,460

REGENT DIAMOND SXS—top-of-the-line Prussian side by side.

$5,250	$4,650	$3,800	$3,200	$2,700	$2,250	$2,025

EMPIRE SINGLE BARREL TRAP—12 ga., 30-34 in. barrel, Anson & Deeley boxlock, ejector, vent rib, finely engraved with select walnut, chopper lump extension, top quality. Discontinued in 1933.

$2,150	$1,675	$1,375	$1,100	$960	$850	$750

SEXTUPLE SINGLE BARREL TRAP—12 ga., 30-34 in. barrel, six locking bolts, ejector, vent rib, elaborately engraved and checkered. Regent Diamond Model has better engraving and wood.

Empire Quality

$2,600	$2,100	$1,700	$1,400	$1,100	$900	$750

Regent Diamond Quality

$3,300	$2,850	$2,400	$1,950	$1,650	$1,350	$995

DRILLING MODEL—3 barrel combination gun, available in 12, 16, 20 ga.'s and .25-20, .25-35, and .30-30 cal.'s, extractors, double triggers, engraved action, select walnut. Discontinued in 1933.

Superior Quality

$2,600	$1,950	$1,690	$1,430	$1,300	$1,170	$1,040

Grading	100%	98%	95%	90%	80%	70%	60%

Diamond Quality—deluxe engraving and walnut.

	$4,200	$3,150	$2,730	$2,310	$2,100	$1,750	$1,425

Regent Diamond Quality—top-of-the-line model.

	$5,500	$4,125	$3,575	$3,025	$2,750	$2,475	$2,200

COMMANIDER O&U—12, 16, 20, 28, and .410 ga.'s, Anson & Deeley boxlock action, single or double triggers, ejectors. Made in Belgium circa 1939.

Model 100

	$500	$375	$325	$275	$250	$225	$200

Add $100 for single trigger.

Model 200—similar to Model 100, except has deluxe walnut.

	$650	$490	$425	$360	$325	$300	$260

For 28 and .410 ga.'s — add 10% - 30%.

RIFLES

BOLT ACTION GRADE I—.22 Hornet, manufactured by F. Jaeger & Co. of Suhl, Germany, 5 shot mag., 24 in. barrel, miniature Mauser bolt action, deluxe walnut. Discontinued.

	$820	$615	$535	$455	$410	$370	$330

DAN ARMS OF AMERICA

MANUFACTURED IN ITALY BY SILMA. IMPORTED BY DAN ARMS OF AMERICA, LOCATED IN ALLENTOWN, PA. PREVIOUSLY IMPORTED BY DAN ARMS OF NORTH AMERICA (PREVIOUSLY CALLED SPORTSMAN'S EMPORIUM LTD.)

Firearms previously imported by the former Dan Arms of North America (Sportsman's Emporium Ltd.) do not carry their warranty periods into current Dan Arms of America importation.

All shotguns listed below were discontinued in early 1988. Dan Arms of America has limited quantities remaining of these models, and values below reflect discontinuance.

SHOTGUNS: OVER AND UNDER

LUX GRADE I—12 and 20 ga.'s, 3 in. Mag. chambers, 26, 28, and 30 in. barrels, vent rib, extractors, pistol grip, double trigger, European walnut.

	$280	$220	$210	$200	$190	$180	$170

Last Mfg.'s Sug. Retail was $350.

LUX GRADE II—12 ga. only, 3 in. Mag. chambers, 26, 28, and 30 in. barrels, vent rib, extractors, pistol grip, single trigger, European walnut.

	$320	$250	$240	$230	$215	$200	$190

Last Mfg.'s Sug. Retail was $395.

LUX GRADE III—20 and 12 ga.'s, 3 in. Mag. chambers, 26, 28, and 30 in. barrels, vent rib, ejectors, pistol grip, single trigger, checkered European walnut.

	$375	$300	$285	$270	$255	$240	$220

Last Mfg.'s Sug. Retail was $450.

LUX GRADE IV—12 ga. only, 3 in. Mag. chambers, 28 in. barrels, vent rib, ejectors, pistol grip, single trigger, checkered European walnut, multi-choked with 5 tubes.

	$460	$390	$350	$310	$285	$265	$245

Last Mfg.'s Sug. Retail was $550.

SKEET MODEL—12 ga. only, 26½ in. barrels, 10mm vent rib, anatomical pistol grip.

	$550	$450	$400	$355	$320	$300	$285

Last Mfg.'s Sug. Retail was $650.

TRAP MODEL—12 ga. only, 30 in. barrels, 10mm vent rib, anatomical pistol grip.

	$550	$450	$400	$355	$320	$300	$285

Last Mfg.'s Sug. Retail was $650.

Grading	100%	98%	95%	90%	80%	70%	60%

SILVERSNIPE—12 and 20 ga.'s, made to customer specifications, sideplates, select high grade walnut, name engraving upon request.

	$1,300	$1,200	$1,050	$900	$800	$700	$600

Last Mfg.'s Sug. Retail was $1,475.

SHOTGUNS: SIDE-BY-SIDE

FIELD MODEL—12, 16, 20, 28, and .410 ga.'s, double triggers, extractors, 26 and 28 in. barrels.

	$285	$220	$210	$200	$190	$180	$170

Last Mfg.'s Sug. Retail was $350.

DELUXE FIELD MODEL—12 and 20 ga.'s, single triggers, ejectors, 26 and 28 in. barrels.

	$440	$375	$340	$310	$290	$260	$230

Last Mfg.'s Sug. Retail was $500.

DARDICK

PREVIOUSLY MANUFACTURED IN HAMDEN, CT.

PISTOLS

SERIES 1100—.38 Dardick Tround, double action, 10 round mag.

	$560	$420	$365	$310	$255	$225	$200

Dardick ammunition in itself is collectible - currently, individual rounds are selling in the $5-$10 range.

SERIES 1500—.22, .30, and .38 Dardick Tround, double action.

	$875	$660	$570	$490	$440	$395	$350

Subtract $400 for .30 cal.

Note: carbine conversion units (.22 or .38 cal) add $175 — $400.

DARNE S.A.

MANUFACTURED BETWEEN 1881-1979 IN SAINT ETIENNE, FRANCE.

Please refer to the Bruchet section in this text for current prices/information regarding Darne patterned shotguns.

DARNE SLIDING BREECH SHOTGUN—double barrel, s x s, a unique and high quality gun, 12, 16, 20, and 28 ga., 27½ in. barrel standard, but other lengths available, any choke combination, either straight grip or pistol grip stock, checkered, models differ in amount of engraving and grade of wood.

Bird Hunter Model R11

	$1,000	$715	$635	$550	$495	$440	$360

Pheasant Hunter Model R15

	$2,300	$1,950	$1,750	$1,625	$1,500	$1,425	$1,300

Magnum Model R16

	$1,650	$1,450	$1,350	$1,250	$1,125	$1,000	$900

Quail Hunter Model V19

	$3,350	$2,750	$2,500	$2,250	$2,000	$1,800	$1,650

Model V22

	$3,750	$3,300	$3,000	$2,600	$2,300	$2,050	$1,850

Hors Series No. 1 Model V

	$4,400	$3,850	$3,575	$3,300	$3,080	$2,750	$2,200

DAVIDSON FIREARMS

MAKER: FABRICA DE ARMAS, EIBAR, SPAIN.

MODEL 63B—12, 16, 20, 28, and .410 ga.'s, double barrel, 25, 26, 28, and 30 in. barrels, Anson & Deeley boxlock, engraved and nickel plated frame, various chokes, walnut checkered stock, made 1963-disc.

	$275	$260	$220	$200	$175	$165	$155

Model 63B Magnum—similar to 63B, except 10 ga. Mag., 12, and 20 ga. Mag., 32 in. barrel.

12 and 20 ga.'s	$360	$340	$310	$275	$230	$195	$165
10 ga.	$385	$370	$340	$305	$250	$220	$195

MODEL 69SL—12 and 20 ga.'s, true detachable sidelock action, engraved nickel plated action, 26 in. and 28 in. barrels, imp. cyl. and mod., mod. and full, checkered walnut stock, made 1963-1976.

	$415	$395	$375	$340	$320	$290	$260

MODEL 73 STAGECOACH—12 and 20 ga.'s, detachable sidelock exposed hammers, 3 in. chambers, 20 in. mod. and full barrels, checkered walnut stock, made 1976-disc.

	$275	$260	$220	$200	$175	$165	$155

DAVIS INDUSTRIES

MANUFACTURED IN CHINO, CA

Davis Industries provides a lifetime warranty to the original purchaser of all models listed below.

D-22 SERIES DERRINGER—.22 LR, .22 Mag., .25 ACP, and .32 ACP cal.'s, O/U steel construction, 2.4 in. vent rib barrel, 9½ oz., black teflon or chrome finish.

Mfg.'s Sug. Retail	$69	$60	$50	$45	$40	$35	$30	$30

P-32—.32 ACP, semi-auto, 6 shot mag., 2.8 in. barrel, black teflon or chrome finish, 22 oz. New in 1987.

Mfg.'s Sug. Retail	$87	$75	$65	$55	$45	$40	$35	$30

P-380—.380 ACP, single action semi-auto, similar to P-32, 5 shot mag., 2.8 in. barrel, 22 oz., bright chrome or black Teflon finish, internal shock resister for recoil, wood grips. New in 1989.

Values were not released on this model by publication deadline.

DEMRO

T.A.C. MODEL 1 RIFLE—.45 ACP or 9mm Luger, blow back operation, 16⅞ in. barrel, also available in carbine model and fully auto.

	$360	$310	$260	$220	$200	$180	$165

XF-7 WASP CARBINE—.45 ACP or 9mm Luger, blow back operation, 16⅞ in. barrel, also available in fully auto.

	$360	$310	$260	$220	$200	$180	$165

Add $45 for case.

DETONICS MANUFACTURING CORPORATION

PREVIOUSLY NAMED DETONICS FIREARMS INDUSTRIES. MANUFACTURED AND DISTRIBUTED IN BELLEVUE, WA 1976 TO DATE. DETONICS WAS SOLD IN EARLY 1988 TO THE NEW DETONICS MANUFACTURING CORPORATION, A WHOLLY OWNED SUBSIDIARY OF "1045 INVESTERS GROUP LIMITED".

Note: All pistols listed below are derivatives of the Colt Model 1911 (except the Pocket 9) and are manufactured from high quality stainless steel.

PISTOLS: STAINLESS STEEL

MARK I—.45 ACP, matte blue. Discontinued in 1981.
$610 $460 $390

MARK II—.45 ACP, satin nickel finish. Discontinued in 1979.
$460 $345 $300

MARK III—.45 ACP, hard chrome finish. Discontinued in 1979.
$520 $390 $325

MARK IV—.45 ACP, polished blue. Discontinued in 1981.
$539 $410 $360

COMBAT MASTER MC1 (FORMERLY MARK I)—.45 ACP, 9mm, and .38 Super cal.'s, 3½ in. barrel, dull, non-glare combat finish, fixed sights.
Mfg.'s Sug. Retail $725 $635 $525 $425
    Add $15 for OM-3 model (polished slide - disc. in 1983).
    Add $100 for 9mm or .38 Super cal.

This model was originally the MC1, then changed to the Mark I, then changed back to the MC1.

COMBAT MASTER MARK V—.45 ACP, 9mm, and .38 Super cal.'s, matte stainless finish, fixed sights, 29 ozs. empty, 6 round mag. in .45 ACP, 7 round in 9mm and .38 Super, 3½ in. barrel. This model was discontinued in 1985.
$620 $550 $495

    Add $100 for 9mm or .38 Super cal.

Last Mfg.'s Sug. Retail was $689.

COMBAT MASTER MARK VI—.45 ACP, 9mm, or .38 Super cal., 3½ in. barrel, 6 shot mag., adj. sights and polished stainless slide sides.
Mfg.'s Sug. Retail $795 $685 $575 $450
    Add $100 for 9mm or .38 Super cal.

   .451 Detonics Mag. Cal.—limited mfg. 1,000. Discontinued in 1985.
$1,000 $900 $775

Last Mfg.'s Sug. Retail was $1,165.

COMBAT MASTER MARK VII—same as Mark VI, only no sights, special order only, 25 oz.
$895 $775 $600

    Add $100 for 9mm or .38 Super cal.
    Add $350 for .451 Detonics Mag., (disc. in 1982).

MILITARY COMBAT MC2—.45 ACP, 9mm, and .38 Super cal.'s, dull, non-glare combat finish, fixed sights. Add $55 for 9mm and .38 Super. Comes with camouflaged pile line wallet, and Pachmayr grips. Discontinued in 1984.
$621 $560 $500

SCOREMASTER—.45 ACP and .451 Mag. cal.'s, match gun with closer-tolerances, 5 or 6 in. barrel. Millett adj. sights, grip safety, 7 or 8 shot mag., 42 oz.
Mfg.'s Sug. Retail $1,110 $940 $825 $695
    Add $40 for 6 in. barrel.

   Janus Competition Scoremaster—.45 ACP only, similar to Scoremaster, except is fully compensated. New in 1988.
Mfg.'s Sug. Retail $1,650 $1,450 $1,200 $950

SERVICEMASTER—.45 ACP only, shortened version of the Scoremaster, non-glare combat finish, 4¼ in. barrel, coned barrel system, interchangeable front and adj. rear sights, 39 oz. Discontinued in 1986.
$625 $555 $495

Last Mfg.'s Sug. Retail was $686.

Grading	100%	98%	95%	90%	80%	70%	60%

Servicemaster II—similar to Servicemaster, except has polished stainless steel finish. New in 1986.

Mfg.'s Sug. Retail	$975	$795	$675	$595			

POCKET 9—9mm, double action, 3 in. barrel, 6 shot mag., soft matte sheen finish, 26 oz. Made in 1985-86 only.

		$410	$370	$325			

Last Mfg.'s Sug. Retail was $458.

The entire Pocket 9 series was disc. in 1986.

Pocket 9 LS—similar to Pocket 9, except has 4 in. barrel. Made in 1986 only.

		$410	$370	$325			

Last Mfg.'s Sug. Retail was $458.

Pocket .380—similar to Pocket 9, except is .380 ACP cal., 23 oz. Made in 1986 only.

		$410	$370	$325			

Last Mfg.'s Sug. Retail was $458.

POWER 9—9mm, similar to Pocket 9, except has polished slide sides and is supplied with 2 mag.'s. Discontinued in 1986.

		$455	$410	$350			

Last Mfg.'s Sug. Retail was $509.

DIARM S.A.

MANUFACTURING CONGLOMERATE (25 COMPANIES) LOCATED IN DEBA, SPAIN. PREVIOUSLY IMPORTED AND DISTRIBUTED BY AMERICAN ARMS, INC. LOCATED IN NORTH KANSAS CITY, MO. OLDER DIARM MODELS CAN BE FOUND UNDER THE AMERICAN ARMS, INC. HEADING IN THIS PUBLICATION. DIARM IMPORTATION BEGAN IN 1986. AT PUBLICATION RELEASE, DIARM IS ON STRIKE AND ALL PRODUCTION HAS STOPPED.

DIXIE GUN WORKS

SEE "MODERN BLACK POWDER GUNS" SECTION

DOMINGO ACHA

MANUFACTURED IN SPAIN.

LOOKING GLASS—.25 and .32 cal. auto pistol.

	$150	$125	$105	$85	$75	$60	$50

DOMINO

CURRENTLY IMPORTED FROM ITALY BY MANDALL SHOOTING SUPPLIES LOCATED IN SCOTTSDALE, AZ.

MODEL OP 601 MATCH PISTOL—.22 short, 5 shot, 5.6 in. barrel, match sights, full target grips, vent barrel and slide to reduce recoil, adj. and removable trigger.

Mfg.'s Sug. Retail	$1,295	$1,225	$1,000	$715	$635	$550	$495	$440

MODEL SP 602 MATCH PISTOL—.22 LR, 5½ in. barrel, same as 601, but .22 LR and slightly different trigger.

Mfg.'s Sug. Retail	$1,295	$1,225	$1,000	$715	$635	$550	$495	$440

DREYSE PISTOL

MANUFACTURED BY RHEINISCHE METALLWAREN AND MACHINENFABRIK, LOCATED IN SOMMERDA, GERMANY.

MODEL 1907 AUTOMATIC—7.65mm, 8 shot, 3½ in. barrel, blue, fixed sights, hard rubber grips, made 1907-1914.

	100%	98%	95%	90%	80%	70%	60%
	$200	$170	$150	$120	$95	$75	$50

MODEL 1910—9mm Luger, 3½ in. barrel, mfg. 1912-1915.

	100%	98%	95%	90%	80%	70%	60%
	$760	$570	$495	$420	$380	$345	$305

VEST POCKET AUTOMATIC—.25 ACP, 6 shot, 2 in. barrel, blue, fixed sights, hard rubber grips, made 1912-1915.

	100%	98%	95%	90%	80%	70%	60%
	$225	$190	$165	$130	$100	$75	$50

DRILLINGS

A drilling is a three-barrel combination gun (two shotgun barrels arranged in a side by side configuration with a rifle barrel placed directly below them or vice versa). Normally two triggers fire the shotgun barrels and one of them activates the rifle barrel when the barrel selector is moved forward (usually located on the upper tang). For over 125 years Drillings have been the classic hunting gun of many European countries, especially Germany and Austria. Because a single hunting trip may require shooting both wildfowl and animals (oftentimes within several hours), Europeans have long favored a single long arm that could afford both rifle and shotgun shooting, be reliable, and not wear the hunter out while transporting it in the field. Americans, on the other hand, have never really accepted this combination gun principle, and more often than not, have chosen to buy both a rifle and shotgun for each specific hunting application. Since Drillings never did catch on (or sell well) in the U.S., collectibility has been somewhat limited in this country, except for those who see the utility and functionability of these mostly hand assembled weapons. Very few Drillings manufactured before WWII are alike today.

DRILLING VALUES

Rather than list the various manufacturers of Drillings (there are hundreds), it should be noted that guns with major trademarks and established provenences (i.e. Charles Daly, Colt Sauer, Ferlach addressed, Heym, Krieghoff, J.P. Sauer, Suhl addressed, etc.) will be more collectible than other lesser known brands - even if the quality of worksmanship is similar. Also, Drillings with American calibers and smaller gauges will be more desirable (and expensive) than the European metric calibers (i.e. a gun configured 20 ga. X 20 ga. by .243 Win. will outperform a similar gun in 16 ga. X 16 ga. by 6.5 X 58R cal.). In addition, a sidelock action will be more desirable than a boxlock. Features and embellishments become very critical in ascertaining Drilling values also - a gun with deep relief engraving, carved stock, claw mounts w/scope, bone trigger guard, cocking indicators, adj. trigger, cartridge trap, and rear tang activated pop-up rear sight is going to be A LOT more collectible than a plain-Jane hammer model with a loose action. Condition is another major consideration - a gun that shows much use and is not operationally intact/correct may bring several thousand dollars less than another similar specimen showing little wear and excellent original finish (including the case colors). Most good boxlock Drillings in the above mentioned trademarks start in the $1,750 range and can go to $4,000 and higher if the configuration, features, and condition are all desirable. Average Drillings usually sell in the $650 - $1,500 range assuming worn condition, metric calibers and few features. For these reasons, Drillings have to be evaluated one at a time and a COMPETENT appraisal/evaluation should be procurred before buying or selling a specimen.

DUBIEL ARMS COMPANY

MANUFACTURER LOCATED IN SHERMAN, TX. DUBIEL ARMS HAS BEEN MAKING CUSTOM BOLT ACTION RIFLES FOR MANY YEARS (SINCE 1973 IN SHERMAN, TX).

BOLT ACTION RIFLE—custom made bolt action, .22-250-.458 Win. Mag. cal's available, barrel length and weight to order, no sights, Canjar trigger, all steel parts, custom made rifle stocks available in five styles.

Mfg.'s Sug. Retail	$2,500	$2,500	$2,100	$1,870	$1,760	$1,650	$1,375	$1,225

DUMOULIN

MANUFACTURED IN HERSTAL, BELGIUM. IMPORTED AND RETAILED BY MIDWEST GUN SPORT LOCATED IN ZEBULON, NC. (FORMERLY FROM ELLISVILLE, MO.).

Note: Most Ernest Dumoulin rifles and shotguns are essentially custom ordered firearms with a long list of options available which, in some cases, can easily double the values of models shown below. Because of this, these options are not listed individually. To determine the exact price on a specific model with certain options, Midwest Gun Sport should be contacted to obtain a firm price (dependent on the fluctuation of the U.S. dollar and other domestic and foreign regulations).

RIFLES: BOLT ACTION

BAVARIA DELUXE—.243 Win. through .458 Win. cal.'s, 21½, 24, and 25½ in. octagonal barrel, French walnut stock with rosewood forend tip and pistol grip cap, no sights, custom made essentially with Sako (disc.) or Mauser action. Many engraving options available from $510-$1,900. Disc. in 1985.

Series I	$995	$890	$775	$650	$575	$530	$460

Add 15% for .375 H&H and .458 Win. Mag. cal's. Last Mfg.'s Sug. Retail was $1,080.

RIFLE MOUSQUETON—.240 Win. through .338 Win. cal.'s, 20 in. barrel, Mannlicher style, French walnut stock and pistol grip cap, no sights, custom made essentially with Sako or Mauser action. Many engraving options available from $510 - $1,900. Discontinued.

$720	$620	$560	$510	$470	$420	$360

CENTURION MODEL—.270 Win. through .458 Win. cal.'s, 21½, 24, and 25½ in. barrels, French walnut stock with rosewood forearm tip and pistol grip cap, no sights, custom made essentially with Sako or Mauser action. Many engraving options available from $510 - $1,900. Importation discontinued in 1986.

$660	$590	$535	$480	$425	$390	$360

Last Mfg.'s Sug. Retail was $740.

CENTURION CLASSIC—similar to Centurion, standard cal.'s only, Mauser 98 action only and has better wood.

Mfg.'s Sug. Retail	$1,525	$1,525	$1,375	$1,175	$975	$800	$700	$600

These models are also available in Mag. cal.'s that are divided into 4 groups — 1, 2, 3, and 4 Mag. Series. These options retail in the $50 - $300 price range.

Diane—grade up from Centurion Classic, 22 in. barrel, Mauser 98 action, M-70 safety, adj. steel trigger.

Mfg.'s Sug. Retail	$1,450	$1,450	$1,250	$1,000	$825	$700	$600	$500

Above values represent base price with no options.

Amazone—grade up from Diane, 20 in. barrel, full stock.

Mfg.'s Sug. Retail	$1,750	$1,750	$1,525	$1,325	$1,075	$865	$750	$600

Above values represent base price with no options.

Bavaria Deluxe—.243 Win. through .458 Win. cal.'s, 21½, 24, and 25½ in. octagonal barrel, French walnut stock with rosewood forend tip and pistol grip cap, no sights, custom made essentially with Sako (discontinued) or Mauser action. Many engraving options available from $510 - $1,900.

Mfg.'s Sug. Retail	$1,900	$1,900	$1,675	$1,450	$1,200	$995	$775	$650

Above values represent base price with no options.

Safari—Mag. cal.'s only.

Mfg.'s Sug. Retail	$2,350	$2,350	$1,775	$1,475	$1,200	$995	$775	$650

Above values represent base price with no options.

MANNLICHER MODEL—Mauser type bolt action, various cal.'s, full stocked. Discontinued in 1985.

$730	$660	$580	$520	$470	$430	$395

Last Mfg.'s Sug. Retail was $825.

Mannlicher Classic—same as basic Mannlicher, except has better walnut. Discontinued in 1985.

$995	$890	$775	$650	$575	$530	$460

Last Mfg.'s Sug. Retail was $1,065.

Grading	100%	98%	95%	90%	80%	70%	60%

MATCH MODEL—match target rifle, adj. sights and stock. Discontinued in 1985.

	$1,640	$1,490	$1,300	$1,050	$900	$800	$700

Last Mfg.'s Sug. Retail was $1,860.

Match NATO—7.62 cal. match rifle. Discontinued in 1985.

	$2,640	$2,400	$2,175	$1,850	$1,595	$1,400	$1,195

Last Mfg.'s Sug. Retail was $3,000.

ST. HUBERT MODEL—Sako action, various cal.'s and barrel lengths. Discontinued in 1985.

	$1,900	$1,700	$1,495	$1,300	$1,150	$995	$850

Last Mfg.'s Sug. Retail was $2,125.

SAFARI SPORTSMAN—Mauser 98 action, .416 Rigby, .375 H&H, .505 Gibbs, and .404 Jeffreys cal.'s, 4 shot mag., limited availability in 1986.

Mfg.'s Sug. Retail	$4,000	$4,000	$3,550	$3,250	$2,800	$2,400	$2,000	$1,750

Add $300 for .505 Gibbs cal.

Above values represent base price with no options.

AFRICAN PRO—similar to Safari Sportsman except has ebony or buffalo horn forearm tip, tilting hood for the front sight, multiple folding rear sight.

Mfg.'s Sug. Retail	$4,800	$4,800	$4,000	$3,550	$3,250	$2,800	$2,400	$2,000

Above values represent base price with no options.

DOUBLE RIFLES

EUROPA I—.22 Hornet, .222 Rem., .222 Rem. Mag., 6mm Rem., .243 Win., .25-06, .30-06, 6.5 X 57R, 7 X 57R, 8 X 57JRS, or 9.3 X 74R cal., Anson & Deeley boxlock action, moderate engraving. New in 1989.

Mfg.'s Sug. Retail	$4,800	$4,800	$4,200	$3,800	$3,500	$3,250	$2,995	$2,700

Above values represent base price with no options.

CONTINENTAL I—same calibers as Europa I, sidelock action, 12 engraving options to choose from, many options available on special order. New in 1989.

Mfg.'s Sug. Retail	$8,600	$8,600	$7,700	$6,995	$6,400	$5,600	$4,750	$4,150

Above values represent base price with no options.

"PIONNIER" JUXTAPOSED EXPRESS RIFLES—assorted cal.'s from .22 Hornet through .600 Nitro Express, S x S configuration, heavily engraved, select walnut. Limited production, Anson & Deeley triple lock action, sideplates available at extra charge.

P-I and P-II—English style scroll or bouquet (P-II) engraving.

Mfg.'s Sug. Retail	$7,850	$7,850	$6,500	$5,825	$5,200	$4,650	$4,160	$3,700

Add $400 for P-II engraving.

P III—English style lace engraving (tapestry style).

Mfg.'s Sug. Retail	$8,640	$8,640	$7,750	$7,000	$6,400	$5,600	$4,750	$4,150

P-IV through P-VIII—various styles of royal engraving with or without hunting scenes.

Mfg.'s Sug. Retail	$9,100	$9,100	$7,995	$7,450	$6,800	$6,000	$5,000	$4,350

Add $400 for gold inlays.

P-IX through P-XII—Louis XVI style engraving.

Mfg.'s Sug. Retail	$9,540	$9,540	$8,600	$7,800	$7,250	$6,400	$5,250	$4,500

Pionnier Magnum—.338 Win. Mag., .375 H&H, .416 Rigby, .416 Hoffman, .458 Win. Mag., .577 Nitro Express, and .600 Nitro Express. Boxlock action with Greener crossbolt.

Mfg.'s Sug. Retail	$10,900	$10,900	$9,400	$8,650	$7,800	$7,000	$6,450	$5,825

Above values represent base price with no options.

ARISTOCRATE MODEL—available in all cal.'s up to .375 H&H (also in 20 ga.), single shot action with low profile, exhibition oil finished walnut stock and forearm. Values below assume standard model (12 engraving options available). Imported 1987-1988 only.

	$9,100	$8,450	$7,775	$7,000	$6,450	$5,825	$5,275

Last Mfg.'s Sug. Retail was $10,400.

Above values represent base price with no options.

Grading	100%	98%	95%	90%	80%	70%	60%

PRESTIGE RIFLE (SIDELOCK)—best quality sidelock, various cal.'s, triple locking, 10 different presentation options available, values below reflect standard model without options. Custom order only, 1 year waiting period. New in 1986.

Mfg.'s Sug. Retail	$17,900	$17,900	$15,000	$12,500	$9,995	$8,000	$7,000	$6,000

Add $600 for Mag. cal.'s over .416 Rigby.

SHOTGUNS

EUROPA MODEL—12, 20, 28, or .410 ga., Anson & Deeley boxlock action, single or double trigger, moderately engraved, oil finished stock and forearm, choice of 6 engraving options. New in 1989.

Mfg.'s Sug. Retail	$3,300	$3,300	$2,750	$2,350	$2,000	$1,800	$1,575	$1,400

LEIGE JUXTAPOSED SHOTGUN (SxS)—12, 16 (discontinued in 1986), 20, and 28 ga.'s, Anson & Deeley locking action, elaborate engraving, deluxe walnut. New in 1986.

Luxe Model

	$5,300	$4,600	$3,900	$3,300	$2,900	$2,600	$2,300

Last Mfg.'s Sug. Retail was $5,900 (disc. in 1988).

Grand Luxe

Mfg.'s Sug. Retail	$6,900	$6,900	$6,000	$5,000	$4,300	$3,600	$3,200	$2,875

Add 15% for 28 ga.
Add 15% for sideplates.

Many engraving options and other special order features can be added to the above models.

CONTINENTAL MODEL—12, 20, 28, or .410 ga., side lock action, double or single trigger, deluxe oil finished walnut stock, choice of 6 engraving options. New in 1989.

Mfg.'s Sug. Retail	$7,400	$7,400	$6,250	$5,200	$4,400	$3,700	$3,200	$2,875

Above values represent base price with no options.

ETENDART JUXTAPOSED SHOTGUN (SxS)—12, 20 and 28 ga., full sidelock, exhibition grade walnut, double triggers, top-of-the-line quality, built to special order. Values listed assume standard gun (12 engraving options available). New in 1987.

Mfg.'s Sug. Retail	$14,400	$14,400	$12,250	$9,995	$9,100	$8,450	$7,775	$7,000

Add 6% for 28 ga.

BOSS ROYAL SUPERPOSED (O/U)—12, 20 and 28 ga., full sidelock, exhibition grade walnut, double triggers, top-of-the-line quality, built to special order. Values listed assume standard gun (12 engraving options available). New in 1987.

Mfg.'s Sug. Retail	$18,500	$18,500	$16,000	$13,750	$11,000	$9,775	$8,000	$6,950

Add 6½% for 28 ga.

SUPERPOSED EXPRESS "INTERNATIONAL"—O/U shotgun, includes extra set of rifle barrels, 20 ga., 7 choices of rifle cal.'s, deluxe walnut. Elaborate engraving patterns available at extra charge, limited production. Discontinued in 1985.

	$2,400	$2,000	$1,800	$1,575	$1,400	$1,200	$1,050

Last Mfg.'s Sug. Retail was $2,490.

COMBINATION GUNS

EAGLE MODEL—O/U configuration (shotgun barrel on bottom), 12 or 20 ga., .22 Hornet, .222 Rem., .222 Rem. Mag., 6mm Rem., .243 Win., .25-06, .30-06, 6.5 X 57R, 7 X 57R, 8 X 57JRS, or 9.3 X 74R cal., boxlock action. New in 1989.

Mfg.'s Sug. Retail	$2,700	$2,700	$2,400	$2,175	$1,850	$1,595	$1,400	$1,195

Above values represent base price with no options.

NOTES

E

E.M.F. CO., INC.
CURRENT IMPORTER AND DISTRIBUTOR LOCATED IN SANTA ANA, CA.

Grading	100%	98%	95%	90%	80%	70%	60%

REVOLVERS: REPRODUCTIONS

1875 REMINGTON OUTLAW—.357 Mag., .44-40, and .45 LC cal.'s, copy of the Rem. Model 1875 SA, 7½ in. barrel only, casehardened frame, walnut grips, blue only.

Mfg.'s Sug. Retail	$485	$325	$250	$185	$165	$155	$145	$135

Add $35 for nickel plating.
Add $115 for engraving.

1890 REMINGTON SINGLE ACTION—.357 Mag., .44-40, and .45 LC cal.'s, 5½ in. barrel, lanyard ring in butt stock, blue frame, walnut grips. New in 1986.

Mfg.'s Sug. Retail	$500	$345	$240	$190	$165	$155	$145	$135

Add $40 for nickel plating.
Add $100 for engraving.

DERRINGERS: REPRODUCTIONS

STANDARD MODEL—.38 Spl., Rem. Model 41 copy, top hinged, vent rib, spur trigger, teflon blue finish. Discontinued in 1986.

	$60	$50	$40	$35	$30	$25	$20

Add $7 for nickel finish.

Last Mfg.'s Sug. Retail was $75.

DAVIS DERRINGER—.22 LR, .22 Mag., .25 ACP, or .32 ACP cal., O/U steel construction.

Mfg.'s Sug. Retail	$65	$50	$40	$35	$30	$25	$20	$20

Add $70 for double cased set.
Add $30 for cased Derringer.
Add $30 for .38 Spl.

RIFLES: MODERN REPRODUCTIONS

These models are authentic shooting reproductions mfg. in Italy.

AP 74—.22 LR or .32 ACP cal., copy of the Colt M-16, semi-auto, 15 round mag., 20 in. barrel, 6¾ lbs.

Mfg.'s Sug. Retail	$295	$240	$175	$165	$155	$145	$135	$125

Add $25 for .32 cal.

Sporter Carbine—wood sporter stock, .22 LR only.

Mfg.'s Sug. Retail	$320	$250	$185	$170	$160	$150	$140	$130

Assault-Paratrooper Carbine—.22 LR only, folding wire stock, black nylon on Assault Model. Importation disc. in 1987.

	$260	$190	$175	$165	$155	$145	$135

Add $10 for wood folding stock.

Last Mfg.'s Sug. Retail was $325.

"Dressed" Military Model—with Cyclops scope, Colt bayonet, sling, and bipod. Discontinued in 1986.

	$330	$265	$240	$220	$200	$185	$170

Last Mfg.'s Sug. Retail was $450.

E.M.F. CO., INC., cont.

ISRAELI GALIL—.22 LR only, reproduction of the Israeli Galil, semi-auto. Importation began in 1988.

Mfg.'s Sug. Retail	$295	$240	$175	$165	$155	$145	$135	$125

KALASHNIKOV AK-47—.22 LR only, reproduction of the Russian AK-47, semi-auto. Importation began in 1988.

Mfg.'s Sug. Retail	$295	$240	$175	$165	$155	$145	$135	$125

FRENCH M.A.S.—.22 LR only, reproduction of the French Bull-Pup Combat Rifle, semi-auto with carrying handle, 29 round mag. Importation began in 1988.

Mfg.'s Sug. Retail	$320	$255	$185	$165	$155	$145	$135	$125

M1 CARBINE—.30 cal. only, copy of the U.S. Military M1 Carbine. Discontinued in 1985.

	$175	$150	$140	$130	$120	$110	$100

Add $43 for Paratrooper variation.

Last Mfg.'s Sug. Retail was $205.

RIFLES: WINCHESTER REPRODUCTIONS

DELUXE HENRY RIFLE—.44-40 cal. only, deluxe walnut, reproduction of New Haven Arms Co.'s Henry Rifle. New in 1987.

Mfg.'s Sug. Retail	$1,380	$1,025	$850	$600	$450	$330	$295	$260

Engraved Henry Rifle—similar to deluxe Henry Rifle except has hand engraved receiver. New in 1987.

Mfg.'s Sug. Retail	$1,598	$1,200	$975	$700	$525	$400	$340	$295

1866 YELLOWBOY CARBINE—.22 LR, .38 Spl., and .44-40 cal.'s, 19 in. barrel, saddle-ring carbine, brass frame.

Mfg.'s Sug. Retail	$870	$600	$400	$325	$250	$235	$220	$200

1866 Rifle—same cal.'s as 1866 Yellowboy Carbine, 24¼ in. barrel.

Mfg.'s Sug. Retail	$900	$615	$400	$325	$250	$235	$220	$200

Engraved Yellowboy Carbine—.38 Spl., and .44-40 cal.'s only.

Mfg.'s Sug. Retail	$1,080	$800	$575	$440	$330	$295	$260	$230

1873 CARBINE—.22 Mag., .357 Mag., and .44-40 cal.'s, 19 in. barrel, copy of the Winchester Model 1873, case hardened receiver.

Mfg.'s Sug. Retail	$1,060	$800	$575	$440	$330	$295	$260	$230

Rifle Variation—24¼ in. barrel, available only in .357 Mag. and .44-40 cal.'s.

Mfg.'s Sug. Retail	$1,100	$825	$575	$440	$330	$295	$260	$230

Engraved Rifle—available in .357 Mag. and .44-40 cal.'s only. Importation disc. in 1987.

	$895	$635	$500	$450	$400	$360	$325

Last Mfg.'s Sug. Retail was $850.

PREMIER 1873 CARBINE & RIFLE—.45 LC, case hardened frame, uncheckered walnut stock and forearm, full mag., rifle has 24¼ in. barrel, carbine has 19 in. barrel. Importation began in 1988.

Mfg.'s Sug. Retail	$1,160	$850	$595	$450	$330	$295	$260	$230

Add $38 for rifle variation.

RIFLES: SHARPS REPRODUCTIONS

SHARPS OLD RELIABLE RIFLE—.45-70 cal., copy of the Sharp's Single Shot, 28 in. octagonal barrel, case hardened frame, double set triggers. Discontinued in 1986.

	$430	$260	$240	$220	$200	$185	$170

Last Mfg.'s Sug. Retail was $600.

Carbine Model—saddle-ring carbine with 22 in. round barrel, single trigger. Discontinued in 1986.

	$440	$330	$295	$260	$230	$210	$195

Last Mfg.'s Sug. Retail was $550.

84 GUN CO.

EIGHTY FOUR, PA. EARLY 1970'S.

RIFLES

CLASSIC RIFLE—Bolt action, various calibers. Grades 1-4.

	100%	98%	95%	90%	80%	70%	60%
Grade 1	$420	$315	$275	$235	$210	$190	$170
Grade 2	$780	$585	$512	$430	$390	$355	$315
Grade 3	$860	$645	$560	$475	$430	$390	$345
Grade 4	$1,580	$1,185	$1,030	$870	$790	$715	$640

LOBO RIFLE—bolt action, various calibers. Grades standard, 1-4.

	100%	98%	95%	90%	80%	70%	60%
Standard	$415	$315	$270	$230	$210	$190	$170
Grade 1	$540	$405	$355	$300	$270	$245	$220
Grade 2	$795	$600	$520	$440	$400	$360	$320
Grade 3	$1,600	$1,200	$1,040	$880	$800	$720	$640
Grade 4	$2,350	$1,765	$1,530	$1,295	$1,175	$1,060	$940

PENNSYLVANIA RIFLE—bolt action, various calibers. Grades standard, 1-4.

	100%	98%	95%	90%	80%	70%	60%
Standard	$420	$315	$275	$235	$210	$190	$170
Grade 1	$540	$405	$355	$300	$270	$245	$220
Grade 2	$795	$600	$520	$440	$400	$360	$320
Grade 3	$1,600	$1,200	$1,040	$880	$800	$720	$640
Grade 4	$2,350	$1,765	$1,530	$1,295	$1,175	$1,060	$940

ENFIELD

ROYAL SMALL ARMS FACTORY, MIDDLESEX, ENGLAND.

NO. 2 MK. I REVOLVER—.380 British Service (based on .38 S&W with a 200 grain bullet), double action, 6 shot, 5 in. barrel, fixed sights, blue, composition grips, top break, issued to British army 1932.

100%	98%	95%	90%	80%	70%	60%
$195	$175	$140	$130	$120	$110	$100

RIFLES

NO. 1 MK. III SMLE—.303 British, bolt action, 10 round mag., 25.2 in. barrel, open sights, long range volley sights, magazine cut-off, adopted by British Army in 1907.

100%	98%	95%	90%	80%	70%	60%
$195	$150	$125	$100	$90	$75	$55

NO. 1 MK. III SMLE—a simplified rifle adopted by the British during WWI, volley sights and magazine cut-off deleted, the most common variation of SMLE.

100%	98%	95%	90%	80%	70%	60%
$195	$150	$125	$100	$90	$75	$55

NO. 3 MK. I PATTERN 14 RIFLE—modified Mauser type bolt action, .303 British, issued as substitute standard by British Army during WWI, manufactured in U.S. (the later U.S. 1917 Enfield is identical except for caliber and sights).

100%	98%	95%	90%	80%	70%	60%
$195	$150	$125	$100	$90	$75	$55

NO. 3 MK. I—.22 cal., single shot military training model.

100%	98%	95%	90%	80%	70%	60%
$300	$275	$250	$225	$200	$175	$150

NO. 4 MK. I—an improved SMLE with aperture rear sight, stronger receiver and more easily manufactured parts, adopted in 1939 by the British Army.

100%	98%	95%	90%	80%	70%	60%
$185	$145	$120	$95	$75	$55	$40

Sniper Model—cased, with or without scope.

	100%	98%	95%	90%	80%	70%	60%
Cased	$750	$675	$595	$540	$480	$420	$350
Uncased	$595	$540	$480	$420	$350	$295	$250

NO. 5 MK. I JUNGLE CARBINE—a shorter, lighter version of the No. 4 MK. I with a 20.5 in. barrel, flash hider, recoil pad and shortened forend and hand guard, 7.2 lbs., developed during WWII.

100%	98%	95%	90%	80%	70%	60%
$250	$200	$150	$125	$100	$85	$75

SMLE stands for Rifle, Short, Magazine, Lee-Enfield. The SMLE rifles served the British Military from 1902-1954.

ENFIELD AMERICA, INC.
MANUFACTURED IN ATLANTA, GA.

MP-45—.45 ACP, semi-auto assault pistol, 4½, 6, 8, 10, or 18½ in. shrouded barrel, Parkerized finish, 10, 30, 40, or 50 round mag.'s, 6 lbs. Manufactured in 1985 only.

	100%	98%	95%	90%	80%	70%	60%
	$295	$260	$240	$220	$200	$185	$170

Last Mfg.'s Sug. Retail was $350.

ERA
MANUFACTURED IN BRAZIL

ERA O/U SHOTGUN—12 or 20 ga., 28 in. vent rib barrel, full and mod., double triggers, extractors, checkered hardwood stock.

	100%	98%	95%	90%	80%	70%	60%
	$275	$250	$225	$200	$170	$150	$125
Trap version	$300	$275	$250	$225	$200	$175	$150
Skeet version	$300	$275	$250	$225	$200	$175	$150

ERA DOUBLE BARREL—12, 20, and .410 ga.'s, 26, 28, or 30 in. barrels, various chokes, double triggers, extractors, checkered pistol grip stock.

	$165	$150	$135	$125	$110	$100	$85

ERA DOUBLE RIOT MODEL—same as Double Barrel, except 12 and 20 ga., 18 in. barrel.

	$185	$175	$150	$140	$125	$110	$95

ERA QUAIL MODEL—same as Standard, except 12 and 20 ga., 20 in. barrel.

	$185	$175	$150	$140	$125	$110	$95

ERMA-WERKE
MANUFACTURED IN DACHAU, WEST GERMANY. PREVIOUSLY DISTRIBUTED BY EXCAM. CURRENTLY DISTRIBUTED BY BEEMAN PRECISION ARMS INC. LOCATED IN SANTA ROSA, CA AND MANDALL'S SHOOTING SUPPLIES, INC. LOCATED IN SCOTTSDALE, AZ.

PISTOLS: SEMI-AUTO

ERMA KGP68A/BEEMAN MP-08—Luger type toggle action, .32 ACP (disc. in 1987) or .380 ACP, 3½ (Beeman) or 4 in. barrel, 6 shot mag., blue, 1.4 lbs., made 1968-present.

Mfg.'s Sug. Retail	$390	$335	$275	$240	$185	$145	$115	$95

In 1988, Beeman took over importation of this model in .380 ACP cal. only with new Luger style checkered walnut grips and 3½ in. barrel. Previous models had plastic grips.

ERMA KGP69/BEEMAN P-08—Luger type toggle action, .22 LR, 8 shot mag., 3¾ in. barrel, blue, plastic (disc.) or checkered walnut grips, made 1969-present.

Mfg.'s Sug. Retail	$390	$335	$275	$240	$185	$145	$115	$95

Beeman is the sole importer of this model currently (Model P-08).

MODEL ESP 85A—.22 LR and .32 S & W Long Wadcutter, blow back semi-auto, 6 in. barrel, 5 or 8 (.32 S & W only) shot mag., adj. stippled match grips with thumbrest, fully adj. and interchangeable sights, gun is supplied with 2 barrels (.22 LR and .32 S & W), several extra mag.'s, sights, disassembly tools, and attache style case with foam rubber cutouts, 2½ lbs. Importation began in 1989.

Mfg.'s Sug. Retail	$1,095	$1,050	$900	$800	$700	$625	$550	$495

This model is imported exclusively by Mandall's Shooting Supplies, Inc. located in Scottsdale, AZ.

ET-22 LUGER CARBINE—.22 LR, 11¾ in. barrel, blue rear ramp sight, checkered walnut grips and uncheckered forearm, adj. artillery type rear sight, rarely seen.

	$395	$335	$275	$240	$200	$175	$140

Add 20% for leatherette case.

Grading	100%	98%	95%	90%	80%	70%	60%

REVOLVERS: DOUBLE ACTION

This series of revolvers is imported exclusively by Mandall's Shooting Supplies, Inc. located in Scottsdale, AZ.

ER 777—.357 Mag., 6 shot, 4 or 5½ in. barrel, solid rib and full barrel shroud, adj. target rear sight, blued steel, checkered sport grips, 2¾ lbs. Importation began in 1989.

Mfg.'s Sug. Retail	$495	$450	$400	$360	$330	$300	$275	$250

ER 772 MATCH—.22 LR, match gun with special adj. contoured grips with stippling, 6 in. barrel, action similar to ER 777, fully adj. and extended rear sight, interchangeable front sight, 3 lbs. Importation began in 1989.

Mfg.'s Sug. Retail	$495	$450	$400	$360	$330	$300	$275	$250

ER 773 MATCH—.32 S & W Long, otherwise same as ER 772 Match, 2.9 lbs. Importation began in 1989.

Mfg.'s Sug. Retail	$495	$450	$400	$360	$330	$300	$275	$250

RIFLES

EM1 .22 CARBINE—M1 copy .22 LR cal., 10 or 15 round mag., 18 in. barrel. 1966-1976 mfg.

	$195	$155	$145	$130	$120	$110	$100

EGM-1—same as EM1 except for unslotted buttstock, 5 round mag.

	$195	$155	$145	$130	$120	$110	$100

EG72 PUMP—outsidM o?Xmer, .22 LR cal., 15 shot mag., 18½ in. barrel. 1970-1976 mfg.

	$125	$95	$90	$75	$70	$65	$60

EG712 LEVER-ACTION—Win. Model 94 copy, .22 LR cal., tube mag., 18½ in. barrel. Mfg. 1976 to date.

	$204	$160	$145	$130	$120	$110	$100

EG-73—same as EG712 except .22 Mag. cal., 12 round mag. Mfg. 1973 to date.

	$229	$180	$160	$155	$130	$115	$100

EXCAM

IMPORTER AND DISTRIBUTOR LOCATED IN HIALEAH, FL. EXCAM DISTRIBUTES DART, ERMA, TANARMI, TARGA, & WARRIOR EXCLUSIVELY FOR THE U.S. THESE TRADEMARKS WILL APPEAR UNDER EXCAM ONLY IN THIS BOOK.

All Targa and Tanarmi pistols are manufactured in Gardone V.T., Italy. All Erma and Warrior pistols and rifles are manufactured in W. Germany. Senator O/U shotguns are manufactured by A. Zoli located in Brescia, Italy.

ERMA PISTOLS

RX 22—.22 LR only, double action-Walther copy, 3¼ in. barrel, 8 round mag., 17 oz., blue only, plastic grips. Assembled in the U.S. Disc. in 1986.

	$140	$125	$105	$95	$90	$85	$80

Last Mfg.'s Sug. Retail was $139.

KGP 22—.22 LR only, Luger type toggle action, 3.78 in. barrel, 8 round mag., 29 oz., blue only, plastic grips. Importation disc. in 1986.

	$220	$195	$175	$155	$135	$120	$105

Last Mfg.'s Sug. Retail was $220.

KGP 380—.380 ACP only, Luger type toggle action, 3½ in. barrel, 5 round mag., 23 oz., blue only, plastic grips. Discontinued in 1986.

	$250	$215	$185	$160	$145	$135	$125

Last Mfg.'s Sug. Retail was $230.

ERMA RIFLES

EG 712—.22 LR only, lever action copied after the Win. Model 92, 18½ barrel, 15 shot, iron sights. Discontinued in 1985.

	$180	$160	$140	$125	$115	$100	$90

Last Mfg.'s Sug. Retail was $204.

Grading	100%	98%	95%	90%	80%	70%	60%

EG 712L—.22 LR only, lever action copied after the Win. Model 92, 18½ octagonal barrel, deluxe walnut silver plated receiver and barrel bands, 15 shot, iron sights. Discontinued.

	$300	**$241**	**$220**	**$180**	**$150**	**$130**	**$115**

EG 73—.22 Mag. only, lever action copied after the Win. Model 92, 19¼ barrel, 12 shot, iron sights, blue only. Discontinued in 1985.

	$205	**$185**	**$160**	**$140**	**$130**	**$120**	**$105**

Last Mfg.'s Sug. Retail was $229.

EG 722—.22 LR only, slide action, 18½ barrel, 15 shot, iron sights, blue only. Discontinued in 1985.

	$180	**$160**	**$140**	**$125**	**$115**	**$100**	**$90**

Last Mfg.'s Sug. Retail was $204.

EM 1 CARBINE—.22 LR and .22 Mag., gas semi-auto, copy of the original M1 carbine, 19½ in. barrel, 15 shot, iron sights, blue only. ESG 22 is 22 Mag. (12 shot) — add $100. Discontinued in 1985.

	$175	**$155**	**$140**	**$125**	**$115**	**$100**	**$90**

Last Mfg.'s Sug. Retail was $195.

SENATOR OVER/UNDER SHOTGUNS

SENATOR MODEL—12, 20, and .410 ga.'s, 3 in. chambers, 26 or 28 in. F/M barrels, folding action, double triggers, extractors, vent barrels and rib, checkered walnut stock and forearm, engraved silver finished receiver. Imported 1986-1987.

	$235	**$200**	**$180**	**$165**	**$150**	**$140**	**$130**

Last Mfg.'s Sug. Retail was $275.

TANARMI PISTOLS

MODEL TA 76 S.A.A.—.22 LR, single action revolver, 4¾ in barrel, 6 shot, 32 oz., blue finish only, wood grips.

Mfg.'s Sug. Retail	**$95**	**$85**	**$65**	**$55**	**$50**	**$45**	**$40**	**$35**

Add $4 for chrome finish or brass backstrap and trigger guard.

Model TA 76M Combo—includes .22 LR and .22 Mag. cylinders, 4¾ (standard), 6, or 9 in. barrel, blue finish, wood grips.

Mfg.'s Sug. Retail	**$105**	**$95**	**$75**	**$65**	**$60**	**$55**	**$50**	**$45**

Add $16 for chrome plated finish (4¾ in. barrel only).
Add $10 for 6 (Model TA 766) or 9 (Model TA 769) in. barrel.
Add $16 for brass backstrap and trigger guard (N/A in 9 in. barrel).

Model TA 22 SLM—steel frame. Discontinued in 1985.

	$95	**$81**	**$70**	**$60**	**$55**	**$50**	**$45**

Last Mfg.'s Sug. Retail was $103.

TANARMI TA 38SB O/U DERRINGER—38 Spl. only, O/U Derringer-copy of Rem. Model 41, 3 in. barrels, 14 oz., with safety, blue finish only, checkered nylon grips. Importation disc. in 1985.

	$90	**$75**	**$65**	**$55**	**$50**	**$45**	**$40**

Last Mfg.'s Sug. Retail was $80.

MODEL TA 41 SERIES—.41 Action Express cal., action similar to TA 90 Series, 11 shot mag., matte blue (Model TA 41B) or matte chrome (Model TA 41C) finish, combat sights, black neoprene grips, 38 oz. Importation began in 1989.

Mfg.'s Sug. Retail	**$490**	**$450**	**$390**	**$360**	**$330**	**$295**	**$265**	**$240**

Add $70 (retail) for adj. target sights (Model TA 41BT).

Model TA 41C—matte chrome finish.

Mfg.'s Sug. Retail	**$550**	**$485**	**$430**	**$395**	**$360**	**$330**	**$295**	**$270**

Add $50 (retail) for adj. target sights (Model TA 41CT).

Model TA 41 SS—.41 AE, compensated variation of the Model TA 41 except has 5 in. ported barrel and slide, blue/chrome finish, competition sights, 40 oz. Importation began in 1989.

Mfg.'s Sug. Retail	**$650**	**$575**	**$450**	**$420**	**$385**	**$350**	**$325**	**$300**

Grading	100%	98%	95%	90%	80%	70%	60%

MODEL TA 90 SERIES—9mm, double action, copy of the CZ-75, 4¾ in. barrel, steel frame, 15 shot mag., matte blue (Model TA 90B) or matte chrome finish (Model TA 90C), combat sights, wood (discontinued in 1985) or neoprene grips, 38 oz. New in 1985.

Mfg.'s Sug. Retail	$415	$365	$300	$260	$225	$205	$190	$180

Add $85 (retail) for adj. target sights (TA 90BT).

Earlier models featured a polished blue finish and nickel steel alloy frame (35 oz.).

Model TA 90C—matte chrome finish.

Mfg.'s Sug. Retail	$430	$380	$315	$270	$235	$210	$190	$180

Add $95 (retail) for adj. target sights (TA 90CT).

Model BTA 90B and C—9mm, smaller version of TA 90, 3½ in. barrel, 12 shot mag., neoprene grips. New in 1986.

Mfg.'s Sug. Retail	$430	$380	$315	$270	$235	$210	$190	$180

Add $20 for chrome finish (BTA 90C).

Model TA 90 SS—9mm, compensated variation of the Model TA 90 except has 5 in. ported barrel and slide, blue/chrome finish, competition sights, 40 oz. Importation began in 1989.

Mfg.'s Sug. Retail	$650	$575	$450	$420	$385	$350	$325	$300

TA 90BK—convertible kit including 2 barrels (9mm and .41 AE) and 2 mag.'s. Released in mid 1989.

Prices have yet to be announced on this model as of this printing.

TARGA PISTOLS

GT 26 and GT 27B OR C—.25 ACP, 2½ in. barrel, 6 shot mag., single action, 13 oz., available in either satin chrome alloy (GT 27 B or C) or steel frame (GT 26 S), wooden grips became standard in 1986.

Mfg.'s Sug. Retail	$69	$60	$50	$45	$35	$30	$30	$25

Add $46 for GT 26 S (steel frame).
Add $6 for chrome finish (Model GT 27C).

GT 22 SERIES—.22 LR, 3.88 in. barrel, 10 round mag., single action 26 oz., steel frame, either satin chrome (GT 22 C) or standard blue (GT 22 B) finish, wooden grips became standard in 1986. GT 22 T is 6 in. barrel target version. (12 shot mag.).

Mfg.'s Sug. Retail	$200	$170	$140	$125	$110	$95	$80	$70

Add $15 for chrome finish.

GT 32 SERIES—.32 ACP, 3.88 in. barrel, 7 round mag., single action, steel frame, 26 oz., either satin chrome (GT 32 C) or standard blue (GT 32 B), wooden grips became standard in 1986.

Mfg.'s Sug. Retail	$200	$170	$140	$125	$110	$95	$80	$70

Add $15 for chrome finish.

GT 380 ACP SERIES—.380 ACP, 3.88 in. barrel, 6 round mag., single action, steel frame, 26 oz., either satin chrome (GT 380 C) or standard blue (GT 380 B), wooden grips became standard in 1986.

Mfg.'s Sug. Retail	$212	$175	$145	$135	$125	$115	$105	$95

Add $8 for chrome finish.

GT 380 BE or CE—engraved models, either blue (BE) or chrome (CE) finish, wood grips.

Mfg.'s Sug. Retail	$220	$180	$155	$145	$135	$125	$115	$105

Add $25 for chrome finish.

GT 380 XE—.380 ACP, 3.88 in. barrel, 11 round mag., 28 oz., blue only, wood grips.

Mfg.'s Sug. Retail	$235	$190	$165	$155	$145	$135	$125	$115

GT 32 XEB—same as GT 380 XE, only 32 ACP, 12 round mag. Discontinued in 1985.

	$165	$145	$135	$125	$115	$100	$95

Last Mfg.'s Sug. Retail was $189.

Grading	100%	98%	95%	90%	80%	70%	60%

UBERTI REVOLVERS

Importation of these revolvers by Excam was stopped in 1986.

ALDO UBERTI CATTLEMAN SA REVOLVER—.375 Mag., .44 Mag., and 45 long Colt cal.'s, 6 shot, single action, 5½, 6, and 7½ in. barrels, target sights, wood grips, blued finish. New in 1985. Discontinued in 1986.

| | | $295 | $250 | $195 | $165 | $150 | $140 | $130 |

Add $10 for .44 Mag. cal.

Last Mfg.'s Sug. Retail was $222.

ALDO UBERTI DA INSPECTOR—.38 Spl., double action, 3 or 4 in. barrel, blue finish, wood grips, 6 shot. New in 1985. Discontinued in 1986.

| | | $325 | $250 | $200 | $180 | $165 | $150 | $140 |

Add $17 for adj. sights.

Last Mfg.'s Sug. Retail was $240.

WARRIOR REVOLVERS

Importation of these revolvers by Excam was stopped in 1986.

WARRIOR DOUBLE ACTION MODEL W 722 (B)—.22 LR and 22 Mag. only, double action, 6 in. barrel, 8 shot, 35 oz., blue only, plastic grips. Discontinued in 1986.

| | | $100 | $80 | $70 | $65 | $60 | $55 | $50 |

Add $50 for 22 Mag. extra cyl.

Last Mfg.'s Sug. Retail was $98.

WARRIOR DOUBLE ACTION MODEL W 384 (B)—38 Spl. only, double action, 4 and 6 in. barrels, 6 shot, 30 oz., blue only, plastic grips. Vent rib standard. Discontinued in 1986.

| | | $135 | $110 | $100 | $90 | $80 | $70 | $65 |

Add $5 for 6 in. barrel (W 386 B).

Last Mfg.'s Sug. Retail was $125.

WARRIOR DOUBLE ACTION MODEL W 357—357 Mag. only, double action, 4 and 6 in. barrels, 6 shot, 36 oz., blue only, plastic grips. Vent rib standard. 6 in. barrel (W 3576). Discontinued in 1986.

| | | $190 | $165 | $145 | $135 | $130 | $125 | $120 |

Last Mfg.'s Sug. Retail was $185.

EXEL ARMS OF AMERICA, INC.

PREVIOUS IMPORTER LOCATED IN GARDENER, MA. EXEL ARMS PREVIOUSLY IMPORTED LANBER (SERIES 100), UGARTECHEA (SERIES 200), AND LAURONA (SERIES 300) SHOTGUNS. LANBER, UGARTECHEA, AND LAURONA, ARE LISTED ALPHABETICALLY BELOW.

LANBER SHOTGUNS: OVER AND UNDER

Lanber shotguns are not being imported currently. The last Mfg.'s Sug. Retail on all models listed below reflects 1987 pricing, the last year they were imported. Any future importation could reflect pricing changes.

EXEL SERIES 100: MODELS 101 THROUGH 104—12 ga., boxlock action, vent rib, extractors, single trigger. Add $16 for 103 Mag., $92 for ejectors (Model 104 only).

| | | $400 | $350 | $310 | $270 | $240 | $225 | $200 |

Last Mfg.'s Sug. Retail was $451.

These models were previously designated the 844ST Series.

Grading	100%	98%	95%	90%	80%	70%	60%

EXEL MODEL 105—12 ga., boxlock action, single trigger, ejectors, Lanber screw-in chokes, deluxe wood, engraved satin finish action.

	$575	$495	$440	$405	$370	$345	$310

Last Mfg.'s Sug. Retail was $644.

This model was previously designated the Model 2004LCH.

EXEL MODELS 106 AND 107—12 ga., similar to 105, only more deluxe version with vent barrels and rib, blued receiver only, interchangeable Lanber screw-in chokes. Trap model is Model 107.

	$725	$625	$550	$500	$475	$450	$425

Last Mfg.'s Sug. Retail was $845.

These models were previosly designated 2008LCH and 2009LCH respectively.

UGARTECHEA SHOTGUNS: SIDE-BY-SIDE

Ugartechea shotguns are not being imported currently. The last Mfg.'s Sug. Retail on all models listed below reflects 1986-87 pricing, the last years they were imported. Any future importation could reflect pricing changes.

EXEL 200 SERIES—these side by sides are available in 12 and 20 ga. (3 in.) only. Model 201 is basic gun with 213 being the highest grade.

Model 201, 202, and 203—double triggers, extractors, straight grip, matted rib, various chokes and barrel lengths.

	$375	$325	$260	$240	$215	$180	$165

Last Mfg.'s Sug. Retail was $429.

Previously designated Model 30.

Model 281—same as 201 series, except 28 ga.

	$420	$325	$275	$250	$235	$210	$195

Last Mfg.'s Sug. Retail was $472.

Previously designated Model 30.

Model 240—same as 201 series, except .410 ga.

	$450	$355	$295	$270	$250	$235	$210

Last Mfg.'s Sug. Retail was $472.

Previously designated Model 30.

Models 204, 205, and 206—single trigger optional, ejectors, straight grip, silver finish, various chokes and barrel lengths. Importation discontinued in 1986.

	$550	$470	$415	$370	$340	$315	$280

Last Mfg.'s Sug. Retail was $627.

Models 207 and 207A—12 ga. only, sidelock, case hardened action. 207A is deluxe model with ejectors. Model 201 discontinued in 1986.

	$725	$650	$580	$515	$465	$400	$345

Last Mfg.'s Sug. Retail was $836.
    Deduct 33% without ejectors (Model 207).

Previously designated Milano EX.

Models 208 and 208A—same as 207/207A, only engraved coin finished receiver. 208A is deluxe model with ejectors. Model 208 discontinued in 1986.

	$775	$695	$625	$550	$485	$420	$360

Last Mfg.'s Sug. Retail was $925.
    Deduct 33% without ejectors (Model 208).

Previously designated Model 75 EX.

Models 209 and 210—better engraving and walnut than 207/207A. Model 210 is 20 ga. Importation discontinued in 1986.

	$580	$505	$450	$415	$375	$340	$310

Last Mfg.'s Sug. Retail was $672.

Grading	100%	98%	95%	90%	80%	70%	60%

Models 211, 212, and 213—top of the line model, best quality engraving and walnut. Special order only.

	$2,350	$2,000	$1,780	$1,475	$1,200	$1,000	$850

Last Mfg.'s Sug. Retail was $3,100.

Previously designated Model 110.

MODEL 251—.410-3 in. ga., folding design, 26 in. barrels only, DT's, extractors, walnut stock and forearm. New in 1987.

	$185	$165	$140	$120	$105	$ 95	$ 85

Last Mfg.'s Sug. Retail was $215.

LAURONA SHOTGUNS: OVER AND UNDER

Laurona shotguns are no longer being imported by Exel Arms of America, Inc. Currently, Laurona shotguns are being imported by Galaxy Imports located in Victoria, TX and these new models can be located in the Laurona section of this text. Model nomenclature has changed from the discounted Exel 300 Series below.

EXEL 300 SERIES—These over and unders are available in 12 and 20 ga. only. Model 301 is basic gun with 310 being the highest grade.

Models 301 and 302—12 ga., double selective trigger system, ejectors, pistol grip, vent rib, lightly engraved chrome finish receiver, various chokes and barrel lengths. Importation discontinued in 1986.

	$485	$415	$380	$340	$300	$275	$250

Last Mfg.'s Sug. Retail was $553.

Models 303 and 304—12 ga., similar to 301/302, except has better engraving on coin finish receiver, vent barrels. Importation disc. in 1987.

	$545	$470	$430	$385	$340	$315	$270

Last Mfg.'s Sug. Retail was $623.

Previously designated Model 82G Super.

Models 305(A) and 306(A)—12 and 20 ga., similar to 303/304, except has better engraving on coin finish receiver, screw-in choke tubes. Importation disc. in 1987.

	$625	$535	$470	$430	$390	$350	$315

Last Mfg.'s Sug. Retail was $711.

Previously designated Models 83MG and 85MS.

Models 307 and 308—12 ga., trap model, 29 in. barrels, extensive engraving, Monte Carlo stock. Importation disc. in 1987.

	$580	$500	$460	$420	$380	$340	$300

Last Mfg.'s Sug. Retail was $668.

Previously designated Model 82U Trap.

Models 309 and 310—super trap model, 29 in. vent barrels, more extensive engraving than Models 307/308. Importation disc. in 1987.

	$630	$545	$495	$460	$415	$385	$340

Last Mfg.'s Sug. Retail was $726.

Previously designated Model 82 S. Trap.

Model 82—double selective trigger system, ejectors, pistol grip, vent rib, various chokes and barrel lengths. Discontinued.

	$549	$410	$380	$340	$300	$275	$250

F

FAS

MANUFACTURED IN ITALY. PREVIOUSLY IMPORTED BY BEEMAN PRECISION ARMS, INC. LOCATED IN SANTA ROSA, CA AND OSBORNE'S LOCATED IN CHEBOYGAN, MI.

Grading	100%	98%	95%	90%	80%	70%	60%

PISTOLS: SEMI-AUTO

MODEL 601—.22 short only, semi-auto competition pistol, 5½ in. barrel, 5 shot mag., 41½ oz., wrap-around matchwood grips. Importation disc. in 1988.

	100%	98%	95%	90%	80%	70%	60%
	$995	$875	$695	$640	$565	$480	$420

Last Mfg.'s Sug. Retail was $1,200.

MODEL 602—.22 LR only, semi-auto competition pistol, 5.6 in. barrel, 5 shot mag., 40 oz., wrap-around match wood grips. Importation disc. in 1987.

	100%	98%	95%	90%	80%	70%	60%
	$975	$850	$725	$635	$555	$475	$415

Last Mfg.'s Sug. Retail was $936.

MODEL 603—.32 S&W wadcutter only, semi-auto competition pistol, 5.6 in. barrel, 5 shot mag., 40 oz., wrap-around adj. or non-adj. match wood grips. Importation disc. in 1987.

	100%	98%	95%	90%	80%	70%	60%
	$975	$850	$725	$640	$565	$480	$420

Last Mfg.'s Sug. Retail was $942.

FEG

THESE MODELS CAN BE FOUND UNDER THE INTERARMS SECTION IN THIS TEXT.

F.I.E.

FIREARMS IMPORT & EXPORT LOCATED IN HIALEAH, FL. CURRENT IMPORTERS FOR FRANCHI AND ARMINIUS.

ARMINIUS REVOLVERS: DOUBLE ACTION

All pistols under this heading are manufactured in W. Germany under the trademark Arminius. .22 cal. is 8 shot, 32 S&W is 7 shot, all others 6 shot.

MODEL 522TB—.22 LR, blue finish, 4 in. barrel, 8 shot.

	100%	98%	95%	90%	80%	70%	60%
Mfg.'s Sug. Retail	$155	$120	$95	$85	$75	$70	$65	$60

Add $25 for walnut grips.

722 SERIES—.22 LR, blue (standard) or chrome finish (disc. in 1985), 6 in. barrel, 8 shot.

	100%	98%	95%	90%	80%	70%	60%
Mfg.'s Sug. Retail	$155	$120	$100	$90	$80	$70	$65	$60

Add $25 for walnut grips.
Add $45 for .22 LR/.22 Mag. combo.
Add $15 for chrome finish.

STANDARD REVOLVER—.32 Mag. or .38 Spl., 2 or 4 in. barrel, blued finish, fixed sights, without ejector assembly. Mfg. in USA starting in 1989.

	100%	98%	95%	90%	80%	70%	60%
Mfg.'s Sug. Retail	$130	$100	$80	$70	$65	$60	$55	$50

MODEL 532TB—.32 S&W, blue (standard) or chrome finish (disc. in 1985), adj. sights, 4 in. barrel, 7 shot.

	100%	98%	95%	90%	80%	70%	60%
Mfg.'s Sug. Retail	$160	$130	$110	$95	$80	$75	$70	$65

Add $25 for walnut grips.
Add $15 for chrome finish.

Grading	100%	98%	95%	90%	80%	70%	60%

Model 732B—similar to Model 532TB, except has 6 in. barrel and fixed sights. Imported in 1988 only.

	$120	$100	$90	$80	$70	$65	$60

Last Mfg.'s Sug. Retail was $140.

MODEL N-38 (TITAN TIGER)—.38 Spl., blue (standard) or chrome finish, (disc. in 1985) 2 or 4 in. barrel, fixed sights. U.S. manufacture.

Mfg.'s Sug. Retail	$175	$130	$110	$95	$80	$75	$65	$60

Add $25 for walnut grips.
Add $15 for chrome finish.

MODEL 384TB—.38 Spl., blue (standard) or chrome finish (disc. in 1985), 6 shot, 4 in. barrel.

Mfg.'s Sug. Retail	$185	$145	$120	$105	$85	$80	$70	$65

Add $25 for walnut grips.
Add $13 for chrome finish.

MODEL 386TB—.38 Spl., blue (standard) or chrome finish (disc. in 1985), 6 shot, 6 in.barrel.

Mfg.'s Sug. Retail	$185	$145	$120	$105	$85	$80	$70	$65

Add $25 for walnut grips.
Add $13 for chrome finish.

MODELS 3573TB, 3574TB, and 3576TB—.357 Mag., blue (standard) or chrome finish (disc. in 1985), 6 shot, 3, 4, or 6 in. barrels.

Mfg.'s Sug. Retail	$240	$195	$165	$135	$120	$110	$100	$90

Add $25 for walnut grips.
Add $15 for chrome finish.

REVOLVERS: SNUB-NOSE

222 SERIES—.22 LR & .22 Mag. cal., blue (standard) or chrome finish, 2 in. snub-nose barrel. Discontinued in 1985.

	$135	$115	$90	$85	$75	$65	$60

Add $15 for walnut grips.
Add $45 for .22 LR/.22 Mag. combo.

Last Mfg.'s Sug. Retail was $120.

222B SERIES—.22 LR only starting 1989, similar to 222 Series, reintroduced in 1987.

Mfg.'s Sug. Retail	$185	$150	$120	$105	$85	$80	$70	$65

Add $45 for .22 LR/.22 Mag. combo (disc. in 1988).

232 SERIES—.32 S&W, blue (standard) or chrome finish, 2 in. barrel. Discontinued.

	$120	$90	$85	$75	$65	$60	$55

Add $15 for walnut grips.
Add $14 for adj. sights.
Add $28 for chrome finish.

232B SERIES—similar to 232 Series, 2 in. barrel. Reintroduced in 1987.

Mfg.'s Sug. Retail	$185	$150	$125	$110	$95	$85	$75	$70

Add $5 for adj. sights.

MODEL 382TB—.38 Spl., blue (standard) or chrome finish, 2 in. barrel. Discontinued in 1985.

	$125	$110	$100	$90	$80	$75	$65

Add $15 for walnut grips.
Add $16 for chrome finish.

Last Mfg.'s Sug. Retail was $145.

MODEL 3572—.357 Mag., blue (standard) or chrome finish, 2 in. barrel. Discontinued in 1984.

	$223	$170	$160	$135	$125	$115	$100

Add $15 for walnut grips.
Add $17 for chrome finish.

Grading	100%	98%	95%	90%	80%	70%	60%

REVOLVERS: SINGLE ACTION

Combo designations on below listed models indicate 2 cylinders (.22 LR/.22 Mag.).

COWBOY—.22 LR or .22 LR/Mag. combo, 3¼ or 6 in. barrel, blued finish, square butt grip, without ejector tube, fixed sights. Mfg. in the USA starting in 1989.

Mfg.'s Sug. Retail	$100	$75	$65	$50	$45	$40	$35	$30

Add $15 for combo.

GOLD RUSH—.22 LR or .22 LR/Mag. combo, 3¼, 4¾, or 6½ in. barrel, round (3¼ in. barrel only) or square butt grip, gold band on barrel and cylinder, ivory-tex grips. Mfg. in USA starting in 1989.

Mfg.'s Sug. Retail	$185	$155	$125	$110	$95	$85	$75	$70

Add $45 for combo.

TEXAS RANGER (TEX 22 SERIES)—.22 LR or .22 Mag. (combo only), 3¼ (new in 1986), 4¾, 6½ (new in 1989), 7, or 9 in. barrel, 6 shot, blue only. Made in USA.

Mfg.'s Sug. Retail	$105	$80	$70	$60	$50	$45	$40	$35

Add $20 for combo.

This model with a 3¼ in. barrel is called the Little Ranger.

BUFFALO SCOUT (E15 SERIES)—.22 LR or .22 Mag., blue (standard) or chrome finish, 4¾ in. barrel. Made in Brescia, Italy.

Mfg.'s Sug. Retail	$93	$70	$55	$45	$35	$35	$30	$30

Add $25 for walnut grips.
Add $20 for combo.
Add $22 for chrome or blue/gold finish.

The Yellow Rose Combo—all metal parts 24 Kt. gold plated, smooth walnut grips. New in 1986.

Mfg.'s Sug. Retail	$155	$130	$110	$95

Add $195 for scrimshawed ivory grips - cased (new in 1989).

LEGEND S.A.A. (PL-22 SERIES)—.22 LR or .22 Mag., blue only. Made in Brescia, Italy. Discontinued in 1984.

	$120	$90	$85	$75	$65	$60	$55

Add $3 for walnut grips.
Add $17 for combo.

HOMBRE MODEL—.357 Mag., .44 Mag., or .45 cal., color case hardened receiver, 5½ (discontinued in 1985), 6, or 7½ in. barrel, 45 oz., smooth walnut grips. Made in W. Germany.

Mfg.'s Sug. Retail	$260	$215	$180	$145	$130	$120	$110	$100

Add $25 for brass back strap and trigger guard (disc.).

24 Kt. Hombre—same general specifications as Hombre, except all metal surfaces are plated in 24Kt. gold.

Mfg.'s Sug. Retail	$340	$295	$210	$145

Add $65 for ivory grips (new in 1989).

TITAN PISTOLS: SEMI-AUTO

TITAN II (E32 SERIES)—.32 ACP (disc. in 1988), or .380 ACP, single action, blue (standard) or chrome finish. Made in USA.

Mfg.'s Sug. Retail	$220	$195	$160	$135	$120	$105	$95	$85

Add $25 for walnut grips.
Add $10 for chrome finish.

This series was redesigned in 1988 to be shorter and more compact. Older series Titans are worth approx. $50 less than values shown above.

SUPER TITAN II—.32 ACP (disc. in 1988), or .380 ACP, single action, 12 round mag. in .32 ACP, 11 for .380 cal., walnut grips, standard blue only. Made in USA.

Mfg.'s Sug. Retail	$260	$215	$185	$155	$135	$120	$105	$95

.22 TITAN II (E22)—.22 LR, single action, 10 shot mag., blue finish only. Walnut grips standard.

Mfg.'s Sug. Retail	$155	$125	$105	$90	$80	$70	$65	$60

Grading	100%	98%	95%	90%	80%	70%	60%

THE BEST (A27)—.25 ACP, single action, blue only, deluxe finish, walnut grips, steel frame, 6 shot mag. Manufactured in Spain by Astra. Importation disc. in 1988.

	$125	$105	$90	$80	$70	$65	$60

Last Mfg.'s Sug. Retail was $155.

.25 TITAN (E27 SERIES)—.25 ACP, single action, blue (standard) or Dyna-chrome finish.

Mfg.'s Sug. Retail	$70	$55	$50	$45	$40	$35	$30	$30

Add $5 for Dyna-chrome finish.

Add $30 for gold trim (new in 1986).

Add $62 for Misty Gold finish (1988 only).

Titan Tigress—similar to .25 Titan except is entirely gold plated and cased, ladies pistol. Importation began in 1989.

Mfg.'s Sug. Retail	$160	$130	$110	$95

TZ-75—9mm Para., double action, 4.72 in. barrel, steel frame and slide, 15 shot mag., patterned after the CZ-75 action, 35 oz. New in 1982.

Mfg.'s Sug. Retail	$440	$375	$325	$290	$270	$250	$235	$220

Add $20 for satin chrome finish (new in 1986).

Add $20 for black rubber grips.

TZ-75 SERIES 88—9mm Para. or .41 Action Express, improved TZ-75 action, 4.72 in. barrel, steel frame and slide, 11 (.41 AE) or 15 (9mm) round mag., fixed removable rear sight, derived from CZ-75 action, 35 oz. New in 1988.

Mfg.'s Sug. Retail	$460	$390	$335	$300	$280	$260	$240	$225

Add $40 for .41 Action Express cal.

Add $20 for satin chrome on 9mm, $50 on .41 AE.

Add $20 for black rubber grips.

This model is also available with a blue slide/chrome frame (I.P.S.C. configuration) at no extra charge.

The TZ-75 Series 88 was re-engineered in 1988 to include: frame mounted sear locking safety (cocked and locked), Colt style firing pin safety block, improved recessed slide serrations, muzzle barrel swell, bobbed hammer design, elongated combat style slide stop, new mag. release, and removable rear sight.

SPECTRE PISTOL—9mm Para., double action, assault configuration, adj. sights, 30 or 50 (opt.) shot mag. (unique 4 column configuration). New in 1989.

Mfg.'s Sug. Retail	$650	$550	$425	$375	$330	$295	$260	$230

Add $50 for mag. loading tool.

KG-99—9mm, assault pistol, 36 round mag. Mini-99 also available with 20 shot mag. and 3 in. barrel. Discontinued in 1984.

	$450	$340	$300	$250	$225	$210	$180

DERRINGERS

MODEL D38—.38 Spl., O/U, chrome finish only, no transfer bar. Discontinued in 1985.

	$70	$60	$55	$45	$40	$35	$30

Add $17 for walnut grips.

Last Mfg.'s Sug. Retail was $82.

MODEL D86—.38 Spl., single shot, 3 in. barrel, internal transfer bar safety, ammo storage compartment, blue or Dyna-chrome finish, 11 oz. New in 1986.

Mfg.'s Sug. Retail	$93	$80	$65	$55	$50	$45	$40	$35

Add $7 for Dyna-chrome finish.

Add $25 for deluxe model (walnut stocks).

This model is also available in both Dyna-Chrome and Misty Gold finishes — add $25 and $60 respectively.

Grading	100%	98%	95%	90%	80%	70%	60%

RIFLES: SEMI-AUTO

GR-8 BLACK BEAUTY—.22 cal. only, 14 shot, 19½ in. barrel, 64 oz., tubular feed, black nylon stock, patterned after Rem. Nylon 66. Made by C.B.C. of Brazil. Importation disc. in 1988.

		$90	$75	$70	$65	$60	$55	$50

Last Mfg.'s Sug. Retail was $100.

PARA RIFLE—.22 LR, assault styled military rifle with case, takedown, 11 shot, matte black receiver finish. Manufactured by L. Franchi between 1979-1984. Imported into the U.S. from 1985-present.

Mfg.'s Sug. Retail	$225	$195	$155	$140	$130	$120	$110	$100

8,000 of this model were manufactured by L. Franchi. 5,000 went to the Italian Government and were used as training rifles (with German scopes). The remainder has been imported by F.I.E. (without scopes).

SPECTRE CARBINE—9mm Para., assault configuration carbine, double action, collapsible metal butt stock, 30 or 50 (opt.) shot mag., adj. rear sight, with pistol and forearm grip. New in 1989.

Mfg.'s Sug. Retail	$700	$595	$450	$395	$340	$295	$260	$230

RIFLES: BOLT-ACTION

MODEL 122—.22 LR, 6 or 10 shot clip mag., 21 in. tapered barrel, Monte Carlo walnut stock, adj. sights. Manufactured by Hamilton & Hunter. New in 1986.

Mfg.'s Sug. Retail	$115	$100	$80	$70	$60	$55	$50	$45

SHOTGUNS

Except for the SPAS-12, all other Franchi shotguns can be located in the Franchi section of this text.

S.O.B.—12, 20, or .410 ga., 18½ in. single barrel, pistol grip only. Discontinued in 1984.

		$100	$90	$80	$70	$60	$55	$50

SINGLE SHOT—12, 20, or .410 ga., 25, 26, 28, and 30 in. barrel, button break action, ejector, 3 in. chamber. Made in Brazil. New in 1985.

Mfg.'s Sug. Retail	$100	$85	$70	$65	$55	$50	$45	$40

Add $5 for Dove & Quail or Junior Models (disc. in 1986).

Snake Charmer—12, 20, or .410 ga., 18 in. barrel with shortened buttstock, 28 in. overall length.

Mfg.'s Sug. Retail	$125	$100	$90	$75	$65	$55	$50	$45

THE STURDY O/U—12 or 20 ga., 3 in. chambers, 28 in. barrels, vent rib and barrels, engraved silver finish receiver, double triggers, extractors, manufactured by Maroccini of Italy. Imported 1985-1988.

		$300	$275	$250	$235	$220	$205	$190

Last Mfg.'s Sug. Retail was $350.

Sturdy Deluxe Priti—similar to The Sturdy model except has deluxe walnut. Importation disc. in 1988.

		$325	$290	$260	$240	$225	$205	$195

Add $70 for ejectors, SST, and choke tubes.

Last Mfg.'s Sug. Retail was $380.

Model 12 Deluxe—12 ga. only, SST, auto ejectors, multi-choked barrels, select walnut. Imported in 1988 only.

		$320	$290	$260	$240	$225	$205	$195

Last Mfg.'s Sug. Retail was $380.

THE BRUTE—12, 20, or .410 ga.'s, 19 in. barrels, 30 in. overall length. Side x side action, discontinued in 1984.

		$195	$150	$140	$120	$110	$100	$90

SPAS 12—12 ga. combat shotgun that offers pump or semi-auto operation, 9 shot capacity, alloy receiver, folding stock, 21½ in. barrel, 9.6 lbs.

Mfg.'s Sug. Retail	$600	$495	$440	$390	$330	$300	$270	$240

This model is manufactured by Franchi in Italy. Models SAS-12 and LAW-12 may be located in the Franchi section.

FABARM

MANUFACTURED IN BRESCIA, ITALY. CURRENTLY IMPORTED AND DISTRIBUTED BY ST. LAWRENCE SALES INC. (STARTING IN 1988) LOCATED IN LAKE ORION, MI. PREVIOUSLY IMPORTED UNTIL 1986 BY BEEMAN PRECISION ARMS LOCATED IN SANTA ROSA, CA.

SHOTGUNS: DISCONTINUED O/U

The Field Model and Skeet/Trap Combination Set listed below were previously imported by Beeman Precision Arms, Inc.

FIELD MODEL—12 ga. only, 29⅛ in. barrels, VR, single trigger ejectors, silver finished receiver, also available in Skeet and Trap models. Discontinued in 1985.

		$695	$595	$550	$500	$460	$420	$390

Last Mfg.'s Sug. Retail was $795.

SKEET/TRAP COMBINATION SET—12 ga. only, is supplied with both skeet and trap barrel assemblies, cased. Discontinued in 1986.

	$1,050	$900	$840	$780	$720	$670	$600

Last Mfg.'s Sug. Retail was $1,195.

SHOTGUNS: COMPETITION O/U

Models below have boxlock actions with coin finished receivers and light engraving. A high gloss wood finish is also available at $39 extra, and auto safety is an additional $30.

GAMMA SPORTING COMPETITON—12 ga. only, designed for sporting clays competition, SST, 29 in. VR, (10mm) and barrels supplied with 5 innerchokes, special recoil pad, ejectors, checkered walnut stock and forearm. Importation began in 1989.

Mfg.'s Sug. Retail	$1,010	$895	$795	$725	$650	$575	$495	$400

GAMMA SKEET—12 ga. only, 27½ in. VR, and barrels, SST, ejectors, supplied with 5 innerchokes, special recoil pad, checkered walnut stock and forearm. Importation began in 1989.

Mfg.'s Sug. Retail	$999	$895	$775	$700	$635	$550	$450	$375

GAMMA TRAP—12 ga. only, 29 in. VR, and barrels with special trap chokes, SST, ejectors, checkered Monte Carlo stock and forearm, 7½ lbs. Importation began in 1989.

Mfg.'s Sug. Retail	$960	$860	$720	$660	$600	$525	$425	$350

SHOTGUNS: SPORTING O/U

Models below have boxlock actions with coin finished receivers and light engraving.

GAMMA FIELD—12 or 20 ga., SST, ejectors, 26, 28, or 29 in. VR, and barrels (fixed chokes), checkered walnut stock and forearm, 6½ lbs. Importation began in 1989.

Mfg.'s Sug. Retail	$920	$840	$695	$625	$550	$475	$400	$325

Add $80 for 5 innerchokes with wrench (3 in. chambers in 12 ga.).
Add $55 for 20 ga. (3 in. chambers).

Gamma AL Superlight—12 ga. only, similar to Gamma Field except receiver is made from Ergal light alloy, 6 lbs. Importation began in 1989.

Mfg.'s Sug. Retail	$960	$875	$760	$695	$625	$550	$450	$375

Add $50 for 5 innerchokes with wrench.

This model is chambered for 2¾ in. shells only.

GAMMA PARADOX—12 ga. only, 25 in. VR and barrels with top barrel rifled and lower barrel supplied with 3 innerchokes, SST, ejectors, checkered walnut stock and forearm, 6 lbs. 6 oz. Importation began in 1989.

Mfg.'s Sug. Retail	$1,010	$895	$795	$725	$650	$575	$495	$400

Gamma Paradox AL Superlight—similar to Gamma Paradox except receiver is made from Ergal light alloy, 5 lbs. 7 oz. Importation began in 1989.

Mfg.'s Sug. Retail	$1,050	$925	$825	$750	$675	$595	$515	$420

FABARM, cont.

EURALFA—12 ga., 2¾ in. chambers, 26 or 28 in. VR barrels with fixed chokes, DT or SNT, extractors, blued receiver with photo engraving, 6½ lbs. Importation began in 1989.

Mfg.'s Sug. Retail	$560	$495	$460	$420	$390	$350	$310	$275

Euralfa AL Superlight—12 ga., similar to Euralfa except receiver is made from Ergal light alloy, 6 lbs. Importation began in 1989.

Mfg.'s Sug. Retail	$589	$515	$475	$430	$400	$360	$320	$285

Euralfa Magnum—12 ga., 3 in. chambers, 26, 28, or 29 in. VR (10mm wide) barrels with fixed chokes, rubber recoil pad. Importation began in 1989.

Mfg.'s Sug. Retail	$589	$515	$475	$430	$400	$360	$320	$285

EURALFA PARADOX—12 ga. only, similar to Euralfa except 25 in. VR barrels with top barrel rifled and lower barrel supplied with 3 innerchokes, 6 lbs. 6 oz. Importation began in 1989.

Mfg.'s Sug. Retail	$685	$590	$525	$475	$430	$400	$360	$320

Euralfa Paradox AL Superlight—similar to Euralfa Paradox except receiver is made from Ergal light alloy, 5 lbs. 7 oz. Importation began in 1989.

Mfg.'s Sug. Retail	$685	$590	$525	$475	$430	$400	$360	$320

SHOTGUNS: SEMI-AUTO

The models listed below are gas operated self compensating, have 4 shot mag.'s, aluminum receivers, twin action bars, blued receiver with photo etched game scene engraving, and checkered walnut stock and forearm. Add $38 for De Luxe engraving.

ELLEGI STANDARD—12 ga. only, 28 in. VR barrel with fixed choke, blued receiver, gold trigger, 6 lbs. 9 oz. Importation began in 1989.

Mfg.'s Sug. Retail	$690	$595	$495	$425	$375	$335	$300	$265

Ellegi Multichoke—similar to Ellegi Standard except 5 different choke tubes extend length of barrel up to 6 in., average weight is 6 lbs. 9 oz. Importation began in 1989.

Mfg.'s Sug. Retail	$690	$595	$495	$425	$375	$335	$300	$265

The standard barrel length on this model is 24½ in. (30½ in. with full extra-long choke tube).

Ellegi Innerchoke—12 ga. only, 3 in. chamber, 28 in. VR barrel with 5 innerchokes supplied, 7 lbs. Importation began in 1989.

Mfg.'s Sug. Retail	$715	$625	$525	$450	$395	$350	$320	$285

Ellegi Magnum—12 ga. only, 3 in. chamber, 30 in. VR barrel with fixed choke, recoil pad, 7¼ lbs. Importation began in 1989.

Mfg.'s Sug. Retail	$715	$625	$525	$450	$395	$350	$320	$285

Ellegi Super Goose—12 ga. only, 3 in. chamber, 35½ in. VR (12mm wide) barrel with fixed choke, adj. rifle rear sight, supplied with rail for mounting scope rings, rubber recoil pad, designed especially for long range shooting, 7½ lbs. Importation began in 1989.

Mfg.'s Sug. Retail	$790	$695	$595	$525	$465	$415	$365	$315

Ellegi Slug—12 ga. only, 24½ in. barrel, adj. rear sight and bead front, 6 lbs. 9 oz. Importation began in 1989.

Mfg.'s Sug. Retail	$775	$665	$550	$475	$415	$365	$325	$290

Ellegi Police—12 ga. only, 20 in. cylinder bored barrel, matte black receiver, non-glare stock and forearm. Importation began in 1989.

Mfg.'s Sug. Retail	$570	$495	$440	$385	$345	$295	$260	$225

SHOTGUNS: SIDE X SIDE

The models listed below have boxlock actions with added sideplates.

BETA MODEL—12 ga. only, 2¾ in. chambers, standard model with checkered walnut stock and forearm, ST, ejectors. Importation began in 1989.

Mfg.'s Sug. Retail	$920	$800	$695	$625	$550	$450	$375	$300

BETA EUROPE—12 ga. only, deluxe model with coin finished game scene engraved sideplates, 26½ or 27½ in. barrels with fixed chokes, ejectors, DT or SST, checkered English stock and splinter forearm, 6 lbs. 6 oz. Importation began in 1989.

Mfg.'s Sug. Retail	$1,750	$1,525	$1,275	$1,000	$850	$700	$575	$495

Add $55 for semi-beavertail forend.
Add $39 for high gloss finish.

Grading	100%	98%	95%	90%	80%	70%	60%

SHOTGUNS: SLIDE ACTION

The models listed below are variations of the same action based on a twin bar slide system, alloy receiver with anti-glare finish (including barrel), rear trigger guard safety, and 2¾ or 3 in. shell interchangeability.

MODEL S.D.A.S.S.—12 ga. only, 3 in. chamber, originally designed for police and self defense use, 8 shot tube mag., 20 or 24½ in. barrel threaded for external choke tubes, approx. 6 lbs. 6 oz. Importation began in 1989.

Mfg.'s Sug. Retail	$480	$420	$325	$285	$260	$230	$195	$160

This model with 24½ in. barrel is threaded for external multi-chokes which can add up to 6 in. to the barrel length - available at no extra charge.

Special Police—similar to Model S.D.A.S.S. except has special heavy 20 in. cylinder bored barrel VR, cooling jacket, 6 shot mag., rubber recoil pad. Importation began in 1989.

Mfg.'s Sug. Retail	$520	$450	$330	$290	$260	$230	$195	$160

Martial—12 ga. only, 18, 20, 28, 30, or 35½ in. barrel, fixed sights and choke, approx. 6¼ lbs. Importation began in 1989.

Mfg.'s Sug. Retail	$480	$420	$325	$285	$260	$230	$195	$160

Add $20 for 35½ in. barrel.

Add $20 for innerchoke (includes 1 choke and wrench).

SHOTGUNS: SINGLE BARREL

The models listed below have receivers made out of aluminum alloy, rear trigger guard safety, and matte black finish metal surfaces.

OMEGA STANDARD—12, 20, or .410 ga., 3 in. chamber, 26 or 28 (12 ga. only) in. barrel, checkered beech stock and forearm, approx. 5 lbs. 5 oz. Importation began in 1989.

Mfg.'s Sug. Retail	$140	$120	$95	$80	$70	$60	$55	$50

Add $5 for .410 ga.

Goose Gun—similar to Omega Standard except is 12 ga. only with a 35½ in. barrel, 6 lbs. Importation began in 1989.

Mfg.'s Sug. Retail	$159	$135	$115	$90	$80	$70	$60	$55

FABBRI, ARMI

MANUFACTURER LOCATED IN GORDONE V.T., ITALY. CAN BE ORDERED FROM NEW ENGLAND ARMS CO. LOCATED IN KITTERY POINT, ME.

SIDE BY SIDE SHOTGUN—12 or 20 ga., one of the world's best current production guns, highest-quality sidelock, ejectors, full engraving.

Mfg.'s Sug. Retail	$22,500	$17,250	$14,000	$11,000	$8,500	$7,500	$6,500	$5,500

O/U SHOTGUN—12 or 20 ga., top-of-the-line quality with almost any special order available.

Mfg.'s Sug. Retail	$27,500	$24,500	$20,000	$16,500	$14,000	$12,500	$10,000	$7,500

FABRIQUE NATIONALE

MANUFACTURER LOCATED IN HERSTAL AND LIEGE, BELGIUM. ESTABLISHED A CONTRACT WITH JOHN M. BROWNING IN 1902 FOR EXCLUSIVE MANUFACTURE OF VARIOUS BROWNING PATENT FIREARMS.

Also See: Browning Arms under Rifles, Shotguns, and several Pistols.

There will be some overlapping of models found in this section and under Browning Arms.

Grading	100%	98%	95%	90%	80%	70%	60%

PISTOLS: SEMI-AUTO

MODEL 1900—7.65mm cal., first Belgium Browning, 4 in. barrel. Made 1899-1910. 724,500 manufactured.

	100%	98%	95%	90%	80%	70%	60%
	$325	$300	$275	$250	$225	$195	$150

Add 30% for early pistols with "pistol logo" grips.

MODEL 1903—9mm Browning Long cartridge, 5 in. barrel. Manufactured by Fabrique Nationale, Herstal-Belgium. Made 1903-1939. 58,400 produced.

	100%	98%	95%	90%	80%	70%	60%
	$450	$400	$350	$300	$260	$220	$180

This variation was also manufactured with a detachable shoulder stock — this accessory is rare and can add as much as 400% to values listed above.

MODEL 1903-SWEDISH CONTRACT—9mm cal., manufactured by Husqvarna and Swedish Arsenal (so marked), many were imported into U.S. and converted to .380 ACP from original Browning 9mm Long.

	100%	98%	95%	90%	80%	70%	60%
	$300	$260	$230	$200	$180	$150	$125

Subtract 25% for .380 ACP conversion.

MODEL 1905 (VEST POCKET)—6.35 mm (.25 ACP), dubbed "Vest Pocket" model, manufactured by Fabrique Nationale, Herstal-Belgium. Made 1906-1959. 1,086,133 produced.

First Variation—no slide lock/safety lever.

	100%	98%	95%	90%	80%	70%	60%
	$375	$325	$300	$280	$225	$195	$150

Add 10% for nickel finish.

Second Variation—post-1908, with slide lock/safety lever.

	100%	98%	95%	90%	80%	70%	60%
	$325	$300	$275	$250	$225	$195	$150

Add 10% for nickel finish.

MODEL 1910—7.65mm (.32 ACP) and Browning 9mm short (.380 ACP) 4 in. barrel. FN manufacture. Made 1912-1980. 701,266. This model was sold 1954-68 with BAC trademark — commonly designated the Model 1955.

	100%	98%	95%	90%	80%	70%	60%
	$325	$300	$275	$250	$225	$195	$150

Add 20% if BAC marked and .380 ACP.
Add 30% if BAC marked and 7.65mm.

BAC marked pistols were imported 1954-1968.

MODEL 1922 OR 10/22—7.65mm or .380 ACP cal.'s, modified Model 1910 with 4½ in. barrel, longer grip frame and mag., made for commercial sale as well as military contracts. Several hundred thousand made by Nazis during the occupation of Liege, Belgium 1940-1944. Manufactured between 1912-1959.

	100%	98%	95%	90%	80%	70%	60%
	$240	$215	$195	$175	$150	$125	$110

Add 10% for .380 ACP.
Add 10% for Waffenamt proofing.
Add 20% for foreign contracts.

The Model 10/22 and M1922 are the same pistol, Model 1910 modified by FN technicians for sale to Serbian Armed Forces in 1923. Also sold to France, Holland, Yugoslavia, and other countries. Also made by the German military 1940-1944.

"BABY" MODEL—6.35mm (.25 ACP) cal., lighter, smaller modification of Browning Model 1905 Vest Pocket .25, has no grip safety or slide lock, imported under BAC trademark from 1954-1970 in standard blue finish, lightweight nickel and engraved Renaissance models, manufactured 1931-1983. Total production is over 510,000.

FN Marked—slide marked Fabrique Nationale, blued finish standard.

	100%	98%	95%	90%	80%	70%	60%
	$395	$350	$310	$280	$245	$225	$200

BAC Slide Marked—slide marked Fabrique Nationale, blued finish standard.

	100%	98%	95%	90%	80%	70%	60%
	$300	$265	$225	$195	$180	$165	$150

Lightweight model—nickel frame, with pearl grips.

	100%	98%	95%	90%	80%	70%	60%
	$395	$350	$310	$280	$245	$225	$200

Renaissance model—engraved, satin grey finish.

	100%	98%	95%
	$875	$760	$600

Grading	100%	98%	95%	90%	80%	70%	60%

FN/BROWNING MODEL 10/71—4½ in. barrel, modified version of Model 1922 (10/22) in .380 ACP cal. with target sights and grips in addition to incorporating a magazine finger tip extension designed to comply with GCA of 1968. Sold in U.S. by BAC 1970-1974 as the "Standard .380", still manufactured by FN as Model 125.

	100%	98%	95%	90%	80%	70%	60%
	$375	$295	$250	$220	$205	$190	$160
Renaissance or Gold Line model	$995	$850	$775				

PISTOLS: HI-POWERS

The F.N. Hi-Power (also known as P-35) was Browning's last pistol design. A single-action semi-auto 9mm pistol, it was the first to incorporate a staggered high capacity magazine. It has a 4⅝ in. barrel, 13 round mag., hammer and mag. safeties, a wide variety of finishes and sight options. It's probably the most widely used military pistol in the world.

PRE-WAR COMMERCIAL HP—semi-auto pistol, 9mm, blue, wood grips, fixed or tangent rear sight, 13 shot mag., slotted for stock.

	100%	98%	95%	90%	80%	70%	60%
Fixed sight	$650	$575	$500	$450	$400	$350	$300
Tangent sight	$1,000	$850	$750	$600	$500	$400	$375

Add $300 for wooden holster stock.

PRE-WAR MILITARY CONTRACT—manufactured under military contract for various European countries.

	100%	98%	95%	90%	80%	70%	60%
Lithuanian Crest	$1,300	$1,175	$950	$750	$600	$450	$375
Latvian Contract	$1,550	$1,325	$1,150	$950	$800	$550	$400
Estonian Contract	$1,200	$1,000	$850	$700	$600	$500	$400

Since so many variations have been manufactured for military contract, the listing above represents a few of the more interesting (and collectable) models.

WWII Production: Waffenampt Proofed

There is a range of finishes during Nazi production that varies from the excellent pre-war commercial finish on early guns assembled from captured parts to the roughly milled, poorly finished specimens mfg. late in the war. Values below assume all major parts (slide, barrel, and frame) are matching.

In recent years, many Nazi production Hi-Powers have had the rear grip strap milled out and slotted to accept a shoulder stock. Careful observation is advised before purchasing a "rare" (and expensive) slotted and tangent sight specimen.

PRE-WAR COMMERCIAL—Nazi captured and so proofed, no milling marks with smooth metal polishing, slotted and tangent rear sight.

Type I: Tangent sights — slotted—assembled from existing pre-war Belgian army parts, quality is excellent, correct ser. range is quite limited, approx. from 48,000-52,000. All are proofed WaA 613.

	100%	98%	95%	90%	80%	70%	60%
	$1,500	$1,200	$1,000	$800	$700	$600	$500

Type II—tangent rear sight only, approx. 50,000 mfg. with generally good quality finish.

	100%	98%	95%	90%	80%	70%	60%
	$850	$750	$620	$475	$450	$400	$325

Type III Standard Fixed Sights

	100%	98%	95%	90%	80%	70%	60%
	$490	$445	$410	$350	$310	$275	$240

POST-WAR COMMERCIAL CONTRACT—not manufactured until 1950, first imported with BAC markings in 1954 (see Browning HP section).

Tangent sight only

	100%	98%	95%	90%	80%	70%	60%
	$725	$670	$645	$590	$535	$425	$350

Tangent sight—slotted for stock.

	100%	98%	95%	90%	80%	70%	60%
	$1,200	$950	$835	$780	$725	$500	$450

Fixed sight—ring hammer.

	100%	98%	95%	90%	80%	70%	60%
	$450	$400	$375	$350	$325	$300	$275

Add $50 for pre-1970 models with round hammer.

Grading	100%	98%	95%	90%	80%	70%	60%

POST-WAR MILITARY CONTRACT—manufactured from 1946-present, early models are identifiable by an "A" serial number prefix and are not fitted with a magazine safety. In 1947 the rear slide bushing became hardened by a new heat treatment process. Other design modifications were added in 1950 making post 1950 barrels not interchangeable with earlier frames. Many thousands manufactured under various government contracts.

Tangent sight and slotted

	$1,200	$950	$890	$725	$650	$600	$525

Tangent sight only

	$780	$725	$670	$550	$525	$500	$475

Fixed sight

	$525	$450	$425	$325	$300	$275	$250

MUSCAT AND OMAN CONTRACT

First Model—9 guns.

	$4,500	$2,750	$1,495

Second Model—27 guns.

	$3,000	$1,700	$995

INGLIS MANUFACTURED HI-POWERS—SEE INGLIS SECTION.

RIFLES

MODEL 1949—semi-auto, 7mm, 7.65mm, 7.92mm, or .30-06 cal., gas operated 10 round mag., 23 in. barrel, military rifle, tangent rear sight, military stock, 160,000 produced.

	$375	$325	$275	$250	$225	$185	$155

Add 10% for .30-06 cal.

Add 100% for sniper variation.

FN SNIPER RIFLE (BOLT ACTION)—.308 cal., this model was a Mauser actioned Sniper Rifle equipped with 20 in. extra heavy barrel, flash hider, diopter sights, Hensoldt 4X scope, hard case, bipod, and sling. Approximately 50 were imported into the U.S. with the last retail price (1988) being $2,950. When encountered today, values will range from $3,500 and higher (depending on condition).

RIFLES: FAL/LAR/FNC SERIES

After tremendous price increases between 1985-1988, Fabrique Nationale decided in 1988 to discontinue this series completely. Not only are these rifles not exported to the U.S. any longer, but all production has ceased in Belgium as well. The only way FN will produce these models again is if they are given a large military contract - in which case a "side-order" of commercial guns may be built. Currently, there is a rather wide range of prices on these models since some dealers have a few remaining models purchased at 1985 prices (i.e. inexpensive) which they can sell for less while other collectors/dealers are using FN's last suggested retail price as a reason to ask considerably more for these models than a short time before. Considering current (and pending) federal and state legislation regarding assualt rifles, these models may even be more prone to rapid price fluctuations than they have been recently.

F.N. FAL—semi-auto, French designation for the FN L.A.R. (light automatic rifle), otherwise same as LAR. See values for LAR model listed below.

F.N. L.A.R. COMPETITION (LIGHT AUTOMATIC RIFLE)—.308 Win. (7.62 x 51), semi-auto, competition rifle with match flash hider, 21 in. barrel, adj. 4 position fire selector on automatic models, wood stock, aperture rear sight adj. from 100-600 meters, 9.4 lbs., mfg. 1950-1988.

	$1,150	$995	$800	$700	$640	$575	$500

This model was designated by the factory as the 50.00 Model.

Mid-1987 retail on this model was $1,258. The last Mfg.'s Sug. Retail was $3,179 (this price reflected the last exchange rate and special order status of this model).

Grading	100%	98%	95%	90%	80%	70%	60%

Heavy barrel rifle—barrel is twice as heavy as standard LAR, includes wood or synthetic stock, short wood forearm, and bi-pod, 12.2 lbs. Importation disc. in 1988.

	$1,400	$1,175	$975	$800	$700	$640	$575

Add $400 for walnut stock.

There were 2 variations of this model. The Model 50.41 had a synthetic buttstock while the Model 50.42 had a wood buttstock with steel buttplate incorporating a top extension used for either shoulder resting or inverted grenade launching.

Mid-1987 retail on this model was $1,497 (Model 50.41) or $1,654 (Model 50.42). The last Mfg.'s Sug. Retail was $3,776 (this price reflected the last exchange rate and special order status of this model).

Paratrooper rifle—similar to LAR model, except has folding stock, 8.3 lbs., made 1950-1988.

	$950	$825	$700	$640	$575	$500	$460

There were 2 variations of the Paratrooper LAR Model. The Model 50.63 had a stationary aperture rear sight and 18 in. barrel. The Model 50.64 was supplied with a 21 in. barrel and had a rear sight calibrated for either 150 or 200 meters. Both models retailed for the same price.

Mid-1987 retail on this model was $1,310 (both the Model 50.63 and 50.64). The last Mfg.'s Sug. Retail was $3,239 (this price reflected the last exchange rate and special order status of this model).

FNC MODEL— .223 Rem. (5.56mm), lightweight combat carbine, 18½ in. barrel, NATO approved, 30 round mag., 8.4 lbs. Disc. in 1987.

	$595	$550	$500	$460	$435	$400	$375

Add $50 for Paratrooper model (16 or 18½ in. barrel).

While rarer, the 16 in. barrel model incorporated a flash hider that did not perform as well as the flash hider used on the standard 18½ in. barrel.

Mid-1987 retail on this model was $749 (Standard Model) and $782 (Paratrooper Model). The last Mfg.'s Sug. Retail was $2,204 (Standard Model) and $2,322 (Paratrooper Model) - these prices reflected the last exchange rate and special order status of these models.

F.N. MAUSER SPORTER DELUXE—available in popular American and European calibers, 24 in. barrel, adj. sight, checkered pistol grip stock, made 1947-1963.

	$550	$495	$460	$300	$275	$250	$225

F.N. PRESENTATION GRADE—same as Deluxe, except engraved and select wood.

	$935	$855	$770	$500	$475	$450	$400

F.N. SUPREME BOLT ACTION—.243, .270, 7mm, .308, and .30-06, 24 in. barrel, peep sight, checkered pistol grip stock, made 1957-1975.

	$550	$495	$460	$300	$275	$250	$225

F.N. SUPREME MAGNUM—same as Bolt Action, .264 Mag., 7mm Mag., and .300 Win. Mag.

	$595	$540	$495	$325	$275	$250	$225

FALCON FIREARMS

MANUFACTURED IN NORTHRIDGE, CA. DISTRIBUTED BY FALCON FIREARMS LOCATED IN NORTHRIDGE, CA. NEW IN 1986.

PORTSIDER—.45 ACP, patterned after Colt M 1911 A-1, stainless steel, fixed sights, 5 in. barrel, 7 shot mag. Available in left only. New in 1986.

Mfg.'s Sug. Retail	$580	$500	$425	$375

Portsider Set—features right and left hand models with matching serial numbers, only 100 sets manufactured in 1986-87.

Mfg.'s Sug. Retail	$1,400	$1,400	$1,150	$925

GOLD FALCON—.45 ACP, machined receiver made from solid 17 Kt gold alloy, stainless steel slide, diamond sighting system, choice of grips, standard or personalized engraving options, total manufacture - 50.

Mfg.'s Sug. Retail	$30,500	$30,500	$22,500	$16,400

FEATHER INDUSTRIES, INC.

MANUFACTURED AND DISTRIBUTED BY FEATHER INDUSTRIES LOCATED IN
BOULDER, CO.

DERRINGERS

GUARDIAN ANGEL—9mm Para., O/U design, stainless steel, double action backup
derringer. New in 1988.

| *Mfg.'s Sug. Retail* | $140 | $130 | $95 | $75 |

This model has interchangeable loading blocks that allow shooting 9mm Para. or .38 Spl.
There is no exposed hammer and trigger is totally enclosed.

PISTOLS

MINI-AT—.22 LR, pistol variation of the AT-22, 5½ in. shrouded barrel, 20 shot mag., about
2 lbs. Mfg. 1986-1989.

| | $195 | $165 | $145 | $135 | $130 | $125 | $115 |

Last Mfg.'s Sug. Retail was $220.

RIFLES

AT-22—.22 LR, semi-auto blowback action, 17 in. detachable shrouded barrel, collapsible metal
stock, adj. rear sight, with sling and swivels, 20 shot mag., 3¼ lbs. New in 1986.

| *Mfg.'s Sug. Retail* | $240 | $220 | $175 | $155 | $145 | $135 | $125 | $115 |

AT-9—9mm Para., semi-auto blowback action, 16 in. barrel, paramilitary design, available with
either 32 or 100 (optional) mag., 5 lbs. New in 1988

| *Mfg.'s Sug. Retail* | $500 | $425 | $360 | $310 | $280 | $260 | $240 | $200 |

Add $80 for 100 round drum mag.

KG-9—9mm Para., semi-auto blowback action, 25 or 50 shot mag., assualt configuration. New
in 1989.

| *Mfg.'s Sug. Retail* | $560 | $450 | $385 | $330 | $295 | $260 | $240 | $200 |

SAR-180—.22 LR, semi-auto blowback action, 17½ in. barrel, 165 shot drum mag., fully adj.
rear sight, walnut stock with combat style pistol grip and forend, 6¼ lbs. New in 1989.

| *Mfg.'s Sug. Retail* | $500 | $425 | $360 | $310 | $280 | $260 | $240 | $200 |

Add $105 for retractable stock.
Add $395 for lazer sight.

KG-22—.22 LR, similar to KG-9 except is .22 LR and has 20 shot mag. New in 1989.

| *Mfg.'s Sug. Retail* | $300 | $260 | $220 | $175 | $155 | $145 | $135 | $125 |

FEDERAL ENGINEERING CORPORATION

CHICAGO, IL.

XC-220—.22 LR semi-auto assault-type rifle, 16⁵⁄₁₆ in.barrel length, 7½ lbs., 28 round mag.,
machined steel action. New in 1984.

| | $348 | $278 | $250 | $230 | $210 | $200 | $175 |

XC-450—.45 ACP only, semi-auto assault carbine, 16½ in. barrel length, 8½ lbs., 30 round
mag., fires from closed bolt, machined steel action. New in 1984.

| | $587 | $470 | $440 | $400 | $360 | $320 | $285 |

XC-900—9mm only, semi-auto assault carbine, 16½ in. barrel length, 8 lbs., 32 round mag.,
fires from closed bolt, machine steel action. New in 1984.

| | $534 | $430 | $390 | $340 | $300 | $280 | $260 |

FEDERAL ORDNANCE INC.

MANUFACTURER/IMPORTER/DISTRIBUTOR LOCATED IN SOUTH EL MONTE, CA.

Federal Ordnance has been importing or distributing both foreign and domestic military handguns and rifles since 1966. In addition, they also fabricate firearms using mostly original older parts. Listed below are those models which have been recently manufactured or remanufactured.

In addition to the models listed below, Fed. Ord. also distributes used M-1 Carbines, AK-47's, SKS's, Finnish 39's, Lee Enfields, Baby Carbines, P-14's, M-1 Garands, Hakims, Mauser 98's, and other rifles. Most of these are in good to excellent overall condition and prices typically are in the $165-$400 range (except the M-1 Garand), depending on the model and quality.

CARBINES

MODEL 713 DELUXE MAUSER CARBINE—7.63 Mauser cal., 16 in. barrel, detachable stock, 2-20 shot detachable mag.'s, deluxe walnut, leather case with accessories, adj. sights to 1,000 meters, 5 lbs., 1,500 mfg. in 1986.

Mfg.'s Sug. Retail **$1,986 $1,775 $1,450 $1,050**

Field Grade Mauser Carbine—7.63 Mauser or 9mm Para. (new in 1989) cal., 16 in. barrel, 10 shot fixed mag., non detachable walnut stock. New in 1987.

Mfg.'s Sug. Retail **$1,200 $995 $795 $695 $595 $500 $450 $400**

PISTOLS

In addition to the Broomhandle models listed below, Federal Ordnance also manufactures other special editions. These models include the British Model, Cut-Away, Cartridge Counter, Para La Guerra, and others. Prices are in the $800-$950 price range (retail).

MODEL 714 BROOMHANDLE—7.63 Mauser or 9mm Para. cal., 5½ in. barrel, new frame, exterior completely refinished, 10 shot detachable mag., "fair" bore, adj. rear sight. New in 1986.

Mfg.'s Sug. Retail **$820 $750 $595 $500 $440 $400 $375 $350**
Add $100 for new barrel.
Subtract $20 for 7.63 Mauser cal.

Model 714 Bolo—similar to Model 714 Broomhandle, except has smaller grips, 3.9 in. barrel, 10 shot mag. standard. Mfg.in 1988 only.

$775 $600 $500 $440 $400 $375 $350

Last Mfg.'s Sug. Retail was $890.

STANDARD BROOMHANDLE—7.63 Mauser or 9mm Para. cal., refurbished (new barrels, completely refinished, etc.) C-96 pistols, replaced springs, includes original Chinese shoulder/holster stock.

Mfg.'s Sug. Retail **$735 $625 $500 $460 $430 $400 $375 $350**

RANGER 1911A1—.45 ACP, 5 in. barrel, 7 round mag., steel construction throughout, checkered walnut grips, 38 oz. New in 1988.

Mfg.'s Sug. Retail **$440 $385 $350 $310 $280 $260 $240 $200**
Add $10 for extended model.
Add $20 for ambidextrous safety.

This pistol is new manufacture and is patterned after the Colt Model 1911A1.

RIFLES

M-14 S.A.—.308 cal., legal for private ownership (no selector), 20 shot mag., refinished original M-14 parts, available in either wood (filled) or camouflaged stock. New in 1986.

Mfg.'s Sug. Retail **$625 $575 $520 $485 $430 $385 $335 $285**

CHINESE RPK 86S-7—7.62 X 39mm cal., semi-auto version of the P.R.C.-RPK light machine gun, 75 shot drum mag., 23¾ in. barrel, with bipod. Importation began in 1989.

Mfg.'s Sug. Retail **$500 $465 $420 $385 $350 $325 $300 $280**

FEINWERKBAU

MANUFACTURED IN OBERNDORF, WEST GERMANY. CURRENTLY IMPORTED BY
BEEMAN PRECISION ARMS IN SANTA ROSA, CA.

Feinwerkbau manufactures some of the world's finest quality target rifles and pistols (.22
LR rimfire and airgun).

Prices below reflect the recent devaluation of the U.S. dollar against some foreign currencies.
While the manufacturer's suggested retails have gone up considerably, prices for used
specimens (98% or less original condition) have not increased proportionately, and in some
cases, have changed very little.

MODEL 2000—.22 LR only, single shot, match target bolt action rifle, fully adj. trigger,
walnut stocks, four variations featuring different specifications. Importation disc. on these
models in 1988.

Universal Model—26⅜ in. barrel, aperture sights, stippled pistol grip and forearm, 9¾
lbs.

	100%	98%	95%	90%	80%	70%	60%
	$1,150	$925	$850	$735	$650	$595	$550

Add $445 for electronic trigger.
Add $160 for left-hand variation.

Last Mfg.'s Sug. Retail was $1,395.

Mini 2000 (Junior)—22 in. barrel, aperture sights, stippled pistol grip, 9⅛ lbs.

	100%	98%	95%	90%	80%	70%	60%
	$1,025	$875	$825	$700	$625	$575	$525

Add $450 for electronic trigger.
Add $150 for left-hand variation.

Last Mfg.'s Sug. Retail was $1,225.

Match Model—26¼ in. barrel, adj. cheekpiece on stock, stippled pistol grip and
forearm, aperture sights.

	100%	98%	95%	90%	80%	70%	60%
	$1,075	$895	$825	$700	$625	$575	$525

Add $390 for electronic trigger.
Add $113 for left-hand variation.

Last Mfg.'s Sug. Retail was $1,285.

Running Target—adj. cheekpiece on stock, thumb hole stippled pistol grip, no sights,
for running bore competition.

	100%	98%	95%	90%	80%	70%	60%
	$1,150	$925	$850	$735	$650	$595	$550

Add $142 for left-hand variation.

Last Mfg.'s Sug. Retail was $1,398.

MODEL 2600—.22 LR only, similar design to Model 600 air rifle, single shot, 26.3 in. barrel,
aperture sights, 10.6 lbs. New in 1986.

	100%	98%	95%	90%	80%	70%	60%
Mfg.'s Sug. Retail	$1,375	$1,125	$925	$850	$735	$650	$595	$550

Add $175 for left-hand variation.

MODEL 2600 ULTRA MATCH FREE RIFLE—.22 LR, single shot match gun based
on Model 2600 action, laminate stock with thumb hole, fully adj. aperture sights, 14 lbs. 1
oz. New in 1986.

	100%	98%	95%	90%	80%	70%	60%
Mfg.'s Sug. Retail	$1,995	$1,775	$1,400	$1,150	$925	$850	$735	$650

Add $380 for electronic trigger (disc. in 1988).
Add $100 for left-hand variation.

FERLACH GUNS

INCLUDES THOSE FIREARMS MANUFACTURED IN FERLACH, AUSTRIA FROM THE
MID-1600'S TO PRESENT.

Grading	100%	98%	95%	90%	80%	70%	60%

Many people are confused that Ferlach is a trademark - it is not. Rather, it is a small village in Austria where a gun guild was started as early as 1558. At that time, it was absolutely neccesary that all the people involved in fabricating a firearm were located together in close proximity. This enabled the barrel maker, the stock maker, and the lock mechanism maker to work together closely to ensure that everyone was performing their task(s) correctly, effectively and efficiently. As the individual skills became better and more refined, more and more firearms were manufactured. Eventually, individual gunsmiths began to put their name on the barrel or frame of those guns which they had either manufactured solely or with the help of their fellow Ferlach craftsman. Since all Ferlach firearms are essentially hand made per individual special order, very few are exactly alike. In the past the gunsmiths of Ferlach have produced almost every type of shoulder arm imaginable including such modern weapons as superposed and juxtaposed rifles and shotguns, hammerless drillings, repeating rifles, 3 barrel rifles, combination guns, 4 barrel rifles/shotguns/combination guns (called Vierlings), hammer guns of every type, etc. Some of these specimens represent the highest refinement in the gunmakers trade. Because of the almost unlimited variety of Ferlach variations, it is recommended that a COMPETENT appraisal is procurred before buying or selling a specimen.

As is the case with many other European weapons, those models with desirable American features will outperform those with European specifications (i.e. a Ferlach sidelock combination gun that is 20 ga. X .243 Win. will be more valuable than a similar specimen chambered for 16 ga. X 5.6 by 50R mm with sling swivels). Things to consider when contemplating buying or selling a Ferlach long arm are: type of action, difficulty of fabrication (Vierlings are very complicated to construct), caliber/gauge desirability, notoriety of gunsmith on barrel legand, elaborateness of embellishments, condition, rarity, accessories, and any provenance a specimen might have.

Today's master gunsmiths of Ferlach carry on the old world tradition of quality in every respect. Most guns manufactured today are by individual special order with a wide range of calibers/gauges and other special features and options. As of this writing, these gunsmiths in alphabetical order are: LUDWIG BOROVNIK, JOHANN FANZOJ, WILFRIED GLANZNIG, JOSEF HAMBRUSCH, KARL HAUPTMANN, GOTTFRIED JUCH, JOSEF JUST, JAKOB KOSCHAT, JOHANN MICHELITSCH, WALTER OUTSCHAR, HERBERT SCHEIRING, BENEDIKT WINKLER, AND JOSEF WINKLER. Anyone wishing to contact these master gunmakers should either write to the guild or address them individually at: Ferlach, Waagplatz,6, A-9170 Ferlach, AUSTRIA. Please allow at least 4-6 weeks for a response.

FEMARU

FEMARU-FEBYVER-ES GEPGYAR R.T., BUDAPEST, HUNGARY.

MODEL 1910—7.65mm Roth/Steyr cal., rare and only infrequently encountered.

Rarity factor excludes accurate pricing evaluation — one specimen sold for over $400 in 70% condition.

FROMMER STOP POCKET AUTO—.32 ACP, .380 ACP, 6 or 7 shot, 3⅞ in. barrel, fixed sights, blue, rubber grips, locked breech, outside hammer, made 1912-1920.

	$150	$135	$125	$110	$90	$75	$50

FROMMER BABY POCKET AUTO—similar to Stop Pocket Auto, but 2 in. barrel, 5 or 6 shot.

	$175	$165	$150	$135	$100	$85	$65

FROMMER LILIPUT AUTO—blowback action, .25 auto, 6 shot, 2.14 in. barrel, blue, hard rubber grips, made in early twenties.

	$225	$200	$175	$145	$115	$90	$75

FERLIB

MANUFACTURED IN GORDONE V.T., ITALY. DISTRIBUTED BY QUALITY ARMS LOCATED IN HOUSTON, TX, AND NEW ENGLAND ARMS CO. LOCATED IN KITTERY POINT,ME. PREVIOUSLY IMPORTED BY W.L. MOORE & COMPANY LOCATED IN WESTLAKE VILLAGE, CA.

Grading	100%	98%	95%	90%	80%	70%	60%

SHOTGUNS: SIDE-BY-SIDE

Values on below listed Ferlib shotguns reflect 1988 pricing as no information was forwarded to this writer by publication deadline regarding 1989 prices.

HAMMER GUN—boxlock action, exposed hammers, deluxe checkered walnut stock and forearm, blued action.

Mfg.'s Sug. Retail $2,875 $2,575 $2,200 $1,850 $1,500 $1,200 $995 $800

MODEL F.VI—12, 16, 20, 28, or .410 ga., Anson & Deeley boxlock action, ejectors, double triggers, case hardened frame, select checkered stock and forearm.

Mfg.'s Sug. Retail $3,750 $3,400 $2,750 $2,500 $2,275 $1,950 $1,700 $1,575

Add $375 for single trigger.

Add 12% for .28 or .410 ga.

MODEL F.VII—12, 16, 20, 28, or .410 ga., Anson & Deeley boxlock action, ejectors, double triggers, coin finish, full coverage English scroll engraving, select checkered stock and forearm.

Mfg.'s Sug. Retail $4,750 $4,300 $3,600 $3,200 $2,800 $2,400 $2,200 $2,000

Add 12% for 28 or .410 ga.

Add $375 for single trigger.

MODEL F.VII/SC—12, 16, 20, 28, or .410 ga., Anson & Deeley boxlock action, ejectors, double triggers, coin finish, game scene with scroll accent engraving with gold inlays, select checkered stock and forearm.

Mfg.'s Sug. Retail $6,100 $5,400 $4,700 $4,200 $3,600 $3,100 $2,800 $2,400

Add $375 for single trigger.

MODEL F.VII SIDEPLATE—12, 16, 20, 28, or .410 ga., Anson & Deeley boxlock action with sideplates, ejectors, single trigger, coin finish, extensive game scene and scroll accent engraving, select checkered stock and forearm.

Mfg.'s Sug. Retail $5,400 $5,150 $4,700 $4,200 $3,600 $3,100 $2,800 $2,400

F.VII/SC Gold—same as F.VII Sideplate, except with gold inlays.

Mfg.'s Sug. Retail $7,100 $6,300 $5,500 $4,900 $4,300 $3,500 $3,150 $2,800

Add 12% for .28 or .410 ga. on both models.

F.V. SIDELOCK—various ga.'s, full sidelock action, special order to customer specifications. Values start in the $8,500 range and go up.

FIALA OUTFITTERS INCORPORATED

NEW YORK CITY, NY.

FIALA REPEATING PISTOL—.22 LR, 10 shot, 3, 7½, or 20 in. barrels, blue, plain wood grips, resembles an auto loader, but is actually hand operated by moving the slide to eject load and cock, made 1920-1923.

$475 $400 $340 $280 $230 $200 $175

Add 50% for 3-barrel set.

Add $150 for original case.

Add $250 for stock.

Add $300 for canvas holster stock.

FINNISH LION

MANUFACTURED IN VALMET, SWEDEN.

RIFLES

MATCH RIFLE—.22 LR, bolt action, single shot, 29 in. barrel, extended aperture sight, globe front sight, thumbhole stock, adj. hook butt, made 1937-1972.

$495 $415 $360 $305 $250 $210 $195

Grading	100%	98%	95%	90%	80%	70%	60%

CHAMPION FREE RIFLE—.22 LR, bolt action, single shot, 29 in. barrel, double set trigger, full target and accessories, made 1965-1972.

	$580	$495	$440	$385	$330	$290	$265

STANDARD ISU TARGET RIFLE—.22 LR, bolt action, single shot, 27 in. barrel, full target stock and accessories, made 1966-1977.

	$330	$275	$250	$205	$180	$165	$150

FIOCCHI OF AMERICA, INC.

IMPORTER/DISTRIBUTOR LOCATED IN OZARK, MO.

Fiocchi of America imports Pardini target pistols and Antonio Zoli shotguns. These trademarks can be found in their respective sections of this text.

FIREARMS INTERNATIONAL

PREVIOUS IMPORTER/ASSEMBLER LOCATED IN WASHINGTON, D.C.

F.I. imported various pistols of which some were copied after the Colt .25 ACP. While some models are relatively rare, collectability to date has been minimal and most models sell in the $125-$250 range.

FOX, A. H.

PREVIOUSLY MANUFACTURED IN PHILADELPHIA, PA 1903-1930. MANUFACTURED BY SAVAGE SINCE 1930.

Mr. Ansley H. Fox first started manufacturing shotguns in the 1896 circa. This first company was called the Fox Gun Co. located in Baltimore, MD. Relatively few guns were made and surviving specimens today are very rare. After this venture he was employed by the Baltimore Gun Co. for several years (approx. circa 1900-1903). Following this period, he formed the Philadelphia Gun Co. where the predecessors to the A.H. Fox Gun Co. were manufactured. These Philadelphia Gun Co. models (circa 1904) were the same as the newer Fox shotguns except that the hinge pin was removed. Sources indicate that the lowest grade was an "A" with the highest being an "E" (fully engraved and ultra rare). Following this tenure, Mr. Fox went on to form the A.H. Fox Gun Co. that was started approximately 1905. In addition to being an entrepreneur and trend setter, Mr. Fox also had the reputation of being an expert shot in his own right, winning more than a few events on the East Coast around the turn of the century.

The A.H. Fox Gun Company of Philadelphia, Pennsylvania, began production in 1905 and produced high quality double barrel shotguns until 1930. The Savage Arms Company, then of Utica, New York, acquired the Fox Company and produced these guns until 1942, when all but the utilitarian model B series guns were discontinued.

A.H. Fox guns are rapidly being considered an American classic as is the L.C. Smith and Parker. Collector interest is high and will undoubtedly grow. The guns do not command quite as high a price as the Smith and Parker guns, but represent a fine investment collectible value.

The Savage made guns from 1930-1942 usually are valued at about 25% less than the early A.H. Fox guns. The current production B series are just not in the same class and are obviously not intended to be. They are lower priced by today's standards and are designed as a utility grade hunting gun.

100%	98%	95%	90%	80%	70%	60%	50%	40%	30%	20%	10%

SHOTGUNS

A.H. Fox serialization indicates the following: 12 ga. guns are encountered in the 100,000 up to 200,000 serial range, 20 ga. shotguns are in the 200,000 up to 300,000 serial range, and 16 ga. specimens are encountered in the 300,000 serial range.

STERLINGWORTH SXS—12, 16, or 20 ga., 26, 28, or 30 in. barrels, various chokes, boxlock, extractors, double trigger, checkered pistol grip stock, made 1905-1930.

| $1,200 | $900 | $825 | $750 | $625 | $525 | $400 | $365 | $335 | $300 | $275 | $250 |

Add 33% for auto ejectors.

Add 50% for 20 ga.

A single trigger was not an option on this model.

STERLINGWORTH DELUXE—same as Sterlingworth, with recoil pad and ivory bead, 32 in. barrel available.

| $1,500 | $1,200 | $950 | $850 | $775 | $675 | $600 | $540 | $460 | $400 | $365 | $330 |

Add $200 for auto ejectors.

Add 50% for 20 ga.

A single trigger was not an option on this model.

STERLINGWORTH SKEET—same as Sterlingworth, with 26 or 28 in. skeet boring, straight grip stock.

This model is very scarce (only several are known) and the extreme rarity factor precludes accurate price evaluation.

SUPER HE GRADE—12 ga., 2¾ (very rare) or 3 in. chambered long range gun, 30 and 32 in. full choke, auto ejectors, otherwise same as Sterlingworth.

| $2,500 | $2,000 | $1,700 | $1,400 | $1,100 | $995 | $900 | $825 | $750 | $675 | $600 | $550 |

Add $300 for SST.

Original 3 in. chambered HE grades are marked "not warranteed, see instruction tag" on barrel flats. The HE grade was also manufactured in 20 ga. but is extremely rare. 2¾ in. chambers are rarer than 3 in. guns in this model.

HIGHER GRADE MODELS (A-F)—the following higher grade Fox shotguns are similar to the Sterlingworth in configuration. The grades differ in engraving and inlays, grade of wood and general workmanship. The E designation means auto ejectors.

Early A and B grades have very little engraving and are much less desirable than later models. Values below are for later guns.

Values below are for 12 ga. Notice ga. add-ons listed below FE grade.

A Grade

| $1,500 | $1,200 | $950 | $850 | $775 | $675 | $600 | $540 | $460 | $400 | $365 | $330 |

AE Grade (ejectors)

| $1,800 | $1,500 | $1,200 | $1,000 | $900 | $800 | $725 | $650 | $575 | $500 | $450 | $400 |

BE Grade (ejectors)

| $3,000 | $2,500 | $2,200 | $1,800 | $1,500 | $1,150 | $995 | $900 | $825 | $750 | $675 | $600 |

This model is rarely encountered.

CE Grade (ejectors)

| $3,000 | $2,500 | $2,200 | $1,800 | $1,500 | $1,150 | $995 | $900 | $825 | $750 | $675 | $600 |

XE Grade (ejectors)

| $6,000 | $5,000 | $4,000 | $3,000 | $2,500 | $2,200 | $1,800 | $1,500 | $1,150 | $995 | $900 | $825 |

DE Grade (ejectors)

| $9,000 | $8,000 | $6,500 | $5,500 | $4,500 | $3,500 | $2,500 | $2,200 | $1,800 | $1,500 | $1,250 | $1,000 |

100%	98%	95%	90%	80%	70%	60%	50%	40%	30%	20%	10%

FE Grade (ejectors)—top of the line model, only infrequently encountered.

$25,000	$20,000	$15,000	$12,000	$10,000	$9,000	$8,000	$7,250	$6,500	$5,800	$5,250	$4,500

Add $200-$1,000 for vent. rib, depending on grade.
Add $200-$1,000 for SST, depending on grade.
Add $200-$1,000 for beavertail forearm, depending on grade.
16 ga. guns were made on same frame as 20 ga. - add 30%.
Add 60% for 20 ga.
Subtract 25% for Savage mfg.

Note: These guns were discontinued in 1942 by Savage Arms after they produced them for 12 years. Pre-1930 guns were made by A.H. Fox Company.

SINGLE BARREL TRAP—12 ga., 30 or 32 in. vent. rib barrel, full choke, boxlock, auto ejector, checkered trap style stock and recoil pad. The grades differ in wood, engraving, and overall quality. ME grade is custom built and extremely high quality with gold inlays. These models were discontinued in 1942. Guns made between 1932-1942 have Monte Carlo stock.

Even though trap guns may be rarer than their side X side counterparts, to date their desirability is less since there are simply fewer collectors.

Grading	100%	98%	95%	90%	80%	70%	60%
Grade JE	$1,760	$1,540	$1,430	$1,320	$1,100	$990	$880
Grade KE	$2,420	$2,200	$2,090	$1,980	$1,760	$1,650	$1,540
Grade LE	$3,300	$3,080	$2,970	$2,860	$2,640	$2,420	$2,200
Grade ME	$8,250	$7,700	$7,150	$6,600	$6,050	$5,500	$4,950

MODEL B DOUBLE BARREL—12, 16, 20, or .410 ga., 24-30 in. barrels, various chokes, vent rib on newer models, boxlock, extractors, double triggers, checkered pistol grip stock, made 1940-86.

	$230	$210	$205	$185	$165	$145	$120

Last Mfg.'s Sug. Retail was $250.

MODEL B-ST—same as model B, with single trigger, made 1955-1966.

	$275	$250	$220	$195	$165	$140	$120

MODEL B-DL—same as model B-ST, with satin chrome receiver, select wood, made 1962-1965.

	$315	$275	$240	$220	$195	$165	$140

MODEL B-DE—same as B-DL, with less checkering, made 1965-1966.

	$295	$255	$230	$210	$180	$155	$125

MODEL B-SE—same as model B, with auto ejectors and single trigger, made 1966-1988.

	$350	$275	$250	$225	$200	$180	$160

Last Mfg.'s Sug. Retail was $525.

FRANCHI, LUIGI

MANUFACTURED IN BRESCIA, ITALY. CURRENTLY IMPORTED BY FIE CORP. LOCATED IN HIALEAH, FL. AND AMERICAN ARMS, INC. LOCATED IN NORTH KANSAS CITY, MO.

Also see Sauer/Franchi heading in the S section.

RIFLES

CENTENNIAL SEMI-AUTO—.22 LR, 21 in. barrel, open sight to commemorate Franchi's 100th anniversary, made 1968 only.

	$330	$250	$220	$195	$165	$150	$140

Engraved deluxe model

	$415	$330	$305	$275	$240	$200	$165

Gallery model

	$220	$195	$160	$120	$100	$80	$60

Grading	100%	98%	95%	90%	80%	70%	60%

SHOTGUNS: SEMI-AUTO

BLACK MAGIC GAME—12 ga. only, 3 in. chamber with gas metering system, interchangeable shell handling, two-tone black alloy receiver with gold accents and trigger, 24, 26, or 28 in. VR barrel with Franchokes, checkered walnut stock and forearm, 7 lbs. Importation began in 1989.

Mfg.'s Sug. Retail	$599	$495	$440	$390	$330	$300	$270	$240

The Black Magic Model Series is imported exclusively by American Arms, Inc. located in North Kansas City, MO.

Black Magic Skeet—skeet variation of the Black Magic Game, 2¾ in. chamber, 26 in. ported VR barrel with fixed choke, skeet dimensioned stock, 7¼ lbs. Importation began in 1989.

Mfg.'s Sug. Retail	$669	$540	$460	$425	$350	$325	$300	$275

Black Magic Trap—trap variation of the Black Magic Game, 2¾ in. chamber, 30 in. VR barrel with Franchoke system, trap dimensioned stock, 7½ lbs. Importation began in 1989.

Mfg.'s Sug. Retail	$689	$565	$475	$425	$350	$325	$300	$275

STANDARD MODEL (48/AL)—12 or 20 ga., 24, 26, 28, or 30 in. VR barrel, recoil operated, alloy frame, checkered pistol grip stock, VR standard, Franchokes became available in 1989, 12 ga., 6 lbs. 4 oz. and 20 ga., 5 lbs. 2 oz. Made 1950-present.

Mfg.'s Sug. Retail	$520	$440	$385	$320	$295	$270	$250	$230

Add $70 for internal Franchokes (3).

This model is imported exclusively by F.I.E. located in Hialeah, FL.

STANDARD MAGNUM (48/AL)—same as Standard, except 28 in. (disc. in 1988) or 32 in. Mag. chamber, recoil pad, made 1954-present. Vent. rib standard.

Mfg.'s Sug. Retail	$560	$475	$425	$380	$325	$310	$295	$275

This model is imported exclusively by F.I.E. located in Hialeah, FL.

HUNTER MODEL (48/AL)—same as Standard, except etched receiver, better wood, VR standard, Franchokes became available in 1989. Made 1950-present.

Mfg.'s Sug. Retail	$560	$475	$395	$325	$310	$295	$275	$255

Add $70 for internal Franchokes (3).

This model is imported exclusively by F.I.E. located in Hialeah, FL.

HUNTER MAGNUM—made 1954-1973.

	$430	$380	$370	$340	$315	$290	$275

PRESTIGE MODEL—12 ga. only, gas operated, vent. rib, various barrel lengths, alloy receiver, Franchokes became available in 1989. New in 1985.

Mfg.'s Sug. Retail	$720	$575	$475	$395	$325	$310	$295	$275

Add $40 for internal Franchokes (3).

This model is imported exclusively by F.I.E. located in Hialeah, FL.

Turkey Model—similar to Prestige Model except has dull matte black finish, Franchokes standard. New in 1989.

Mfg.'s Sug. Retail	$760	$615	$515	$425	$350	$320	$300	$280

This model is imported exclusively by F.I.E. located in Hialeah, FL.

ELITE MODEL—same general specifications as the Prestige Model, only etched receiver, Franchokes became available in 1989.

Mfg.'s Sug. Retail	$740	$595	$500	$425	$350	$320	$300	$280

Add $45 for internal Franchokes (3).

This model is imported exclusively by F.I.E. located in Hialeah, FL.

SPAS 12—12 ga. combat shotgun that offers pump or semi-auto operation, 9 shot capacity, alloy receiver, folding stock, 21½ in. barrel, 9.6 lbs.

Mfg.'s Sug. Retail	$600	$495	$440	$390	$330	$300	$270	$240

This model is imported exclusively in the U.S. by F.I.E. located in Hialeah, FL.

TURKEY GUN—same as Standard Mag., 12 ga., 3 in. barrel only, turkey scene engraved, made 1963-1965.

	$415	$385	$370	$340	$315	$290	$275

Grading	100%	98%	95%	90%	80%	70%	60%

SLUG GUN—22 in. plain barrel, and rifle sights.

	$360	$330	$315	$295	$275	$255	$240

SKEET GUN—26 in. skeet choke, vent rib, select wood, made 1972-1974.

	$385	$370	$350	$330	$310	$285	$265

ELDORADO—fancy wood and gold filled engraved receiver, made 1954-1975.

	$450	$420	$395	$380	$360	$340	$320

CROWN GRADE—engraved hunting scene, made 1954-1975.

	$1,540	$1,320	$1,210	$1,045	$965	$910	$855

DIAMOND GRADE SILVER INLAID SCROLL—manufactured 1954-1975.

	$1,980	$1,735	$1,540	$1,430	$1,210	$1,045	$965

IMPERIAL GRADE—gold inlaid hunting scene.

	$2,420	$2,090	$1,925	$1,760	$1,595	$1,485	$1,320

Note: Standard, Skeet and Slug with steel frame made 1965-1972, designated "Dynamic" 12 in., values are the same.

MODEL 500 STANDARD—12 ga,, 26 or 28 in. barrel, various chokes, vent rib, gas operated, checkered pistol grip stock, made 1976-present.

	$330	$310	$305	$265	$230	$195	$165

MODEL 520 DELUXE—engraved receiver.

	$385	$365	$330	$290	$260	$220	$195

MODEL 520 ELDORADO GOLD—fine wood, engraved gold, inlaid receiver, made 1977-present.

	$990	$770	$715	$660	$580	$525	$470

MODEL 530 AUTO TRAP—similar to 500, except 30 in. and 32 in. full, very high rib, special trap stock, pad.

	$660	$550	$525	$440	$415	$385	$330

SHOTGUNS - O/U

DE LUXE MODEL PRITI—12 or 20 ga., boxlock action, ST, ejectors, 26 or 28 in. VR barrels with fixed chokes. Importation began in 1988.

Mfg.'s Sug. Retail	$460	$395	$350	$315	$285	$240	$215	$185

This model is imported exclusively by F.I.E. located in Hialeah, FL.

ALCIONE MODEL—12 ga., 28 in. barrels, less engraving than Alcione SL, separated barrels.

Mfg.'s Sug. Retail	$800	$675	$550	$495	$460	$430	$380	$335

Previously designated Diamond Model.

This model is imported exclusively by F.I.E. located in Hialeah, FL.

ALCIONE SL—12 ga., 27 or 28 in. barrels, 6 lbs. 13 oz., separated barrels, ejectors, single trigger, silver finished receiver engraved with luggage case. Importation discontinued in 1986.

	$1,400	$1,200	$1,035	$880	$800	$720	$640

Last Mfg.'s Sug. Retail was $1,595.

BLACK MAGIC SPORTING HUNTER—12 ga. only, 3 in. chambers, 28 in. separated barrels with VR and Franchokes, blued receiver with gold accents and trigger, SST, ejectors, checkered walnut stock and forearm, 7 lbs. Importation began in 1989.

Mfg.'s Sug. Retail	$1,199	$1,025	$875	$800	$725	$650	$575	$495

The Black Magic Model Series is imported exclusively by American Arms, Inc. located in North Kansas City, MO.

Black Magic Lightweight Hunter—similar to Black Magic Sporting Hunter except 2¾ in. chambers only, 26 in. separated barrels with VR and Franchokes, alloy receiver, 6 lbs. Importation began in 1989.

Mfg.'s Sug. Retail	$1,159	$995	$850	$775	$700	$625	$550	$475

The Black Magic Model Series is imported exclusively by American Arms, Inc. located in North Kansas City, MO.

Grading	100%	98%	95%	90%	80%	70%	60%

ARISTOCRAT FIELD—12 ga., 26, 28, or 30 in. barrels, various chokes, vent rib, auto ejectors, boxlock, selective single trigger, checkered pistol grip stock, made 1960-1969.

	$660	$470	$440	$395	$375	$340	$310

ARISTOCRAT MAGNUM—same as Field, except 32 in. barrel, 3 in. chamber, full choke, pad, made 1962-1965.

	$660	$470	$440	$395	$375	$340	$310

ARISTOCRAT SKEET—same as Field, but 26 in. vent rib, bored skeet no. 1 and no. 2, made 1960-1969.

	$715	$525	$495	$450	$430	$395	$365

ARISTOCRAT TRAP—30 in. vent rib barrel, bored mod. and full, trap stock, made 1960-1969.

	$745	$550	$525	$480	$455	$415	$380

ARISTOCRAT SILVER KING—select wood, engraved coin finished receiver, made 1962-1969.

	$750	$560	$535	$485	$470	$430	$400

ARISTOCRAT DELUXE—finer wood, more engraving, made 1960-1966.

	$990	$870	$835	$810	$770	$715	$660

ARISTOCRAT SUPREME—gold inlaid game birds, made 1960-1966.

	$1,430	$1,265	$1,155	$1,075	$990	$935	$880

ARISTOCRAT IMPERIAL—high grade wood, more engraving, made 1967-1969.

	$2,640	$2,200	$2,090	$1,925	$1,815	$1,650	$1,430

ARISTOCRAT MONTE CARLO—highest grade wood, elaborate engraving and inlay, made 1967-1969.

	$3,520	$3,080	$2,915	$2,640	$2,420	$2,090	$1,870

FALCONET S—12 ga., lightweight model of the Alcione SL, 27 or 28 in. barrels, 6 lbs. 1 oz., separated barrels, moderate engraving on silver finish receiver. Discontinued in 1985.

	$895	$765	$660	$560	$510	$460	$410

Last Mfg.'s Sug. Retail was $1,015.

FALCONET FIELD—12, 16, 20, 28, or .410 ga., 24-30 in. barrels, various chokes, auto ejectors, select single trigger, engraved alloy receiver, checkered walnut stock, made 1968-1975.

	100%	98%	95%	90%	80%	70%	60%
Buckskin (light)	$550	$495	$470	$440	$415	$385	$360
Ebony (black)	$550	$495	$470	$440	$415	$385	$360
Silver	$605	$550	$525	$495	$470	$415	$385

28 ga. and .410 — add 25%.

FALCONET SKEET—26 in. barrels, bored skeet no. 1 and no. 2, wide vent rib, case hardened steel receiver, made 1970-1974.

	$935	$855	$825	$770	$715	$690	$650

FALCONET INTERNATIONAL SKEET—higher grade wood, more engraving, made 1970-1974.

	$1,045	$935	$865	$825	$770	$745	$700

FALCONET STANDARD TRAP—12 ga., 30 in. mod. and full, wide vent rib, trap stock, pad, made 1970-1974.

	$935	$855	$825	$770	$715	$690	$650

FALCONET INTERNATIONAL TRAP—higher grade wood, more engraving, made 1970-1974.

	$1,045	$935	$865	$825	$770	$745	$700

PEREGRINE MODEL 451—12 ga., 26-28 in. barrels, various chokes, vent rib, auto ejectors, alloy receiver, selective single trigger, checkered pistol grip stock, made 1975.

	$605	$550	$525	$495	$440	$415	$360

PEREGRINE MODEL 400—same as 451, except steel receiver, made 1975.

	$660	$605	$570	$540	$495	$460	$385

Grading	100%	98%	95%	90%	80%	70%	60%

MODEL 2003 TRAP—12 ga., 30 or 32 in. barrels, imp. mod. and full, or full and full, boxlock, auto ejectors, single selective trigger, high vent rib, trap style stock, pad, cased, made 1976. Discontinued.

| | $1,205 | $1,090 | $1,045 | $910 | $855 | $770 | $660 |

MODEL 2004 TRAP—same as 2003, except single barrel, cased, made 1976. Discontinued.

| | $1,205 | $1,090 | $1,045 | $910 | $855 | $770 | $660 |

MODEL 2005 COMBINATION TRAP—two sets of barrels, one single, one O/U, cased, made 1976. Discontinued.

| | $1,815 | $1,595 | $1,515 | $1,320 | $1,210 | $1,075 | $935 |

MODEL 2005/3 COMBINATION TRAP—three sets of barrels, cased, made 1976. Discontinued.

| | $2,420 | $2,090 | $1,980 | $1,705 | $1,515 | $1,485 | $1,320 |

UNDERGUN MODEL 3000—radical competition trap, very high rib separated barrels, single and O/U, set cased. Discontinued.

| | $2,750 | $2,530 | $2,310 | $2,090 | $1,980 | $1,870 | $1,760 |

SHOTGUNS: SIDE-BY-SIDE

AIRONE—.12 ga., double barrel, choice of barrel length and chokes, box lock, Anson & Deeley, auto ejectors, double triggers, checkered English style stock, engraved, made 1940-1950.

| | $1,320 | $1,100 | $935 | $825 | $745 | $715 | $660 |

ASTORE—double barrel, similar to Airone, except less engraving, extractors, made 1937-1960.

| | $990 | $910 | $770 | $715 | $635 | $580 | $550 |

ASTORE 5—same as Astore, except higher grade wood, more engraving, auto ejectors. Discontinued.

| | $2,200 | $1,925 | $1,650 | $1,540 | $1,460 | $1,375 | $1,320 |

ASTORE II—similar to Astore 5, except less elaborate, currently made in Spain for Franchi.

| | $1,210 | $1,045 | $935 | $880 | $800 | $715 | $660 |

SIDELOCK DOUBLE BARREL—12, 16, or 20 ga., barrels and choke custom order, stock to order, hand detachable side lock, self-opening action, auto ejectors, six grades offered, they differ only in overall quality and ornamentation, and grade of wood used.

	100%	98%	95%	90%	80%	70%	60%
Condor	$7,700	$6,600	$6,050	$5,720	$5,500	$4,620	$3,960
Imperial	$10,450	$9,350	$8,800	$8,250	$7,480	$6,600	$5,720
Imperiales	$10,670	$9,570	$9,020	$8,470	$7,700	$6,820	$5,940

SIDE-LOCK DOUBLE BARREL

No. 5 Imperial Monte Carlo

| | $15,400 | $13,200 | $11,000 | $9,900 | $9,350 | $8,250 | $7,150 |

No. 11 Imperial Monte Carlo

| | $16,500 | $14,300 | $12,100 | $11,000 | $10,450 | $9,350 | $8,250 |

Imperial Monte Carlo Extra

| | $19,800 | $17,050 | $14,300 | $13,200 | $12,650 | $11,000 | $9,900 |

Note: Imperial Monte Carlo Extra is currently being produced on special order only; the other models are discontinued.

FRANCOTTE, AUGUSTE & CIE. S.A.

MANUFACTURED IN LIEGE, BELGIUM SINCE 1805. CURRENTLY IMPORTED BY ARMES DE CHASSE LOCATED IN CHADDS FORD, PA. PREVIOUSLY IMPORTED BY VL&O BETWEEN 1900-1930'S, ABERCROMBIE & FITCH UNTIL APPROX. 1982. ROYAL ARMS INTERNATIONAL LOCATED IN WOODLAND HILLS, CA ALSO IMPORTS A. FRANCOTTE ON A LIMITED BASIS.

Prices below reflect the recent devaluation of the U.S. dollar against some foreign currencies. While the manufacturer's suggested retails have gone up considerably, prices for used specimens (98% or less original condition) have not increased proportionately, and in some cases, have changed very little.

Grading	100%	98%	95%	90%	80%	70%	60%

SHOTGUNS

BOXLOCK SXS—premium grade Belgium side by side, double triggers standard, auto ejectors, sideplates (except Knockabout). Available in 12, 16, 20, and 28 ga.'s., with gold inlaid bird scenes, Anson & Deeley boxlock action.

Mfg.'s Sug. Retail	$5,625	$5,150	$4,500	$4,020	$3,650	$3,285	$2,960	$2,560

Deluxe Anson & Deeley—gold inlaid game scenes.

Mfg.'s Sug. Retail	$6,875	$6,275	$5,500	$4,850	$4,365	$3,900	$3,450	$2,900

Normal Boxlock Action—available in 12, 16, 20, or 28 ga., Arabesque scroll engraving.

Mfg.'s Sug. Retail	$5,190	$4,700	$4,150	$3,765	$3,320	$2,975	$2,575	$2,175

This boxlock action is also available with sideplates - add $625. .410 ga. can also be ordered - add $940.

SIDELOCK SXS—true sidelock action, available in 12, 16, 20, 28, or .410 ($1,200 extra) ga., Arabesque scroll engraving, various chokes and barrel lengths, custom order only.

Mfg.'s Sug. Retail	$12,625	$11,600	$10,500	$9,000	$8,350	$7,700	$7,100	$6,550

Deluxe sidelock—same as above, except with gold inlaid game scenes.

Mfg.'s Sug. Retail	$15,000	$13,500	$12,000	$10,750	$9,500	$8,400	$7,300	$6,850

JUBILEE

	100%	98%	95%	90%	80%	70%	60%
	$1,595	$1,430	$1,265	$1,100	$990	$825	$715
No. 14	$2,000	$1,900	$1,800	$1,650	$1,500	$1,450	$1,200
No. 18	$2,500	$2,400	$2,250	$2,000	$1,800	$1,600	$1,300
No. 20	$3,000	$2,600	$2,350	$2,100	$1,900	$1,700	$1,500
No. 25	$3,500	$3,000	$2,500	$2,200	$2,100	$1,900	$1,700
No. 30	$5,000	$4,500	$4,000	$3,500	$2,500	$2,200	$2,000

KNOCKABOUT

	100%	98%	95%	90%	80%	70%	60%
	$1,265	$1,100	$935	$825	$715	$635	$550

Add 20% for 20 ga.
Add 30% for 28 ga.
Add 40% for .410 ga.

NO. 45 EAGLE GRADE

	100%	98%	95%	90%	80%	70%	60%
	$3,300	$2,970	$2,640	$2,365	$2,090	$1,870	$1,705

RIFLES

BOLT ACTION MODEL—many calibers available between .243 Win., .458 Win. Mag., select checkered walnut stock, engraved mag. floor plate, available by special order only.

Mfg.'s Sug. Retail	$3,125	$2,875	$2,500	$2,150	$1,900	$1,700	$1,500	$1,350

ARMES DE CHASSE SAFARI EXPRESS—available in cal.'s up to 470 Nitro Express, boxlock action, English scroll or border engraving, coin finished or case colored receiver, oil finished walnut stock with checkering. These guns are manufactured to Armes de Chasse specifications by several different European manufacturers.

Mfg.'s Sug. Retail	$3,300	$3,300	$2,800	$2,500	$2,200	$2,000	$1,850	$1,700

Add $600 for English scroll engraving.

This rifle is available on a custom order basis only.

ARMES DE CHASSE NORTH AMERICAN SAFARI EXPRESS—available in most standard U.S. cal.'s, otherwise similar to Safari Express model.

Mfg.'s Sug. Retail	$3,300	$3,300	$2,800	$2,500	$2,200	$2,000	$1,850	$1,700

This rifle is available on a custom order basis only. Options include a set of 20 ga. shotgun barrels with factory scope mounts.

FRASER, DANL. & CO.

MANUFACTURED IN EUROPE. LIMITED IMPORTATION INTO THE UNITED STATES.

Danl. Fraser & Co. has been building rifles since 1873 (originally in Edinburgh, Scotland).

Grading	100%	98%	95%	90%	80%	70%	60%

HIGHLANDER SINGLE SHOT—.22 LR or .22 Hornet cal., underlever falling block action (color case hardened), 24 in. (½ round, ½ octagon) barrel, folding express-style sights, pistol grip walnut stock with fine checkering.

Mfg.'s Sug. Retail	$475	$415	$335	$300	$280	$260	$240	$220

Royal Highlander—.22 LR or .22 Hornet cal., mfg. in Scotland, rose and scroll engraving with 18Kt. inlays. Special order only — prices available upon request.

FRASER FIREARMS CORP.

MANUFACTURED BY R.B. INDUSTRIES, LTD. DISTRIBUTED BY FRASER FIREARMS CORP.

FRASER 25 CAL.—.25 cal. only, copy of the Bauer semi-auto pocket model, 6 round mag., 2¼ in. barrel, stainless steel construction.

Mfg.'s Sug. Retail	$133	$120	$100	$90

Add $17 for Model 2 (black nylon grips).
Add $115 for Model 3 (24 Kt. gold plated).

FREEDOM ARMS

MANUFACTURED AND DISTRIBUTED IN FREEDOM, WY.

Percussion mini-revolvers can be found in the Blackpowder Section of this text.

MINI-REVOLVERS: STAINLESS STEEL

FA-S-22LR (PATRIOT)—.22 LR cal., 5 shot, 1, 1¾ (disc. in 1988), or 3 (disc. in 1988) in. barrel, Hi-Gloss finish.

Mfg.'s Sug. Retail	$153	$125	$95	$75

Add $15 for 3 in. barrel model (FA-BG-22LR, Minute-Man, disc. in 1988).

FA-S-22M (IRONSIDES)—.22 Mag. cal., 5 shot, 1, 1¾ (disc. in 1988), or 3 in. barrel, Hi Gloss finish.

Mfg.'s Sug. Retail	$177	$150	$110	$85

Add $43 for 3 in. barrel model (Bostonian).

FA-S-22-LR CELEBRITY BUCKLE REVOLVER—.22 LR, 1 in. barrel, gun pivots on belt buckle.

Mfg.'s Sug. Retail	$193	$165	$135	$110

.22 Mag. cal.

Mfg.'s Sug. Retail	$216	$185	$150	$125

MAGNUM REVOLVERS

CASULL SAA PREMIER GRADE—.44 Rem. Mag., .44 Win. Mag., .45 LC, or .454 Casull cal., 5 shot stainless steel single action revolver, the .454 Casull shoots 225 grain bullet at over 2000 fps., 4¾, 6, 7½, 10, and 12 (disc. in 1988) in. barrels, walnut grips. Manufactured 1983-present.

Mfg.'s Sug. Retail	$1,045	$935	$785	$650

Adj. sights

Mfg.'s Sug. Retail	$1,150	$985	$825	$725

Add $75-$95 for Mag-na-porting.
Add $112 for SSK Industries T'SOB 3-ring scope mount.

CASULL FIELD GRADE SAA—.454 Casull only, 4¾ (fixed sight only), 7½, or 10 in. barrel, stainless steel matte finish with Pachmayr presentation grips. New in 1988.

Mfg.'s Sug. Retail	$761	$675	$590	$500

Add $73 for adj. sights.

Grading	100%	98%	95%	90%	80%	70%	60%

SIGNATURE EDITION .454 CASULL—.454 Casull, high polish stainless steel, 7½ in. barrel only, rosewood grips, cased with accessories ser. no.'s DC1-2000. Discontinued.

	$1,950	$1,625	$1,250				

PRIMUS INTER PARES—1 of every 100 guns is made in this variation, includes octagonal barrel, ivory grips, 7½ in. barrel, and cased. Contact the factory directly for prices on this model.

FRENCH MILITARY

MANUFACTURED IN VARIOUS LOCATIONS IN FRANCE.

Some French Military models may be found under the MAS section of this text.

MODEL 1886 LEBEL—bolt action, 8mm Lebel, 32 in. barrel, adj. sight, military stock, made 1886 - WWII.

	$125	$100	$75	$65	$50	$40	$25

1936 MAS MILITARY RIFLE—bolt action, 7.5mm MAS, 22 in. barrel, adj. sight, military stock, bayonet in forearm, made 1936-1940.

	$125	$100	$75	$65	$50	$40	$25

MODEL 1935A AUTO PISTOL—7.65mm long, 8 shot, 4.3 in. barrel, fixed sights, blue, checkered wood grips, French service sidearm, made 1935-1945.

	$195	$175	$150	$125	$110	$100	$90

M.A.B. MODEL C—7.65mm, design based on FN Browning Model 1910, 6.1 in. barrel, introduced in 1933.

	$250	$220	$190	$170	$150	$125	$110

M.A.B. MODEL D—7.65mm, 7 in barrel, single action, similar to Model C, produced commercially 1933-1940, many thousands mfg. for the German military during WWII (marked "Pistole MAB Kaliber 7.65mm")

	$275	$225	$200	$175	$150	$125	$110

MODEL M.A.B. PA - 15—9mm, single action semi-auto, 16 shot, currently used by French military.

	$700	$595	$450				

MODEL M.A.B. PA - 15 TARGET—rare target variation of PA-15, adj. sight, 6 in. barrel, cased.

	$1,600	$1,200	$750				

FRIGON

MANUFACTURED BY MAROCCHI IN ITALY. DISTRIBUTED BY FRIGON GUNS LOCATED IN CLAY CENTER, KS.

FT I—12 ga. only, single barrel trap gun, blued finish, 32 or 34 in. VR barrel, quick-change stock. New in 1986.

Mfg.'s Sug. Retail	$875	$750	$585	$475	$425	$375	$350	$295

FTC—12 ga. only, quick-change stock, trap combination gun includes 1 single barrel and 1 set of O/U barrels, cased. New in 1986.

Mfg.'s Sug. Retail	$1,600	$1,350	$1,175	$1,000	$875	$775	$685	$620

FS-4—4-barrel skeet set including 12, 20, 28, or .410 ga., individual forearms, quick-change stock, vent barrels (except for .410 ga.), cased. New in 1986.

Mfg.'s Sug. Retail	$2,340	$2,050	$1,775	$1,625	$1,500	$1,350	$1,250	$1,150

FROMMER PISTOLS

FEMARU-FEBYVER-ES GEPGYAR R.T., BUDAPEST, HUNGARY.

Please refer to the Femaru listing in this section.

FURR ARMS

MANUFACTURER LOCATED IN OREM, UT.

Please refer to the Gatling Gun Company listing in this text.

G

GALEF SHOTGUNS (IMPORTERS)

ZABAL HERMANOS, SPAIN. ANTONIO ZOLI, ITALY.

Grading	100%	98%	95%	90%	80%	70%	60%

COMPANION FOLDING SINGLE BARREL—12, 16, 20, 28, or .410 ga., 28 in. barrel, full choke, 30 in. full, 12 ga. only, hammerless, underlever, checkered pistol grip stock.

	$110	$95	$85	$75	$65	$55	$45

MONTE CARLO TRAP—12 ga., single barrel, 32 in. full vent rib, hammerless, underlever, recoil pad, checkered pistol grip Monte Carlo stock, current production.

	$185	$175	$150	$135	$125	$100	$90

SILVER SNIPE—12 or 20 ga., O/U, 3 in. chambers, 26, 28, or 30 in. barrels, imp. cyl. and mod. or full and mod. vent rib, checkered pistol grip stock, boxlock, extractors, single trigger, made by A. Zoli, current production.

	$350	$325	$295	$275	$250	$220	$190

GOLDEN SNIPE—O/U, same as Silver Snipe, except auto ejectors.

	$395	$380	$340	$300	$275	$250	$225

SILVER HAWK—12 or 20 ga., SxS, 3 in. chambers, 26, 28, or 30 in. barrels, imp. cyl. and mod. or mod. and full, boxlock, extractors, checkered pistol grip and beavertail forearm, made by A. Zoli, 1968-1972.

	$400	$375	$360	$320	$280	$255	$225

GALEF ZABALA DOUBLE—10, 12, 16, or 20 ga., s x s, 22, 26, 28, or 30 in. barrels, boxlock, extractors.

	100%	98%	95%	90%	80%	70%	60%
10 gauge	$250	$2?0	$200	$175	$150	$140	$125
Other gauges	$200	$175	$150	$130	$120	$110	$100

GALIL

MANUFACTURED BY ISRAEL MILITARY INDUSTRIES (IMI). FORMERLY IMPORTED BY MAGNUM RESEARCH, INC., MINNEAPOLIS, MN. CURRENTLY IMPORTED BY ACTION ARMS, LTD. LOCATED IN PHILADELPHIA, PA.

MODEL AR—.223 cal. (5.56mm) or .308 cal., semi-auto assault rifle, gas operated - rotating bolt, 16.1 in. (.223 only) or 19 in. (.308 only) barrel, parkerized, folding stock. Flip-up Tritium night sights. 8.6 lbs.

Mfg.'s Sug. Retail	$950	$825	$725	$640	$590	$530	$460	$420

Add $38 for .308 cal.

MODEL ARM—similar to Model AR, except includes folding bipod, vented hardwood handguard, and carrying handle.

Mfg.'s Sug. Retail	$1,050	$925	$800	$700	$620	$550	$475	$430

Add $75 for .308 cal.

HADAR II—.308 cal., gas operated, hunting rifle configuration, 1 piece walnut thumbhole stock with pistol grip and forearm, 18½ in. barrel, adj. rear sight, recoil pad, 4 shot (standard) or 25 shot mag., 10.3 lbs. Importation began in 1989.

Mfg.'s Sug. Retail	$998	$850	$740	$650	$600	$540	$475	$425

SNIPER OUTFIT—.308 cal., semi-auto, limited production, sniper model built to exact specifications for improved accuracy, 20 in. heavy barrel, hardwood folding stock (adj. cheekpiece) and forearm, includes Tritium night sights, bipod, detachable 6 X 40mm Nimrod scope, two 25 shot mag.'s, carrying/storage case, 14.1 lbs. Importation began in 1989.

Mfg.'s Sug. Retail	$3,995	$3,500	$3,000	$2,650	$2,150	$1,750	$1,300	$1,125

GAMBA, RENATO
MANUFACTURED IN GARDONE V.T., ITALY.

Renato Gamba firearms were last imported on a limited basis by Armes de Chasse located in Chadds Ford, PA, 19317. Armes de Chasse models imported were Principessa, Oxford 90, and London. The information and values listed below regarding Renato Gamba firearms reflect 1987 information - the last year this quality trademark was imported in it's entirety. As of this writing, Gamba is negotiating with several U.S. importers for exclusive domestic distribution. Any future importation could reflect pricing increases.

PISTOLS

SAB G90—7.65 P or 9 x 18mm Ultra cal.'s, double action, 4.72 in. barrel, 15 shot side release mag., blue or chrome finish, smooth walnut grips, 2.2 lbs.

Mfg.'s Sug. Retail	$680	$550	$440	$390	$345	$300	$270	$245

Add $65 for chrome finish.

SAB G91 COMPACT—similar to SAB G90, except has 3.54 in. barrel, 12 shot mag., and weighs 1.87 lbs.

Mfg.'s Sug. Retail	$695	$555	$445	$390	$345	$300	$270	$245

Add $65 for chrome finish.

REVOLVERS

TRIDENT FAST ACTION—.32 S&W or .38 Spl. cal., 2½ or 3 in. barrel, double action, blued receiver with checkered walnut grips, 6 shot, 23 oz.

Mfg.'s Sug. Retail	$595	$495	$395	$360	$330	$295	$270	$245

TRIDENT SUPER—.32 S&W or .38 Spl. cal., 4 in. vent rib barrel, 6 shot, double action, checkered walnut grips, 25 oz.

Mfg.'s Sug. Retail	$645	$530	$425	$380	$345	$300	$270	$245

TRIDENT MATCH 900—.32 W.C. or .38 Spl. cal., match gun featuring 6 in. heavy barrel and anatomically compatible checkered walnut grips, target sights, 2.2 lbs.

Mfg.'s Sug. Retail	$995	$750	$660	$590	$525	$475	$430	$390

Trident Match 901—similar to Trident Match 900.

Mfg.'s Sug. Retail	$995	$750	$660	$590	$525	$475	$430	$390

RIFLES

SAFARI EXPRESS—7 x 65R, 9.3 x 74R, or .375 H&H cal., 25 in. barrels with open sights, underlug locking with Greener crossbolt, ejectors except on .375 H&H, coin finished receiver with scroll work and game scene engraving, DT's, deluxe checkered walnut stock with cheekpiece and recoil pad, 9.9 lbs.

Mfg.'s Sug. Retail	$6,630	$5,685	$4,575	$3,950	$3,575	$3,175	$2,850	$2,500

MUSTANG—5.6 x 50, 6.5 x 57R, 7 x 65R, .222 Rem., .270 Win., or .30-06 cal., single 25½ in. barrel configuration with highly engraved sidelock action, double-set triggers, best quality checkered walnut stock and forearm, 6.17 lbs.

Mfg.'s Sug. Retail	$12,930	$11,000	$8,750	$7,950	$7,275	$6,600	$6,000	$5,450

RGZ 1000—7 x 64, .270 Win., 7mm Rem. Mag., .300 Win. Mag., modified Mauser K-98 action, 20½ in. barrel, pistol grip stock with cheekpiece, 7 lbs.

Mfg.'s Sug. Retail	$1,310	$1,100	$885	$825	$760	$700	$640	$575

RGX 1000 Express—similar to RGZ 1000, except has 23¾ in. barrel and double set triggers, 7.7 lbs.

Mfg.'s Sug. Retail	$1,475	$1,255	$960	$875	$795	$725	$650	$575

SHOTGUNS: OVER AND UNDER

COUNTRY MODEL—12 or 20 ga., DT's, extractors, checkered walnut stock and forearm.

Mfg.'s Sug. Retail	$765	$650	$520	$485	$455	$430	$395	$365

GRIFONE MODEL—12 or 20 ga., engraved, silver finished boxlock action, vent barrels and rib, deluxe checkered walnut, SST, ejectors, 7.05 lbs.

Mfg.'s Sug. Retail	$935	$795	$630	$575	$525	$475	$430	$390

Add $50 for single trigger.
Add $98 for multi-choke option.

Grading	100%	98%	95%	90%	80%	70%	60%

EUROPA 2000—12 ga. only, engraved, silver finished boxlock action with sideplates, vent rib, single trigger, ejectors, deluxe checkered stock and forearm, 6.84 lbs.

Mfg.'s Sug. Retail	$1,475	$1,250	$995	$895	$835	$775	$715	$650

EDINBURGH SUPER SLUG—12 ga. only, trap model, SST, ejectors, engraved action, deluxe checkered stock and forearm.

Mfg.'s Sug. Retail	$1,425	$1,225	$980	$895	$835	$775	$715	$650

GRIFONE SPORTING TRAP—12 ga. only, trap model, SST, ejectors, moderately engraved action, deluxe checkered stock and forearm.

Mfg.'s Sug. Retail	$1,425	$1,225	$980	$895	$835	$775	$715	$650

GRINTA TRAP/SKEET—12 ga. only, trap/skeet model, SST, ejectors, medium engraving coverage.

Mfg.'s Sug. Retail	$1,710	$1,460	$1,250	$995	$895	$835	$775	$715

VICTORY TRAP/SKEET—similar to Grinta Model, except has better walnut and more engraving.

Mfg.'s Sug. Retail	$1,905	$1,620	$1,295	$1,100	$995	$895	$835	$775

EDINBURG MATCH—similar to Victory Model, except has different style of engraving.

Mfg.'s Sug. Retail	$1,930	$1,630	$1,300	$1,100	$995	$895	$835	$775

BAYERN 88 COMBINATION GUN—12 ga. over same cal.'s listed for Mustang Model, coin finished boxlock action with game scene engraving, double DT's, extractors, deluxe checkered walnut stock with recoil pad, 7½ lbs.

Mfg.'s Sug. Retail	$1,595	$1,365	$1,050	$950	$860	$775	$715	$665

SHOTGUNS: SIDE X SIDE

HUNTER SUPER—12 ga. only, Anson & Deeley engraved boxlock action with silver finish, DT's, extractors, 6.84 lbs.

Mfg.'s Sug. Retail	$1,506	$1,395	$1,100	$865	$760	$630	$575	$525

PRINCIPESSA—12 or 20 ga., similar to Hunter Super except has English straight grip stock and better engraving, 6.62 lbs.

Mfg.'s Sug. Retail	$2,000	$1,895	$1,500	$1,275	$995	$885	$770	$650

Also available in 28 ga. on a 28 ga. frame as an option.

OXFORD 90—12 or 20 ga., side-lock action with Purdey locking system, DT's, ejectors, deluxe checkered straight grip walnut stock with recoil pad, 6.84 lbs.

Mfg.'s Sug. Retail	$2,753	$2,500	$2,050	$1,750	$1,395	$1,175	$995	$885

Also available in 28 ga. on a 28 ga. frame as an option.

LONDON—12 or 20 ga., H&H side-lock system, ejectors, DT or SST, deluxe checkered straight grip stock and forearm, 6.84 lbs.

Mfg.'s Sug. Retail	$7,953	$7,500	$5,875	$4,975	$3,950	$3,575	$3,175	$2,850

Also available in 28 ga. on a 28 ga. frame as an option.

LONDON ROYAL—similar to London Model except has extensive game scene engraving.

Mfg.'s Sug. Retail	$6,730	$5,725	$4,600	$3,950	$3,575	$3,175	$2,850	$2,500

AMBASSADOR GOLDEN BLACK—12 or 20 ga., H&H side-lock system, gold-line engraving on barrels and receiver, single trigger, ejectors, deluxe checkered walnut stock and forearm, 6.4 lbs.

Mfg.'s Sug. Retail	$14,650	$12,450	$10,000	$8,750	$7,950	$7,275	$6,600	$6,000

Also available with deluxe English engraving at no extra charge (Ambassador English Model).

Also available in 28 ga. on a 28 ga. frame as an option.

AMBASSADOR EXECUTIVE—12 or 20 ga. only, top-of-the-line model, made to individual order only, every possible refinement.

Mfg.'s Sug. Retail	$23,410	$19,995	$15,750	$12,450	$10,000	$8,750	$7,950	$7,275

Also available in 28 ga. on a 28 ga. frame as an option.

Grading	100%	98%	95%	90%	80%	70%	60%

SHOTGUNS: FOLDING ACTION

MILANO 1—all gauges, single barrel with vent rib, checkered stock and forearm with sling swivels, 5¾ lbs.

Mfg.'s Sug. Retail	$365	$315	$250	$220	$185	$150	$125	$105

Milano 2—similar to Milano 1.

Mfg.'s Sug. Retail	$380	$320	$255	$220	$185	$150	$125	$105

Milano 3—similar to Milano 2.

Mfg.'s Sug. Retail	$390	$320	$255	$220	$185	$150	$125	$105

LS 2000—12, 20, 28, and .410 ga.'s, O/U configuration, single trigger, extractors, vent rib, engraved action, 6.3 lbs.

Mfg.'s Sug. Retail	$630	$545	$390	$330	$295	$260	$235	$205

SHOTGUNS: SLIDE ACTION

MODEL 2100—12 ga. Mag., 19½ in. barrel, 7 shot mag., law enforcement configuration with matte black metal and wood, 6.62 lbs.

Mfg.'s Sug. Retail	$715	$610	$480	$390	$330	$275	$220	$195

SHOTGUNS: DISCONTINUED

MONTREAL MODEL 81—12 ga. only, boxlock, interchangeable trigger assembly, select walnut, vent rib. Available in International Trap, American Skeet, Sporting, and Field models. Add $50 for adj. single barrel.

	$1,995	$1,500	$1,300	$1,100	$1,000	$900	$800

MONTREAL 81 AMERICAN TRAP COMBO—12 ga. only, 32 in. barrels and adj. impact, single 34 in. barrel, interchangeable trigger assembly.

	$2,800	$2,100	$1,820	$1,540	$1,400	$1,260	$1,120

SINGLE BARREL TRAP-MODEL 496—12 ga. only, boxlock, vent rib.

	$1,150	$865	$750	$635	$575	$520	$460

S. VINCENT 580 EXTRA DELUXE SXS—12 ga. only, custom made to individual preferences,very high quality, sidelock action, engraving coverage 100%.

	$3,250	$2,440	$2,115	$1,790	$1,625	$1,465	$1,300

GARBI

MANUFACTURED IN EIBAR, SPAIN. DISTRIBUTED BY W.L. MOORE & CO. OF WESTLAKE VILLAGE, CA.

SHOTGUNS: DISCONTINUED SIDE-BY-SIDE

51 A—12 ga. only, extractors, case hardened finish, straight grip.

	$450	$350	$325	$300	$280	$260	$240

51 B—12, 16, or 20 ga., ejectors, case hardened or coin finish receiver, straight grip.

	$850	$650	$590	$540	$500	$460	$420

60 A—12 ga. only, extractors, case hardened finish, true sidelock, large scroll engraving, cocking indicators, hand checkered butt, choice of grip.

	$725	$575	$530	$475	$440	$400	$360

60 B—12, 16, or 20 ga., ejectors, case hardened or coin finish receiver, extensive engraving, straight grip.

	$1,200	$850	$790	$735	$680	$630	$575

62 A—12 ga. only, extractors, case hardened finish, true sidelock, light engraving, cocking indicators, hand checkered butt, choice of grip.

	$725	$575	$530	$475	$440	$400	$360

62 B—12, 16, or 20 ga. only, ejectors, case hardened or coin finish receiver, extensive engraving, straight grip.

	$1,200	$850	$790	$735	$680	$630	$575

Grading	100%	98%	95%	90%	80%	70%	60%

SHOTGUNS: SXS RECENT MFG.

For the following models — add $250 for 28 ga., $300 for single trigger, $75-$150 for beavertail forearm, $600-$1,300 per extra set of barrels (depending on grade), and $150 for Churchill style level file-cut rib.

71—12, 16, or 20 ga., Holland-pattern detachable sidelock ejector double, fine English scroll engraving, oil finish, select walnut, articulated trigger. Importation disc. in 1988.

	$2,250	**$1,825**	**$1,500**	**$1,300**	**$1,075**	**$980**	**$900**

Last Mfg.'s Sug. Retail was $2,600.

100—12, 16, or 20 ga., Holland-pattern detachable sidelock ejector double, Purdy style scroll engraving, chopper lump barrels, oil finish, select walnut, articulated trigger.

Mfg.'s Sug. Retail	**$3,375**	**$2,700**	**$2,100**	**$1,650**	**$1,450**	**$1,200**	**$1,025**	**$930**

101—12, 16, or 20 ga., Holland-pattern sidelock ejector double with chopper lump barrels, Continental style floral and scroll engraving, selected walnut stock.

Mfg.'s Sug. Retail	**$4,125**	**$3,300**	**$2,700**	**$2,250**	**$1,900**	**$1,650**	**$1,400**	**$1,200**

102—12, 16, 20, or 28 ga., Holland-pattern sidelock ejector double with chopper lump barrels, Holland-type large scroll engraving, selected walnut stock. Importation disc. in 1988.

	$4,100	**$3,250**	**$2,500**	**$2,200**	**$1,900**	**$1,650**	**$1,400**

Last Mfg.'s Sug. Retail was $4,500.

103A—12, 16, 20, or 28 ga., Holland-pattern sidelock ejector double with chopper lump barrels, Purdey-type fine scroll and rosette engraving, selected walnut stock.

Mfg.'s Sug. Retail	**$5,500**	**$4,400**	**$3,450**	**$2,700**	**$2,350**	**$2,000**	**$1,750**	**$1,500**

103B—12, 16, 20, or 28 ga., Holland-pattern sidelock ejector double with chopper lump barrels of nickel-chrome steel, H&H type easy opening mechanism, Purdey-type fine scroll and rosette engraving, well figured walnut stock.

Mfg.'s Sug. Retail	**$7,500**	**$6,000**	**$5,150**	**$4,250**	**$3,500**	**$3,150**	**$2,700**	**$2,300**

120—12, 16, 20, or 28 ga., Holland-pattern sidelock ejector double with chopper lump barrels of nickel-chrome steel, H&H type easy opening mechanism, game scene engraving-3 patterns available. Well figured walnut stock.

Mfg.'s Sug. Retail	**$7,000**	**$5,600**	**$4,750**	**$4,000**	**$3,250**	**$2,995**	**$2,575**	**$2,150**

200—12, 16, 20, or 28 ga., Holland-pattern sidelock ejector double with chopper lump barrels of nickel-chrome steel, heavy-duty locks, magnum proofed, very fine Continental style floral and scroll engraving, well figured walnut stock.

Mfg.'s Sug. Retail	**$7,250**	**$5,800**	**$4,950**	**$4,125**	**$3,375**	**$3,075**	**$2,650**	**$2,225**

SPECIAL WLM—12, 16, 20, or 28 ga., top of the line Holland-pattern sidelock ejector double with chopper lump barrels, full coverage large scroll engraving, fancy-figured walnut stock. Importation disc. in 1988.

	$5,400	**$4,325**	**$3,500**	**$3,150**	**$2,700**	**$2,300**	**$2,000**

Last Mfg.'s Sug. Retail was $6,250.

SPECIAL AG—12, 16, 20, or 28 ga., top of the line Holland-pattern sidelock ejector double with chopper lump barrels, large scroll engraving patterned after Labeau-Courally, fancy figured walnut stock.

Mfg.'s Sug. Retail	**$7,625**	**$6,100**	**$5,200**	**$4,300**	**$3,550**	**$3,150**	**$2,700**	**$2,300**

GATLING GUN COMPANY

MANUFACTURED SINCE 1961 BY FURR ARMS LOCATED IN PRESCOTT, AZ. DISTRIBUTED BY J & G SALES, INC. LOCATED IN PRESCOTT, AZ.

The Gatling Gun Company manufactures high quality ⅙, ⅓, ½, ¾ and full scale brass reproductions of famous, antique machine guns and cannons. Models include the 1874 Gatling Gun on carriage (includes 225 round Broadwell feed drum and 10 exposed barrels), 1876 Camel Gun (includes 225 round Broadwell feed drum), 1883 Gatling Gun on carriage (Accles feed drum, 10 enclosed barrels), 1893 Police, British Naval Cannon, and the James Six Pounder. Prices vary according to the complexity of each model, and are available by contacting the distributor.

Grading	100%	98%	95%	90%	80%	70%	60%

⅙ Scale 1874 Carriage Gatling
Mfg.'s Sug. Retail $5,000 $5,000 $4,000 $3,500

⅓ Scale 1874 Carriage Gatling
Mfg.'s Sug. Retail $6,500 $6,500 $5,250 $4,250

½ Scale 1876 Carriage Gatling
Mfg.'s Sug. Retail $12,000 $12,000 $9,000 $7,500

¾ Scale 1876 Carriage Gatling
Mfg.'s Sug. Retail $19,000 $19,000 $15,000 $12,000

⅙ Scale 1874 Camel Tripod
Mfg.'s Sug. Retail $4,000 $4,000 $3,000 $2,500

⅓ Scale 1874 Camel Tripod
Mfg.'s Sug. Retail $4,500 $4,500 $3,500 $2,800

½ Scale 1876 Camel Tripod
Mfg.'s Sug. Retail $8,000 $8,000 $6,500 $5,250

¾ Scale 1876 Camel Tripod
Mfg.'s Sug. Retail $12,000 $12,000 $9,000 $7,500

Full Scale 1876 Camel Tripod
Mfg.'s Sug. Retail $18,000 $18,000 $14,500 $11,500

⅙ Scale 1893 Police Gatling
Mfg.'s Sug. Retail $2,500 $2,500 $2,100 $1,650

⅓ Scale 1893 Police Gatling
Mfg.'s Sug. Retail $3,200 $3,200 $2,550 $2,000

⅙ Scale 1883 Carriage Gatling
Mfg.'s Sug. Retail $5,000 $5,000 $4,000 $3,500

⅓ Scale 1883 Carriage Gatling
Mfg.'s Sug. Retail $6,500 $6,500 $5,250 $4,250

⅙ Scale James Six Pounder Cannon
Mfg.'s Sug. Retail $900 $900 $750 $575

⅕ Scale James Six Pounder Cannon
Mfg.'s Sug. Retail $2,200 $2,200 $1,850 $1,400

⅓ Scale James Six Pounder Cannon
Mfg.'s Sug. Retail $3,200 $3,200 $2,550 $2,000

1/10 Scale H.M.S. Victory Naval Cannon
Mfg.'s Sug. Retail $500 $500 $375 $325

1/10 Scale H.M.S. Victory Naval Cannon—this cannon is mounted on an oak ship deck section complete with planking, port lid, and working block and tackle.
Mfg.'s Sug. Retail $900 $900 $750 $575

⅓ Scale H.M.S. Victory Naval Cannon
Mfg.'s Sug. Retail $3,200 $3,200 $2,550 $2,000

GERMAN WWII MILITARY PISTOLS

ALSO SEE: FABRIQUE NATIONALE, LUGER, MAUSER, AND WALTHER FOR OTHER MILITARY PISTOLS.

P.38—double action, 9mm, 5 in. barrel, fixed sights, brown or black composite grips, blued finish. Many variations exhibiting a variety of metal finishes and codings, 34 oz. Over 1,000,000 manufactured during WW II.

Note: This model was adopted as the standard service pistol of the German Military in 1938. The P.38 was manufactured by Walther - code "ac" (manufactured 1939-1945), Mauser - code "byf" (manufactured Nov. of 1942-1945), and Spreewerke - code "cyq." (manufactured 1943-1945). The finish on most WWII 1942 and later P.38's is not of the same quality as the pre and early war Walther guns with the Spreewerke (cyq) models being the poorest. Pre-war Walther commercial manufactured P.38's command a 10-35% premium (models MP, AP, and Walther Banner HP's) over Zero-series prices listed below.

Grading	100%	98%	95%	90%	80%	70%	60%

ZERO-SERIES HP—"Heeres Pistole", with Mauser banner, high polish finish. Manufactured in 1939 and 1940. 5-digit number without suffix. Add 10% for matching mag.

Zero Series - 1st Issue—internal extractor, square firing pin.

	$3,500	$3,000	$2,250	$1,800	$1,500	$1,200	$1,000

Zero Series - 2nd Issue—external extractor, square firing pin.

	$2,750	$2,200	$2,000	$1,700	$1,400	$1,100	$900

Zero Series - 3rd Issue—external extractor, round firing pin.

	$1,800	$1,400	$1,000	$800	$700	$600	$500

480 code—"480" appears on slide.

	$1,850	$1,400	$1,100	$850	$725	$625	$525

"ac-40" CODE—add 20% for matching Mag. The 480 code was dropped in October of 1940, and the "ac" code was started.

	$1,100	$800	$700	$600	$500	$430	$380

"ac-41" OR "ac-42" CODE—add 20% for matching Mag.

	$600	$475	$425	$380	$340	$300	$275

"ac" OR "byf" CODED 43-45—letters are followed by two digit code corresponding to year of manufacture 1943-1945. Two line codes are more desirable than single line models. Highest P.38 production occurred in 1943 and 1944.

	$400	$350	$285	$250	$225	$200	$175

Add 20% for "dual tone" (phosphate finish — byf-44 date).

"cyq" CODE AND "ac-45" MISMATCH—found in "c" serial suffix range, mismatched slide and frame on ac-45 model.

	$375	$320	$265	$240	$210	$190	$165

Deduct 20% for ac-45 mismatch.

LATE WAR (1945)—Zero Series with rough milled finish.

	$700	$600	$500	$425	$350	$300	$250

1945 "svw" CODE—Mauser manufactured after January, 1945.

	$300	$265	$230	$200	$185	$175	$165

Recent importation has decreased values substantially in the last several years.

1946 "svw" CODE—Mauser manufactured in 1946.

	$395	$350	$295	$265	$235	$210	$195

GEVARM

STE. ETIENNE, FRANCE.

E-1 AUTOLOADING RIFLE—.22 LR, 19 in. barrel, open sights, walnut pistol grip stock.

	$165	$130	$110	$100	$85	$65	$55

GIB

10 GAUGE MAGNUM SHOTGUN—10 ga., 3½ in. chambers, 32 in. full choke barrel, case hardened receiver, matted rib, rubber pad, checkered pistol grip walnut stock. Discontinued.

	$275	$250	$235	$220	$200	$175	$150

GIBBS GUNS, INC.

PREVIOUSLY MANUFACTURED BY VOLUNTEER ENTERPRISES IN KNOXVILLE, TN AND PREVIOUSLY DISTRIBUTED BY GIBBS GUNS, INC. LOCATED IN GREENBACK,TN.

MARK 45 CARBINE—.45 ACP only, based on TS M6 Thompson machine gun, 16½ in. barrel, 5, 15, 30, or 90 shot clip, U.S. manufactured. Disc. in 1988.

	$275	$225	$180	$165	$155	$145	$135

Add $60 minimum for nickel plating.

Last Mfg.'s Sug. Retail was $279.

GLOCK

MANUFACTURED BY GLOCK GES.m.b.H. IN AUSTRIA SINCE 1983. IMPORTED AND DISTRIBUTED BY GLOCK, INC., LOCATED IN SMYRNA, GA.

GLOCK 17—9mm, double action, unique polymer frame, mag., trigger and other pistol parts. Steel barrel, slide, and springs, 17 shot mag., 27.9 oz. loaded, adj. (Sport) or fixed (Military) rear sight, includes extra mag., case, and spare rear sight. Importation began in late 1985.

Mfg.'s Sug. Retail $512 $450 $365 $300

Add $15 for adj. sights.

The retail price is the same for fixed or adj. rear sight. Currently, however, a small premium is being charged for the adj. sight because of demand.

Glock 17L Competition Model—competition version of the Glock 17, includes internally compensated 6 in. barrel, recalibrated trigger pull (3½ lb. pull), adj. rear sight. New in 1988.

Mfg.'s Sug. Retail $774 $625 $495 $400

GLOCK 19 COMPACT—similar to Glock 17, except has scaled down dimensions with 4 in. barrel and serrated grip straps, 15 or 17 round mag. New in 1988.

Mfg.'s Sug. Retail $512 $475 $380 $320

GOLDEN EAGLE

NIKKO LIMITED, TOCHIGI, JAPAN.

RIFLES

MODEL 7000 GRADE I—bolt action, all popular American calibers, including .270, and .300 Wby., 24 and 26 in. barrels, select skipline checkered walnut stock, rosewood pistol grip and forearm tip, recoil pad, made 1976. Discontinued.

| | $495 | $440 | $360 | $305 | $275 | $220 | $195 |

MODEL 7000 GRADE I AFRICAN—same as 7000, except .375 H&H and .458 Win. Mag., open sights.

| | $535 | $470 | $385 | $330 | $255 | $230 | $210 |

MODEL 7000 GRADE II—scroll engraving, better grade wood.

SHOTGUNS

| | $605 | $495 | $415 | $330 | $275 | $220 | $200 |

MODEL 5000 GRADE I—O/U shotgun, 12 and 20 ga., 26, 28, and 30 in. barrels, various chokes, vent rib, engraved receiver, gold eagle head inlay, auto ejectors, SST, checkered pistol grip beavertail stock, made 1975. Discontinued.

| | $880 | $855 | $715 | $635 | $525 | $470 | $415 |

MODEL 5000 GRADE I SKEET—same as 5000, except 26 and 28 in. skeet bored, wide rib.

| | $935 | $880 | $745 | $660 | $550 | $495 | $385 |

MODEL 5000 GRADE I TRAP—same as Field, except 30 or 32 in. barrel, mod. and full, imp. mod. and full, or full and full choke, wide rib, trap stock with pad.

| | $965 | $910 | $770 | $690 | $605 | $525 | $440 |

MODEL 5000 GRADE II—available in Field, Trap, and Skeet, more engraving, better grade wood, with or without screaming eagle on receiver in gold.

	$990	$965	$825	$635	$550	$470	$385
Skeet	$1,020	$980	$880	$800	$715	$660	$550
Trap	$1,045	$1,020	$935	$855	$770	$715	$605

GRANDEE GRADE III—same as 5000 Grade II, except elaborate engraving, inlays, and better grade wood.

| | $2,500 | $2,150 | $1,750 | $1,300 | $1,125 | $1,000 | $850 |

GONCZ CO.

MANUFACTURER AND DISTRIBUTOR LOCATED IN NORTH HOLLYWOOD, CA SINCE 1984.

Early 3-digit serial numbers can bring premiums of 25% or more. Currently, all Goncz firearms have match barrels and are built completely in the U.S. The Goncz action is unique since it is not a copy of any other major design.

MODEL GA SERIES PISTOL—7.63 Mauser, .38 Super, 9mm, or .45 ACP cal., 9½ in. shrouded barrel, black matte finish, one piece grip, 16 or 18 shot mag., except in .45 ACP cal. (10 or 20 shot), 3 lbs. 2 oz. New in 1985.

Mfg.'s Sug. Retail	$425	$375	$295	$250	$220	$200	$185	$170

Stainless steel frame became standard in 1987.

Model GAT-9—9mm, similar to GA Series, except has adj. trigger and hand polished parts.

Mfg.'s Sug. Retail	$550	$480	$395	$350	$300	$275	$2250	$225

Stainless steel frame became standard in 1987.

Stainless Steel Collector's Issue—all internal and external parts precision polished, cased, low serial numbers, limited mfg.

Mfg.'s Sug. Retail	$750	$750	$595	$475

MODEL GS SERIES PISTOL—similar to GA Series, except has 5 in. non-shrouded barrel, 2 lbs. 10 oz.

	$350	$280	$250	$220	$200	$185	$170

Stainless steel frame became standard in 1987. Last Mfg.'s Suggested Retail on the steel model was $340.

Model GS Stainless—similar to GS Series, except is 100% stainless steel. New in 1987.

Mfg.'s Sug. Retail	$415	$375	$340	$300

Stainless Steel Collector's Issue—all internal and external parts precision polished, cased, low serial numbers, limited mfg.

Mfg.'s Sug. Retail	$725	$725	$575	$475

GC CARBINE—same cal.'s as GA Series pistols, 16.1 in. barrel, uncheckered walnut stock, 4 lbs. 10 oz.

Mfg.'s Sug. Retail	$440	$395	$350	$315	$285	$260	$240	$220

Model GC Stainless—similar to GC Carbine, except is 100% stainless steel. New in 1987.

Mfg.'s Sug. Retail	$550	$550	$425	$330

Stainless Steel Collector's Issue—all internal and external parts precision polished, cased, low serial numbers, limited mfg.

Mfg.'s Sug. Retail	$800	$800	$595	$495

Halogen Carbine—9mm or .45 ACP only, similar to carbine, except is supplied with halogen lighting unit underneath barrel, can be trigger activated. New in 1986.

Mfg.'s Sug. Retail	$550	$485	$425	$350	$325	$300	$280	$260

Laser Carbine—similar to Halogen Carbine, except laser sighting replaces halogen light — accuracy to 400 yds. New in 1986.

Mfg.'s Sug. Retail	$1,500	$1,375	$1,100	$935	$825	$770	$700	$650

GRANGER, G.

MANUFACTURER LOCATED IN SAINT ETIENNE, FRANCE SINCE 1902, IMPORTED AND DISTRIBUTED BY WES GILPIN LOCATED IN DALLAS, TX.

G. Granger manufactures high quality, limited production side by side shotguns in 12, 16, or 20 ga. All guns are made on a custom order basis with prices starting at $13,500. Prices will vary per customer specifications and appointments. Quotations are available on application to Wes Gilpin directly.

GRANT, STEPHEN

PREVIOUSLY MANUFACTURED IN LONDON, ENGLAND.

Manufacturer specializing in custom order only SxS rifles and shotguns. Shotguns (12, 16, or 20 ga.) can be top or side lever and are equipped with sidelocks and a self-opening mechanism. Very limited production making values hard to establish. Prices are at par with similar quality H&H firearms.

GREENER, W.W., LIMITED

PREVIOUSLY MANUFACTURED IN BIRMINGHAM, ENGLAND.

SHOTGUNS

FARKILLER GRADE F35—double barrel, 12 ga., 28, 30, or 32 in. barrels, hammerless boxlock, checkered straight or semi-pistol grip stock.

	100%	98%	95%	90%	80%	70%	60%
	$2,420	$2,200	$2,090	$1,870	$1,760	$1,650	$1,540
Auto ejectors	$3,300	$3,025	$2,750	$2,475	$2,035	$1,925	$1,650

FARKILLER GRADE F35 LARGE BORE—same as F35 above, except 8 or 10 ga.

	100%	98%	95%	90%	80%	70%	60%
	$2,750	$2,585	$2,310	$2,090	$1,980	$1,815	$1,650
Auto ejectors	$3,575	$3,300	$3,080	$2,860	$2,640	$2,090	$1,925

HAMMERLESS EJECTOR MODELS—12, 16, 20, 28, and .410 ga.'s, 26, 28, or 30 in. barrels supplied with any choke combination, auto ejectors, single or double triggers, straight or semi-pistol grip stock, grades differ as follows:

Jubilee Grade DH35

	100%	98%	95%	90%	80%	70%	60%
	$2,420	$2,255	$2,090	$1,925	$1,650	$1,540	$1,375

Sovereign Grade DH40

	100%	98%	95%	90%	80%	70%	60%
	$2,860	$2,695	$2,420	$2,200	$1,980	$1,815	$1,595

Crown Grade DH55

	100%	98%	95%	90%	80%	70%	60%
	$3,300	$3,080	$2,915	$2,750	$2,420	$2,035	$1,760

Royal Grade DH75

	100%	98%	95%	90%	80%	70%	60%
	$4,400	$4,180	$3,850	$3,300	$3,080	$2,915	$2,640

Add $400 for SST.

Note: Degree of engraving and grade of wood are the basic differences between models.

EMPIRE—double barrel, 12 ga. only, 2¾ or 3 in., any choke, 28, 30, or 32 in. barrel, hammerless, boxlock, straight stock or semi pistol grip.

	100%	98%	95%	90%	80%	70%	60%
	$1,760	$1,540	$1,320	$1,100	$935	$825	$770
Auto ejectors	$1,980	$1,760	$1,540	$1,320	$1,155	$1,045	$990

EMPIRE DELUXE—double barrel, same as Empire, only better grade wood.

	100%	98%	95%	90%	80%	70%	60%
	$1,980	$1,760	$1,540	$1,320	$1,155	$1,045	$990
Auto ejectors	$2,200	$1,980	$1,760	$1,540	$1,375	$1,265	$1,100

GENERAL PURPOSE—12 ga., improved Martini action, single shot, 26, 30, or 32 in. barrel, full or mod., auto ejectors, straight checkered stock.

	100%	98%	95%	90%	80%	70%	60%
	$330	$305	$275	$220	$195	$165	$160

GREIFELT AND COMPANY

SUHL, GERMANY.

SHOTGUNS: SIDE-BY-SIDE

MODEL 22—12 and 20 ga., 28 or 30 in. mod. and full, hammerless, boxlock, false sideplates, extractors, checkered pistol grip or English style stock, post WWII.

	100%	98%	95%	90%	80%	70%	60%
	$2,200	$1,760	$1,595	$1,320	$1,100	$990	$825

Grading	100%	98%	95%	90%	80%	70%	60%

MODEL 22E—same as 22, except auto ejectors.

	100%	98%	95%	90%	80%	70%	60%
	$2,750	$2,200	$1,980	$1,760	$1,540	$1,430	$1,265

MODEL 103—12 and 16 ga., 28 and 30 in. mod. and full, extractors, double triggers, checkered pistol grip or English stock, post war.

	$1,980	$1,650	$1,485	$1,210	$990	$880	$715

MODEL 103E—same as model 103, except auto ejectors.

	$2,200	$1,760	$1,595	$1,320	$1,100	$990	$825

SHOTGUNS: OVER/UNDER & DRILLING

GRADE NO. 1—O/U, 12, 16, 20, 28, and .410 ga.'s, any barrel 26-32 in., choke, vent or solid rib, Anson & Deeley boxlock, auto ejectors, checkered pistol grip or English stock, pre-war.
12 and 20 ga.

	$3,600	$3,200	$2,850	$2,500	$2,100	$1,750	$1,500

Deduct 10% for 16 ga.
Add 30% for 28 and .410 ga.'s
Add $300 for vent rib.
Add $400 for SST.

GRADE NO. 3—same as No. 1, except less elaborate engraving, pre WWII.
12 ga.

	$2,850	$2,500	$2,200	$2,000	$1,650	$1,350	$1,200

Deduct 10% for 16 ga.
Add 20% for 28 and .410 ga.'s.
Add $300 for vent rib.
Add $400 for SST.

MODEL 143E—O/U, similar to model 1, except not as high quality as pre-war model, not available in 28 or .410 ga., made post-WWII.

	$2,400	$2,150	$1,850	$1,550	$1,350	$1,175	$1,000

Add 10% for vent rib and SST.

O/U COMBINATION GUN—12, 16, 20, 28, and .410 ga.'s, shotgun barrel, rifle in any rimmed caliber, 24 or 26 in. solid rib barrel, pre-WWII.

	$5,200	$4,800	$4,400	$4,000	$3,600	$3,150	$2,800

Add $700 for auto ejectors.
Deduct 10% for 16 ga.
Add 20% for 28 and .410 ga.'s.
Deduct 40-50% for obsolete rifle caliber.

Above values for 12 or 20 ga. over obtainable rifle cartridge.

DRILLING—12, 16, and 20 ga., SxS over any rimmed rifle caliber, 26 in. barrels, boxlock, extractors, double triggers, rifle sight activated by barrel selector, pre WWII.

	$3,500	$3,000	$2,750	$2,550	$2,300	$2,000	$1,750

Deduct 10% for 16 ga.
Deduct 40-50% for obsolete cal.'s.

Previous values for 12 and 20 ga. over available caliber.

GRENDEL, INC.

MANUFACTURER LOCATED IN ROCKLEDGE, FL SINCE 1984.

Grendel firearms are noted for their precision manufacture, outstanding accuracy, and lightweight characteristics.

P-10 SERIES PISTOL—.380 ACP, semi-auto, double action, 10 shot mag., small dimensions, hammerless, matte blue finish, 15 oz.

Mfg.'s Sug. Retail	$150	$135	$120	$110	$100	$95	$90	$85

Add $15 for electroless nickel finish.
Add $5 for green finish.

Grading	100%	98%	95%	90%	80%	70%	60%

SRT-20F COMPACT RIFLE—.308 cal., bolt action based on the Sako A-2 action, 20 in. match grade finned barrel with muzzle brake, folding synthetic stock, integrated bipod rest, no sights, 9 shot mag., 6.7 lbs.

Mfg.'s Sug. Retail	$525	$475	$395	$365	$340	$320	$300	$285

Grendel previously manufactured the SRT-20L and SRT-24 - both were discontinued in 1988. Values are approximately the same as the SRT-20F.

GRIFFIN & HOWE

U.S. CUSTOM GUNSMITH/MANUFACTURER THAT STARTED IN 1923 - LOCATED IN NEW YORK, NY.

Griffin & Howe are custom gunsmiths who do a variety of gunsmithing services (including building custom rifles), almost totally by individual customer order. Prices vary greatly depending on configuration desirability, condition, and special orders/features. Most Griffin & Howe custom rifles (in average condition) start in the $1,200 + range and rise according to the nature of the gun. Less than 2,700 custom rifles were manufactured between 1923 and 1966. In 1930 G & H became a subsidiary of Abercrombie & Fitch. Because all G & H rifles were essentially special ordered, accurate pricing can only be ascertained by examining one specimen at a time. Elaborate specimens in this trademark will command $4,000 and higher. Engraving by Joseph Fugger (employed by G & H) will add considerably to the value.

.30-06 SPRINGFIELD BOLT ACTION—a classic sporter based on the U.S. 1903 Springfield military rifle.

	$1,900	$1,675	$1,300	$1,200	$1,050	$975	$850

Above values represent a base gun with normal wood and no options.

GUNWORKS, LTD.

PREVIOUSLY MANUFACTURED AND DISTRIBUTED IN BUFFALO, NY. EARLY GUNS WERE MADE IN TONAWANDA, NY.

MODEL 9—O/U derringer, .357 Mag., 9mm or .38 Super, and .38 Spl. cal.'s, electroless nickel finish, 2½ in. barrel, wood grips, Millett sights, 15 oz. Discontinued in 1986.

	$135	$120	$105	$95	$65	$55	$50

Last Mfg.'s Sug. Retail was $149.

GUSTAF, CARL

MANUFACTURED IN ESKILSTUNA, SWEDEN.

MODEL 2000—6.5 x 55, .243, .270, .30-06, and .308 cal.'s, bolt action, Monte Carlo walnut stock with checkering, open sights, cold-swaged barrel and receiver, 60 degree bolt. Discontinued in 1985.

	$650	$560	$520	$480	$440	$415	$380

Last Mfg.'s Sug. Retail was $750.

STANDARD BOLT ACTION RIFLE—6.5 x 55, 7 x 64, .270, 7mm Mag., .308, .30-06, and 9.3 x 62, 24 in. barrel, folding rear sight, checkered classic style stock, made 1970-1977.

	$495	$415	$360	$330	$310	$275	$250

Monte Carlo stock

	$525	$440	$385	$360	$335	$305	$275

GUSTAF, CARL, cont.

Grading	100%	98%	95%	90%	80%	70%	60%

GRADE II—same as Monte Carlo Standard, in .22-250, .25-06, 6.5 x 55, .270, 7mm Mag., .308, .30-06, and .300 Win. Mag., select stock and rosewood pistol grip cap, and forearm tip.

	$605	$525	$470	$440	$420	$385	$330

GRADE III—same as Grade II, except fancy wood, deluxe high gloss finish.

	$715	$635	$580	$550	$530	$495	$440

DELUXE—same as Grade III, except engraved floorplate and trigger guard, Deluxe French walnut, and jeweled bolt.

	$800	$715	$635	$605	$580	$525	$495

VARMINT TARGET MODEL—bolt action, fast lock time, .222, .22-250, .243, and 6.5 x 55, 27 in. barrel, no sights, large bakelite bolt knob, target type stock, made 1970. Discontinued.

	$550	$495	$440	$385	$360	$320	$290

GRAND PRIX SINGLE SHOT TARGET—fastest lock time bolt action, .22 LR, 27 in. heavy barrel with adj. weight, no sights, target stock, adj. buttplate, made 1970. Discontinued.

	$550	$495	$440	$385	$360	$320	$290

NOTES

H

H.J.S. INDUSTRIES, INC.

BROWNSVILLE, TX.

Grading	100%	98%	95%	90%	80%	70%	60%

FRONTIER FOUR DERRINGER—4 shot derringer, .22 LR only, stainless steel construction, 5½ oz.

	$115	**$90**	**$80**

LONE STAR DERRINGER—single shot derringer, .38 S&W only, stainless steel construction, 6 oz.

	$137	**$105**	**$95**

HWP INDUSTRIES

MANUFACTURER LOCATED IN MILWAUKEE, WI.

THE SLEDGEHAMMER—.500 HWP Mag. cal., 5 shot revolver, double action, stainless steel, full shrouded 4 in. barrel (quick change), pachmayr grips. New in 1989.

Mfg.'s Sug. Retail   **$1,295 $1,150 $895 $750**

HAENEL, C.G.

PREVIOUS MANUFACTURER LOCATED IN SUHL, GERMANY. MFG. BETWEEN 1925-1940.

RIFLES

MAUSER-MANNLICHER SPORTING RIFLE—M/88 Mauser type action, 7 x 57, 8 x 57, or 9 x 57 cal., 22 or 24 in. octagon barrel, Mannlicher box mag., double set triggers, raised rib on barrel leaf sight, sporter stock.

	$440	**$360**	**$330**	**$275**	**$250**	**$220**	**$165**

88 MAUSER SPORTER—same as Mauser-Mannlicher, with Mauser 5 shot mag.

	$525	**$450**	**$375**	**$325**	**$275**	**$240**	**$200**

PISTOLS

SCHMEISSER MODEL 1 & 2—.25 ACP, similar to Baby Browning.

	$385	**$340**	**$300**	**$275**	**$230**	**$200**	**$180**

MODELS 200-205—See Hammerli-Walther

HAMBUSH, JOSEPH

MANUFACTURED IN FERLACH, AUSTRIA.

SHOTGUN—boxlock or sidelock SxS, various ga.'s, most specimens exhibit game scene engraving, ejectors, SST or DT. Not many specimens are encountered in this trademark - boxlock prices typically start in the $1,000 on up range and sidelocks begin in the $2,000 range.

HAMMERLI

MANUFACTURED IN LENZBURG, SWITZERLAND. CURRENTLY IMPORTED AND DISTRIBUTED BY MANDALL SHOOTING SUPPLIES, INC. LOCATED IN SCOTTSDALE, AZ AND BEEMAN PRECISION ARMS LOCATED IN SANTA ROSA, CA. PREVIOUSLY IMPORTED BY OSBORNE'S LOCATED IN CHEBOYGAN, MI.

PISTOLS

MODEL 100 FREE PISTOL—.22 LR, 11½ in. octagon barrel, blue, martini action single shot, set trigger, micro rear sight, walnut stock and forearm, made 1933-1949.

	$880	$660	$605	$550	$470	$440	$385

Deluxe model—carved stock.

	$990	$770	$715	$660	$580	$550	$495

MODEL 101—similar to 100, but heavy round barrel, improved action and sights, matte finish, made 1956-1960.

	$880	$660	$605	$550	$470	$440	$385

MODEL 102—same as 101, except high polished finish, made 1956-1960.

	$880	$660	$605	$550	$470	$440	$385
Deluxe model.	$990	$770	$715	$660	$580	$550	$495

MODEL 103 FREE PISTOL—same as model 101, except lighter octagon polished barrel, made 1956-1960.

	$935	$715	$660	$605	$580	$550	$495

MODEL 104 MATCH PISTOL—similar to 103, except lighter round barrel, redesigned stock, made 1961-1965.

	$760	$660	$550	$495	$470	$440	$385

MODEL 105 MATCH PISTOL—similar to 103, except redesigned action and stock, made 1962-1965.

	$935	$715	$660	$605	$580	$550	$495

MATCH PISTOL—similar to 105, except improved trigger.

	$910	$690	$580	$525	$495	$470	$415

MODEL 107 MATCH PISTOL—similar to 105, except improved trigger.

	$990	$770	$660	$550	$525	$495	$440

Deluxe model—engraved and carved wood.

	$1,320	$990	$880	$660	$635	$605	$550

MODEL 120-1 SINGLE SHOT FREE PISTOL—.22 LR, bolt action, 9.9 in. barrel, blue barrel and receiver, side lever operated, anodized aluminum lever and frame, walnut checkered grips.

	$440	$360	$305	$275	$220	$200	$175

MODEL 120-2—same as 120-1, except stocks hand contoured.

	$470	$385	$330	$305	$250	$220	$195

MODEL 120 HEAVY BARREL—same as 120-1, with 5.7 in. bull barrel.

MODEL 150 FREE PISTOL—.22 LR cal., 11.3 in. barrel, improved Martini-type action, set trigger, innovative design incorporating many unusual features.

Mfg.'s Sug. Retail	$1,980	$1,850	$1,495	$1,275	$1,120	$980	$900	$850

Add $89 for left-hand variation.

MODEL 152 FREE PISTOL—.22 LR cal., 11.3 in. barrel. improved Martini-type action, electronic trigger release, innovative design incorporating many unusual features. State of the art target pistol.

Mfg.'s Sug. Retail	$2,105	$2,000	$1,600	$1,350	$1,195	$1,090	$990	$895

Add $90 for left-hand variation.

MODELS 200-205—See Hammerli-Walther

	$440	$360	$305	$275	$220	$200	$175

Grading	100%	98%	95%	90%	80%	70%	60%

INTERNATIONAL MODEL 206—.22 LR, .22 S, semi-auto, 7¹⁄₁₆ in. barrel with muzzle brake, adj. sights, walnut grips, blue, made 1962-1969.

	$690	$605	$495	$470	$385	$360	$330

INTERNATIONAL MODEL 207—same as 206, except adj. grip heel.

	$705	$635	$505	$480	$395	$370	$340

INTERNATIONAL MODEL 208—.22 LR, semi-auto, 9 shot, 6 in. barrel, blue, adj. sights, checkered walnut grips with adj. heel, made 1966-1988.

	$1,700	$1,495	$1,275	$1,120	$980	$900	$850

Last Mfg.'s Sug. Retail was $1,960.

Model 208S—similar to Model 208, except has redesigned trigger guard and interchangeable rear sight element. Imported in 1988 only.

	$1,200	$935	$875	$820	$760	$600	$550

Last Mfg.'s Sug. Retail was $1,417.

This model was also distributed by Mandall Shooting Supplies located in Scottsdale, AZ.

Model 208 Deluxe—similar to Model 208, except has carved grips and elaborate engraving. Importation disc. in 1988.

	$2,995	$2,500	$1,995

Last Mfg.'s Sug. Retail was $3,250.

Model 208C (Commemorative)—limited edition commemorative. Disc. in 1987.

	$2,100	$1,750	$1,400

Last Mfg.'s Sug. Retail was $2,225.

INTERNATIONAL MODEL 209—.22 Short, semi-auto, 5 shot, 4¾ in. barrel, muzzle brake, adj. sights, blue, walnut stock, made 1966-1970.

	$800	$690	$635	$550	$525	$485	$440

INTERNATIONAL MODEL 210—same as 209, but grips have adj. heel, made 1966-1970.

	$800	$715	$660	$590	$540	$525	$495

MODEL 211—.22 LR, semi-auto, 9 shot, 6 in. barrel, adj. sights, blue, similar to Model 208 except non-adj. walnut stocks.

Mfg.'s Sug. Retail	$1,570	$1,495	$1,250	$1,050	$950	$880	$835	$770

MODEL 212—.22 LR, semi-auto, hunter's pistol, 9 shot, 5 in. barrel, adj. sights, blue, walnut stocks.

Mfg.'s Sug. Retail	$1,550	$1,450	$1,200	$935	$875	$820	$760	$600

MODEL 215—.22 LR, semi-auto, Model 208 specs on commercial target model, 9 shot, 5 in. barrel, adj. sights, blue, walnut stocks.

Mfg.'s Sug. Retail	$1,305	$1,250	$1,000	$895	$775	$695	$650	$600

MODEL 230 RAPID FIRE PISTOL—.22 S, semi-auto, 5 shot, 6.3 in. barrel, blue, adj. sights, smooth walnut grips, made 1970-1983.

	$705	$635	$580	$530	$485	$450	$415

MODEL 230-2—same as 230, except checkered grips with adj. heel, made 1970-1983.

	$735	$655	$605	$570	$515	$485	$470

MODEL 232 RAPID FIRE PISTOL—.22 S, semi-auto, 6 shot, 5.1 in. barrel, blue, adj. sights, contoured walnut grips.

Mfg.'s Sug. Retail	$1,445	$1,350	$1,100	$950	$850	$750	$700	$650

Add $210 for wrap-around grips sizes S-M-LG (Model 232-2).

MODEL 280—.22 LR or .32 Wadcutter, new modular pistol design utilizing carbon fiber synthetic material to replace frame and other critical parts, adj. grips, trigger, and rear sight, 4.6 in. barrel, 5 or 6 shot mag., approx. 2.2 lbs. New in 1988.

Mfg.'s Sug. Retail	$1,800	$1,750	$1,450	$1,200	$935	$875	$820	$760

MODEL P-240—see S.I.G.- HAMMERLI for this model.

Grading	100%	98%	95%	90%	80%	70%	60%

RIFLES: TARGET

OLYMPIC 300 METER—.30-06 or .300 H&H Mag., bolt action, single shot free rifle, U.S.A. import, 7 x 57mm overseas, 20½ in. heavy barrel, double set trigger, aperture rear sight, globe front, free rifle stock with thumbhole pistol grip, beavertail forearm, Swiss style target butt, made 1945-1959.

	$880	$745	$605	$550	$470	$440	$415

HAMMERLI-TANNER 300 METER FREE RIFLE—similar to Olympic 300 , except 7.5mm standard, can be ordered in other calibers, made 1962-discontinued.

	$895	$825	$770	$715	$660	$580	$520

Last Mfg.'s Sug. Retail was $935.

MODEL 45 SMALLBORE MATCH RIFLE—.22 LR, bolt action, single shot, 27½ in. heavy barrel, same sights and stock type as Hammerli-Tanner, made 1945-1957.

	$660	$550	$470	$440	$385	$360	$330

MODEL 54 SMALLBORE MATCH RIFLE—similar to 45 Smallbore, except adj. butt, made 1954-1957.

	$670	$560	$480	$450	$395	$370	$340

MODEL 503 SMALLBORE FREE RIFLE—similar to 54 Smallbore, except free style stock.

	$660	$550	$470	$440	$385	$360	$330

MODEL 506 SMALLBORE MATCH RIFLE—similar to 503 Smallbore, made 1963-1966.

	$690	$580	$495	$470	$415	$385	$360

SPORTING RIFLE—various calibers, set triggers. Hunting Model-single shot.

	$650	$490	$425	$360	$325	$300	$260

HAMMERLI-WALTHER

TARGET PISTOLS MANUFACTURED UNDER JOINT EFFORT.

PISTOLS: SEMI-AUTO

MODEL 200 OLYMPIA—.22 Short or LR, 7½ in. barrel, 1952 type, adj. sights, barrel weight, blue, checkered walnut grips, made 1952-1958.

	$660	$605	$550	$440	$415	$385	$360

MODEL 200 OLYMPIA—1958 type, same as 1952 type, except has muzzle brake, made 1958-1963.

	$715	$605	$550	$495	$470	$415	$385

MODEL 201—same as 200, 1952 type, except 9½ in. barrel, made 1955-1957.

	$660	$605	$550	$440	$415	$385	$360

MODEL 202—same as 201, except adj. heel grips, made 1955-1957.

	$715	$605	$550	$495	$470	$415	$385

MODEL 203—same as 200, except has adj. heel grip.

1955 type—no muzzle brake.

	$715	$605	$550	$495	$470	$415	$385

1958 type—muzzle brake.

	$770	$660	$605	$550	$525	$470	$440

MODEL 204—similar to 200, except .22 LR only.

1956 type—no muzzle brake.

	$745	$635	$580	$525	$495	$470	$440

1958 type—muzzle brake.

	$800	$690	$635	$550	$525	$495	$470

MODEL 205—.22 LR, same as 204, except adj. heel grips.

	100%	98%	95%	90%	80%	70%	60%
1956 type	$800	$690	$635	$550	$525	$495	$470
1958 type, M.B.	$855	$745	$715	$635	$580	$525	$495

HARRINGTON & RICHARDSON, INC.

GARDNER, MA - FORMERLY FROM WORCHESTER, MA. SUCCESSORS TO WESSON & HARRINGTON, MANUFACTURED FROM 1871 UNTIL JANUARY 24, 1986.

A manufacturer of utilitarian firearms for over 115 years, H & R ceased operation on January 24, 1986. The discontinuance of this trademark may produce premiums on the older, discontinued models in either N.I.B. or mint condition, but probably will not affect values on those handguns only recently discontinued.

Even though this trademark has been discontinued for over 3 years, collector interest to date has been mimimal. Most H & R firearms are still purchased for their shooting value rather than collecting potential.

PISTOLS: PRE-1942

MODEL 4—.32 S&W Long 6 shot, or .38 S&W Long 5 shot, (1904), double action, 2½, 4½, and 6 in. barrels, blued or nickel, hard rubber grips, solid frame, fixed sights.

$95	$85	$70	$55	$45	$35	$30

MODEL 5—.32 S&W Long, 5 shot only, (1905), double action, same as Model 4.

$95	$85	$70	$55	$45	$35	$30

MODEL 6—.22 LR, 7 shot only, (1906), double action, same as Model 4.

$95	$85	$70	$55	$45	$35	$30

AMERICAN—.32 S&W, 6 shot, .38 S&W, 5 shot, double action, 2½, 4, and 6 in. barrels, fixed sights, blue or nickel.

$95	$85	$70	$55	$45	$35	$30

YOUNG AMERICAN—.22 Long, 7 shot, .32 S&W, 5 shot, double action, 2, 4½, or 6 in. barrel, fixed sights, blue or nickel.

$95	$85	$70	$55	$45	$35	$30

VEST POCKET—double action, 1⅛ in. barrel, blue or nickel, solid frame, spurless hammer.

$95	$85	$70	$55	$45	$35	$30

HUNTER—.22 LR, double action, 10 in. octagon barrel, 9 shot, checkered walnut grips.

$140	$110	$100	$85	$65	$55	$45

TRAPPER—.22 LR, double action, 7 shot, 6 in. octagon barrel, checkered walnut stocks.

$140	$120	$100	$85	$65	$55	$45

MODEL 922—.22 LR, first issue, 9 shot, 10 in. octagon barrel on early models, 6 in. round barrel on later models, checkered walnut grips.

$140	$120	$100	$85	$65	$55	$45

AUTOMATIC EJECTING—.32 S&W, 6 shot, .38 S&W, 5 shot, double action, 3¼, 4, 5, and 6 in. barrels, hinged break open, fixed sights, black rubber grips.

$160	$150	$105	$90	$75	$65	$55

PREMIER—.22 LR, 7 shot, .32 S&W, 5 shot, double action, break open, small frame.

$95	$85	$70	$55	$45	$35	$30

HAMMERLESS—.22 LR, 7 shot, .32 S&W, 5 shot, double action, 2, 3, 4, 5, or 6 in. barrels, small frame, break open, blue or nickel, black rubber grips.

$125	$110	$100	$85	$65	$55	$45

HAMMERLESS—.32 S&W, 6 shot, .38 S&W, 5 shot, double action, 3¼, 4, 5, or 6 in. barrels, large frame, break open.

$125	$110	$100	$85	$65	$55	$45

TARGET MODEL—.22 LR, .22 WRF, 7 shot, double action, 6 in. barrel, fixed sights, break open, small frame, blue only, walnut grips.

$140	$120	$100	$85	$70	$60	$50

.22 SPECIAL—.22 LR, .22 WRF, 7 shot, double action, 6 in. barrel, break open, large frame, blue only, gold plated front sight, walnut grips.

$165	$140	$120	$100	$85	$70	$60

EXPERT—double action, same as .22 Special, except 10 in. barrel.

$150	$140	$120	$100	$85	$70	$60

Grading	100%	98%	95%	90%	80%	70%	60%

SPORTSMAN NO. 199—.22 LR, 9 shot, single action, 6 in. barrel, adj. target sights, break open, blue only, checkered walnut grips.

	$195	$165	$140	$110	$90	$75	$65

DEFENDER—.38 S&W, double action, 4 or 6 in. barrel, fixed sights, blue, break open, black plastic grips, made during WWII for police reserves and major corporation guards.

	$140	$120	$110	$100	$85	$65	$55

ULTRA SPORTSMAN—.22 LR, 9 shot, single action, 6 in. barrel, blue, break open, adj. sights, walnut grips, short cylinder action, wide hammer spur.

	$220	$200	$180	$150	$120	$100	$85

NEW DEFENDER—.22 LR, 9 shot, double action, 2 in. barrel, break open, adj. sights, blue, round butt, checkered walnut grip.

	$220	$200	$180	$150	$120	$100	$85

USRA SINGLE SHOT TARGET—.22 LR, 7, 8, or 10 in. barrel, blue, hinged break open, adj. sights, walnut grips, made 1928-1941.

	$440	$415	$385	$330	$290	$250	$195

Nickel finish — add $10%.

25 SELF LOADING PISTOL—.25 ACP, 6 shot, 2 in. barrel, fixed sights, blue, black rubber grips.

	$330	$305	$250	$195	$165	$140	$110

32 SELF LOADING PISTOL—.32 ACP, 8 shot, 3½ in. barrel, fixed sights, black rubber grips.

	$330	$305	$250	$195	$165	$140	$110

HANDY GUN—shotgun or rifle pistol manufactured between 1901-1933, available in either 8 in. or 12¼ in. barrel, either .410 or 28 ga. in shotgun configuration, centerfire rifle cal.'s also were available, although not as common. Guns were either case hardened (in Tiger stripe colors), or blued. Case hardened frames have "Handy Gun" stamped on side. Serial numbers on barrel lug and back of frame-numbers should match. .410 ga in 12¼ in. barrel length is most common. These guns had to be registered during the Amnesty period pre-1968. Guns that are not cannot be bought or sold legally. Purchasing a Handy Gun requires a $5 treasury stamp necessary for class 6 registration. Centerfire Handy Guns do not need the $5 stamp. Add $50 for original box or H & R holster.

	$600	$550	$520	$485	$450	$425	$395

REVOLVERS: RECENT PRODUCTION

MODEL 504 SQUARE BUTT—.32 H&R Mag., 5 shot, 4 or 6 in. bull barrels, adj. rear sight, swing out cylinder, blue, black plastic and walnut grips. Made 1984 and 1985.

	$165	$145	$135	$120	$110	$100	$90

Last Mfg.'s Sug. Retail was $185.

Model 504 Round Butt—compact design available with 3 or 4 in. barrel only. Discontinued in 1985.

	$165	$145	$135	$120	$110	$100	$90

Last Mfg.'s Sug. Retail was $185.

MODEL 532—.32 H&R Mag., 5 shot, 2½ and 4 in. barrels, solid frame revolver, blue, pull pin cylinder, black plastic and walnut grips. Made 1984 and 1985.

	$100	$90	$80	$70	$60	$50	$45

Last Mfg.'s Sug. Retail was $115.

MODEL 586—.32 H&R Mag., 5 shot, Western-style revolver, double action, 4½, 5½, 7½, and 10 in. barrels, adj. rear sight, fixed cylinder, antique finish, black plastic or walnut grips. Made 1984 and 1985.

	$175	$155	$135	$120	$110	$100	$90

Last Mfg.'s Sug. Retail was $195.

MODEL 603—.22 Mag. cal., 6 in. barrel, double action. Discontinued.

	$159	$120	$110	$95	$90	$80	$70

MODEL 604—same specifications as the Model 603, only has 6 in. bull barrel.

	$170	$130	$115	$95	$90	$80	$70

Grading	100%	98%	95%	90%	80%	70%	60%

MODEL 622—.22 short, long, or LR, solid frame, 6 shot, 2½, 4, or 6 in. barrels, blue, plastic grips, made 1957-1985.

	$95	**$82**	**$70**	**$60**	**$55**	**$50**	**$45**

Last Mfg.'s Sug. Retail was $104.

MODEL 623—same basic specifications as the Model 622, only nickel finish. Discontinued.

	$115	**$95**	**$75**	**$60**	**$55**	**$50**	**$45**

MODEL 632 GUARDSMAN—.32 S&W, 6 shot, 2½ or 4 in. barrel, solid frame, checkered tenite grips, blue, model 633 chrome, manufactured 1953-1984.

	$104	**$82**	**$70**	**$60**	**$55**	**$50**	**$45**

MODEL 633—same basic specifications as the Model 632, only nickel finish. Discontinued.

	$115	**$95**	**$75**	**$60**	**$55**	**$50**	**$45**

MODEL 642—.22 Mag cal., 2½ or 4 in. barrel. Discontinued.

	$95	**$70**	**$65**	**$60**	**$50**	**$45**	**$40**

MODEL 649 CONVERTIBLE—.22 LR and .22 Mag. cal.'s, furnished with extra cylinder, Western style, double action, side loading, 5½ or 7½ in. barrel, 6 shot, walnut grips, blued finish, made 1976-1985.

	$140	**$120**	**$110**	**$95**	**$90**	**$80**	**$70**

Last Mfg.'s Sug. Retail was $160.

MODEL 650 CONVERTIBLE—same as Model 649, except with nickel finish and only available with 5½ in. barrel. Discontinued in 1985.

	$150	**$130**	**$115**	**$100**	**$90**	**$80**	**$70**

Last Mfg.'s Sug. Retail was $175.

MODEL 666—.22 LR, .22 Win. Mag., 6 shot, 6 in. barrel, blue, plastic grips, convertible, made 1976-1982.

	$100	**$90**	**$70**	**$50**	**$45**	**$35**	**$30**

MODEL 676—.22 LR and .22 Win. Mag., 6 shot, 4½, 5½, 7½, and 12 in. barrel, side load and eject, convertible, blue, case hardened frame, one piece walnut stock, made 1976-1982.

	$140	**$120**	**$100**	**$85**	**$60**	**$45**	**$35**

MODEL 686 CONVERTIBLE—.22 LR and .22 Mag. cal.'s, furnished with extra cylinder, Western style, double action, side loading, 5½, 7½, 10 or 12 in. barrel, 6 shot, walnut grips, color case hardened frame, adj. rear sight, 12 in. barrel. Discontinued in 1984.

	$185	**$160**	**$140**	**$125**	**$110**	**$90**	**$80**

MODEL 732—.32 S&W and .32 H&R Mag., 6 shot, 2½ and 4 in. barrels, fixed sights, swing out cylinder, blue, black plastic grips. Add $15 for .32 H&R Mag. cal., made 1958-discontinued.

	$127	**$100**	**$85**	**$75**	**$65**	**$55**	**$45**

MODEL 733—same specifications as the Model 732, only nickel finish and available only with 2½ in. barrel. Add $15 for .32 H&R Mag. cal.

	$140	**$125**	**$110**	**$85**	**$75**	**$60**	**$50**

MODEL 900—.22 S, L, or LR, 9 shot, 2½, 4, or 6 in. barrels, snap out cylinder, blue, black plastic grips, made 1962-1973.

	$90	**$85**	**$70**	**$55**	**$50**	**$40**	**$30**

MODEL 901—same as 900, but chrome with white tenite grips, made 1962-1963.

	$110	**$100**	**$90**	**$70**	**$50**	**$40**	**$30**

MODEL 904—.22 cal., double action, 4 or 6 in. bull barrel, target grade, 9 shot. Discontinued in 1985.

	$150	**$135**	**$120**	**$105**	**$95**	**$80**	**$70**

Last Mfg.'s Sug. Retail was $168.

MODEL 905—same as Model 904, except with nickel finish and 4 in. barrel only. Discontinued in 1985.

	$160	**$140**	**$125**	**$105**	**$95**	**$80**	**$70**

Last Mfg.'s Sug. Retail was $185.

Grading	100%	98%	95%	90%	80%	70%	60%

MODEL 922—Second Issue, .22 LR, 9 shot, 2½, 4, and 6 in. barrels, solid frame, blue, plastic grips, made 1950-1982.

	$85	$70	$60	$45	$40	$30	$25

MODEL 923—same as 922, only nickel.

	$90	$75	$65	$50	$45	$35	$30

MODEL 925 DEFENDER—.38 S&W, 5 shot, 2½ in. barrel, blue, break open, adj. sight, wrap-around one piece grip, made 1964-1984.

	$130	$120	$100	$85	$70	$60	$50

Model 935—same as Model 925, except with nickel finish.

	$145	$135	$115	$100	$70	$60	$50

MODEL 926—.22 LR, 9 shot, .38 S&W, 5 shot, 4 in. barrel, blue, adj. rear sight, break open, walnut grips, made 1968-1982.

	$130	$120	$100	$85	$70	$60	$50

MODEL 929 SIDEKICK—.22 LR, 9 shot, 2½, 4, or 6 in. barrels, swing out cylinder, plastic grips, blue, made 1956-1985.

	$115	$100	$70	$55	$45	$35	$30

Last Mfg.'s Sug. Retail was $127.

MODEL 930 SIDEKICK—same as 929 Sidekick, only nickel finish and not available with 6 in. barrel. Discontinued in 1985.

	$125	$110	$80	$65	$55	$45	$40

Last Mfg.'s Sug. Retail was $140.

MODEL 939 ULTRA SIDEKICK—.22 S, L, or LR, 9 shot, 6 in. barrel, swing out cylinder, vent rib, adj. sights, blue, made 1958-1982.

	$110	$100	$85	$70	$55	$45	$30

MODEL 940 ULTRA SIDEKICK—same as 939, only round barrel. Discontinued.

	$105	$95	$75	$65	$50	$40	$30

MODEL 949 "FORTY NINER"—.22 S, L, or LR, 5½ in. barrel, double action, solid frame, 9 shot, side load and Western style ejection, adj. rear sight, walnut grips, made 1960-1985.

	$115	$100	$85	$70	$55	$50	$45

Last Mfg.'s Sug. Retail was $127.

MODEL 950—same as Model 949, except with nickel finish. Discontinued in 1985.

	$125	$105	$90	$70	$55	$50	$45

Last Mfg.'s Sug. Retail was $145.

MODEL 976—same as 949, only color case hardened frame. Discontinued.

	$100	$90	$85	$70	$60	$50	$35

MODEL 999 SPORTSMAN—Second Issue, .22 LR, 9 shot, 4 and 6 in. vent rib barrel, break open, adj. sights, walnut grips, made 1950-1985.

	$195	$170	$155	$145	$130	$120	$110

Last Mfg.'s Sug. Retail was $215.

This model was also made in a Sportsman Centennial Commemorative. Add 15%-25% if NIB.

MODEL 999 ENGRAVED—same as 999, only engraved throughout, 6 in. barrel only. Discontinued in 1985.

	$425	$375	$300	$260	$225	$190	$175

Last Mfg.'s Sug. Retail was $525.

RIFLES

REISING MODEL 60—semi-auto, .45 ACP, 12 and 20 shot, 18¼ in. barrel, detachable mag., made 1944-1946.

	$360	$340	$310	$275	$220	$200	$175

MODEL 65 MILITARY—.22 LR, 10 shot mag., 23 in. barrel, Redfield aperture rear sight, made 1944-1946 for USMC.

	$250	$230	$200	$165	$145	$130	$110

Grading	100%	98%	95%	90%	80%	70%	60%

MODEL 150—semi-auto, .22 LR, 5 shot, made 1949-1953.

	$95	$85	$70	$55	$40	$35	$30

MODEL 155—single shot, .44 Mag. and .45-70, break open, made 1972-discontinued.

	$120	$110	$100	$85	$65	$45	$30

MODEL 157—single shot, .22 Mag., .22 Hornet, and .30-30, break open, made 1976-discontinued.

	$122	$100	$90	$70	$60	$40	$30

MODEL 158—.30-30, .22 Hornet, .357 Mag & .44 Mag. cal.'s, single shot break open, 22 in. barrel, side lever action release, ejector, case hardened frame. Discontinued in 1985.

	$105	$90	$80	$60	$50	$40	$30

Last Mfg.'s Sug. Retail was $115.

Model 158 Combination—supplied with rifle barrel and 20 ga., 26 in. barrel. Discontinued in 1985.

	$130	$110	$95	$85	$75	$70	$65

Last Mfg.'s Sug. Retail was $145.

MODEL 165—.22 LR, 10 shot, made 1945-1961.

	$120	$110	$95	$85	$70	$55	$50

MODEL 171—.45-70 Model 1873 Trap door copy, 22 in. barrel, Model 174 is the deluxe model. Discontinued.

	$295	$260	$230	$210	$190	$175	$160

MODEL 171-DL—single shot, .45-70 gov't cal., Springfield copy, 22 in. barrel. Made 1984 and 1985.

	$345	$305	$265	$225	$205	$190	$170

Last Mfg.'s Sug. Retail was $385.

MODEL 174—Little Big Horn commercial carbine, made 1972.

	$395	$350	$310	$280	$240	$220	$200

MODEL 300 ULTRA—bolt action, .22-250, .243 Win., .270 Win., .30-06, .308 Win., 7mm Mag., and .300 Win. Mag., 22 or 24 in. barrel, made 1965-1978.

	$440	$415	$360	$305	$250	$210	$195

MODEL 301 CARBINE—same as 300, but 18 in. barrel, full length Mannlicher stock, N/A .22-250.

	$440	$415	$360	$305	$250	$220	$195

MODEL 317 ULTRA WILDCAT—short action Sako, .17 Rem., .17-223, .222 Rem., and .223 Rem., 20 in. barrel, no sights, made 1968-1976.

	$440	$415	$360	$305	$275	$220	$195

MODEL 317P PRESENTATION—same as 317, but deluxe wood basketweave checkering, made 1968-1976.

	$550	$525	$495	$440	$400	$360	$305

MODEL 333—same as 300, in 7mm Mag., plainer version, made in 1974 only.

	$250	$230	$215	$180	$160	$140	$120

MODEL 340—bolt action in .243 Win. Mag., .270 Win. Mag., .30-06, .308 Win. Mag., 7mm Mauser, 5 shot, 22 in. barrel, checkered walnut. Discontinued.

	$395	$300	$275	$240	$220	$200	$180

MODEL 360 ULTRA AUTOMATIC—.243 Win. and .308 Win., 3 shot, 22 in. barrel, made 1965-1978.

	$350	$330	$315	$275	$240	$220	$200

MODEL 370 ULTRA MEDALIST TARGET—Varmint Rifle, .22-250, .243 Win., and 6mm Rem., 24 in. varmint weight barrel, semi-beavertail forearm, made 1968-1973.

	$440	$415	$360	$305	$275	$220	$195

MODEL 422—slide action, .22 S, L, and LR, made 1956-1958.

	$110	$100	$85	$65	$45	$40	$30

Grading	100%	98%	95%	90%	80%	70%	60%

MODEL 451 MEDALIST—bolt action, .22 LR, 5 shot, 26 in. barrel, made 1948-1961.

	$165	$150	$140	$110	$100	$85	$55

Model 450—same as Model 451, only no sights.

	$150	$140	$120	$110	$95	$70	$55

MODEL 700—.22 Win. Mag., semi-auto, 5 shot, clip mag., 22 in. barrel, made 1977-1985.

	$185	$165	$140	$120	$100	$80	$65

Last Mfg.'s Sug. Retail was $210.

MODEL 700DL—same as Model 700, except deluxe checkered walnut. 4-power scope is standard, recoil pad. Discontinued in 1985.

	$315	$270	$230	$195	$175	$150	$135

Last Mfg.'s Sug. Retail was $360.

MODEL 750—.22 cal. single-shot bolt action, 22 in. barrel, open sights, youth stock dimensions. Discontinued in 1985.

	$85	$75	$60	$50	$45	$40	$35

Last Mfg.'s Sug. Retail was $95.

MODEL 865—.22 cal. bolt action. 5 shot mag., 22 in. barrel. Discontinued in 1985.

	$90	$80	$65	$55	$50	$45	$40

Last Mfg.'s Sug. Retail was $105.

MODEL 5200—.22 cal. target rifle, heavy 28 in. barrel, adj. trigger, no sights, single shot. 11 lbs. Discontinued in 1985.

	$395	$350	$295	$260	$230	$200	$175

Last Mfg.'s Sug. Retail was $450.

MODEL 5200 SPORTER—.22 cal., bolt action, 5 shot, 24 in. barrel, adj. sights, checkered walnut. Discontinued in 1983.

	$440	$385	$330	$295	$260	$230	$200

SHOTGUNS

HARRICH NO. 1—single barrel Trap Gun, 12 ga., 32 and 34 in. full choke, high quality, engraved, vent rib, made by Ferlach of Austria from 1971-1975.

	$1,650	$1,595	$1,485	$1,320	$1,100	$880	$770

MODEL 3 HAMMERLESS—same as 8, but no visible external hammer, made 1908-1942.

	$85	$75	$70	$55	$45	$40	$30

MODEL 5 LIGHTWEIGHT—24, 28 ga., and .410 only, made 1908-1942.

	$95	$90	$75	$65	$55	$40	$35

MODEL 6 HEAVY BREECH—same as 8, only 10 ga. - 20 ga., heavier barrels, made 1908-1942.

	$95	$85	$75	$60	$50	$45	$35

MODEL 7 OR 9 BAY STATE—same as 8, only 12, 16, 20 ga., and .410, rounded pistol grip, made 1908-1942.

	$85	$75	$70	$55	$45	$40	$30

MODEL 8 STANDARD—single shot, 12, 16, 20, 24, 28, and .410 ga.'s, 26-32 in. barrels, plain pistol grip stock, auto ejector, break open, made 1908-1942.

	$85	$75	$70	$55	$45	$40	$30

FOLDING GUN—hinged frame, barrel folds against stock, made 1908-1942.

	$95	$90	$75	$65	$55	$40	$35

TOPPER—single shot, break open, 10 different models of this pistol, all are very similar and values run too close to differentiate, made 1946-discontinued.

	$95	$85	$70	$55	$45	$35	$30

MODEL 088—12, 16, 20, 28, and .410 ga.'s, single shot, hammer model, ejector, blue barrel finish with case hardened frame. Discontinued in 1985.

	$85	$75	$55	$50	$45	$40	$35

Last Mfg.'s Sug. Retail was $95.

Grading	100%	98%	95%	90%	80%	70%	60%

MODEL 099—12, 16, 20, and .410 ga.'s, similar to Model 088, only electroless nickel finish, ejector. Discontinued in 1984.

	$95	$80	$60	$55	$50	$45	$40

MODEL 162—12 and 20 ga.'s, single shot, 24 in. slug barrel with rifle sights, case hardened frame, 20 ga. Discontinued in 1984.

	$115	$105	$90	$80	$65	$55	$45

MODEL 176—3½ in. 10 ga. Mag., single shot, 36 in. heavy barrel, break open, made 1977-1985.

	$110	$95	$80	$70	$60	$50	$45

Last Mfg.'s Sug. Retail was $125.

MODEL 400 PUMP ACTION—12, 16, and 20 ga.'s, 28 in. full choke, made 1955-1967.

	$155	$145	$125	$110	$90	$75	$55

MODEL 401 PUMP—same as 400, but H&R variable choke, made 1956-1963.

	$165	$155	$140	$120	$100	$90	$65

MODEL 402 PUMP—same as 400, only .410 ga., lightweight, made 1959-1967.

	$175	$165	$150	$140	$110	$100	$85

MODEL 403 AUTOLOADER—.410 ga., 26 in. full choke, takedown, made in 1964 only.

	$195	$180	$165	$155	$120	$100	$85

MODEL 404—double barrel, s x s, 12, 20, and .410 ga.'s, 26 and 28 in. barrel, boxlock, extractors, double triggers, made by Rossi of Brazil 1969-1972.

	$185	$175	$165	$145	$110	$90	$70

MODEL 404C—same as 404, only checkered stock.

	$200	$185	$175	$155	$120	$100	$85

MODEL 440—pump action, 12, 16, and 20 ga.'s, 26, 28, and 30 in. barrels, available in various chokes, plain pistol grip and slide, made 1968-1973.

	$145	$130	$110	$100	$85	$70	$55

MODEL 442—pump action, same as 440, only vent rib, checkered stock, made 1969-1973.

	$175	$165	$155	$140	$100	$85	$65

MODEL 490—20 and .410 ga.'s, made for junior shooters, Greenwing finish - add $10. Discontinued in 1984.

	$85	$65	$60	$50	$45	$40	$40

MODEL 1212—O/U, Field, 12 ga., 2¾ in., 28 in. vent rib barrels, various chokes, checkered walnut stocks, made by Landbar Arms, Spain, from 1976-discontinued.

	$310	$295	$275	$250	$200	$175	$155

MODEL 1212 WATERFOWL—same as 1212, except 3 in. 12 ga., 30 in. barrel.

	$320	$310	$285	$260	$210	$185	$165

SINGLE SHOT COMBINATION GUNS

MODEL 058—20 ga./.30-30, .22 Hornet, .44 Mag., .357 Mag. combination - 2 separate barrels supplied, blue only. Discontinued in 1985.

	$130	$110	$95	$85	$75	$65	$60

Last Mfg.'s Sug. Retail was $145.

MODEL 258 COMBINATION HANDY GUN II—supplied with 20 ga., 22 in. barrel and 22 in. rifle barrel in .22 Hornet, .30-30 Win., or .357 Mag. cal.'s, electroless, matte nickel finish, side lever action release, cased, 6½ lbs. Discontinued in 1985.

	$175	$155	$140	$130	$120	$100	$95

Last Mfg.'s Sug. Retail was $195.

COMMEMORATIVES & REPLICAS

H&R 100TH ANNIVERSARY—1871-1971, Commemorative Officer's Model, Springfield 1873 Replica, trap door, .45-70 cal., engraved metal work, 26 in. barrel, anniversary plaque on stock, 10,000 produced in 1971.

	$425	$390	$360

MODEL 171 AND 171 DELUXE—listed in previous rifle section.

MODEL 173—.45-70, same as Officer's Model, no plaque on stock, made 1972-1983.

	$320	$265	$250

Grading	100%	98%	95%	90%	80%	70%	60%

MODEL 174—.45-70, Little Big Horn Commercial Carbine, made 1972.

	$395	$350	$320				

MODEL 178—.45-70, Infantry Musket Replica, 32 in. barrel, made 1973-1984.

	$325	$275	$260				

CUSTER MEMORIAL ISSUE—.45-70 cal., limited production, deluxe walnut stock, highly engraved, gold inlaid, mahogany display case and two volumes on Custer history. Each weapon bears the name of one who fell at Little Big Horn.

Officer's Model—25 made new with original box/accessories.

	$2,650	$2,150	$1,575				

Enlisted Men's Model—243 made new with original box/accessories.

	$1,350	$900	$650				

HARTFORD ARMS & EQUIPMENT COMPANY

HARTFORD ARMS WAS THE FORERUNNER OF HIGH STANDARD ARMS CO., WHO ACQUIRED THEM IN 1932.

HARTFORD AUTOMATIC TARGET—.22 LR, 10 shot, 6¾ in. barrel, blue, black rubber grips, made 1929-1930.

	$575	$500	$450	$375	$300	$275	$250

HARTFORD REPEATING PISTOL—.22 cal., similar in appearance to Automatic, except a hand operated repeater, made 1929-1930.

	$495	$425	$360	$310	$260	$250	$225

HARTFORD SINGLE SHOT TARGET—similar in appearance to Automatic, .22 LR, 6¾ in. barrel, target sights, case colored frame and slide, blue barrel, rubber or wood grips, made 1929-1930.

	$475	$390	$350	$310	$260	$250	$225

HATFIELD RIFLE COMPANY

MANUFACTURED AND DISTRIBUTED BY HATFIELD RIFLE COMPANY LOCATED IN ST. JOSEPH, MO.

Hatfield also manufactures flintlock and percussion black powder rifles which can be located in the Modern Black Powder Guns section of this text. Hatfield Rifle Company was named Hatfield International until 1988.

SHOTGUNS: SIDE BY SIDE

UPLANDER GRADE I—20 ga. only, 3 in. chambers, 26 in. IC/M, matted rib barrels, case hardened boxlock action, single trigger, ejectors, deluxe checkered straight grip walnut stock and forearm, 5¾ lbs, leather cased. New in 1987.

Mfg.'s Sug. Retail	$1,120	$1,000	$800	$650	$540	$460	$430	$410

UPLANDER GRADE II PIGEON—similar to Grade I, except has scroll engraving on top lever, sides, floor plate, and trigger guard, leather cased. New in 1987.

Mfg.'s Sug. Retail	$1,995	$1,775	$1,425	$1,200	$995	$875	$700	$600

UPLANDER GRADE III SUPER PIGEON—includes heavy relief scroll engraving (total coverage) on frame, top lever, floor plate, and trigger guard, leather cased. New in 1987.

Mfg.'s Sug. Retail	$2,495	$2,200	$1,900	$1,700	$1,495	$1,200	$1,025	$900

UPLANDER GRADE IV GOLDEN QUAIL—more extensive engraving including six 24 Kt. gold inlays on frame and floor plate, 2 gold barrel bands, leather cased. New in 1987.

Mfg.'s Sug. Retail	$3,995	$3,575	$2,750	$2,350	$1,900	$1,700	$1,495	$1,200

UPLANDER GRADE V WOODCOCK—top-of-the-line model with best quality engraving and 7 gold inlays, leather cased. New in 1987.

Mfg.'s Sug. Retail	$5,595	$4,800	$3,950	$3,475	$2,950	$2,500	$2,150	$1,800

HAWES FIREARMS

MANUFACTURED BY J.P. SAUER & SOHN IN ECKERNFORDE, W. GERMANY.
IMPORTED BY HAWES FIREARMS IN VAN NUYS, CA.

Rather than give an individual listing of the various single action revolvers that have been imported, a generalized price range is as follows: centerfire single actions usually are in the $130 - $250 range while .22 rimfire models are typically valued between $60 - $140.

HECKLER & KOCH

MANUFACTURED IN OBERNDORF/NECKAR, W. GERMANY. DISTRIBUTED AT U.S. HEADQUARTERS LOCATED IN CHANTILLY, VA.

PISTOLS: SEMI-AUTO, RECENT MANUFACTURE

HK4—double action auto, .380, .32 auto, .25 auto, and .22 LR, available with all caliber conversion units, $3\frac{1}{13}$ in. barrel, blue, plastic grips. In recent years, used HK 4's have been imported into the U.S. at discount prices - thus affecting used HK 4 prices. Discontinued in 1984.

	100%	98%	95%	90%	80%	70%	60%
.25 or .32 ACP cal.	$295	$260	$230	$215	$180	$150	$130
.22 or .380 cal.	$430	$345	$300	$250	$195	$160	$140
.380 with .22 conversion							
	$480	$385	$350	$325	$310	$290	$280
.380 with all conversions							
	$590	$475	$450	$420	$390	$375	$360

This model was also mfg. in a French model in .22 LR and/or .32 ACP (about 500 imported).

P9S—.45 ACP and 9mm parabellum, double action combat model, 4 in. barrel, parkerized finish, sculptured plastic grips, fixed sights. Production ceased in 1984.

Mfg.'s Sug. Retail	$1,299	$600	$480	$400	$360	$320	$290	$265

Although discontinued in 1984, modest quantities are still available from the distributor on this model.

P9S TARGET—.45 ACP and 9mm parabellum, 5½ in. barrel, blue, adj. sights and trigger. Discontinued in 1984.

Mfg.'s Sug. Retail	$1,382	$850	$700	$600	$540	$500	$465	$430

Although discontinued in 1984, modest quantities are still available from the distributor on this model.

P9S COMPETITION KIT—same as Target, except extra 5½ in. barrel and weight, competition walnut grip, 2 slides. Discontinued in 1984.

	$1,150	$950	$875	$800	$720	$640	$550

P7 PSP—9mm Para., older variation of the P7 M8, without extended finger guard or ambidextrous safety. Disc. in 1986.

	$650	$550	$495	$450	$410	$390	$370

P7 M8—9mm Para., unique squeeze cocking single action, extended square combat type trigger guard with heat shield, 4.13 in. fixed barrel, 28 oz., 8 round mag., ambidextrous mag. release, fixed 3-dot sighting system, stippled black plastic grips, blue finish.

Mfg.'s Sug. Retail	$895	$650	$550	$495	$450	$410	$390	$370

P7 M13—similar to P7 M8, only with staggered 13 shot mag., 40 oz.

Mfg.'s Sug. Retail	$1,115	$825	$740	$680	$630	$580	$530	$480

P7 K3—.380 ACP, uses unique oil-filled buffer to decrease recoil, 3.8 in. barrel, 8 round mag., 1.65 lbs. New in 1988.

Mfg.'s Sug. Retail	$895	$660	$560	$495	$450	$410	$390	$370

Add $467 for .22 LR conversion kit.

Grading	100%	98%	95%	90%	80%	70%	60%

VP 70Z—9mm, 18 shot, double action only, 4½ in. barrel, blue, plastic receiver/grip assembly. Discontinued in 1984.

	$365	$320	$275	$250	$230	$210	$195

Limited quantities of this rifle are still available at $399 suggested retail.

RIFLES: SEMI-AUTO

MODEL 91 A-2—.308 cal. (7.62mm), semi-auto assault rifle, delayed roller lock bolt system, antennuated recoil, black cycolac stock, 17.7 in. barrel, 20 round mag., 9.7 lbs.

Fixed stock model

Mfg.'s Sug. Retail	$946	$775	$620	$580	$500	$460	$430	$400

Model 91 A-3—with retractable metal stock.

Mfg.'s Sug. Retail	$1,114	$895	$720	$645	$560	$500	$470	$430

Add $516 for .22 LR conversion kit.

Model 91 A-2 Package—includes A.R.M.S. mount, B-Square rings, Leupold 3 x 9 compact scope with matte finish. Importation disc. in 1988.

	$1,050	$895	$710	$645	$560	$500	$470

Add $156 for retractable stock.

Last Mfg.'s Sug. Retail was $1,285.

MODEL 93 A-2—.223 cal. (5.56mm), otherwise same as H&K 91, 25 round mag., 16.14 in. barrel, 8 lbs.

Fixed stock model

Mfg.'s Sug. Retail	$946	$775	$620	$580	$500	$460	$430	$400

Model 93 A-3—with retractable metal stock.

Mfg.'s Sug. Retail	$1,114	$895	$720	$645	$560	$500	$470	$430

Model 93 A-2 Package—includes A.R.M.S. mount, B-Square rings, Leupold 3 x 9 compact scope with matte finish. Importation disc. in 1988.

	$1,050	$895	$710	$645	$560	$500	$470

Add $156 for retractable stock.

Last Mfg.'s Sug. Retail was $1,285.

MODEL 94 CARBINE A-2—9mm, semi-auto carbine, 16.54 in. barrel, aperture rear sight, 15 shot mag. New in 1983.

Fixed stock model

Mfg.'s Sug. Retail	$946	$780	$625	$580	$500	$460	$430	$400

Model 94 Carbine A-3—retractable metal stock.

Mfg.'s Sug. Retail	$1,114	$895	$720	$645	$560	$500	$470	$430

Model 94 A-2 Package—includes A.R.M.S. mount, B-Square rings, Leupold 3 x 9 compact scope with matte finish. Importation disc. in 1988.

	$1,050	$895	$710	$645	$560	$500	$470

Add $156 for retractable stock.

Last Mfg.'s Sug. Retail was $1,285.

Model 94 SGI—9mm, semi-auto, target rifle, aluminum alloy bipod, Leupold 6X scope, 15 or 30 shot mag. Imported in 1986 only.

	$1,175	$1,000	$900	$820	$740	$660	$590

Last Mfg.'s Sug. Retail was $1,340.

MODEL 270—.22 LR cal. semi-auto, sporting rifle, 5 or 20 round mag., high luster blue, checkered walnut. Discontinued in 1985.

	$300	$250	$215	$200	$180	$160	$150

Last Mfg.'s Sug. Retail was $200.

MODEL 300—semi-auto, .22 Mag., otherwise same as H&K 270. Importation disc. in 1988.

	$595	$550	$485	$440	$400	$380	$360

Last Mfg.'s Sug. Retail was $426.

Grading	100%	98%	95%	90%	80%	70%	60%

Model 300 Package—includes A.R.M.S. mount, B-Square rings, Leupold 3 x 9 compact scope with matte finish. Importation disc. in 1988.

	$750	$700	$650	$600	$550	$500	$460

Last Mfg.'s Sug. Retail was $689.

MODEL 630—.223 cal., semi-auto, delayed roller lock bolt system, 17.7 in. barrel, reduced recoil, checkered walnut, 4 or 10 shot mag., 7.04 lbs. Importation discontinued in 1986.

	$675	$550	$495	$460	$430	$400	$380

Last Mfg.'s Sug. Retail was $784.

Because of the significant price increases since 1986 triggered by the devaluation of the American dollar, the importation of this model was stopped. Above values are indicative of current market prices, which could fluctuate due to regional supply and demand.

MODEL 770—.308 cal., 3 or 10 shot mag., 19.7 in. barrel, 7.92 lbs., otherwise same as model 630. Importation discontinued in 1986.

	$750	$640	$595	$560	$530	$500	$485

Last Mfg.'s Sug. Retail was $797.

Because of the significant price increases since 1986 triggered by the devaluation of the American dollar, the importation of this model was stopped. Above values are indicative of current market prices, which could fluctuate due to regional supply and demand.

Approximately 10 Model 770's were imported in .243 Win. Values for the .243 cal. will be considerably higher than listed above for the .308 cal.

MODEL 940—.30-06 cal., 21.6 in. barrel, 8.62 lbs., otherwise same as model 770. Importation discontinued in 1986.

	$795	$685	$620	$560	$500	$465	$430

Last Mfg.'s Sug. Retail was $917.

Because of the significant price increases since 1986 triggered by the devaluation of the American dollar, the importation of this model was stopped. Above values are indicative of current market prices, which could fluctuate due to regional supply and demand.

MODELS SL6 & SL7 CARBINE—.223 or .308 cal., 17.71 in. barrel, semi-auto, delayed roller lock bolt system, reduced recoil, vent wooden hand guard, 3 or 4 round mag, 8.36 lbs., matte black metal finish, HK-SL6 is .223 cal., HK-SL7 is .308 cal.

	$595	$525	$450	$420	$390	$375	$360

PSG-1—.308 cal. only, high precision marksman's rifle, 5 shot mag., complete with accessories (including Hensholdt 6 x 42 power scope), 17.8 lbs.

Mfg.'s Sug. Retail	$8,728	$7,000	$5,975	$4,995	$4,485	$3,850	$3,400	$3,000

Add $529 for fully adj. butt stock.

RIFLES: BOLT ACTION

BASR—.22, .22-250, 6mm PPC, 300 Win. Mag., .30-06, or .308 cal., Kevlar stock, stainless steel barrel, limited production, custom order only rifle with approx. 6 week delay. Special order only. Manufactured in 1986 only.

	$1,775	$1,485	$1,295	$1,075	$960	$840	$740

Last Mfg.'s Sug. Retail was $1,685.

Less than 100 of this variation were manufactured and they are extremely rare.

SHOTGUNS

H & K imported Benelli shotguns can be found under their own heading.

HENRY RIFLE

PLEASE REFER TO THE WINCHESTER SECTION IN THIS TEXT.

HEROLD RIFLE

FRANZ JAEGER, SUHL, GERMANY.

BOLT ACTION SPORTING RIFLE—miniature Mauser action, .22 Hornet, 24 in. barrel, leaf sight, double set trigger, select checkered stock, imported by Daly & Stoeger, pre-WWII.

	$990	$880	$825	$770	$660	$550	$495

HEYM, FRIEDRICH WILH.

ORIGINALLY FOUNDED IN 1865 BY F.H. HEYM WITH LOCATION IN SUHL. IMPORTED AND DISTRIBUTED BY HEYM AMERICA, INC. LOCATED IN FORT WAYNE, IN. PREVIOUSLY IMPORTED BY PAUL JAEGER INC. LOCATED IN GRAND JUNCTION, TN.

OVER AND UNDERS

MODEL 22 SAFETY—rifle/shotgun combination, 12, 16, or 20 ga. (3 in.), x 22 Hornet, 8 x 57 I(R)S, (10 cal.'s available), single set trigger, coin finish, 5½ lbs. Add $370 for takedown feature.

Mfg.'s Sug. Retail	$2,400	$2,100	$1,760	$1,525	$1,325	$1,100	$990	$920

MODEL 55 BF—rifle/shotgun combination, popular U.S. and European cal.'s, shotgun barrels interchangeable in 12, 16, and 20 ga.'s, 25 or 28 in. barrels, boxlock, auto ejectors, silver finish, fine German engraving, folding leaf sight, checkered pistol grip stock. Extra barrels — add $3,250 for O/U rifle and $2,250 for O/U shotgun or shotgun/rifle combination.

Mfg.'s Sug. Retail	$5,200	$4,950	$4,525	$3,950	$3,615	$3,210	$2,775	$2,300

Model 55 B—O/U rifle only, various cal.'s, engraving similar to Model 55 BF.

Mfg.'s Sug. Retail	$7,230	$6,875	$5,925	$5,100	$4,650	$3,975	$3,300	$2,780

Model 55 BS—O/U rifle only with different caliber for each barrel, double set triggers, "Bergstutzen" design.

Mfg.'s Sug. Retail	$7,400	$6,950	$5,950	$5,125	$4,650	$3,975	$3,300	$2,780

Model 55 F—O/U shotgun, ejectors, 20 and 16 ga., engraved, 6.6 lbs.

Mfg.'s Sug. Retail	$5,200	$4,950	$4,525	$3,950	$3,615	$3,200	$2,775	$2,300

Model 55 SS—sidelock version of Model 55 F, large engraved hunting scenes.

Mfg.'s Sug. Retail	$9,200	$8,700	$7,900	$6,550	$6,000	$5,560	$4,825	$3,975

DRILLINGS

MODEL 33 BOXLOCK STANDARD—16 or 20 ga., boxlock, Arabesque engraving, shotgun barrels over popular European cal.'s, and .222, .243, .270, .308, and .30-06 rifle barrel, 25 in. full and mod. barrels, set trigger on rifle, checkered pistol grip stock.

Mfg.'s Sug. Retail	$6,000	$5,600	$4,950	$4,525	$3,950	$3,615	$3,210	$2,775

Model 33 Deluxe—same specifications as Standard Model, only hunting scene engraved.

Mfg.'s Sug. Retail	$6,400	$5,850	$5,075	$4,600	$4,025	$3,650	$3,210	$2,775

MODEL 37 SIDELOCK STANDARD—shotgun barrels (12, 16, or 20 ga.) over rifle, detachable sidelocks, select French walnut, border engraving, 8 lbs.

Mfg.'s Sug. Retail	$9,400	$8,800	$8,050	$6,650	$6,050	$5,560	$4,825	$3,975

Model 37 Deluxe—same as Model 37 Standard, except has large engraved hunting scenes.

Mfg.'s Sug. Retail	$11,000	$9,950	$8,200	$7,475	$6,500	$5,650	$4,875	$4,200

MODEL 37 B STANDARD—rifle barrels over shotgun (20 ga.), sidelock, border engraved, about 8.6 lbs.

Mfg.'s Sug. Retail	$12,000	$10,875	$9,500	$8,400	$7,550	$6,500	$5,650	$4,875

Model 37 B Deluxe—similar to Model 37 B Standard, except has large hunting scene engraving.

Mfg.'s Sug. Retail	$13,900	$12,000	$10,700	$9,450	$8,200	$7,050	$6,000	$5,575

RIFLES

MODEL SR 20N—available in 18 cal.'s, Mauser type bolt action, set trigger, French walnut, Krupp barrels. Add $125 for Mag. cal.'s (G suffix), 24 in. barrel except Mag. (25 in.), also available in left-hand.

Mfg.'s Sug. Retail	$1,450	$1,275	$1,075	$900	$800	$700	$600	$500

Add $350 for left-hand variation.
Add $125 for single-set trigger.

Grading	100%	98%	95%	90%	80%	70%	60%

Model SR 20 Hunter—similar to Model SR 20N, except has classic style fiberglass stock with either matte blue or parkerized metal finish. New in 1988.

Mfg.'s Sug. Retail	$1,650	$1,475	$1,225	$1,050	$900	$800	$700	$600

Model SR 20L—Mannlicher style stock, 21 in. barrel, 7 lbs.

Mfg.'s Sug. Retail	$1,600	$1,450	$1,225	$985	$895	$785	$720	$650

SR 20 TROPHY—available in 8 cal.'s between 7 X 57mm and .357 H&H, bolt action, 22 or 24 (Mag. cal.'s only) in. octagonal barrel, classic stock configuration with cheekpiece and recoil pad. Importation began in 1989.

Mfg.'s Sug. Retail	$1,700	$1,500	$1,250	$985	$895	$785	$720	$650

SR 20 CLASSIC SPORTSMAN—available in 8 cal.'s between 2.43 Win. and .357 H&H, bolt action, 22 or 24 in. round barrel, steel grip cap. Importation began in 1989.

Mfg.'s Sug. Retail	$1,700	$1,500	$1,250	$985	$895	$785	$720	$650

SR 20 ALPINE—available in 8 cal.'s between .243 Win. and 8 X 57JS, mountain style rifle with full stock, schnabel forend cap, supplied with mounted open sights. Importation began in 1989.

Mfg.'s Sug. Retail	$2,600	$2,300	$1,875	$1,550	$1,325	$1,100	$990	$920

SR 20 CLASSIC SAFARI—.404 Jeffrey, .425 Express, or .458 Win. Mag., 24 in. barrel only, express rear sight and large front post sights, extra fancy walnut. Importation began in 1989.

Mfg.'s Sug. Retail	$3,500	$3,150	$2,875	$2,525	$2,150	$1,900	$1,620	$1,425

EXPRESS SERIES RIFLE—available in most Mag. cal.'s between .404 Jeffrey and .500 A-Square, express sights, Timney single trigger. Importation began in 1989.

1989 retail values were not forwarded this writer by publication release.

MODEL HR 30N SINGLE SHOT—available in many cal.'s, Ruger No. 1 falling block action, 24 in. barrel, French walnut with Bavarian cheekpiece, round barrel, Sporter or full length carbine style French walnut stock, engraved coin finished receiver, 6.6 lbs.

Mfg.'s Sug. Retail	$3,100	$2,875	$2,525	$2,150	$1,900	$1,620	$1,425	$1,300

Add $400 for Mannlicher stocked Carbine Model.
Add $1,700 for sideplates with hunting scenes.
Add $490 for octagon barrel.
Add $150 for Mag. cal.'s.

MODEL 88 B—SxS double rifle, 7 mm-375 H&H cal.'s, boxlock, Krupp steel barrels, double underlocking lugs with greener crossbolt, ejectors, checkered circassian walnut, built to customer specifications, 7½ lbs.

Mfg.'s Sug. Retail	$9,600	$8,850	$8,150	$6,850	$6,225	$5,420	$4,575	$3,975

Model 88 BSS—sidelock model with interceptor sears.

Mfg.'s Sug. Retail	$13,800	$12,250	$10,550	$9,550	$8,150	$7,025	$6,000	$5,575

Model 88 B Safari—available in .375 H&H, .458 Win Mag., .470 Nitro Express, or .500 Nitro Express cal., 25 in. barrels, 9.9 lbs.

Mfg.'s Sug. Retail	$13,600	$12,000	$10,700	$9,450	$8,200	$7,050	$6,000	$5,575

HIGGINS, J.C.

TRADEMARK USED ON SEARS & ROEBUCK RIFLES AND SHOTGUNS MANUFACTURED BETWEEN 1946-1962.

The J.C. Higgins trademark has appeared literally on hundreds of various models (shotguns and rifles) sold through the Sears & Roebuck retail network. Most of these models were manufactured through subcontracts with both domestic and international firearms manufacturers. Typically, they were "spec." guns made to sell at a specific price to undersell the competition. Most of these models were derivatives of existing factory models with less expensive wood and perhaps missing the features found on those models from which they were derived. To date, there has been very little interest in collecting J.C. Higgins guns, regardless of rarity. Rather than list J.C. Higgins' models, a general guideline is that values generally are under those of their "1st generation relatives". The Ranger trademark was also used by Sears & Roebuck - it is not any more desirable than those guns marked J.C. Higgins. As a result, prices are ascertained by the shooting value of the gun, rather than its' collector value.

HIGH STANDARD

MANUFACTURED FROM 1932-1984. FORMERLY HIGH STANDARD MFG. CO. FROM NEW HAVEN, CT. LATTER GUNS WERE MANUFACTURED IN EAST HARTFORD, CT.

High Standard closed its doors in 1984. Premiums for older discontinued models will be greater than for those handguns only recently discontinued.

PISTOLS: SEMI-AUTO

MODEL A—.22 LR, 10 shot, 4½ or 6¾ in. barrel, blue, adj. sights, checkered walnut grips, hammerless automatic, 7,300 mfg. 1938-1942.

	100%	98%	95%	90%	80%	70%	60%
	$415	$350	$295	$250	$210	$190	$170

The Model A is actually a Model B with a larger, squared off grip. Approximately 7,000 were mfg.

MODEL H-A—similar to Model A, except with visible hammer, no thumb safety, and lighter weight barrel, approx. 1,000 made 1940-1942.

	$495	$410	$350	$295	$240	$225	$195

This model is extremely hard to find in 100% condition.

MODEL B—.22 LR, the original High Standard hammerless, 4¾ or 6¾ in. barrel, blue, fixed sights, hard rubber grips, approx. 65,000 mfg. 1932-1942.

	$405	$350	$300	$270	$225	$200	$180

Model B-US—similar to Model B, except marked "Property of U.S." on right side of frame, approx. 14,000 mfg. 1942-1943.

	$475	$375	$325	$295	$240	$225	$195

MODEL H-B—similar to Model B, except visible hammer, with or without safety, approx. 25,000 mfg. made 1940-1942 and 1949-1954.

	$460	$360	$310	$285	$240	$225	$195

Add 10% for early model with no safety.

MODEL C—same as Model B, except .22 short only, approx. 5,000 mfg. 1935-1942.

	$495	$375	$325	$295	$240	$225	$195

This model is very desireable.

MODEL D—same as Model A, except heavier barrel, approx. 2,500 mfg. 1938-1942.

	$465	$375	$325	$295	$240	$225	$195

MODEL H-D—same as Model D, except visible hammer, no safety, excellent quality, approx. 7,000 mfg. 1940-1949.

	$440	$350	$315	$265	$220	$200	$180

Model HD-USA—similar to Model H-D, except has external safety, bull barrel, fixed sights, and parkerized finish, "Property of U.S.A." barrel or slide marking, approx. 44,000 mfg. 1943-1946.

	$415	$325	$295	$250	$210	$190	$150

Add 20% for early blue finish.

This model was also produced with a silencer for the O.S.S. called the Model USA-HD-MS — requires N.F.A. transfer. Add 100% to above values.

MODEL H-D Military—same as Model H-D, with thumb safety, sometimes called H-D military, approx. 150,000 mfg. 1946-1955.

	$370	$300	$275	$250	$210	$190	$150

The Model H-DM was the highest production High Standard.

MODEL E—similar to Model A, except extra heavy barrel, thumb rest grips, very high quality, approx. 2,500 mfg. 1938-1942.

	$585	$465	$400	$350	$275	$240	$210

MODEL H-E—same as Model E, except visible hammer, with or without safety, approx. 1,000 mfg. 1940-1942.

	$795	$625	$550	$475	$350	$295	$250

The Model H-E is the rarest of the High Standard semi-auto's and a 100% specimen is seldomly encountered.

Grading	100%	98%	95%	90%	80%	70%	60%

MODEL G-380—.380 auto, 6 shot, 5 in. barrel, blue, lever takedown, thumb safety, fixed sights, checkered plastic grips, approx. 7,400 mfg. 1947-1950.

	$545	$425	$395	$325	$275	$240	$210

MODEL G-B—.22 LR, 10 shot, 4½ or 6¾ in. interchangeable barrels, blue, lever takedown, plastic grips, average quality, hammerless, approx. 5,000 mfg. 1949-1950.

	$415	$350	$300	$250	$210	$190	$170
Both barrels	$475	$365	$315	$275	$240	$210	$190

MODEL G-D—similar to G-B, except target sight, lever takedown, walnut grips, approx. 3,300 mfg. 1948-1951.

	$415	$350	$300	$250	$210	$190	$170
Both barrels	$475	$365	$315	$275	$240	$210	$190

MODEL G-E—similar to G-D, with extra heavy barrel, quality at par with Models E and HE, thumb rest grips, lever takedown, approx 3,000 mfg. during 1949-1950 .

	$585	$465	$400	$350	$275	$240	$210
Both barrels	$650	$500	$435	$365	$335	$275	$240

OLYMPIC AUTOMATIC 1ST MODEL (G-O)—similar to Model G-E with lever takedown, except .22 short only, alloy slide, thumb rest grips, approx. 1,200 mfg. 1949-1950.

	$695	$575	$495	$425	$340	$305	$275

This model can be differentiated by its distinctive curved magazine.

Both barrels	$750	$595	$520	$440	$380	$340	$315

SPORT KING 1ST MODEL—.22 LR, 4½ or 6¾ in. barrel, blue, fixed sights, plastic grips, made 1951-1954 with lever takedown (G-takedown), made 1954-1958 with push button takedown.

Lever takedown	$365	$300	$250	$195	$155	$140	$120
Push button T.D.	$325	$280	$225	$190	$145	$135	$120

Add 20% for extra barrel.

FLITE KING 1ST MODEL—similar to Sport King, only .22 short, alloy frame, made 1953-1958.

	$355	$275	$250	$200	$160	$140	$125
Both barrels	$400	$295	$250	$220	$200	$180	$160

FIELD KING—similar to Sport King, except target sights and heavy barrel, made 1951-1958.

	$365	$280	$200	$175	$140	$120	$100
Both barrels	$385	$290	$245	$195	$175	$150	$135

SUPERMATIC—.22 LR, 10 shot, 4½ or 6¾ in. barrels, target sights, lever takedown, hammerless, adj. barrel weights, plastic grips, made 1951-1958.

	$405	$350	$300	$250	$210	$190	$170
Both barrels	$465	$385	$325	$295	$265	$240	$210

QUICK CHANGE CONVERSION KIT—includes a barrel with weights, aluminum slide, and magazine for converting .22 LR to .22 Short, these kits were first available in 1951.

	$300	$250	$200				

OLYMPIC SECOND MODEL—similar to Supermatic, except .22 short, alloy slide, made 1951-1958.

	$505	$400	$350	$300	$240	$200	$180
Both barrels	$565	$445	$375	$320	$275	$225	$210

Grading	100%	98%	95%	90%	80%	70%	60%

DURAMATIC—.22 LR, 4½ or 6½ in. barrels, blue, fixed sights, screw takedown, wood grips, made 1954-1970.

	$365	$325	$250	$200	$155	$140	$120

Add 20% for extra barrel.

The Duramatic was sold by Sears Roebuck & Co. as the J.C. Higgins Model 80. This Sears variation had some minor exterior differences, but mechanically it was the same.

SPORT KING SECOND MODEL—.22 LR, 4½ or 6¾ in. interchangeable barrels, blue, fixed sights, plastic grips, made 1958-1970.

	$350	$285	$225	$200	$165	$150	$140

Both barrels

	$415	$335	$270	$240	$210	$190	$170

PLINKER—similar to Duramatic, thumb-screw takedown, made 1971-1973.

	$365	$325	$250	$200	$155	$140	$120

Add 20% for extra barrel.

This model was designated #9215 when in manufacture.

SPORT KING THIRD MODEL—similar to Second Model, also available in nickel - add $30, made 1974-1984.

	$295	$250	$195	$175	$140	$130	$120

This model was designated #9209 when in manufacture.

SPORT KING "M"—military type grips.

	$295	$250	$195	$175	$140	$130	$120

This model was designated #9259 when in manufacture.

FLITE KING SECOND MODEL—similar to Sport King Second Model, except .22 short only, alloy frame, made 1958-1966.

	$295	$250	$195	$175	$140	$130	$120

SHARPSHOOTER—.22 LR, 5½ in. bull barrel, adj. rear sight, push button takedown, brown plastic grips, made 1971-1981.

	$295	$250	$195	$175	$140	$130	$120

This model was designated #9210 when in manufacture.

SUPERMATIC TOURNAMENT—.22 LR, 10 shot, 5½ in. bull barrel or 6¾ in. heavy tapered barrel, blue, barrel weights, checkered wood grips, made 1958-1966.

	$415	$360	$325	$295	$240	$225	$195

This model does not have the plated roll marks (gold or silver) that the Citation and Trophy Models did.

SUPERMATIC CITATION MILITARY—similar to Citation, except straight military grip. There also was a Supermatic Citation made in a .22 Short - 8 in. barrel and a .22 LR - 10 in. barrel, which came with barrel weights, made only for a short time. Discontinued.

	$450	$375	$325	$295	$240	$225	$195

This model was designated #9242 and was next to the Supermatic Trophy in quality when in manufacture.

SUPERMATIC TROPHY—same as Supermatic Citation, except 5½ in. bull barrel or 7½ in. fluted barrel, walnut thumb rest grips, made 1963-1966.

	$475	$395	$325	$295	$240	$225	$195

This model was designated #9206 when in manufacture and was the top-of-the-line model.

SUPERMATIC TROPHY MILITARY—same as Trophy, with straight military grips, made 1965-1984.

	$475	$395	$325	$295	$240	$225	$195

1972 OLYMPIC COMMEMORATIVE MODEL—limited edition issued for only American made .22 to win an Olympic gold medal, highly engraved, gold inlaid Olympic rings, presentation case, made 1972 only.

	$995	$840	$640				

Grading	100%	98%	95%	90%	80%	70%	60%

OLYMPIC THIRD MODEL—same as Trophy, with .22 short, made 1963-1966.

	$485	$375	$325	$295	$240	$210	$190

OLYMPIC MILITARY—same as Third Model, with straight military grips, made 1965.

	$485	$375	$325	$225	$175	$155	$150

OLYMPIC ISU—similar to Citation, only .22 short, 6¾ or 8 in. barrels with weights made 1958-1984.

	$495	$425	$325	$275	$240	$225	$195

OLYMPIC ISU MILITARY—same as ISU, with military grip bracket sight, made 1965-1984.

	$495	$425	$325	$275	$240	$225	$195

This model was designated #9238 when in manufacture.

1980 Olympic Commemorative—has 5 Olympic rings on right side of receiver. 1,000 mfg. (USA prefix) in 1980 only. Presentation case.

	$595	$500	$365

This model was designated #9239 when in manufacture. It was supplied with a felt-lined presentation case.

VICTOR—.22 LR, 10 shot, 4½ in. solid (discontinued) or 5½ in. vent rib, target sights, push button or allen screw takedown, 47 oz., blue, checkered walnut grips. Discontinued in 1984.

	$510	$425	$350	$285	$240	$215	$190

This model was designated #9206 when in manufacture.

Last Mfg.'s Sug. Retail was $405.

Victor models with a "SH" prefix (allen screw takedown - #9217) are not as desireable (subtract 20%) as the early models.

10-X PUSH BUTTON—specifically designed for top flight match shooting, push button barrel release. Mfg. 1982-84.

	$850	$695	$575	$450	$395	$360	$330

This model was designated #9372 when in manufacture. This model used hand-picked parts and was precisely assembled by a High Standard Master Gunsmith (with his initials on the gun). All 10-X models are extremely rare. Prices may vary due to the extreme rarity of this model.

10-X Allen Screw—later production with allen screw barrel release.

	$595	$525	$450	$395	$360	$330	$295

TROPHY—.22 LR, 10 shot, 5½ in. bull or 7¼ in. fluted barrel, target sights, takedown, 45 oz., blue, checkered walnut grips. Discontinued in 1984.

	$475	$395	$325	$295	$220	$200	$180

This model was designated #9247 when in manufacture.

CITATION II—.22 LR, 10 shot, 5½ or 7¼ in. bull barrel, 45 oz., blue, checkered military type wood grips, allen screw takedown, mfg. 1982-84.

	$450	$375	$325	$295	$220	$200	$175

This model was designated #9348 when in manufacture. This model was also available with a flat-sided (slab) barrel.

Citation models with a "SH" prefix are not as desireable (subtract 20%) as the early models.

SHARPSHOOTER "M"—.22 LR, 5½ in. bull barrel, adj. rear sight, military type plastic grips, blue. Mfg. 1982-1984.

	$350	$300	$275	$200	$160	$140	$115

Deduct 20% for late model ("SH" prefix) - allen screw takedown.

This model was designated #9424 when in manufacture.

The last pistols manufactured by High Standard can be differentiated by the "SH" serial number prefix with an allen screw takedown. These specimens were poorly fitted and polished — thus the difference in value. Mfg. 1982-1984.

Grading	100%	98%	95%	90%	80%	70%	60%

SURVIVAL PACK—Sharpshooter "M" Model with electroless nickel finish, included canvas carrying case and extra nickel magazine, mfg. 1982-84.

	$435	$375	$300	$235	$200	$180	$165

This model was designated #9424 when in manufacture.

DERRINGER—double action only O/U, .22 S, L, or LR, or .22 WMR, 2 shot, 3½ in. barrels, blue or nickel, plastic grips. Discontinued in 1984.

Blue Finish—.22 LR or .22 Mag.

	$165	$135	$110	$95	$70	$65	$60

This model was designated #9194 when in manufacture.

Nickel Finish—.22 Mag.

	$185	$150	$115	$90	$85	$80	$75

Electroless nickel—included walnut grips.

	$205	$150	$115				

This model was designated #9420-21 when in manufacture.

Silver plated—includes presentation case. 500 mfg.

	$250	$200	$175				

This model was designated #9341 when in manufacture.

Gold plated—includes presentation case.

	$275	$225	$175				

This model was designated #9196 when in manufacture.

Matched consecutive—gold plated, cased.

	$440	$370	$330				

CONVERSION KITS—converts .22 LR to .22 Short, contains alloy slide with vent rib, barrel weight, and two .22 Short mag.'s, kit comes in "gun size box" set in styrofoam.

This model was designated #9370-71 when in manufacture.

Victor Kit

	$300	$200	$160				

This model was designated #9370 when in manufacture.

Trophy/Citation Kit

	$300	$200	$160				

This kit also includes a stabilizer.

This model was designated #9371 when in manufacture.

REVOLVERS

SENTINEL—.22 LR, 9 shot, swing out cylinder, 3, 4, or 6 in. barrel, aluminum frame, made 1955-1956.

	100%	98%	95%	90%	80%	70%	60%
Blue finish	$120	$110	$100	$95	$85	$70	$55
Nickel finish	$130	$120	$110	$105	$95	$85	$65
Pink finish	$150	$135	$120	$110	$100	$95	$85
Yellow finish	$150	$135	$120	$110	$105	$95	$85

SENTINEL IMPERIAL—same as Sentinel, with adj. sights, walnut grips, made 1962-1965.

	100%	98%	95%	90%	80%	70%	60%
Blue finish	$140	$125	$115	$110	$100	$90	$75
Nickel finish	$150	$140	$125	$120	$110	$100	$90

SENTINEL DELUXE—same as Sentinel, except adj. sights, wide trigger, 4 and 6 in. barrel, square butt, made 1957-1974.

	100%	98%	95%	90%	80%	70%	60%
Blue finish	$140	$125	$115	$110	$100	$90	$75
Nickel finish	$150	$140	$115	$120	$110	$100	$90

SENTINEL SNUB—same as Deluxe, except checkered bird's-head grip, 2⅜ in. barrel.

	100%	98%	95%	90%	80%	70%	60%
Blue finish	$145	$140	$130	$120	$110	$90	$85
Nickel finish	$155	$150	$145	$130	$120	$100	$95

Grading	100%	98%	95%	90%	80%	70%	60%

DURANGO—.22 LR, double action, steel frame, 4½ and 5½ in. barrel, wood grips, made 1971-1973.

	100%	98%	95%	90%	80%	70%	60%
Blue finish	$145	$130	$120	$95	$85	$70	$55
Nickel finish	$150	$140	$125	$105	$95	$85	$65

HOMBRE DOUBLE ACTION—similar to Double Nine steel frame, but no ejector rod housing, 4½ in. barrel, made 1971-1973.

Blue finish	$125	$120	$110	$105	$95	$85	$65
Nickel finish	$140	$130	$120	$115	$105	$95	$75

LONGHORN STEEL FRAME—similar to Double Nine, except 9½ in. barrel.

Fixed sights	$210	$170	$150	$120	$110	$105	$85
Adj. sights	$165	$155	$150	$130	$120	$115	$95

HIGH SIERRA—similar to Double Nine steel frame, except 7 in. octagon barrel, gold plated grip frame. Discontinued in 1984. Add $10 for adj. sights.

Fixed sights	$235	$175	$150	$130	$120	$105	$90

KIT GUN—.22 LR, swing out cylinder, 9 shot, 4 in. barrel, adj. sights, blue, walnut grips, made 1970-1973.

	$155	$145	$140	$125	$115	$105	$85

DOUBLE NINE—.22 LR, Western style double action, 5½ in. barrel, aluminum frame, simulated stag, ebony or ivory grips, made 1959-1984.

Blue finish	$235	$180	$160	$140	$120	$105	$90
Nickel finish (disc. in 1982)	$245	$190	$170	$150	$130	$115	$100

POSSE—similar to Double Nine aluminum, except 3½ in. barrel, blue, brass grip frame, walnut grips, made 1961-1966.

	$120	$110	$95	$90	$85	$70	$55

NATCHEZ—similar to Double Nine aluminum, except has bird's-head grip, made 1961-1966.

	$120	$110	$100	$90	$85	$70	$55

LONGHORN ALUMINUM FRAME—similar to Natchez, but 4½, 5½, and 9½ in. barrel, longhorn hammer spur, made 1961-1966.

	$145	$130	$110	$100	$85	$70	$55

9½ in. model—Discontinued in 1984.

	$250	$190	$160	$140	$120	$100	$90

CAMP GUN DOUBLE ACTION—.22 LR or .22 Win. Mag., 6 in. barrel, blue, adj. rear sight, checkered walnut grips, made 1976-1984.

	$250	$185	$165	$145	$125	$110	$100

SENTINEL 1 DOUBLE ACTION—.22 LR, 2, 3, and 4 in. barrel, 9 shot, smooth walnut grips, made 1974-present.

Blue finish	$235	$180	$160	$140	$120	$105	$90
Nickel finish	$250	$195	$175	$150	$130	$110	$95

Blue w/adj. sights — add $15 to above prices.

SENTINEL MARK IV DOUBLE ACTION—same as Sentinel 1, except .22 WRM.

Blue finish	$145	$140	$125	$120	$115	$95	$90
Nickel finish	$155	$150	$140	$130	$125	$105	$100

Adj. sights

	$160	$155	$150	$145	$125	$115	$100

SENTINEL MARK II DOUBLE ACTION—.357 Mag., 6 shot, double action, 2½, 4, and 6 in. barrel, blue, fixed sights, wood grips, made 1974-1976.

	$225	$190	$165	$155	$150	$140	$130

SENTINEL MARK III DOUBLE ACTION—same as Mark II, except adj. sights.

	$250	$220	$185	$175	$170	$160	$150

CRUSADER—.357 Mag., .44 Mag. or .45 LC, double action, swing-out cylinder, unique action, adj. sights, limited mfg. because of expensive fabrication.

	$575	$495	$440	$395	$360	$320	$295

Add 10& for NIB condition.

Anniversary Editions—ser. no.'s 1 - 50 for years 1927-1977. Very rare with asking prices sometimes over $3,500. Sets were also available.

Grading	100%	98%	95%	90%	80%	70%	60%

RIFLES

SPORT KING FIELD MODEL—.22 S (hi-speed), .22 L, .22 LR, semi-auto, tube mag., 22 in. barrel, open sight, plain pistol grip stock, made 1960-1966.

	$100	$90	$85	$75	$65	$55	$45

SPORT KING SPECIAL—same as Field, except beavertail forearm and Monte Carlo stock.

	$140	$120	$95	$90	$75	$65	$55

SPORT KING CARBINE—same as Field, except 18 in. barrel, straight grip, barrel band and sling, made 1964-1973.

	$170	$150	$120	$110	$100	$90	$85

SPORT KING DELUXE—same as Special, but stock checkered, made 1966-1975.

	$185	$160	$140	$115	$90	$75	$65

HI-POWER FIELD BOLT ACTION—Mauser type action, .270, .30-06, 4 shot mag., 22 in. barrel, folding rear sight, plain stock, made 1962-1966.

	$295	$230	$210	$195	$180	$165	$150

HI-POWER DELUXE—same as Field, except checkered Monte Carlo stock, swivels, made 1962-1966.

	$350	$285	$240	$220	$205	$195	$165

FLITE KING SLIDE ACTION—.22 S, L, or LR, 24 in. barrel, tube mag., hammerless, partridge sight, Monte Carlo stock with pistol grip, semi beavertail forearm, made 1962-1975.

	$120	$105	$95	$85	$65	$60	$50

SHOTGUNS

SUPERMATIC FIELD GRADE—12 ga., 28 and 30 in. barrel, mod. or full, gas operated semi-auto, plain pistol grip stock, made 1960-1966.

	$205	$185	$175	$160	$145	$140	$120

SUPERMATIC SPECIAL—12 ga., same as Field, 27 in. barrel, adj. choke, made 1960-1966.

	$210	$195	$180	$165	$150	$145	$125

SUPERMATIC DELUXE—same as Field, except vent rib, checkered stock and forearm, made 1961-1966.

	$265	$225	$200	$175	$160	$155	$140

SUPERMATIC TROPHY—same as Deluxe, except 27 in. barrel, adj. choke.

	$235	$215	$205	$180	$165	$160	$145

SUPERMATIC DUCK—same as Field, except 3 in. Mag., 30 in. full barrel, recoil pad, made 1961-1966.

	$275	$235	$190	$160	$145	$125	$110

SUPERMATIC DUCK VENT RIB—same as Duck, vent rib, checkered stock and forearm, made 1961-1966.

	$295	$250	$210	$175	$150	$130	$115

SUPERMATIC DEER GUN—same as Field, except 22 in. cylinder bore barrel, rifle sights, checkered stock and forearm, recoil pad, made 1965.

	$230	$210	$200	$185	$165	$155	$140

SUPERMATIC SKEET—same as Deluxe Rib, except 26 in. barrel, skeet bore, made 1962-1966.

	$300	$260	$225	$195	$175	$160	$150

SUPERMATIC TRAP—same as Skeet, except 30 in. full barrel, trap stock with pad, made 1962-1966.

	$245	$230	$220	$205	$185	$170	$160

Note: All preceding models, except Deer and Trap, chambered only for 20 ga., 3 in. Mag. values are $10 higher.

High Standard restyled the Supermatic Autoloader in 1966. The new model Supermatics are recognized by the new checkering pattern and jeweled bolt. All models previously listed are offered, 12 and 20 ga. values are $25 higher per model. All are considered deluxe models. They were discontinued in 1975.

Grading	100%	98%	95%	90%	80%	70%	60%

FLITE KING PUMP FIELD GRADE—12 or 20 ga., slide action, 26, 28, or 30 in. barrel, imp. cyl., mod., or full choke, plain pistol grip stock and slide, made 1960-1966.

	$165	$150	$140	$130	$120	$110	$100

FLITE KING SPECIAL—12 and 20 ga., same as Pump Field, except 27 in. barrel, adj. choke, made 1960-1966.

	$185	$160	$150	$145	$130	$120	$110

FLITE KING DELUXE RIB—12 or 20 ga., same as Pump Special, except vent rib, checkered stock, made 1961-1966.

	$195	$175	$170	$165	$155	$140	$125

FLITE KING TROPHY—same as Deluxe Rib, except 27 in. vent rib barrel, adj. choke, made 1960-1966.

	$200	$180	$175	$170	$160	$145	$130

FLITE KING BRUSH—12 ga. only, same as Field, except 18 or 20 in. cylinder bore barrel, rifle sights, made 1962-1964.

	$185	$170	$165	$160	$150	$140	$120

FLITE KING BRUSH DELUXE—12 ga. only, same as Brush, except adj. aperture rear sight, checkered stock, recoil pad, swivels and sling, 20 in. barrel only, made 1964-1966.

	$265	$230	$195	$170	$155	$145	$130

FLITE KING SKEET—12 ga. only, same as Deluxe Rib, except 26 in. vent rib, skeet bore, made 1962-1966.

	$265	$230	$195	$170	$155	$145	$130

FLITE KING TRAP—12 ga. only, same as Deluxe Rib, except 30 in. vent rib, full choke and pad, made 1962-1966.

	$250	$220	$195	$165	$150	$140	$125

Note: Flite King is available in 16 ga. also, except for the Brush, Skeet, and Trap models. Values are about $20 less per model. A .410 bore was offered in all models that were offered in 20 ga., except the Special and Trophy models. Values are generally the same per model.

High Standard restyled the Flite King in 1966. The new models have a jeweled bolt and new checkering pattern. These new guns were available as Deluxe, Deluxe Rib, Brush, Brush Deluxe, Skeet Deluxe, and Trap Deluxe. Their values are about $20 higher per model.

The new redesigned Flite King was also offered in Deluxe, Deluxe Rib, and Deluxe Skeet, in 20, 28, and .410 ga.'s. The 28 and .410 ga.'s will bring an additional 10-40%.

MODEL 10B—12 ga. combat shotgun, 18 in. barrel, semi-auto, unique design incorporates raked pistol grip in front of receiver and metal shoulder pad attached directly to rear of receiver, black cycolic plastic shroud and pistol grip, folding carrying handle, provisions made for attaching a small flashlight to receiver top, extended blade front sight, very compact size (28 in. overall). Discontinued.

	$440	$395	$360	$325	$290	$270	$250

RIOT SHOTGUN—18 or 20 in. barrel, police riot gun was also offered until 1975. This was a reliable weapon available with or without rifle sights, 12 ga. only on the Flite King Action.

	$165	$155	$140	$130	$120	$115	$110

SUPERMATIC INDY O/U—This model was made in Japan and imported in 1974 and 1975, boxlock, fully engraved receiver, selective auto ejectors and single trigger, 12 ga., 27½ sk & sk, 29½ imp. mod. and full, or full and full, air flow vent rib, checkered (skipline) pistol grip stock with pad and vent forearm.

	$815	$720	$635	$590	$550	$495	$440

SUPERMATIC SHADOW SEVEN O/U—same as Indy O/U, except less elaborate engraving, unvented forearm, standard vent rib, regular checkering, no recoil pad, imported 1974-1975.

	$670	$590	$540	$495	$470	$425	$385

SUPERMATIC SHADOW AUTO—12 and 20 ga., 2¾ or 3 in. chambers in 12 ga., air flow rib, 26 in. imp. cyl. or skeet, 28 in. mod., imp. mod. or full and 30 in. full or trap, checkered walnut stock, gas operated, imported 1974-1975.

	$340	$285	$240	$210	$180	$165	$155

HOFER-JAGDWAFFEN, PETER

MASTER GUNSMITH LOCATED IN FERLACH, AUSTRIA. CUSTOM ORDER ONLY, BEST QUALITY RIFLES MADE PER INDIVIDUAL ORDER — PRICES TYPICALLY START AT $10,000 + . INFORMATION CAN BE OBTAINED BY WRITING TO MR. HOFER DIRECTLY AT: PETER HOFER-JAGDWAFFEN, FRANZ-LANG-STRABE 13, A-9170 FERLACH, AUSTRIA.

HOLLAND & HOLLAND LIMITED

MANUFACTURED SINCE 1835 IN LONDON, ENGLAND. NEW ENGLAND ARMS LOCATED IN KITTERY POINT, ME IS AN IMPORT AGENT FOR H&H AND SPECIAL ORDER GUNS MAY BE ORDERED PER INDIVIDUAL SPECIFICATIONS.

Holland & Holland over the years has justly earned the reputation of producing some of the finest firearms ever manufactured. Their Double Rifles chambered for the Large Black Powder Express Cartridges are still among the most powerful rifles ever made, while exhibiting outstanding quality and superior craftsmanship. Most of these fine arms were made to order for the famous, wealthy, or royalty of their day. Because of the individual nature of each firearm, these early guns, as with any high grade item, must be individually appraised.

The early Double Rifles were proofed and regulated with the Black Powder of their day. These exposed hammer rifles were almost exclusively sold cased with accessories by Holland & Holland. They are seldom found on the market, and then not in the best of condition. Purchase of these as well as any high grade firearm should include trusted appraisal.

Due to the recent devaluation of the U.S. dollar, prices may fluctuate rapidly on this trademark. Values below reflect the dollar/pound exchange rates at this writing ($1.75 per pound).

RIFLES: MODERN

BEST QUALITY MAGAZINE RIFLE—Mauser or Enfield action, various cal.'s, incl. .300 H&H Mag., .375 H&H Mag., 4 shot mag., 24 in. barrel, folding leaf sight, checkered French walnut stock.

Mfg.'s Sug. Retail	$7,700	$7,700	$5,300	$4,400	$3,500	$2,800	$2,400	$2,000

The values above represent the standard model without additional options (of which there are a wide array). Mfg. to customer specifications.

DE LUXE MAGAZINE RIFLE—similar to Best Quality, with engraving and exhibition grade wood, very limited mfg.

Mfg.'s Sug. Retail	$10,445	$10,445	$7,300	$5,300	$4,150	$3,400	$2,750	$2,400

NO. 2 MODEL DOUBLE RIFLE S x S—various British and American cal.'s, 24-28 in. barrels, sidelock, folding leaf sight, checkered French walnut stock, auto ejectors.

$15,000	$13,000	$11,000	$10,000	$9,000	$7,000	$6,500

ROYAL DOUBLE S x S RIFLE—similar to No. 2, except has de luxe finish and more engraving.

Mfg.'s Sug. Retail	$52,935	$52,935	$40,250	$29,500	$24,250	$19,000	$16,000	$14,250

ROYAL DE LUXE S x S RIFLE—top-of-the-line model, every refinement, built to individual order only with almost any option possible.

Mfg.'s Sug. Retail	$56,435	$56,435	$42,350	$30,350	$25,000	$18,500	$16,000	$14,250

H&H 700 BORE DOUBLE RIFLE—.700 H&H cal., 1,000 grain jacketed bullet, approx. 19 lbs with 26 in. barrels chambered 3½ in. Delivery of this rifle is expected to commence in 1990. Prices have yet to be set but Holland & Holland would forward a written estimate if they are written directly.

Grading	100%	98%	95%	90%	80%	70%	60%

SHOTGUNS: SINGLE SHOT AND SIDE BY SIDE

Holland & Holland currently manufactures the Royal De Luxe Game Gun, Royal Game Gun, Badminton Game Gun, and the Dominion Game Gun models in sidelock configuration (and are listed below). In addition to the sidelock models, H&H also manufactures the boxlock models Cavalier De Luxe, Cavalier, Northwood De Luxe, and Northwood. The values below assume standard model without single trigger, vent rib, de luxe walnut, or casing. These special orders will add considerable value to the price of a new custom order.

Several years ago, Holland & Holland absorbed W & C Scott and is currently manufacturing the Chatsworth, Bowood, and Kinmount boxlock models. H&H is planning to phase this trademark out in the future, and current models can be found in the W & C Scott section of this text.

SINGLE BARREL TRAP GUN—12 ga., 30 or 32 in. full choke barrel, vent rib, boxlock, auto ejectors, Monte Carlo pistol grip stock, pad.

Standard Grade	$5,000	$4,500	$4,000	$3,250	$2,500	$2,250	$2,000
De Luxe Grade	$7,500	$6,250	$5,000	$4,500	$3,750	$3,000	$2,750
Exhibition Grade	$8,950	$7,500	$6,000	$5,500	$5,000	$4,250	$3,500

Note: This model is not currently available.

NORTHWOOD S x S BOXLOCK—12, 16, 20, and 28 ga.'s, 28 and 30 in. barrels, scalloped-case colored receiver, boxlock, auto ejectors, double triggers, checkered pistol grip or straight stock. The values shown below are for standard model.

Mfg.'s Sug. Retail	$7,435	$7,435	$5,900	$5,100	$4,450	$3,850	$3,300	$2,950
Add $615 for 20 or 28 ga.							

Northwood De Luxe—12, 16, 20, or 28 ga., scalloped-case colored receiver with moderate engraving and select walnut, double triggers. Current mfg.

Mfg.'s Sug. Retail	$8,310	$8,310	$6,850	$6,175	$5,000	$4,450	$3,850	$3,300
Add $785 for 20 or 28 ga.							

CAVALIER S x S BOXLOCK—12, 20, or 28 ga., best quality model boxlock with scalloped frame, double triggers, ejectors, and case colored receiver. Current mfg.

Mfg.'s Sug. Retail	$12,685	$12,685	$9,575	$8,650	$7,400	$6,100	$5,500	$4,850
Add $785 for 20 or 28 ga.							

Cavalier De Luxe—similar to Cavalier Model, except has de luxe walnut and better engraving. Current mfg.

Mfg.'s Sug. Retail	$14,435	$14,435	$11,750	$9,625	$8,400	$6,925	$6,000	$5,250
Add $960 for 20 or 28 ga.							

DOMINION SIDELOCK—12, 16, and 20 ga.'s, 25-30 in. barrels, any choke, sidelock, auto ejectors, double triggers, checkered straight grip stock.

	$5,000	$4,000	$3,500	$3,250	$3,000	$2,750	$2,500
20 gauge — add 20%.							

Above values are for older, previously manufactured specimens.

Dominion Game Gun—12 ga. only, single or double triggers. Current mfg.

Mfg.'s Sug. Retail	$28,000	$28,000	$19,950	$16,750	$14,250	$11,950	$9,500	$8,250

ROYAL HAMMERLESS EJECTOR SIDELOCK—12, 16, 20, 28, and .410 ga.'s, customer specifications as to barrel length and chokes, hand detachable sidelocks and a self opening action, stocked in pistol grip or straight style to specifications, made from 1885-present.

	$12,000	$10,750	$8,500	$7,750	$6,950	$6,350	$5,250
20 gauge — add 20%.							
28 gauge — add 40%.							
.410 — add 60%.							
Without SST — subtract $1,000.							

Above values are for older, previously manufactured specimens.

Royal Game Gun—12, 16, or 20 ga., best quality sidelock game gun. Mfg. per individual customer specifications.

Mfg.'s Sug. Retail	$36,925	$36,925	$25,750	$19,950	$16,500	$12,750	$10,500	$9,000
Add $2,450 for 28 or .410 ga.							

HOLLAND & HOLLAND, LIMITED, cont.

Grading	100%	98%	95%	90%	80%	70%	60%

DE LUXE MODEL—similar to Royal Hammerless Ejector, except with more elaborate engraving and exhibition wood, self-opening gun.

	$15,000	**$13,000**	**$11,000**	**$9,000**	**$7,500**	**$6,500**	**$5,750**

    20 gauge — add 20%.
    28 gauge — add 40%.
    .410 ga. — add 60%.
    Without SST - subtract $1,000.

Above values are for older, previously manufactured specimens.

Royal De Luxe Game Gun—12, 16, or 20 ga., top-of-the-line sidelock shotgun. Mfg. per individual customer specifications.

Mfg.'s Sug. Retail   **$42,350 $42,350 $28,950 $22,000 $17,500 $14,000 $11,250 $9,000**
    Add $2,625 for 28 or .410 ga.

BADMINTON SIDELOCK—same as Royal model, without self opening action, made 1902-present.

	$10,500	**$9,000**	**$8,000**	**$7,000**	**$6,000**	**$5,000**	**$4,000**

    20 gauge — add 20%.
    28 gauge — add 40%.
    .410 ga. — add 60%.
    SST — add $1,000.

Above values are for older, previously manufactured specimens.

Badminton Game Gun—12 or 20 ga., double or single trigger. Discontinued in 1988.

	$28,000	**$20,000**	**$17,000**	**$14,500**	**$12,250**	**$10,000**	**$8,500**

Last Mfg.'s Sug. Retail was $28,000.

RIVIERA SIDELOCK—same as Badminton model, with two sets of barrels, made until 1967.

	$15,000	**$11,500**	**$9,500**	**$7,950**	**$7,100**	**$6,350**	**$5,600**

    20 gauge — add 20%.
    28 gauge — add 40%.
    .410 — add 60%.

CENTENARY SIDELOCK—12 ga., 2 in. chambers, lightened version of Royal, Badminton, and Dominion grades. The values would be the same as for the standard models, made until 1962.

SHOTGUNS: O/U

ROYAL MODEL O/U SHOTGUN OLD MODEL—12 ga., customer specifications as to barrel length and choke, hand detachable sidelocks, auto ejectors, checkered straight grip stock, made until 1951. Rare, fewer than 30 made.

	$21,500	**$18,000**	**$16,000**	**$14,500**	**$13,000**	**$11,000**	**$10,000**

    Single trigger — add $1,000.

ROYAL NEW MODEL O/U—same as Old Model, with improved narrow action, made until 1960.

	$24,000	**$22,000**	**$19,500**	**$18,500**	**$17,000**	**$15,500**	**$13,250**

ROYAL O/U GAME GUN—H&H is resuming production of the O/U Game Gun, and delivery is set for Autumn of 1990. Currently, pricing is set to start at approx. $41,125 and deposits are being taken at this time.

HOLLOWAY ARMS CO.

MANUFACTURED IN FORT WORTH, TX.

Holloway firearms did not make many rifles or carbines before operations ceased. While rare, they still are not particularly collectible at this point.

Grading	100%	98%	95%	90%	80%	70%	60%

HAC MODEL 7—7.62mm NATO (.308), gas operated semi-auto assault rifle, 20 in. barrel, adj. front and rear sights, 20 round mag., side folding stock. Manufactured 1984-1985 only. Also available in fully auto (class III dealers only) — add $80. Add $50 for left-hand variation.

		$595	$525	$465	$420	$380	$345	$315

Last Mfg.'s Sug. Retail was $675.

Model 7C—16 in. carbine, same general specifications as Model 7. Discontinued in 1985.

		$595	$525	$465	$420	$380	$345	$315

Last Mfg.'s Sug. Retail was $675. Also available from the manufacturer were the models 7S and 7M (Sniper and Match models).

HOLMES FIREARMS

MANUFACTURED IN WHEELER, AR. DISTRIBUTED BY D.B. DISTRIBUTING, FAYETTEVILLE, AR.

These pistols were mfg. in very limited numbers, most were in prototype configuration and exhibit changes from gun to gun.

MP-83—9mm and .45 ACP cal.'s, assault pistol, 6 in. barrel, walnut stock and forearm, blued finish, 3½ lbs. Add $75 for deluxe package and $220 for conversion kit. Manufactured 1985 only.

		$400	$360	$320	$285	$250	$225	$200

Last Mfg.'s Sug. Retail was $450.

MP-22—.22 LR cal., 2½ lbs., steel and aluminum construction, 6 in. barrel, similar appearance to MP-83. Manufactured 1985 only.

		$360	$320	$285	$250	$230	$210	$190

Last Mfg.'s Sug. Retail was $400.

COMBAT 12—12 ga., riot configuration, cylinder bore barrel. Discontinued in 1983.

		$795	$720	$650	$595	$550	$500	$450

Last Mfg.'s Sug. Retail was $750.

HOWA

MANUFACTURER LOCATED IN JAPAN.

Recently, Howa rifles have been imported by both Smith & Wesson (pre-1985) and Mossberg (1986-87). Currently, Howa sporting rifles are being imported by Interarms and this trademark will appear in the Interarms section in this text. Older Howa models will appear in both the S&W and Mossberg sections of this text.

HUNTER ARMS COMPANY

MANUFACTURER LOCATED IN FULTON, NY BETWEEN 1891 AND 1945.

The Hunter Arms Company was formed to manufacture L.C. Smith shotguns. Please refer to the L.C. Smith section in this text for further information regarding this manufacturer (including Fulton, Fulton Special, and Hunter Special models).

HUSQVARNA

MANUFACTURED IN HUSQVARNA, SWEDEN.

Also see: Lahti Pistols

RIFLE: BOLT ACTION

HI-POWER—Mauser type action, .220 Swift, .270, and .30-06 cal.'s, open sight, checkered beech wood, made 1946-1951, early models found 6.5 x 55, 8 x 57, 9.3 x 57 cal.'s.

		$330	$265	$250	$220	$195	$175	$165

Grading	100%	98%	95%	90%	80%	70%	60%

MODEL 1951—same as Hi-Power, except high combination stock.

	$340	$275	$260	$230	$205	$185	$175

SERIES 1100 DELUXE—same as 1951, except has European walnut and jeweled bolt, made 1952-1956.

	$440	$360	$330	$310	$290	$275	$250

SERIES 1000 SUPER GRADE—same as 1951, has walnut Monte Carlo stock, made 1952-1956.

	$440	$360	$330	$310	$290	$275	$250

SERIES 3100 CROWN GRADE—improved HVA Mauser action, .243, .270, .30-06, 7mm, and .308 cal.'s, 24 in. barrel, walnut stock, black forend tip and pistol grip cap, made 1954-1972.

	$470	$385	$360	$330	$315	$305	$275

SERIES 3000 CROWN GRADE—same as 3100, except has Monte Carlo stock.

	$470	$385	$360	$330	$315	$305	$275

SERIES 4100 LIGHTWEIGHT—HVA Mauser action, calibers same as 3100, 20½ in. barrel, open sights, lightweight walnut stock, pistol grip, Schnabel forend, made 1954-1972.

	$470	$385	$360	$330	$315	$305	$275

SERIES 4000 LIGHTWEIGHT—same as 4100, except has Monte Carlo stock, no sights.

	$470	$385	$360	$330	$315	$305	$275

MODEL 456 LIGHTWEIGHT—same as 4000/4100, except full length stock, made 1959-1970.

	$495	$415	$385	$360	$330	$310	$290

SERIES 6000 IMPERIAL GRADE—same as 3100, except has select wood, 3 leaf folding sight, made 1968-1970.

	$580	$495	$470	$440	$395	$365	$330

SERIES 6000 IMPERIAL LIGHTWEIGHT—same as 6000 Imperial, except 20½ in. barrel, lightweight stock.

	$580	$495	$470	$440	$395	$365	$330

SERIES P-3000 PRESENTATION—same as Crown, except engraved action, special wood, made 1968-1970.

	$770	$660	$635	$605	$550	$510	$485

MODEL 9000 CROWN GRADE—Husqvarna action, .300 Win. Mag. added to line, 23½ in. barrel, adj. trigger, adj. sight, walnut stock, made 1971-1972.

	$470	$385	$360	$330	$315	$305	$275

MODEL 8000 IMPERIAL—same as 9000, but jeweled bolt, engraved floor plate, no sights and deluxe stock, made 1971-1972.

	$605	$525	$495	$470	$415	$385	$350

HY-HUNTER INC. FIREARMS MANUFACTURING CO.

PREVIOUSLY MANUFACTURED IN W. GERMANY, IMPORTED BY HY-HUNTER INC.

Previous importer of single action revolvers in various calibers. Typically, prices are determined by their shooting value rather than their collector value. Prices generally range from $100-$175 depending on caliber and finish.

HYPER

PREVIOUSLY MANUFACTURED IN JENKS, OK.

SINGLE SHOT RIFLE—all calibers, all standard lengths and contours, falling block trigger guard lever activated, adj. trigger, no sights, stocked to customer specifications, in AA grade walnut. Discontinued in 1984.

	$2,200	$1,980	$1,925	$1,870	$1,650	$1,540	$1,375

Stainless barrel — add $75.
Octagon barrel — add $75.

I

I A B SHOTGUNS

MANUFACTURED BY INDUSTRIA ARMI BRESCIANE, ITALY. PREVIOUSLY DISTRIBUTED BY SPORTING ARMS INTERNATIONAL,INC. LOCATED IN INDIANOLA, MS.

I A B manufactures high quality competition (O/U and single barrel trap or skeet) shotguns in various styles and configurations including combo sets. These guns employ a boxlock action, have ejectors, and various amounts of engraving. Prices for 100% condition usually start in the $550-$900 price range. I A B shotguns are not being imported currently — values for older models will be determined by the prices shooters, not collectors, are willing to pay for them.

I G A SHOTGUNS

MANUFACTURED IN VERANOPOLIS, BRAZIL. CURRENTLY IMPORTED BY STOEGER INDUSTRIES.

Grading	100%	98%	95%	90%	80%	70%	60%
STANDARD GRADE S X S—12, 20, 28, or .410 ga., 3 in. chambers, underlug lockup, double triggers, extractors.							
Mfg.'s Sug. Retail	$300	$235	$185	$165	$145	$130	$115	$100
COACH GUN S X S—12 or 20 ga., same as standard grade, only 20 in. barrels.							
Mfg.'s Sug. Retail	$285	$220	$175	$155	$140	$125	$110	$100
DOUBLE TRIGGER O & U—12 or 20 ga., sliding underlug action, vent rib, checkered walnut, separated barrels. Discontinued in 1986.							
	$255	$220	$205	$190	$175	$160	$150
Last Mfg.'s Sug. Retail was $297.							
SINGLE TRIGGER O & U—12 or 20 ga., 3 in. chambers, sliding underlug action, vent rib, deluxe checkered walnut, separated barrels.							
Mfg.'s Sug. Retail	$450	$350	$275	$250	$225	$210	$195	$180
DELUXE O & U—12 ga. only, single trigger, ejectors, presentation walnut, chrome lined bores. Discontinued in 1985.							
	$580	$500	$450	$410	$375	$350	$325
Last Mfg.'s Sug. Retail was $667.							
SINGLE BARREL—12, 20, or .410 ga., exposed hammer with half-cock, extractor.							
Mfg.'s Sug. Retail	$110	$85	$70	$60	$50	$45	$40	$35

INDIAN ARMS

PREVIOSLY MFG. BY INDIAN ARMS CORPORATION LOCATED IN DETROIT, MI.

INDIAN ARMS .380 SEMI-AUTO—.380 ACP, patterned after Walther PPK, stainless steel, 3¼ in. barrel, 6 shot mag., natural or blue finish, with (early specimens) or without key lock safety, with or without VR barrel, walnut grips, 20 oz., manufactured 1975-1977.

$450 $350 $275

This model had limited manufacture with approx. 1,000 guns being made.

INDUSTRIA ARMI GALESI

MANUFACTURED IN BRESCIA, ITALY.

PISTOL: SEMI-AUTO

GALESI MODEL 6 POCKET AUTO—.22 long, .25 auto, 6 shot, 2¼ in. barrel blue, fixed sights, plastic grips, mfg. 1930-disc.

	$130	$120	$105	$90	$75	$65	$55

GALESI MODEL 9 POCKET AUTO—.22 LR, .32 auto, .380 auto, 8 shot, 3¼ in. barrel, blue, fixed sights, plastic grips, mfg. 1930-disc.

	$140	$125	$110	$100	$85	$65	$55

INGLIS HI-POWERS

MANUFACTURED BY JOHN INGLIS CO. LIMITED OF TORONTO, CANADA. OVER 151,000 INGLIS HI-POWERS WERE MANUFACTURED BETWEEN FEBRUARY 1944 AND SEPTEMBER 1945 UNDER MILITARY CONTRACTUAL AGREEMENT.

CHINESE CONTRACT PATTERN 35

Chinese No. 1—with markings, slotted for stock and tangent sights.

	$1,775	$1,475	$1,100	$995	$900	$800	$700

Add $200 for wooden holster stock.

CH SERIES CHINESE CONTRACT—recently being imported again, market is currently somewhat flooded.

MK 1-slotted—tangent sights.

	$1,200	$1,000	$900	$800	$700	$600	$500

CANADIAN MILITARY

MK 1-No. 1 Inglis—tangent sight, slotted.

	$1,150	$975	$850	$725	$650	$550	$450

Add $200 for wooden holster stock.

MK 1-No. 2 Inglis—fixed sight, no slot.

	$550	$475	$450	$425	$400	$350	$275

MK 1-No. 2 Inglis—fixed sight, slotted. Inspect slot carefully.

	$1,150	$975	$850	$725	$650	$550	$450

Add $200 for wooden holster stock.

T SERIES CANADIAN MILITARY

	100%	98%	95%	90%	80%	70%	60%
1 T	$725	$600	$550	$500	$450	$400	$350
2 T	$600	$500	$450	$395	$345	$295	$275
3 T	$550	$450	$400	$350	$300	$260	$240
4 T	$550	$450	$400	$350	$300	$260	$240
5 T	$550	$450	$400	$350	$300	$260	$240
6 T	$550	$450	$400	$350	$300	$260	$240
7 T	$550	$450	$400	$350	$300	$260	$240
8 T	$800	$695	$595	$550	$530	$460	$395
9 T	$860	$750	$650	$550	$530	$460	$395

INGRAM

MILITARY ARMAMENT CORP. (MAC), PREVIOUSLY LOCATED IN ATLANTA, GA. DISCONTINUED LATE 1982.

MAC 10—.45 ACP or 9mm cal., semi-auto, open bolt, pistol version of the sub machine gun, 16 and 32 round mag., compact construction, all metal construction, rear aperture and front blade sight. Discontinued 1982.

	$850	$775	$700	$650	$600	$550	$495

Add approx. $160 for accessories (barrel extension, case, and extra mag).

Grading	100%	98%	95%	90%	80%	70%	60%

MAC 10A1—similar to MAC 10 except fires from a closed bolt.

	100%	98%	95%	90%	80%	70%	60%
	$295	$275	$250	$230	$215	$200	$190

MAC 11—same as MAC 10 except in .380 ACP cal.

	100%	98%	95%	90%	80%	70%	60%
	$650	$595	$550	$525	$500	$480	$460

INTERARMS
MANUFACTURER - IMPORTER - DISTRIBUTOR LOCATED IN ALEXANDRIA, VA.

Interarms has imported a multitude of trademarks and models since the early 1960's. Most of the models shown below are recent imports, and specific information on older, limited import models can be obtained by contacting Interarms directly. The Astra, Rossi, Star, and Walther trademarks will be found in their own sections listed alphabetically in this text.

FEG PISTOLS

FEG pistols were imported from Hungary during 1986-87 only.

FEG MODEL R-9—9mm Para., patterned after Browning Hi-Power, double action, 13 shot mag., blued finish, steel construction, checkered wood grips. Imported in 1986-87 only.

	100%	98%	95%	90%	80%	70%	60%
	$275	$230	$200	$180	$165	$155	$145

Last Mfg.'s Sug. Retail was $375.

FEG MODEL PPH—.380 ACP, patterned after Walther PP, alloy frame, double action, plastic grips with thumbrest, blued finish. Imported in 1986-87 only.

	100%	98%	95%	90%	80%	70%	60%
	$200	$170	$140	$125	$115	$105	$95

Last Mfg.'s Sug. Retail was $225.

HELWAN PISTOLS

BRIGADIER—9mm Para., single action, 4.5 in. barrel, all steel construction, 8 round mag. with finger extension, black plastic grips, 32.6 oz.. Importation began in 1988.

	100%	98%	95%	90%	80%	70%	60%
Mfg.'s Sug. Retail	$260	$205	$170	$140	$125	$115	$105	$95

This design was originally initiated and produced by Pietro Beretta.

VIRGINIAN REVOLVERS: SINGLE ACTION

Virginian Revolvers were previously imported from Europe by various manufacturers (including Hammerli of Switzerland). They were also manufactured in Midland, VA from 1976-1984. Older models with exceptional quality (including Hammerli guns) are worth a premium over values listed below.

VIRGINIAN DRAGOON STANDARD—improved action patterned after Colt S.A. design, 6 shot, .44 Mag. cal. only, 6, 7½, 8⅜, or 12 (Buntline) in. barrel, blue finish, smooth walnut grips, adj. rear sight, 51 oz. with 7½ in. barrel.

	100%	98%	95%	90%	80%	70%	60%
	$255	$225	$205	$190	$180	$170	$160

Add 15% for Buntline Model.

Last Mfg.'s Sug. Retail was $315.

Dragoon Standard Stainless—.44 Mag., 6 (disc.), 7½ (disc.), or 8⅜ in. barrel, same general specifications as Standard Dragoon.

	100%	98%	95%
	$265	$230	$210

Last Mfg.'s Sug. Retail was $315.

DRAGOON SILHOUETTE—.357 or .44 Mag. cal., stainless steel, 7½, 8⅜, or 10½ in. (standard on .357 Mag.) barrel, special sights and grips.

	100%	98%	95%
	$365	$320	$275

Last Mfg.'s Sug. Retail was $425.

DRAGOON ENGRAVED—.44 Mag. only, choice of stainless steel or blue finish, 6 or 7½ in. barrel.

	100%	98%	95%	90%	80%	70%	60%
	$545	$470	$430	$395	$360	$320	$285

Add $75 for presentation case.

Last Mfg.'s Sug. Retail was $625.

Grading	100%	98%	95%	90%	80%	70%	60%

DRAGOON "DEPUTY"—.357 or .44 Mag. cal., blued barrel, case hardened frame, 5 in. barrel only.

	$250	$215	$195	$180	$165	$155	$145

Last Mfg.'s Sug. Retail was $295.

Stainless Deputy—same as above, except .44 Mag. available in 6 in. barrel only, stainless steel.

	$255	$225	$205				

Last Mfg.'s Sug. Retail was $295.

VIRGINIAN .22 CONVERTIBLE—.22 LR/.22 Mag. cylinders, 5½ in. barrel only, adj. rear sight, 38 oz.

	$185	$155	$145	$135	$125	$115	$105

Last Mfg.'s Sug. Retail was $219.

Virginian .22 Convertible Stainless—stainless steel fabrication, otherwise same as above.

	$200	$170	$155				

Last Mfg.'s Sug. Retail was $239.

RIFLES: HOWA MFG.

MODEL 1500 HUNTER—.22-250, .223, .243, .270, .308, .30-06, .300 Win. Mag., or 7mm Rem. Mag. cal.'s, 3 (Mag. cal.'s only) or 5 shot, 22 or 24 in. barrel, adj. rear sight and trigger, checkered walnut stock. Importation with Interarms in 1988 only.

	$360	$310	$285	$260	$240	$225	$205

Last Mfg.'s Sug. Retail was $440.

Model 1500 Lightning—.270, .30-06, or 7mm Rem. Mag. cal., lightweight variation of the Model 1500 Hunter featuring lightweight Carbolite (synthetic) stock, 7 lbs. Importation began in 1988.

Mfg.'s Sug. Retail	$495	$390	$325	$285	$260	$240	$225	$205

Add $15 for 7mm Rem. Mag. cal.

MODEL 1500 TROPHY—.22-250, .223, .243, .270, .308, .30-06, .300 Win. Mag., or 7mm Rem. Mag. cal.'s, 3 (Mag. cal.'s only) or 5 shot, 22 or 24 in. barrel, adj. rear sight and trigger, select Monte Carlo stock with skipline checkering. Importation with Interarms began in 1988.

Mfg.'s Sug. Retail	$495	$390	$325	$285	$260	$240	$225	$205

Add $15 for 7mm Rem. Mag./.300 Win. Mag. cal.

Model 1500 Varmint—.22-250 or .223 cal., 24 in. heavy barrel without sights, 5 round mag., 7 lbs. 1 oz. Importation began in 1988.

Mfg.'s Sug. Retail	$535	$410	$335	$295	$270	$250	$230	$210

RIFLES: MAUSER ACTIONS

Whitworth rifles are manufactured in England. Mark X rifles are currently manufactured in Yugoslavia.

MARK X VISCOUNT—.22-250, .243, .25-06, .270, 7 x 57mm, 7mm Mag., .308, .30-06, or .300 Win. Mag. cal.'s, 5 shot, 3 shot mag., 24 in. barrel, adj. rear sight and trigger, classic style Monte Carlo stock. Discontinued in 1983, re-introduced in 1985.

Mfg.'s Sug. Retail	$460	$370	$315	$285	$260	$240	$225	$205

Add $15 for 7mm Rem. Mag./.300 Win. Mag. cal.

This model is often referred to as the Viscount. Early manufacture was done in Manchester, England. Recent manufacture is in Yugoslavia. Earlier Manchester guns (before approx. 1980) will bring a slight premium over the values listed above.

Mini Mark X—.223 only, miniature M98 Mauser System action, 20 in. barrel with iron sights, checkered hardwood stock, 5 shot mag., adj. trigger, 6.35 lbs. New in 1987.

Mfg.'s Sug. Retail	$385	$315	$260	$240	$220	$200	$185	$170

Grading	100%	98%	95%	90%	80%	70%	60%

Lightweight Mark X—.270, .30-06, or 7mm Rem. Mag. cal., similar to Mark X Viscount, except has Carbolite (synthetic) stock and 20 in. barrel, 7 lbs. New in 1988.

Mfg.'s Sug. Retail	$480	$410	$365	$330	$300	$270	$240	$215

Add $15 for 7mm Rem. Mag. cal.

MARK X AMERICAN FIELD—same cal.'s as Mark X Rifle, Mauser action, 24 in. barrel, open sights, 5 shot Mag.(.300 Win. Mag. is only 3), checkered deluxe walnut with ebony forearm tip, thumb safety with sling swivels, adj. trigger, rubber recoil butt plate, 7 lbs. Imported since 1984.

Mfg.'s Sug. Retail	$570	$445	$385	$340	$310	$275	$250	$235

Add $15 for 7mm Rem. Mag./.300 Win. Mag. cal.

This model was the Whitworth American Field Series until 1987. Early manufacture was done in Manchester, England. Recent manufacture is in Yugoslavia. Earlier Manchester guns (before approx. 1980) will bring a slight premium over the values listed above.

WHITWORTH MANNLICHER STYLE CARBINE—.243, .270, .308, 7 x 57mm, or .30-06 cal., bolt action with full length walnut Mannlicher style stock, open sights, sling swivels, thumb safety, 20 in. barrel, 5 shot mag., 7 lbs. Imported in 1984-87.

		$570	$495	$455	$410	$375	$340	$310

Last Mfg.'s Sug. Retail was $675.

WHITWORTH EXPRESS RIFLE—.375 H&H or .458 Win. Mag. cal., 3 shot, 24 in. barrel, 3 leaf express sight, English style stock of walnut, checkered pistol grip forearm, 8½ lbs., made 1974-present.

Mfg.'s Sug. Retail	$710	$585	$480	$440	$400	$375	$350	$335

RIFLES: SEMI-AUTO

22-ATD—.22 LR only, patterned after the Browning Semi-Auto, 19.4 in. barrel, 11 shot mag. in stock, blued finish, checkered hardwood stock, take-down design, adj. rear sight, 4.6 lbs. New in 1987.

Mfg.'s Sug. Retail	$179	$150	$120	$110	$105	$100	$95	$90

Add $16 for camo case.

This model is manufactured by Norinco in China.

RIFLES: DISCONTINUED

CAVALIER—same as Viscount, except modern style stock, roll over cheekpiece, rosewood pistol grip cap and forend tip, recoil pad. Discontinued.

	$365	$330	$305	$290	$265	$230	$195

MANNLICHER STYLE CARBINE—same as Cavalier, except 20 in. barrel, full length stock, no Magnum or varmint calibers. Discontinued.

	$365	$330	$305	$290	$265	$230	$195

CONTINENTAL CARBINE—same as Mannlicher Style, except with double set trigger. Discontinued.

	$395	$365	$330	$310	$285	$255	$220

THE MARQUIS—.243, .270, .308, 7x51mm, or .30-06 cal., 20 in. barrel, adj. trigger. Mannlicher style carbine. Discontinued in 1984.

	$430	$325	$300	$275	$250	$230	$215

ALASKAN—same as Mark X, except .375 H&H and .458 Win. Mag. cal.'s, recoil pad and extra stock crossbolt. Discontinued in 1984.

	$460	$350	$330	$310	$290	$250	$210

INTERDYNAMIC OF AMERICA, INC.

PREVIOUSLY DISTRIBUTED 1981-84 UNDER THE ABOVE HEADING OUT OF MIAMI, FL.

KG-9—9mm Para., 3 in. barrel, open bolt, semi-auto assault pistol, disc. approx. 1983.

	$750	$700	$650	$600	$575	$550	$525

KG-99—9mm Para., 3 in. barrel, semi-auto assault pistol, closed bolt, 36 round mag, 5 in. vent shroud barrel, blue only, also available in fully auto version (Class III only — add $140), a stainless steel version of the KG 99. Made by Interdynamic in 1984 only.

	$260	$200	$180	$160	$145	$130	$120
KG-99M, mini pistol	$213	$165	$155	$145	$135	$125	$115

INTRATEC

MANUFACTURED AND DISTRIBUTED OUT OF MIAMI, FL.

TEC-9—9mm only, semi-auto assault pistol, 5 in. shrouded barrel, matte black finish, 36 shot mag. New in 1985.

Mfg.'s Sug. Retail	$267	$225	$175	$155	$140	$130	$120	$110

TEC-9S—matte stainless version of the TEC-9.

Mfg.'s Sug. Retail	$329	$275	$230	$185

For above TEC-9 with accessory package (deluxe case, 3-36 shot mag.'s, assault grip, and recoil compensator), add $150.

TEC-9M—mini version of the Model TEC-9, including 3 in. barrel and 20 shot mag.

Mfg.'s Sug. Retail	$245	$200	$165	$150	$140	$130	$120	$110

Tec-9MS—matte stainless version of the TEC-9M.

Mfg.'s Sug. Retail	$307	$255	$215	$180

TEC-9C—9mm, carbine variation with 16½ in. barrel, 36 shot mag. Made in 1987 only.

	$280	$240	$205

Last Mfg.'s Sug. Retail was $318.

TEC-22 "SCORPION"—.22 LR, semi-auto pistol, assault configuration, 4 in. barrel, ambidextrous safety, military matte finish, 30 shot mag., adj. sights, 30 oz.

Mfg.'s Sug. Retail	$173	$155	$130	$110	$100	$90	$85	$80

Add $12 for threaded barrel (Model Tec-22T).

TEC-38 DERRINGER—.38 Spl., O/U, derringer, 3 in. barrel, blue frame, double action, 13 oz. Mfg. 1986-1988.

	$110	$95	$85	$75	$65	$60	$55

Last Mfg.'s Sug. Retail was $125.

IRWINDALE ARMS, INC. (IAI)

MANUFACTURER LOCATED IN IRWINDALE, CA. MANUFACTURE BEGAN IN 1988.

PISTOLS

AUTOMAG III—.30 Carbine, stainless steel only, 6⅜ in. barrel, gas assisted action, Millett adj. sights with white outline, grooved Lexan grips, 8 shot mag., 43 oz. New in 1989.

Mfg.'s Sug. Retail	$695	$625	$550	$495

BACKUP PISTOL—.22 LR or .380 ACP cal., semi-auto action, 2½ in. barrel, stainless steel, Lexan grips, formerly TDE, 5 shot mag. in 380, 8 shot mag. in .22 LR, 18 oz. Older discontinued walnut grip models are worth a slight premium.

Mfg.'s Sug. Retail	$243	$200	$165	$135

AMT previously manufactured this model.

ISRAELI MILITARY INDUSTRIES (IMI)

MANUFACTURER LOCATED IN ISRAEL.

IMI manufactured guns (Galil, Magnum Research, Uzi, and others) can be located in their respective sections of this text.

ITALIAN MILITARY RIFLES

ITALY.

MODEL 1891 MANNLICHER-CARCANO—bolt action, 6.5mm, 6 shot, 31 in. barrel, straight handle, adj. sight, military stock.

	$120	$100	$85	$70	$55	$40	$30

Grading	100%	98%	95%	90%	80%	70%	60%

MODEL 38 TERNI MILITARY RIFLE—7.35mm, similar to 1891, except turned down bolt handle, 21 in. barrel and folding bayonet.

	$120	$100	$85	$70	$55	$40	$30

Gilisenti Auto Pistol—9mm (2 different models).

	$425	$350	$285	$250	$225	$200	$185

Warning: 9mm Parabellum ammunition cannot be used in this pistol - only 9mm Gilisenti.

ITHACA GUN

MANUFACTURED IN ITHACA, NY, 1886 TO NOV. OF 1986. REOPENED IN EARLY 1987 AS ITHACA ACQUISITION CORP. USING THE OLD TRADEMARK. IN THE PAST, ITHACA ALSO ABSORBED COMPANIES INCLUDING SYRACUSE ARMS CO., LEFEVER ARMS CO., UNION FIRE ARMS CO., WILKES-BARRE GUN CO., AS WELL AS OTHERS.

ON MARCH 6,1987 THE ITHACA GUN COMPANY WAS SOLD TO ITHACA ACQUISITION CORPORATION DOING BUSINESS AS ITHACA GUN COMPANY. CURRENTLY, ITHACA IS MANUFACTURING THE MODEL 87 SLIDE ACTION SHOTGUN (PREVIOUSLY DESIGNATED THE MODEL 37) AND WILL MANUFACTURE A SINGLE SHOT HANDGUN LATER IN 1988.

HANDGUNS

X-CALIBER SINGLE SHOT—.22 LR or .44 Mag. cal., break open action with contoured wooden grip and forearm, 10 or 15 in. barrel, unique dual firing pin detonates both rimfire and centerfire cartridges. Model 20 is target model (blued finish with Goncalo Alves wood grips), or Model 30 Hunting (sandblasted teflon finish with American walnut grips). Frames and barrels can be purchased separately. New in 1988.

Mfg.'s Sug. Retail	$270	$230	$210	$190	$175	$165	$155	$150

Add $95 for combo set (.44 Mag./.22 LR barrels).

RIFLES: BOLT ACTION

LSA-55 STANDARD—Mauser type action, .222, .22-250, 6mm, .243, or .308 cal., 22 in. barrel, leaf sight, 3 shot clip mag., checkered Monte Carlo stock, made in Finland by Tikka from 1969 to 1977.

	$375	$350	$330	$290	$255	$230	$210

LSA-55 DELUXE—same as Standard, except rollover cheek, rosewood pistol grip cap and forend tip, skipline checkering, no sights, scope mounts furnished.

	$415	$385	$365	$330	$285	$260	$240

LSA-55 HEAVY BARREL—same as LSA-55, except .222 and .22-250 only, target heavy barrel, special beavertail stock 8½ lbs.

	$440	$420	$390	$360	$310	$275	$255

LSA-65—same as LSA-55, except long action for calibers .25-06, .270, and .30-06. Made 1969 to 1977.

	$375	$350	$330	$290	$255	$230	$210

LSA-65 DELUXE—same as LSA-55 Deluxe, except .25-06, .270, and .30-06.

	$415	$385	$365	$330	$285	$260	$240

COMBINATION GUNS

LSA-55 TURKEY GUN—O/U shotgun-rifle combo, 12 ga., .222 Rem., 24½ in. ribbed barrel, exposed hammer, folding rear sight, checkered Monte Carlo stock, made by Tikka, Finland. Made from 1970-1981.

	$605	$550	$415	$495	$425	$385	$330

RIFLES: SEMI-AUTO

MODEL X5-C—.22LR cal., 7 round Mag., semi-auto action, made 1958 to 1964. Model X5-T has tube mag.

	$95	$70	$65	$60	$55	$50	$35

MODEL X-15—.22 LR cal., same as X5-C only forearm is not grooved. Made 1964 to 1967.

	$95	$70	$65	$60	$55	$50	$35

Grading	100%	98%	95%	90%	80%	70%	60%

RIFLES: LEVER ACTION

MODEL 49 SADDLEGUN—.22 LR cal., lever-action, single shot. Made 1961 to 1978. Martini-style action Mag. — add $15, deluxe model — add $45.

	$65	$50	$45	$40	$35	$30	$30

MODEL 49 PRESENTATION—like model 49, except gold-plated trigger, hammer, engraved receiver, fancy walnut. Made 1962 to 1974.

	$220	$165	$155	$130	$120	$110	$100

MODEL 149 ST. LOUIS BICENTENNIAL—like deluxe model 149, except inscription on receiver, 200 made in 1964.

	$210	$160	$150	$125	$115	$105	$95

MODEL 72 SADDLEGUN—.22 or .22 mag., lever action, 18½ in. barrel, hooded front sight. Made 1973 to 1978 by Erma Werke, W. Germany.

	$185	$140	$130	$110	$100	$90	$85

MODEL 72 DELUXE—same as Model 72, except has silver finished engraved receiver, deluxe walnut, octagon barrel. Made 1974 to 1976.

	$260	$195	$185	$155	$145	$130	$120

SHOTGUNS: SIDE X SIDE - EARLY PRODUCTION

ITHACA HAMMERLESS DOUBLE BARREL—12, 16, 20, 28 and .410 ga.'s, 26-32 in. barrels, boxlock, extractors, double triggers, any standard choke, checkered pistol grip stock and forearm. Prices shown for guns made between 1925-1948, when discontinued for 12 ga. only. Grades shown differ in overall quality, ornamentation, grade of wood and style of checkering.

> SST — add $200.
>
> Non-SST — add $150.
>
> Vent rib on grades 4, 5, 7, and $2,000 Grade — add $350.
>
> Vent rib - lower grades — add $200.
>
> Beavertail forearm — add $175.
>
> Auto ejectors - for grades No. 1, 2, and 3 — add 33%.
>
> Without ejectors on grades 4E-7E — subtract 33%.
>
> NOTE: Shotguns made before 1925 have less value (ser. no.'s before 400,000 with underbolt - rib extension locking system) because modern ammunition cannot be shot safely in these earlier models. In 1925 the rotary bolt and stronger frame were adapted (ser. no.'s after 400,000). Once again, it is recommended that these guns (pre-400,000 ser. range) are not shot with modern ammo.

100%	98%	95%	90%	80%	70%	60%	50%	40%	30%	20%	10%

FIELD GRADE

10 ga. Mag.

$2,000	$1,800	$1,500	$1,400	$1,300	$1,200	$1,100	$950	$825	$700	$575	$495

3½ in. chambered 10 ga. Mag.'s are serial numbered over 500,000. Total production was approx. 850 guns. 2⅞ in. chambered 10 ga.'s are priced the same as a 12 ga.

12 ga.

$1,000	$800	$600	$550	$500	$450	$415	$380	$350	$325	$300	$265

16 ga.

$1,000	$800	$600	$550	$500	$450	$415	$380	$350	$325	$300	$265

20 ga.

$1,200	$1,000	$800	$675	$575	$500	$450	$415	$380	$350	$325	$300

28 ga.

$2,000	$1,800	$1,500	$1,400	$1,300	$1,200	$1,100	$1,000	$925	$850	$775	$695

.410 ga.

$2,000	$1,800	$1,500	$1,400	$1,300	$1,200	$1,100	$1,000	$925	$850	$795	$750

	100%	98%	95%	90%	80%	70%	60%	50%	40%	30%	20%	10%

GRADE NO. 2

10 ga. Mag.

100%	98%	95%	90%	80%	70%	60%	50%	40%	30%	20%	10%
$2,400	$2,000	$1,800	$1,600	$1,400	$1,300	$1,200	$1,100	$950	$825	$700	$575

3½ in. chambered 10 ga. Mag.'s are serial numbered over 500,000. Total production was approx. 850 guns. 2⅞ in. chambered 10 ga.'s are priced the same as a 12 ga.

12 ga.

100%	98%	95%	90%	80%	70%	60%	50%	40%	30%	20%	10%
$1,500	$1,200	$1,000	$800	$600	$550	$500	$450	$415	$380	$350	$325

16 ga.

100%	98%	95%	90%	80%	70%	60%	50%	40%	30%	20%	10%
$1,500	$1,200	$1,000	$800	$600	$550	$500	$450	$415	$380	$350	$325

20 ga.

100%	98%	95%	90%	80%	70%	60%	50%	40%	30%	20%	10%
$1,800	$1,500	$1,200	$1,000	$800	$600	$550	$500	$450	$415	$380	$350

28 ga.

100%	98%	95%	90%	80%	70%	60%	50%	40%	30%	20%	10%
$2,500	$2,000	$1,800	$1,500	$1,400	$1,300	$1,200	$1,100	$1,000	$925	$850	$775

.410 ga.

100%	98%	95%	90%	80%	70%	60%	50%	40%	30%	20%	10%
$2,500	$2,000	$1,800	$1,500	$1,400	$1,300	$1,200	$1,100	$1,000	$925	$850	$795

GRADE NO. 3

10 ga. Mag.

100%	98%	95%	90%	80%	70%	60%	50%	40%	30%	20%	10%
$3,000	$2,500	$2,100	$1,800	$1,600	$1,400	$1,300	$1,200	$1,100	$950	$825	$700

3½ in. chambered 10 ga. Mag.'s are serial numbered over 500,000. Total production was approx. 850 guns. 2⅞ in. chambered 10 ga.'s are priced the same as a 12 ga.

12 ga.

100%	98%	95%	90%	80%	70%	60%	50%	40%	30%	20%	10%
$1,850	$1,500	$1,200	$1,000	$800	$600	$550	$500	$450	$415	$380	$350

16 ga.

100%	98%	95%	90%	80%	70%	60%	50%	40%	30%	20%	10%
$1,850	$1,500	$1,200	$1,000	$800	$600	$550	$500	$450	$415	$380	$350

20 ga.

100%	98%	95%	90%	80%	70%	60%	50%	40%	30%	20%	10%
$1,800	$1,500	$1,200	$1,000	$800	$600	$550	$500	$450	$415	$380	$350

28 ga.

100%	98%	95%	90%	80%	70%	60%	50%	40%	30%	20%	10%
$3,200	$2,800	$2,400	$2,100	$1,800	$1,500	$1,400	$1,300	$1,200	$1,100	$1,000	$925

.410 ga.

100%	98%	95%	90%	80%	70%	60%	50%	40%	30%	20%	10%
$3,400	$2,950	$2,500	$2,150	$1,800	$1,500	$1,400	$1,300	$1,200	$1,100	$1,000	$925

GRADE NO. 4E—auto ejectors.

10 ga. Mag.

100%	98%	95%	90%	80%	70%	60%	50%	40%	30%	20%	10%
$4,000	$3,500	$3,000	$2,500	$2,100	$1,800	$1,600	$1,400	$1,300	$1,200	$1,100	$950

3½ in. chambered 10 ga. Mag.'s are serial numbered over 500,000. Total production was approx. 850 guns. 2⅞ in. chambered 10 ga.'s are priced the same as a 12 ga.

12 ga.

100%	98%	95%	90%	80%	70%	60%	50%	40%	30%	20%	10%
$3,000	$2,500	$2,200	$1,850	$1,500	$1,200	$1,000	$800	$600	$550	$500	$450

16 ga.

100%	98%	95%	90%	80%	70%	60%	50%	40%	30%	20%	10%
$3,000	$2,500	$2,200	$1,850	$1,500	$1,200	$1,000	$800	$600	$550	$500	$450

20 ga.

100%	98%	95%	90%	80%	70%	60%	50%	40%	30%	20%	10%
$4,000	$3,500	$3,000	$2,500	$2,200	$1,850	$1,500	$1,200	$1,000	$800	$600	$550

28 ga.

Extreme rarity factor precludes accurate pricing evaluation.

.410 ga.

Extreme rarity factor precludes accurate pricing evaluation.

GRADE NO. 5E—auto ejectors.

10 ga. Mag.

100%	98%	95%	90%	80%	70%	60%	50%	40%	30%	20%	10%
$5,000	$4,500	$4,000	$3,500	$3,000	$2,500	$2,100	$1,800	$1,600	$1,400	$1,200	$1,000

3½ in. chambered 10 ga. Mag.'s are serial numbered over 500,000. Total production was approx. 850 guns. 2⅞ in. chambered 10 ga.'s are priced the same as a 12 ga.

	100%	98%	95%	90%	80%	70%	60%	50%	40%	30%	20%	10%

12 ga.

100%	98%	95%	90%	80%	70%	60%	50%	40%	30%	20%	10%
$4,250	$3,250	$2,600	$2,200	$1,850	$1,500	$1,200	$1,000	$800	$600	$550	$500

16 ga.

100%	98%	95%	90%	80%	70%	60%	50%	40%	30%	20%	10%
$4,250	$3,250	$2,600	$2,200	$1,850	$1,500	$1,200	$1,000	$800	$600	$550	$500

20 ga.

100%	98%	95%	90%	80%	70%	60%	50%	40%	30%	20%	10%
$4,800	$4,100	$3,500	$3,000	$2,500	$2,200	$1,850	$1,600	$1,400	$1,200	$1,000	$895

28 ga.

Extreme rarity factor precludes accurate pricing evaluation.

.410 ga.

Extreme rarity factor precludes accurate pricing evaluation.

GRADE NO. 6E—auto ejectors.

10 ga. Mag.

100%	98%	95%	90%	80%	70%	60%	50%	40%	30%	20%	10%
$5,600	$5,000	$4,500	$4,000	$3,500	$3,000	$2,500	$2,100	$1,800	$1,600	$1,400	$1,200

3½ in. chambered 10 ga. Mag.'s are serial numbered over 500,000. Total production was approx. 850 guns. 2⅞ in. chambered 10 ga.'s are priced the same as a 12 ga.

12 ga.

100%	98%	95%	90%	80%	70%	60%	50%	40%	30%	20%	10%
$4,750	$4,000	$3,250	$2,600	$2,200	$1,850	$1,500	$1,200	$1,000	$800	$600	$550

16 ga.

100%	98%	95%	90%	80%	70%	60%	50%	40%	30%	20%	10%
$4,750	$4,250	$3,250	$2,600	$2,200	$1,850	$1,500	$1,200	$1,000	$800	$600	$550

20 ga.

100%	98%	95%	90%	80%	70%	60%	50%	40%	30%	20%	10%
$5,350	$4,675	$4,100	$3,500	$3,000	$2,500	$2,200	$1,850	$1,600	$1,400	$1,200	$995

28 ga.

Extreme rarity factor precludes accurate pricing evaluation.

.410 ga.

Extreme rarity factor precludes accurate pricing evaluation.

GRADE NO. 7E—auto ejectors.

10 ga. Mag.—extreme rarity factor precludes accurate pricing evaluation.

3½ in. chambered 10 ga. Mag.'s are serial numbered over 500,000. Total production was approx. 850 guns. 2⅞ in. chambered 10 ga.'s are priced the same as a 12 ga.

12 ga.

100%	98%	95%	90%	80%	70%	60%	50%	40%	30%	20%	10%
$9,250	$8,300	$7,400	$6,500	$5,650	$4,750	$4,000	$3,250	$2,600	$2,100	$1,600	$1,150

16 ga.

100%	98%	95%	90%	80%	70%	60%	50%	40%	30%	20%	10%
$9,250	$8,300	$7,400	$6,500	$5,650	$4,750	$4,000	$3,250	$2,600	$2,100	$1,600	$1,150

20 ga.

100%	98%	95%	90%	80%	70%	60%	50%	40%	30%	20%	10%
$10,400	$9,250	$8,300	$7,400	$6,500	$5,650	$4,750	$4,000	$3,250	$2,600	$2,100	$1,600

28 ga.

Extreme rarity factor precludes accurate pricing evaluation.

.410 ga.

Extreme rarity factor precludes accurate pricing evaluation.

$2,000 GRADE—12 ga., top-of-the-line model, auto ejectors, single selective trigger.

100%	98%	95%	90%	80%	70%	60%	50%	40%	30%	20%	10%
$11,000	$9,500	$8,450	$7,400	$6,500	$5,650	$4,750	$4,000	$3,250	$2,600	$2,100	$1,600

Rarity on 16 or 20 ga. precludes accurate pricing.

PRE-WAR $1,000 GRADE—12 ga., top-of-the-line models, auto ejectors, single selective trigger.

100%	98%	95%	90%	80%	70%	60%	50%	40%	30%	20%	10%
$13,000	$11,000	$9,500	$8,450	$7,400	$6,500	$5,650	$4,750	$4,000	$3,250	$2,600	$2,100

Rarity on 16 or 20 ga. precludes accurate pricing.

SOUSA GRADE—has mermaids on trigger guard in gold, only 11 manufactured (including one .410 ga.). This model is too rare to accurately evaluate but values would exceed $50,000 (assuming all original and 80% or better condition).

This model had help in development by the famous band director and composer, John Phillip Sousa.

Grading	100%	98%	95%	90%	80%	70%	60%

TRAP GUNS

SINGLE BARREL TRAP—12 ga., 30, 32, and 34 in. barrels, vent rib, boxlock, auto ejector, checkered pistol grip and forearm, grades differ in engraving, overall workmanship, and grade or wood and checkering. Values on these models sometimes vary greatly depending on originality of finish, customer alterations, and other variations trap shooters might use to alter dimensions for their particular shooting requirements. Below values represent trap guns in original, unaltered condition.

Note: Flues model made prior to 1921 with serial numbers under 400,000 have less value than those models made afterward as pre-400,000 serial no. shotguns cannot be fired safely with modern ammunition.

Trap guns under 60% original condition will be within 25% of the value shown in the 60% column.

Knick Model—made 1921-discontinued. Serial numbered above 400,000. Can be distinguished by triple underbolt locking.

	100%	98%	95%	90%	80%	70%	60%
	$1,395	$1,000	$900	$800	$675	$600	$550

Victory Grade—discontinued 1938.

	$995	$850	$775	$675	$575	$495	$440

No. 4E—discontinued in 1976.

	$1,500	$1,200	$1,000	$875	$750	$650	$595	$550

No. 6E—this model was available by special order only. Rarity factor precludes accurate pricing.

No. 7E—discontinued in 1964.

	$3,950	$3,450	$3,000	$2,750	$2,475	$2,225	$1,995

$5,000 Grade—same as Pre-War $1,000 grade.

	$9,500	$8,900	$8,175	$7,650	$6,725	$5,825	$4,950

Sousa Grade—extremely rare.

Extreme rarity factor precludes accurate pricing evaluation. Prices will be higher than the $5,000 Grade.

AUTO BURGLAR S X S—20 ga., 10 or 14 in. barrels, with or without cocking indicators, blue finish, pistol grip, class 3 weapon - must be registered, offered in Model A or B (squared grips), manufactured from early 1900's-1933.

	$1,045	$935	$770	$715	$660	$635	$580

MODEL 66 LEVER ACTION—20 and .410 ga. single shot lever action, field gun only. Manufactured 1963 to 1978. Add 33% to .410 ga.

	$125	$95	$90	$75	$70	$65	$55

Model 66 RS—20 ga. slug gun with 22 in. barrel and rifle type sights, recoil pad.

	$150	$130	$110	$90	$80	$70	$60

Note: Ventilated ribs were also available on special order in the 20 ga. only — add 25%.

SKB SHOTGUNS: PREVIOUSLY IMPORTED BY ITHACA

Note: Can be found under SKB heading.

SINGLE BARREL TRAP SHOTGUNS: RECENT MANUFACTURE

CENTURY TRAP GRADE SINGLE BARREL—12 ga., 32 or 34 in. vent rib barrel, engraved, auto ejector, full choke, checkered walnut stock. Made 1973 and 1976 by SKB.

	$550	$525	$470	$440	$385	$360	$320

CENTURY II—improved trap stock version of Century, Monte Carlo stock.

	$600	$550	$495	$470	$415	$385	$350

5E GRADE—12 ga., 32 or 34 in. barrel, custom order only, elaborate engraving, quality workmanship throughout. Originally mfg. 1925-1986, mfg. resumed again in 1988.

Mfg.'s Sug. Retail	$7,500	$7,500	$2,950	$2,550	$2,175	$1,900	$1,725	$1,495

Grading	100%	98%	95%	90%	80%	70%	60%

DOLLAR GRADE—12 ga., 32 or 34 in. barrel. Top-of-the-line model custom built to customer specifications. Original mfg. was stopped in 1986 and resumed again in 1988.

Mfg.'s Sug. Retail	$10,000	$10,000	$5,800	$5,000	$4,400	$3,850	$3,250	$2,775

SHOTGUNS: SLIDE ACTION

In 1987, Ithaca Acquisition Corp. reintroduced the Model 37 as the Model 87. New Model 87's are listed below and also include pre-1986 mfg. (Model 37's). Unless a particular Model 37 specimen has rare features, special wood, or was a deluxe order, values will approximate most older models as well.

MODEL 37 FEATHERLIGHT STANDARD—12, 16, and 20 ga.'s, bottom ejection, 4 shot mag., 26, 28, and 30 in. barrel, hammerless, take down, any standard choke, made 1937-discontinued.

	$260	$225	$205	$185	$165	$150	$135

MODEL 37V—same as 37, except vent rib, made 1962-discontinued.

	$315	$260	$240	$195	$180	$170	$165

All currently manufactured Model 37's have the Featherlight designation. Prices above are for older manufactured Model 37's.

MODEL 37D—same as 37, except recoil pad, beavertail forearm, checkered, made 1954-1981.

	$360	$275	$255	$205	$195	$185	$175

MODEL 37DV—same as 37D, except vent rib, made 1962-1981.

	$395	$320	$295	$245	$225	$200	$185

MODEL 37 FIELD GRADE MAGNUM—12 and 20 ga., 3 in. chambers, vent rib, walnut stock and corncob forearm, supplied with three choke tubes. Mfg. 1984-1986.

	$300	$240	$195	$180	$170	$165	$150

Last Mfg.'s Sug. Retail was $428.

MODEL 87 DELUXE MAGNUM—12 and 20 ga., 3 in. chambers, vent rib, deluxe wood with checkered forearm. Mfg. 1981-1986, production resumed in 1988 only.

	$320	$270	$230	$210	$200	$185	$165

Add $77 for Combo package (extra 28 in. barrel).

Last Mfg.'s Sug. Retail was $395.

New mfg. 20 ga. shotguns were available with a 25 in. barrel only (with choke tubes).

MODEL 37 FIELD GRADE STANDARD—12 or 20 ga., economy model, corncob forearm, 26, 28, or 30 in. barrel. Manufactured 1983-1985 only.

	$260	$225	$205	$180	$165	$150	$135

Last Mfg.'s Sug. Retail was $298.

MODEL 87 BASIC FIELD COMBO—12 or 20 ga., includes 20/25 in. deer barrel with special bore and 28 in. VR multi-choke field barrel, uncheckered walnut stock and corncob forearm, 7 lbs. New in 1989.

Mfg.'s Sug. Retail	$427	$340	$280	$240	$200	$175	$160	$145

Add $32 for rifled bore barrel.

MODEL 87 FIELD GRADE—12 or 20 ga., 3 in. chamber, economy model, walnut stock and forearm with pressed checkering, 26, 28, or 30 in. barrel with 3 choke tubes standard. Reintroduced in 1989.

Mfg.'s Sug. Retail	$458	$375	$325	$275	$230	$205	$185	$165

Model 87 Camo Field—12 ga. only, all metal and wood surfaces camouflaged with Camoseal paint, 28 in. VR barrel with choke tubes. New in 1989.

Mfg.'s Sug. Retail	$524	$430	$360	$300	$250	$220	$190	$170

Model 87 Turkey Gun—12 ga. only, 24 in. VR barrel with choice of fixed full choke or full choke tube, camo or matte blue finish. New in 1989.

Mfg.'s Sug. Retail	$409	$330	$275	$235	$195	$175	$160	$145

Add $105 for camo finish.
Add $11 for full choke tube.

Model 87 Deluxe—similar to Model 87 Field Grade except has cut checkering, high gloss lacquer finish, and gold trigger. New in 1989.

Mfg.'s Sug. Retail	$495	$410	$345	$285	$240	$210	$190	$170

Grading	100%	98%	95%	90%	80%	70%	60%

MODEL 87 ULTRALITE FIELD—12 or 20 ga., 3 in. chamber, aluminum receiver, 20 (disc. in 1988), 24, 25 (disc. in 1988), or 26 in. barrel. 20 ga. weighs 5 lbs., 12 ga. weighs 5¾ lbs, multi-chokes (3) became standard in 1989. Originally mfg. 1988-86, reintroduced in 1988.

Mfg.'s Sug. Retail	$481	$400	$340	$285	$240	$210	$190	$170

Add $50 for slim grip model (12½ in. stock - discontinued in 1985).
Subtract $42 if without multiple choke feature.

The 20 and 25 in. barrels were discontinued when mfg. was resumed in 1988.

Model 87 Ultra Deluxe—similar to Ultralite Field except has cut checkering, high gloss lacquer finish, and gold trigger. New in 1989.

Mfg.'s Sug. Retail	$514	$425	$360	$300	$250	$220	$190	$170

MODEL 37 ENGLISH ULTRALITE—12 and 20 ga., 25 or 26 in. barrels. World's lightest pump. 20 ga. weighs 4¾ lb., 12 ga. weighs 5½ lbs., checkered straight stock. Mfg. 1983-1986.

	$350	$310	$275	$250	$225	$200	$180.

Last Mfg.'s Sug. Retail was $522.

MODEL 37R—solid rib, made 1937-1967.

Plain stock	$340	$200	$175	$145	$130	$110	$90
Checkered stock	$380	$220	$200	$175	$165	$145	$120

MODEL 37R DELUXE—same as 37R, except fancy wood, made 1937-1955.

	$440	$275	$255	$230	$210	$195	$165

MODEL 37S SKEET GRADE—similar to 37, except vent rib, large forearm, fancy wood, made 1937-1955.

	$380	$310	$290	$270	$230	$200	$195

MODEL 37T TRAP GRADE—similar to 37S, except trap stock, select walnut, recoil pad, made 1937-1955.

	$400	$360	$320	$290	$270	$230	$210

MODEL 37T TARGET GRADE—replaced 37S and 37T, made from 1955-1961.

	$425	$375	$340	$310	$285	$260	$240

MODEL 87 SUPREME GRADE—12 or 20 ga., presentation walnut, high luster blue, limited production, previously available in either trap, skeet, or field models, fixed chokes. Originally manufactured 1967-86, reintroduced 1988.

Mfg.'s Sug. Retail	$819	$695	$495	$425	$395	$360	$315	$280

BASIC DEERSLAYER—12 ga. only, 20 or 25 in. special bore barrel, oil finished stock and corncob forearm with no checkering, iron sights, matte metal finish, 7 lbs. New in 1989.

Mfg.'s Sug. Retail	$391	$320	$265	$230	$195	$175	$160	$145

MODEL 87 FIELD DEERSLAYER—12 or 20 ga., rifle slug barrel, 20 or 25 in. special bore barrel, open sights, made 1959-86, reintroduced 1988.

Mfg.'s Sug. Retail	$407	$330	$275	$235	$195	$175	$160	$145

Model 87 Deluxe Deerslayer—similar to Field Deerslayer except has cut checkering, high gloss lacquer finish, and gold trigger. New in 1989.

Mfg.'s Sug. Retail	$429	$340	$280	$240	$200	$175	$160	$145

Add $120 for combo package (28 in. multi-choke barrel).
Add $33 for rifled bore.

Model 87 Ultra Deerslayer—similar to Deluxe Deerslayer except has aluminum frame. New in 1989.

Mfg.'s Sug. Retail	$444	$350	$285	$245	$200	$175	$160	$145

MODEL 37 SUPER DELUXE DEERSLAYER—similar to Model 37 (87) Deerslayer, except fancy wood, made 1962-1985.

	$390	$335	$300	$270	$235	$210	$185

Last Mfg.'s Sug. Retail was $447.

MONTE CARLO DEERSLAYER II—12 ga. only, 25 in. barrel with rifling, Monte Carlo stock and forearm with cut checkering, receiver is drilled and tapped for scope mounting, 7 lbs. New in 1989.

Mfg.'s Sug. Retail	$525	$435	$360	$300	$250	$220	$190	$170

Grading	100%	98%	95%	90%	80%	70%	60%

MODEL 87 CAMO VENT—12 ga. only, 3 in. chamber, 26 in. vent rib barrel, camo-seal rust resistant finish on exterior parts. Available in either green or brown, includes sling and swivels. Mfg. began in 1986, resumed in 1988.

Mfg.'s Sug. Retail	$524	$430	$360	$300	$250	$220	$190	$170

MODEL 87 MILITARY & POLICE—12 or 20 (new in 1989) ga., short barrel Model 37 w/normal stock or pistol grip only, 18½ or 20 in. barrel, 5 or 8 shot. Originally discontinued in 1983, reintroduced in 1988.

Mfg.'s Sug. Retail	$391	$325	$265	$230	$200	$180	$170	$160

Add $16 for normal stock and corncob forearm.
Subtract $35 without parkerizing (disc.).

MODEL 37 BICENTENNIAL—12 ga., engraved, fancy wood, cased with pewter buckle, 1,776 produced in 1976, 100% value assumes NIB condition with case and belt buckle.

		$425	$375	$340	$315	$295	$270	$250

MODEL 37 2500 SERIES CENTENNIAL—12 ga., customized version of the Model 37 commemorating Ithaca's 100th year anniversary. Silver plated, etched antique finish receiver, deluxe walnut. Made 1980-1984.

		$850	$690	$600	$505	$460	$415	$370

Last Mfg.'s Sug. Retail was $919.

MODEL 37 PRESENTATION—12 ga., blued, engraved, gold mounted receiver with extra-fancy walnut, cased, limited production. Manufactured 1981-86.

		$1,475	$1,245	$1,080	$915	$830	$745	$665

Last Mfg.'s Sug. Retail was $1,658.

MODEL 37 DUCKS UNLIMITED—12 ga., vent rib.

		$385	$305	$275

MODEL 37 $1000 GRADE—all gauges, deluxe engraving and checkering, gold inlaid, select figured walnut, hand-finished parts, made 1937-1940.

		$5,995	$5,500	$4,950	$4,400	$3,960	$3,520	$2,750

MODEL 37 $5000 GRADE—same as $1000 Grade, post-war designation, made 1947-1967.

		$5,720	$5,060	$4,675	$4,290	$3,740	$3,300	$2,530

SHOTGUNS: SEMI-AUTO

MODEL 51A STANDARD—12 and 20 ga., 30 in. full, 28 in. full or mod., 26 in. imp. cyl., gas operated, autoloading, checkered pistol grip stock, made 1970-1985. Vent rib became standard during late production.

Older models (no VR)	$285	$230	$200	$180	$165	$150	$130

Recent production—with vent. rib.

	$395	$360	$325	$295	$260	$235	$210

Last Mfg.'s Sug. Retail with VR was $477.

MODEL 51A MAGNUM—same as 51 Standard, except 3 in. shells only, blue finish, recoil pad, vent rib became standard in 1984. Discontinued for 1985.

Older models with no VR	$310	$255	$220	$205	$180	$165	$150
Vent rib	$410	$370	$330	$300	$270	$245	$215

MODEL 51A MAGNUM WATERFOWLER—same as 51 Standard, except 3 in. shells only, matte finished metal & flat finished walnut, recoil pad. Vent rib standard. Mfg. 1984-1986. Add $80 for camouflaged exterior finish.

	$420	$380	$335	$310	$270	$245	$215

Last Mfg.'s Sug. Retail was $625.

MODEL 51A CAMO VENT—similar to Waterfowler, except has camo-seal rust resistant exterior finish. Mfg. in 1986 only.

	$450	$360	$325

Last Mfg.'s Sug. Retail was $770.

MODEL 51A SUPREME TRAP—same as 51 Standard, except 12 ga. only, 30 in. barrel, 7 post rib, full choke, select wood, pad, trap style stock. Add $36 for Monte Carlo. Mfg. 1970-1986.

	$425	$365	$315	$295	$270	$250	$230

Last Mfg.'s Sug. Retail was $869.

Grading	100%	98%	95%	90%	80%	70%	60%

MODEL 51A SUPREME SKEET—same as 51 Standard, except 26 in. vent rib barrel, skeet choke, select wood, made 1970-present. 20 ga. was available 1983. Disc. in 1986.

	$450	$390	$340	$300	$280	$260	$240

Last Mfg.'s Sug. Retail was $858.

MODEL 51A DEERSLAYER—same as 51 Standard, with 24 in. slug barrel, rifle sights, recoil pad, no rib, made 1972-1983.

	$350	$300	$260	$230	$195	$180	$165

Last Mfg.'s Sug. Retail was $477.

MODEL 51A TURKEY GUN—.12 ga. Mag. only, 26 in. barrel, matte finish, sling and swivels included. Mfg. 1984-1986.

	$360	$305	$275	$265	$250	$230	$210

Last Mfg.'s Sug. Retail was $625.

MODEL 51 DUCKS UNLIMITED—same as 51 Deluxe, with D/U emblem on receiver.

	$475	$400	$350	$300	$280	$260	$230

MODEL 51 PRESENTATION—12 ga., blued, engraved, gold engraved receiver with deluxe walnut. Mfg. 1984-1986.

	$1,475	$1,245	$1,080	$915	$830	$745	$665

Last Mfg.'s Sug. Retail was $1,658.

SEMI-AUTO: MAG-10 SEMI-AUTO

All Ithaca Mag-10's were discontinued in 1986.

MAG-10—10 ga., 3½ in. Mag., semi-auto, various barrel lengths, stainless steel breech block assembly, gas operated, various chokes, plain barrel, 11 lb., manufactured 1975-1986.
100% values assume NIB condition - if without, subtract 10%.

Standard Grade—no checkering, ribless barrel, dull finished wood.

	$650	$600	$550	$495	$450	$400	$375

Last Mfg.'s Sug. Retail was $726.

Standard Grade with VR—available in 22, 26, 28, and 32 in. barrel lengths - otherwise same as Standard grade. Add $60 for camouflaged exterior finish.

	$775	$700	$650	$595	$530	$495	$465

Interchangeable choke tubes (3) became available in 1986 — add $60.

Last Mfg.'s Sug. Retail was $781.

Deluxe Vent—select checkered walnut stock and forearm, 22, 26, 28, and 32 in. barrels, high lustre wood finish.

	$825	$750	$675	$625	$550	$525	$495

Last Mfg.'s Sug. Retail was $924.

Supreme Grade—extra-select checkered walnut stock and forearm, otherwise same as Deluxe Vent.

	$995	$850	$725	$675	$595	$550	$525

Last Mfg.'s Sug. Retail was $1,124.

Mag. 10 Roadblocker—22 in. cylinder bored ribless barrel, parkerized finish.

	$595	$525	$500	$475	$450	$425	$400

Last Mfg.'s Sug. Retail was $741.

National Wild Turkey Fed. Special Edition—mfg. in 1985 only.

	$850	$775	$700				

MAG-10 PRESENTATION—10 ga. Mag., blued, engraved, gold inlaid receiver, extra fancy walnut. Limited production. Approx. 200 mfg. 1983-1986.

	$1,875	$1,550	$1,300	$1,050	$915	$830	$745

Last Mfg.'s Sug. Retail was $1,727.

PERAZZI SHOTGUNS

NOTE: Ithaca was sole importer for Perazzi in the 70's. All new and used models will be in the P section under Perazzi. Perazzi today distributes their own firearms.

NOTES

J

JAPANESE MILITARY RIFLES
WWII MANUFACTURE IN TOKYO, JAPAN.

Grading	100%	98%	95%	90%	80%	70%	60%

NOTE: All Japanese rifles: deduct 20% if National Crest (chrysanthemum flower) has been ground off front receiver ring, deduct 20% if serial numbers are not matching, deduct 10-40% for training rifles of each type.

MODEL 38 ARISAKA RIFLE—Jap. Mauser type action, 6.5mm, 31 in. barrel, adj. sight, adapted 1905.

	100%	98%	95%	90%	80%	70%	60%
	$150	$130	$105	$95	$75	$65	$50

MODEL 38 CAVALRY CARBINE—same as T38 Rifle, except shorter barrel, made 1911.

	$155	$135	$110	$100	$80	$70	$55

MODEL 44 CAVALRY ARISAKA CARBINE—same as T38 Carbine, 6.5mm with 19 in. barrel, folding bayonet.

	$260	$235	$210	$190	$170	$155	$135

MODEL 99 SERVICE RIFLE—WWII version of 38, 7.7mm.

	$155	$135	$110	$100	$80	$70	$55

Add 20% for monopod.

PARATROOPER TAKEDOWN VERSION—adopted 1940, crossbolt barrel lock.

Type 2

	$350	$305	$265	$220	$190	$165	$135

NAMBU PISTOLS—See Nambu.

JEFFERY, W.J. & CO. LTD
PREVIOUSLY MANUFACTURED IN LONDON, ENGLAND.

In addition to making a complete line of their own shotguns and rifles, W.J. Jeffery also was subcontracted by many other exporters, distributors, and retailers (including Londons' famous Army & Navy department store). Many models were produced and rather than list them individually, a generalized format has been adopted for determining values on both rifles and shotguns.

RIFLES

SINGLE SHOT—various cal.'s, falling block action, checkered walnut stock and forearm, usually multiple folding leave rear sight (also tangent), excellent quality. Prices start in the $600 range for poor condition specimens in obsolete or undesirable cal.'s and can go up to $5,000 for 100% condition in .600 Nitro Express.

Subtract substantially for the Martini action variation.

BOXLOCK DOUBLE RIFLE—many cal.'s, various engraving patterns, top or under (usually large cal.'s) lever opening, multiple folding leave rear sight, checkered walnut stock and forearm. Prices usually start in the $1,500 range for poor condition in undesirable cal.'s and can exceed $8,000 if encountered with elaborate engraving in .475 Express or larger cal.'s.

Subtract approx. 40% if with hammers, over 50% if with damascus barrels.

SIDELOCK DOUBLE RIFLE—various cal.'s, available in No. 1 or No. 2 grade, top-lever opening, best quality engraving, deluxe checkered walnut stock and forearm, almost any custom order could be filled. Prices start in the $3,250 range for 60% condition in smaller cal.'s and can easily go to $12,000 + when found in excellent condition in the larger cal.'s

Subtract approx. 40% if with hammers, over 50% if with damascus barrels.

Grading	100%	98%	95%	90%	80%	70%	60%

SHOTGUNS

BOXLOCK SHOTGUN—most ga.'s, many combinations of options available, top-lever opening, many ranges of engraving, high quality and worksmanship. Values usually start in the $650 range if in poor condition and can go to $4,500 + if in a small ga. in near new condition ($1,750 for 12 ga.).

Subtract approx. 40% if with hammers, over 50% if with damascus barrels.

SIDELOCK SHOTGUN—most ga.'s, many combinations of options available, top-lever opening, many ranges of engraving, high quality and worksmanship. Values usually start in the $1,250 range if in poor condition and can go to $8,500 + if in a small ga. in near new condition ($3,950 for 12 ga.).

JENNINGS FIREARMS, INC.

MANUFACTURED BY CALWESTCO IN CHINO, CA AND BY BRYCO FIREARMS LOCATED IN CARSON CITY, NV. DISTRIBUTED BY JENNINGS FIREARMS, INC. IN CARSON CITY, NV.

PISTOLS: SEMI-AUTO

Bryco Arms will also appear in this section. All pistols below are single action.

MODEL J-22—.22 LR cal., 6 shot, semi-auto, 2½ in. barrel, satin nickel, bright chrome or black teflon or bright chrome finish, 13 oz.

Mfg.'s Sug. Retail	$75	$65	$50	$40	$35	$30	$30	$30

BRYCO 25 (J-25)—.25 cal., aluminum alloy frame, 2.5 in. barrel, single action, impregnated wood grips, positive safety, 11 oz. New in 1988.

Mfg.'s Sug. Retail	$90	$75	$65	$50	$40	$35	$30	$30

This model is available in either satin nickel, bright chrome, or black teflon finish.

BRYCO 38—.22 LR, .32 ACP, or .380 ACP cal., semi-auto, 2.8 in. barrel, choice of nickel, chrome, or black teflon finish, alloy receiver, 15 oz. New in 1988.

Mfg.'s Sug. Retail	$110	$90	$75	$60	$55	$50	$45	$40

Add $20 for .380 ACP cal.

BRYCO 48—.22 LR, .32 ACP, or .380 ACP, semi-auto, black or chrome finish, black grips, 4 in. barrel, 19 oz. New in 1989.

Mfg.'s Sug. Retail	$139	$120	$95	$75	$60	$55	$50	$45

JERICHO

TRADEMARK OF ISRAELI MILITARY INDUSTRIES (I.M.I.) IMPORTED EXCLUSIVELY BY K.B.I. INC. LOCATED IN HARRISBURG, PA.

JERICHO 941—9mm Para./.41 Action Express, semi-auto double action, 4.72 in. barrels (includes both 9mm and .41 AE), all steel fabrication, polygonal rifling, 3 dot Tritium sights, ambidextrous safety, polymer grips, includes case, 2 boxes of ammo, and Rig cleaning kit. New in 1989.

Mfg.'s Sug. Retail	$849	$775	$675	$575	$525	$475	$425	$400

This model is sold as a package only.

JOHNSON AUTOMATICS, INC.

MANUFACTURED IN PROVIDENCE, RI.

MODEL 1941—.30-06 or 7mm cal., semi-auto, 22 in. removable air cooled barrel, recoil operated, perforated metal handguard, aperture sight, military stock. Most were made for Dutch military, some used by Marine Paratroopers, during WWII all .30-06 and 7mm were ordered by South American governments.

	$850	$770	$720	$650	$600	$550	$500

7mm caliber—subtract $50 because not original U.S. Military cal. Also deduct 10% if ser. no.'s don't match.

IVER JOHNSON ARMS, INC.

MANUFACTURED IN FITCHBURG, MA, 1883-1984 AND JACKSONVILLE, AR 1984 TO DATE. FORMERLY JOHNSON BYE & CO. 1871-1883. RENAMED IVER JOHNSON & CO. IN 1871 UNTIL 1891. RENAMED IVER JOHNSON'S ARMS & CYCLE WORKS IN 1891 WITH MANUFACTURING MOVING TO FITCHBURG, MA. IN 1975 THE NAME CHANGED TO IVER JOHNSON'S ARMS, INC. AND TWO YEARS LATER, COMPANY FACILITIES WERE MOVED TO MIDDLESEX, MA. IN 1982, PRODUCTION WAS MOVED TO JACKSONVILLE, AR UNDER THE TRADE NAME IVER JOHNSON ARMS, INC. IN 1983 UNIVERSAL FIREARMS, INC. WAS ACQUIRED BY IVER JOHNSON ARMS, INC.

IVER JOHNSON ARMS WAS SOLD IN MARCH OF 1987 AND WAS ACQUIRED BY AMERICAN MILITARY ARMS CORPORATION (AMAC). CURRENTLY, AMAC HAS REINTRODUCED SOME OLDER MODELS, MOSTLY USING PREVIOUSLY EXISTING PARTS. IN ADDITION, AMAC IS ALSO IN THE PROCESS OF RELEASING SOME NEWLY DESIGNED MODELS.

REVOLVERS

MODEL 1900—.22, .32 S&W, or .38 S&W cal., double action, 2½, 4½, or 6 in. barrel, fixed sights, blue or nickel, rubber grips, made 1900-1947.

	100%	98%	95%	90%	80%	70%	60%
	$125	$80	$70	$60	$55	$45	$40

MODEL 1900 TARGET—.22 LR, 6 shot, 6 or 9½ in. barrel, blue, fixed sights, made 1925-1942.

	$140	$90	$80	$70	$65	$55	$50

TARGET SEALED 8—.22 LR, 8 shot, 6 or 10 in. barrel, blue, fixed sights, rubber grips, made 1931-1957.

	$150	$100	$95	$80	$75	$65	$60

TARGET 9 SHOT—same as Target Sealed 8, except 9 shot, made 1929-1946.

	$145	$90	$80	$70	$65	$55	$50

SAFETY HAMMER MODEL—.22 LR, .32 S&W, or .38 S&W cal., 3½, 4, 5, or 6 in. barrel, fixed sights, blue or nickel, break open, made 1892-1950.

	$150	$80	$70	$60	$55	$45	$40

SAFETY HAMMERLESS—double action only, same cal.'s and barrels as Safety Hammer, break open, fixed sights, rubber grips, blue or nickel, made 1895-1950.

	$145	$100	$95	$80	$75	$65	$60

.22 SUPERSHOT—.22 LR, 6 in. barrel, blue, fixed sights, checkered wood grips, break open, no counterbore, made 1929-1949.

	$150	$80	$70	$60	$55	$45	$40

TRIGGER COCKING SINGLE ACTION—.22 LR, 8 shot, 6 in. barrel, break open, counterbored, clue, checkered wood grips, first pull on trigger cocks, second fires, made 1940-1947. Rare in 100% condition.

	$175	$120	$110	$95	$80	$75	$65

.22 TARGET SINGLE ACTION—.22 LR, 8 shot, 6 in. barrel, break open, counterbored, checkered wood, adj. grips and sights, made 1938-1948.

	$160	$120	$110	$95	$80	$75	$65

SUPERSHOT SEALED 8—.22 LR, 8 shot, break open, blue, adj. sights, checkered wood grips, made 1931-1957.

	$175	$130	$120	$110	$90	$85	$75

SUPERSHOT 9—same as Sealed 8, only 9 shot, not counterbored, made 1929-1949.

	$135	$90	$80	$75	$60	$50	$40

PROTECTOR SEALED 8—.22 LR, 8 shot, 2½ in. barrel, break open, fixed sights, blue, wood grips, made 1933-1949.

	$175	$135	$125	$110	$90	$80	$75

Grading	100%	98%	95%	90%	80%	70%	60%

SUPERSHOT MODEL 844—.22 LR, 8 shot, 4½ or 6 in. barrel, adj. sights, break open, blue, wood grips, made 1955-1956.

	$100	$90	$85	$80	$75	$60	$50

ARMSWORTH MODEL 855—.22 LR, single action, 8 shot, 6 in. barrel, break open, blue, adj. sights, wood grips, adj. finger rest, made 1955-1957.

	$135	$125	$120	$110	$90	$80	$75

MODEL 55A TARGET—.22 LR, 8 shot, 4½ or 6 in. barrel, solid frame, blue, fixed sights, wood grips, loading gate, made 1955-1984.

	$75	$65	$55	$45	$35	$30	$15

CADET—.22 LR, .22 WRM, .32 S&W, .38 S&W, or .38 Spl. cal., 2½ in. barrel, blue, fixed sights, plastic grips, made 1955-1984.

	$110	$90	$80	$75	$65	$55	$50

MODEL 57A TARGET—.22 LR, 8 shot, 4½ or 6 in. barrel, solid frame, blue, adj. sights, wood grips, made 1955-1975.

	$100	$80	$75	$65	$55	$45	$40

MODEL 66 TRAILSMAN—.22 LR, 6 in. barrel, break open, blue, adj. sights, rebounding hammer, wood grips, made 1958-1975.

	$110	$90	$85	$75	$65	$55	$50

SIDEWINDER—.22 LR, 6 or 8 shot, 4¾ or 6 in. barrel, solid frame, blue, nickel, or case hardened plastic grips, wood on case color model, made 1961-present, 8 shot pre-1975.

	$110	$90	$85	$75	$65	$55	$50

SIDEWINDER S—same as Sidewinder, except .22 WMR, interchangeable cylinder.

	$125	$100	$95	$85	$75	$65	$60

MODEL 67 VIKING—.22 LR, 8 shot, 4½ or 6 in. barrel, break open, blue, adj. sights, wood grips with thumbrest, made 1964-1975.

	$135	$110	$100	$95	$85	$75	$65

MODEL 67S VIKING—.22 LR, .32 S&W, or .38 S&W cal., 8 shot in .22, 5 shot in .32 and .38, 2¾ in. barrel, break open, adj. sights, plastic grips, made 1964-1975.

	$130	$100	$95	$85	$75	$60	$50

AMERICAN BULLDOG—.22 LR, .22 WRM, or .38 Spl. cal., 6 shot in .22, 5 shot in .38, 2½ and 4 in. barrel, blue or nickel, adj. sights, plastic grips, made 1974-1976.

	$135	$110	$100	$90	$80	$65	$60

ROOKIE—.38 Spl., 5 shot, 4 in. barrel, solid frame, blue or nickel, plastic grips, made 1975-1984.

	$100	$80	$75	$65	$55	$45	$35

SPORTSMAN—.22 LR, 6 shot, 4¾ or 6 in. barrel, solid frame, blue, fixed sights, plastic grips, made 1974-1976.

	$100	$80	$75	$65	$55	$45	$35

DELUXE TARGET—same as Sportsman, adj. sights, made 1975-1976.

	$110	$90	$85	$75	$65	$55	$40

SWING OUT—.22 LR, .22 WRM, .32 S&W, or .38 S&W cal., 6 shot in .22, 5 shot in .32 and .38, 2, 3, or 4 in. barrel, vent. rib, 4 or 6 in., blue or nickel, fixed or adj. sights, made 1977-1984.

	$130	$110	$100	$90	$80	$75	$65

VR Barrel—4 or 6 in. vent. rib barrel, adj. sights.

	$170	$150	$140	$130	$125	$120	$100

PISTOLS: SEMI-AUTO

AMAC also manufactures a Super Enforcer .30 cal. and a Delta 786 9mm machine gun which are not listed in this text.

MODEL 9—9mm, double action, 6 shot mag., 3 in. barrel, blue or matte blue only, ambidextrous safety, smooth hardwood grips, 26 oz. Has not been released to date..

IVER JOHNSON ARMS, INC., cont.

Grading	100%	98%	95%	90%	80%	70%	60%

TRAILSMAN PISTOL—.22 LR only, semi-auto, all steel construction, 4½ or 6 in. barrel, blue finish, black checkered composition grips, 10 shot mag., about 30 oz. Add $24 for hardwood stocks and high polish blue. Mfg. in 1985 and 1986 only.

	$160	$145	$130	$120	$110	$100	$95

Last Mfg.'s Sug. Retail was $191.

PONY PISTOL (PO380 SERIES)—.380 ACP only, semi-auto single action, 3 in. barrel, 6 shot mag., all steel construction, 20 oz., blue or matte blue finish. Mfg. 1985-1986.

	$245	$220	$195	$185	$175	$165	$155

Last Mfg.'s Sug. Retail was $287.

Pony Pistol—with nickel finish. Manufactured 1985 only.

	$260	$230	$215	$200	$185	$170	$160

Last Mfg.'s Sug. Retail was $290 for nickel finish.

POCKET PISTOL (TP SERIES)—.22 LR or .25 ACP cal., semi-auto, double action, 2.8 in. barrel, 7 shot finger tip extension mag., 15 oz., black plastic grips, fixed sights. Previously mfg. 1985-86, reintroduced in 1988.

Mfg.'s Sug. Retail	$192	$165	$135	$120	$110	$100	$90	$80

Add $15 for nickel finish.

AMAC-22 COMPACT—.22 Short or .25 ACP cal., semi-auto, single action, 5 shot mag., 2 in. barrel, plastic grips. New in 1988.

Mfg.'s Sug. Retail	$157	$135	$120	$110	$100	$90	$85	$80

Add $13 for nickel finish.

SUPER ENFORCER (MODEL 3000)—.30 cal. only, pistol version of the Carbine with 11 in. shrouded barrel. Add $40 for stainless steel (discontinued for 1986). Manufactured 1985-1986 only.

	$225	$200	$180	$170	$160	$150	$140

Last Mfg.'s Sug. Retail was $255.

Enforcer—similar to Super Enforcer model, except as 9½ in. barrel. Reintroduced in 1988.

Mfg.'s Sug. Retail	$333	$280	$240	$210	$180	$165	$150	$140

CATTLEMAN MAGNUM—.357 Mag., .44 Mag., or .45 Colt, single action, 6 shot, Colt replica, 4¾, 5½, or 7½ in. barrel, case color frame, blue barrel, and brass grip frame, smooth walnut grips, fixed sights. Discontinued in 1984.

	$190	$175	$150	$140	$130	$125	$110
.44 Mag.	$220	$190	$175	$165	$145	$135	$125

BUCKHORN MAGNUM—same as Cattleman, except flat top, adj. sights.

	$210	$190	$175	$165	$145	$140	$125

BUNTLINE BUCKHORN MAGNUM—same as Buckhorn, only 18 in. barrel, detachable stock.

	$345	$310	$295	$275	$260	$250	$225
.44 Mag.	$375	$325	$310	$295	$280	$275	$250

TRAIL BLAZER—.22 LR, or .22 Mag. cal., interchangeable cylinder, 5½ or 6½ in. barrel, blue.

	$175	$145	$130	$120	$110	$100	$80

RIFLES

AMAC also manufactures a full-auto M2 Carbine that is not listed in this text.

MODEL X—.22 Short, Long, or LR, bolt action, single shot, 22 in. barrel, open sight, pistol grip with knob forend, made 1928-1932.

	$90	$60	$50	$40	$35	$30	$25

MODEL 2X—improved Model X, 24 in. heavy barrel larger stock, adj. sights, made 1932-1955.

	$120	$95	$75	$50	$40	$35	$30

Grading	100%	98%	95%	90%	80%	70%	60%

LI'L CHAMP—.22 LR only, single shot bolt action, 16¼ in. barrel, black molded stock, nickel plated bolt, youth dimensions, (32½ in. overall length), 3 lbs. Introduced in 1986, reintroduced in 1988 only.

	$75	$60	$50	$45	$40	$35	$35

Last Mfg.'s Sug. Retail was $92.

LONG RANGE RIFLE—.50 BMG cal., bolt action design, single shot, 29 in. stainless steel fluted barrel with muzzle brake, adj. trigger pull, built in bipod, adj. rail stock, includes Leupold M-1 Ultra 20X scope, 36 lbs. New in 1988.

Mfg.'s Sug. Retail	$7,056	$6,500	$5,200	$4,250	$3,800	$3,400	$2,995	$2,600

Custom rifles in either military or sporting configuration are also available in the AMAC 338/416 cal.

9MM CARBINE (JJ9MM SERIES)—9mm only, copy of U.S. military M1, 16 in. barrel, blue finish only, 20 shot mag. Mfg. 1985-86 only.

Hardwood Stock Model—discontinued in 1986.

	$230	$200	$180	$170	$160	$150	$140

Last Mfg.'s Sug. Retail was $255.

Standard Model—with plastic stock. Discontinued in 1985.

	$225	$200	$180	$170	$160	$150	$140

Last Mfg.'s Sug. Retail was $250.

Folding Plastic Stock Model—discontinued in 1985.

	$255	$225	$200	$180	$170	$160	$150

Last Mfg.'s Sug. Retail was $281.

DELTA-786—9mm Para., semi-auto, patterned after the U.S. military M1, 16 in. barrel, matte black finish. New in 1989.

Mfg.'s Sug. Retail	$665	$575	$425	$360	$325	$295	$260	$230

.30 CAL. CARBINE—.30 cal. only, semi-auto, 18 in. barrel, available in various stock configurations, hardwood stock. Mfg. 1985-86, reintroduced in 1988.

Mfg.'s Sug. Retail	$265	$225	$180	$170	$160	$150	$140	$130

Add $26 for walnut stock or Parkerized finish.

Paratrooper Model—similar to standard model, except has folding synthetic stock. Mfg. in 1988 only.

	$240	$195	$180	$165	$150	$140	$130

Last Mfg.'s Sug. Retail was $291.

Stainless Steel Variation—discontinued in 1985.

	$230	$200	$180

Last Mfg.'s Sug. Retail was $250.

5.7mm Johnson Cal.—add $30 for stainless steel.

	$195	$175	$165	$155	$145	$135	$125

Last Mfg.'s Sug. Retail was $219.

.22 CAL. U.S. CARBINE—.22 LR or .22 Mag. cal., 18½ in. barrel, except for Mag. (19.3 in.), 5.8 lbs., 15 shot mag., sling swivels. Mfg. 1985-86, reintroduced in 1988 only.

	$150	$120	$110	$100	$90	$85	$80

Add $120 for .22 Mag. model (gas operated — disc. in 1986).

Last Mfg.'s Sug. Retail was $183 for .22 Mag. cal.

Last Mfg.'s Sug. Retail was $166 for .22 LR cal.

TARGETMASTER SLIDE ACTION—.22 LR or Mag. (disc. in 1986) cal.'s, 18½ in. barrel, 12 shot (LR) tube mag., 5¾ lbs. Mfg. 1985 only, reintroduced in 1988.

Mfg.'s Sug. Retail	$167	$150	$130	$120	$110	$100	$90	$80

This model was designated EW.22 HBP previously.

Grading	100%	98%	95%	90%	80%	70%	60%

MODEL EW.22 HBL LEVER ACTION (WAGONMASTER)—.22 S, L, and LR or .22 Mag. cal., 18½ in. barrel, walnut finish, hardwood stock, blue finish, 5¾ lbs., grooved for scope mounts. Mfg. 1985-86, reintroduced 1988.

Mfg.'s Sug. Retail	$167	$150	$130	$120	$110	$100	$90	$80

Add $21 for .22 Mag. cal. (19 in. barrel).

This model was designated EW.22 HBL previously. It was also available in a Junior model featuring smaller dimensions; values same as listed above.

TRAIL BLAZER SEMI-AUTO (MODEL IJ.22 HB)—.22 LR only, 10 shot clip mag., 18½ in. barrel, 5.8 lbs. Manufactured 1985 only.

	$115	$100	$90	$85	$80	$75	$70

Last Mfg.'s Sug. Retail was $125.

SHOTGUNS

CHAMPION—10, 12, 16, 20, 24, 28, 32, or .410 ga., also available in .44, .45, 12mm, or 14mm rifle cal., single barrel shotgun or rifle, 26-32 in. full barrel, exposed hammer, auto ejector, plain pistol grip stock, made 1909-1956.

	$145	$100	$80	$60	$40	$35	$25

Values on both smaller gauge shotguns and rifles would be considerably higher than those listed above. A mint .410 ga. might command 400% more than the above values.

MATTED RIB GRADE—similar to Champion, except in 12, 16, and 20 ga. only, solid rib, checkered stock, made 1909-1948.

	$165	$115	$95	$70	$50	$45	$40

This model has either a semi-octagon (with top matted) or jacketed breech.

TRAP GRADE—similar to Matted Rib, except 32 in. full barrel, 12 ga., vent rib, made 1909-1942.

	$275	$165	$140	$120	$100	$90	$80

HERCULES GRADE—12, 16, 20, or .410 ga., double barrel, 26-32 in. barrel, hammerless, boxlock, various chokes, extractors and double triggers standard, checkered pistol grip or straight stock, made until 1948.

	$600	$400	$375	$365	$335	$310	$290

Auto ejectors — add $100.
SST — add $100.
16 ga. — deduct 10%.
.410 ga. — add 20%.

SKEETER MODEL—similar to Hercules, except offered in 28 ga. also, super select wood, beavertail forend, made until 1946.

	$1,095	$800	$600	$525	$450	$410	$390

Auto ejectors — add 20%.
SST — add 20%.
28 and .410 ga.'s — add 50%.

SUPER TRAP—12 ga. only, 32 in. full vent rib, boxlock, extractors, checkered pistol grip stock, beavertail forend and recoil pad, made until 1942. Very rare.

	$1,095	$750	$550	$475	$415	$395	$370

Auto ejectors — add $100.
SST — add $100.

SILVER SHADOW—O/U, 12 ga., 26 or 28 in. barrels, various chokes, extractors, vent rib, checkered pistol grip stock, Italian manufactured. Discontinued.

	$375	$325	$300	$275	$225	$185	$175

Single trigger — add $100.

JURRAS

CUSTOM PISTOLSMITH LOCATED IN PRESCOTT, AZ. DISTRIBUTED BY J & G SALES LOCATED IN PRESCOTT, AZ.

Ammunition for Jurras pistols is exclusively manufactured by Robert Davis, Jr. located in Athens, TN.

PISTOLS

Lee E. Jurras manufactures custom pistols in larger calibers. Almost any caliber is available by special order and the below listings represent a few of his more standard items. Special order inquiries may be directed to Mr. Jurras, in Prescott, AZ.

HOWDAH—available in .375, .416, .460, .475, .500, or .577 cal., action based on Thompson/Center Contender receiver, 12 in. bull barrel, nitex finish, adj. rear sights, limited mfg. (100).

Custom Grade

	100%	98%	95%	90%	80%	70%	60%
	$1,150	$925	$800	$725	$650	$575	$500

Presentation Grade—.375 Jurras or .460 Jurras, deluxe Claro walnut stock and forearm.

	100%	98%	95%	90%	80%	70%	60%
	$2,000	$1,750	$1,500	$1,250	$1,050	$950	$825

.416, .475, .500, or .577 calibers command a premium on this model.

K

KBI INC.
IMPORTER/MANUFACTURER LOCATED IN HARRISBURG, PA.

KBI Inc. imports C.B.C. from Brazil and the Jericho pistol manufactured by I.M.I. from Israel. The Jericho pistol may be found under it's own heading in this text.

Grading	100%	98%	95%	90%	80%	70%	60%

PSP-25—.25 ACP, semi-auto, single action, patterned after the Baby Browning, all steel construction, mfg. in the U.S.A. under license from Fabrique Nationale, dual safety system. New in 1989.

Mfg.'s Sug. Retail	$249	$225	$200	$185	$170	$160	$150	$140

KDF INC. (KLEINGUENTHER DISTINCTIVE FIREARMS)
PREVIOUSLY MANUFACTURED BY VOERE UNTIL 1986 IN VOHRENBACH, W. GERMANY. MANUFACTURE IN 1987 WAS ABSORBED BY MAUSER-WERKE IN OBERNDORF, W. GERMANY. PRESENTLY IMPORTED BY KDF, INC. IN SEGUIN, TX.

Older KDF rifles were private labeled by Voere and were marked KDF. Since Voere was absorbed by Mauser-Werke in 1987, model designations have changed. Mauser-Werke does not private label (i.e. newer guns are marked Mauser-Werke), and these rifles can be found under the Mauser-Werke heading in this text.

In 1987, KDF became the sole importer for Mauser-Werke long arms. They can be found under their heading in this publication.

RIFLES

K-22 (MAUSER 201)—.22 LR cal., bolt action, free floating 21 in. barrel, clip 5 shot mag., adj. trigger, scale down version of the K-15, unusual action incorporates two front-located locking lugs on bolt face that engage Stellite inserts on the front receiver portion, guaranteed 1 in. groupings at 100 yards, blue only, no sights, select walnut stock with cheekpiece, standard model disc. in 1987. Add $50 for .22 Mag. cal. on the K-22 models listed below.

	$310	$285	$260	$240	$225	$210	$195

Last Mfg.'s Sug. Retail was $345.

K-22 Deluxe (Mauser 201)—better walnut and stock options. Model notation changed in 1988.

	$410	$360	$295	$275	$250	$235	$210

This model has been redesignated KDF-Mauser Model 201 since current distributer/dealer inventories have been depleted.

Last Mfg.'s Sug. Retail was $495.

K-22 Deluxe Custom—richly layered walnut and stock options. Importation disc. in 1987.

	$655	$595	$550	$495	$450	$395	$350

Last Mfg.'s Sug. Retail was $725.

K-22 Deluxe Special Select—top-of-the-line bolt action, double set triggers. Importation disc. in 1987.

	$1,060	$950	$850	$750	$695	$650	$595

Last Mfg.'s Sug. Retail was $1,225.

K D F INC. (KLEINGUENTHER) , cont.

Grading	100%	98%	95%	90%	80%	70%	60%

TITAN SPORTER SERIES—various cal.'s, bolt action, 24 or 26 in. barrel length, select walnut, pistol grip stock.

This series is available with either European Monte Carlo high-luster stock or in classic featherweight configuration with Schnabel forend — add $50-$200.

Titan Menor—.222 or .223 cal. Importation disc. in 1987.

	$675	$615	$560	$495	$450	$395	$350

Add $100 for Match or Competition model (.223 cal.).

Last Mfg.'s Sug. Retail was $765.

Titan II Standard—many cal.'s, between .243 and .30-06. Disc. in 1988.

	$950	$825	$725	$625	$550	$500	$450

Add $100 for Match or Competition model (.308 cal.).

Last Mfg.'s Sug. Retail was $1,075.

Titan II Magnum—available in cal.'s between 7mm Rem. and .375 H&H. Disc. in 1988.

	$995	$875	$750	$650	$575	$520	$475

Last Mfg.'s Sug. Retail was $1,125.

Titan .411 KDF Mag.—.411 KDF cal., 26 in. barrel with recoil arrestor, 3 shot mag., blue or electroless nickel finish, 9¼ lbs. Imported 1986-1988.

	$1,175	$965	$810	$725	$650	$575	$520

Last Mfg.'s Sug. Retail was $1,300.

MODEL 2005—.22 LR only, semi-auto, 19½ in. barrel, Monte Carlo stock, 5 shot clip mag., iron sights, 6 lbs. Imported in 1986 only.

	$135	$115	$100	$90	$85	$80	$75

Last Mfg.'s Sug. Retail was $165.

This model was ruled no longer importable by the BATF.

Model 2005 Deluxe—similar to Model 2005, except has deluxe checkered walnut. Made in 1986-87 only.

	$160	$135	$110	$95	$85	$80	$75

Last Mfg.'s Sug. Retail was $185.

MODEL 2107—.22 LR or .22 Mag. cal., bolt action, 19½ in. barrel, 5 shot clip mag., adj. iron sights, 6 lbs. Imported 1986-87 only.

	$175	$150	$125	$105	$95	$85	$80

Add $42 for .22 Mag. cal.

Last Mfg.'s Sug. Retail was $197.

Model 2107 Deluxe (Mauser 107)—similar to Model 2107, except has deluxe checkered walnut. Imported 1986-1988.

	$185	$165	$140	$125	$110	$105	$100

Add $50 for .22 Mag. cal.

This model has been redesignated KDF-Mauser Model 107 since current distributer/dealer inventories have been depleted.

Last Mfg.'s Sug. Retail was $219.

MODEL 2112—.22 LR or .22 Mag. cal., similar to Model 2107, except has extra select walnut. Imported in 1988 only.

	$235	$200	$180	$160	$145	$135	$125

Add $50 for .22 Mag. cal.

Last Mfg.'s Sug. Retail was $279.

K-14 INSTA FIRE RIFLE—.22-250, .458 Win. Mag., .270, or .300 Wby. Mag. cal., 24 or 26 in. barrel, no sights, ultra fast lock time, hidden detachable mag., checkered Monte Carlo stock, recoil pad.

	$605	$580	$550	$525	$470	$415	$330
K15 (.22 cal.)	$165	$145	$120	$105	$95	$85	$70

Grading	100%	98%	95%	90%	80%	70%	60%

K-15 (MODEL 225)—available in 13 cal.'s between .243 Win. and .300 Wby. Mag., bolt action, 60 degree bolt lift with 3 locking lugs, ultra fast lock time, adj. trigger, 24 or 26 (Mag. only) in. barrel, 3 or 5 shot mag., no sights, guaranteed ½ in. accuracy at 100 yards, many stock options available at extra cost. Left-handed action available in certain cal.'s at a $50 charge.

Deluxe Standard Sporter—standard model available in 6 regular cal.'s and 9 Mag. cal.'s. Disc. in 1988.

	$1,075	$950	$810	$700	$625	$550	$495

Add $50 for Magnum action.
Add $525 for .411 KDF cal.

In addition to the 15 regular cal.'s, it is also possible to order various other factory cal.'s as a $200 option.

This model has been redesignated KDF-Mauser Model 225 (standard cal.'s) since current distributer/dealer inventories have been depleted.

Last Mfg.'s Sug. Retail was $1,275.

K-15 Fiberstock Pro-hunter—similar to the K-15, except is supplied with fiberglass stock (various colors), choice of parkerized, matte blue, or electroless nickel metal finish, and recoil arrestor installed. Imported 1986-1988.

	$1,420	$1,200	$950

Add $50 for Magnum action.

This model has been redesignated KDF-Mauser Model 225 (standard cal.'s) since current distributer/dealer inventories have been depleted.

Last Mfg.'s Sug. Retail was $1,680.

K-15 Dangerous Game—.411 KDF Mag. (new cartridge in 1985), choice of finishes, oil finished deluxe American walnut stock. Imported 1986-1988.

	$1,895	$1,500	$1,150

This model has been redesignated KDF-Mauser Model 225 since current distributer/dealer inventories have been depleted.

Last Mfg.'s Sug. Retail was $2,100.

K-15 Swat Rifle—.308 cal. standard, 24 or 26 in. barrel, parkerized metal, oil finished target walnut stock, 3 or 4 shot detachable mag., 10 lbs. Importation disc. in 1988.

	$1,475	$1,250	$1,000	$850	$725	$650	$575

Last Mfg.'s Sug. Retail was $1,725.

K-16—available in 6 standard cal.'s between .243 Win. and .300 Win. Mag. in addition to optional cal.'s, modified Remington Model 700 action, standard features include KDF accurizing and instant fire ignition, single stage adj. trigger, Dupont Rynite stock (camel or grey), choice of finishes (high-gloss blue standard), recoil pad and quick detachable sling swivels, many options available. Imported in 1988 only.

	$765	$675	$615	$560	$495	$450	$395

Add $120 for KDF muzzle brake.
Add $250 for optional cal.'s.
Add $350 for .411 KDF Mag. cal.

Last Mfg.'s Sug. Retail was $876.

SHOTGUNS

CONDOR O/U—12 ga., 28 in. barrel, various chokes, selective single trigger, auto ejectors, wide vent rib, boxlock, checkered pistol grip stock, Italian made.

	$660	$635	$605	$580	$525	$470	$415

BRESCIA S X S—12 ga., 28 in. barrel, full and mod., double triggers, engraved, checkered pistol grip stock.

	$330	$305	$275	$250	$195	$165	$140

K.F.C.

FORMERLY MANUFACTURED BY KAWAGUCHIYA FIREARMS CO., LTD. PREVIOUSLY IMPORTED AND DISTRIBUTED BY LA PALOMA MARKETING, INC. LOCATED IN TUCSON, AZ.

SHOTGUNS

MODEL 250—12 ga. only, semi-auto incorporating a patented, cushioned piston assembly, 26, 28, or 30 in. barrel, matte blue finish, vent rib standard, checkered premium walnut, 7 lbs. Manufactured 1980-86.

	$360	$290	$270	$250	$235	$220	$205

Add $60 for multi-chokes.

Last Mfg.'s Sug. Retail was $485.

Model 250 Deluxe—same specifications as Model 250, except has scrolled acid etching panels on both sides of normally black receiver. Discontinued in 1986.

	$395	$310	$290	$270	$250	$225	$210

Last Mfg.'s Sug. Retail was $520.

FIELD GUN O/U—12 ga. only, vent rib, premium grade walnut, semi pistol grip stock, F&IC chokes. Discontinued in 1986.

	$645	$565	$530	$495	$470	$445	$410

Last Mfg.'s Sug. Retail was $748.

E-1 TRAP OR SKEET O/U—12 ga. only, vent rib, oil finished premium grade walnut, semi pistol grip stock, engraved.

Discontinued in 1986.

	$935	$800	$750	$700	$625	$550	$495

Last Mfg.'s Sug. Retail was $1,070.

E-2 TRAP OR SKEET O/U—12 ga. only, vent rib, oil finished premium grade walnut, semi pistol grip stock, detailed engraving. Discontinued in 1986.

	$1,450	$1,250	$1,075	$950	$850	$750	$650

Last Mfg. Sug. Retail was $1,660.

KASSNAR IMPORTS, INC.

IMPORTER AND DISTRIBUTOR LOCATED IN HARRISBURG, PA.

Kassnar also imports Omega shotguns which can be found in their individual section.

PISTOLS

PJK-9HP—9mm, single action, patterned after the Browning Hi-Power, 4¾ in. barrel, 13 shot mag., cone hammer, checkered walnut grips, 32 oz.

	$225	$200	$185	$175	$165	$155	$145

Add $15 for Vent Rib barrel.

This pistol was imported from Hungary. Approximately 18,000 (including the MBK-9HP) were imported until importation was discontinued because of Federal ramifications.

MBK-9HP—9mm, double action, patterned after the Browning Hi-Power, 4⅔ in. barrel, spur hammer, blued metal, checkered walnut grips, 14 shot mag., 36 oz. Limited importation was stopped in late 1985.

	$295	$260	$230	$190	$175	$165	$155

PMK-380—.380 ACP, double action, patterned after the Walther PP, plastic grips with thumbrest, 4 in barrel, 7 shot mag., 21 oz. Limited importation.

	$275	$235	$200	$185	$175	$165	$155

This model was imported in very limited quantities before Interarms began exclusive importation.

KEBERST INTERNATIONAL

PREVIOUSLY MANUFACTURED AND DISTRIBUTED BY KENDALL INTERNATIONAL LOCATED IN PARIS, KY.

KEBERST MODEL 1A—.338 Lapua Mag., .338-416 Rigby, or .338-06 cal., bolt action, muzzle brake and unique recoil pad, camouflaged synthetic stock, package includes 3-9 power Leupold scope, stainless steel cleaning rod, custom designed case, built to special order only. Mfg. 1987-1988 only.

	$3,475	$2,850	$2,475	$2,100	$1,750	$1,400	$1,150

Add $275 for 10X Ultra scope.

Last Mfg.'s Sug. Retail was $3,750.

KENDALL INTERNATIONAL

PREVIOUS IMPORTER/DISTRIBUTOR LOCATED IN PARIS, KY. KENDALL INTERNATIONAL ALSO IMPORTED AUSTRALIAN AUTOMATIC ARMS, THE KEBERST RIFLE, AND SEVERAL AIR RIFLES THAT CAN BE FOUND IN THEIR RESPECTIVE SECTIONS IN THIS TEXT.

KEPPLINGER, ING. HANNES

MANUFACTURER LOCATED IN KUFSTEIN, AUSTRIA. NO CURRENT IMPORTER.

RIFLES

Kepplinger rifles are essentially built per individual order. In addition to his unique bolt action, he also makes O/U rifles as well.

3-S SYSTEM RIFLE—various cal.'s, unique short action allows for staight on cartridge loading, high strength alloy main parts, grip safety on lower pistol grip, unique uncocking device allowing manual cocking/decocking of the firing pin spring, 23.6 in. standard barrel, 3 shot detachable mag., iron sights, receiver drilled for scope mounts, best quality wood, available in either Schnabel forearm or Mannlicher configuration, many styles of engraving are optional, 7.14 lbs.

Price quotations are available upon request by writing Mr. Kepplinger at the following address: ING. HANNES KEPPLINGER, A-6330 Kufstein, Carl-Wagner-Strabe 1, AUSTRIA.

KESSLER ARMS CORPORATION

MANUFACTURED IN SILVER CREEN, NY.

LEVERMATIC SHOTGUN—level action, 12, 16, and 20 ga.'s, 26 and 28 in. full choke, takedown, plain pistol grip stock. Discontinued in 1953.

	$125	$75	$60	$50	$45	$45	$45

BOLT ACTION SHOTGUN—12, 16, or 20 ga., 26 or 28 in. full, takedown, plain stock, made 1951-1953.

	$90	$65	$50	$45	$35	$35	$35

KIMBER OF OREGON, INC.

MANUFACTURED AND DISTRIBUTED IN CLACKAMAS, OR. SINCE 1980.

RIFLES: BOLT ACTION

Note: No suffix in Kimber models denotes pre-1986 action design, "A" suffix models refer to the new action in right or left-hand, "B" suffix models also incorporate the new action with improved cocking system, faster lock time, swept-back bolt design, improved recoil lug, and are right handed.

Grading	100%	98%	95%	90%	80%	70%	60%

MODEL 82 SERIES—.22 LR, .22 Mag., or .22 Hornet cal., Mauser type rear locking bolt action, 3(.22 Hornet), 4(.22 Mag.), or 5(.22 LR) shot mag., 22 in. (Sporter) or 24 in. (Varmint) barrel, deluxe claro walnut, steel buttplate, rocker style safety, 6½ lbs. Add $45 for .22 Hornet or .22 Mag. cal. for all variations of this model.

Classic Model—disc. in 1988.

	$600	$500	$400	$350	$295	$250	$225

Add $55 for disc. Cascade Model (Monte Carlo cheekpiece).

Last Mfg.'s Sug. Retail was $750.

Custom Classic Model—higher grade claro walnut, ebony forearm tip, Niedner style steel buttplate. Disc. in 1988.

	$795	$675	$550	$475	$395	$340	$295

Also previously available in the .218 Bee or .25-20 (single shot only) cal.'s. These cal.'s may bring a slight premium. Manufactured in 1985 only (retail price was $695).

Last Mfg.'s Sug. Retail was $995.

Deluxe Grade—similar to Custom Classic Model, AA walnut, 5 or 10 (optional) shot mag., 6½ lbs. New in 1989.

Mfg.'s Sug. Retail	$995	$895	$700	$595	$525	$450	$395	$350

A left-hand variation is also available - priced on request from factory.

Mini Classic—.22 LR only, Model 82 action, 18 in. barrel, steel buttplate, sling swivels. Mfg. in 1988 only.

	$510	$460	$415	$375	$340	$300	$275

Last Mfg.'s Sug. Retail was $589.

Government Model 82 A Target—.22 LR only, specifically designed for U.S. Army training, 25 in. heavy target barrel including scope blocks, oversized stock, 10¾ lbs. Production began late 1987.

Mfg.'s Sug. Retail	$575	$525	$480	$440	$400	$365	$325	$295

20,000 rifles were manufactured in 1987-1989 to fill the initial U.S. government contract. Commercial guns are now being manufactured for the private sector with values listed above.

Continental—.22 LR, .22 Mag., or .22 Hornet cal., Sporter action only, full length Mannlicher stock, open sights, deluxe walnut. New in 1987.

Mfg.'s Sug. Retail	$850	$660	$540	$425	$370	$310	$265	$240

Above values represent 1988 pricing. This model is now only available as a special order with prices on request from the factory.

Super Continental—similar to Continental, except has AAA claro walnut with 22 lines/in. checkering. Mfg. in 1987-1988.

	$1,250	$1,000	$875	$795	$740	$680	$620

Last Mfg.'s Sug. Retail was $1,465.

Super America—top-of-the-line model, includes detachable scope mounts, Niedner checkered steel buttplate and best quality walnut, available in Sporter configuration only. Disc. in 1988.

	$995	$860	$730	$600	$520	$440	$365

Last Mfg.'s Sug. Retail was $1,150.

Super Grade—similar to Super America, AAA walnut, beaded cheekpiece, 5 or 10 (optional) shot mag., 6½ lbs. New in 1989.

Mfg.'s Sug. Retail	$1,095	$950	$775	$625	$550	$475	$425	$375

Brownell—.22 LR, only 500 manufactured to commemorate the late Leonard Brownell, Mannlicher style extra deluxe claro walnut stock. Manufactured in 1986 only.

	$1,250	$1,000	$800

Last Mfg.'s Sug. Retail was $1,500.

Grading	100%	98%	95%	90%	80%	70%	60%

Centennial—.22 LR only, limited edition (100 rifles) to commemorate centennial of .22 LR cal., includes hand-picked checkered walnut, moderate engraving, special Wilson Arms match barrel, skeleton butt plate and other refinements, serial numbered C1-C100. Manufactured in 1987 only.

$2,600 $2,350 $1,900

Last Mfg.'s Sug. Retail was $2,950.

MODEL 84 CENTERFIRE—.17 Rem., .17 Mach IV (disc. in 1987), 6 x 45 or 47mm (disc. in 1987), 5.6 x 50mm (disc. in 1987), .221 Fireball, .222 Rem., .222 Rem. Mag. (disc. in 1987), or .223 Rem. cal., Mauser type head locking bolt action, 5 shot mag., 22 (Sporter) or 24 (Varmint) in. barrel, deluxe claro walnut, steel buttplate, rocker style safety, 6½ lbs.

Classic Model—disc. in 1988.

	$705	$625	$540	$450	$375	$300	$260

Add $55 for disc. Cascade Model (Monte Carlo cheekpiece).

Last Mfg.'s Sug. Retail was $885.

Custom Classic Model—higher grade claro walnut, ebony forearm tip, Niedner style steel buttplate. Disc. in 1988.

	$970	$825	$720	$595	$500	$440	$365

Last Mfg.'s Sug. Retail was $1,130.

Deluxe Grade Sporter—.17 Rem., .221 Rem., or .223 Rem. cal., Mauser action, AA walnut, similar to Custom Classic Model, 6¼ lbs. New in 1989.

Mfg.'s Sug. Retail	$1,150	$975	$795	$650	$575	$500	$450	$395

Add $100 for left-hand action (.223 cal. only).

Continental—.221 Fireball (new in 1988), .222 Rem. or .223 Rem. cal., Sporter action only, full length Mannlicher stock, open sights, deluxe walnut. New in 1987.

Mfg.'s Sug. Retail	$985	$790	$675	$550	$475	$395	$340	$295

Above values represent 1988 pricing. This model is now only available as a special order with prices on request from the factory.

Super Continental—similar to Continental (same cal.'s), except has AAA claro walnut with 22 lines/in. checkering. Mfg. 1987-1988.

	$1,325	$1,060	$920	$830	$740	$680	$620

Last Mfg.'s Sug. Retail was $1,600.

Super America—top-of-the-line, with detachable scope mounts, available in Sporter configuration only. Disc. in 1988.

	$1,015	$865	$760	$640	$520	$465	$400

Super Grade—.17 Rem., .221 Rem., or .223 Rem. cal., Mauser action, AAA walnut, similar to Super America, 6¼ lbs. New in 1989.

Mfg.'s Sug. Retail	$1,250	$1,050	$850	$695	$600	$500	$450	$395

Ultra Varmint—.17 Rem., .221 Rem., or .223 Rem. cal., 24 in. medium weight stainless steel barrel, laminated birch stock, plain buttstock, 7¾ lbs. New in 1989.

Mfg.'s Sug. Retail	$1,165	$985	$800	$650	$575	$500	$450	$395

Super Varmint—similar to Ultra Varmint except has steel barrel, AAA walnut stock with beaded cheekpiece, 7¼ lbs. New in 1989.

Mfg.'s Sug. Retail	$1,265	$1,050	$850	$695	$600	$500	$450	$395

MODEL 89 BIG GAME RIFLE (BGR)—.270 Win., .280 Rem., 7mm Rem. Mag., 30-06, .300 Win. Mag., .338 Win. Mag., or 375 H&H cal., new action incorporates features from both Mauser 98 and Win. pre-64 Model 70, three position safety, 22 or 24 in. barrel. New in 1987.

Classic Model—deluxe claro walnut checkered 18 lines/in. with steel buttplate. Disc. in 1988.

	$790	$675	$550	$475	$395	$340	$295

Add $200 for .375 H&H cal.

Last Mfg.'s Sug. Retail was $985.

Grading	100%	98%	95%	90%	80%	70%	60%

Custom Classic Model—higher grade claro walnut, ebony forearm tip, Niedner style steel buttplate. Disc. in 1988.

	$1,025	$865	$750	$625	$500	$440	$365

Add $200 for .375 H&H cal.

Last Mfg.'s Sug. Retail was $1,230.

Deluxe Grade—similar to Custom Classic Model, round top frame, AA walnut, 22 or 24 in. barrel, plain buttstock, 7½-8½ lbs. New in 1989.

Mfg.'s Sug. Retail	$1,395	$1,200	$950	$775	$650	$525	$475	$425

Add $100 for .375 H&H cal.

Add $100 for matte blue metal finish.

The 24 in. barrel is available in Mag. cal.'s only.

Super America—top-of-the-line, with detachable scope mounts, recoil pad optional. Disc. in 1988.

	$1,075	$915	$795	$660	$530	$465	$400

Add $200 for .375 H&H cal.

Last Mfg.'s Sug. Retail was $1,385.

Super Grade—similar to Super America Model, square top frame, AAA walnut, 22 or 24 in. barrel, plain buttstock, 7½-8½ lbs. New in 1989.

Mfg.'s Sug. Retail	$1,495	$1,275	$995	$825	$695	$550	$500	$450

Add $100 for .375 H&H cal.

Add $100 for matte blue metal finish.

The 24 in. barrel is available in Mag. cal.'s only.

PISTOLS

PREDATOR MODEL—.221 Fireball, .223 Rem., 6mm TCU (disc. in 1987), 7mm TCU, or 6 x 45mm (disc. in 1987) cal., single shot Model 84 action with shortened 14⅞ in. barrel, scope use only, one piece deluxe walnut stock with contoured pistol grip, 5¼ lbs. Mfg.in 1987-1988 only.

Hunter Grade—AA claro walnut without checkering. Disc. in 1988.

	$795	$675	$550	$475	$395	$340	$295

Last Mfg.'s Sug. Retail was $995.

Super Grade—similar to Hunter Grade, except has select French walnut with ebony forend tip and 22 lines/in. checkering. Disc. in 1988.

	$1,010	$875	$740	$600	$520	$440	$365

Last Mfg.'s Sug. Retail was $1,195.

KOLIBRI

MANUFACTURED 1914-1925 BY H. GRABNER LOCATED IN KREMS/DONAU, AUSTRIA.

KOLIBRI SEMI-AUTO PISTOL—2.7 or 3mm centerfire, unrifled barrel, 5 shot box mag., world's smallest semi-automatic centerfire pistol.

	$1,200	$1,000	$875	$740	$600	$520	$440

Individual rounds of 2.7 or 3mm (rarer) ammunition are currently trading in the $75 range as it has the distinction of being the world's smallest centerfire shell (shooting a 3 grain bullet).

KORRIPHILA

MANUFACTURED IN WEST GERMANY. PREVIOUSLY IMPORTED AND DISTRIBUTED BY OSBORNE'S LOCATED IN CHEBOYGAN, MI.

Currently, this trademark has very limited U.S. distribution. Values below reflect 1988 price information.

Due to the recent devaluation of the U.S. dollar, prices may fluctuate rapidly on this trademark.

Grading	100%	98%	95%	90%	80%	70%	60%

HSP 701 TYPE I—7.65 Luger, .38 Spl., 9mm Luger, 9mm Police, 9mm Steyr, .45 ACP, or 10mm auto cal., semi-auto, double action, 40% stainless steel parts, 4 in. barrel, blue or satin finish, very limited production.

Mfg.'s Sug. Retail	$2,395	$2,000	$1,675	$1,375	$1,100	$995	$820	$740

Type II—similar to Type I, except has 5 in. barrel.

Mfg.'s Sug. Retail	$2,615	$2,150	$1,750	$1,475	$1,200	$1,075	$850	$760

Type III—similar to Type II, except single action trigger.

Mfg.'s Sug. Retail	$2,785	$2,200	$1,800	$1,550	$1,200	$1,075	$850	$760

KORTH

MANUFACTURED IN WEST GERMANY. LIMITED PRODUCTION. IMPORTED BY BEEMAN PRECISION ARMS, LOCATED IN SANTA ROSA, CA AND PREVIOUSLY BY OSBORNE'S IN CHEBOYGAN, MI.

Korth handguns are very high quality and are literally manufactured one-at-a-time. Importation to date has been quite limited.

Due to the recent devaluation of the U.S. dollar, prices have fluctuated rapidly on this trademark.

REVOLVERS

SPORT/COMBAT RIMFIRE—.22 LR only, 3, 4 (Combat only), or 6 in. vent rib barrel, 6 shot, micro adj. sights (Sport), adj. trigger, shrouded ejector rod, cylinder automatically ejects empties when opened, checkered and oil finished walnut grips, 2.6 lbs.

Mfg.'s Sug. Retail	$2,420	$2,150	$1,775	$1,525	$1,325	$1,080	$950	$800

Add $430 for extra .22 Mag. cylinder.
Add $530 for stainless steel.

SPORT/COMBAT CENTERFIRE—.32 S&W Long (disc.), .38 Spl. (disc.), or .357 Mag. cal., 3, 4 (Combat only), or 6 in. vent rib barrel, 6 shot, micro adj. sights (Sport), adj. trigger, shrouded ejector rod, cylinder automatically ejects empties when opened, checkered and oil finished walnut grips, 2.1 - 2.6 lbs.

Mfg.'s Sug. Retail	$2,420	$2,150	$1,775	$1,525	$1,325	$1,080	$950	$800

Add $430 for interchangeable 9mm cylinder.
Add $530 for stainless steel (limited availability).

PRESENTATION MODEL .357 MAG.—6 in. barrel only, deluxe variation of the Sport/Target Model.

Mfg.'s Sug. Retail	$3,850	$3,400	$2,900	$2,600

Add $350 for interchangeable 9mm cylinder.

PISTOLS: SEMI-AUTO

KORTH SEMI-AUTO—9mm, double action, 4 in. barrel, all steel construction, 13 round mag., adj. sights, checkered walnut stocks, very limited production — special order only. Introduced in 1986.

Mfg.'s Sug. Retail	$3,075	$2,950	$2,500	$2,000

This model has very limited importation and above values reflect 1987 manufacturer's information (last importers retail price).

KRAG-JORGENSEN

U.S. MAGAZINE MILITARY RIFLE. FIRST SMALL CALIBER (.30-40) MILITARY REPEATING RIFLE TO SHOOT SMOKELESS POWDER AMMUNITION. MANUFACTURED 1892-1902.

There have been many conversions of Krag-Jorgensen rifles - many of which are hard to identify. As a rule, these conversions are not as desirable as these specific models listed below.

Grading	100%	98%	95%	90%	80%	70%	60%

M1892-DATED 1894, 1895, OR 1896—Springfield Armory, with cleaning rod. Note: designated Type I, has wide, solid upper barrel band.

	100%	98%	95%	90%	80%	70%	60%
	$4,180	$3,960	$3,740	$3,575	$3,300	$3,000	$2,600

Dated 1894 or 1895—designated Type II. Upper band has double strap instead of being solid as in Type I.

	$1,870	$1,705	$1,540	$1,210	$880	$720	$595

FACTORY — ALTERED TO M1896 STYLE

	$250	$220	$195	$165	$140	$125	$105

M1896—Dated 1896, 1897, 1898, Springfield Armory.

	$470	$440	$330	$250	$220	$185	$155

M1896 CARBINE

	$660	$580	$495	$385	$360	$320	$280

M1895 CARBINE—This is a variant that was dated 1895 and 1896 and omits the word "Model".

	$880	$800	$660	$550	$440	$385	$330

M1896 CADET RIFLE

	$3,025	$2,750	$2,530	$2,200	$1,815	$1,500	$1,200

M1898 RIFLE

	$440	$360	$330	$250	$220	$190	$160

M1898 CARBINE

	$1,450	$1,225	$950	$800	$660	$580	$525

M1899 CARBINE

	$635	$525	$495	$470	$440	$395	$360

M1899 CARBINE, PHILIPPINE CONSTABULARY

	$1,100	$990	$825	$715	$550	$480	$400

KRICO

MANUFACTURED IN STUTTGART, W. GERMANY BY SPORTWAFFENFABRIK KRIEGESKORTE G.M.B.H. PREVIOUSLY IMPORTED (UNTIL (1988) BY BEEMAN PRECISION FIREARMS INC. LOCATED IN SANTA ROSA, CA.

Due to the recent devaluation of the U.S. dollar, prices have fluctuated rapidly on this trademark.

RIFLES: BOLT ACTION

SPORTING RIFLE—.22 Hornet or .222 Rem. cal., miniature Mauser action, 4 shot, 22, 24, or 26 in. barrel, single or double set triggers, open sights, checkered walnut stock, pistol grip, made 1956-1962.

	$605	$550	$495	$440	$400	$360	$305

CARBINE—same as Sporting Rifle, except 20 or 22 in. barrel, full length stock.

	$635	$580	$415	$470	$420	$375	$320

SPECIAL VARMINT RIFLE—same as Sporting Rifle, except heavy barrel, no sights.

	$605	$550	$495	$440	$400	$360	$300

MODEL 300 SPORTER—.22 LR only, select walnut with straight, checkered stock and fuller forearm, 23½ in. barrel, 5 shot mag., grooved receiver, 6½ lbs. Importation disc. in 1988.

	$665	$565	$500	$450	$400	$360	$300

This model was designated Model 302 Sporter until 1986.

Last Mfg.'s Sug. Retail was $775.

Grading	100%	98%	95%	90%	80%	70%	60%

MODEL 311 SMALL BORE RIFLE—.22 LR only, bolt action, 5 or 10 shot, 22 in. barrel, single or double set trigger, open sights, checkered stock. Discontinued.

	$330	$275	$250	$220	$195	$165	$155

Add 30% for Kaps 2½ power scope.

MODEL 320 MANNLICHER SPORTER—.22 LR only, full stock sporter, 19½ in. barrel, 5 shot mag., double set triggers, 6 lbs. Importation disc. in 1988.

	$675	$565	$500	$450	$400	$360	$300

This model was designated Model 304 Mannlicher Sporter until 1986.

Last Mfg.'s Sug. Retail was $800.

MODEL 340—.22 LR only, silhouette model, 21 in. bull barrel, match trigger, no sights, 5 shot mag., stippled pistol grip and forearm, 7½ lbs. Importation disc. in 1988.

	$725	$575	$500	$450	$400	$360	$300

Last Mfg.'s Sug. Retail was $850.

Model 340 Kricotronic—same as above, except with Krico electronic trigger. Importation disc. in 1988.

	$1,295	$995	$900	$800	$690	$600	$550

Last Mfg.'s Sug. Retail was $1,450.

Model 340 Mini-Sniper—non-glare wood and metal finish, military style barrel with muzzle brake, vent forearm, no sights, match trigger (interchangeable), 5 shot, raised cheekpiece. Importation disc. in 1988.

	$1,050	$825	$725	$600	$550	$500	$450

Last Mfg.'s Sug. Retail was $1,200.

MODEL 400 SPORTER—.22 Hornet, 23½ in. barrel, select checkered walnut with European style curved cheekpiece, 5 shot mag., open sights, 6.8 lbs. Importation disc. in 1988.

	$725	$600	$525	$450	$400	$360	$300

Last Mfg.'s Sug. Retail was $900.

MODEL 420 MANNLICHER SPORTER—.22 Hornet only, full stock sporter, 19½ in. barrel, double set triggers, 5 shot, 6½ lbs. Importation disc. in 1988.

	$895	$725	$575	$525	$450	$400	$360

Last Mfg.'s Sug. Retail was $1,000.

MODEL 440—.22 Hornet, otherwise same as Model 340. Importation disc. in 1988.

	$900	$725	$575	$525	$450	$400	$360

Last Mfg.'s Sug. Retail was $1,025.

MODEL 600 SPORTER—9 cal.'s available from .17 Rem. - .308 Win., 23½ in. barrel, select checkered walnut with curved European style cheekpiece, 3 shot mag., open sights, single set trigger, 7 lbs. Importation disc. in 1988.

	$1,150	$985	$880	$760	$695	$650	$590

Last Mfg.'s Sug. Retail was $1,350.

MODEL 620 MANNLICHER SPORTER—same cal.'s as Model 600, full stock sporter, 20¾ in. barrel, double set triggers, 3 shot mag., 6.8 lbs. Importation disc. in 1988.

	$1,165	$965	$875	$760	$695	$650	$590

Last Mfg.'s Sug. Retail was $1,300.

MODEL 640 VARMINT—.22-250, .222 Rem., or .223 Rem. cal., 23¾ in. heavy barrel, high Monte Carlo comb and full cheekpiece, rosewood forearm tip and grip cap, Wundhammer hand swell, double set triggers, 4 shot mag., 9.6 lbs. Importation disc. in 1988.

	$1,165	$965	$875	$760	$695	$650	$590

Last Mfg.'s Sug. Retail was $1,300.

Model 640 Sniper—same as Model 640, except has non-adj. cheekpiece. Importation disc. in 1988.

	$1,325	$1,075	$965	$875	$760	$695	$650

Last Mfg.'s Sug. Retail was $1,500.

Grading	100%	98%	95%	90%	80%	70%	60%

MODEL 640 DELUXE/SUPER SNIPER—.223 Rem. or .308 Win., 23 in. barrel, select walnut stock has stippled hand grip, adj. cheekpiece and vent forearm, engine turned bolt assembly, 3 shot mag., match trigger, 10 lbs. Importation disc. in 1988.

	$1,495	$1,175	$1,025	$875	$760	$695	$650

This model was known as the 650 Sniper/Match until 1986.

Last Mfg.'s Sug. Retail was $1,725.

MODEL 700 SPORTER—.270 or .30-06 cal., 23½ in. barrel, curved European cheekpiece, select walnut, 3 shot Mag., single set trigger, open sights, 7 lbs. Importation disc. in 1988.

	$995	$880	$760	$695	$650	$590	$535

Last Mfg.'s Sug. Retail was $1,375.

MODEL 720 MANNLICHER SPORTER—same as Model 700, only has 20¾ in. barrel, double set triggers, 6.8 lbs. Importation disc. in 1988.

	$995	$880	$760	$695	$650	$590	$535

Last Mfg.'s Sug. Retail was $1,400.

Model 720 Limited Edition—.270 cal. only, 24Kt. gold scroll work on bolt handle, receiver, barrel and mounts. Trigger and front side are gold plated. Serial numbered in gold. Discontinued in 1986.

	$2,310	$1,990	$1,700	$1,450	$1,200	$1,050	$950

Last Mfg.'s Sug. Retail was $2,659.

H. KRIEGHOFF GUN CO. (SHOTGUNS OF ULM)

MANUFACTURED SINCE 1886 IN SUHL, GERMANY. IMPORTED AND DISTRIBUTED BY KRIEGHOFF INTERNATIONAL INC. LOCATED IN OTTSVILLE, PA. WWII KRIEGHOFF LUGERS APPEAR IN THE LUGER SECTION OF THIS TEXT.

SHOTGUNS: OVER AND UNDER

MODEL 32 STANDARD—O/U, 12, 20, 28, or .410 ga., 26½ - 32 in. barrels, auto ejector, boxlock, single trigger, select wood. Discontinued in 1980.

	$1,995	$1,795	$1,600	$1,450	$1,300	$1,175	$1,000

Low Rib—28 or .410 ga., two-barrel set, 50% premium.

	$3,520	$2,860	$2,640	$2,200	$1,980	$1,870	$1,540

MODEL 32 4-BARREL SKEET SET—O/U, 12, 20, 28, or .410 ga., matched barrels in case, grades differ in engraving and wood quality, available as follows:

	100%	98%	95%	90%	80%	70%	60%
Standard	$5,500	$4,400	$3,960	$3,300	$3,080	$2,970	$2,750
Munchen Grade	$7,920	$6,820	$6,050	$5,720	$5,500	$5,225	$4,950
San Remo Grade	$9,020	$7,920	$7,150	$6,820	$6,600	$6,325	$6,050
Monte Carlo Grade	$16,500	$14,300	$12,650	$11,000	$9,900	$9,350	$8,800
Crown Grade	$19,800	$16,500	$14,300	$13,200	$12,100	$10,340	$9,680
Super Crown Grade	$24,200	$19,800	$16,500	$15,400	$14,300	$12,650	$11,000
Exhibition Grade	$39,500	$33,000	$27,500	$24,750	$22,000	$19,800	$16,500

MODEL 32 SINGLE BARREL TRAP—same action as O/U, 12 ga., 32-34 in. barrel, vent rib, mod., imp. mod., or full choke.

	$1,850	$1,400	$1,200	$1,000	$895	$795	$695

KS-5 SINGLE BARREL TRAP—12 ga. only, adj. point of impact, innovative trigger configuration, optional choke tubes. New in 1985.

Mfg.'s Sug. Retail	$2,670	$2,350	$1,850	$1,575	$1,275	$1,075	$900	$795

Add $325 for screw-in choke option.

Add $320 for hard case.

H. KRIEGHOFF GUN CO., cont.

K-80 TRAP—12 ga. only, available in O/U, Unsingle (top barrel plugged), Top Single (single top barrel), and Combo (O/U with extra trap barrel) configurations, standard model has silver finished receiver. In O/U configuration the barrels are separated, about 8½ lbs. A wide variety of custom order options can be ordered on this model.

For the Model K-80, extra barrels vary between $1,895 (O/U) - $2,400 (single barrel), add $285 for single release trigger. Add $480 for double release trigger. Add $325 for screw-in chokes (single barrel guns only) - add $475 for O/U screw in chokes (5 tubes).

Standard Model O/U—add 3% for Top Single, 17% for Unsingle, and 50% for Combo Standard K-80 variations.

Mfg.'s Sug. Retail	$4,850	$4,500	$4,175	$3,550	$3,000	$2,600	$2,295	$2,000

Add $375 for screw-in chokes (5 tubes).

Bavaria Model O/U—game scene engraved silver receiver with light scroll perimeter scroll work, select walnut. Add 1% for Top Single, 8% for Unsingle, and 29% for Combo Bavaria variations.

Mfg.'s Sug. Retail	$8,475	$7,890	$6,595	$5,875	$5,000	$4,375	$3,950	$3,300

Add $375 for screw-in chokes (5 tubes).

Danube Model O/U—fine English scrollwork on receiver sides and floorplate. Add 1% for Top Single, 7% for Unsingle, and 25% for Combo Danube variations.

Mfg.'s Sug. Retail	$10,490	$9,800	$8,330	$7,475	$6,860	$6,000	$5,250	$4,800

Add $375 for screw-in chokes (5 tubes).

Gold Target Model—deep chiseled scroll engraving with gold line accents, 100% coverage finest quality walnut. Add $65 for Top Single, 5% for Unsingle, and 18% for Combo Gold Target variations.

Mfg.'s Sug. Retail	$13,875	$12,500	$10,950	$9,700	$8,600	$7,595	$6,570	$5,850

Add $375 for screw-in chokes (5 tubes).

Centennial Model—12 ga. only, available in combo configuration only, 100 only made in 1986 to commemorate Krieghoff's centennial year, ser. no. 14501-14600. H. Krieghoff's signature inlaid in gold on frame sides. Add $150 for screw-in interchangeable chokes, $1,755 for 4-barrel set.

	$6,000	$5,000	$4,400

Last Mfg.'s Sug. Retail was $5,995.

K-80 SKEET O/U—12 ga. only, available in Lightweight (8mm rib), Standardweight (8mm rib), and International (12mm rib) configurations, muzzle vents on lower barrel, 28 in. barrels only, 8.2 lbs.

International Skeet models are supplied with hard case. Standardweight and Lightweight models include soft case.

Standard Model—available with either lightweight (Dural aluminum) or standardweight frame. Hard case optional.

Mfg.'s Sug. Retail	$4,750	$4,250	$3,685	$3,200	$2,800	$2,450	$2,125	$1,900

Add $350 for Skeet Special (choke tubes & tapered flat rib).
Add $350 for International Model.
Add $200 for Tula choking (even patterning).

Bavaria Model O/U—game scene engraved silver receiver with light perimeter scroll work, select walnut. Available in either Standardweight or Lightweight configuration.

Mfg.'s Sug. Retail	$8,375	$7,700	$5,525	$5,840	$4,975	$4,375	$3,950	$3,300

Add $325 for Skeet Special (choke tubes & tapered flat rib).
Add $325 for International Model.
Add $200 for Tula choking (even patterning).

Danube Model O/U—fine English scrollwork on receiver sides and floorplate. Available in either Standardweight or Lightweight configuration.

Mfg.'s Sug. Retail	$10,390	$9,200	$8,000	$7,395	$6,825	$5,995	$5,250	$4,800

Add $310 for Skeet Special (choke tubes & tapered flat rib).
Add $310 for International Model.
Add $200 for Tula choking (even patterning).

Grading	100%	98%	95%	90%	80%	70%	60%

Gold Target Model—deep chiseled scroll engraving with gold line accents, 100% coverage finest quality walnut. This model is available in Standardweight frame only.

Mfg.'s Sug. Retail	$13,775	$11,500	$9,950	$8,650	$7,595	$6,570	$5,850	$4,850

  Add $125 for Skeet Special (choke tubes & tapered flat rib).
  Add $125 for International Model.
  Add $200 for Tula choking (even patterning).

Centennial Skeet—available in skeet configuration — special features as noted above on Centennial Model description listed under K-80 Trap. Manufactured in 1986 only.

	$3,675	$3,150	$2,700

Last Mfg.'s Sug. Retail was $3,980.

K-80 2-BARREL SKEET SET—12 ga. Tula and tubing barrel, 8mm rib, hard case standard. New in 1988.

Standard Grade

Mfg.'s Sug. Retail	$8,475	$7,300	$5,850	$4,700	$4,175	$3,875	$3,300	$3,000

Bavaria Model O/U—game scene engraved silver receiver with light perimeter scroll work, select walnut. Importation began in 1988.

Mfg.'s Sug. Retail	$12,195	$10,750	$8,750	$7,500	$6,825	$5,995	$5,250	$4,800

Danube Model O/U—fine English scrollwork on receiver sides and floorplate. Importation began in 1988.

Mfg.'s Sug. Retail	$14,300	$12,000	$9,950	$8,750	$7,595	$6,570	$5,850	$5,450

Gold Target Model—deep chiseled scroll engraving with gold line accents, 100% coverage finest quality walnut.

Mfg.'s Sug. Retail	$17,750	$14,750	$11,500	$9,900	$8,700	$7,500	$7,000	$6,650

K-80 4-BARREL SKEET SET—1 barrel each of 12, 20, 28, and .410 ga.'s, 12 ga. is Tula choked (even patterning), 8mm vent rib., includes hard case.

Standard Grade—satin finished receiver with no engraving.

Mfg.'s Sug. Retail	$9,650	$8,800	$7,950	$7,050	$6,100	$5,250	$4,500	$3,700

Bavaria Model O/U—game scene engraved silver receiver with light perimeter scroll work, select walnut.

Mfg.'s Sug. Retail	$13,750	$12,000	$10,550	$9,250	$7,975	$6,900	$5,400	$4,750

Danube Model O/U—fine English scrollwork on receiver sides and floorplate.

Mfg.'s Sug. Retail	$15,800	$13,450	$11,750	$9,950	$8,600	$7,725	$6,900	$5,750

Gold Target Model—deep chiseled scroll engraving with gold line accents, 100% coverage finest quality walnut.

Mfg.'s Sug. Retail	$20,500	$18,250	$15,000	$11,875	$9,950	$8,700	$7,500	$6,700

K-80 PIGEON O/U—12 ga. only, available with 28, 29, or 30 in. barrels, standard tapered step rib, IM/SF choking, available in Lightweight or Standardweight configuration (no extra charge).

Standard Grade—satin finished receiver with no engraving.

Mfg.'s Sug. Retail	$4,850	$4,450	$4,175	$3,550	$3,000	$2,600	$2,295	$1,950

Bavaria Model O/U—game scene engraved silver receiver with light scroll perimeter scroll work, select walnut.

Mfg.'s Sug. Retail	$8,475	$7,550	$6,400	$5,875	$5,000	$4,375	$3,950	$3,300

Danube Model O/U—fine English scroll work on receiver sides and floorplate.

Mfg.'s Sug. Retail	$10,490	$9,300	$8,325	$7,475	$6,860	$6,000	$5,250	$4,400

Gold Target Model—deep chiseled scroll engraving with gold line accents, 100% coverage finest quality walnut.

Mfg.'s Sug. Retail	$13,875	$11,350	$9,800	$8,650	$7,595	$6,500	$5,750	$4,995

K-80 SPORTING CLAYS O/U—12 ga. only, 28 in. barrels with 5 choke tubes, choice of 8mm VR Skeet, tapered flat (broadway) or tapered step rib, sporting clay stock dimensions. New in 1988.

Grading	100%	98%	95%	90%	80%	70%	60%

Standard Grade—satin finished receiver with no engraving.

Mfg.'s Sug. Retail	$5,350	$4,800	$4,350	$3,995	$3,550	$3,000	$2,600	$2,100

Bavaria Model O/U—game scene engraved silver receiver with light scroll perimeter scroll work, select walnut.

Mfg.'s Sug. Retail	$8,950	$7,900	$6,850	$6,000	$5,150	$4,375	$3,950	$3,300

Danube Model O/U—fine English scroll work on receiver sides and floorplate.

Mfg.'s Sug. Retail	$10,970	$9,500	$8,475	$7,600	$6,950	$6,000	$5,250	$4,400

Gold Target Model—deep chiseled scroll engraving with gold line accents, 100% coverage finest quality walnut.

Mfg.'s Sug. Retail	$14,350	$11,950	$9,995	$8,700	$7,575	$6,570	$5,600	$4,800

VANDALIA TRAP—high rib, two barrel combination.

	$4,180	$3,520	$3,300	$2,860	$2,640	$2,530	$2,200

O/U TECK SHOTGUN OR COMBINATION GUN—O/U shotgun or rifle/shotgun combo., 12 and 16 ga., various cal.'s, boxlock, Kersten double crossbolt, auto ejectors, 7½ lbs.

Mfg.'s Sug. Retail	$5,450	$4,995	$4,550	$4,175	$3,550	$3,000	$2,600	$2,295

Teck Dural—Dural aluminum frame variation of the Teck, 6.8 lbs.

Mfg.'s Sug. Retail	$5,450	$4,995	$4,550	$4,175	$3,550	$3,000	$2,600	$2,295

ULM—same as Teck, except sidelock and fully engraved with leaf arabesques.

Mfg.'s Sug. Retail	$10,500	$8,875	$7,850	$7,000	$6,100	$5,250	$4,400	$3,500

Ulm Dural—Dural aluminum frame variation of the Ulm.

Mfg.'s Sug. Retail	$10,500	$8,875	$7,850	$7,000	$6,100	$5,250	$4,400	$3,500

ULM PRIMUS—same as Ulm, except game scene engraved with English arabesques.

Mfg.'s Sug. Retail	$13,500	$11,250	$9,250	$7,950	$6,850	$5,975	$5,450	$4,995

Ulm Primus Dural—Dural aluminum frame variation of the Ulm Primus.

Mfg.'s Sug. Retail	$13,500	$11,250	$9,250	$7,950	$6,850	$5,975	$5,450	$4,995

ULTRA—combination O/U, 12 ga. only, various calibers (lower barrel), 25 in. barrels, "Kickspannar" mechanism allows manual cocking from thumb safety, satin finish receiver, vent rib, 6 lbs. New in 1985.

Mfg.'s Sug. Retail	$2,895	$2,425	$1,850	$1,550	$1,350	$1,200	$1,050	$900

Ultra-B—same as Ultra, except features a selector to switch the front set trigger to the top shotgun barrel.

Mfg.'s Sug. Retail	$3,150	$2,575	$1,950	$1,625	$1,375	$1,175	$990	$895

ULM-P—O/U shotgun, 12 ga. only, live pigeon gun with hand detachable sidelocks, standard grade has light scrollwork engraving.

Mfg.'s Sug. Retail	$13,250	$10,850	$9,250	$7,900	$6,800	$5,850	$5,450	$4,995

Bavaria Grade—same as Ulm-P, only with elaborate game scene engraving.

Mfg.'s Sug. Retail	$16,000	$12,850	$10,450	$8,950	$7,750	$6,400	$5,700	$5,300

KS-2 SERIES—any ga., full H&H type sidelocks, priced by individual special order. Prices start at $24,000.

DOUBLE RIFLES

Various grades differ in style and amount of engraving, choice of walnut and various options that can be special ordered.

TECK O/U—American and metric calibers, 25 in. barrel, boxlock action, cocking indicators.

Mfg.'s Sug. Retail	$7,400	$6,500	$5,500	$4,750	$4,000	$3,650	$3,300	$3,000

Add 15% for .375 H&H (disc. in 1988) or .458 Win. Mag. cal.

Add $750 for DT's with front set trigger.

Teck-Handspanner—manual cocking, 16 ga. only.

Mfg.'s Sug. Retail	$8,750	$7,700	$6,625	$5,900	$5,000	$4,375	$3,950	$3,200

H. KRIEGHOFF GUN CO., cont.

Grading	100%	98%	95%	90%	80%	70%	60%

ULM—same as Teck Double Rifle, with sidelocks and more elaborate engraving.

Mfg.'s Sug. Retail $12,500 $10,750 $8,900 $7,550 $6,575 $6,100 $5,500 $4,950

     Add $450 for hand detachable sidelocks.

     Add $1,400 with single/double trigger.

     Ulm Primus—deluxe sidelock.

     Mfg.'s Sug. Retail $15,500 $12,250 $10,200 $8,725 $7,500 $6,350 $5,700 $5,300

     Ulm Dekor—sidelock with light scroll engraving.

     Mfg.'s Sug. Retail $11,500 $9,800 $8,750 $7,750 $6,650 $5,600 $5,000 $4,400

TRUMPF - SxS—boxlock action, similar to Teck model.

     Mfg.'s Sug. Retail $8,950 $8,050 $7,150 $6,100 $5,300 $4,800 $4,400 $4,000

NEPTUN - SxS—sidelock double rifle, same features as the Ulm model.

     Mfg.'s Sug. Retail $14,500 $12,000 $10,000 $8,500 $7,250 $6,000 $5,450 $4,995

DRILLINGS

H.Krieghoff drillings can be ordered with a variety of cal.'s and special order features. Prices shown below are for standard guns with no options. Better models will have a finer grade walnut and exhibit more elaborate deep relief engraving.

PLUS MODEL—12 or 20 ga. over rifle barrel (.222 Rem., 243 Win., 270, or .30-06 cal.), boxlock action, light engraving. New in 1988.

     Mfg.'s Sug. Retail $3,795 $3,300 $2,850 $2,450 $2,100 $1,825 $1,525 $1,200

TRUMPF MODEL—12, 16, or 20 ga. O/U, or rifle shotgun combo., various cal.'s, boxlock, 25 in. barrels, 7½ lbs.

     Mfg.'s Sug. Retail $6,990 $6,275 $5,250 $4,700 $3,950 $3,200 $2,750 $2,200

     Add $950 for single trigger.

     Trumpf Dural—Dural aluminum frame variation of the Trumpf. 6.8 lbs., cased.

     Mfg.'s Sug. Retail $6,990 $6,275 $5,250 $4,700 $3,950 $3,200 $2,750 $2,200

     Add $950 for single trigger.

NEPTUN MODEL—12 or 20 ga., variety of cal.'s, elaborate engraving, sidelocks.

     Mfg.'s Sug. Retail $11,850 $9,975 $8,700 $7,650 $6,800 $5,900 $5,100 $4,150

     Neptun Dural—Dural aluminum frame variation of the Neptun, cased.

     Mfg.'s Sug. Retail $11,850 $9,975 $8,700 $7,650 $6,800 $5,900 $5,100 $4,150

NEPTUN PRIMUS MODEL—same as Neptun Model, only hand detachable sidelocks and elaborate deep relief engraving.

     Mfg.'s Sug. Retail $14,600 $12,000 $10,300 $9,000 $7,700 $6,675 $5,850 $4,950

     Neptun Primus Dural—Dural aluminum frame variation available at no extra charge.

     Mfg.'s Sug. Retail $14,600 $12,000 $10,300 $9,000 $7,700 $6,675 $5,850 $4,950

L

L.A.R. MANUFACTURING, INC.

MANUFACTURED AND DISTRIBUTED IN WEST JORDAN, UT.

Grading	100%	98%	95%	90%	80%	70%	60%

GRIZZLY WIN. MAG. MARK I—.357 Mag. or .45 Win. Mag., single action, semi-auto based on the Colt 1911 design, 5.4 in. (new in 1986), 6½ in., 8 in. (new in 1987), or 10 in. (new in 1987) barrel, parkerized finish, 7 round mag., ambidextrous safeties, checkered rubber grips, adj. sights, 48 oz. empty, also can be converted to .45 ACP, 10mm (new in 1988), .357 Mag., and .30 Mauser (disc.). New in 1984.

Short Barrel Lengths—5.4 or 6.5 in. barrel.

Mfg.'s Sug. Retail	$725	$650	$600	$575	$525	$495	$475	$450

    Add $25 if purchased in .357 Mag.
    Add $164 - $179 for cal. conversion units.

Conversion units include .357 Mag., 10mm, and .45 ACP cal.'s.
    Add $119 for hard chrome frame.
    Add $188 for full hard chrome.

Long Barrel Lengths—8 or 10 in. barrel, extended slides.

Mfg.'s Sug. Retail	$1,250	$1,150	$950	$875	$800	$725	$650	$575

    Add $63 for 10 in. barrel.
    Add $25 if purchased in .357 Mag.
    Add $88 for scope mounts.
    Add $74 for muzzle compensator.

GRIZZLY WIN. MAG. MARK II—similar to Mark I, except has fixed sights, standard safeties, and different metal finish. Manufactured in 1986 only.

			$595	$550	$525	$495	$475	$450	$425

    Add $25 for .357 Mag.

Last Mfg.'s Sug. Retail was $550.

L E S INCORPORATED

MANUFACTURED IN SKOKIE, ILLINOIS.

PISTOL: SEMI-AUTO

P-18 ROGAK DOUBLE ACTION—9mm, double action, 18 shot, 5½ in. barrel, stainless steel. Discontinued.

		$325	$295	$265

High polish finish

		$375	$330	$295

LAHTI PISTOL

MANUFACTURED IN HUSQVARNA, SWEDEN & VKT (STATE RIFLE FACTORY IN JYVASKYLA), FINLAND.

LAHTI AUTOMATIC—9mm, 4¾ in. barrel, blue, fixed sights, plastic grips.

	$400	$365	$330	$295	$260	$240	$200

Grading	100%	98%	95%	90%	80%	70%	60%

SWEDISH MODEL 40—made 1940-1944.

	$375	$335	$300	$275	$260	$250	$240

Add 10% for Holster-Rig.

FINNISH L-35—made 1935-1944.

	$1,250	$1,050	$900	$760	$680	$620	$575

Note: It is important to note that there are diversely marked variations of this pistol, such as RPLT (Danish State Police); such police markings reduce value by about 10%.

LAMES

MANUFACTURED IN ITALY.

SHOTGUNS

FIELD MODEL O/U—12 ga., 26, 28, or 30 in. barrels, various chokes, VR, engraving, SST, auto ejectors, checkered pistol grip stock with pad.

	$400	$380	$365	$350	$325	$300	$275

Separated barrels

	$500	$480	$465	$450	$425	$400	$375

STANDARD TRAP O/U—same as Field, 30 or 32 in. various trap bore barrels, with wide vent rib, trap style Monte Carlo stock.

	$600	$575	$550	$525	$425	$400	$450

CALIFORNIA TRAP O/U—same as Standard Trap, with separated barrels.

	$700	$675	$650	$625	$525	$500	$450

SKEET MODEL—same as Field, with 26 in. skeet bore barrels, skeet stock and separated barrels.

	$600	$575	$550	$525	$425	$400	$350

LANBER SHOTGUNS

MANUFACTURED IN ZALDBAR, SPAIN. PREVIOUSLY IMPORTED BY EXEL ARMS OF AMERICA, INC., LOCATED IN GARDENER, MA. AND BY LANBER ARMS OF AMERICA LOCATED IN ADRIAN, MI.

SHOTGUNS: O/U RECENT MANUFACTURE

Please refer to discontinued Exel Models 101-104 and 105-107 in the "E" section of this text.

SHOTGUNS: O/U DISCONTINUED MANUFACTURE

The following models were imported by Lanber Arms of America, Inc. located in Adrian, MI until business ceased in late 1986.

844 ST—12 ga. only, boxlock, 26 or 28 in. barrels, choked IC/IM, extractors, SST, automatic safety, vent rib, European walnut with hand checkering, blued finish with engraved receiver, 7⅛ lbs. Importation discontinued in 1986.

	$395	$340	$320	$300	$285	$270	$255

Last Mfg.'s Sug. Retail was $450.

844 MST—12 ga. only, 3 in. chambers, 30 in. F & M barrels, otherwise same as 844 ST. Importation discontinued in 1986.

	$405	$350	$335	$320	$310	$300	$295

Last Mfg.'s Sug. Retail was $470.

2004 LCH—12 ga. only, boxlock action, 28 in. barrels, SST, ejectors, supplied with 5 screw-in choke tubes, engraved satin finish receiver, checkered European walnut, 7⅜ lbs. Importation discontinued in 1986.

	$575	$485	$460	$440	$420	$395	$380

Last Mfg.'s Sug. Retail was $650.

Grading	100%	98%	95%	90%	80%	70%	60%

2004 LCH SKEET—12 ga. only, 28 in. barrels supplied with 5 choke tubes, blued finish, moderately engraved, select checkered walnut, 7⅜ lbs. Importation discontinued in 1986.

	$740	$635	$585	$560	$540	$520	$495

Last Mfg.'s Sug. Retail was $845.

2004 LCH TRAP—12 ga. only, 30 in. barrels supplied with 3 choke tubes, European walnut has trap dimensions, blued finish. Importation discontinued in 1986.

	$675	$625	$585	$560	$540	$520	$495

Last Mfg.'s Sug. Retail was $845.

LASALLE

MANUFACTURED IN FRANCE.

SLIDE ACTION SHOTGUN—12 or 20 ga., 26, 28, or 30 in. barrels, various chokes, alloy frame, checkered pistol grip stock.

	$250	$225	$200	$175	$150	$125	$100

AUTOMATIC SHOTGUN—12 ga., 26, 28, or 30 in. barrels, various chokes, gas operated, checkered pistol grip stock.

	$300	$275	$250	$225	$200	$175	$150

LAURONA

MANUFACTURED IN EIBAR, SPAIN. CURRENTLY IMPORTED AND DISTRIBUTED BY GALAXY IMPORTS LOCATED IN VICTORIA, TX.

SHOTGUNS: O/U DISC. MANUFACTURE

Please refer to the Exel 300 Series in the ''E'' section.

SHOTGUNS: O/U RECENT MANUFACTURE

Laurona shotguns come standard with a black chrome metal finish that is extremely resistant to oxidation.

Suffix designations on Laurona shotguns refer to the following: G - twin single triggers, S - selective single trigger, M - multi-chokes, T - Tulip, BV - beavertail.

MODEL 82—double selective trigger system, ejectors, pistol grip, vent rib, various chokes and barrel lengths. Discontinued.

	$549	$410	$380	$340	$300	$275	$250

This model was imported by Exel Arms of America, Inc.

SUPER GAME MODELS—12 or 20 ga., boxlock, 28 in. barrels, unique twin single triggers, ejectors, extensive fine scroll engraving on a satin finished receiver, anti-rust black chrome barrel finish, vent. rib, elongated forcing cones, checkered walnut stock and forearm.

Twin single triggers can function as conventional double triggers in addition to each firing either of the two barrels.

82 G Super Game—new designation for 82 Super Game, with T forend, 2¾ in. chambers, 28 in. separated barrels choked F/M or IC/IM with 8mm VR, twin single triggers.

Mfg.'s Sug. Retail	$984	$875	$795	$675	$625	$550	$495	$460

This model was previously designated 82 Super Game.

82 Pigeon Competition—same as 82 Trap Competition, except 28 in. barrels with different chokings. Importation discontinued in 1986.

	$545	$465	$440	$420	$405	$390	$375

Last Mfg.'s Sug. Retail was $630.

Grading	100%	98%	95%	90%	80%	70%	60%

82 Trap Combo—trap model, 8mm vent rib, non-selective single trigger. Importation discontinued in 1986.

| | $485 | $390 | $375 | $360 | $350 | $340 | $330 |

Last Mfg.'s Sug. Retail was $566.

82 Trap Competition—29 in. barrels, oil finished Monte Carlo stock, 13mm VR, non-selective single trigger, motif engraving, rubber recoil pad, 8.1 lbs. Importation discontinued in 1986.

| | $540 | $460 | $435 | $420 | $405 | $390 | $375 |

Last Mfg.'s Sug. Retail was $625.

83 MG SUPER GAME—12 or 20 ga., similar to 82 G Super Game except has multi-chokes, 2¾ or 3 in. Mag. chambers.

| *Mfg.'s Sug. Retail* | $995 | $895 | $795 | $675 | $625 | $550 | $495 | $460 |

83 MS Super Game 2 Barrel Set—includes 2 sets of barrels (12 and 20 ga.).

| *Mfg.'s Sug. Retail* | $1,385 | $1,200 | $985 | $875 | $775 | $700 | $625 | $550 |

83 M Puma Hunting—importation discontinued in 1986.

| | $485 | $445 | $425 | $410 | $395 | $380 | $375 |

Last Mfg.'s Sug. Retail was $529.

84 S SUPER GAME—similar to 82 G Super Game except has SST and available with 3 in. Mag. chambers.

| *Mfg.'s Sug. Retail* | $984 | $875 | $795 | $675 | $625 | $550 | $495 | $460 |

84 S SUPER TRAP—29 in. barrels, extensive fine scroll engraving, separated barrels with 13mm aluminum VR, rubber recoil pad, full pistol grip stock with orthopedic grip, beavertail forearm, single selective trigger, elongated forcing cones, choked IM/F or M/F, 7¾ lbs.

| *Mfg.'s Sug. Retail* | $1,095 | $950 | $825 | $695 | $625 | $550 | $495 | $460 |

85 MS SUPER GAME—available in 12 or 20 ga., similar to 83 MG Super Game, except has single trigger.

| *Mfg.'s Sug. Retail* | $995 | $895 | $795 | $675 | $625 | $550 | $495 | $460 |

85 MS Super Game 2 Barrel Set—includes 2 sets of barrels (12 and 20 ga.).

| *Mfg.'s Sug. Retail* | $1,385 | $1,200 | $985 | $875 | $775 | $700 | $625 | $550 |

85 MS SUPER TRAP—similar to 84 S Super Trap except chokes are full over multi-choke.

| *Mfg.'s Sug. Retail* | $1,135 | $985 | $875 | $775 | $650 | $525 | $475 | $420 |

85 MS Super Pigeon—similar to 85 Super Trap except choked and stocked for live pigeon shooting, 7¼ lbs.

| *Mfg.'s Sug. Retail* | $1,117 | $975 | $875 | $775 | $650 | $525 | $475 | $420 |

Add $40 for pigeon stock.

85 S SUPER SKEET—12 ga. only, 28 in. barrels, 2¾ in. chambers with elongated forcing cones, extensive fine scroll engraving, rust resistant black chrome finish, separated barrels, rubber recoil pad, 13mm aluminum VR, mechanical triggers with 5 lb. pull, 7¼ lbs.

| *Mfg.'s Sug. Retail* | $1,061 | $940 | $825 | $695 | $625 | $550 | $495 | $460 |

85 MS Special Sporting—12 ga. only, similar to 85 S Super Skeet except designed for sporting clays competition, SST, 28 in. barrels choked full over multi-choke, 7¼ lbs., importation began in 1988.

| *Mfg.'s Sug. Retail* | $1,085 | $950 | $825 | $695 | $625 | $550 | $495 | $460 |

SILHOUETTE 300 SPORTING CLAYS—12 ga. only, 3 in. chambers, 28 in. barrels with 11mm VR, field stock with special recoil pad designed for dropped stock style shooting, 7¼ lbs. New in 1988.

| *Mfg.'s Sug. Retail* | $1,019 | $900 | $795 | $675 | $625 | $550 | $495 | $460 |

Available with either flush or knurled multi-chokes.

SIHOUETTE 300 TRAP—12 ga. only, same as 85 MS Super Trap except has 29 in. steel barrels with 11mm VR, flush or knurled multi-chokes, black chrome finish, distinctive silver striped receiver, 8 lbs. New in 1988,

| *Mfg.'s Sug. Retail* | $1,159 | $995 | $895 | $775 | $650 | $525 | $475 | $420 |

LAW ENFORCEMENT ORDNANCE CORPORATION

MANUFACTURED AND DISTRIBUTED IN RIDGWAY, PA.

STRIKER-12—12 ga. only, assault shotgun featuring 12 shot rotary mag., 12 or 18¼ in. barrel, semi-auto, alloy shrouded barrel with PG extension, 9.2 lbs., folding or fixed assault stock. New in 1986.

	Mfg.'s Sug. Retail	$725	$650	$575	$500	$475	$450	$425	$400

Add $100 for Marine variation ("Metal Life" finish).

Earlier variations were imported and available to law enforcement agencies only. In 1987, manufacture was started in PA and these firearms can be sold to individuals (18 in. barrel only).

LEBEAU-COURALLY

MANUFACTURED SINCE 1865 IN LIEGE, BELGIUM. CURRENTLY IMPORTED BY MIDWEST GUN SPORT IN ZEBULON, NC. PREVIOUSLY IMPORTED BY W.L. MOORE & CO. IN WEST LAKE VILLAGE, CA.

Prices could differ from values shown below because of the fluctuating U.S. dollar.

RIFLES: SIDE-BY-SIDE

BOXLOCK EJECTOR—8 x 57 JRS, 9.3 x 74 R, .375 H&H, or .458 Win. Mag., Anson & Deeley boxlock, ejectors, select French walnut stock, quarter rib with ramp front sight, about 8 lbs. Add $1,800 for .375 H&H or .458 Win. Mag. cal. Importation disc. in 1988.

		$9,200	$7,950	$7,250	$6,500	$5,500	$4,500	$3,750

Add $1,400 for standard cal.'s.

This model was imported by W.L. Moore & Co. only.

Last Mfg.'s Sug. Retail was $10,200.

SIDELOCK EJECTOR—8 x 57 JRS, 9.3 x 74 R, .375 H&H, or .458 Win. Mag., chopper lump barrels, reinforced action, select French walnut stock, quarter rib with ramp front sight, about 8 lbs.

	Mfg.'s Sug. Retail	$22,500	$19,950	$16,600	$14,000	$11,850	$10,250	$8,900	$7,000

SHOTGUNS

For currently manufactured shotguns — add $1,500 for single trigger, and $700 for false sideplates.

SOLOGNE SXS—12, 16, or 20 ga., Anson & Deeley boxlock action, various chokes and barrel lengths, select walnut, no engraving. Add $530 for false side plates.

	Mfg.'s Sug. Retail	$7,320	$6,725	$5,950	$5,475	$4,950	$4,620	$4,400	$4,125

GRAND RUSSE MODEL—grade up from Sologne Model.

	Mfg.'s Sug. Retail	$8,480	$7,625	$7,000	$6,750	$5,500	$4,950	$4,400	$4,125

BOXLOCK EJECTOR SXS—12, 16, 20, or 28 ga., choice of classic or rounded action, with or without side plates, select French walnut stock, choice of numerous engraving patterns (optional), 26, 28, or 30 in. barrels, double trigger. Add 10% for 28 or .410 ga.'s. Importation discontinued in 1986.

		$8,450	$7,500	$6,500	$5,500	$4,500	$3,750	$3,000

Last Mfg.'s Sug. Retail was $9,400.

Boxlock with side plates.

		$8,950	$7,900	$6,750	$5,600	$4,500	$3,750	$3,000

Last Mfg.'s Sug. Retail was $10,000.

SIDELOCK EJECTOR SXS—12, 16, 20, or 28 ga., choice of classic or rounded action, chopper lump barrels, select French walnut stock, choice of numerous engraving patterns (optional), 26, 28, or 30 in. barrels, double triggers. Add 10% for 28 or .410 ga.'s.

	Mfg.'s Sug. Retail	$20,600	$18,250	$14,000	$12,000	$9,995	$8,750	$7,500	$6,350

Grading	100%	98%	95%	90%	80%	70%	60%

SIDELOCK O/U—similar to Boss Model, except less engraving, and different quality wood.

Mfg.'s Sug. Retail	$19,600	$17,000	$13,725	$11,400	$9,995	$8,750	$7,500	$6,350

BOSS MODEL O/U—12 or 20 ga. only, Boss pattern sidelock with low profile action, top of the line O/U individually made to customer specifications.

Mfg.'s Sug. Retail	$28,000	$24,800	$21,750	$19,000	$16,000	$13,000	$10,750	$9,700

LEFEVER ARMS COMPANY

MANUFACTURED IN SYRACUSE, NY.

SHOTGUNS

The Lefever was the first commercially successful hammerless double barrel shotgun made in America. They were made in Syracuse, NY from 1885-1916, at which time the company was acquired by Ithaca Gun Company. Ithaca made the Lefever until 1916. In 1921 the Box Lock Nitro Special was introduced and in 1934 the Lefever Grade A was introduced. Production of Lefever guns ceased in 1948.

THE FOLLOWING IS A PERCENTAGE BREAKDOWN OF GAUGES MADE BETWEEN 1885-1916 (TOTALING 100%): 8 GA.—½%, 10 GA.—25%, 12 GA.—60%, 14 GA.—½%, 16 GA.—8%, 20 GA.—6%. TOTAL MANUFACTURE WAS APPROX. 72,000 DURING THIS PERIOD. IT IS IMPORTANT TO NOTE THAT DAMASCUS BARRELED GUNS IN 90% ORIGINAL CONDITION OR BETTER ARE VERY COLLECTIBLE AND VALUES CAN APPROXIMATE THOSE OF STEEL BARREL MODELS IF THE BORE IS EXCELLENT WITH NO PITTING. DAMASCUS SPECIMENS BELOW 90% CONDITION ARE NOT AS COLLECTIBLE, HOWEVER, AND VALUES FALL OFF RAPIDLY IF UNDER 90%. PRICES SHOWN BELOW FOR 90% AND UP CONDITION ARE VERY DIFFICULT TO EVALUATE AND ARE MEANT AS A GUIDE ONLY - ANY LEFEVER SHOTGUN IS RARE AND HARD TO EVALUATE IF IN OVER 95%.

SIDELOCK DOUBLE BARREL SHOTGUN—10, 12, 16, or 20 ga., 26-32 in. barrels, any choke, cocking indicators on all but DS and DSE grades, double triggers standard, checkered straight or pistol grip stock, auto ejectors designated by letter E after grade, made 1885-1919.

16 ga. — deduct 10%.

20 ga. — add 20%.

SST — add 10%.

	100%	98%	95%	90%	80%	70%	60%
DS grade	$1,250	$1,000	$800	$700	$525	$470	$415
DSE grade	$1,650	$1,300	$1,100	$950	$700	$575	$500
H grade	$1,400	$1,100	$950	$800	$625	$580	$525
HE grade	$1,825	$1,650	$1,450	$1,200	$900	$775	$625
G grade	$1,550	$1,425	$1,200	$1,000	$800	$700	$595
GE grade	$1,950	$1,800	$1,575	$1,325	$1,175	$1,000	$800
F grade	$1,700	$1,550	$1,325	$1,125	$925	$800	$750
FE grade	$2,200	$1,950	$1,750	$1,475	$1,250	$1,100	$1,045
E grade	$2,000	$1,675	$1,500	$1,325	$1,100	$975	$950
EE grade	$2,700	$2,200	$1,875	$1,600	$1,400	$1,250	$1,155
D grade	$2,400	$2,000	$1,750	$1,500	$1,430	$1,375	$1,265
DE grade	$3,200	$2,750	$2,400	$2,000	$1,750	$1,595	$1,485
C grade	$4,000	$3,400	$2,950	$2,400	$2,000	$1,815	$1,705
CE grade	$6,000	$5,500	$5,000	$4,200	$3,200	$2,200	$1,750
B grade	$5,750	$5,100	$4,600	$3,850	$2,750	$2,300	$1,900
BE grade	$10,000	$9,000	$7,500	$5,500	$3,500	$2,875	$2,310

A grade—auto ejectors standard.

	$20,000	$15,000	$11,000	$8,000	$5,000	$3,650	$2,530

AA grade—auto ejectors standard.

	$30,000	$20,000	$15,000	$11,000	$7,750	$5,500	$3,500

Optimus Grade—auto ejectors standard. Extreme rarity precludes accurate percentage pricing.

Thousand Dollar Grade—auto ejectors standard. Extreme rarity precludes accurate percentage pricing.

Grading	100%	98%	95%	90%	80%	70%	60%

NITRO SPECIAL DOUBLE BARREL SHOTGUN—12, 16, 20, or .410 ga., 26-32 in. barrels, various chokes, boxlock, extractors, checkered pistol grip stock, made 1921-1948.

	$400	$375	$350	$300	$250	$225	$200

Single trigger — add $75.
16 ga. — deduct 10%.
20 ga. — add 20%.
.410 ga. — add 100%.

GRADE A DOUBLE BARREL SHOTGUN—12, 16, 20, or .410 ga., 26-32 in. barrels, various chokes, boxlock, checkered pistol grip stock, made 1934-1942.

	$880	$770	$715	$660	$550	$495	$440

Auto ejectors — add 33%.
Single trigger — add $75.
Beavertail forearm — add $75.
16 ga. — deduct 10%.
20 ga. — add 20%.
.410 — add 100%.

GRADE A SKEET MODEL—same as Grade A, with 26 in. skeet bore barrels, auto ejector, single trigger and beavertail forearm standard.

	$1,155	$1,045	$990	$935	$825	$770	$715

16 ga. — deduct 10%.
20 ga. — add 20%.
.410 — add 100%.

SINGLE BARREL TRAP GUN—12 ga. only, 30 or 32 in. VR barrel, full choke, boxlock, auto ejector, checkered pistol grip stock, made 1972-1942.

	$550	$440	$385	$330	$275	$250	$195

LONG RANGE SINGLE BARREL FIELD—12, 16, 20, or .410 ga., 26-32 in. barrel, boxlock, extractor, checkered pistol grip stock, made 1972-1942.

	$330	$275	$250	$220	$165	$140	$120

LEFEVER, D.M. & SON

MANUFACTURED IN BOWLING GREEN, OH.

SHOTGUNS

"Uncle Dan" Lefever, founder of Lefever Arms, designed and manufactured the first breech loading double hammerless shotgun made in the U.S. Production started in 1872 and continued in the Syracuse, NY plant until he sold his interest in the Lefever Arms Company during the early 1900's. He then moved to Ohio and started another factory under the name D.M. Lefever & Son. After his death a few years later the Ohio factory was closed, while his old company (Lefever Arms Co.) continued manufacturing Lefever's until being sold to Ithaca Gun Company in the early 20's. From that point, Lefever Arms Co. was a branch of Ithaca and continued to make shotguns until shortly after WWII.

Grading	80%	70%	60%	50%	40%	30%	20%	10%

TOTAL PRODUCTION ON D.M. LEFEVER SHOTGUNS BETWEEN 1901-1904 TOTALED LESS THAN 1,200. BECAUSE OF THEIR INHERENT RARITY, VALUES LISTED BELOW SHOW ONLY 10%-80% CONDITION SPECIMENS. D.M. LEFEVER SPECIMENS ARE SO RARE IN 80% + CONDITION THAT PRICES CANNOT BE ACCURATELY ASCERTAINED.

NEW LEFEVER DOUBLE BARREL SHOTGUN—12, 16, or 20 ga., any length barrel and choke on order, auto ejectors standard on all grades except O Excelsior, double triggers standard on all except Uncle Dan grade, optional single triggers available, checkered walnut pistol grip or straight stock, grades differ as to engraving, wood, checkering and overall quality, made 1904-1906.

16 ga. — deduct 10%.
20 ga. — add 20%.
SST — add 10%.

Grading	80%	70%	60%	50%	40%	30%	20%	10%
O Excelsior Grade								
	$2,365	$1,925	$1,650	$1,430	$1,210	$990	$770	$605
Excelsior Grade w/ejectors								
	$2,640	$2,310	$1,925	$1,595	$1,320	$1,045	$825	$660
F Grade, No. 9								
	$3,000	$2,640	$2,310	$1,925	$1,595	$1,320	$1,045	$825
G Grade—10 ga., sidelock, damascus barrels.								
	$3,450	$2,950	$2,500	$2,000	$1,650	$1,375	$1,100	$875
E Grade, No. 8								
	$4,000	$3,350	$2,875	$2,300	$1,980	$1,650	$1,320	$990
D Grade, No. 7								
	$4,400	$4,125	$3,850	$3,300	$2,750	$2,475	$2,200	$1,650
C Grade, No. 6								
	$4,950	$4,400	$4,125	$3,850	$3,300	$2,750	$2,420	$2,050
B Grade, No. 5								
	$6,600	$5,500	$4,400	$4,125	$3,850	$3,300	$3,000	$2,600
AA Grade, No. 4								
	$8,800	$7,700	$6,600	$5,500	$4,400	$3,630	$3,250	$2,850

UNCLE DAN GRADE—too rare to accurately determine values.

SINGLE BARREL TRAP GUN—12 ga., 26-32 in. full choke, auto ejector, boxlock, checkered pistol grip stock, made 1904-1906. Too rare to accurately determine values.

LE FORGERON

MANUFACTURED IN BELGIUM. CURRENTLY DISTRIBUTED BY MIDWEST GUN SPORT IN ZEBULON, NC.

Grading	100%	98%	95%	90%	80%	70%	60%

SHOTGUNS

Prices could differ from values shown below because of the fluctuating U.S. dollar.

BOXLOCK EJECTOR SXS—20 or 28 ga. only, with or without sideplates, select French walnut stock, choice of engraving patterns (optional), single trigger.

Mfg.'s Sug. Retail	$4,400	$3,975	$3,650	$3,325	$2,995	$2,600	$2,250	$1,900

Add $1,000 for sideplates.

SIDELOCK EJECTOR SXS—20 or 28 ga. only, select French walnut stock, choice of engraving patterns (optional), rounded action, single trigger.

Mfg.'s Sug. Retail	$11,600	$10,200	$9,250	$8,500	$7,900	$7,100	$6,300	$5,500

RIFLES

MODEL 6020—9.3 x 74R cal., boxlock action, beavertail forearm, pistol grip stock.

Mfg.'s Sug. Retail	$4,900	$4,450	$4,025	$3,750	$3,475	$3,100	$2,800	$2,550

Add $700 for side plates (Model 6040).

MODEL 6030—sidelock action, engraved action with deluxe French walnut stock and forearm.

Mfg.'s Sug. Retail	$8,950	$8,475	$7,900	$7,100	$6,300	$5,500	$4,700	$4,000

LE FRANCAIS PISTOLS

MANUFACTURED IN FRANCAIS D'ARMES ET CYCLES, STE. ETIENNE, FRANCE.

STAFF OFFICER MODEL AUTOMATIC—.25 auto, 2½ in. barrel, blue, fixed sights, rubber grips, no visible cocking piece, made 1914-disc.

$275	$230	$200	$165	$140	$115	$80

POLICEMAN MODEL AUTOMATIC—.32 auto, double action, 7 shot, 3½ in. barrel, hinged barrel, blue, fixed sights, rubber grips, made 1914-disc.

$850	$800	$700	$575	$435	$350	$275

Only limited quantities of this model were made during the early 1960's.

ARMY MODEL AUTOMATIC—9mm Browning, 8 shot, 5 in. barrel, blue, fixed sights, checkered walnut grips, made 1928-1938.

$1,200	$1,100	$850	$700	$550	$425	$350

LIEGEOISE D'ARMES

MANUFACTURED IN BELGIUM.

Small manufacturer specializing in boxlock shotguns, normally engraved and with ejectors. Prices usually start in the $600 + range.

LIGNOSE (BERGMAN)

MANUFACTURED IN SUHL, GERMANY.

EINHAND MODEL 2A POCKET AUTOMATIC—.25 auto, 6 shot, 2 in. barrel, blue, rubber grips, can be cocked by rearward pressure on trigger guard.

$220	$205	$195	$165	$140	$110	$85

MODEL 3A POCKET AUTOMATIC—same as 2A, except longer grip, 9 shot capacity.

$220	$205	$195	$165	$140	$110	$85

MODEL 2 POCKET AUTOMATIC—similar to 2A, without one hand cocking trigger guard.

$165	$155	$140	$110	$90	$75	$55

LJUNGMAN

CARL GUSTAF, SWEDEN.

AG 42—semi-auto rifle, 6.5mm, 10 shot mag., wood stock, tangent rear sight, hooded front, bayonet lug, designed in 1941. This was the first mass produced, direct gas operated rifle. This weapon was also used by the Egyptian armed forces and was known as the Hakim.

$715	$660	$580	$525	$440	$360	$275

LJUTIC INDUSTRIES, INC.

MANUFACTURED IN YAKIMA, WA.

Prior to 1960, Ljutic was doing business as Ljutic Gun Co.

TRAP SHOTGUNS

To date approximately 2,500 target shotguns have been manufactured.
ALL CURRENT LJUTIC SHOTGUNS LISTED BELOW ARE SUBJECT TO 11% FEDERAL EXCISE TAX.

Grading	100%	98%	95%	90%	80%	70%	60%

DYNATRAP SINGLE BARREL SHOTGUN—12 ga., 33 in. barrel, full choke, push button opening, extractor, trap stock.

	$2,000	$1,800	$1,600	$1,475	$1,300	$1,200	$1,100

Release trigger — add $75.
Custom stock — add $200.
Extra release trigger — add $200.
Extra pull trigger — add $150.

MODEL X-73 SINGLE BARREL—12 ga., 33 in. full, push button opening, high rib fancy Monte Carlo stock.

	$2,500	$2,250	$2,000	$1,850	$1,700	$1,600	$1,500

Extra barrel — add $500.
Extra pull trigger — add $200.
Extra release trigger — add $250.

MONO GUN SINGLE BARREL—12 ga., 34 in. barrel, custom choked, custom stocked, pull or release trigger, a "built to customers specifications" trap gun. Also known as Standard Rib or Olympic model.

Standard Rib Model

Mfg.'s Sug. Retail	$3,795	$3,795	$3,200	$2,950	$2,575	$2,200	$2,000	$1,850

Add $100 for medium rib.
Add $200 for screw-in choke tubes.

LTX (Deluxe Mono Trap)—similar to Mono Gun except has 33 in. medium rib barrel and exhibition wood and checkering.

Mfg.'s Sug. Retail	$4,995	$4,995	$4,250	$3,750	$3,300	$2,950	$2,500	$2,250

Add $1,000 for choke tube option.
Extra barrel — add $1,895 for standard rib.
Extra release trigger — add $700.
Add $550 for pull trigger.

SPACE GUN—12 ga. only, single barrel, unusual design permits in-line round stock with recoil pad, circular forearm wraps around barrel, high post rib on muzzle half of barrel.

Mfg.'s Sug. Retail	$3,795	$3,795	$3,200	$2,950	$2,575	$2,200	$2,000	$1,850

BI GUN COMBO—12 ga. only, supplied with one set of O/U barrels in addition to a high rib single barrel, deluxe wood and checkering, separated barrels on O/U.

Mfg.'s Sug. Retail	$16,995	$16,950	$13,250	$11,000	$9,450	$8,600	$8,000	$7,450

BI Gun - O/U Only—supplied with O/U barrels only.

Mfg.'s Sug. Retail	$9,984	$9,984	$8,500	$7,700	$6,950	$6,250	$5,600	$4,950

BI MATIC AUTO LOADER—12 ga., 2 shot, 26-32 in. barrels, low recoil, trap or skeet models available, stock and choking to customer specifications.

	$2,000	$1,850	$1,650	$1,500	$1,375	$1,225	$1,075

Extra barrel — add $700.
Extra release trigger — add $250.

LLAMA PISTOLS

MANUFACTURED IN GABILONDO Y CIA, VICTORIA, SPAIN. CURRENTLY IMPORTED AND DISTRIBUTED BY STOEGER INDUSTRIES LOCATED IN SOUTH HACKENSACK, NJ.

PISTOLS: SEMI-AUTO

MODEL IIIA—.380 auto, 7 shot, 3 in. barrel, adj. sights, blue, plastic grips, made 1951-discontinued.

	$235	$200	$180	$160	$140	$120	$110

MODEL XA—same as model IIIA, except .32 auto.

	$235	$200	$180	$160	$140	$120	$110

MODEL XV—same as model XA, except .22 LR.

	$235	$200	$180	$160	$140	$120	$110

Grading	100%	98%	95%	90%	80%	70%	60%

MODELS C-IIIA, C-XA, C-XV—same as model C, except engraved chrome.

	$305	$260	$230	$205	$180	$155	$140

MODELS BE-IIIA, BE-XA, BE-XV—same as model CE, except engraved, blue.

	$290	$250	$220	$195	$165	$140	$125

Deluxe Models, all blue or chrome engraved with simulated pearl grips, add $20.

MODEL G-IIIA—same as IIIA, except gold engraved, simulated pearl grips.

	$1,515	$880	$825	$660	$550	$440	$330

MODEL VIII—.38 Super, 9 shot, 5 in. barrel, fixed sights, wood grips, made 1952-discontinued.

	$305	$255	$220	$195	$180	$165	$140

MODEL IXA—same as model VIII, except .45 ACP.

	$305	$255	$220	$195	$180	$165	$140

MODEL XI—same as model IXA, except 9mm.

	$305	$255	$220	$195	$180	$165	$140

MODELS C-VIII, C-IXA, C-XI—same as VIII, except satin chrome.

	$360	$315	$285	$260	$220	$195	$165

MODELS CE-VIII, CE-IXA, CE-XI

	$385	$330	$310	$285	$265	$220	$195

MODELS BE-VIII, BE-IXA, BE-XI—same as model CE, except blue, engraving.

	$365	$320	$295	$275	$250	$210	$180

Deluxe Models, same as above, except simulated pearl grips - add $20.

OMNI—.45 ACP or 9mm, double action, all steel construction, 2 sear bars, 3 safeties, 4¼ in. barrel, 7 round mag. in .45 cal., 13 round mag. in 9mm, blue finish. Importation discontinued in 1986.

9mm Caliber

	$440	$380	$330	$295	$260	$225	$200

Last Mfg.'s Sug. Retail was $546.

.45 ACP Caliber

	$395	$360	$320	$285	$250	$220	$195

Last Mfg.'s Sug. Retail was $500.

SMALL FRAME MODEL—.22 LR, .32 ACP, or .380 ACP cal., Colt 1911 A1 design, semi-auto, single action, 3¹¹⁄₁₆ in. barrel, 23 oz., 7 round mag. Also available in satin chrome, optional engraving patterns.

Mfg.'s Sug. Retail	$315	$245	$195	$155	$130	$120	$110	$100

Add $75 for chrome finish.

COMPACT FRAME MODEL—9mm or .45 ACP cal., scaled down variation of the Large Frame Model, 4¼ in. barrel, 7 or 9 shot mag., 34 or 37 oz. New in 1986.

Mfg.'s Sug. Retail	$365	$270	$230	$190	$170	$160	$155	$150

LARGE FRAME MODEL—9mm (disc.), .38 Super (new in 1988), or .45 ACP cal., similar to small-frame model, 5⅛ in. barrel, 36 oz., 9 round mag. in 9mm, 7 round mag. in .45 ACP. Engraved and deluxe models available also.

Mfg.'s Sug. Retail	$365	$270	$230	$190	$170	$160	$155	$150

Add $120 for satin chrome finish (.45 ACP only).

MODEL 82—9mm Para., double action, 4¼ in. barrel, blue finish, 3-dot sighting system, 15 shot mag., ambidextrous safety, loaded chamber indicator, black polymer grips, 39 oz. New in 1988.

Mfg.'s Sug. Retail	$975	$860	$675	$550	$495	$450	$395	$365

MODEL 87 COMPETITION—9mm Para., competition variation of the Model 82, includes built in ported compensator, oversize magazine and safety release, fixed barrel bushing, bevelled rapid load magazine well, 14 shot mag., extended and serrated trigger guard, and adj. trigger. New in 1989.

Mfg.'s Sug. Retail	$1,450	$1,300	$995	$850	$750	$650	$575	$500

Grading	100%	98%	95%	90%	80%	70%	60%

REVOLVERS

MARTIAL DOUBLE ACTION REVOLVER—.22 LR, .38 Spl., 6 shot, 4 and 6 in. barrels, target sights, blue, checkered wood grips, made 1969-1976.

	100%	98%	95%	90%	80%	70%	60%
	$220	$200	$180	$165	$140	$120	$100

DELUXE MARTIAL—same as Martial, except finish as follows:

	100%	98%	95%	90%	80%	70%	60%
Satin chrome	$275	$250	$220	$195	$165	$140	$120
Chrome, engraved	$305	$275	$250	$220	$195	$165	$140
Blue, engraved	$290	$265	$235	$210	$180	$155	$120
Gold, engraved	$1,430	$880	$770	$660	$550	$495	$415

COMANCHE I—same as Martial .22, double action, made 1977-1982.

	100%	98%	95%	90%	80%	70%	60%
	$255	$220	$195	$165	$155	$140	$110

COMANCHE II—same as Martial .38, double action, made 1977-1982 and 1986 in .22 LR and .22 Mag. only.

	100%	98%	95%	90%	80%	70%	60%
	$240	$220	$195	$165	$155	$140	$110

Last Mfg.'s Sug. Retail was $272.

COMANCHE III—.22 LR (discontinued) or .357 Mag., double action, 6 shot, 4, 6, and 8½ (discontinued in 1986) in. barrel, blue, adj. sights, checkered walnut grips, made 1975-present. Before 1977, it was called "Comanche".

	100%	98%	95%	90%	80%	70%	60%
Mfg.'s Sug. Retail	$325	$270	$240	$200	$165	$155	$140	$130

Satin Chrome Finish

	100%	98%	95%	90%	80%	70%	60%
Mfg.'s Sug. Retail	$380	$320	$265	$230	$205	$185	$170	$160

Gold Finish (disc.)

	100%	98%	95%	90%	80%	70%	60%
	$1,100	$880	$825	$660	$550	$440	$330

SUPER COMANCHE IV—.44 Mag., double action, 6 or 8½ in. vent rib barrel, adj. sights, blue only.

	100%	98%	95%	90%	80%	70%	60%
Mfg.'s Sug. Retail	$420	$340	$280	$235	$220	$205	$185	$175

SUPER COMANCHE V—.357 Mag., double action, 6 shot, 4, 6, or 8½ in. vent rib barrel, adj. sights, blue only. Importation disc. in 1988.

	100%	98%	95%	90%	80%	70%	60%
	$335	$275	$230	$210	$200	$190	$180

Last Mfg.'s Sug. Retail was $414.

LORCIN ENGINEERING CO., INC.

MANUFACTURED IN RIVERSIDE, CA.

L-25 MODEL—.25 ACP, semi-auto single action, 7 shot mag., anatomically designed grips to fit hand better, choice of black and gold, chrome and pearl, satin chrome and pearl, or black and pearl finish, 13.5 oz. New in 1989.

	100%	98%	95%	90%	80%	70%	60%
Mfg.'s Sug. Retail	$80	$70	$60	$50	$45	$40	$35	$35

LUGERS WITH VARIATIONS

Note: The Luger section in this book is arranged chronologically by year of manufacture (1900 models to Post-War production), under individual manufacturer headings.

Often times, year of production can be hard to nail down, especially on commercial models. An easier way to initially identify your Luger is to categorize by toggle marking first - then by chamber marking within groups (chronologically for dated chambers). Once you know period of manufacture, simply refer to the appropriate subheading in this section. While some rare variations will be excluded in this generalized overview, it will be very helpful to establish correct, basic knowledge about your particular Luger.

In 1984, Federal legislation once again allowed importation of non-domestic WWI and WWII military handguns. As a result, many military Lugers (including DWM and Mauser variations) plus a few commercial models have been recently seen at gun shows in some quantity. Condition on most of these recent imports is 50% or lower (with pitting on some) and prices typically start in the $200 range. While many of these newer imports would make workable shooters, they have in no way lowered prices on 90% + condition specimens due to normal collector activity in top quality only pistols. Recently imported Lugers should have the importer's name visibly stamped on an exterior surface. Most of these imports are in the 9mm - 4 in. barrel configuration.

More and more importation of Lugers has resulted in prices for less than 90% condition variations to drop in the last 12 months. Many Swiss models have surfaced recently and while most appear to be in mint condition, they have been refinished. Every year more and more reblued, restrawed, regripped, reframed, rebarrelled Lugers are sold to unknowing military handgun collectors as rare variations. On any expensive contract variation, careful inspection on all parts must be made before potentially purchasing. If in doubt, secure 2 or 3 additional appraisals/observations from qualified individuals. Lugers are a field in themselves and an experienced Winchester dealer would not be qualified to guestimate the originality of these German handguns.

A FINAL NOTE ON LUGERS: ORIGINAL PISTOLS IN 98%-100% CONDITION HAVE NOT BEEN AFFECTED BY THE INFLUX OF RECENT IMPORTS AS THESE NEWLY IMPORTED GUNS ARE USUALLY IN 80% AND LOWER CONDITION OR HAVE BEEN REBLUED. TOP QUALITY LUGERS ARE STILL VERY MUCH IN DEMAND AND SOME DEALERS ARE REPORTING THAT MINT SPECIMENS ARE NOT AS FREQUENTLY ENCOUNTERED AS IN THE PAST. BECAUSE OF THIS, PRISTINE EXAMPLES COULD EVEN EXCEED VALUES LISTED BELOW.

REFERENCE GUIDE BY TOGGLE MARKING
DWM TOGGLE IDENTIFICATION

DWM MODELS—produced from 1900 to 1930 in Berlin, Germany.

    1900 Models—grip safety and "Dished" Toggles, ser. no.'s 1-24,999.

    1906 Models—grip safety, many chamber markings, ser. no.'s 25,000-74,000.

    1908 Commercial Models—no grip safety, 9mm, ser. no.'s 39,000-74,000.

    1908 Military Models—no stock lug.

    1914 Military Models—stock lug, dated 1913-1918.

    1920 Commercial Models—no grip safety, usually 3⅞ in. barrel. Most common Luger, undated chamber, 7.65 mm or 9mm.

Note: Lugers with 4 inch barrels are most frequently encountered in military and commercial models. 6 in. barrels usually denote "Navy" models. 8 in. barrels usually denote "Artillery" models. Guns with barrels over 8 inches are rare and should be checked carefully for originality.

DWM COMMERCIAL LUGERS

DWM MEANS DEUTSCHE WAFFEN & MUNITIONS FABRIKEN

These are models manufactured from 1900-1923 found in the five digit serial range.

MODEL 1900—Serial range 1-20,000. Configuration: 4¾ in. x .30 Commercial, American Eagle, Swiss.

MODEL 1900—Serial range 20,001-21,000. Configuration: 4¾ in. x .30 Bulgarian.

MODEL 1902—Serial range 21,001-25,000. Configuration: 9 mm x 4 in. "fat barrels" and 11¾ in. x .30 Carbine models, intermixed with 4¾ x .30 American Eagles and Commercials.

LUGERS WITH VARIATIONS, cont.

Grading	100%	98%	95%	90%	80%	70%	60%

MODEL 1906—Serial range 25,001-39,000. Configuration: Commercial American Eagle, Navy Commercial and Swiss, both 4¾ in. x .30 and 9 mm x 4 in. grip safety models.

MODEL 1908—Serial range 39,001-71,000. Configuration: First 9 mm x 4 in. without grip safety, M1908 Commercials were interspersed with .30 and 9 mm Eagles, Commercials, Navy Commercials, and a few Carbines and Swiss.

MODEL 1914—Serial range 71,001-74,000. Configuration: Last pre-WWI Commercial Lugers, made with stock lug, with a few 9mm Commercials mixed in.

MODEL 1923—Serial range 74,001-89,000. Configuration: Post-WWI Commercials, mostly 3⅞ in. x .30 cal.

MODEL 1923—Serial range 89,001-91,000. Configuration: The last thousand or so made have "safe" on lever and "loaded" on the extractor, 3⅞ in. x .30 barrels.

ERFURT TOGGLE IDENTIFICATION

ERFURT MODELS—Produced from 1911-1918 in Erfurt, Germany. Military Model - Chamber dated 1911-1918. Erfurt models exhibit the most proof marks and individual parts numbering. Walnut grips.

SIMSON & CO. TOGGLE IDENTIFICATION

SIMSON & CO.—Manufactured 1922 to 1932 in Suhl, Germany. Most Simson Lugers are military models (9mm - 4 in. barrels). During this 10 year period, Simson supplied the German Army Lugers exclusively. Can be dated 1925-1928. Many reworks of WWI DWM Military Lugers were refurbished by Simson, and can be detected by the Simson "Eagle-over-6" proof on repaired parts. A very few Simsons made in 1934 have just an "S" on the toggle (very rare).

SWISS TOGGLE IDENTIFICATION

SWISS BERN MODELS—Manufactured 1924 to 1929 by WAFFENFABRIK Bern, Switzerland. Relatively rare - these Swiss models have "improved" changes (flat and curved front grip strap), 4¾ in. barrels, walnut or plastic grips, grip safety. 1929 model has Geneva Cross in shield on front link.

LUGERS WITH VARIATIONS, cont.

MAUSER TOGGLE IDENTIFICATION

MAUSER VARIATIONS—Manufactured 1934-1942 in Obendorf, Germany. Between 1930 and 1934 Mauser Werke was primarily engaged in reworking older Lugers, since transfer of machinery and personnel to the DWM plant in Berlin was completed in 1931. Mauser "Banner" models were made from 1934 to 1942, many are dated from 1939-1942 on the chamber. S/42 models are MOSTLY MILITARY contract guns manufactured between 1934 and 1940, usually chamber marked. "42" toggle marked guns (Mauser code) were made in 1939 and 1940 and are dated. "byf" marked toggles indicate guns made for german military use after 1940 and are more common than other military models. The Mauser Werke trademark also appears on those Lugers made in the 1970's.

KRIEGHOFF TOGGLE IDENTIFICATION

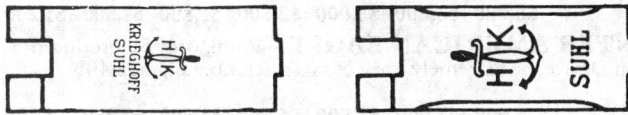

KRIEGHOFF MODELS—Manufactured between 1934-1946 in Suhl, Germany. Early Krieghoffs are side frame inscribed. The German Luftwaffe contracted Kreighoff for military guns in 1935. Early military Krieghoffs have "S" marked chambers, most are chamber dated between 1936 and 1945. Krieghoff Lugers are prized for their quality fit and finish and command higher prices because of their rarity factor.

VICKERS TOGGLE IDENTIFICATION

VICKERS—Manufactured by Vickers, Ltd. between 1915-1917 in England from DWM parts for military contract sale to the Netherlands. Added barrel date is a date of arsenal refinish or refurbishing. Distinguishable by Vickers toggle and "rust" marked safety. Serial range is 1-10,100. Grips can be finely checkered with shallow contour or very coarsely checkered. Configuration is 9mm, 4 in. barrel, and grip safety.

PRE-1900 AND 1900 DWM MANUFACTURED LUGERS

1898/99 BORCHARDT LUGER TRANSITIONAL—7.65mm, 5 in. barrel, this is perhaps one of the most desirable Lugers, only 10 were produced.

	100%	98%	95%	90%	80%	70%	60%
	$20,000	$14,000	$10,000	$7,500	$7,000	$6,000	$5,000

1899/1900 SWISS TEST MODEL—7.65mm, 4¾ in. barrel, 100 or less produced, the very first true luger. Engraved "Swiss Cross" chamber marking.

	100%	98%	95%	90%	80%	70%	60%
	$15,000	$10,000	$7,500	$6,800	$6,500	$6,000	$5,000

This variation is serial numbered in the 1-50 range approximately.

1900 COMMERCIAL DWM—7.65mm, 4¾ in. barrel, 5,500 produced.

	100%	98%	95%	90%	80%	70%	60%
	$2,850	$2,000	$1,400	$1,000	$750	$600	$500

Grading	100%	98%	95%	90%	80%	70%	60%

1900 SWISS COMMERCIAL DWM—7.65mm, 4¾ in. barrel, 2,000 commercially produced and 3000 military produced. Add 15% for wide trigger (only in ser. no. range 4000).

	$2,850	$2,000	$1,200	$1,000	$800	$600	$500

1900 AMERICAN EAGLE DWM—7.65mm, 4¾ in. barrel, approximately 12,000 produced. Add 30% for U.S. Test Model (approx. ser. no. range 6200-7400).

	$2,500	$2,000	$1,500	$1,000	$700	$600	$500

1900 BULGARIAN DWM—7.65mm, 4¾ in. barrel, 1,000 produced, very rare in U.S., most often seen in the 60% and lower condition, deduct 30% if rebarreled.

	$8,500	$5,500	$4,500	$3,500	$2,700	$2,200	$1,800

LUGERS: 1902-DWM MANUFACTURE

1902 COMMERCIAL—9mm, 4 in. barrel, serial number range 22,300-22,400 and 22,900-23,500 (500-600 produced). Commonly called "Fat Barrel" model.

	$5,500	$4,000	$3,400	$3,000	$2,700	$2,000	$1,450

1902 AMERICAN EAGLE—9mm, 4 in. barrel, 600-700 produced, commonly called the "fat barrel". Same ser. range as 1902 Commercial Model.

	$5,000	$3,500	$3,000	$2,500	$1,800	$1,500	$1,200

1902 CARTRIDGE COUNTER AMERICAN EAGLE—9mm, only 50 produced with the Powell Indication Device; be extremely wary of fakes. ser. no. range 22,401-22,450.

	$14,000	$11,000	$8,500	$6,500	$4,500	$3,850	$3,000

1902 DANZIG TEST—7.65 or 9mm, blank toggle, 4 in. barrel, Crown D proofs.

	$8,000	$4,600	$3,700	$3,000	$2,200	$1,800	$1,500

1902 CARBINE—7.65mm, 11¾ in. barrel, approximately 2500 produced.

Gun w/matching stock	$10,000	$7,500	$6,500	$5,000	$3,500	$3,000	$2,000
Gun only	$6,000	$4,500	$4,000	$3,200	$2,700	$2,200	$1,800

1902/06 TRANSITIONAL CARBINE—11¾ in. barrel, 50-100 produced, may have new model frame. Ser. #'s start at 50,000, deduct 20% if no matching stock.

	$12,000	$7,500	$5,500	$4,500	$4,200	$4,000	$3,800

1903 COMMERCIAL—7.65mm, 4 in. barrel, 50 produced, extractor marked "charge". Ser. No. Range (25,000-25,050).

	$10,000	$6,500	$6,000	$5,500	$5,000	$3,000	$2,500

LUGERS: 1904-DWM MANUFACTURE

1904 NAVY DWM—9mm, 6 in. barrel, 1200-1500 produced, a Transitional Navy.

	$15,000	$11,000	$8,000	$6,000	$4,600	$3,800	$3,200

LUGERS: 1906-DWM MANUFACTURE

1906 COMMERCIAL—7.65mm, 4¾ in. barrel, "Geischert" marked safety, long frame, approximately 750 produced.

	$2,400	$1,700	$1,300	$1,100	$900	$750	$600

1906 COMMERCIAL—9mm, 4 in. barrel, 3500-4000 produced. Scarcer than 7.65mm.

	$2,000	$1,800	$1,400	$1,000	$800	$650	$500

1906 COMMERCIAL—7.65mm, 4¾ in. barrel, area under safety polished bright, 5000 produced.

	$1,600	$1,350	$1,000	$800	$600	$500	$400

1906 AMERICAN EAGLE - 9MM—9mm, 4 in. barrel, American Eagle stamped in front of breech, 3000 produced.

	$2,250	$1,900	$1,500	$1,100	$700	$550	$450

Grading	100%	98%	95%	90%	80%	70%	60%

1906 AMERICAN EAGLE - 7.65MM—7.65mm, 4¾ in. barrel, 7,500-8,000 produced. Add 40% for long frame.

	100%	98%	95%	90%	80%	70%	60%
	$2,000	$1,650	$1,200	$750	$600	$475	$400

1906 NAVY COMMERCIAL—9mm, 6 in. barrel, approximately 2,500 produced. Add 50% for 7.65 cal. with 6 in. barrel.

	$3,800	$3,000	$2,400	$1,800	$1,600	$1,200	$950

1906 NAVY MILITARY—9mm, 6 in. barrel, first issue, 19,000 produced, mostly altered safety marking. Unaltered rare add 25%. ("Geischert" in lower position). Ser. no. range 1-9,000a.

	$3,000	$2,500	$2,000	$1,600	$1,200	$875	$600

1906 NAVY MILITARY—9mm, 6 in. barrel, second issue, 2,000 produced. Ser. range 9,000a-1,000b.

	$2,700	$2,200	$1,800	$1,600	$1,300	$1,075	$900

LUGERS: 1906-1918 DWM AND ERFURT MANUFACTURE

Most common variations in good supply within this section in 50% or less condition will approximate the 60% value. This reflects its value as a representative shooter rather than a higher priced collector's gun.

1906 SWISS COMMERCIAL—7.65 and 9mm, 4¾ in. barrel, less than 1,000 produced, Swiss "Cross in Sunburst," short frame.

	$2,800	$2,000	$1,750	$1,500	$1,350	$1,200	$1,100

1906 SWISS MILITARY—7.65mm, 4¾ in. barrel, long frame, Swiss Police has Cross in Shield. Either "Cross in Shield" or "Cross in Sunburst".

	$2,500	$2,000	$1,600	$1,200	$900	$800	$700

1906/23 DUTCH—9mm, 4 in. barrel, approximately 4,000 produced, often seen as arsenal rework. Deduct 30% if arsenal reblued and/or rebarreled.

	$1,850	$1,600	$1,400	$900	$750	$600	$525

1906 BRAZILIAN—7.65mm, 4¾ in. barrel, 5,000 produced, extremely rare in fine condition.

	$2,000	$1,300	$1,000	$900	$850	$700	$650

1906 BULGARIAN—7.65mm, 4¾ in. barrel, 1,500 produced, most rebarrelled to 9mm (deduct 30%).

	$4,800	$4,200	$3,500	$3,500	$2,000	$1,850	$1,450

1908 BULGARIAN—9mm, 4 in. barrel, DWM on chamber, 10,000 produced, extremely rare in mint condition.

	$2,400	$1,500	$1,000	$900	$825	$750	$675

1906 PORTUGUESE ARMY—7.65mm, 4¾ in. barrel, Manuel II crest on chamber, approximately 5000 produced.

	$1,350	$1,000	$825	$600	$525	$450	$350

1906 ROYAL PORTUGUESE NAVY—9mm, 4 in. barrel, Anchor & Crown on chamber, very rare.

	$8,000	$7,000	$6,500	$6,000	$5,000	$4,500	$4,000

1906 REPUBLIC OF PORTUGAL NAVY—Anchor R.P. on chamber, very rare.

	$8,000	$7,000	$6,500	$6,000	$5,000	$4,500	$4,000

1906 RUSSIAN—9mm, 4 in. barrel, approximately 1,000 produced, only 6 reported.

	$10,000	$8,500	$7,000	$4,300	$3,200	$2,600	$2,000

1906 VICKERS DUTCH—9mm, 4 in. barrel, approximately 10,000 assembled by Vickers Ltd. from DWM supplied parts.

	$2,250	$1,800	$1,200	$750	$650	$600	$495

1906 FRENCH COMMERCIAL—7.65mm, 4¾ in. barrel. Add 30% if cased with accessories.

	$2,400	$2,150	$1,800	$1,575	$1,400	$1,200	$995

Grading	100%	98%	95%	90%	80%	70%	60%

1908 COMMERCIAL AND MILITARY—DWM, 9mm, 4 in. barrel, Test/Acceptance Model, approximately 500 produced. Ser. # range 69,000-71,200.

	$1,200	$1,000	$800	$700	$575	$475	$400

1908 NAVY COMMERCIAL—9mm, 6 in. barrel. Add 50% for 7.65mm with 6 in. barrel.

	$4,200	$3,500	$2,700	$2,200	$1,800	$1,500	$1,300

1908 DWM MILITARY—9mm, 4 in. barrel, approximately 20,000 produced. Each year, undated 1st issue or dated 1910-1913. No stock lug. Add 20% for undated or for 1913 date w/stock lug.

	$1,000	$700	$600	$450	$400	$350	$300

1908 DWM COMMERCIAL—9mm, 4 in. barrel, no stock lug or hold open, blank chamber.

	$1,000	$800	$600	$450	$400	$350	$300

1911-1913 DATED 1908 ERFURT MILITARY—9mm, 4 in. barrel (dated 1911-1913). No stock lug. Add 20% for 1913 w/stock lug.

	$1,000	$700	$595	$350	$250	$220	$195

WWI ERFURT MILITARY SERIAL RANGES

CHAMBER DATE	OBSERVED LOW SERIAL	OBSERVED HIGH SERIAL	APPROXIMATE QTY. MADE
1910	non observed		
1911	2545	9548	10,000
1912	255	866b	22,000
1913	575	303b	22,000
1914	2137	3029	5,000
1915	non observed		
1916	733	5764g	*80,000
1917	579	9592k	*120,000
1918	304	9018r	*180,000

These quantities are unrealistically high. Serial numbers were probably used in scattered blocks. We estimate 30,000 Lugers maximum for each year 1916-1918.

Production data appears courtesy of the late Bernard A. Lafferty.

1908 NAVY—9mm, 6 in. barrel, scarce. Ser. # range 1,000b-10,000b, 9,000 manufactured.

	$2,700	$2,200	$1,700	$1,300	$1,100	$950	$800

1908 BOLIVIAN CONTRACT—9mm, 4 in. barrel.

	$3,600	$3,000	$2,500	$1,700	$1,300	$1,100	$900

1913 COMMERCIAL DWM—9mm, 4 in. barrel, grip safety and stock lug, horizontal "N" proof mark, 71,000 ser. range, rare.

	$1,800	$1,420	$1,250	$1,050	$900	$780	$700

1914 COMMERCIAL DWM—9mm, 4 in. barrel, undated, stock lug, horizontal crown-N proofed.

	$1,400	$1,000	$800	$550	$450	$400	$350

1914 NAVY—9mm, 6 in. barrel, scarce. Dated 1916 and 1917.

	$2,500	$2,000	$1,500	$1,250	$1,050	$950	$800

1914-1918 DATED ERFURT MILITARY—9mm, 4 in. barrel. Dated 1914-1918.

	$850	$650	$450	$300	$250	$225	$195

Add 20% for 1914 date.
Add $75 for original holster in average + condition.
Add 10% for matching mag.
Add 25% for 2 matching mag.'s.

Note: Date stamped on top frame is date of production; thus dates could be 1914, 1915, 1916, 1917, or 1918. All are Military P.08's, however.

Grading	100%	98%	95%	90%	80%	70%	60%

1914 ERFURT ARTILLERY—9mm, 1914 date is only one seen, 8 in. barrel.

	$1,650	$1,350	$1,150	$850	$600	$500	$375

1913-1918 DATED WWI DWM MILITARY—9mm, 4 in. barrel. 1913-1918 dated.
Most frequently encountered WWI military Luger, stock lug.

	$1,000	$700	$530	$300	$250	$225	$200

Add $75 for original holster in average + condition.
Add 10% for matching mag.
Add 25% for 2 matching mag.'s.

Note: Date stamped on top frame is date of production; thus dates could be 1914, 1915, 1916, 1917, or 1918. All are Military P.08's, however.

WWI DWM MILITARY SERIAL RANGES

DWM MILITARY LUGER SERIAL RANGES

CHAMBER DATE	OBSERVED LOW SERIAL	OBSERVED HIGH SERIAL	APPROXIMATE QTY. MADE
1908 (Undated)	3483	2636b	22,500
1910	2487b	5266d	14,500
1911	155e	6747e	13,000
1912	599	8050	10,000
1913	892	1028b	22,000
1914	4003	920c	32,000
1915	3528	9410i	100,000
1916	2448	6057k	120,000
1917	1058	73681	130,000
1918	3838	3548m	135,000

Production data appears courtesy of the late Bernard A. Lafferty.

1914-1918 DATED DWM ARTILLERY—9mm, 8 in. barrel. Dated 1914-1918. 1914 rare - add 40%. Correct matching stock - add $275, original leather holster and shoulder strap - add $200.

	$1,600	$1,300	$1,000	$800	$600	$500	$400

LUGERS: 1920-1930 DWM

Most common variations in good supply within this section in 50% or less condition will approximate the 60% value. This reflects its value as a representative shooter rather than a higher priced collector's gun.

1920 DWM OR ERFURT—9mm, 4 in. barrel, military and police, reworked and issued to police units, many thousand reworked, double date also, 1920 and 1921 dated.

	$850	$700	$540	$300	$250	$225	$200

1920 COMMERCIAL—7.65mm, 3⅞-4 in. barrel, many thousand produced. Add 20%-50% for "long barrel" variations.

	$650	$450	$350	$250	$200	$175	$150

1920 NAVY COMMERCIAL—9mm, 6 in. barrel, very rare rework, Navy rear sight. Add 20% for 7.65mm with 6 in. barrel.

	$2,000	$1,550	$1,250	$1,000	$900	$800	$700

1920 COMMERCIAL ARTILLERY—9mm, 8 in. barrel, very rare rework.

	$1,500	$1,250	$950	$800	$600	$500	$400

While this variation is undoubtedly rarer than the 1914-1918 military Artillery models, it is less desireable.

Grading	100%	98%	95%	90%	80%	70%	60%

1920 "LONG BARREL" COMMERCIAL—7.65mm or 9mm, 10-20 in. barrel, extremely rare.

	$1,850	$1,400	$1,100	$1,000	$750	$655	$600

1920 NAVY CARBINE—7.65mm, 11¾ in. barrel, long frame (if short frame, be wary of fakes, very few produced). Navy rear sight, no forearm under barrel.

	$2,500	$2,000	$1,600	$1,100	$1,025	$950	$850

1920 CARBINE—7.65mm, 11¾ in. barrel, very rare.

Gun only	$5,000	$4,500	$4,000	$3,000	$2,500	$2,000	$1,750
Gun with stock	$7,500	$6,000	$5,000	$4,000	$3,400	$2,900	$2,500

1920 SWISS REWORK—7.65mm 3⅝-6 in. barrel, several hundred produced.

	$1,650	$1,400	$1,100	$1,000	$750	$655	$600

ABERCROMBIE & FITCH COMMERCIAL—7.65mm or 9mm, long frame, 4¾ in. barrel, 100 produced, total for both cal.'s. A few 6 in. barrels - add 30%.

	$4,800	$4,000	$3,500	$3,000	$2,500	$2,100	$1,850

1920/21-DWM—9mm, 4 in. barrel. Deduct 20% if arsenal reworked.

	$850	$700	$600	$450	$400	$350	$300

1920/23 STOEGER EAGLE—7.65mm or 9mm, 3⅝-24 in. barrels, less than 1000 produced, made by DWM for Stoeger, sold in USA, longer barrel models have higher value, also produced by Mauser - 50% more valuable.

3⅞ - 6 in. barrels	$2,400	$1,750	$1,450	$1,200	$1,050	$950	$825
8 in. barrel							
	$3,000	$2,675	$2,300	$2,000	$1,650	$1,200	$995

1923 DWM COMMERCIAL—7.65mm, 3⅝ in. barrel, 14,000 produced. (Ser No. Range 74,000-89,000).

	$750	$650	$465	$300	$250	$225	$200

1923 DWM "SAFE AND LOADED" COMMERCIAL—"safe and loaded" marked on frame and ejector, 7.65mm, 3⅞ in. barrel, safety and extractor marked in English, 2000 produced. (Ser. No. Range 89,000-91,000).

	$1,250	$1,000	$850	$600	$500	$420	$350

1923 FINNISH LUGER—7.65mm, approx. 5,000-7,000 units made for Finnish military contract (Army and Navy), marked "SA" surrounded by a rectangle, most have been recently imported into the U.S.

	$650	$550	$465	$375	$325	$295	$260

LUGERS: KRIEGHOFF

1923 DWM/KRIEGHOFF COMMERCIAL—7.65mm x 3⅞ in. or 9mm x 4 in. barrels, few made, reworked by Krieghoff, chamber dated 1921 or unmarked, most in "in" range, Krieghoff stamped on back-frame. Be wary of fakes.

	$1,800	$1,375	$1,210	$1,100	$880	$770	$660

DWM/KRIEGHOFF COMMERCIAL—7.65mm or 9mm, 4 in. barrel, a few hundred made, side frame marked Krieghoff. Be wary of fakes.

	$2,800	$2,400	$2,000	$1,650	$1,300	$1,000	$800

KRIEGHOFF COMMERCIAL SIDE FRAME—7.65mm or 9mm, 4 or 6 in. barrel, 1500 produced, 1000 with side frame marked, and 500 without. "P" prefix ser. no.'s. Add 30% for side frame marked 7.65mm.

	$3,200	$2,400	$2,000	$1,650	$1,300	$1,000	$800

KRIEGHOFF S CODE EARLY—9mm, 4 in. barrel, 1800 produced, German Luftwaffe. Has fat walnut grips, "H-K Suhl" toggle.

	$2,400	$1,700	$1,450	$1,200	$995	$895	$775

KRIEGHOFF S CODE MID SERIES—9mm, 4 in. barrel, 500-700 produced, Luftwaffe, ser. no. range 1600-2500, fine-checkered plastic grips.

	$2,800	$1,975	$1,775	$1,200	$995	$800	$700

Grading	100%	98%	95%	90%	80%	70%	60%

KRIEGHOFF S CODE LATE—9mm, 4 in. barrel, 1800 produced, Luftwaffe, ser. no. range 2300-4200.

	$2,000	$1,550	$1,225	$950	$750	$600	$500

KRIEGHOFF 36 DATE—9mm, 4 in. barrel, 500-700 made, Luftwaffe military, 2 digit date, coarse checkered plastic grips.

	$2,800	$2,400	$2,000	$1,650	$1,300	$1,000	$800

KRIEGHOFF 1936-1945 DATED—9mm, 4 in. barrel, approx. 9,000 produced, 4 digit chamber date, 1936, 1937 and 1940 most common; 1938 and 1941 through 1945 dates command 70-200% premiums. 1945 is extremely rare - add 500%.

	$2,250	$1,975	$1,825	$1,550	$1,320	$1,225	$1,100

POST-WAR KRIEGHOFF TYPE I—9mm, 4 in. barrel, 150 produced for occupation forces, H-K marked toggle link.

	$1,700	$1,500	$1,300	$1,200	$1,100	$995	$875

POST-WAR KRIEGHOFF TYPE II—9mm, 4 in. barrel, 150 produced, unmarked toggle link, many parts proofed "Eagle-over-2".

	$1,450	$1,200	$1,100	$1,000	$900	$800	$775

POST-WAR KRIEGHOFF COMMERCIAL—7.65mm, 4 in. barrel, 100-200 produced, unmarked toggle, many parts proofed "Eagle-over-2".

	$1,450	$1,200	$1,100	$1,000	$900	$800	$775

LUGERS: MAUSER

Most common variations in good supply within this section in 50% or less condition will approximate the 60% value. This reflects its value as a representative shooter rather than a higher priced collector's gun.

1935/06 PORTUGUESE GNR—7.65mm, 4¾ in. barrel, 564 produced, GNR on chamber, Portuguese marked safety and extractor.

	$2,200	$1,500	$1,200	$900	$700	$650	$425

1934/06 MAUSER SWISS COMMERCIAL—7.65mm, 4¾ in. barrel, a few hundred produced, cross in sunburst or blank chamber, grip safety.

	$4,200	$2,800	$2,400	$2,000	$1,500	$1,250	$850

1934 MAUSER BANNER COMMERCIAL—7.65mm or 9mm, 4 in. barrel, hundreds produced, unmarked chamber, "v" suffix to ser. no. Add 15% for "Kal. 7.65" barrel marked.

	$2,800	$1,800	$1,600	$1,400	$1,150	$950	$725

S/42 K DATE—manufactured in 1934 only, 9mm, 4 in. barrel, approx. 10,000 produced, military. Add 50% for "large eagle over M Navy" proofed.

	$3,000	$1,850	$1,400	$900	$800	$700	$550

S/42 G DATE—manufactured in 1935 only, 9mm, 4 in. barrel, many thousand produced. Add 20% for Navy markings.

	$1,200	$700	$595	$500	$450	$400	$375

S/42 DATED CHAMBER—9mm, 4 in. barrel, many thousands produced, "S/42" stamped rear toggle, chamber dated 1936-1940. One of the most frequently encountered WWII military Lugers.

	$850	$700	$595	$450	$395	$360	$330

Add $75 for original holster in average + condition.
Add 10% for matching mag.
Add 25% for 2 matching mag.'s.
Add 20% for Navy markings.

Grading	100%	98%	95%	90%	80%	70%	60%

WWII MAUSER MILITARY SERIAL RANGES

TOGGLE CODE	CHAMBER DATA	SERIAL RANGES OBSERVED LOW #	OBSERVED HIGH #	APPROXIMATE QTY. MADE
S/42	K(1934)	179	622a	11,000
S/42	G(1935)	1788a	4459f	56,000
S/42	1936	8977f	901p	98,000
S/42	1937	7764p	9503a	119,000
S/42	1938	1204b	3051a	124,000
S/42	1939	5937n	5023r	38,000
42	1939	300r	1595z	86,000
42	1940	5355	6668n	137,000
42	1941	3707n	3773o	10,000
byf	1941	8395o	9975	122,000
byf	1942	597	2197n	130,000

Production data appears courtesy of the late Bernard A. Lafferty.

MAUSER PERSIAN CONTRACT—9mm, 4 and 8 in. barrels, 1,000 — 8 in. produced, and 1,000 — 4 in. produced, Farsi numerals.

	100%	98%	95%	90%	80%	70%	60%
4 in. barrel	$6,500	$5,350	$4,200	$3,750	$3,300	$2,950	$2,500
Artillery (8 in.)	$2,850	$2,400	$2,000	$1,800	$1,650	$1,475	$1,200

1936-1942 DATED MAUSER BANNER—9mm, 4 in. barrel, over 1,000 produced, commercial and contract sales. No sear safety, often have strawed small parts.

$1,800	$1,350	$1,050	$800	$700	$600	$500

MAUSER BANNER DUTCH CONTRACT—9mm, 4 in. barrel, 1,000 produced, safety marked "Rust". Dated 1936-1940. 10% premium on 1936-1838 dates.

$1,695	$1,300	$750	$695	$600	$500	$400

MAUSER BANNER SWEDISH CONTRACT—275 produced in 9mm, 4¾ in. barrels, dated 1938, 25 produced in 9mm, dated 1939, and 30 produced in 7.65mm, dated 1939. Add 15% for 7.65mm.

$2,000	$1,750	$1,300	$750	$695	$600	$500

CODE "S/42" COMMERCIAL CONTRACT—9mm, 4 in. barrel, a few hundred produced, dated 1938. Commercial proof marks only.

$1,600	$1,200	$975	$750	$650	$550	$500

CODE "42"—9mm, 4 in. barrels, dated 1939-1940, rear toggle marked "42". One of the most frequently encountered WWII military Lugers. Add 40% for Navy markings.

$900	$650	$495	$375	$325	$275	$250

Add $75 for original holster in average + condition.

MAUSER BANNER POLICE—approx. 30 thousand produced, dated 1939-1942, police contract, have sear safeties, blued small parts. A few observed dated 1938 — add 30%.

$1,400	$1,100	$875	$600	$500	$400	$350

CODE "41-42"—9mm, 4 in. barrel, 2-digit date, 20,000 produced, "41" dated chamber, "42" code, most 42 dates are reworks.

$1,000	$675	$425	$350	$300	$265	$240

Add $75 for original holster in average + condition.

LUGERS: MAUSER, cont.

Grading	100%	98%	95%	90%	80%	70%	60%

CODE "byf"—9mm, 4 in. barrel, thousands made, chamber dated 41 and 42. Rear toggle is stamped "byf", standard magazine was "fxo" marked and had an un-numbered plastic bottom. One of the most frequently encountered WWII military Lugers.

	$800	$650	$495	$300	$275	$250	$225

Add 10% for original black bakelite grips.

Add $75 for original holster in average + condition.

Code "byf" Lugers with black bakelite grips are referred to as the "Black Widow" variation.

AUSTRIAN BUNDES HEER—9mm, 4 in. barrel, several hundred produced, Austrian Federal Army, no serial letter suffix-same ser. placement as KU. Rarely encountered in mint condition.

	$1,600	$1,400	$1,000	$950	$825	$750	$650

MAUSER 1934 CODE BYF, S/42 AND 42 KU—3,500 manufactured. Post-1942 Luftwaffe subcontract.

	$1,800	$1,500	$1,150	$950	$825	$750	$650

LUGER: REWORKS

DEATH'S HEAD REWORK—9mm, 4 in. barrel, very rare, SS unit marked. Watch for fakes.

	$1,000	$800	$700	$600	$500	$450	$400

SIMSON REWORK—9mm, 4 in. barrel, DWM toggles, Simpson Eagle proofs on reworked parts.

	$775	$650	$550	$450	$375	$325	$295

DOUBLE DATED DWM/ERFERT—9mm, 4 in. barrel, very scarce. 1920 over 1910-1918 chamber dates. Often with sear safety and mag. safety remnant. Add 30% for intact mag. safety.

	$650	$550	$420	$300	$275	$250	$225

KADETTEN INST. REWORK—9mm, 4 in. barrel, a few hundred marked KI 1933.

	$1,000	$800	$650	$550	$475	$400	$350

LUGERS: SIMSON

SIMSON & COMPANY—7.65mm or 9mm, 3⅞ or 4 in. barrel, military and limited commercial sales, many thousands produced, but rarely found.

	$1,400	$950	$750	$650	$500	$450	$375

SIMSON GRIP SAFETY—9mm, 3⅞ in. barrel, very rare, production unknown. Be wary of fakes.

	$2,450	$1,800	$1,600	$1,200	$975	$675	$475

SIMSON MILITARY DATED—9mm, 4 in. barrel, 2,000 produced, dated 1925-1928.

	$2,250	$1,750	$1,200	$1,000	$800	$675	$550

This model is most commonly encountered with a 1925 chamber date.

SIMSON S CODE—9mm, 4 in. barrel, less than 1,000 produced. Rare.

	$2,800	$1,600	$1,200	$975	$675	$550	$475

LUGERS: SWISS BERN

1906 BERN—7.65mm, 4¾ in. barrel, "Waffenfabrik Bern" on toggle, Swiss military, bordered checkered walnut grips, exactly 17,874 produced.

	$2,000	$1,600	$1,400	$1,000	$800	$600	$500

1929 SWISS BERN—7.65mm, 4¾ in. barrel, 29,857 produced, many machining changes to simplify production, straight front grip strap, P prefix designates commercial model, brown or black plastic grips.

	$1,600	$1,450	$1,100	$900	$800	$600	$500

LUGERS: KDF, INTERARMS, STOEGER, & RECENT IMPORTATION

Note: These Lugers have been manufactured by Mauser Werke in Oberndorf, W. Germany in the 1970's and again recently. Earlier importation was by Interarms of Alexandria, VA (and so marked on these guns). Currently, Mauser Werke 7.65 and 9mm Lugers are available in various configurations including the Karabiner (Carbine), Cartridge Counter, and special order variations (4 in. standard barrel and Artillery).

Currently, only KDF located in Seguin, TX is importing the Mauser manufactured P.08 (on a special basis only). Prices start at $3,210 for the standard model. Engraved or limited production models typically start at approx. $7,200 and go up according to the amount of workmanship needed to complete the fabrication.

Prices below for 100% condition Lugers assume N.I.B. status. If without box and accessories, deduct 10-15%.

Prices below reflect the recent devaluation of the U.S. dollar against some foreign currencies. While the manufacturer's suggested retails have gone up considerably, prices for used specimens (98% or less original condition) have not increased proportionally, and in some cases, have changed very little.

MAUSER P.O8—imported by KDF in various configurations including engraved models. Prices start in the $3,210 range (4 in. barrel) and vary substantially depending on model, type(s) of finish, and amount of engraving.

INTERARMS MAUSER P.O8—7.65 and 9mm, 4 or 6 in. barrel, fully-contoured front grip strap.

		$750	$600	$450	$400	$375	$350	$300

INTERARMS "SWISS-STYLE" MAUSER EAGLE—9mm or 7.65mm, "straight" front grip strap, American eagle logo on top of frame. Add 10% for 6 in. barrel in 9mm.

		$600	$500	$450	$400	$375	$350	$325

STOEGER .22 CAL. LUGER—.22 LR cal., toggle action, all steel construction, 4½ in. barrel, 10 round mag. capacity, previously mfg. in the U.S. until 1985.

		$175	$150	$135	$125	$100	$85	$75

Last Mfg.'s Sug. Retail was $200.

NEW MODEL CARBINE WITH STOCK—manufacture discontinued but limited quanities are still available through Interarms.

Mfg.'s Sug. Retail		$6,500	$4,300	$3,000	$2,500

CARTRIDGE COUNTER—left grip is slotted and contains a numbered metal strip. Introduced in 1983.

Mfg.'s Sug. Retail		$3,600	$2,500	$1,900	$1,350

Manufacture has been discontinued but limited quanities are still available through Interarms.

COMMEMORATIVE BULGARIAN—100 available on U.S. market.

		$1,800	$1,600	$1,400	$1,000	$750	$600	$500

COMMEMORATIVE RUSSIAN—100 available on U.S. market.

		$1,800	$1,600	$1,400	$1,000	$750	$600	$500

Matched pair of each

		$4,000	$3,175	$1,950

MAUSER SPORT PARABELLUM—10 each, 7.65mm and 9mm, imported target barrel and adj. sights.

		$2,500	$2,000	$1,250

MAUSER SPORT PARABELLUM

Consecutive pair—7.65mm or 9mm.

		$4,250	$3,175	$1,950

LUGERS: SPECIAL INTEREST

SPANDAU LUGER—200 produced as prototype in 1918, 10 known. Controversial.

Prices vary substantially on this "variation" and are not predictable.

1945 CHAMBER DATED KREIGHOFF—100 produced, 3 known.

			$8,000	$6,000	$4,800	$3,500	$2,900	$2,400	$1,850

1900 SWISS LUGER NO. 33—pre-production, 1898-1900.

MO4/05 G.L. BABY LUGER—9 mm, 3¼ in. barrel, G.L. proofed, Georg Luger's personal hand-made weapon, one known to exist. Made by shortening barrel, mag., and grip frame with 1902 9mm fat barrel.

BABY LUGER 1925/26—Prototype, 380/32 ACP, 4 manufactured, only 1 known is .380. Only Luger documented by the manufacturer.

VONO REWORK—7.54mm or 9mm, 4 in. barrel, commercial, rework by W.P. VonNordheim, extremely rare variation.

		$1,500	$1,275	$1,050	$900	$800	$700	$600

1900 DWM CARBINE—7.65mm, 11¾ in. barrel, 100 produced, only one known to exist. Characterized by "Ski slope" sight on rear toggle.

1907 U.S. ARMY TEST TRIAL—.45 cal., at least three produced, three known to exist.

KRIEGHOFF GRIP SAFETY—9mm, 4 in. barrel, extremely rare, test trial gun.

		$3,800	$3,500	$3,000

1906/29 SWISS SPECIAL ASSEMBLY—7.65mm, 4¾ in. barrel.

		$2,200	$1,650	$1,200

1929 SWISS 9MM PROTOTYPE—4¾ in. barrel.

		$4,200	$3,000	$2,100

CONVERSIONS: JOHN MARTZ—John Martz of CA has converted P.38's and WWI or WWII Lugers into various configurations for some time. Below is a generalized listing of variations he has fabricated and their values.

.380 ACP Baby Luger—approx. 5 mfg.

		$3,000	$2,400	$1,850

9mm Baby Luger—approx. 96 mfg.

		$1,500	$1,150	$895

Luger Carbine—approx. 60 mfg.

		$4,000	$3,000	$2,100

P.38 Carbine—9mm, approx. 35 mfg.

		$3,500	$2,750	$1,995

P.38 Carbine—.45 ACP, approx. 7 mfg.

		$3,000	$2,400	$1,850

Baby P.38—9mm, shortened barrel, approx. 31 mfg.

		$1,500	$1,150	$895

.45 ACP Navy—adj. sight.

		$3,500	$2,750	$1,995

.45 ACP Navy—fixed sight, approx. 19 mfg.

		$3,000	$2,400	$1,850

LUGERS: ACCESSORIES

.22 CALIBER CONVERSION UNITS:

ERMA—(POSTWAR-GREEN CARD BOARD BOX)

		$350	$320	$295	$275	$250	$225	$200

ERMA-PREWAR IN WOODEN BOX—Pre-war in wooden box - deduct 20% for mismatched. Add 20% for Nazi Navy property numbered.

		$650	$600	$550	$550	$430	$400	$360

Grading	100%	98%	95%	90%	80%	70%	60%

DETACHABLE STOCKS:
ARTILLERY TYPE FLAT BOARD

	100%	98%	95%	90%	80%	70%	60%
	$200	$180	$160	$135	$120	$110	$100

NAVAL-TYPE FLAT BOARD

	$750	$625	$550	$500	$450	$410	$350

CARBINE CONTOURED

	$1,200	$1,000	$900	$850	$750	$700	$600

HOLLOW ARTILLERY HOLSTER TYPE—hollow wood broomhandle type-very rare (watch for fakes).

	$6,000	$5,500	$5,000	$4,500	$4,000	$3,500	$3,000

IDEAL TELESCOPING WITH GRIPS—made in U.S. by Ideal Corp.

	$1,200	$750	$675	$625	$575	$530	$500

DRUM MAGAZINE:
1ST ISSUE

	$500	$450	$400				

2ND ISSUE

	$400	$350	$300				

LOADING TOOL OR UNLOADING TOOL (2 TYPES)

	$425	$375	$350				

ARTILLERY HOLSTER RIG, COMPLETE

	$395	$325	$275				

If shoulder strap is missing — deduct 20%.

NAVAL HOLSTER RIG, COMPLETE

	$1,200	$800	$675	$600	$575	$525	$450

LUNA
GERMANY.

SINGLE SHOT

SINGLE SHOT TARGET RIFLE—falling block action, .22 LR and .22 Hornet, 20 in. barrel, adj. sights, target type stocks, pre-WWII.

	$990	$880	$800	$690	$605	$550	$495

MODEL 200 FREE PISTOL—.22 LR, 11 in. barrel, blue, target sights, checkered target grips, pre-WWII.

	$1,100	$990	$855	$770	$660	$605	$525

M

MAC (MILITARY ARMAMENT CORP.)

PLEASE REFER TO THE INGRAM SECTION IN THIS TEXT.

MBA GYROJET

PREVIOUSLY MANUFACTURED (1966-1969) IN SAN RAMON, CA.

Grading	100%	98%	95%	90%	80%	70%	60%

MARK I GYROJET PISTOL—12 or 13mm (no cartridge case), uses spin-stabilized rocket projectiles that accelerate to 1,250 FPS in .12 seconds, 2 in. (rare) or 5 in. barrel, 6-shot semi-auto action drives rocket projectile (primer activated) into fixed firing pin, smooth walnut grips, black or antique nickel finish, 13 or 16 oz. Not particularly accurate.

	100%	98%	95%	90%	80%	70%	60%
	$600	$525	$475	$425	$375	$325	$295

The rocket ammunition for this model is rare and reports of $20 + /round are not uncommon.

Mark I Presentation Model—cased with 10 dummy rounds and bronze medal honoring rocket pioneer Robert H. Goddard.

	100%	98%	95%
	$995	$800	$600

MARK I CARBINE—13mm, same action as Mark I pistol, full stock with pistol grip extension, 18 in. barrel, nickel finish, 4½ lbs. Limited manufacture.

	100%	98%	95%	90%	80%	70%	60%
	$1,300	$1,000	$850	$700	$600	$525	$450

MK ARMS INC.

MANUFACTURER AND DISTRIBUTOR LOCATED IN IRVINE, CA.

MK 760—9mm, semi-auto, assault carbine configuration, steel frame, 16 in. shrouded barrel, fires from closed bolt, 14, 24, or 36 shot mag., parkerized finish, folding metal stock, fixed sights. Manufactured in CA since 1983.

	100%	98%	95%	90%	80%	70%	60%
Mfg.'s Sug. Retail	$495	$450	$375	$340	$310	$280	$250	$225

New full-auto models are still available from Automatic Weaponry located in Brentwood, TN - retail price is $1,195. Earlier MK 760 SMG's were manufactured in AL in 1983.

MKE

MANUFACTURED IN ANKARA, TURKEY. CURRENTLY DISTRIBUTED BY MANDALL SHOOTING SUPPLIES, INC., LOCATED IN SCOTTSDALE, AZ.

KIRIKKALE DOUBLE ACTION AUTOMATIC—7.65mm (discontinued), or .380 auto, 7 shot, blue, fixed sights, checkered plastic grips, this is a close copy of Walther's PP and the Turkish Army's standard service pistol.

	100%	98%	95%	90%	80%	70%	60%
Mfg.'s Sug. Retail	$395	$365	$295	$240	$215	$185	$170	$155

M.O.A. CORPORATION

MANUFACTURED AND DISTRIBUTED IN DAYTON, OH.

Grading	100%	98%	95%	90%	80%	70%	60%

PISTOLS

MAXIMUM—available in 21 cal.'s between .22 Hornet and .44 Mag., single shot lever action pistol, falling block action, chromoly steel receiver, 8¾ (new in 1989), 10, or 14 in. barrel, transfer bar safety, adj. open sights, walnut grips and forearm. New in 1986.

Mfg.'s Sug. Retail	$499	$445	$375	$340	$310	$280	$250	$225

Add $139 per extra barrel.

Barrels must be fitted to individual receivers at the factory initially.

Add $49 for scope mount.

Carbine Model—similar to Maximum, except has 18 in. barrel. Mfg. 1986-87 only.

	$495	$430	$365	$330	$300	$275	$250

Last Mfg.'s Sug. Retail was $575.

MAGNUM RESEARCH, INC.

MANUFACTURED BY ISRAEL MILITARY INDUSTRIES. DISTRIBUTED BY MAGNUM RESEARCH, INC., IN MINNEAPOLIS, MN.

In addition to the models listed below, Magnum Research can also provide a variety of special order options through their custom shop. Prices can be obtained by contacting Magnum Research directly.

Magnum Research also offers a Collector's Edition Presentation Series. Special models include a Gold Edition (serial numbered 1-100), a Silver Edition (serial numbered 101-500), and a Bronze Edition (serial numbered 501-1,000). Each pistol from this series is supplied with a walnut presentation case, 2 sided medallion, and certificate of authenticity. Prices are available upon request by contacting Magnum Research directly.

.357 MAG. DESERT EAGLE—.357 Mag., gas operated, semi-auto pistol, 6, 10, and 14 in. barrel lengths, steel (58.3 oz.) or alloy (47.8 oz.) frame, adaptable to .44 Mag with optional kit, 9 round mag. (8 for .44 Mag.). New in 1983.

Mfg.'s Sug. Retail	$629	$565	$500	$455	$415	$380	$355	$330

Add $129 for choice of finishes.

Choice of finishes includes nickel, polished blue, or hardchrome (matte, polished, or brushed).

Add $170 for 14 in. barrel.

Add $495 for .357 Mag. to .44 Mag. conversion kit (6 in. barrel).

Add $685 for .357 Mag. to .44 Mag. conversion kit (10 or 14 in. barrel).

Stainless Steel .357 Mag.—similar to .357 Mag. Desert Eagle, except has stainless steel frame, 58.3 oz. New in 1987.

Mfg.'s Sug. Retail	$669	$600	$510	$455

Add $170 for 14 in. barrel.

.41 MAG. DESERT EAGLE—.41 Mag., similar to .357 Desert Eagle, 6 in. barrel only, 8 shot mag., steel (62.8 oz.) or alloy (52.3 oz.) frame. New in late 1988.

Mfg.'s Sug. Retail	$739	$665	$550	$500	$450	$415	$390	$365

Add $129 for choice of finishes.

Choice of finishes includes nickel, polished blue, or hardchrome (matte, polished, or brushed).

Stainless Steel .41 Mag.—similar to .41 Mag. Desert Eagle, except has stainless steel frame, 58.3 oz. New in late 1988.

Mfg.'s Sug. Retail	$779	$685	$560	$500

Grading	100%	98%	95%	90%	80%	70%	60%

.44 MAG. DESERT EAGLE—.44 Mag., similar to .357 Desert Eagle, 8 shot mag., steel (62.8 oz.) or alloy (52.3 oz.) frame. Introduced late in 1986.

Mfg.'s Sug. Retail	$749	$675	$575	$520	$465	$420	$390	$360

Add $129 for choice of finishes.

Choice of finishes includes nickel, polished blue, or hardchrome (matte, polished, or brushed).

Add $150 for 10 or 14 in. barrel.
Add $475 for .44 Mag. to .357 Mag. conversion kit (6 in. barrel).
Add $675 for .44 Mag. to .357 Mag. conversion kit (14 in. barrel only).
Add $395 for .44 Mag. to .41 Mag. conversion kit (6 in. barrel).

Stainless Steel .44 Mag.—similar to .44 Mag. Desert Eagle, except has stainless steel frame, 58.3 oz. New in 1987.

Mfg.'s Sug. Retail	$789	$695	$585	$530

Add $150 for 10 or 14 in. barrel.

HUNTER EDITION—.357 or .44 Mag., 6 in. barrel with extra 14 in. hunting barrel, includes Simmons 2X x 20 compact scope, scope mount, cherry hardwood presentation case. New in late 1987.

Mfg.'s Sug. Retail	$1,139	$1,025	$895	$785	$550	$470	$385	$330

Add $132 for .44 Mag. cal.
Add $149 for choice of finishes.

Choice of finishes includes nickel, polished blue, or hardchrome (matte, polished, or brushed).

MALIN, F.E.

MANUFACTURED IN ENGLAND. CURRENTLY SOLD ON A LIMITED BASIS BY CAPE HORN OUTFITTERS LOCATED IN CHARLOTTE, NC. PREVIOUSLY IMPORTED BY SAXON ARMS, INC. LOCATED IN CLEARWATER, FL.

Once existing supplies of F.E. Malin shotguns have been depleted, this trademark will be discontinued. Charles Boswell will take the place of F.E. Malin (please refer to the Charles Boswell section in this text).

SHOTGUNS: OVER-AND-UNDER AND SIDE-BY-SIDE

BOXLOCK—Made to individual order, choice of game scene engraving, Anson & Deeley boxlock actions, select European hybrid walnut, double triggers, leather cased, current manufacture. Prices start at $3,750 and each shotgun is priced per individual special order.

SIDELOCK—Made to individual order, choice of game scene engraving, H&H sidelock action, select European hybrid walnut, double triggers, leather cased, current manufacture. Prices start at $5,000 and each shotgun is priced per individual special order.

MANDALL SHOOTING SUPPLIES INC.

RETAILER/DISTRIBUTOR/IMPORTER LOCATED IN SCOTTSDALE, AZ.

Mandall Shooting Supplies distributes/imports various firearms including pistols, revolvers, rifles, shotguns, as well as other models. Most of these firearms can be located under their individual trademark headings and include Bretton, Britarms, Cabanas, Erma-Werke, igi Domino, Hammerli, Mandall private label shotguns, Sig, Sig-Hammerli, Valmet, Zanardini, and A. Zoli shotguns and rifles. This importer also carries a line of Spanish mfg. shotguns that are both hammer and hammerless. Values range from $350 - $550 depending on features and engraving.

MANNLICHER SCHOENAUER SPORTING RIFLES

MANUFACTURED BY STEYR, DAIMLER, PUCH, IN AUSTRIA FROM 1850's - PRESENT. PLEASE REFER TO STEYR-MANNLICHER IN THIS TEXT FOR CURRENT MANUFACTURED RIFLES.

PRE-WAR

MODEL 1903 CARBINE—bolt action, 6.5 x 53mm, 5 shot, 17.7 in. barrel, rotary mag., two leaf rear sight, double set trigger, full length stock.

	$1,050	$875	$770	$550	$470	$385	$330

MODEL 1905 CARBINE—same as 1903, except 9 x 56mm, 19.7 in. barrel.

	$1,200	$950	$825	$660	$580	$495	$415

MODEL 1908 CARBINE—same as 1905, except 7 x 57mm and 8 x 56mm.

	$1,050	$875	$770	$550	$470	$385	$330

MODEL 1910 CARBINE—same as 1905, except 9.5 x 57mm.

	$1,050	$875	$770	$550	$470	$385	$330

MODEL 1924 CARBINE—same as 1905, except .30-06.

	$1,200	$1,050	$990	$770	$715	$605	$525

HIGH VELOCITY SPORTING RIFLE—bolt action, 7 x 64 Brenneke, .30-06, 8 x 60 Mag., 9.3 x 62mm, 10.75 x 68mm, 23.6 in. barrel, 3 leaf sight, half stock.

	$1,320	$1,100	$825	$660	$580	$495	$415

Takedown Model

	$2,200	$1,980	$1,650	$1,320	$880	$715	$635

RIFLES: POST-WAR

MODEL 1950—.257 Roberts, .270 Win., and .30-06 cal.'s, bolt action, 5 shot rotary mag., 24 in. barrel, low bolt handle, half length stock, ebony forearm, made 1950-1952.

	$795	$725	$650	$575	$500	$460	$420

MODEL 1950 CARBINE—same as 1950, except 20 in. barrel, full length stock, made 1950-1952.

	$1,000	$875	$770	$675	$580	$525	$440

MODEL 1950 CARBINE 6.5—same as 1950 Carbine, except 6.5 x 54mm cal., 18½ in. barrel, made 1950-1952.

	$1,000	$875	$770	$675	$580	$525	$440

IMPROVED MODEL 1952—same specifications as 1950, except swept back bolt handle, made 1952-1956.

	$795	$725	$650	$575	$500	$460	$420

IMPROVED MODEL 1952 CARBINE—.257 Roberts, .270 Win., 7 x 57mm, and .30-06 cal.'s, swept back handle, otherwise same as 1950 Carbine.

	$1,000	$875	$770	$675	$580	$525	$440

IMPROVED MODEL 1952 6.5 CARBINE—same as 1952 Carbine, except 6.5mm, 18½ in. barrel, made 1952-1956.

	$1,000	$875	$770	$675	$580	$525	$440

MODEL 1956 RIFLE—similar to 1952, except .243 and .30-06 cal.'s, new high comb. stock design, 22 in. barrel, half length stock, made 1956-1960.

	$795	$725	$650	$575	$500	$460	$420

MODEL 1956 CARBINE—similar to 1956 Rifle, except .243, 6.5 x 53mm, .257 Roberts, .270, 7mm, .30-06, or .308 cal., 20 in. barrel, full length stock, made 1956-1960.

	$1,000	$875	$770	$675	$580	$525	$440

MODEL 1961 MCA RIFLE—same as Model 1956, except Monte Carlo stock, made 1961-1971.

	$795	$725	$650	$575	$500	$460	$420

Grading	100%	98%	95%	90%	80%	70%	60%

MODEL 1961 MCA CARBINE—same as 1956 Carbine, except Monte Carlo stock, made 1961-1971.

	100%	98%	95%	90%	80%	70%	60%
	$1,000	$875	$770	$675	$580	$525	$440

MODEL M72 L/M RIFLE—M72 bolt action, .243, .308, .270, .30-06, 7 x 57, and 7 x 64 cal.'s, 23 in. barrel, single or double set triggers, made 1972-1980.

	$795	$725	$650	$575	$500	$460	$420

RIFLES: CURRENT MANUFACTURE

Current production guns are now called Steyr-Mannlicher models and can be located under this trademark in the S section.

MANUFRANCE

MANUFACTURED IN ST. ETIENNE, FRANCE SINCE 1902.

Manufrance currently manufactures many models in both rifles and shotguns that are not being imported in the U.S. at this time. These models are not covered in this book.

AUTO SHOTGUN—12 ga., 26, 28, and 30 in. imp. cyl., mod. and full, 2¾ or 3 in. chamber, gas operated, walnut stock, black matte receiver, vent rib.

	$330	$305	$290	$275	$255	$240	$220

FALCOR—O/U, 12 ga., vent rib, 26 in. imp. cyl. and mod., 28 in. mod. and full, SST, auto ejector, chrome lined barrel, walnut checkered stock.

	$715	$665	$635	$605	$550	$495	$470

MANURHIN

MANUFACTURED IN MULHOUSE, FRANCE BY MATRA MANURHIN DEFENSE. CURRENTLY IMPORTED AND DISTRIBUTED EXCLUSIVELY IN THE U.S. BY ATLANTIC BUSINESS ORGANIZATIONS, INC., LOCATED IN NEW YORK, NY. PREVIOUSLY IMPORTED (1984-86) DIRECTLY BY MATRA-MANURHIN INTERNATIONAL, INC., LOCATED IN FORT LAUDERDALE, FL.

Manurhin in France has been manufacturing models PP, PPK, and PPK/S since 1952. Previously, they were imported by Interarms out of Alexandria, VA. In 1984, Manurhin imported their new models directly and they were marked Manurhin on the left front slide assembly. This differs from the previous Walther stamped guns. Also, no Interarms logo appears on the right side.

HANDGUNS: CURRENT IMPORTATION

All models listed below are imported exclusively through Atlantic Business Organizations, Inc., located in New York, NY.

MODEL PP—.380 ACP cal., 3⅞ in. barrel, 7 round mag. blue only, 24 oz., all steel construction, double action with positive steel block safety. Imported resumed in 1988.

Mfg.'s Sug. Retail	$415	$360	$320	$275	$230	$205	$185	$170

MODEL PPK/S—.380 ACP cal., 3¼ in. barrel, 7 round mag. blue only, 23 oz., all steel construction, double action with positive steel block safety. Imported resumed in 1988.

Mfg.'s Sug. Retail	$415	$360	$320	$275	$230	$205	$185	$170

MODEL 73 DEFENSE REVOLVER—.357 Mag./.38 Special, 6 shot, 2½, 3, or 4 in. barrel, checkered wood stocks, mfg. to precise tolerances, 31-33½ oz. Importation began in 1988.

Mfg.'s Sug. Retail	$1,122	$1,000	$850	$725	$600	$500	$425	$350

MODEL 73 GENDARMERIE—.357 Mag./.38 Special, 6 shot, similar to Model 73 Defense except has adj. sighting components and also is offered in 5¼, 6, or 8 in. barrel lengths. Manufactured for police requirements. Importation began in 1988.

Mfg.'s Sug. Retail	$1,220	$1,075	$900	$750	$625	$525	$450	$375

MANURHIN, cont.

MODEL 73 SPORT—.357 Mag./.38 Special, 6 shot, sport shooting feaures include minimized hammer stroke, micrometer rear sight, and free release trigger with fitted adj. Importation began in 1988.

Mfg.'s Sug. Retail $1,220 $1,075 $900 $750 $625 $525 $450 $375

MODEL 73 CONVERTIBLE—includes choice of .22 LR/.38 Special or .22 LR/.32 cal. cylinders and barrels (5¾ in. for .38 Spl. and 6 in. for .22 LR/.32). Importation began in 1988.

Mfg.'s Sug. Retail $1,847 $1,675 $1,325 $1,125 $950 $800 $700 $600

3 Cylinder Model 73 Convertible

similar to Model 73 Convertible except includes 3 calibers (.22 LR, .32, and .38 Special). Importation began in 1988.

Mfg.'s Sug. Retail $2,230 $1,950 $1,700 $1,375 $1,150 $975 $850 $750

MODEL 73 SILHOUETTE—.22 LR or .357 Mag. cal., Silhouette variation with fully adj. rear sight and either 10 (.22 LR) or 10¾ (.357 Mag.) in. heavy barrel with full shroud, contoured wooden target grips, approx. 4 lbs. Importation began in 1988.

Mfg.'s Sug. Retail $1,189 $1,050 $875 $735 $615 $525 $450 $375

Add $13 for .357 Mag. cal.

PISTOLS: PREVIOUS IMPORTATION

P-1—9mm, similar to W. German P-38, double action, 5 in. barrel.

   $440 $380 $325 $275 $230 $205 $185

MODEL P4—9mm, P.38 variation issued to the French Police when in Berlin during post-WWII.

   $495 $440 $380 $325 $275 $230 $200

MODEL PP—.22 LR, .32 ACP, and .380 ACP cal.'s, 3⅞ in. barrel, 10 round mag.-.22 LR, 8 round mag.-.32 ACP, 7 round mag.-.380 ACP, blue only, 24 oz., all steel construction, double action with positive steel block safety. Add $10 for .22 LR cal., $46 for durgarde finish. Imported 1984-86.

   $360 $320 $275 $230 $205 $185 $170

Last Mfg.'s Sug. Retail was $419.

Collector Model—blue finish, special engraving. Imported in 1986 only.

   $465 $415 $350

Last Mfg.'s Sug. Retail was $529.

Presentation Model—blue finish, special ornamentation. Imported in 1986 only.

   $720 $650 $500

Last Mfg.'s Sug. Retail was $819.

Also available with various engraving options in either blue, nickel, or gold finish - prices range from $222 - $540.

MODEL PPK/S—.22 LR, .32 ACP, and .380 ACP cal.'s, 3¼ in. barrel, 10 round mag.-.22 LR, 8 round mag.-.32 ACP, 7 round mag.-.380 ACP, blue only, 23 oz., all steel construction, double action with positive steel block safety. Add $10 for .22 LR cal. Imported 1984-86.

   $360 $320 $275 $230 $205 $185 $170

Last Mfg.'s Sug. Retail was $419.

PPK/S Durgarde—same as above, only with bonded brushed chrome finish. Add $14 for .22 LR cal.

   $410 $365 $325 $290 $265 $250 $240

Last Mfg.'s Sug. Retail was $465.

Collector Model—blue finish, special engraving. Imported in 1986 only.

   $465 $415 $350

Last Mfg.'s Sug. Retail was $529.

Presentation Model—blue finish, special ornamentation. Imported in 1986 only.

   $720 $650 $500

Last Mfg.'s Sug. Retail was $819.

Also available with various engraving options in either blue, nickel, or gold finish - prices range from $222 - $540.

Grading	100%	98%	95%	90%	80%	70%	60%

PP SPORT—.22 LR cal. only, double action, 6.1 or 8.1 in. barrel, blue finish only, 25 oz., precision adj. sights, contoured plastic grips with thumb rest. New Manurhin design for 1985. Imported 1984-86.

	$545	$485	$430	$385	$325	$290	$270

Last Mfg.'s Sug. Retail was $635.

PP Sport-C—same as PP Sport, except has single action with softened trigger.

	$540	$475	$415	$370	$310	$280	$260

Last Mfg.'s Sug. Retail was $635.

MARATHON PRODUCTS, INC.

PREVIOUSLY MANUFACTURED BY SANTA BARBARA ARMAMENTS EXCLUSIVELY FOR MARATHON PRODUCTS, INC. MOST OF THE BELOW LISTED MODELS WERE ALSO AVAILABLE IN KIT FORM BUT ARE NOT SHOWN IN THIS BOOK.

.22 FIRST SHOT—.22 cal., single shot bolt action, 16½ in. barrel, hardwood stock, open sights, 31 in. total length, 3.8 lbs. Mfg. 1985-87.

	$55	$45	$40	$35	$35	$30	$30

Last Mfg.'s Sug. Retail was $60.

.22 Super Shot—same as First Shot, except with 24 in. barrel and regular dimension stock. Mfg. 1985-87.

	$55	$45	$40	$35	$35	$30	$30

Last Mfg.'s Sug. Retail was $60.

.22 Hot Shot Pistol—.22 LR only, bolt action, single shot, fixed sights, 14¾ in. barrel, hardwood stock with target grip configuration. Mfg. 1986-87.

	$55	$45	$40	$35	$35	$30	$30

Last Mfg.'s Sug. Retail was $60.

CENTERFIRE MODEL—.243, .270 Win., 7 x 57, 7mm Rem. Mag., .30-06, .300 Win. Mag., and .308 Mag. cal.'s, Mauser type bolt action, 5 shot fixed box mag., 24 in. barrel, select walnut with recoil pad, adj. trigger, open sights, 7.9 lbs. Available in 1985-86 only.

	$295	$240	$215	$195	$180	$170	$160

Last Mfg.'s Sug. Retail was $320.

MARBLE'S GAME GETTER

PREVIOUS MANUFACTURER LOCATED IN GLADSTONE, MI.

In addition to axes and compasses, Marble's also manufactured their Game Getter O/U combination gun from approximately 1907 to the late 1920's. During this period of production, the gun underwent quite a few changes including sights (an aperture sight mounted on the rear backstrap was standard until changed to a top frame sight), different configuration folding metal stock, and other changes.

GAME GETTER MODEL—.22 S, L, or LR cal., upper rifled barrel over choice of .44-40 Game Getter/.410 ga. (2 in.) or .410 ga. (2½ in.) smooth bore lower barrel, choice of 12, 15, or 18 in. separated barrels, folding steel skeleton attached stock, pivoting hammer striker mechanically selects upper or lower barrel, tip-up barrels are opened by pulling trigger guard back, gutta percha or walnut stocks, approx. 3½ lbs.

	$795	$725	$650	$600	$550	$520	$480

Add $100 for original leather holster in good condition.

Above values assume 18 in. barrels or correct registration on 12 or 15 in. models. Those 12 or 15 in. barreled Game Getter's not registered during the 1968 BATF ammnesty program are not legally transferable today. If not a legal configuration, values will drop considerably.

The lower barrel of this model was capable of shooting .410 ga. 2 in. paper or brass shotshells, .410 ga. 2½ in. paper shotshell (standard configuration), and .410 or .44 cal. round ball cartridges.

MARGOLIN

RUSSIAN TARGET PISTOL MANUFACTURED IN THE U.S.S.R.

TARGET MODEL—.22 LR, semi-auto, manufactured to precise tolerances, used by some members of the Russian shooting team, basically individually made to shooters specifications, seldomly encountered in the U.S.A., while rare, desirablity to date has been limited, current mfg.

Margolin pistols are typically priced in the $475-$750 range, depending on features and assuming 95% + original condition.

MARLIN FIREARMS COMPANY

PREVIOUSLY MANUFACTURED 1870-1969 IN NEW HAVEN, CT. MANUFACTURED 1969-PRESENT IN NORTH HAVEN, CT.

Research is underway to include the Ballard rifles — forerunners of the Marlin, mfg. 1875-1881 by John M. Marlin and 1881-1891 by Marlin Fiearms Company. Approx. total is 40,000 rifles.

RIFLES: ANTIQUE MANUFACTURE

Values below are for standard models only without special order features.

MODEL 1881 LEVER ACTION—.32-40, .38-55, .40-60, .45-70, and .45-85 cal.'s, tube mag., 28 in. octagonal barrel standard, top ejection, blued finish with case hardened hammer, lever, and butt plate. First models (pre ser. no. 600) are rare, add 200-300% premium. Approximately 20,000 manufactured between 1881-1892.

	$1,850	$1,500	$1,200	$1,000	$900	$800	$700

This model came in 2 or 3 frame thicknesses for various caibers

MODEL 1888 LEVER ACTION—.32-20, .38-40, and .44-40 cal.'s, 24 in. octagonal barrel most frequently encountered, top ejection, blued finish with case hardened hammer, lever, and butt plate, short throw lever action principle. Approx. 4,800 mfg. between 1888-1889. Ser. range approximately 19,560 - 27,850.

	$2,100	$1,750	$1,500	$1,350	$1,100	$950	$750

MODEL 1889 LEVER ACTION—.25-20 (very rare), .32-20, .38-40, and .44-40 cal.'s, 24 in. octagonal barrel most frequently encountered, side ejection with solid top frame, blued finish with case hardened hammer, lever, and butt plate, short throw lever action principle. Approximately 55,000 mfg. between 1889-1899. Ser. range approximately 25,000-100,000. Also available as Carbine (15 in. barrel-add 50%) or Musket (30 in. barrel-add 300-500%, very rare).

	$780	$695	$650	$580	$500	$400	$395

MODEL 1891 LEVER ACTION—.22 Rimfire and .32 Rimfire/Centerfire, 24 in. octagonal barrel most often encountered, blued finish with case hardened hammer, lever, and butt plate, sear safety system on lever action, approx. 18,650 mfg. between 1891-1897. Ser. No. range is approx. 37,500-118,000.

	$1,450	$1,100	$900	$780	$600	$475	$400

MODEL 1892 LEVER ACTION—.22 S, L, or LR, .32 S or L, 16, 24, 26, and 28 in. barrel, tubular mag., open sight, plain straight stock, made 1892-1916.

	$935	$825	$745	$660	$550	$495	$415

.22 cal.'s will bring a premium in this model.

MODEL 1893 LEVER ACTION—.25-36 Marlin, .30-30, .32 Spl., .32-40, and .38-55 cal.'s, 28-32 in. round or octagonal barrels, 10 shot tube mag., straight or pistol grip stock, made 1893-1936. Musket model also manufactured-30 in. barrel and military style forearm.

	$950	$850	$750	$600	$500	$400	$295

MODEL 1893 CARBINE—.30-30, .32 Spl., 20 in. round barrel, 7 shot tube mag., straight or pistol grip stock, made 1893-1936.

	$950	$850	$750	$600	$500	$400	$295

MARLIN FIREARMS COMPANY, cont.

Grading	100%	98%	95%	90%	80%	70%	60%

MODEL 1894 LEVER ACTION—.25-20, .32-20, .38-40, and .44-40 cal.'s, 10 shot tube mag., 24 in. round or octagon barrel, straight or pistol grip stock, made 1894-1934.

	$950	$850	$750	$600	$500	$400	$295

MODEL 1895 LEVER ACTION—.33 WCF, .38-56, .40-65, .40-70, .40-82, and .45-70 cal.'s, 9 shot tube mag., 24 in. round or octagon barrel standard, other lengths were available, open sights, plain straight or pistol grip stock, made 1895-1915.

	$1,250	$950	$800	$700	$600	$500	$395

MODEL 1897 LEVER ACTION—.22 S, L, or LR, tube mag., 16, 24, 26, and 28 in. barrel, takedown, open sights, plain straight or pistol grip stock, made 1897-1922.

	$2,500	$1,450	$995	$795	$650	$450	$295

RIFLES: MODERN PRODUCTION

Year of manufacture can be determined from 1946-1968 by the following letter prefix: 1946-C, 1947-D, 1948-E, 1949-F, 1950-G, 1951-H, 1952-J, 1953-K, 1954-L, 1955-M, 1956-N, 1957-P, 1958-R, 1959-S, 1960-T, 1961-U, 1962-V, 1963-W, 1964-Y,Z, 1965-AA, 1966-AB, 1967-AC, 1968-AD.

MODEL 18 SLIDE ACTION—.22 S, L, or LR, tube mag., 20 in. round or octagon barrel, open sight, exposed hammer, plain straight grip stock, made 1906-1909.

	$330	$250	$195	$140	$110	$100	$85

MODEL 20 SLIDE ACTION—.22 S, L, or LR, 24 in. octagon barrel, open sight, exposed hammer, takedown, plain straight grip stock, made 1907-1922.

	$330	$250	$195	$140	$110	$100	$85

MODEL 25 SLIDE ACTION—.22 short, tube mag., 23 in. barrel, open sight, exposed hammer, takedown, plain straight grip stock, made 1909-1910.

	$360	$275	$220	$165	$140	$120	$95

MODEL 27 SLIDE ACTION—.25-20, .32-20 cal.'s, ⅔ tube mag., 7 shot, 24 in. octagon barrel, open sight, plain straight grip stock, made 1910-1916.

	$330	$250	$195	$140	$110	$100	$85

MODEL 27S—same as 27, with round or octagonal barrel.

	$330	$250	$195	$140	$110	$100	$85

MODEL 29 SLIDE ACTION—similar to 20, with 23 in. round barrel, ½ tube mag., made 1913-1916.

	$330	$250	$195	$140	$110	$100	$85

MODEL 32 SLIDE ACTION—.22 S, L, or LR, ⅔ tube mag., 24 in. octagon barrel, open sight, plain pistol grip stock, hammerless, made 1914-1915.

	$330	$250	$195	$140	$110	$100	$85

MODEL 1936 CARBINE LEVER ACTION—.30-30 and .32 Spl., 6 shot, 20 in. barrel, tubular mag., open sights, pistol grip stock, barrel band, made 1936-1948.

	$275	$220	$195	$165	$140	$110	$95

MODEL 36A—same as 36 Carbine, with 24 in. barrel, ⅔ tube mag.

	$275	$220	$195	$165	$140	$110	$95

MODEL 36A-DL—same as 36A, with deluxe checkered stock, sling and swivels.

	$305	$250	$220	$195	$165	$140	$110

MODEL 37 SLIDE ACTION—same as 29, with 24 in. barrel, full length tube mag., made 1913-1916.

	$330	$250	$195	$140	$110	$100	$85

MODEL 38 SLIDE ACTION—.22 S, L, or LR, ⅔ tube mag., 24 in. octagon barrel, open sights, hammerless, takedown, plain pistol grip stock, made 1920-1930.

	$330	$250	$195	$140	$110	$100	$85

MODEL 39 LEVER ACTION—.22 S, L, or LR, tube mag., 24 in. octagon barrel, open sight, takedown, case hardened receiver, plain pistol grip stock, made 1922-1947.

	$750	$650	$500	$400	$300	$200	$150

MODEL 39A—same as 39, with blued or color case hardened receiver, round barrel, made 1938-1960.

	$225	$175	$150	$130	$110	$95	$85

GOLDEN 39A—same as 39A, with gold plated trigger, sling swivels, made 1960-1983.

	$170	$155	$140	$110	$95	$85	$70

MARLIN FIREARMS COMPANY, cont.

Grading	100%	98%	95%	90%	80%	70%	60%

MODEL 39A "MOUNTIE"—straight grip stock, slim forearm, otherwise same as 39A, made 1953-1960.

	$165	$150	$130	$110	$90	$75	$70

90TH ANNIVERSARY 39A—same as 39A, with chrome barrel and action, select checkered walnut stock, carved squirrel on side of butt stock, 500 produced in 1960.

	$550	$385	$330	$275	$220	$165	$110

90TH ANNIVERSARY MODEL 90 CARBINE—same as 90th Anniversary 39A, except 20 in. barrel, straight stock, 500 produced in 1960.

	$550	$385	$330	$275	$220	$165	$110

MODEL 39A-DL—same as 90th Anniversary, with blue barrel and action, regular production, made 1960-1963.

	$250	$195	$165	$140	$110	$100	$85

MODEL 39A OCTAGON—same as Golden 39A, with octagon barrel, no pistol grip cap, made 1972-73.

	$195	$165	$150	$130	$110	$90	$85

MODEL 39M "MOUNTIE" CARBINE—same as "Mountie", with 20 in. barrel, made 1954-1960.

	$165	$150	$130	$110	$90	$75	$70

MODEL 39 CARBINE—same as 39M, with light barrel, ¾ tube mag., made 1963-1967.

	$165	$150	$130	$110	$90	$75	$70

MODEL 39D—same as 39M, with pistol grip stock, made 1970-1974.

	$175	$155	$140	$120	$100	$85	$70

MODEL 39AS—.22 LR cal., current production model, lever action, tube mag., 19 shot, 24 in. barrel, walnut stock, open sights, gold trigger, takedown, 6½ lbs.

Mfg.'s Sug. Retail	$339	$245	$185	$155	$145	$130	$110	$100

This model was previously designated the Model 39A. In 1988, the Model 39AS became the standard production model and included a rebounding hammer and hammer block safety.

MODEL 39TDS—.22 LR cal., carbine variation of the Model 39AS, 16½ in. barrel with open sights, 5¼ lbs. New in 1988.

Mfg.'s Sug. Retail	$377	$275	$195	$160	$150	$130	$110	$100

MODEL 39M—carbine version of Model 39A, 20 in. lightweight barrel, 16 shot tube mag., squared finger lever, 6 lbs. Disc. in 1987.

	$225	$180	$155	$145	$130	$110	$100

Last Mfg.'s Sug. Retail was $304.

MODEL 39M OCTAGON—same as 39M, with octagon barrel, made 1973.

	$225	$175	$165	$150	$135	$115	$105

MODEL GOLDEN 39M CARBINE—same as 39M, with gold plated trigger, sling swivels, made 1960-1982.

	$170	$155	$140	$110	$95	$85	$70

MODEL 39 CENTURY LTD—Marlin Centennial 1870-1970 Commemorative, 20 in. octagon barrel, select walnut straight stock, brass forearm cap and buttplate, name plate in butt, 35,388 produced in 1970.

	$275	$195	$180	$155	$140	$110	$95

MODEL 39A ARTICLE II—NRA Centennial Commemorative 1871-1971, "Right to Bear Arms" medallion in receiver, 24 in. octagon barrel, fancy pistol grip stock, brass butt plate and forearm cap, 6,244 produced in 1971.

	$265	$180	$165	$150	$120	$100	$85

MODEL 39M ARTICLE II CARBINE—same as 39A Article II, with 20 in. barrel, straight grip stock, 3,824 produced.

	$275	$195	$175	$160	$130	$110	$95

MODEL 56—same as 57, with clip mag., made 1955-1964.

	$130	$100	$85	$70	$55	$40	$30

MODEL 57 LEVERMATIC—.22 S, L, or LR, tube mag., 22 in. barrel, open sight, Monte Carlo pistol grip stock, made 1959-1965.

	$130	$100	$85	$70	$55	$40	$30

Grading	100%	98%	95%	90%	80%	70%	60%

MODEL 57 M—Mag. version of Model 57 Levermatic.

	$195	$180	$165	$155	$140	$120	$110

MODEL 62 LEVERMATIC—.256 Mag., .30 Carbine cal.'s, 4 shot clip mag., 23 in. barrel, open sight, pistol grip Monte Carlo stock, made 1963-1969.

	$165	$140	$120	$100	$85	$70	$55

MODEL 322 BOLT ACTION VARMINT—Sako Mauser type action, .222 Rem., 3 shot clip mag., 24 in. medium weight barrel, 2 position aperture sight, checkered stock, made 1954-1957.

	$385	$305	$275	$220	$195	$165	$140

MODEL 336—.219 Zipper, 20 in. carbine barrel, ⅔ magazine, 5 shot.

	$275	$225	$190	$150	$130	$110	$95

MODEL 336A—improved 36A, .30-30, .35 Rem., and .32 Spl. cal.'s, round breech bolt, 24 in. barrel with ⅔ mag., made 1948-1963, re-introduced 1973-1983.

	$210	$180	$165	$150	$130	$110	$95

MODEL 336 CS CARBINE LEVER ACTION—.30-30 Win., .35 Rem., or .375 Win. (disc. in 1988) cal., 6 shot tube mag., 20 in. barrel, hammer block safety, American black walnut pistol grip stock, 7 lbs. Add $5 for Model 336C (without hammer block safety-discontinued in 1984). Introduced 1983.

Mfg.'s Sug. Retail	$338	$245	$190	$160	$150	$140	$130	$120

MODEL 375—same as 336 CS, except is .375 Win. cal. Discontinued 1983.

	$230	$175	$165	$150	$140	$130	$120

MODEL 336 TS TEXAN—same as 336 CS, except is .30-30 cal., 18½ in. barrel, straight grip stock and squared finger lever. Add $5 for Model 336T (discontinued in 1984). Disc. in 1987.

	$240	$185	$160	$150	$140	$130	$120

Last Mfg.'s Sug. Retail was $314.

MODEL 336 LTS CARBINE—.30-30 cal. only, 16¼ in. barrel, 5 shot tube mag., 6½ lbs. New in 1988.

Mfg.'s Sug. Retail	$346	$255	$190	$160	$150	$140	$130	$120

MODEL 30 AS LEVER ACTION—.30-30 cal. only, 20 in. barrel, walnut finish hardwood, open sights, no frills version of the 336 CS, 7 lbs. New in 1985.

Mfg.'s Sug. Retail	$287	$220	$180	$145	$130	$125	$120	$115

Add $48 for 4X scope.

MODEL 336 ER—.307 (discontinued in 1984) and .356 Win. cal.'s, 5 shot tube mag., 20 in. barrel, walnut pistol grip stock, open sights, 7 lbs. Mfg. 1983-87.

	$270	$210	$190	$175	$165	$155	$140

Last Mfg.'s Sug. Retail was $350.

MODEL 336A CARBINE—same as 336A, with 20 in. barrel, made 1948-1963.

	$200	$180	$165	$150	$130	$110	$95

MODEL 336 MICRO GROOVE ZIPPER—same as 336A Carbine, in caliber .219 Zipper, made 1955-1961.

	$495	$415	$360	$330	$275	$250	$220

MODEL 336T CARBINE "TEXAN"—same as 336A Carbine, with straight stock, made 1963-1967, .44 Mag. also available, made 1963-1967.

	$185	$170	$160	$145	$130	$120	$100

MODEL 336DT CARBINE "TEXAN"—select stock version of 336T, longhorn and map of Texas carved on butt stock, made 1962-1964.

	$275	$220	$195	$165	$155	$140	$120

MODEL 336 RC—carbine.

	$275	$220	$195	$165	$155	$140	$120

MODEL 336 SC—.35 Rem., carbine variation, disc.

	$265	$215	$190	$165	$155	$140	$120

Grading	100%	98%	95%	90%	80%	70%	60%

MARLIN CENTENNIAL MATCHED PAIR—Model 336 and Model 339 serial numbered the same, .30-30 and .22 LR cal.'s, engraved, deluxe wood, inlaid medallions, cased, 1,000 sets produced in 1970.

| | $955 | $750 | $500 | | | | |

MODEL 336 ZANE GREY CENTURY—same as 336A, with .30-30 cal., 22 in. octagon barrel, Zane Grey medallion inlaid in receiver, select walnut stock, pistol grip, brass butt plate and forearm cap, 10,000 produced in 1972.

| | $330 | $250 | $195 | $165 | $150 | $130 | $110 |

MODEL 336 OCTAGON—same as 336T, .30-30 cal. only, with 22 in. octagon barrel, made 1973.

| | $205 | $175 | $165 | $155 | $140 | $120 | $100 |

MODEL 336 MARAUDER—same as 336T Carbine, with 16¼ in. barrel, made 1963-1964.

| | $250 | $200 | $180 | $165 | $155 | $140 | $120 |

MODEL 444 LEVER ACTION—.444 Marlin cal., 4 shot tube mag., 24 in. barrel, open sights, straight grip, Monte Carlo stock, recoil pad, swivels, sling, made 1965-1971.

| | $180 | $160 | $140 | $120 | $110 | $100 | $85 |

MODEL 444 SS SPORTER—same as 444 Rifle, with 22 in. barrel, pistol grip stock without Monte Carlo configuration, Model 444 S does not have hammer block safety (discontinued in 1984 — add $10), 7½ lbs., made 1972-present.

| *Mfg.'s Sug. Retail* | $409 | $340 | $305 | $270 | $230 | $195 | $180 | $170 |

MODEL 455 BOLT ACTION SPORTER—FN Mauser action with Sako trigger, .270, .30-06, and .308 cal.'s, 24 in. barrel, stainless steel barrel, Lyman aperture sight, checkered Monte Carlo pistol grip stock, made 1957-1959.

| | $415 | $330 | $305 | $250 | $220 | $195 | $165 |

MODELS 780, 781, 782, and 783 BOLT ACTION—.22 LR and .22 Mag. (Models 782 and 783), tube or clip mag., 22 in. barrel. Disc. in 1988.

| | $110 | $85 | $75 | $70 | $65 | $55 | $50 |

Add $17-$25 for Models 782 and 783.

Last Mfg.'s Sug. Retail was $162.

MODELS 880, 881, 882, and 883 BOLT ACTION—.22 LR or .22 Mag. cal., replacements for Models 780, 781, 782, and 783, Model 880 is .22 LR with 7 shot clip mag. and 22 in. barrel, Model 881 is .22 LR with 17 shot tube mag. and 22 in. barrel, Model 882 is .22 Mag. with 7 shot clip mag. and 22 in. barrel, Model 883 is .22 Mag. with 12 shot tube mag. and 22 in. barrel, approx. 6 lbs. on all models. Mfg. began in 1989.

| *Mfg.'s Sug. Retail* | $189 | $155 | $120 | $100 | $85 | $75 | $70 | $65 |

Add $11 for Model 882.

Add $19 for Model 883.

MODEL 25MB—.22 Mag. cal., bolt action, 16¼ in. micro-groove barrel, 7 shot clip mag., hardwood stock, takedown action, 6 lbs. Mfg. in 1987-88 only.

| | $145 | $115 | $95 | $85 | $75 | $70 | $65 |

This model included both a scope and gun case.

Last Mfg.'s Sug. Retail was $173.

MODEL 25MN—.22 Mag. cal., bolt action, 7 shot clip mag., 22 in. barrel, walnut finished hardwood stock, grooved receiver, 6 lbs. Mfg. began in 1989.

| *Mfg.'s Sug. Retail* | $151 | $120 | $100 | $90 | $80 | $75 | $70 | $65 |

MODEL 9 CAMP CARBINE SEMI-AUTO—9mm only, 16½ in. barrel, 12 or 20 (optional) shot mag., sand blasted steel receiver, open sights, last shot automatic hold-open, 6¾ lbs. New for 1985.

| *Mfg.'s Sug. Retail* | $312 | $245 | $185 | $165 | $150 | $140 | $130 | $125 |

A new high visibility orange front sight post with cutaway hood was added in 1989.

MODEL 45 CARBINE—.45 ACP only, 7 shot clip mag., sandblasted steel receiver, 16½ in. barrel, last shot hold open device, adj. rear sight, 6¾ lbs. New in 1986.

| *Mfg.'s Sug. Retail* | $312 | $245 | $185 | $165 | $150 | $140 | $130 | $125 |

A new high visibility orange front sight post with cutaway hood was added in 1989.

Grading	100%	98%	95%	90%	80%	70%	60%

MODEL 990 SEMI-AUTO—.22 LR only, 18 shot tube mag., 22 in. barrel, last shot automatic bolt hold-open, Monte Carlo American black walnut stock with pistol grip, 5½ lbs. Disc. in 1987.

	100%	98%	95%	90%	80%	70%	60%
	$115	$90	$75	$65	$60	$55	$50

Last Mfg.'s Sug. Retail was $159.

MODEL 995 SEMI-AUTO—.22 LR only, 7 shot clip mag., 18 in. barrel, Monte Carlo walnut stock, 5 lbs.

	100%	98%	95%	90%	80%	70%	60%
Mfg.'s Sug. Retail	$166	$120	$95	$75	$70	$65	$60	$55

MODEL 70P (PAPOOSE)—.22 LR only, semi-auto, takedown carbine with 16¼ in. barrel, 7 shot clip mag., rustproof receiver, bolt hold open, is supplied with floating nylon carrying case. New in 1986.

	100%	98%	95%	90%	80%	70%	60%
Mfg.'s Sug. Retail	$156	$130	$100	$90	$85	$80	$75	$70

Add $20 for 4X scope.

This model was supplied with a 4X scope until 1989.

MODEL 1894 CS (CARBINE)—copy of original Model 1894, .357 Mag./.38 Spl., 9 shot mag., 18½ in. round barrel, open sights, straight grip stock, squared finger lever, 6 lbs., made 1969-present. Model 1894 C does not have hammer block safety - subtract $20.

	100%	98%	95%	90%	80%	70%	60%
Mfg.'s Sug. Retail	$380	$290	$215	$180	$165	$150	$140	$130

MODEL 1894 S (SPORTER)—.41 Mag., .44 Mag./.44 Spl., or .45 Long Colt (new in 1988), 20 in. barrel, 10 shot tube mag., adj. sights, 6 lbs., straight grip walnut stock and forearm.

	100%	98%	95%	90%	80%	70%	60%
Mfg.'s Sug. Retail	$380	$290	$215	$180	$165	$150	$140	$130

MODEL 1894 M (.22 MAG.)—.22 Mag., with 20 in. barrel, 11 shot tube mag., straight grip walnut stock and forearm, 6¼ lbs. Disc. in 1989.

	100%	98%	95%	90%	80%	70%	60%
	$275	$210	$180	$150	$135	$125	$115

Last Mfg.'s Sug. Retail was $358.

MODEL 1894 CL—.25-20 or .32-20 cal., 6 shot (two-thirds length) tube mag., 22 in. barrel, 6¼ lbs. New in 1988.

	100%	98%	95%	90%	80%	70%	60%
Mfg.'s Sug. Retail	$407	$300	$225	$185	$155	$140	$125	$115

MODEL 1894 OCTAGON—same as 1894 Carbine, with octagon barrel, made 1973.

	100%	98%	95%	90%	80%	70%	60%
	$260	$195	$175	$165	$150	$130	$120

MODEL 1895 LEVER ACTION—.45-70 Gov't., 4 shot tube mag., 22 in. barrel, open sights, straight grip stock, forearm cap, sling and swivels, made 1972-1984.

	100%	98%	95%	90%	80%	70%	60%
	$265	$210	$185	$175	$165	$150	$140

MODEL 1895 SS—same as Model 1895 only with hammer block safety. New in 1983.

	100%	98%	95%	90%	80%	70%	60%
Mfg.'s Sug. Retail	$409	$300	$225	$185	$155	$140	$125	$115

MARLIN PROMOTIONAL MODELS—Models 15, 15Y, 15YN (new in 1989), 25, 25M, 25N (new in 1989), 60, 70, 70HC (new in 1989), and 75C are inexpensive, utilitarian .22 LR or .22 Mag. cal. (Model 25M only), rifles meant for shooting, not for collecting. All the above models retail for approximately $125-$140, but can be purchased for less, depending on discounting.

Series 15 and 25 Models designate bolt action, Series 60 and 70 designate semi-auto design.

RIFLES: BOLT ACTION, SINGLE SHOT

Between 1930 and the present, Marlin made a number of .22 cal. rimfire rifles, bolt action single shots, bolt action repeaters and auto loaders. These were good quality, low priced weapons. In 1960 the name Glenfield was also used in connection with these guns. They are valued from a high of about $100 for a 100% gun to about $25 for a 60% or less gun that is still in working order. We will list these models for reference purposes.

Grading	100%	98%	95%	90%	80%	70%	60%

Model 65 — 1932-1938.
Model 65E — 1932-1938.
Model 100 — 1936-1941.
Model 100SB — 1936-1941.
Model 101 — 1951-disc.
Model 101 DL — disc.
Model 101G — 1960-1965, Marlin Glenfield.
Model 10 — 1966-disc., Marlin Glenfield.
Model 122 — 1966-disc.

BOLT ACTION: REPEATING RIFLES

Model 80 — 1934-1939.
Model 80E — 1934-1940.
Model 80C — 1940-1970.
Model 80DL — 1940-1965.
Model 80G — 1960-1965, Marlin Glenfield.
Model 20 — 1966-disc., Marlin Glenfield.
Model 780 — 1971-1988.
Model 781 — 1971-1988.
Model 782 — 1971-1988, .22 WRM.
Model 783 — 1971-1988, .22 WRM.
Model 980 — 1962-1970, .22 WRM.
Model 81 — 1937-1940.
Model 81E — 1937-1940.
Model 81C — 1940-1970.
Model 81DL — 1940-1965.
Model 81G — 1960-1965 Marlin Glenfield.

AUTOLOADING RIFLES

Model 50 — 1931-1934.
Model 50E — 1931-1934.
Model A-1 — 1935-1946.
Model A-1E — 1935-1946.
Model A-1C — 1940-1946.
Model A-1DL — 1940-1946.
Model 88-C — 1947-1956.
Model 88-DL — 1953-1956.
Model 89-C — 1950-1961.
Model 89-DL — 1950-1961.
Model 98 — 1950-1961.
Model 99 — 1959-1961.
Model 99C — 1962-disc.
Model 99G — 1960-1965, Marlin Glenfield.
Model 60 — 1960-present, Marlin Glenfield.
Model 99DL — 1960-1965.
Model 49 — 1968-1971.
Model 49DL — 1971-disc.
Model 99M1 — 1966-disc.
Model 99M2 — 1966-disc.
Model 989 — 1962-1966.
Model 70 — 1966-1969, Marlin Glenfield.
Model 989G — 1962-1964, Marlin Glenfield.
Model 990 — disc.
Model 995 — disc.

Grading	100%	98%	95%	90%	80%	70%	60%

SHOTGUNS

MODEL 1898 SLIDE ACTION—12 ga., 5 shot tube mag., 26-32 in. barrels, various chokes, exposed hammer, pistol grip stock, grades differ in quality of wood and engraving on C and D, made 1898-1905.

Grade A	$495	$385	$330	$305	$250	$195	$165
Grade B	$580	$495	$440	$415	$360	$305	$275
Grade C	$880	$715	$635	$580	$525	$495	$440
Grade D	$1,760	$1,540	$1,320	$1,210	$1,045	$965	$880

MODEL 16—16 ga. only, 26 or 28 in. barrel, various chokes, takedown, pistol grip stock, made 1904-1910.

Grade A	$385	$305	$250	$220	$195	$165	$140
Grade B	$495	$415	$360	$330	$305	$275	$250
Grade C	$635	$525	$495	$440	$415	$385	$330
Grade D	$1,320	$1,100	$990	$825	$715	$635	$550

MODEL 17 SLIDE ACTION—12 ga., 30 or 32 in. full choke barrel, solid frame, straight stock, made 1906-1908.

	$440	$330	$305	$250	$220	$180	$150

MODEL 17 BRUSH GUN—same as 17, with 26 in. cylinder bore barrel, made 1906-1908.

	$470	$360	$330	$275	$250	$220	$165

MODEL 17 RIOT GUN—same as 17, with 20 in. barrel, made 1906-1908.

	$415	$330	$275	$250	$195	$180	$160

MODEL 19 SLIDE ACTION—improved lightened version of 1898, matte top surface on barrel, made 1906-1907.

Grade A	$385	$305	$250	$220	$195	$165	$140
Grade B	$495	$415	$360	$330	$305	$275	$250
Grade C	$635	$525	$495	$440	$415	$385	$330
Grade D	$1,320	$1,100	$990	$825	$715	$635	$550

MODEL 21 SLIDE ACTION—straight grip version of 19.

Grade A	$385	$305	$250	$220	$195	$165	$140
Grade B	$495	$415	$360	$330	$305	$275	$250
Grade C	$635	$525	$495	$440	$415	$385	$330
Grade D	$1,320	$1,100	$990	$825	$715	$635	$550

MODEL 24—improved 21, takedown, automatic recoil lock on slide, solid matte rib, made 1908-1915.

Grade A	$330	$305	$275	$250	$220	$195	$165
Grade B	$525	$440	$385	$360	$330	$305	$275
Grade C	$660	$550	$525	$470	$440	$415	$360
Grade D	$1,375	$1,155	$1,045	$880	$770	$660	$580

MODEL 26—same as 24 Grade A, with solid frame, 30 or 32 in. full choke barrel, made 1909-1915.

	$275	$230	$210	$195	$165	$150	$140

MODEL 26 BRUSH GUN—26 in. cylinder bore barrel, made 1909-1915.

	$305	$275	$250	$220	$195	$165	$150

MODEL 26 RIOT GUN—20 in. cylinder bore barrel, made 1909-1915.

	$250	$195	$180	$165	$150	$140	$120

MODEL 28 HAMMERLESS—12 ga., 26-32 in. barrels, various chokes, takedown, matte top barrel, pistol grip stock, made 1913-1922.

Grade A	$385	$305	$250	$220	$195	$165	$140
Grade B	$495	$415	$360	$330	$305	$275	$250
Grade C	$635	$525	$495	$440	$415	$385	$330
Grade D	$1,320	$1,100	$990	$825	$715	$635	$550

MODEL 28TS TRAP GUN—same as 28, with 30 in. matte rib barrel, full choke, high combination straight grip stock, made 1915.

	$415	$330	$275	$250	$220	$195	$165

MODEL 28T—same as 28TS, with fancy wood, checkering, better finish, made 1915.

	$605	$525	$495	$470	$415	$360	$305

Grading	100%	98%	95%	90%	80%	70%	60%

MODEL 30—same as 16, with automatic recoil lock on slide, made 1910-1914.

Grade A	$385	$305	$250	$220	$195	$165	$140
Grade B	$495	$415	$360	$330	$305	$275	$250
Grade C	$635	$525	$495	$440	$415	$385	$330
Grade D	$1,320	$1,100	$990	$825	$715	$635	$550

MODEL 30 FIELD GRADE—same as 30 Grade B, with 25 in. mod. barrel, straight stock, made 1913-1914.

	$360	$275	$220	$180	$160	$130	$115

MODEL 31—scaled down small ga. (16 and 20 ga.) version of the Model 28, has 26 and 28 in. barrels, various chokes, made 1915-1922.

Grade A	$385	$305	$250	$220	$195	$165	$140
Grade B	$495	$415	$360	$330	$305	$275	$250
Grade C	$636	$525	$495	$440	$415	$385	$330
Grade D	$1,320	$1,100	$990	$825	$715	$635	$550

MODEL 31F FIELD GUN—25 in. mod. barrel, made 1915-1917.

	$495	$415	$360	$330	$305	$275	$250

MODEL 42A—similar to 24, but less quality finishing, made 1922-1934.

	$250	$220	$195	$165	$140	$120	$100

MODEL 43 HAMMERLESS—similar to 28, with less quality finish, made 1923-1930.

	$330	$250	$220	$195	$165	$140	$110

MODEL 43TS—same as 28T, lower quality.

	$525	$440	$415	$385	$360	$305	$275

MODEL 44A—similar to 31A, 20 ga. only, made 1923-1935.

	$360	$275	$250	$220	$195	$165	$140

MODEL 44S—select checkered stock.

	$470	$385	$360	$330	$195	$165	$140

MODEL 49—lower priced version of 42A. They were given to purchasers of 4 shares of Marlin stock, 3,000 produced in 1925-1928.

	$440	$360	$305	$275	$220	$195	$165

MODEL 53—similar to 43A, made 1929-1930.

	$330	$275	$250	$220	$195	$165	$140

MODEL 63—same as 43, later model, made 1931-1935.

	$330	$250	$220	$195	$165	$140	$110

MODEL 63TS—similar to 43TS, with trap style stock.

	$385	$305	$250	$220	$195	$165	$140

MODEL .410 LEVER ACTION—.410 ga., 22 or 26 in. barrel, full choke, lever action, similar to 1893, exposed hammer, plain pistol grip stock, made 1929-1932 as a stockholders promotional firearm.

	$495	$420	$375	$335	$290	$260	$230

Model .410 Deluxe—includes deluxe checkered walnut stock and forearm.

	$675	$595	$500	$425	$350	$300	$275

MODEL 60 SINGLE BARREL—12 ga., 30 or 32 in. barrel, full choke, top lever, break open, exposed hammer, pistol grip stock, 60 produced in 1923.

	$220	$195	$165	$140	$120	$110	$100

MODEL 90 O/U—12, 16, 20, and .410 ga.'s, 26, 28, and 30 in. barrels, boxlock, extractors, checkered pistol grip stock, made 1937-1958, guns made from 1937-1949 had vent separated barrels, after 1949, solid barrels.

	$495	$385	$360	$330	$290	$265	$230

With single trigger

	$605	$495	$470	$440	$400	$375	$340

MODEL 120 MAGNUM—slide action, 12 ga., 3 in. chamber, 26-38 in. barrel, takedown, various chokes, checkered pistol grip stock, made 1971-1985. Deduct $35 if without vent rib.

	$290	$225	$215	$205	$195	$180	$165

Last Mfg.'s Sug. Retail was $370.

Grading	100%	98%	95%	90%	80%	70%	60%

MODEL 778—12 ga. Mag. slide action, 20-38 in. barrels, 7¾ lbs. Discontinued in 1984.

	$225	$190	$175	$155	$140	$125	$110

PREMIER MARK I SLIDE ACTION—12 ga. only, aluminum receiver, takedown, manufactured in France for Marlin.

	$200	$180	$160	$150	$140	$120	$95

PREMIER MARK II—same as Mark I, except with engraved receiver and checkering, made 1960-1963 in France.

	$260	$205	$170	$155	$145	$125	$100

PREMIER MARK IV—same as Mark II, only deluxe grade with better wood, more engraving, made 1960-1963 in France.

	$305	$250	$220	$195	$165	$140	$110
With vent rib	$330	$275	$250	$220	$195	$165	$140

SHOTGUNS: BOLT ACTION

MODEL 55—12, 16, and 20 ga.'s, 2 shot detachable mag., 26 and 28 in. full choke barrel, plain pistol grip stock, made 1950-1965.

	$90	$70	$55	$40	$35	$30	$25

With adj. choke

	$100	$85	$65	$50	$45	$40	$30

MODEL 55 GOOSE GUN—same as 55, except 12 ga. only, 36 in. full choke barrel, 3 in. chamber, 2 shot clip mag., 8 lbs., leather carrying strap and detachable swivels, rubber recoil pad, made 1962-present.

Mfg.'s Sug. Retail	$229	$175	$140	$120	$100	$90	$85	$80

MODEL 55 SWAMP GUN—same as 55, 12 ga., 20 in. adj. choke barrel, 3 in. mag., made 1963-1965.

	$105	$90	$70	$55	$50	$45	$35

MODEL 55S SLUG GUN—24 in. barrel, cylinder bore, rifle sights, made 1974-1983.

	$140	$120	$110	$95	$85	$55	$40

MODEL 5510—10 ga., 3½ in. mag., 2 shot clip mag., 34 in. barrel, leather carrying strap and detachable swivels, rubber recoil pad, 10½ lbs. Made 1976-1985.

	$220	$170	$160	$150	$140	$130	$120

Last Mfg.'s Sug. Retail was $282.

MAROCCHI

MANUFACTURED SINCE 1922 BY ARMI MAROCCHI IN BRESCIA, ITALY. CURRENTLY IMPORTED AND DISTRIBUTED BY MAROCCHI USA, INC. IN CHICAGO, IL AND SILE DISTRIBUTORS INC., LOCATED IN NEW YORK, NY.

Marocchi makes a wide variety of target shotguns and O/U rifles. Currently, these firearms are available on a very limited basis domestically and Marocchi USA, Inc. should be contacted to determine availability and price for each model in their line. Frigon guns (manufactured by Marocchi) appear under the F section in this text.

The models listed below are currently distributed by Sile Distributors Inc., located in New York, NY.

SHOTGUNS

FIELD MASTER I O/U—12 ga. only, 26 or 28 in. VR barrels and rib with choke tubes, engraved coin finished receiver, SNT, checkered walnut stock and forearm.

No Mfg.'s Retail	$385	$330	$290	$265	$230	$210	$195

Field Master II—similar to Field Master I except has SST.

No Mfg.'s Retail	$415	$350	$300	$270	$235	$210	$195

MODEL 2000 SINGLE SHOT—12 ga. only, 3 in. chamber, hammer, 28 in. barrel, ejector, lightly engraved receiver.

No Mfg.'s Retail	$85	$60	$55	$50	$45	$40	$35

Grading	100%	98%	95%	90%	80%	70%	60%

COMBINATION GUNS

VALLEY COMBO—12 ga. over .222 Rem. cal., 23½ in. separated barrels with VR, 3 in. chamber, fold down rear sight and will accept claw scope mounts, fixed cylinder choke, DT's, engraved silver receiver, satin finish walnut Monte Carlo stock with checkering and recoil pad, 8¼ lbs.

Mfg.'s Sug. Retail	$680	$575	$475	$415	$375	$325	$295	$275

MASQUELIER S.A.

MANUFACTURED IN BELGIUM. PREVIOUSLY DISTRIBUTED (UNTIL 1986) BY AMBEL LTD., INC. LOCATED IN SUGAR LAND, TX.

SHOTGUNS

BOXLOCK SxS—12 ga. only, 2¾ in. chambers, Anson & Deeley boxlock action, ejectors, fine scroll engraving with French walnut. Importation discontinued in 1986.

	$4,400	$4,000	$3,650	$3,300	$2,995	$2,600	$2,200

Last Mfg.'s Sug. Retail was $4,780.

SIDELOCK SxS—12 ga. only, 2¾ in. chambers, H&H style sidelocks, auto ejectors, English style fine scroll engraving with French walnut. Importation discontinued in 1986.

	$12,500	$10,000	$8,750	$7,600	$6,700	$5,800	$5,000

Last Mfg.'s Sug. Retail was $15,850.

RIFLES

CARPATHE—.243, .270, .30-06, 7 x 57R, and 7 x 65R cal.'s, single shot, hair trigger, push-down cocking system. Importation discontinued in 1986.

	$3,500	$3,200	$2,900	$2,600	$2,300	$2,100	$1,850

Last Mfg.'s Sug. Retail was $3,850.

EXPRESS—.270, .30-06, 8 x 57JRS, and 9.3 x 74R cal.'s, O/U configuration, SST, ejectors. Add $800 for extra set of 20 ga. barrels. Importation discontinued in 1986.

	$3,300	$3,000	$2,800	$2,600	$2,300	$2,100	$1,850

Last Mfg.'s Sug. Retail was $3,600.

ARDENNES MODEL—top-of-the-line model, custom order only. Importation discontinued in 1986.

	$6,600	$6,000	$5,400	$4,800	$4,300	$3,900	$3,450

Last Mfg.'s Sug. Retail was $7,250.

MATRA MANURHIN DEFENSE

PLEASE REFER TO THE MANURHIN HEADING IN THIS SECTION.

MAUSER-WERKE

MANUFACTURED IN OBERNDORF, W. GERMANY 1871 TO DATE. RIFLES ARE CURRENTLY IMPORTED BY KLEINGUETHER DISTINCTIVE FIREARMS (KDF) LOCATED IN SEQUIN, TX (STARTING IN 1987). LUGER PISTOLS ARE ALSO IMPORTED BY KDF ON A CUSTOM ORDER BASIS AND MAY BE FOUND IN THE BACK OF THE LUGER SECTION IN THIS TEXT.

PISTOLS: SEMI-AUTO

WTP MODEL I VEST POCKET AUTOMATIC—6.35mm, 6 shot, 2½ in. barrel, blue, rubber grips, made 1922-1937.

	$375	$280	$250	$200	$160	$140	$100

WTP MODEL II—similar to Model I, but 2 in. barrel, made 1938-1940.

	$400	$300	$250	$200	$150	$140	$130

Grading	100%	98%	95%	90%	80%	70%	60%

POCKET MODEL 1910—6.35mm, 9 shot, 3 in. barrel, blue fixed sights, checkered walnut or hard rubber grips, made 1910-1934.

	100%	98%	95%	90%	80%	70%	60%
	$295	$225	$180	$165	$150	$140	$130

POCKET MODEL 1914—similar to 1910, but 7.65mm, 3.4 in. barrel, made 1914-1934.

	$300	$200	$175	$165	$150	$145	$135

> Add 10% for Eagle WWI proofs.
> Add 500% for the "humpback" model.

POCKET MODEL 1934—similar to 1914, but one piece grip, made 1934-1939.

	$325	$260	$210	$175	$160	$150	$140

> Add 15% for Waffenamt.
> Add 100% for Nazi Navy marked.

MODEL HSC DOUBLE ACTION—7.65mm (8 shot) or .380 ACP (7 shot), 3.4 in. barrel, blue or nickel, fixed sights, checkered walnut grips, made 1938-present (current mfg. is by R. Gamba in Italy).

Early Commercial—standard pre-war Commercial Model. Most frequently encountered variation.

	$450	$340	$300	$265	$225	$200	$185

Transitional—exhibits features of both early and late models.

	$425	$320	$290	$250	$215	$195	$175

WWII MILITARY VARIATIONS

Early Nazi Army—proofed 655 and 135.

	$400	$340	$300	$265	$225	$200	$185

Early Nazi Navy—marked on front grip strap.

	$750	$595	$540	$500	$440	$395	$350

Early Nazi Police—Eagle L proof only.

	$450	$395	$360	$320	$285	$245	$200

Wartime Nazi Army—proof 135 and WaA 135. Eagle N proofed also

	$375	$325	$290	$250	$200	$180	$150

Wartime Nazi Navy—proofed on left side of trigger guard.

	$500	$450	$400	$340	$295	$260	$230

Wartime Nazi Police—proofed Eagle L. Add 10% if Eagle F.

	$450	$395	$360	$320	$285	$245	$200

Wartime Commercial—standard WWII Commercial Model.

	$375	$325	$290	$265	$200	$180	$150

Swiss Commercial—ser. range 800,000-900,000. Very rare.

	$1,400	$1,250	$1,125	$995	$900	$850	$600

Low Grip Screw—very rare, less than 2,000 produced.

	$2,175	$1,700	$1,350	$995	$875	$775	$650

> Add 20% if Navy marked.

Cutaways—manufactured to visibly show mechanism. Should not be proofed.

	$1,495	$1,000	$900	$850	$800	$750	$700

POST-WWII VARIATIONS

French Manufacture—frequently encountered in poor condition — post-WWII production.

	$325	$275	$245	$220	$180	$155	$130

Mauser Production—.32 and .380 cal.'s. Manufactured 1968-1981.

	$350	$295	$260	$225	$180	$150	$130

> Deduct 20% if not boxed or in .32 cal.

Interarms Import—imported by Interarms from 1983-1985 (Italian manufactured by Gamba).

	$300	$275	$250	$220	$180	$150	$125

Last Mfg.'s Sug. Retail was $415.

Grading	100%	98%	95%	90%	80%	70%	60%

One of Five Thousand Edition—American Eagle edition (marked on gun), 5,000 total mfg. (serial numbered 1-5000).

	$400	$330	$265				

Armes de Chasse Import—previously imported by Armes De Chasse located in Chadds Ford, PA on a limited basis. For G15 variation (9 shot) add $58.

	$525	$425	$330	$300	$260	$240	$220

Add $195 for Limited Series.

Last Mfg.'s Sug. Retail was $695.

MAUSER LUGERS

Both pre-war and post-war Mauser manufactured Lugers will be found in the Luger section of this book (including those variations currently imported by KDF from Sequin, TX).

1896 BROOMHANDLE

Note: Manufactured in Oberndorf, Germany between 1897 & 1938.

While many variations of the famous 1896 Broomhandle exist, most common Broomhandles are pre-war Commercials, Model 1930 Commercials, Red 9's, and Bolo's. They can be found in chronological order in this section. Holster stocks are a very popular accessory in this model. Commercial stocks may be matching or may not be serial numbered to gun (proper stock). Add $300 + for stock depending on overall original condition and if matching/non-matching.

In 1984, Federal legislation once again allowed importation of non-domestic WWI and WWII military handguns. As a result, many Bolo and various commercial Banner models have been recently seen at gun shows in some quantity. Condition on most of these recent imports is 25% or lower (with pitting on many) and prices typically start in the $150 range. While many of these newer imports would make workable shooters, they have in no way lowered prices on 90% + condition specimens due to normal collector activity in top quality only pistols. Recently imported Broomhandles should have the importer's name visibly stamped on an exterior surface.

CONEHAMMER VARIATIONS

STANDARD CONEHAMMER—7.63 Mauser, distinguishable by circular machined upper hammer with concentric rings. 5.5 in. barrel, 23 groove wooden grips, rear adjustable sight available in 1-10, 50-500, 100-300, 50-300, 50-700 meter configurations, 10 shot mag.

	$2,600	$2,000	$1,550	$1,200	$1,050	$925	$700

FIXED SIGHT CONEHAMMER—7.63 Mauser, similar to Standard Conehammer, except has fixed rear sight.

	$3,000	$2,200	$1,600	$1,300	$1,100	$925	$700

6 SHOT CONEHAMMER - FIXED SIGHT—7.63 Mauser, 4¾ in. barrel, 6 shot mag., rare.

	$6,000	$5,200	$4,200	$3,500	$3,000	$2,500	$2,000

6 Shot Conehammer w/adjustable sight—7.63 Mauser, 5.5 in. barrel, very rare.

	$10,000	$7,500	$6,000	$5,000	$4,000	$3,000	$2,500

Sales of this variation are extremely limited.

TURKISH CONEHAMMER—7.63 Mauser, approximately 1,000 made for Turkey in 1898, Farsi serial numbers, 5.5 in. barrel, 10 shot mag.

	$4,000	$3,400	$2,800	$2,400	$2,100	$1,800	$1,500

"SYSTEM MAUSER" CONEHAMMER—7.63 Mauser, "SYSTEM MAUSER" marked on top of chamber, improved 5.5 in tapered barrel, 10 shot mag.

	$5,000	$4,000	$3,000	$2,400	$2,100	$1,800	$1,500

Stepped barrel variation—Similar to System Mauser variation, except has older 5.5 in. stepped barrel with no taper.

	$10,000	$7,500	$6,000	$5,000	$4,000	$3,000	$2,500

20 SHOT CONEHAMMER—7.63 Mauser, 20 shot non-detachable mag., frame can either be flatside or have milled panels, 5.5 in. tapered barrel, extremely rare.

	$15,000	$12,000	$10,000	$7,500	$6,000	$5,000	$4,000

Grading	100%	98%	95%	90%	80%	70%	60%

EARLY TRANSITIONAL LARGE RING HAMMER—7.63 Mauser, distinguishable by large, open centered ring, 10 shot mag., 5.5 in. barrel.

	$2,750	$2,000	$1,550	$1,200	$1,050	$925	$700

This variation is normally found in the 12,000-15,000 serial range only.

FLATSIDE VARIATIONS

ADD APPROX. $400 FOR A MATCHING SHOULDER STOCK ON THE FOLLOWING MODELS, $325 FOR NON-MATCHING.

ITALIAN CONTRACT FLATSIDE—7.63 Mauser, distinguishable by flatside frame and DV/AV proofmarks, 10 shot mag., 5.5 in. barrel.

	$3,000	$2,200	$1,600	$1,300	$1,100	$900	$700

This variation is found in the 1-5,000 serial range only.

FLATSIDE COMMERCIAL—7.63 Mauser, 5.5 in. barrel, 23 groove walnut grips, adj. rear sight typically marked 1-10 or 50-1000.

	$2,200	$1,550	$1,250	$1,000	$800	$600	$400

Early specimens may have pinned rear sights. Found in serial range 20,000-30,000.

POST 1900 VARIATIONS

ADD APPROX. $400 FOR A MATCHING SHOULDER STOCK ON THE FOLLOWING MODELS, $325 FOR NON-MATCHING.

PRE-WAR LARGE RING BOLO—7.63 Mauser, 3.9 in. barrel, floral grips, usually found in 29,000 and 40,000 serial range.

	$3,500	$2,800	$2,000	$1,450	$1,000	$700	$450

Add $700 for short pre-war bolo stock.

LARGE RING SHALLOW MILLING—7.63 Mauser, 5.5 in. barrel, 23 groove walnut or hard rubber grips, normally found in the 30,000-33,000 ser. range.

	$1,850	$1,350	$950	$750	$625	$500	$400

LARGE RING DEEP MILLING—7.63 Mauser, 5.5 in. barrel, 35 groove walnut or hard rubber grips, normally found in the 34,000 ser. range.

	$1,850	$1,350	$950	$750	$625	$500	$400

PRE-WAR SMALL RING BOLO—7.63 Mauser, 3.9 in. barrel, floral/checkered rubber or 31-36 groove walnut grips, usually found in 40,000-44,000 serial range.

	$2,200	$1,600	$1,250	$950	$800	$575	$400

6-SHOT BOLO—7.63 Mauser, distinctive 6 shot mag., 3.9 in. barrel, either fixed rear sight (more common) or adjustable, could have either large ring or small ring hammer.

	$5,000	$4,000	$3,500	$3,000	$2,600	$2,200	$1,500

STANDARD PRE-WAR COMMERCIAL—7.63 Mauser, 5.5 in. barrel, 10 shot mag., 34 groove walnut or checkered black rubber grips, typically 50-1,000 adjustable rear sight.

	$1,200	$1,000	$850	$725	$600	$500	$400

This variation is the most commonly encountered of all M1896 broomhandles. It can be encountered in the 39,000-274,000 serial range. Early guns below serial no. 100,000 are often Von Lengerke and Detmold marked and can be encountered with hard rubber grips. Rifling changed from 4 groove to 6 groove at approximately serial no. 100,000.

Note: This model is once again being imported by domestic distributors/dealers. Condition is somewhat poor, and prices usually start in the $250 range. These specimens usually have been reblued in addition to other reworking because the original condition has generally been very poor.

MAUSER BANNER CHAMBER MARKED—7.63 Mauser or 9mm export (rare), 5.5 in. barrel, distinguishable by Mauser banner trademark on top of chamber, 32 groove walnut grips, approximately 10,000 mfg. in serial range 84,000-94,000.

	$1,850	$1,450	$1,100	$850	$725	$600	$500

This model is very similar in appearance to the Pre-War Commercial.

PERSIAN CONTRACT—7.63 Mauser, 5.5 in. barrel, distinguished by Persian lion crest in left rear frame panel, must be in the 154,000 serial range, 50-1,000 meter adjustable rear sight.

	$3,500	$2,800	$2,200	$1,600	$1,100	$850	$700

This variation is frequently faked - pay close attention to serial no. and Persian crest.

Grading	100%	98%	95%	90%	80%	70%	60%

STANDARD WARTIME COMMERCIAL—7.63 Mauser, 5.5 in. barrel, 10 shot mag., 30 groove walnut grips, adj. 50-1,000 meter rear sight.

	$1,000	$850	$750	$650	$550	$450	$350

This variation is encountered almost as frequently as the Standard Pre-War Commercial. It is usually found in the 290,000-440,000 serial range. It was the first model to utilize the "new safety" design, and can be noticed by the "NS" marking on the back of hammer. Similar features as the Pre-War Commercial, except finish and polishing exhibit more machine and tooling marks.

Note: This model is once again being imported by domestic distributors/dealers. Condition is somewhat poor, and prices usually start in the $250 range. These specimens usually have been reblued in addition to other reworking because the original condition has generally been very poor.

RED-9 ADJ. SIGHT—9mm P, 5.5 in. barrel, 10 shot mag., 24 groove walnut grips usually marked with large red no. 9, adj. 50-500 meter rear sight, standard WWI military contract model with separate serial range 1-150,000, generally poorly finished, manufactured 1916-1918.

	$1,500	$1,200	$1,000	$850	$750	$650	$550

Add 10% if Prussian Eagle proofed on front of magazine well.

Note: With matching stock add $400.00 - for non-matching add $325. For original leather add $200. Be cautious for originality since metal refinishing is prevalent in this model. The last 10,000 guns of this German military contract are not military proofed, are better polished, and will command a slight premium.

RED-9 FIXED SIGHT—9mm P, 3.9 in. barrel, this is a 1920 commercial rework of the Red-9 military, may be dated 1920 and/or have police markings on front grip strap.

	$850	$700	$625	$550	$475	$400	$350

Because of the Treaty of Versailles following WWI, barrels had to be shortened to less than 4 inches and the adj. rear sight removed.

FRENCH GENDARME—7.63 Mauser, 3.9 in. barrel, distinguished by Bolo barrel length on large frame, hard rubber or walnut (rare) grips, found in the serial range 431,000-434,000, adj. 50-500 meter rear sight.

	$2,500	$1,850	$1,100	$850	$700	$550	$400

EARLY POST-WAR BOLO—7.63 Mauser, 3.9 in. barrel, shot extractor, small ring hammer, usually found in the 440,000-500,000 serial range.

	$1,700	$1,300	$925	$725	$600	$500	$375

Add 50% for long barrel Bolo's in approximately the 475,000 serial range.

LATE POST-WAR BOLO—7.63 Mauser, 3.9 in. barrel, similar features of Early Post-War Bolo except has Mauser banner trademark on left rear frame panel, usually encountered in the 500,000-700,000 + serial range.

	$1,850	$1,350	$950	$750	$625	$500	$375

POST 1930 VARIATIONS

ADD APPROX. $400 FOR A MATCHING SHOULDER STOCK ON THE FOLLOWING MODELS, $325 FOR NON-MATCHING.

EARLY MODEL 1930 COMMERCIAL—7.63 Mauser, 5.2 (common) or 5.5 in. stepped barrel, 12 groove walnut grips, adj. 50-1,000 meter rear sight, usually found in the 800,000-890,000 serial range.

	$1,750	$1,325	$950	$750	$625	$500	$375

This was the first broomhandle variation to have a high polish, salt blue finish. Small parts are still fire blued and milling grooves were machined in receiver rails.

LATE MODEL 1930 COMMERCIAL—7.63 Mauser, 5.5 in. stepped barrel, similar appearance to early 1930 Commercial except has solid receiver rails and various small parts are salt blued, serial range 890,000-921,000 with production ending in late 1930's.

	$1,650	$1,300	$950	$750	$625	$500	$375

This model is serial numbered on rear top of breech bolt assembly.

Grading	100%	98%	95%	90%	80%	70%	60%

MODEL 1930 REMOVABLE MAG.—7.63 Mauser, 5.5 in. stepped barrel, 12 groove walnut grips, adj. 50-1,000 meter rear sight, very rare.

| | $9,000 | $7,500 | $6,000 | $5,000 | $4,000 | $3,200 | $2,500 |

Original specimens of this variation have frames without the extra cuts required for the selector switch. Fakes are usually welded up Schnellfeuers made to look original. Only a very few are known in the 84,000-88,000 serial range. They are not slotted for the shoulder stock. Also known as the Model 711.

SCHNELLFEUER (MODEL712)—7.63 Mauser, 5.5 in. stepped barrel, 12 groove walnut grips, adj. 50-1,000 meter rear sight, switchable full auto variation generally with selector switch, separate serial range 1-100,000, 10 or 20 shot detachable mag. 712 stock is internally grooved for selector switch.

| | $3,500 | $3,000 | $2,600 | $2,200 | $1,800 | $1,500 | $1,200 |

Add $500 for correct stock. Deduct 60% if Class III transferable only (dealer sample).

The Model 712 is classified as a machine gun and is subject to registration and payment of a $200 transfer tax.

CARBINES: SEMI-AUTO

FLUTED BARREL MODEL—marked "July 1897".

| | $15,000 | $13,000 | $9,000 | $6,000 | $3,800 | $3,300 | $2,950 |

FLATSIDE CONE HAMMER—7.63mm, 11¾ in. barrel, experimental variation.

| | $12,000 | $9,500 | $7,000 | $4,600 | $3,800 | $3,300 | $2,950 |

FLATSIDE TRANSITIONAL—7.63mm, 11¾ in. barrel.

| | $10,000 | $7,500 | $5,500 | $4,600 | $3,800 | $3,300 | $2,950 |

LARGE RING HAMMER TRANSITIONAL—7.63mm, 11¾ in. barrel.

| | $10,000 | $7,500 | $5,500 | $4,600 | $3,800 | $3,300 | $2,950 |

LARGE RING HAMMER—7.63mm, 14½ in. barrel.

| | $10,000 | $7,500 | $5,500 | $4,600 | $3,800 | $3,300 | $2,950 |

SMALL RING HAMMER—7.63mm, 14½ in. barrel.

| | $9,000 | $6,400 | $5,500 | $4,600 | $3,800 | $3,300 | $2,950 |

BROOMHANDLE COPIES FROM OTHER COUNTRIES

Chinese manufactured copies of the original German design.

HAND-MADE MAUSER CHINESE MARKED AND OTHERS—very poorly made Mauser copies, many thousands made.

| | $475 | $425 | $360 | $320 | $260 | $215 | $150 |

HAND-MADE UNMARKED—poor quality.

| | $595 | $550 | $520 | $440 | $385 | $345 | $310 |

ASIATIC FLATSIDE UNMARKED—better quality, not exceedingly rare.

| | $895 | $800 | $740 | $680 | $600 | $500 | $400 |

TAKU-NAVAL DOCKYARD FLATSIDE—machine-made, better quality, not exceedingly rare, approx. 6,000 produced.

| | $1,100 | $900 | $740 | $680 | $600 | $500 | $400 |

Add 30% with correct stock.
Add 5% if with holster.

SHANSI ARSENAL .45 CAL.—.45 ACP cal., approx. 8,500 manufactured, scarce and desirable in excellent condition.

| | $3,500 | $2,700 | $2,400 | $2,100 | $1,700 | $1,600 | $1,475 |

SPANISH COPIES OF MAUSER BROOMHANDLES

VERY EARLY ASTRA-900—Bolo grips, frame has single-line address, approx. 1,200 produced.

| | $3,000 | $2,500 | $2,200 | $2,000 | $1,750 | $1,600 | $1,475 |

EARLY ASTRA-900—single-line address, approx. ser. range 1,200-12,000.

| | $2,250 | $1,800 | $1,300 | $850 | $700 | $525 | $425 |

MAUSER-WERKE, cont.

Grading	100%	98%	95%	90%	80%	70%	60%

LATE ASTRA-900—two and three-line address, two-line address ser. range is approx. 12,000-20,000, three-line address ser. range is approx. 20,000-34,400.

	$2,000	$1,800	$1,300	$850	$700	$525	$425

Add 25% for Japanese character variation in the 27,000 serial range or if in Nazi procurement range.

ROYAL SEMI-AUTO—early Royals are mostly seen in semi-auto with round bolts.

	$2,650	$2,200	$1,800	$1,300	$850	$700	$600

There were many variations of the Royal's and above values assume standard variation.

ROYAL SELECTIVE FIRE—7.63mm, most of approx. 25,000 Royal's manufactured were selective fire, several variations, transferable only. Add 20% if detachable mag., 100% if equipped with pneumatic rate retarder.

Class III	$2,500	$2,200	$2,000	$1,800	$1,700	$1,600	$1,475

This model had either a fixed mag., detachable mag., or pneumatic rate retarder.

MILITARY RIFLES

Deduct 30% if bolt is not matching.

CZECH MODEL 1924 SHORT—7.92mm, 23.23 in. barrel.

	$395	$350	$275	$250	$195	$165	$140

MODEL 1935 FN

	$440	$375	$300	$220	$160	$140	$120

KAR 98 POLISH CREST—7.92mm.

	$325	$260	$200	$150	$125	$100	$80

SWISS CALVARY CARBINE—K31.

	$1,150	$950	$800	$675	$525	$450	$350

GREEK FN

	$395	$320	$275	$220	$190	$175	$140

GERMAN G 33/40-MOUNTAIN CARBINE, 1940-1943 DATES

	$750	$575	$475	$400	$350	$300	$260

GERMAN G 98/40-MOUNTAIN CARBINE

	$950	$875	$750	$650	$575	$500	$425

G41 SNIPER

Mauser manufacture

	$1,400	$1,200	$900	$700	$650	$600	$550

Walther manufacture

	$950	$900	$850	$700	$600	$500	$450

G43 OR K43 SNIPER RIFLE—add $500 if with scope, Nazi issue.

	$990	$880	$770	$650	$600	$485	$400

KAR 98 ERFURT ROYAL ARSENAL

	$180	$140	$120	$100	$90	$85	$65

GERMAN M98—WWI Gewehr 98 (Mauser, Simson, Danzig, Amberg, Erfut).

	$295	$250	$195	$155	$140	$110	$90

KAR 98 GERMAN WWII—(K 98 K), dated 1936-1945, coded manufacturers, deduct 20% for 1943-1945 dates. Add 100% for K date S/42. Add 50% for G date S/42.

	$395	$325	$250	$165	$145	$120	$100

RADOM MAUSER MODEL 29—7.92mm.

	$395	$320	$275	$220	$190	$175	$140

K98K PORTUGUESE CONTRACT

	$525	$440	$330	$275	$250	$220	$165

TURKISH M1888

	$185	$140	$115	$90	$70	$55	$40

MAUSER-WERKE, cont.

Grading	100%	98%	95%	90%	80%	70%	60%
SWEDISH CONTRACT M98							
	$200	$175	$135	$110	$90	$75	$60
CZECH M98 VZ24—7.92mm.							
	$340	$275	$240	$210	$170	$140	$110
YUGOSLAVIAN M24							
	$250	$200	$150	$120	$110	$100	$85
DANISH 1889 - 10							
	$250	$200	$165	$155	$140	$110	$90
CHILIAN MODEL 1895—7mm, 29.06 in. barrel.							
	$285	$220	$185	$165	$140	$110	$100
98K FRENCH OCCUPATION							
	$285	$220	$180	$165	$140	$110	$100
MODEL 98 COLUMBIAN—.30-06.							
	$285	$220	$175	$155	$110	$90	$85
SIAMESE MAUSER RIFLE—29.13 in. barrel, 8 x 50R.							
	$165	$125	$110	$90	$75	$60	$50
SIAMESE MAUSER CARBINE—8 x 50R.							
	$165	$125	$110	$90	$75	$60	$50
IRANIAN MODEL 98/29—long rifle.							
	$250	$210	$165	$140	$120	$100	$85
IRANIAN MODEL 98/29—7.92mm, 17.91 in. barrel, short.							
	$270	$220	$195	$165	$145	$120	$100
SWEDISH MODEL 94—6.5mm, 17.38 in. barrel carbine.							
	$225	$190	$155	$130	$110	$100	$95
SPANISH MODEL 93—7mm, 29.06 in. barrel.							
	$185	$150	$120	$110	$90	$85	$65
SPANISH MODEL 43 SHORT—7.9mm, 23.62 in. barrel.							
	$200	$160	$125	$100	$90	$85	$75
SOUTH AMERICAN G.E.W. M98—7.92mm.							
	$175	$145	$100	$90	$85	$70	$55
VZ24 ROMANIAN CREST							
	$325	$250	$220	$200	$180	$165	$140
BRAZILIAN M1908—7 x 57mm.							
	$170	$145	$110	$90	$85	$65	$55
ARGENTINE M1909—7.65mm.							
	$225	$190	$150	$120	$110	$95	$85
ARGENTINE M1891—7.65mm.							
	$170	$145	$110	$90	$85	$65	$55
PERUVIAN M1935 SHORT—.30-06, 23 in. barrel.							
	$225	$190	$150	$120	$110	$100	$85
PERUVIAN CREST M98							
	$195	$160	$120	$110	$100	$90	$85
1934 MAUSER BANNER—7.92mm. Characterized by side sling and turn down bolt handle.							
	$375	$280	$250	$220	$195	$165	$140
ITALIAN MAUSER—7.92mm, 1,000 produced for Germany.							
	$250	$210	$160	$120	$110	$95	$85
GERMAN M71/84—11mm, 33.56 in. barrel. Add 60% if M 71 (without tubular mag.)							
	$250	$225	$200	$180	$160	$140	$125

SPORTING RIFLES

BOLT ACTION SPORTING RIFLE—6.5 x 55, 6.5 x 58, 7 x 57, 8 x 57, 9 x 57, 9.3 x 63, and 10.75 x 68 cal.'s, 5 shot mag., 23½ in. barrel, double set trigger, adj. sight, rounded (not capped) pistol grip, Schnabel forearm, sling swivels.

$370	$330	$300	$260	$220	$190	$175

Grading	100%	98%	95%	90%	80%	70%	60%

BOLT ACTION SPORTING RIFLE SHORT MOD.—6.5 x 54 and 8 x 51 cal.'s, 20 in. barrel, same as Standard for other specifications.

	$370	$330	$300	$260	$220	$190	$175

BOLT ACTION SPORTING RIFLE MILITARY TYPE—same as Standard, except stepped military type barrel and military style sights and trigger, 7 x 57, 8 x 57, and 9 x 57 cal.'s.

	$370	$330	$300	$260	$220	$190	$175

BOLT ACTION SPORTING CARBINE—same as Standard, except Mannlicher style full stock, 6.5 x 54, 6.5 x 58, 7 x 57, and 9 x 57 cal.'s, 19¾ in. barrel.

	$400	$350	$300	$260	$220	$190	$175

TYPE A BOLT ACTION—7 x 57, .30-06, 8 x 60, 9 x 57, and 9.3 x 62 cal.'s, 23½ in. barrel, 5 shot, express sights, single trigger, Buffalo Horn forearm tip and pistol grip cap.

	$430	$375	$325	$280	$240	$220	$195

TYPE A SHORT ACTION—same as Bolt Action, .250-3000, 6.5 x 54 cal.'s, and 8½ x 51.

	$430	$375	$325	$280	$240	$220	$195

TYPE A MAGNUM MODEL—same as Short Action, except Mag. cal. .280 Ross, .318 W.R. Express, 10¾ x 68, and .404 Nitro Express.

	$475	$410	$360	$325	$275	$250	$235

Note: Type B, Type K, Type M, and Type S, and the above rifles have great similarity and for the purpose of price evaluation are extremely close to the Type A rifles.

MAUSER STANDARD MODEL RIFLE—refined Kar 98K, 7 x 57 and 8 x 57 cal.'s, made for commercial sale and possesses quality of Oberndorf Sporters.

	$425	$310	$245	$200	$175	$160	$140

RIFLES: RECENT MANUFACTURE

All long arms manufactured by Mauser-Werke are currently being exclusively imported by KDF Inc. located in Seguin, TX. More information pertaining to current Mauser-Werke long arms can be obtained by contacting KDF Inc. directly.

Importation of some of the current models listed below may be somewhat limited, and due to the devaluation of the U.S. dollar, prices (and availability) could differ from what is shown in this section.

MODEL 225—available in 13 cal.'s between .243 Win. and .300 Wby. Mag., bolt action, 60 degree bolt lift with 3 locking lugs, ultra fast lock time, adj. trigger, 24 or 26 (Mag. only) in. barrel, 3 or 5 shot mag., no sights, guaranteed ½ in. accuracy at 100 yards, many stock options available at extra cost. Left-handed action available in certain cal.'s at the same price as Mag. cal.'s (Model 226).

Deluxe Standard Sporter—standard model available in 6 regular cal.'s and 9 Mag. cal.'s.

Mfg.'s Sug. Retail	$1,400	$1,275	$1,000	$875	$750	$625	$550	$495

Add $90 for Mag. cal.'s.

This model was formerly the KDF Model K-15.

MODEL 66A—similar to Model 66S except has American configured laminate stock (wood grain), cal.'s, action, and features are the same as the Model 66S. Importation began in late 1988.

Standard Calibers

Mfg.'s Sug. Retail	$2,100	$1,900	$1,425	$1,150	$925	$800	$700	$650

Add $630 per interchangeable barrel.

The A suffix on this model denotes American.

Magnum Calibers—includes Weatherby Mag. cal.'s also.

Mfg.'s Sug. Retail	$2,270	$2,050	$1,500	$1,200	$975	$825	$700	$650

Add $670 per interchangeable barrel.

Big Game Calibers—includes most popular Mag. cal.'s up to .458 Win. Mag.

Mfg.'s Sug. Retail	$2,700	$2,350	$1,900	$1,425	$1,150	$950	$825	$750

Grading	100%	98%	95%	90%	80%	70%	60%

MODEL 66S—telescoping short action, .243 Win., 6.5 x 57, .270 Win., 7 x 64, .308 Win., and .30-06 cal.'s, 24 in. barrel, standard interchangeable barrels, single or double set triggers, adj. and detachable sights, Monte Carlo walnut stock with checkering, swivels, new safety, rosewood tipped forearm and pistol grip, rubber recoil pad, 7¼ lbs., made 1974-present.

With the introduction of the Model 66A, the Model 66S is now available on a custom order only basis through KDF Inc. Values below represent 1988 prices, and KDF should be contacted directly to obtain more information regarding this European configured model.

Model 66 prices below reflect the recent devaluation of the U.S. dollar against the Deutschmarke. While the manufacturer's suggested retails have gone up considerably, prices for used specimens (98% or less original condition) have not increased proportionately, and in some cases, have changed very little.

Mfg.'s Sug. Retail	$1,440	$1,200	$995	$920	$800	$680	$550	$470

Magnum Model—28 in. barrel, 6.5 x 68, 7mm Rem. Mag., 8 x 68 S, 300 Win. and Wby. Mag.'s, and 9.3 x 64 cal.'s, 8.4 lbs.

Mfg.'s Sug. Retail	$1,537	$1,275	$1,070	$965	$840	$700	$600	$500

Mannlicher and Ultra—21 in. barrel, full stock (Mannlicher only) and half stock, double or single triggers, standard cal.'s only, 7 lbs.

Mfg.'s Sug. Retail	$1,537	$1,275	$1,070	$965	$840	$700	$600	$500

Big Game Rifle—.375 H&H Mag. or .458 Win. Mag. cal.'s only, single trigger, 9¼ lbs.

Mfg.'s Sug. Retail	$1,864	$1,550	$1,300	$1,075	$895	$760	$675	$575

Extra standard barrels are available starting at $513 each.

MODEL 66 SM—telescoping short action, .243 Win., .270 Win., 7 x 64, .308 Win., .30-06, and 6.5 x 57 cal.'s, 24 in. barrel, standard interchangeable barrels, set trigger on tang, adj. and detachable sights, Monte Carlo walnut stock with checkering, swivels, new safety, anatomical gripped select walnut stock with Mauser-nose, cocking lever on tang, rubber recoil pad, 7¼ lbs., made 1981-present.

With the introduction of the Model 66A, the Model 66SM is now available on a custom order only basis through KDF Inc. Values below represent 1988 prices, and KDF should be contacted directly to obtain more information regarding this European configured model.

Model 66 prices below reflect the recent devaluation of the U.S. dollar against the Deutschmarke. While the manufacturer's suggested retails have gone up considerably, prices for used specimens (98% or less original condition) have not increased proportionately, and in some cases, have changed very little.

Mfg.'s Sug. Retail	$1,801	$1,550	$1,260	$1,075	$875	$730	$620	$520

Model 66 SM Ultra—all standard cal.'s, 21 in. barrel, 7¼ lbs.

Mfg.'s Sug. Retail	$1,903	$1,625	$1,325	$1,140	$920	$760	$650	$550

Magnum Calibers—same as Model 66 S, 26 in. barrel, 8.4 lbs.

Mfg.'s Sug. Retail	$1,903	$1,625	$1,325	$1,140	$920	$760	$650	$550

Mannlicher type full stock—all standard cal.'s, 21 in. barrel, 7 lbs.

Mfg.'s Sug. Retail	$1,903	$1,625	$1,325	$1,140	$920	$760	$650	$550

MODEL 66 SL—same as Model 66 SM, except features extra select walnut with special graining, 7¼ lbs. Disc. in 1985.

	$1,370	$1,275	$890	$720	$580	$475	$420

Last Mfg.'s Sug. Retail was $1,470.

Model 66 SL Ultra—7 x 64 and .30-06 cal.'s, 21 in. barrel, 7¼ lbs. Discontinued in 1985.

	$1,475	$1,325	$940	$750	$600	$450	$400

Last Mfg.'s Sug. Retail was $1,520.

Magnum Calibers—same as Model 66 S, 8.4 lbs. Discontinued in 1985.

	$1,475	$1,325	$940	$750	$600	$450	$400

Last Mfg.'s Sug. Retail was $1,520.

Mannlicher type full stock—21 in. barrel, 7 lbs. Discontinued in 1985.

	$1,475	$1,325	$940	$750	$600	$450	$400

Last Mfg.'s Sug. Retail was $1,520.

Grading	100%	98%	95%	90%	80%	70%	60%

MODEL 66SL DIPLOMAT—same specifications as Model 66 SM, except includes selected walnut and special engraving including deer and wild bore game scenes. Add $93 for Mannlicher full stock (21 in. barrel), $387 for Mag. cal.'s.

Mfg.'s Sug. Retail **$3,167 $2,700 $2,220 $1,875 $1,535 $1,385 $1,135 $1,000**

This model is now available on a individual custom order basis only. Values above reflect 1988 pricing information.

MODEL 660—U.S. designation of 66S, imported 1971-1973.

$925 $820 $720 $600 $500 $450 $400

MODEL 66S DELUXE—special order engraved and inlaid, select wood. Priced per individual customer order. All guns are custom made only. Prices usually start in the $2,500 range.

MODEL 66SP SUPER MATCH—telescoping short action, .308 Win., 27½ in. heavy barrel with muzzle break, no sights match trigger, 3 shot mag., select European walnut stock with stippling and thumbhole, adj. cheekpiece and buttplate, includes premium scope, 12 lbs.

Mfg.'s Sug. Retail **$8,160 $7,375 $6,200 $5,500 $4,800 $4,300 $3,900 $3,500**

MODEL 77—.243 Win., .270 Win., 6.5 x 57, 7 x 64, .308 Win., and .30-06 cal.'s, 24 in. barrel, set trigger on tang, adj. and detachable sights, walnut stock with European cheekpiece and hand checkering, swivels, new safety, steel detachable box mag., rubber recoil pad, 7¼ lbs. Discontinued.

$1,130 $950 $875 $810 $750 $675 $595

Last Mfg.'s Sug. Retail was $1,331.

Model 77 Ultra—6.5 x 57, 7 x 64 or .30-06 cal., 20 in. barrel, 7.7 lbs. Discontinued.

$1,175 $975 $895 $835 $760 $675 $595

Last Mfg.'s Sug. Retail was $1,394.

Magnum Calibers—same as Model 66S, 8⅛ lbs. Discontinued.

$1,175 $975 $895 $835 $760 $675 $595

Last Mfg.'s Sug. Retail was $1,394.

Mannlicher type full stock—20 in. barrel, Mauser-set trigger, 7.7 lbs. Discontinued.

$1,175 $975 $895 $835 $760 $675 $595

Last Mfg.'s Sug. Retail was $1,394.

Big Game Model—.375 H&H Mag. cal., 26 in. barrel, 8⅛ lbs. Discontinued.

$1,075 $1,000 $900 $795 $675 $575 $475

Last Mfg.'s Sug. Retail was $1,150.

MODEL 77 SPORTSMAN—.243 or .308 Win. cal., sports version of the Model 77, set trigger on the tang, no sights, 24 in. barrel, 9 lbs. Add $430 for Zeiss 2½-10X scope and mounts. Discontinued.

$1,495 $1,230 $1,075 $985 $895 $820 $740

Last Mfg.'s Sug. Retail was $1,754.

MODEL 83 MATCH SINGLE SHOT—.308 Win. cal.'s only, cylinder locking action with 3 locking lugs in rear, match trigger, anatomical match stock with select walnut, adj. comb and buttplate. Discontinued.

$2,170 $1,815 $1,660 $1,545 $1,400 $1,195 $925

This model is a UIT standard rifle at 300 meters.

Last Mfg.'s Sug. Retail was $2,594.

MODEL 83 MATCH UIT FREE RIFLE—.308 Win. cal.'s only, cylinder locking action with 3 locking lugs in rear, match trigger, anatomical match stock with select walnut, adj. comb and buttplate. Discontinued.

$2,320 $1,940 $1,760 $1,600 $1,430 $1,195 $925

Last Mfg.'s Sug. Retail was $2,771.

MODEL 83 STANDARD RIFLE—similar to Model 83 Match, except has removable 10 shot steel mag., 26 in. barrel. Discontinued.

$2,320 $1,950 $1,800 $1,625 $1,460 $1,250 $1,000

Last Mfg.'s Sug. Retail was $2,766.

Grading	100%	98%	95%	90%	80%	70%	60%

MODEL 86SR MATCH—.308 cal., updated version of the Model 83 action, fiberglass stock, magazine. Importation began in 1989.

Mfg.'s Sug. Retail	$4,140	$3,850	$3,200	$2,750	$2,175	$1,800	$1,500	$1,250

Model 86SR Cism—similar to Model 86SR Match except has wood stock and iron sights. Importation began in 1989.

Mfg.'s Sug. Retail	$4,540	$4,140	$3,500	$3,000	$2,400	$2,100	$1,700	$1,450

MODEL 2000 BOLT ACTION—.270 Win., .308 Win., or .30-06 cal., 5 shot mag., 24 in. barrel, leaf rear sight, checkered walnut stock, made by F.W. Heym for Mauser, 1969-1971.

	$305	$290	$275	$220	$175	$155	$140

MODEL 3000—bolt action, .243 Win., .270 Win., .308 Win., or .30-06 cal., 5 shot mag., 22 in. barrel, no sights, walnut Monte Carlo style stock, rosewood forearm and pistol grip, skipline checkering, recoil pad and swivels, made 1971-1974.

	$500	$450	$425	$400	$375	$325	$275

MODEL 3000 MAGNUM—same as 3000, except 7mm Rem. Mag., .300 Win. Mag., or .375 H&H Mag. cal., 3 shot mag., 26 in. barrel.

	$550	$500	$450	$425	$375	$350	$325

This model was manufactured by Heym for Mauser.

MODEL 4000 VARMINT RIFLE—same as 3000, except smaller action, .222 Rem. or .223 Rem. cal., folding leaf rear sight, rubber buttplate.

	$425	$400	$375	$350	$300	$260	$225

This model was manufactured by Heym for Mauser.

RIFLES: .22 CAL. SPORTING

MODEL 107—.22 LR only, bolt action, 19½ in. barrel, 5 shot clip mag., adj. iron sights, 6 lbs. Importation began in 1988.

Mfg.'s Sug. Retail	$280	$265	$215	$175	$150	$135	$120	$110

This model is the same as KDF's previous Model 2107 mfg. by Voere.

Model 107 Deluxe—.22 LR or .22 Mag. cal., similar to Model 2107, except has deluxe checkered walnut. Importation began in 1988.

Mfg.'s Sug. Retail	$320	$290	$240	$210	$175	$150	$135	$120

Add $90 for .22 Mag. cal.

This model is the same as KDF's previous Model 2107 Deluxe mfg. by Voere.

MODEL 201—.22 LR or .22 Mag. cal., bolt action, free floating 21 in. barrel, clip 5 shot mag., adj. trigger, scale down version of the K-15, unusual action incorporates two front-located locking lugs on bolt face that engage Stellite inserts on the front receiver portion, guaranteed 1 in. groupings at 100 yards, blue only, no sights, select walnut stock with cheekpiece.

Mfg.'s Sug. Retail	$585	$530	$425	$365	$315	$270	$240	$225

Add $65 for .22 Mag. cal.

This model is the same as KDF's previous Model K-22 mfg. by Voere.

Model 201 Deluxe—similar to the Model 201 except has better walnut and stock options.

Mfg.'s Sug. Retail	$650	$595	$525	$425	$365	$315	$270	$240

Add $65 for .22 Mag. cal.

This model is the same as KDF's previous Model K-22 Deluxe mfg. by Voere.

MODEL DSM34—.22 LR, 25 in. barrel. "Deutches Sportmodell" lightweight trainer, side sling, no bayonet lug.

	$325	$300	$260	$225	$200	$175	$150

MODEL MS 420B—.22 LR Sporter, pre-war, 5 shot, clip fed.

	$360	$330	$305	$275	$220	$195	$165

MODEL ES340—.22 LR, single shot, bolt action, 25½ in. barrel, adj. sights, checkered pistol grip, grooved forearm, pre-1935.

	$275	$255	$230	$200	$180	$155	$140

Grading	100%	98%	95%	90%	80%	70%	60%

MODEL ES350—.22 LR, single shot, bolt action, 27½ in. barrel, championship rifle, micrometer rear sight, ramp front sight, checkered full target stock, swivels, pre-1935.

| | $440 | $420 | $395 | $370 | $305 | $275 | $250 |

MODEL M410—.22 LR, bolt action, repeating, 5 shot detachable mag., 23½ in. barrel, adj. sights, sporter stock, checkered pistol grip, swivels, pre-1935.

| | $360 | $340 | $320 | $290 | $240 | $220 | $195 |

MODEL M420—.22 LR, bolt action, repeating, 5 shot detachable mag., 25½ in. barrel, adj. sights, sporter stock, checkered pistol grip, swivels, pre-1935.

| | $360 | $340 | $320 | $290 | $240 | $220 | $195 |

MODEL EN310—.22 LR, single shot, bolt action, 19¾ in. barrel, fixed sights, plain pistol grip stock, pre-1935.

| | $230 | $220 | $210 | $185 | $140 | $120 | $100 |

MODEL EL320—.22 LR, single shot, bolt action, 23½ in. barrel, fixed sights, checkered pistol grip stock.

| | $275 | $255 | $230 | $200 | $180 | $155 | $140 |

MODEL KKW—.22 LR, single shot, bolt action, target, 26 in. barrel, tangent rear sight, military style stock with bayonet lug. This weapon was also produced by Walther, Gustloff, and Anschutz. It was used as a training rifle in addition to commercial sales. Deduct 15% for 4mm KKW Models.

| | $415 | $400 | $385 | $360 | $305 | $250 | $195 |

MODEL MS350B—.22 LR, bolt action, repeating, 5 shot mag., 26¾ in. barrel, grooved receiver for scope or sight, micrometer rear sight, ramp front sight, target stock, checkered pistol grip and forearm, swivels.

| | $470 | $450 | $430 | $415 | $360 | $330 | $305 |

MODEL ES350B—.22 LR, bolt action, single shot, 5 shot mag., 26¾ in. barrel, grooved receiver for scope or sight, micrometer rear sight, ramp front sight, target stock, checkered pistol grip and forearm, swivels.

| | $415 | $400 | $385 | $360 | $320 | $275 | $250 |

MODEL ES340B—.22 LR, bolt action, single shot, 26¾ in. barrel, adj. sight, plain pistol grip stock.

| | $360 | $340 | $320 | $305 | $250 | $220 | $195 |

MODEL MM410BN—.22 LR, bolt action sporter, 5 shot mag., 23½ in. barrel, adj. sights, lightweight stock, checkered pistol grip, swivels.

| | $415 | $395 | $385 | $360 | $305 | $275 | $250 |

MODEL MS420B—.22 LR, bolt action target, 5 shot mag., 26¾ in. barrel, adj. sights, target style stock, checkered pistol grip, swivels.

| | $415 | $395 | $385 | $360 | $305 | $275 | $250 |

SHOTGUNS

Mauser shotguns were sub-contracted to various European firms and were made in field and target configurations. While they are relatively rare (these shotguns were never imported into the U.S.), collectibility to date has been minimal. Values will depend on the grade, configuration, features, engraving, and overall desirability. Most of these shotguns have been priced in the $650-$1,300 range.

MARK X SPORTING RIFLE

Currently imported by Interarms. Consult the Interarms Mark X section.

MAVERICK ARMS, INC.

MANUFACTURER LOCATED IN EAGLE PASS, TX.

MODEL 88—12 ga. only, 3 in. chamber, slide-action, 28 or 30 in. barrel, black synthetic stock and forearm with recoil pad, fixed choke, aluminum alloy receiver, crossbolt safety, approx. 7¼ lbs. New in 1989.

| *Mfg.'s Sug. Retail* | $175 | $160 | $135 | $125 | $115 | $110 | $105 | $100 |

Add $20 for vent. rib.

McMILLAN, G. & CO. INC.
MANUFACTURER/DISTRIBUTOR LOCATED IN PHOENIX, AZ.

McMillan primarily manufactures fiberglass synthetic stocks in a wide variety of configurations and styles (including many camouflaged models). In addition to these, McMillan also custom manufactures the rifles listed below on an individual order basis. More information can be obtained on McMillan's fiberglass stocks by contacting the company directly.

RIFLES: BOLT ACTION

SIGNATURE MODEL—various cal.'s available between .22-250 and .375 H&H, fiberglass stock, buttoning used on rifling for 22 or 24 in. stainless steel barrel, action made from 4340 chrome moly steel (either left or right-handed), 3 or 4 shot mag. supplied with 5 shot test target. New in 1988.

| *Mfg.'s Sug. Retail* | $1,525 | $1,475 | $1,200 | $1,020 | $895 | $800 | $700 | $600 |

Varmint Model—similar to Signature Model, except is available in 9 cal.'s between .22-250 and .25-06, hand bedded fiberglass stock, adj. trigger, 26 in. heavily contoured barrel. New in 1988.

| *Mfg.'s Sug. Retail* | $1,625 | $1,540 | $1,275 | $1,020 | $895 | $800 | $700 | $600 |

Safari Model—available in 8 cal.'s between .300 Win. Mag. and .460 Weatherby, hand bedded fiberglass stock, 4 round mag., 24 in. stainless steel barrel, matte black finish. New in 1988.

| *Mfg.'s Sug. Retail* | $2,750 | $2,650 | $2,100 | $1,850 | $1,600 | $1,350 | $1,100 | $950 |

MODEL 86 SNIPER RIFLE—.300 Win. Mag. or .308 cal., fiberglass stock, variety of optical sights. New in 1988.

| *Mfg.'s Sug. Retail* | $1,600 | $1,520 | $1,275 | $1,020 | $895 | $800 | $700 | $600 |

Model 86 Sniper System—includes Model 86 Sniper Rifle, bipod, Ultra scope, rings, and bases. Cased. New in 1988.

| *Mfg.'s Sug. Retail* | $2,665 | $2,460 | $2,050 | $1,825 | $1,600 | $1,350 | $1,100 | $950 |

MODEL 87 LONG RANGE SNIPER RIFLE—.50 BMG, stainless steel bolt action, 29 in. barrel with muzzle brake, single shot, camo synthetic stock, accurate to 1500 meters, 21 lbs. New in 1988.

| *Mfg.'s Sug. Retail* | $2,950 | $2,700 | $2,400 | $2,200 | $2,000 | $1,850 | $1,700 | $1,575 |

Model 87 Sniper System—includes Model 87 Sniper Rifle, bipod, 20X Ultra scope, rings, and bases. Cased. New in 1988.

| *Mfg.'s Sug. Retail* | $4,200 | $3,950 | $3,400 | $3,000 | $2,750 | $2,450 | $2,200 | $2,000 |

COMPETITION MODELS—available in Metallic Silhouette (.308 or 7mm/08 cal.), National Match (.308 cal. only), Long Range (.300 Win. Mag. only), or Bench Rest (shooter's choice). Each model made specifically for individual competition events. New in 1988.

| *Mfg.'s Sug. Retail* | $1,625 | $1,540 | $1,275 | $1,020 | $895 | $800 | $700 | $600 |

Add $125 for National Match/Long Range models.

MCMILLAN BARRELS
MCMILLAN IN CONJUNCTION WITH BILL WISEMAN MANUFACTURES BOTH CUSTOM RIFLES AND SILHOUETTE PISTOLS. SINCE MCMILLAN FABRICATES THE BARRELS ONLY IN THIS VENTURE, THESE FIREARMS WILL APPEAR UNDER THE WISEMAN HEADING IN THIS TEXT.

MERCURY
MANUFACTURED IN SPAIN.

MAGNUM DOUBLE BARREL—10, 12, and 20 ga. Mag., 28 and 32 in. barrels, full and mod., boxlock, extractors, double triggers, engraved frame, checkered pistol grip stock.

| | $300 | $275 | $250 | $225 | $200 | $180 | $150 |
| 10 gauge | $400 | $375 | $325 | $300 | $275 | $225 | $200 |

MERCURY

MANUFACTURED IN BELGIUM.

MERCURY SEMI-AUTO—.22 LR, 7 shot mag., steel frame, fixed sights.

$400	$375	$325	$300	$275	$225	$200

MERKEL, GEBRUDER

MANUFACTURED IN SUHL, E. GERMANY. CURRENTLY IMPORTED EXCLUSIVELY BY ARMES DE CHASSE LOCATED IN CHADDS FORD, PA, 19317.

SHOTGUNS: DISCONTINUED

MODEL 100 O/U—12, 16, or 20 ga., various barrel lengths and chokes, boxlock, Greener cross bolt, double triggers, extractors, checkered pistol grip or English style stock, pre-WWII.

Plain	$1,450	$1,250	$1,000	$925	$850	$675	$550
Ribbed	$1,550	$1,300	$1,050	$950	$875	$700	$575

MODEL 101—same as 100, except selective extractors, rib barrel, some English style scroll engraving, pre-WWII.

$1,600	$1,325	$1,100	$1,000	$900	$750	$600

MODEL 101E—same as 100, except auto ejectors, pre-WWII.

$1,750	$1,425	$1,250	$1,150	$1,000	$875	$750

MODEL 400—similar to 101, except arabesque engraving and Kersten double cross bolt, pre-WWII.

$1,650	$1,350	$1,200	$1,100	$975	$825	$675

MODEL 400E—same as 400, except auto ejector, pre-WWII.

$1,800	$1,450	$1,325	$1,175	$1,025	$925	$775

MODEL 410—same as 400, except more engraving and fancier wood, pre-WWII.

$1,750	$1,425	$1,250	$1,150	$1,000	$875	$750

MODEL 410E—same as 410, except auto ejectors, pre-WWII.

$1,900	$1,600	$1,450	$1,225	$1,100	$995	$875

MODEL 200 O/U—12, 16, 20, 24, 28, or 32 ga., ribbed barrels in various lengths, Kersten double cross bolt, scalloped frame, boxlock, double triggers, extractors, cocking indicators, either pistol grip or English style checkered stock.

$1,700	$1,350	$1,100	$990	$770	$660	$635

MODEL 210—same as 200, except engraved and better grade wood, pre-WWII.

$1,900	$1,500	$1,300	$1,075	$895	$800	$725

MODEL 201 O/U—12, 16, or 20 ga., Greener crossbolt, hunting engraving or fine arabesque, dark walnut.

$2,000	$1,600	$1,425	$1,200	$995	$900	$800

MODEL 201E—same as 201, except with auto ejectors, pre-WWII.

$2,400	$1,825	$1,600	$1,400	$1,200	$1,075	$950

MODEL 202—same as 201, except with false sideplates, higher quality wood, more profuse engraving, pre-WWII.

$2,800	$2,400	$2,035	$1,700	$1,450	$1,200	$1,050

MODEL 202E—same as 202, with auto ejectors, pre-WWII.

$3,200	$2,800	$2,485	$2,050	$1,700	$1,425	$1,200

MODEL 203E O/U—similar to 202E except better engraving and wood.

$4,000	$3,400	$2,900	$2,500	$2,100	$1,800	$1,425

MODEL 204E O/U—similar to 203E, but fine English scroll engraving and Merkel sidelocks, ejectors, pre-WWII.

$5,650	$4,900	$4,300	$3,850	$3,300	$2,750	$2,100

Grading	100%	98%	95%	90%	80%	70%	60%

MODEL 300 O/U—12, 16, 20, 24, 28, or 32 ga., various lengths and choke ribbed barrels, Merkel-Anson boxlock, Kersten double cross bolt, two underlugs, scalloped frame, either English or pistol grip style stock, cocking indicators, pre-WWII.

$2,100 $1,900 $1,700 $1,550 $1,375 $1,200 $1,050

This model is usually encountered without engraving and has standard wood.

MODEL 300E—same as 300, with auto ejectors, pre-WWII.

$2,500 $2,250 $1,900 $1,750 $1,500 $1,350 $1,175

This model is usually encountered without engraving and has standard wood.

MODEL 301—same as 300, but more profusely engraved and better grade wood pre-WWII.

$5,250 $4,250 $3,995 $3,500 $3,000 $2,600 $2,150

MODEL 310E—same as 300, with auto ejectors, pre-WWII.

$6,250 $5,300 $4,450 $3,900 $3,400 $3,000 $2,550

MODEL 302—similar to 301, but has auto ejectors and more elaborate ornamentation, false side plates and better grade wood.

$10,500 $8,500 $6,500 $5,750 $4,900 $4,150 $3,400

MODEL 304E O/U—special order version of 303E, higher quality and more ornamentation, top of Merkel O/U line.

$16,500 $12,000 $10,500 $8,750 $7,500 $6,250 $5,000

MODEL 130 SxS—all standard gauges, barrel lengths and chokes, Anson & Deeley action with false side plates, boxlock, auto ejectors, English style or pistol grip stock, elaborate game scenes and arabesque engraving, pre-WWII.

$12,000 $9,500 $7,500 $6,350 $5,400 $4,600 $3,950

MODEL 127 SxS—all standard gauges, barrel lengths and chokes, H&H, hand detachable sidelocks, auto ejectors, double triggers, pistol or English style stock elaborately engraved, this is a best grade gun, pre-WWII.

$21,500 $16,500 $12,500 $10,000 $8,800 $7,000 $5,750

O/U RIFLES OR COMBINATION GUNS

COMBINATION GUN—12, 16, or 20 ga., over 5.6 x 35 Vierling, 7 x 57R, 8 x 57JR, 8 x 60R Mag., 9.3 x 53R, and 9.3 x 72R cal.'s, various barrel lengths and chokes, specifications and values are comparable to previous O/U shotguns.

DOUBLE RIFLE—models include 220E, 221, 223, 223E, and 323E, rifle barrels, calibers same as Combination Gun, plus English Bigbore African cal.'s(up to .375 H&H). Rare and very desirable — prices can exceed $20,000.

Most of these models are rare since they were not meant to be exported to the U.S. by Eastern Block countries.

DRILLINGS

MERKEL ANSON DRILLING—usually 2 shotguns over rifle, although 2 rifles over shotgun have been noted, 12, 16, and 20 ga.'s, calibers 7 x 57R, 8 x 57JR, and 9.3 x 74R cal.'s most common, others noted, 25.6 in. or 21.6 in. barrels, boxlock, Anson & Deeley system, double triggers, extractors, checkered pistol grip stock, pre-WWII.

MODEL 142—engraved.

$5,000 $4,000 $3,000 $2,750 $2,500 $2,200 $2,000

MODEL 142—less ornamentation.

$4,000 $3,500 $3,000 $2,500 $2,250 $2,100 $2,000

MODEL 145—least ornamentation.

$3,000 $2,800 $2,700 $2,600 $2,500 $2,100 $1,900

SHOTGUNS: SxS RECENT IMPORTATION

Imported exclusively by Armes de Chasse located in Chadds Ford, PA, 19317.

Available in limited quantities, the models listed below include the 65% duty levied on all firearms imported from Warsaw Pact countries.

Grading	100%	98%	95%	90%	80%	70%	60%

Prices below reflect the recent devaluation of the U.S. dollar against the E. German Deutschmarke. While the manufacturer's suggested retails have gone up considerably, prices for used specimens (98% or less original condition) have not increased proportionately, and in some cases, have changed very little.

MODEL 8—12, 16, or 20 ga., case hardened scalloped boxlock action with light engraving, Greener crossbolt with chopper lump extension, extractors, DT's, standard walnut with checkering, cheekpiece on stock, sling swivels. Importation disc. in 1987.

	100%	98%	95%	90%	80%	70%	60%
	$925	$690	$630	$585	$530	$480	$450

Last Mfg.'s Sug. Retail was $1,010.

MODEL 47E—12, 16, or 20 ga., case hardened scalloped boxlock action with chopper lump extension and Greener crossbolt, DT's, ejectors, deluxe checkered walnut, sling swivels.

	100%	98%	95%	90%	80%	70%	60%
Mfg.'s Sug. Retail	$1,525	$1,325	$1,045	$820	$690	$630	$585	$530

MODEL 147E—12, 16, and 20 ga.'s, 26 in barrels, Anson & Deeley boxlock, any choke, double trigger, auto ejectors, straight or pistol grip stock, hunting scene engraved.

	100%	98%	95%	90%	80%	70%	60%
Mfg.'s Sug. Retail	$1,945	$1,650	$1,375	$995	$875	$780	$700	$640

MODEL 122—12, 16, or 20 ga., coin finished sidelock action with Greener crossbolt and chopper lump extension, cocking indicators, ejectors, DT's, deluxe game scene engraving.

	100%	98%	95%	90%	80%	70%	60%
Mfg.'s Sug. Retail	$3,252	$2,750	$2,200	$1,650	$1,475	$1,350	$1,225	$1,100

MODEL 147S—12, 16, or 20 ga., coin finished sidelock action with Greener crossbolt and chopper lump extension, ejectors, DT's, deluxe game scene engraving.

	100%	98%	95%	90%	80%	70%	60%
Mfg.'s Sug. Retail	$5,436	$4,600	$3,975	$3,250	$2,900	$2,500	$2,200	$1,950

MODEL 247S—12, 16, or 20 ga., similar to Model 147S, except has deluxe scroll engraving.

	100%	98%	95%	90%	80%	70%	60%
Mfg.'s Sug. Retail	$5,436	$4,600	$3,975	$3,250	$2,900	$2,500	$2,200	$1,950

MODEL 347S—12, 16, or 20 ga., similar to Model 247S, except has more elaborate engraving and better walnut.

	100%	98%	95%	90%	80%	70%	60%
Mfg.'s Sug. Retail	$6,102	$5,625	$4,825	$4,200	$3,600	$2,950	$2,425	$2,180

MODEL 447S—similar to Model 347S, except has different type of scroll engraving.

	100%	98%	95%	90%	80%	70%	60%
Mfg.'s Sug. Retail	$6,982	$6,150	$5,000	$4,465	$3,200	$2,725	$2,425	$2,180

MODEL 47S—12, 16, or 20 ga., coin finished sidelock action with scroll engraving, Greener crossbolt, DT's, deluxe walnut stock (with cheekpiece) and forearm, sling swivels.

	100%	98%	95%	90%	80%	70%	60%
Mfg.'s Sug. Retail	$4,370	$3,825	$3,275	$2,700	$2,250	$1,975	$1,625	$1,475

SHOTGUNS: O/U CURRENT IMPORTATION

Imported exclusively by Armes de Chasse located in Chadds Ford, PA, 19317.

Available in limited quantities, the models listed below include the 65% duty levied on all firearms imported from Warsaw Pact countries.

Prices below reflect the recent devaluation of the U.S. dollar against the E. German Deutschmarke. While the manufacturer's suggested retails have gone up considerably, prices for used specimens (98% or less original condition) have not increased proportionately, and in some cases, have changed very little.

The models listed below are also available in either 28 or .410 ga. for an additional charge of $900 and $1,050, respectively.

MODEL 200E—12, 16, or 20 ga., case hardened scalloped boxlock action with minor scroll engraving, checkered heartwood stock and forearm, ejectors, DT's, solid rib.

	100%	98%	95%	90%	80%	70%	60%
Mfg.'s Sug. Retail	$3,944	$3,550	$2,950	$2,500	$1,950	$1,785	$1,650	$1,525

A vent. rib can be obtained on this model for an additional charge.

MODEL 201E—similar to Model 200E, except has coin finished action with light game scene engraving.

	100%	98%	95%	90%	80%	70%	60%
Mfg.'s Sug. Retail	$4,386	$3,750	$3,175	$2,650	$2,100	$1,920	$1,700	$1,560

Grading	100%	98%	95%	90%	80%	70%	60%

MODEL 203E—12, 16, or 20 ga.(24, 28, and 32 ga.'s were once available but are now disc.), various barrel lengths and chokes, VR, ejectors, DT's, elaborate scroll engraving on coin finished receiver, sidelock screws are H&H style but the sidelocks are not, choice of English or pistol grip stock.

Mfg.'s Sug. Retail **$10,606 $9,150 $8,000 $6,950 $5,500 $4,775 $4,100 $3,700**
Add $600 for flat cut game scene engraving.
Add $5,700 for deep relief game scene engraving featuring small animals.
Add $6,500 for deep relief game scene engraving featuring large animals.

MODEL 303E—similar to 203E, except H&H type with hidden thumbnail detachable sidelocks, double underlugs, more ornamentation and better wood.

Mfg.'s Sug. Retail **$16,918 $14,500 $12,300 $10,250 $8,000 $6,950 $5,500 $5,000**

MODEL 304E (LUXUS GRADE)—available in SXS, O/U, Drilling, or Combo configuration, top-of-the-line Merkel with extensive engraving and typically stock carving (with or without inlays).

Values generally start at $16,500 and go up according to engraving and stock work.

Luxus variations are also encountered in the 201 and 203 series in addition to older pre-war models.

MERRILL

SPORTSMAN SINGLE-SHOT PISTOL—.22 S, L, or LR, .22 WMR, .22 Rem. Jet., .22 Hornet, 30 Herrett, .38 Spl., .357 Mag., .256 Win. Mag., .45 Colt, .44 Mag., and .30-30 cal.'s, 9 in. barrel, hinged break open available, smooth walnut grips.

    $275 $250 $235 $210 $190 $175 $150
Add $70 for interchangeable barrels.
Add $25 for wrist support.

MERWIN HULBERT & CO.

HEADQUARTERED IN NEW YORK, NY, FROM 1874-1891. MANUFACTURED BY HOPKINS & ALLEN MANUFACTURING CO.

Merwin Hulbert & Co. were designers and promoters who created a revolver that had such advanced features as an automatic ejection system, streamlined appearance, and ease of shooting. Rather than list the individual variations, each specimen should be examined for originality and condition. Prices have recently escalated and currently these revolvers in average condition start in the $500 + range.

MIIDA

MANUFACTURED IN JAPAN.

MODEL 612—O/U shotgun, 12 ga., 26 and 28 in. barrels, vent rib, various chokes, boxlock, auto ejectors, single selective trigger, checkered pistol grip stock, made 1972-1974.

    $880 $745 $660 $605 $550 $495 $440

MODEL 612 SKEET GUN—same as 612, with 27 in. vent rib, skeet bore barrel, more elaborate engraving, made 1972-1974.

    $990 $855 $770 $715 $660 $605 $550

MODEL 2200T TRAP GUN—same as 612, with 29¾ in. imp. mod. and full choke barrel, wide vent rib, 60% engraved coverage and select wood, made 1972-1974.

    $1,100 $935 $880 $825 $770 $715 $660

MODEL 2200S SKEET GUN—same as 2200T, with 27 in. skeet bore barrel.

    $1,100 $935 $880 $825 $770 $715 $660

Grading	100%	98%	95%	90%	80%	70%	60%

MODEL 2300 SERIES TRAP OR SKEET—same as 2200, with more engraving, made 1972-1974.

	100%	98%	95%	90%	80%	70%	60%
	$1,320	$1,100	$990	$935	$880	$825	$715

MODEL GRT GRANDEE TRAP GUN—12 ga., 29 in. full choke barrels, single selective trigger, auto ejector, boxlock with side plates, receiver fully engraved as well as breech ends of barrel, trigger guard and locking lever, gold inlaid, high grade select walnut stock, made 1972-1974.

	100%	98%	95%	90%	80%	70%	60%
	$2,200	$1,980	$1,760	$1,650	$1,430	$1,320	$1,100

MODEL GRS GRANDEE SKEET GUN—same as GRT, with 27 in. skeet bored barrels.

	100%	98%	95%	90%	80%	70%	60%
	$2,200	$1,980	$1,760	$1,650	$1,430	$1,320	$1,100

MIROKU SHOTGUNS

MANUFACTURED IN MIROKU, JAPAN.

Shotguns marked Miroku only without another trademark listing represent that period of manufacture before Miroku began manufacturing shotguns for other companies (i.e. Charles Daly, SKB, Browning, and others). Most guns marked Miroku only were made on a limited basis and although somewhat rare, collector desirability to date has been minimal. Since model notations were not specified in most instances (many shotguns were made to test market demand), a model rundown is virtually impossible. Values can be approximately ascertained by comparing a Miroku shotgun of similar gauge, features, engraving/wood, and condition to an equivalent Japanese Charles Daly model.

MITCHELL ARMS INC.

IMPORTER AND DISTRIBUTOR LOCATED IN SANTA ANA, CA.

PISTOLS

SKORPION—.32 ACP only, single action, 4⅝ in. barrel, 20 or 30 shot mag., blue finish only, made in Yugoslavia. Imported 1987-1988 only.

	100%	98%	95%	90%	80%	70%	60%
	$615	$520	$480	$440	$395	$360	$330

Last Mfg.'s Sug. Retail was $685.

SPECTRE—9mm, single action, 8 in. shrouded barrel, unique frame/barrel cooling system, 30 or 50 shot mag., approx. 4 lbs. Imported 1987-1988 only.

	100%	98%	95%	90%	80%	70%	60%
	$610	$515	$475	$440	$395	$360	$330

Last Mfg.'s Sug. Retail was $670.

Spectre Carbine—9mm, carbine model with folding butt stock. Imported in 1988 only.

	100%	98%	95%	90%	80%	70%	60%
	$610	$520	$480	$440	$395	$360	$330

Last Mfg.'s Sug. Retail was $680.

REVOLVERS

SINGLE ACTION ARMY—.22 LR, .357 Mag., .44 Mag., and .45 Long Colt cal.'s, 4¾, 5½, 6, and 7½ in. barrel lengths, hammer block safety mechanism, steel construction, case hardened frame, one-piece walnut stock. Add $17 for adj. sight. New in 1986.

Rimfire Model—.22 LR cal.

	100%	98%	95%	90%	80%	70%	60%
Mfg.'s Sug. Retail	$280	$230	$200	$180	$160	$145	$130	$120

Add $30 for adj. rear sight.

Centerfire Model—.357 Mag., .44 Mag., or .45 LC cal.

	100%	98%	95%	90%	80%	70%	60%
Mfg.'s Sug. Retail	$296	$245	$210	$190	$170	$155	$145	$135

Add $32 for adj. rear sight.
Add $86 for silhouette model.

The silhouette model is available with 10, 12, or 18 in. barrel in .44 Mag. or .45 LC cal.
Add $141 for shoulder stock (available with 18 in. barrel only).

The shoulder stock is available with .44 Mag./.44-40 cal.'s only.

Grading	100%	98%	95%	90%	80%	70%	60%

Dual Cylinder—available in either .22 LR/.22 Mag., .22 LR/.22 Mag. stainless (disc. in 1988), or .44 Mag./.44-40. New in 1986.

Mfg.'s Sug. Retail	$310	$265	$230	$200	$180	$165	$150	$135

Add $28 for .44 Mag./.44 Combo.

Add $35 for adj. rear sight.

Stainless Model—available in .22 LR or .357 Mag. (disc. in 1987) only, adj. sights. Imported 1986-1988 only.

	$260	$225	$195

Add $25 for .357 Mag.

Last Mfg.'s Sug. Retail was $301.

BAT MASTERSON MODEL—.45 LC cal., 4¾ in. barrel with full ejector rod housing, nickel plated, one piece walnut stocks, hammer-block safety, rear sight is square notch in frame, two piece backstrap. New in 1989.

Mfg.'s Sug. Retail	$329	$280	$240	$210	$185	$170	$150	$135

RIFLES

M-16—.22 LR, .22 Mag. (disc. in 1987), and .32 ACP cal.'s, patterned after Colt's AR-15. New in 1987.

Mfg.'s Sug. Retail	$280	$235	$195	$160	$150	$140	$130	$120

Add $15 for .22 Mag. cal. or .32 ACP (disc. in 1988).

GALIL—.22 LR or .22 Mag. cal., patterned after Galil semi-auto assault rifle. New in 1987.

Mfg.'s Sug. Retail	$280	$235	$195	$160	$150	$140	$130	$120

MAS—.22 LR or .22 Mag. cal., patterned after French MAS rifle. New in 1987.

Mfg.'s Sug. Retail	$280	$235	$195	$160	$150	$140	$130	$120

Add $15 for .22 Mag. cal. (disc. in 1988).

PPS-50—.22 LR cal., patterned after the Russian WWII PPSh military rifle, full length barrel shroud, 20 shot banana clip, adj. rear sight, walnut stock. New in 1989.

Mfg.'s Sug. Retail	$280	$235	$195	$160	$150	$140	$130	$120

Add $60 for 50 shot drum magazine.

AK-22—.22 LR or .22 Mag. (new in 1988) cal., copy of the famous Russian AK-47, fully adj. sights, built in cleaning rod, high quality European walnut stock, 20 shot clip mag. New in 1985.

Mfg.'s Sug. Retail	$280	$235	$195	$160	$150	$140	$130	$120

AK-47—7.62 x 39 cal., copy of the original SKS AK-47, semi-auto, teak stock and forend, 30 round steel mag., last shot hold open. Mfg. in Yugoslavia. New in 1986.

Mfg.'s Sug. Retail	$675	$565	$495	$450	$400	$360	$310	$270

Add $23 for steel folding butt stock.

Add $150 for 75 shot steel drum mag.

.308 NATO AK-47 (M77B1)—.308 (7.62 NATO) cal., otherwise similar to AK-47 except has scope rail, day/night Tritium sights, and 20 shot mag. New in 1989.

Mfg.'s Sug. Retail	$775	$675	$565	$495	$450	$400	$360	$310

Add $600 for military issue sniper scope and rings.

M76—similar to AK-47, except is 7.9mm cal. and has longer barrel and frame set up for scope mount, counter sniper design, 10 round mag., mfg. to mil. spec.'s. New in 1986.

Mfg.'s Sug. Retail	$1,995	$1,725	$1,535	$1,350	$1,100	$900	$820	$760

SKS-M59—7.62 x 39 cal., copy of the SKS-M59 standard rifle, full walnut stock, fully adj. sights, gas operated. Mfg. in Yugoslavia. New in 1986.

Mfg.'s Sug. Retail	$699	$610	$525	$465	$410	$360	$315	$260

R.P.K.—7.62 X 39mm cal., forged heavy barrel with cooling fins, teak stock, detachable bipod, mil. spec.'s. Importation began in 1989.

Mfg.'s Sug. Retail	$995	$875	$775	$675	$565	$495	$450	$400

MORINI

TARGET PISTOLS MANUFACTURED IN ITALY. IMPORTED AND DISTRIBUTED BY OSBORNE'S, LOCATED IN CHEBOYGAN, MI.

CM-80 STANDARD—.22 LR only, single shot, adj. grips, frame, and sights. Add $50 for left-hand model.

Mfg.'s Sug. Retail	$1,015	$965	$840	$725	$650	$585	$520	$465

CM-80 Super Competition—similar to CM-80 Standard, except has deluxe finish, and unique plexiglass front sighting system. Add $50 for left-hand model.

Mfg.'s Sug. Retail	$1,196	$1,085	$920	$800	$690	$590	$520	$450

MOSSBERG, O.F. & SONS, INC.

MANUFACTURED 1892-1919 UNDER OSCAR F. MOSSBERG IN FITCHBURG & CHICOPEE FALLS, MA. FROM 1919 TO DATE, MANUFACTURER HAS BEEN LOCATED AT NORTH HAVEN, CT.

PISTOLS: DISCONTINUED

BROWNIE—.22 LR, top break open action, rotating firing pin, 4 barrel derringer, double action, 4 shot, limited production.

	$350	$300	$260	$225	$200	$180	$160

RIFLES: DISCONTINUED

MODEL K PUMP RIFLE—.22 S, L, and LR, tube mag., hammerless, 22 in. barrel, takedown, open sights, plain straight stock, made 1922-1931.

	$165	$130	$110	$95	$70	$60	$50

MODEL M PUMP RIFLE—same as K, except 24 in. octagon barrel, made 1928-1931.

	$180	$150	$120	$105	$85	$70	$60

MODEL L—.22 S, L, and LR, falling block action, single shot, 24 in. barrel, takedown, open sights, pistol grip stock, made 1927-1932.

	$305	$240	$220	$195	$165	$155	$130

Note: From 1930 to present, Mossberg has manufactured 40 bolt action .22 rifles, both single and repeating. These guns are very practical and serviceable. Higher priced rifles are listed separately in many places, our concern being values. They are all in a range from about $125 for 100% to $25 for 60% and under.

Mossberg also manufactured 13 different autoloading .22 rifles in the same category. Values are $135 for 100% to $35 for 60% and under.

MODEL 400 PALOMINO—.22 S, L, and LR, lever action, tube mag., open sights, checkered Monte Carlo stock, made 1959-1964.

	$140	$110	$100	$90	$65	$55	$40

MODEL 402 PALOMINO CARBINE—same as 400, except 18½ in. or 20 in. barrel, made 1961-1971.

	$140	$110	$100	$90	$65	$55	$40

MODEL 800—.222, .22-250, .243, and .308 cal.'s, bolt action, 22 in. barrel, folding sight, checkered pistol grip stock, made 1967-discontinued.

	$220	$195	$165	$110	$85	$55	$45

MODEL 800VT—similar to 800, except .222, .22-250, and .243 cal.'s, 24 in. heavy barrel, no sights, made 1968-discontinued.

	$220	$195	$165	$110	$85	$55	$45

MODEL 800M—same as 800, except 20 in. barrel, full length stock, spoon bolt handle, made 1969-1972.

	$275	$240	$220	$205	$175	$160	$145

MODEL 800D—similar to 800, with roll-over combination and cheekpiece, checkered stock with rosewood forearm tip and pistol cap, no .222 available, made 1970-1973.

	$290	$265	$230	$195	$175	$165	$140

Grading	100%	98%	95%	90%	80%	70%	60%

MODEL 810—.270, .30-06, 8mm Rem. Mag., and .338 Win. Mag. cal.'s, bolt action, 22 or 24 in. barrel, leaf sight, checkered Monte Carlo stock, made 1970-discontinued.

	$285	$260	$220	$175	$160	$150	$130

MODEL 472—.30-30 and .35 Rem. cal.'s, lever action carbine, 20 in. barrel, open sights, pistol grip or straight stock, saddle ring on straight model, made 1972-discontinued.

	$180	$155	$145	$130	$120	$110	$90

MODEL 472 RIFLE—same as Carbine, except 24 in. barrel, pistol grip stock, made 1974-1976.

	$195	$165	$155	$145	$130	$120	$100

MODEL 472 BRUSH GUN—same as Carbine, except 18 in. barrel, straight stock only, made 1974-1976.

	$195	$165	$155	$145	$130	$120	$100

MODEL 472 ONE IN FIVE THOUSAND—same as Brush Gun, except Indian scene etched on receiver, brass butt plate, saddle ring and barrel bands, select stock, only 5,000 produced, 1974.

	$415	$210	$195	$175	$165	$145	$120

MODEL 479 PCA—.30-30 lever action, 20 in. barrel, 6 round capacity.

	$195	$135	$120	$110	$95	$85	$75

MODEL 479 RR—limited edition "Roy Rodgers" signature model, 5,000 total production, gold trigger, barrel bands. New in 1983.

	$350	$275	$215				

MODEL 144—.22 cal. only, bolt action, 7 shot detachable mag., 27 in. barrel, target style stock and sights, with swivels, 8½ lbs. Discontinued in 1985.

	$175	$160	$155	$150	$145	$140	$135

Last Mfg.'s Sug. Retail was $210.

MODEL 479—.30-30 cal. only, lever action, 6 shot tube mag., 20 in. barrel with adj. sights, 7 lbs. Manufactured 1985 only.

	$190	$175	$160	$150	$145	$140	$135

Last Mfg.'s Sug. Retail was $232.

Mossberg also has made several .22 bolt action and semi-auto sporters that are in the $115 - $130 price range. While they are good shooting models, they are not covered in this section as they are not collectible.

RIFLES: RECENT MANUFACTURE

In 1985, Mossberg purchased the parts inventory and importing rights for those rifles that Smith & Wesson imported from Howa of Japan. These new models were identical to those models which S&W discontinued.

MODEL 1500 MOUNTAINEER GRADE I—.223, .243, .270, 30-06, and 7mm Mag. cal.'s, bolt action, 22 or 24 (7mm Mag. only) in. barrel, 5 or 6 shot mag., available with or without sights, hardwood stock is satin finished, blued finish, about 7 lbs. 10 oz. Imported 1986-87 only. Add $15 for 7mm Rem. Mag. cal., $25 for iron sights.

	$285	$250	$225	$195	$180	$165	$150

Last Mfg.'s Sug. Retail was $335.

Model 1500 Varmint—.22-250, .223, and .308 cal.'s, similar to Model 1500 Grade I, except has 24 in. heavy barrel only, Monte Carlo stock. Imported 1986-87 only. Add $10 for parkerized finish (oil finished stock with swivels — not available in .22-250 cal.).

	$360	$300	$270	$235	$205	$190	$175

Last Mfg.'s Sug. Retail was $457.

Blued finish and high gloss wood finish available with cal.'s .22-250 and .223 only. Parkerized variation is available in .223 and .308 cal.'s only (matte wood finish, includes swivels).

Grading	100%	98%	95%	90%	80%	70%	60%

MODEL 1500 MOUNTAINEER GRADE II—similar to Grade I Mountaineer, except has select checkered American walnut stock. Also available in .300 and .338 Win. Mag. cal.'s. Imported 1986-87 only.

	$315	$270	$235	$205	$190	$175	$160

> Add $15 for Mag. cal.'s.
> Add $25 for iron sights.

Last Mfg.'s Sug. Retail was $368.

MODEL 1550—similar to Model 1500, except has detachable mag. and available in standard cal.'s (.243, .270, and .30-06), with or without sights. Imported 1986-87 only. Add $24 for iron sights.

	$330	$280	$245	$210	$190	$175	$160

Last Mfg.'s Sug. Retail was $391.

MODEL 1700 LS—.243, .270, or .30-06 cal., no sights, jeweled bolt body and knurled bolt handle, detachable mag., Schnabel forend, deluxe checkering, 7 lbs. Imported 1986-87 only.

	$405	$365	$310	$275	$240	$205	$190

Last Mfg.'s Sug. Retail was $492.

SHOTGUNS

Note: Mossberg made 12 bolt action shotguns from 1940-present. They are good, serviceable guns valued at $125 for 100% to $25 for 60% and under.

In 1985, Mossberg purchased the parts inventory and manufacturing rights for the shotguns that Smith & Wesson discontinued. These new models (manufactured in Japan) are identical to those models which S&W discontinued.

MODEL 200K—slide shotgun, 12 ga., 28 in., select choke, plain pistol grip stock, black nylon slide handle, made 1955-1959.

	$130	$110	$100	$90	$65	$55	$40

MODEL 200D—same as 200K, except interchangeable choke tubes (2), made 1955-1959.

	$130	$110	$100	$90	$65	$55	$40

BOLT ACTION MODEL—12, 20, and .410 ga.'s, 3 shot mag., 26, 28, or 38 in. barrel. Deduct $10 for .410 ga. Discontinued in 1985.

	$115	$105	$100	$90	$65	$55	$40

> Add $20 for 38 in. barrel.

Last Mfg.'s Sug. Retail was $135.

MODEL 500 REGAL SERIES—12 or 20 ga., slide action, 26 or 28 in. barrel, select checkered walnut, vent rib. Add $19 for Accu-choke. Importation disc. in 1987.

	$240	$195	$175	$165	$155	$145	$135

Last Mfg.'s Sug. Retail was $286.

Also available in a combo pack which includes 1 extra 24 in. slugster barrel - add $39.

MODEL 500 FIELD GRADE—12, 20 and .410 ga.'s, slide action, 25-38 in. barrel, various chokes, upper receiver slide safety, C Lect & Accu chokes, or with 24 in. slug barrel, checkered pistol grip stock after 1973, made 1962-present.

Mfg.'s Sug. Retail	$258	$205	$180	$150	$135	$120	$110	$100

> Add $23 for vent rib.
> Add $10 for C Lect (disc.).
> Add $31 for Accu II chokes (VR barrel only).

Also available in a combo pack which includes 1 extra 24 in. slugster barrel — add $40-$60.

Model 500 Steel Shot—12 ga. only, 28 in. vent rib multi-choke barrel capable of shooting steel shot. New in 1987.

Mfg.'s Sug. Retail	$292	$245	$200	$175	$165	$155	$145	$135

> Add $29 for camo stock.

Grading	100%	98%	95%	90%	80%	70%	60%

Model 500 Camo/Speedfeed—12 ga. only, parkerized camo metal and stock finish, 24-30 in. vent rib barrel, includes swivels, camo sling, and drilled and tapped receiver, stock holds 4 extra shells. New in 1986.

Mfg.'s Sug. Retail	$334	$275	$240	$200			

   Subtract $30 without multi-chokes.
   Subtract $30 without speedfeed in syn. stock.
   Add $54 for Camo Combo (includes extra 24 in. slug barrel).

Model 500 Slugster—12 or 20 ga., 18½ or 24 in. barrel with iron sights, drilled and tapped receiver.

Mfg.'s Sug. Retail	$276	$235	$185	$170	$160	$155	$145	$135

   Add $48 with integral scope base and rifled bore (Trophy Slugster).

Model 500 Camper—12, 20, or .410 ga. only, 18½ in. barrel, synthetic pistol grip (no stock), supplied with camo carrying case, blued finish. New in 1986.

Mfg.'s Sug. Retail	$292	$245	$195	$175	$165	$155	$145	$135

   Add $6 for .410 ga.

MODEL 500 HI-RIB TRAP—12 ga. only, high post trap rib, 28 or 30 in. barrel. Add $20 for Accu-choke. Discontinued in 1986.

	$285	$250	$230	$200	$175	$155	$140

Last Mfg.'s Sug. Retail was $334.

MODEL 500 SUPER GRADE—same as Field, except vent rib and checkered, no 16 ga., made 1965-1976.

	$215	$180	$170	$160	$140	$130	$120

MODEL 500 ATR SUPER GRADE—same as Field, except 12 ga., vent rib, 30 in. full, checkered Monte Carlo, made 1968-1971.

	$295	$260	$230	$200	$175	$155	$140

MODEL 500 PIGEON GRADE—same as 500 Super Grade, except etched and scroll engraving, select wood, floating vent rib, made 1971-1975.

	$385	$330	$305	$250	$210	$185	$165

MODEL 500 APTR PIGEON GRADE TRAP—same as 500 ATR, except trap style stock, made 1971-1975.

	$440	$415	$330	$250	$220	$200	$175

MODEL 500 DSPR DUCK STAMP COMMERCIAL—same as Pigeon Grade, except wood duck etching, 1,000 produced in 1975.

	$525	$330	$310	$285	$260	$220	$195

MODEL 500L SERIES—same as 500 Field Grade, except no 16 ga., etched receiver, new style stock and slide, made 1977-1983.

	$250	$220	$210	$200	$175	$165	$140

MODEL 500 PERSUADER—same as 500L, except 12 ga. only, 6 or 8 shot, 18½ or 20 in. plain barrel, optional rifle sights, parkerized, optional bayonet lug, plain pistol grip wood or synthetic stock.

Mfg.'s Sug. Retail	$259	$210	$180	$160	$145	$130	$115	$100

   Add $17 for speedfeed stock.
   Add $40 for parkerized finish.
   Add $7 for pistol grip.
   Add $25 for combo with pistol grip.
   Add $19 for rifle sights.
   Add $37 for 8 shot.

MODEL 500 MARINER—12 ga. only, 18½ or 20 in. barrel, Marinecote finish on all metal parts (more durable than stainless steel), synthetic stock and forearm, 6 or 8 shot.

Mfg.'s Sug. Retail	$358	$295	$255	$200			

   Add $33 for speedfeed stock.
   Add $17 for 8 shot mag. (disc.).
   Add $9 for pistol grip adapter.

MODEL 500 CRUISER—12 or 20 ga., 18½ in. cylinder bore barrel with shroud, 6 shot mag., pistol grip only.

Mfg.'s Sug. Retail	$259	$210	$180	$160	$145	$130	$115	$100

Grading	100%	98%	95%	90%	80%	70%	60%

MODEL 500 BULLPUP—12 ga. only, 18½ or 20 in. barrel, bullpup configuration, includes shrouded barrel, carrying handle, ejection port in stock, employs high impact materials. New in 1986.

Mfg.'s Sug. Retail	$403	$335	$295	$255			

Add $15 for 8 shot mag. (disc.).

MODEL 590—similar to Model 500, except has 9 shot mag., 20 in. barrel with ¾ shroud, and bayonet lug, blued or parkerized finish. New in 1987.

Mfg.'s Sug. Retail	$329	$285	$235	$200	$175	$155	$140	$125

Add $41 for parkerized finish.
Add $16 for speedfeed stock.

Model 590 Mariner—similar to Model 500 Mariner except is 9 shot and has 20 in. barrel. New in 1989.

Mfg.'s Sug. Retail	$428	$365	$310	$260	$220	$190	$165	$150

Add $15 for speedfeed stock.
Add $8 for pistol grip adapter.

Model 590 Bullpup—similar to Model 500 Bullpup except is 9 shot and has 20 in. barrel. New in 1989.

Mfg.'s Sug. Retail	$472	$410	$350	$295	$250	$225	$195	$175

MODEL 835 ULTI-MAG—12 ga. with 3½ in. chamber (new in 1988), slide action, 28 in. VR barrel with Accu-Mag choke tubes, 6 shot mag., safety on top rear of receiver, choice of camo synthetic or checkered hardwood stock. New in late 1988.

Mfg.'s Sug. Retail	$416	$355	$300	$260	$220	$190	$165	$150

Add $27 for synthetic camo field stock.

MODEL 835 WILD TURKEY FED. LIMITED EDITION—12 ga. with 3½ in. chamber, 24 in. VR barrel with Accu-Mag. chokes, camo finish, includes camo sling, medallion in stock, and 10-pack of Federal Turkey loads. New in 1989.

Mfg.'s Sug. Retail	$477	$420	$360	$300	$260	$225	$195	$175

MODEL 3000—12 or 20 ga. only, 3 in. chamber, slide action, steel receiver, double action bars, various chokes and vent rib barrel lengths, checkered walnut stock and forearm, vent recoil pad. Add $25 for multi-choke II. This model was introduced in 1986 and the field version was discontinued in 1987. Law enforcement variations are still available.

	$325	$275	$250	$220	$200	$185	$170

Last Mfg.'s Sug. Retail was $360.

Model 3000 Waterfowler—12 ga. only, similar to Model 3000, except has dull matte finish on wood and metal, includes swivels and camouflaged sling, vent rib only. Add $30 for multi-choke II option, $70 for camo/speedfeed stock. Made in 1986 only.

	$340	$295	$265				

Last Mfg.'s Sug. Retail was $386.

Model 3000 Law Enforcement—12 or 20 ga. only, 18½ or 20 in. cylinder bore only, rifle or bead sights. Add $33 for black speedfeed stock. Imported 1986-87 only.

	$325	$275	$250	$220	$200	$185	$170

Add $25 for rifle sights.

Last Mfg.'s Sug. Retail was $362.

MODEL 1000—12 or 20 ga., gas semi-auto, 2¾ in. chamber, scroll engraved aluminum alloy receiver, plain or vent rib barrel, also available in trap and skeet configuration, checkered walnut stock and forearm. Add $28 for multi-choke II. Imported 1986-87 only. Vent rib became standard in 1987.

	$410	$345	$300	$270	$245	$220	$200

Deduct $50 if without VR.

Last Mfg.'s Sug. Retail was $472.

Model 1000 barrels are not interchangeable with Model 1000 Super barrels.

Model 1000 Junior—similar to Model 1000, except 20 ga. only, shortened stock, and 22 in. VR multi-choke barrel. Imported 1986-87 only.

	$425	$355	$310	$275	$250	$220	$200

Last Mfg.'s Sug. Retail was $499.

Grading	100%	98%	95%	90%	80%	70%	60%

Model 1000 Slug—12 or 20 ga., 22 in. barrel with rifle sights, recoil pad. Imported in 1986-87 only.

	$405	$340	$295	$270	$245	$220	$200

Last Mfg.'s Sug. Retail was $464.

Model 1000 Skeet—12 or 20 ga., steel receiver, 26 in. vent rib barrel bored skeet. Made in 1986 only.

	$395	$335	$295	$270	$245	$220	$200

Last Mfg.'s Sug. Retail was $439.

MODEL 1000 SUPER—12 or 20(Super 20) ga., gas semi-auto, 3 in. chambers, shoots 2¾ and 3 in. shells interchangeably, steel receiver, vent recoil pad, select checkered walnut stock and forearm, multi-choke II is standard (except on slug barrel). Slug models are approximately the same price as values listed directly below. Imported 1986-87 only.

	$495	$405	$365	$330	$295	$270	$245

Last Mfg.'s Sug. Retail was $577.

Model 1000 Super barrels are not interchangeable with Model 1000 barrels.

Model 1000 Super Waterfowler—12 ga. only, matte finished wood and metal, includes swivels and camouflaged sling, 28 in. multi-choke barrel. Imported 1986-87 only.

	$510	$430	$370

Last Mfg.'s Sug. Retail was $605.

Model 1000 Super Skeet—12 or 20 ga., 25 in. barrel, jug choking. Imported 1986-87 only.

	$575	$495	$450	$410	$375	$330	$295

Last Mfg.'s Sug. Retail was $658.

Model 1000 Super Trap—12 ga. only, 30 in. multi-choke II barrel with high vent rib, Monte Carlo stock, recoil pad. Made in 1986 only.

	$470	$380	$345	$320	$285	$270	$250

Last Mfg.'s Sug. Retail was $560.

MODEL 5500 SEMI-AUTO—12 ga., 2¾ or 3 in. mag., gas operated, 18½ - 30 in. barrels. Add $20 for vent rib. Discontinued in 1985.

	$250	$235	$205	$185	$170	$155	$140

Last Mfg.'s Sug. Retail was $307.

Model 5500 Mag.—12 ga. only, 3 in. chamber, 30 in. vent rib barrel. Discontinued in 1985.

	$275	$250	$225	$205	$190	$175	$160

Last Mfg.'s Sug. Retail was $325.

MODEL 5500 MKII—12 ga. only, supplied with 2 VR barrels - 26 in./2¾ in. chamber and 28 in./3 in. chamber barrels, includes 3 Accu-II choke tubes and 2 Accu-Steel choke tubes, checkered hardwood stock and forearm, top receiver safety, recoil pad, 7½ lbs. New in 1989.

Mfg.'s Sug. Retail	$433	$365	$310	$260	$220	$190	$165	$150

Subtract $57 if supplied with only one 26 in. Accu-II barrel.

MODEL 712—12 ga. only, semi-auto, gas operated, shoots 2¾ and 3 in. shells interchangeably, plain barrel or vent rib, top of receiver safety, checkered hardwood stock, rubber recoil pad, fixed or Accu Choke II choking. Imported 1986-1988 only.

	$285	$250	$220	$200	$190	$175	$160

Subtract $25 without Accu II choking.

Also available in a combo pack which includes 1 extra 24 in. slugster barrel — add $90.

Last Mfg.'s Sug. Retail was $345.

Model 712 Steel Shot—similar to Model 712, except has Accu-Steel choking system for steel shot, 28 in. VR barrel. Imported in 1988 only.

	$290	$250	$220	$200	$190	$175	$160

Last Mfg.'s Sug. Retail was $349.

Model 712 Camo/Speedfeed—12 ga. only, similar to Model 712, except has camo finished metal parts, stock, and forearm, 24 or 28 in. barrel. Add $20 for Accu II choke. Imported 1986-87 only.

	$340	$295	$240				

Last Mfg.'s Sug. Retail was $390.

MODEL 712 REGAL—12 or 20 ga., action same as Model 712, special bright bluing, vent rib only, deluxe checkered walnut stock and forearm, gold trigger, inlaid medallion on receiver, top of receiver safety. Add $20 for Accu II choke. Imported 1986-87 only.

	$310	$280	$250	$225	$200	$185	$170

Last Mfg.'s Sug. Retail was $366.

NEW HAVEN BRAND—same as previous models, except plainer finish. Discontinued.

Values are 20% less per model.

MUSGRAVE

MANUFACTURER LOCATED IN THE REPUBLIC OF SOUTH AFRICA.

Currently, this manufacturer has limited importation into the U.S. and listings below represent older models. Newer models manufactured by Musgrave include the Model 90 Standard Rifle, Model 90 Light Rifle, Model 90 De Luxe Rifle, Magnum Rifle in addition to the same series in the Mauser 98 action. More information can be obtained (including prices and availability) by writing this manufacturer directly at: MUSGRAVE MANUFACTURERS & DISTRIBUTORS LTD., P.O. Box 183, Bloemfontein 9300, Jagersfontein Road, Republic of South Africa.

VALIANT BOLT ACTION RIFLE—.243, .270, .30-06, .308, and 7mm Mag. cal.'s, 24 in. barrel, leaf sight, skip checkered straight stock, pistol grip, made 1971-1976.

	$275	$250	$220	$195	$175	$165	$150

PREMIER—same as Valiant, with 26 in. barrel, select Monte Carlo stock, rosewood pistol grip cap and forearm tip.

	$330	$305	$250	$220	$205	$195	$165

RSA SINGLE SHOT TARGET RIFLE—.308 cal. only, 26 in. heavy barrel, target sights and stock, made 1971-1976.

	$310	$285	$260	$250	$220	$200	$180

MUSKETEER RIFLES

FIREARMS INTERNATIONAL COMPANY, WASHINGTON, D.C.

SPORTER—.243, .25-06, .270, .265 Mag., .308, .30-06, 7mm Mag., .300 Win. Mag. cal.'s, bolt action, FN Mauser action, 24 in. barrel, no sights, checkered Monte Carlo stock, made 1963-1972.

	$280	$240	$225	$200	$180	$170	$150

SPORTER DELUXE—adj. trigger, select wood, tear drop pistol grip, skipline checkering.

	$350	$300	$275	$260	$245	$225	$200

CARBINE—same as Sporter, except 20 in. barrel.

	$300	$260	$245	$220	$200	$190	$175

N

NAMBU PISTOLS

MANUFACTURED IN JAPAN FOR THE JAPANESE MILITARY BETWEEN 1902-1945.

Grading	100%	98%	95%	90%	80%	70%	60%

TYPE 14—8mm, semi-auto pistol, recoil operated, 4.7 in. barrel, blued, wood grips, 8 round mag., a simply designed pistol used by Japanese armed forces from 1925-1945.

> Add 10% for matching mag. on models listed below.

Type 14 Nambu's have a 3 digit number just forward of the lanyard ring on the right side of frame (on back of grip). To determine year and month of manufacture add "1925" to the first two digits and the last number will indicate the month (i.e. code 13.3 indicates a gun built in March of 1938).

1925-1930 Mfg.

			$475	$420	$360	$320	$295	$260	$230

1930-1935 Mfg.—small trigger guard.

			$375	$320	$260	$220	$200	$180	$165

1935-1945 Mfg.—large trigger guard.

			$295	$260	$215	$195	$180	$165	$150

> Add 10% for strawed trigger and safety.

TYPE 94—8mm, semi-auto, recoil operated, 3.8 in. barrel, blued, and bakelite wood grips, 6 round mag., made 1934-1945.

			$265	$210	$180	$160	$150	$135	$120

> Add 20% for pre-WWII commercial.

BABY NAMBU—7mm Nambu, semi-auto, 3¼ in. barrel, blued, wood grips, grip safety, one of the most desirable Japanese handguns.

		$2,300	$2,000	$1,800	$1,600	$1,475	$1,300	$1,050

> Add 10% for matching mag.
> Add 50% for chamber marked "TGE" (Tokyo Gas & Electric).

PAPA NAMBU (MODEL 1904)—8mm, semi-auto, 4.7 in. barrel, wood grips, grip safety, 8 round mag., essentially the same action as the Baby, but a larger version, made 1904-1925.

		$1,225	$995	$875	$775	$700	$600	$500

> Add 10% for matching mag.

1893 REVOLVER (MODEL 26)—9mm, double action only, 4.7 in. barrel, blued, wood grips, made 1893-1925.

			$300	$250	$210	$170	$150	$135	$120

NAVY ARMS COMPANY

IMPORTERS SINCE 1958 LOCATED IN RIDGEFIELD, NJ. NAVY ARMS FIREARMS ARE FABRICATED BY VARIOUS MANUFACTURERS INCLUDING THE ITALIAN COMPANIES DAVIDE PEDERSOLI & CO., PIETTA & CO., AND UBERTI & CO.

RIFLES: REPLICA MANUFACTURE

MODEL 1873 RIFLE—.22 LR, .357 Mag., or .44-40 cal., lever action replica of 1873 Winchester, case hardened receiver, 24 in. barrel, made 1972-1984.

			$305	$275	$250	$220	$165	$140	$110

Model 1873 1 of 1,000—only 1,000 mfg., deluxe wood, special engraving.

			$1,000	$775	$550

Grading	100%	98%	95%	90%	80%	70%	60%

MODEL 1873 CARBINE—.44-40 cal., blue receiver, 19 in. round barrel.

	$260	$220	$195	$165	$140	$110	$100

MODEL 1873 TRAPPER—.44-40 cal., same as Carbine, with 16½ in. barrel.

	$260	$220	$195	$165	$140	$110	$100

YELLOWBOY—.38 Spl., or .44-40 cal., lever action replica of Winchester 1866, 24 in. octagon barrel, made 1966-1984.

	$330	$275	$220	$195	$165	$140	$110

YELLOWBOY CARBINE—.44-40 cal., 19 in. round barrel.

	$215	$180	$165	$150	$140	$110	$85

YELLOWBOY TRAPPER—.44-40 cal., 16½ in. barrel.

	$215	$180	$165	$150	$140	$110	$85

REVOLVING CARBINE—.357 Mag., .44-40, or .45 Colt cal., 6 shot cylinder, 20 in. barrel, case hardened frame, straight stock, made 1968-1984.

	$250	$210	$180	$160	$150	$140	$120

REMINGTON ROLLING BLOCK BUFFALO RIFLE—.444 Marlin (discontinued), .45-70, or .50-70 (discontinued), replica of Remington Rolling Block, 26 or 30 in. heavy octagon or ½ round/½ oct. barrel, open sight, straight grip stock, made 1971-present.

Mfg.'s Sug. Retail	$489	$385	$320	$275	$230	$180	$160	$140

Add approx. $25 for long or short Creedmoor sight.

Add $55 for 50 x 3¼ Sharps cal. (disc.).

BUFFALO CARBINE—same as Rifle, with 18 in. barrel. Discontinued in 1985.

	$325	$280	$230	$180	$160	$140	$120

Last Mfg.'s Sug. Retail was $375.

ROLLING BLOCK BABY CARBINE—.22 LR, .22 Hornet, .357 Mag., or .44-40 cal., replica of small frame Remington, 20 in. octagon or 22 in. round barrel, open sight, straight stock, made 1968-1984.

	$160	$130	$110	$90	$65	$55	$40

ROLLING BLOCK CREEDMOOR TARGET—same as Buffalo Rifle, in .45-70 or .50-70 (discontinued) cal., with Creedmoor tang sight, color case hardened receiver, checkered walnut.

Mfg.'s Sug. Retail	$640	$515	$440	$350	$250	$195	$175	$150

SHARPS RIFLE/CARBINE—.54 cal., reproduction of Sharps sporting rifle/carbine, 22 or 28½ in. barrel, case colored frame and hammer, latter typed rear sight. Mfg. 1986-87 only.

	$420	$345	$280	$230	$180	$160	$140

Last Mfg.'s Sug. Retail was $480.

HENRY RIFLE—.44-40 or .44 Rem. cal., reproduction of Winchester's famous Henry Rifle, brass or iron frame. New for 1985.

Add $375 for "A" pattern engraving (25% coverage).

Add $600 for "B" pattern engraving (35% coverage).

Add $1,000 for "C" pattern engraving (50% coverage).

Military Rifle—24 in. barrel, brass frame, blued barrel, walnut stock, original style sling swivels, 9¼ lbs. New for 1985.

Mfg.'s Sug. Retail	$769	$630	$495	$440	$350	$275	$225	$195

Union Pacific Commemorative—.44 RF, only 100 manufactured.

	$795	$575	$475

Engraved Rifle—limited mfg., extensive engraving on brass frame. Disc. in 1988.

	$1,510	$1,275	$1,100	$900	$750	$650	$550

Add $100 for steel frame.

Last Mfg.'s Sug. Retail was $1,850.

Grading	100%	98%	95%	90%	80%	70%	60%

Carbine—24 in. barrel, limited edition of 1,000 units including 50 engraved specimens, no swivels, 8¼ lbs.

Mfg.'s Sug. Retail	$769	$630	$495	$440	$350	$275	$225	$195

Engraved Carbine—limited production, only 50 produced. Disc. in 1988.

	$1,450	$1,225	$1,075	$900	$750	$650	$550

Last Mfg.'s Sug. Retail was $1,750.

Trapper Model—16½ in. barrel, 7¼ lbs., 34¼ in. overall length.

Mfg.'s Sug. Retail	$769	$630	$495	$440	$350	$275	$225	$195

Iron Frame Model—with iron frame and buttplate, 24 in. blued barrel, select walnut, 9¼ lbs.

Mfg.'s Sug. Retail	$769	$675	$600	$520	$460	$420	$380	$325

This model is available with either blued or color case hardened receiver at no extra charge.

RIFLES: MODERN MANUFACTURE

MARTINI TARGET RIFLE—.444, or .45-70 cal., single shot, 26 or 30 in. octagon barrel, tang sight, pistol grip stock, made 1972-1984.

	$480	$420	$350	$250	$195	$175	$150

RPKS-74—.223 or 7.62 X 39mm (new in 1989) cal., semi-automatic version of the Chinese RPK Squad Automatic Weapon, Kalashnikov action, 19 in. barrel, integral folding bipod, 9½ lbs. Importation began in 1988.

Mfg.'s Sug. Retail	$649	$525	$445	$350	$250	$195	$175	$150

PARKER-HALE SNIPER RIFLE—.308 cal., bolt action, extended heavy barrel, 10 shot mag., camo green synthetic stock with stippling, built in adj. bipod, enlarged contoured bolt, adj. recoil pad. Importation began in 1989.

Mfg.'s Sug. Retail	$2,300	$2,100	$1,750	$1,475	$1,275	$1,050	$875	$750

USED MILITARY FIREARMS

Navy Arms sells a wide variety of original military firearms in used condition. Handguns include the Mauser Broomhandle, Japanese Nambu, Colt 1911 Government Model, Browning Hi-Power, S & W Model 1917, and others. Rifles include Mauser contract models, Japanese Type 38's, Enfield's, FN's, Nagant's, M1 Carbines, M1 Garand's, Chinese SKS's, Egyptian Rashid's, French MAS Model 1936's, among others. Most of these firearms are priced in the $75-$500 price range depending on desirability of model and condition. Navy Arms should be contacted directly regarding specific prices for these models.

PISTOLS: LUGERS

LUGER—.22 LR cal. only, 10 round mag., Luger toggle type action, available in blued or matte finish, 4, 6, and 8 in. barrel, checkered walnut stocks. Made in U.S.A. Mfg. 1986-87 only.

	$140	$120	$95	$85	$75	$70	$65

Last Mfg.'s Sug. Retail was $165.

PISTOLS: REPLICA MANUFACTURE

GRAND PRIX SILHOUETTE—.30-30, 7mm Spl., .44 Mag., or .45-70 cal., 13¾ in. barrel, non-glare matte blue finish, walnut forearm and grips, adj. heat dispersing aluminum rib, adj. target sights, 4 lbs. Manufactured in 1985 only.

	$320	$280	$240	$220	$195	$175	$150

Last Mfg.'s Sug. Retail was $375.

SHOTGUNS: RECENT IMPORTATION

MODEL 83 O/U—12 or 20 ga., manufactured in Italy by R. Luciano, 3 in. chambers, extractors, double triggers, engraved chrome receiver, vent barrels and rib. New in 1985.

Mfg.'s Sug. Retail	$389	$335	$280	$240	$215	$195	$170	$160

MODEL 93 O/U—12 or 20 ga., manufactured in Italy by R. Luciano, 3 in. chambers, ejectors, double triggers, engraved chrome receiver, vent barrels and rib. New in 1985.

Mfg.'s Sug. Retail	$450	$390	$325	$285	$250	$220	$200	$185

Grading	100%	98%	95%	90%	80%	70%	60%

MODEL 95 O/U—same as Model 93, except with single trigger and multi-chokes (includes 5 tubes).

Mfg.'s Sug. Retail	$475	$420	$360	$320	$295	$265	$235	$210

MODEL 96 SPORTSMAN O/U—12 ga. only, 3 in. chambers, vent barrels and rib, engraved chrome receiver, gold plated receiver, multi-choked with 5 choke tubes. New in 1985.

Mfg.'s Sug. Retail	$575	$515	$450	$390	$360	$330	$295	$260

MODEL 100 O/U—12, 20, 28, or .410 ga., 3 in. chambers, 26 in. VR barrels, photo-engraved hard chrome receiver, single trigger, extractors, checkered walnut stock and forearm, approx. 6¼ lbs. New in 1989.

Mfg.'s Sug. Retail	$299	$260	$225	$205	$190	$170	$160	$150

MODEL .410 GA. O/U—.410 ga. only, 26 in. barrels with 3 in. chambers, vent rib, engraved chrome receiver, extractors, 6¼ lbs. New in 1985.

Mfg.'s Sug. Retail	$299	$260	$225	$205	$190	$170	$160	$150

MODEL 100 SXS—12 or 20 ga., 3 in. chambers, 27½ in. barrels, checkered European walnut, double triggers, extractors, 6½ or 7 lbs. Imported 1985-87 only.

	$380	$330	$290	$260	$230	$200	$170

Last Mfg.'s Sug. Retail was $475.

MODEL 150 SXS—same as Model 100, except with ejectors. Imported 1985-87 only.

	$455	$395	$350	$310	$280	$250	$220

Last Mfg.'s Sug. Retail was $574.

MODEL 105 SINGLE BARREL—12, 20, or .410 ga., 26 or 28 in. full choke barrel only, folding action, engraved chrome receiver, checkered hardwood stock and forearm. New in 1985.

Mfg.'s Sug. Retail	$100	$90	$80	$70	$65	$60	$55	$50

This model was designated the Model 600 before 1988.

Model 105 Deluxe—same as Model 105, except has European walnut stock and vent rib.

Mfg.'s Sug. Retail	$115	$100	$90	$80	$70	$65	$60	$55

This model was designated the Model 600 Deluxe before 1988.

NEW ENGLAND FIREARMS CO., INC.

MANUFACTURER AND DISTRIBUTOR LOCATED IN GARDNER, MA.

REVOLVERS: D/A

Ultra Models listed below are available in blue finish only.

MODEL R22—.22 LR cal., 9 shot, swing out cylinder, 2½, 4, or 6 in. barrel, blue or nickel finish, hardwood stocks, fixed rear sight, 25-32 oz. New in 1988.

No Mfg.'s Retail	$106	$90	$80	$70	$65	$60	$55

Add $13 for nickel finish (2½ or 4 in. barrel only).
Add $43 for adj. rear sight (Ultra Model - 4 or 6 in. barrel only).

Model R22 - .22 Mag.—.22 Mag. cal., 6 shot, 2½, 4, or 6 (Ultra Model only) in. barrel, blue or nickel finish, 25-28 oz. New in 1988.

No Mfg.'s Retail	$106	$95	$85	$75	$70	$65	$60

Add $13 for nickel finish.
Add $43 for adj. rear sight (Ultra Model - 4 or 6 in. barrel only).

Model R22 - .32 H&R Mag.—.32 H&R Mag. cal., 6 shot, 2½, 4, or 6 (Ultra Model only) in. barrel, blue or nickel finish, 23-26 oz. New in 1988.

No Mfg.'s Retail	$106	$95	$85	$75	$70	$65	$60

Add $13 for nickel finish.
Add $43 for adj. rear sight (Ultra Model - 4 or 6 in. barrel only).

New England Firearms Co. also manufactures blank starter revolvers (.22 or .32 cal.) which are variation of this model.

Grading	100%	98%	95%	90%	80%	70%	60%

SHOTGUNS/COMBINATION GUNS

PARDNER—12, 16 (new in 1989), 20, or .410 ga., single shot, break open action, safety transfer bar mechanism on hammer, side lever release, color case hardened receiver, 24, 26, or 28 in. barrel, extractor, walnut stock and forearm. New in 1987.

No Mfg.'s Retail	$97	$85	$75	$65	$55	$50	$45

Add $4 for Youth Gun (20 or .410 ga. - shorter dimension stock).
Add $27 for rifle sights (12 or 20 ga. - 24 in. cyl. barrel only).

Mini-Pardner—20 or .410 ga. only, shortened stock, sling swivels, 18½ in. barrel. New in 1989.

No Mfg.'s Retail	$97	$85	$75	$65	$55	$50	$45

Pardner Magnum—10 ga. only, 3½ in. chamber, 32 in. barrel, blue finish, recoil pad, 10 lbs. New in 1988.

No Mfg.'s Retail	$162	$140	$120	$100	$90	$80	$75

HANDI-RIFLE—.22 Hornet, .223 Rem., .30-30, or .45-70 cal., 22 in. barrel, blued receiver, ramp front and adj. folding rear sights, sling swivels, 7 lbs. New in 1989.

No Mfg.'s Retail	$160	$140	$120	$100	$90	$80	$75

Add $17 for .223 Rem. or .45-70 cal.

This model in .223 Rem. cal. is supplied with scope mount and no sights.

HANDI-GUN—includes 12 or 20 ga. 22 in. barrel and choice of .22 Hornet, .223 Rem., .30-30 Win., or .45-70 cal. extra barrel, blue or electroless matte finish nickel, 6½ lbs. New in 1988.

No Mfg.'s Retail	$207	$180	$155	$135	$120	$110	$100

Add $15 for blue finish.

NEWTON ARMS CO.

ALSO NAMED CHARLES NEWTON RIFLE CORP. AND BUFFALO NEWTON RIFLE CO. MANUFACTURED IN BUFFALO, N.Y. 1913-1932.

NEWTON-MAUSER RIFLE—Oberndorf bolt action, .256 Newton cal., 24 in. barrel, double set triggers, checkered pistol grip stock, pre-WWI production.

	$800	$650	$550	$440	$385	$330	$275

FIRST TYPE STANDARD RIFLE—Newton bolt action, .22, .256, .280, .30, .33, .35 Newton, and .30-06 cal.'s, 24 in. barrel, double set triggers, open or aperture sights, checkered pistol grip stock, made 1916-1918 by Newton Arms.

	$1,150	$925	$750	$625	$500	$440	$385

SECOND TYPE STANDARD RIFLE—improved Newton action, has Enfield type bolt handle, .256, .30, .35 Newton, and .30-06 cal.'s, open sights, checkered pistol grip stock, made post-WWI by Charles Newton Rifle Corporation.

	$1,000	$825	$660	$600	$500	$440	$385

BUFFALO NEWTON RIFLE—same as Second Type, made 1922-1932 by Buffalo Newton Rifle company.

	$1,000	$825	$660	$600	$500	$440	$385

SPRINGFIELD NEWTON—kit consisting of a Newton barrel and sporter stock, barrels were chambered for Newton calibers, kits were available to adapt Springfield rifles into Newton calibers in the 1920's when the NRA made the Springfields available to its membership.

	$595	$540	$495	$450	$410	$375	$330

NORINCO

MANUFACTURED IN CHINA. IMPORTED AND DISTRIBUTED BY CHINA SPORTS, INC. LOCATED IN DALLAS, TX.

NORINCO, cont.

Norinco pistols, rifles, and shotguns are manufactured in the People's Republic of China by China North Industries Corp. (Norinco - with over 100 factories). They are currently being imported and distributed by China Sports, Inc. Various other new models will be imported in the near future and China Sports, Inc. should be contacted to find out current availability and prices on these upcoming models.

PISTOLS

MODEL 213—9mm Para., single action, satin blue finish. Imported in 1988 only.

	100%	98%	95%	90%	80%	70%	60%
	$185	$150	$135	$125	$115	$105	$100

Last Mfg.'s Sug. Retail was $200.

TYPE 54-1 TOKAREV—7.62 X 25mm cal., single action semi-auto, 4.6 in. barrel, 8 shot mag., fixed sights, blue finish, 29 oz. Importation began in 1989.

	100%	98%	95%	90%	80%	70%	60%
No Mfg.'s Retail	$175	$150	$125	$115	$105	$95	$85

TYPE 59 MAKAROV—9 X 18mm Makarov or .380 ACP, double action semi-auto, 3.58 in. barrel, 8 shot mag., PPK design with additional features, 24 oz. Importation began in 1989.

	100%	98%	95%	90%	80%	70%	60%
No Mfg.'s Retail	$260	$210	$175	$150	$130	$115	$105

ASSAULT CARBINES & RIFLES

TYPE 84S AK RIFLE—.223 cal., semi-auto Kalashnikov action, 16.34 in. barrel, hardwood stock and pistol grip, 30 shot mag., 1,000 meter adj. rear sight, includes bayonet and sheath, 8.87 lbs. Importation began in 1988.

	100%	98%	95%	90%	80%	70%	60%
No Mfg.'s Retail	$350	$300	$250	$225	$200	$185	$165

Type 84S-1—similar to Type 84S AK except has under-folding metal stock. Importation began in 1989.

	100%	98%	95%	90%	80%	70%	60%
No Mfg.'s Retail	$350	$300	$250	$225	$200	$185	$165

Type 84S-3—similar to Type 84S AK except has composite fiber stock (1½ in. longer than wood stock). Importation began in 1989.

	100%	98%	95%	90%	80%	70%	60%
No Mfg.'s Retail	$365	$315	$265	$230	$205	$185	$165

Type 84S-5—similar to Type 84S AK except has side-folding metal stock. Importation began in 1989.

	100%	98%	95%	90%	80%	70%	60%
No Mfg.'s Retail	$350	$300	$250	$225	$200	$185	$165

TYPE SKS—.223 or 7.62 X 39mm cal., SKS action, 20.47 in. barrel, 30 shot clip mag., 1,000 meter adj. rear sight, hardwood stock, new design accepts standard AK mag., folding bayonet included, 8.8 lbs. Importation began in 1988.

	100%	98%	95%	90%	80%	70%	60%
No Mfg.'s Retail	$240	$210	$180	$165	$150	$140	$130

TYPE 81S AK RIFLE—7.62 x 39mm cal., semi-auto Kalashnikov action, 17.5 in. barrel, 5, 30, or 40 shot clip mag., 500 meter adj. rear sight, fixed wood stock, hold open devise after last shot, 8 lbs. Importation began in 1988.

	100%	98%	95%	90%	80%	70%	60%
No Mfg.'s Retail	$385	$325	$275	$240	$220	$200	$185

Type 81S-1—similar to Type 81S AK except has under-folding metal stock. Importation began in 1988.

	100%	98%	95%	90%	80%	70%	60%
No Mfg.'s Retail	$385	$325	$275	$240	$220	$200	$185

TYPE 56S-2—7.62 X 39mm cal., older Kalashnikov design with side-folding metal stock.

	100%	98%	95%	90%	80%	70%	60%
No Mfg.'s Retail	$350	$300	$250	$225	$200	$185	$165

TYPE 86S-7 RPK RIFLE—7.62 X 39mm cal., AK action, 23.27 in. heavy barrel with built in bipod, in-line buttstock, 11.02 lbs. Importation began in 1988.

	100%	98%	95%	90%	80%	70%	60%
No Mfg.'s Retail	$425	$370	$325	$285	$245	$220	$200

TYPE 86S BULLPUP RIFLE—7.62 X 39mm cal., bullpup configuration with AK action, under-folding metal stock, 17¼ in. barrel, ambidextrous cocking design, folding front handle, 7 lbs. Importation began in 1989.

	100%	98%	95%	90%	80%	70%	60%
No Mfg.'s Retail	$400	$350	$300	$265	$225	$200	$185

OFFICERS NINE—9mm, 16.1 in. barrel, action patterned after the IMI Uzi, 32 round mag., black military finish, 8.4 lbs. New in 1988.

	100%	98%	95%	90%	80%	70%	60%
No Mfg.'s Retail	$450	$350	$300	$275	$250	$225	$200

This model is imported exclusively by Pacific International Merchandizing Corporation located in Sacramento, CA.

Grading	100%	98%	95%	90%	80%	70%	60%

SPORTING RIFLES

MODEL EM-321—.22 LR, slide action, 19.5 in. barrel, 10 shot tube mag., hardwood stock and forearm, fixed sights, 6 lbs. Importation began in 1989.

No Mfg.'s Retail	$125	$100	$80	$70	$60	$55	$50

SHOTGUNS

TYPE HL12-203 O/U—12 ga. only, 2¾ in. chambers, boxlock action, ejectors, 30 in. vent. barrels and rib, single trigger, multi-chokes, checkered stock and forearm, 7½ lbs. Importation began in 1989.

No Mfg.'s Retail	$400	$350	$300	$265	$225	$200	$185

TYPE HL12-102 PUMP—12 ga. only, 2¾ in. chamber, 28.4 in. barrel, 3 shot mag., crossbolt safety on rear trigger guard, fixed chokes, 9.3 lbs. Importation began in 1989.

No Mfg.'s Retail	$230	$200	$175	$165	$150	$135	$120

NORTH AMERICAN ARMS

MANUFACTURED BY NORTH AMERICAN ARMS IN SPANISH FORK, UT. OWNED BY TELEFLEX DEFENSE SYSTEMS, ALSO LOCATED IN SPANISH FORK, UT.

MINI REVOLVERS

All mini revolvers have half-way notches cut on the front cylinder face allowing the hammer to lock up the cylinder between cartridges. This allows the gun to be carried fully loaded without the danger of accidental discharge.

NAA .22 S-L-LR—5 shot, single action, 1⅛, 1⅝, or 2½ in. barrel, stainless steel, plastic (disc.) or laminated rosewood grips, approx. 4½ oz., made 1975-present.

Mfg.'s Sug. Retail	$135	$110	$90	$75

Add $14 for 2½ in. barrel.
Add $38 for holster grip accessory.

Viper Belt Buckle Option—belt buckle with built in 1⅛ in. barrel revolver (LR cal.).

Mfg.'s Sug. Retail	$167	$135	$115	$95

NAA .22 MAGNUM—same as .22 LR, except .22 LR Mag. and only available with 1⅝ or 2½ in. barrel.

Mfg.'s Sug. Retail	$156	$125	$105	$85

Add $15 for 2½ in. barrel.

NAA .22 MAGNUM CONVERTIBLE—same as NAA .22 Mag., except has extra LR cylinder in pouch. Add $36 for walnut presentation case.

Mfg.'s Sug. Retail	$187	$165	$125	$105

Add $16 for 2½ in. barrel.

NAA STANDARD SET—3 gun set (.22 Short, .22 LR, and .22 Mag.) in walnut display case with matching serial numbers, high polish finish with matte contours.

Mfg.'s Sug. Retail	$570	$490	$350	$275

NAA DELUXE SET—3 gun set (.22 Short, .22 LR, and .22 Mag.) in walnut display case with matching serial numbers, high polish finish on entire gun.

Mfg.'s Sug. Retail	$622	$520	$380	$300

CASED .22 MAG.—includes .22 Mag. model in walnut display case with high polish finish with matte contours.

Mfg.'s Sug. Retail	$285	$240	$190	$145

Grading	100%	98%	95%	90%	80%	70%	60%

REVOLVERS

NAA SINGLE ACTION REVOLVER—.45 Win. Mag. or .450 Mag. Express, polished stainless steel, transfer bar safety inside the hammer, 5 shot, 7½ in. barrel, walnut grips, includes presentation case. North American Arms might resume production of this model in 1989.

	100%	98%	95%
	$895	**$750**	**$625**
Both cylinders	**$1,500**	**$1,100**	**$925**

Last Mfg.'s Sug. Retail was $650.

Also available by special order with 10½ in. barrel and optional scope. Extra cylinders are also available at $75-$100 extra and must be fitted to the gun. A set including 2 cylinders can also be ordered.

NORTH AMERICAN SAFARI EXPRESS

TRADEMARK FOR THOSE RIFLES (SIDE BY SIDE) ASSEMBLED BY A. FRANCOTTE OF BELGIUM FOR EXCLUSIVE IMPORTATION BY ARMES DE CHASSE LOCATED IN CHADDS FORD, PA.

These models can be located in the A. Francotte section of this text.

O

O.D.I. (OMEGA DEFENSIVE INDUSTRIES)

PREVIOUSLY MANUFACTURED IN MIDLAND PARK, NEW JERSEY FROM APPROXIMATELY 1981-1982. OAK'S WHOLESALE, INC. LOCATED IN ROCKLEDGE, FL HAS ACQUIRED THE REMAINING O.D.I. VIKING INVERTORY OF THE DOUBLE ACTION .45 ACP PISTOLS. PREVIOUSLY, RANDCO MANUFACTURING LOCATED IN MONROVIA, CA., WAS PROVIDING SERVICE (AND HAD PARTS) FOR THESE OLDER O.D.I. PISTOLS.

Oak's Trading Post is planning to reintroduce the Viking Model's in 1989. Firm prices have yet to be established - please contact Oak's Trading Post for more current information regarding the current status of this model.

Grading	100%	98%	95%	90%	80%	70%	60%

VIKING & VIKING COMBAT—.45 ACP or 9mm, Viking Model is Government size and the Combat Model is Commander size. All stainless steel construction, the design utilizes the Seecamp double action, teakwood grips. 9mm advertised but never saw production. 5 in. barrel on the Viking Model and 4 1/4 in. barrel on the Viking Combat Model, 7 round mag., 39 oz. Approximately 200-300 Viking Combat Models were made from kits.

				$575	**$425**	**$325**	

Last Mfg.'s Retail was $579.

OLD-WEST GUN CO.

IMPORTER AND DISTRIBUTOR THAT TOOK OVER THE INVENTORY OF ALLEN FIREARMS AFTER THEY WENT OUT OF BUSINESS IN EARLY 1987. OLD-WEST GUN CO. IN LATE 1987 CHANGED THEIR NAME TO CIMARRON ARMS. REFER TO CIMARRON ARMS IN THIS TEXT FOR APPROXIMATE PRICES ON SIMILAR MODELS FROM OLD-WEST GUN CO.

OLYMPIC ARMS, INC.

MANUFACTURER/DISTRIBUTOR LOCATED IN OLYMPIA, WA.

In late 1987, Olympic Arms, Inc. acquired Safari Arms of Phoenix, AZ and is currently manufacturing/assembling guns from existing parts. Once the parts clean-up is over, the Olympic Arms trademark will appear on their firearms. This company also manufactures barrels (including .38 Super & .45 ACP cal.'s) for the Colt Government Model 1911, Browning Hi-Power, and TZ & CZ 75.

Olympic Arms manufactures single action, semi-auto pistols derived from the Browning M1911 design with modifications.

DEFENSE PISTOLS

ENFORCER—.45 ACP, 3.8 in. barrel, 6 shot mag., shortened grip, available with max hard finish aluminum frame, parkerized, electroless nickel or lightweight anodized finishes, flat or arched mainspring housing, adj. sights, ambidextrous safety, neoprene or checkered walnut grips, 27 oz. (lightweight model).

Mfg.'s Sug. Retail	$629	$550	$500	$450	$425	$400	$375	$350

Match Master—similar to the Enforcer, except has 5 in. barrel and 7 shot mag., 40 oz.

Mfg.'s Sug. Retail	$649	$565	$510	$460	$430	$400	$375	$350

OLYMPIC ARMS, INC., cont.

Grading	100%	98%	95%	90%	80%	70%	60%

BLACK WIDOW—.45 ACP, 3.9 in. barrel, hand-contoured front grip strap, schrimshawed ivory Micarta grips with black widow emblem, 6 shot mag., 27 oz. Inventory was depleted in 1988.

	$565	$510	$460	$430	$400	$375	$350

Last Mfg.'s Sug. Retail was $595.

RIFLES

SGW ULTRA MATCH—.223 cal., AR-15 action with modifications, 20 or 24 in. match stainless steel barrel, handle removed, Williams set trigger, scope mounts. New in 1988.

Mfg.'s Sug. Retail	$995	$840	$700	$640	$575	$530	$475	$430

Add $130 for custom aperture sights.

OMEGA PISTOL

MANUFACTURED AND DISTRIBUTED BY SPRINGFIELD ARMORY LOCATED IN GENESEO, IL.

PISTOLS: SEMI-AUTO

OMEGA—.38 Super, 10mm Norma, or .45 ACP cal., single action, ported slide, 5 or 6 in. interchangeable ported or unported barrel with Polygon rifling, special lock-up system eliminates normal barrel link and bushing, Pachmayr grips, dual extractors, adj. rear sight. New in late 1987.

Mfg.'s Sug. Retail	$849	$775	$650	$575	$495	$425	$360	$295

Add $663 for interchangeable conversion units.

Each conversion unit includes an entire slide assembly, one mag., 5 or 6 in barrel, recoil spring guide mechanism assembly, and factory fitting.

Add $336 for interchangeable 5 or 6 in. barrel (including factory installation).

OMEGA SHOTGUNS

OMEGA IS THE TRADEMARK OF SELECT SHOTGUNS IMPORTED BY KASSNAR IMPORTS LOCATED IN HARRISBURG, PA.

SHOTGUNS

STANDARD O/U—12, 20, 28, or .410 ga., boxlock action, folding design, SNT, 26 or 28 in. VR barrels, extractors, checkered walnut stock and forearm, 5½-7 lbs.

Mfg.'s Sug. Retail	$319	$275	$240	$210	$185	$160	$140	$125

Deluxe O/U—12 ga. only, similar to Standard Model except has better walnut.

Mfg.'s Sug. Retail	$369	$330	$285	$255	$220	$185	$160	$140

STANDARD SXS—20, 28, and .410 ga.'s, boxlock action, folding design, double triggers, hardwood stock and forearm, 26 in. barrels, extractors, 5½ lbs.

Mfg.'s Sug. Retail	$229	$190	$165	$140	$120	$110	$100	$90

Add $40 for 28 or .410 ga.

Deluxe SXS—.410 ga. only, similar to Standard Model except has better walnut.

Mfg.'s Sug. Retail	$249	$200	$185	$170	$155	$140	$130	$120

SINGLE BARREL—12, 20, and .410 ga.'s, various barrel lengths, matte blue finish, extractor. Importation disc. in 1987.

	$85	$75	$65	$55	$45	$40	$35

Last Mfg.'s Sug. Retail was $95.

Grading	100%	98%	95%	90%	80%	70%	60%

STANDARD FOLDING SINGLE BARREL—12, 16, 20, 28, and .410 ga.'s, 28 or 30 in. barrel, checkered hardwood stock, matte chrome receiver, approx. 5½ lbs. Importation disc. in 1987.

	100%	98%	95%	90%	80%	70%	60%
	$160	$135	$115	$100	$85	$70	$65

Last Mfg.'s Sug. Retail was $180.

DELUXE FOLDING SINGLE BARREL—12, 16, 20, 28, and .410 ga.'s, similar to Standard Model, except has checkered walnut stock and forearm, blued receiver. Importation disc. in 1987.

	100%	98%	95%	90%	80%	70%	60%
	$195	$160	$135	$115	$100	$85	$70

Last Mfg.'s Sug. Retail was $220.

OMEGA

MAKER: ARMERO SPECIALISTAS REUNIDAS, EIBAR, SPAIN, 1920'S.

SEMI AUTOMATIC PISTOL—"Eibar" type, marked, Omega on slide, 6 shot mag.

	100%	98%	95%	90%	80%	70%	60%
6.35 cal.	$125	$115	$100	$80	$70	$55	$40
7.65 cal.	$130	$120	$105	$90	$80	$70	$55

OMEGA FIREARMS

PREVIOUSLY MANUFACTURED IN FLOWER MOUND, TX.

SINGLE SHOT BOLT ACTION RIFLE—various cal.'s, premium walnut. Discontinued in late 1960's.

	100%	98%	95%	90%	80%	70%	60%
	$775	$650	$575	$495	$425	$360	$295

OPUS SPORTING ARMS, INC.

PREVIOUSLY MANUFACTURED AND DISTRIBUTED BY OPUS SPORTING ARMS, INC. LOCATED IN LONG BEACH, CA.

OPUS ONE—.243, .270, and .30-06 cal.'s, U.S.R.A. Co. Model 70 action, 24 in. barrel, deluxe checkered walnut stock with ebony forend cap, guaranteed 100 yard accuracy, 6¾ lbs., Halliburton cased. Mfg. 1987-1988 only.

	100%	98%	95%	90%	80%	70%	60%
	$2,350	$1,995	$1,675	$1,250	$1,000	$875	$795

Last Mfg.'s Sug. Retail was $2,700.

OPUS TWO—similar to Opus One, except in 7mm Rem. Mag. and .300 Win. Mag. cal.'s, 7¼ lbs., cased. Mfg. 1987-1988 only.

	100%	98%	95%	90%	80%	70%	60%
	$2,350	$2,050	$1,705	$1,300	$1,000	$875	$795

Last Mfg.'s Sug. Retail was $2,700.

OPUS THREE—similar to Opus Two, except in .375 H&H and .458 Win. Mag. cal.'s, 10¼ lbs., cased. Mfg. 1987-1988 only.

	100%	98%	95%	90%	80%	70%	60%
	$2,600	$2,275	$1,800	$1,375	$1,050	$900	$825

Last Mfg.'s Sug. Retail was $2,850.

ORTGIES PISTOLS

PREVIOUSLY MANUFACTURED BY DEUTSCHE WERKE A.G. LOCATED IN ERFURT, GERMANY.

VEST POCKET AUTOMATIC—.25 auto, 6 shot, 2¾ in. barrel, blue or nickel finish, fixed sights, wood grips, post-WWI.

	100%	98%	95%	90%	80%	70%	60%
	$250	$195	$160	$140	$120	$105	$95

Grading	100%	98%	95%	90%	80%	70%	60%

POCKET AUTOMATIC—.32 auto, 8 shot, .380 auto, 7 shot, 3¼ in. barrel, blue or nickel finish, fixed sights, wood grips.

	$225	$180	$130	$110	$90	$75	$65

Add 10% for .380.

ORVIS

RETAILER/IMPORTER OF PRIVATE LABEL SUBCONTRACTED RIFLES/SHOTGUNS LOCATED IN DALLAS, HOUSTON, TX AND MANY OTHER LOCATIONS. Orvis imports various rifles and shotguns under subcontract with various international manufacturers. These private label models will approximate the values of the equivalent model manufactured by the subcontractor unless there are additional features and/or options which will add to the value.

P

P.A.F.

PETORIA ARMS COMPANY. PREVIOUS MANUFACTURER LOCATED IN S. AFRICA.

Grading	100%	98%	95%	90%	80%	70%	60%

.25 ACP PISTOL—.25 ACP cal., patterned after the Baby Browning, blued finish, approx. 10,000 total manufactured.

	100%	98%	95%	90%	80%	70%	60%
	$375	$300	$275	$250	$225	$200	$180

P.S.M.G. GUN COMPANY

MANUFACTURER/DISTRIBUTOR LOCATED IN ARLINGTON, MA.

SIX IN ONE SUPREME—.22 LR, .30 Luger, .38 Super, .38 Spl., 9mm, or .45 ACP cal., single action semi-auto, 3¼, 5, or 7½ in. barrel with solid cooling rib, adj. rear sight, limited mfg. New in 1988.

Mfg.'s Sug. Retail	$895	$895	$700	$600	$500	$450	$400	$365

    Add $20-$55 for caliber options.
    Add $25 for 7½ in. barrel.
    Add $35 for satin nickel plating.
    Add $225 per extra barrel.
    Add $450 per individual conversion unit.

PTK INTERNATIONAL, INC.

DISTRIBUTOR LOCATED IN ATLANTA, GA.

Please refer to listing under Poly-Technologies in this section.

PARA-ORDNANCE MFG. INC.

MANUFACTURER LOCATED IN SCARBOROUGH ONTARIO, CANADA.

Para-Ordnance also manufactures the Model 85 full or semi-auto paint-shell carbine (styled after the Ingram). This model retails for $300.

14 SHOT .45 ACP PISTOL—.45 ACP cal., patterned after the Colt Model 1911A1 except has alloy frame that has been widened slightly for extra shot capacity, 5 in. barrel, loaded weight with 13 shot staggered mag. is the same as loaded Colt Model 1911A1 (2.6 lbs.). Introduced late 1989.

Mfg.'s Sug. Retail	$675	$640	$575	$525	$475	$435	$400	$360

This model might vary in price somewhat when released.

PARDINI

MANUFACTURED IN ITALY. IMPORTED AND DISTRIBUTED BY FIOCCHI OF AMERICA, INC., LOCATED IN OZARK, MO.

STANDARD PISTOL—.22 LR only, target grips, adj. sights, 4.92 in. barrel, interchangeable grips, detachable mag. New in 1986.

Mfg.'s Sug. Retail	$955	$850	$700	$600	$520	$460	$410	$380

Grading	100%	98%	95%	90%	80%	70%	60%

LADIES PISTOL—similar to Standard Pistol, except grips are suitable for smaller hands. New in 1986.

Mfg.'s Sug. Retail	$955	$850	$700	$600	$520	$460	$410	$380

This variation is imported in limited quantities only.

RAPIDFIRE PISTOL—.22 short, features enclosed style grip assembly, adj. sights, 5.12 in. barrel. New in 1986.

Mfg.'s Sug. Retail	$985	$865	$710	$600	$520	$460	$410	$380

CENTERFIRE PISTOL—.32 S&W Long cal., otherwise similar to Standard Pistol, 4.92 in. barrel. New in 1986.

Mfg.'s Sug. Retail	$995	$865	$710	$600	$520	$460	$410	$380

FREE PISTOL—.22 LR, single shot, sliding rotating bolt, 9.06 in. barrel, hilted grip, top-of-the-line match pistol.

Mfg.'s Sug. Retail	$1,060	$900	$750	$600	$520	$460	$410	$380

PARKER BROTHERS

ORIGINALLY MANUFACTURED IN MERIDEN, CT FROM 1866-1934. REMINGTON TOOK OVER PRODUCTION IN 1934, AND IN 1938, THE PLANT WAS MOVED TO ILION, NY. OVER 5,500 GUNS WERE PRODUCED IN MERIDEN BETWEEN 1934-1937 AND ABOUT 1,800 PARKERS WERE MANUFACTURED AT THE ILION LOCATION BEFORE PRODUCTION STOPPED. TOTAL PRODUCTION REACHED OVER 242,000.

At the 1987 Shot Show, Remington Arms Co. reintroduced the Parker shotgun in an AHE grade - 20 ga., serial numbered 242,502 (consecutively numbered to the last Parker built in Ilion in 1934). These limited mfg. new shotguns will again be manufactured in Ilion, NY to precise quality control standards (see separate listing in this section under the Model AH).

SHOTGUNS: DAMASCUS BARRELS — HAMMER MODELS

PARKER DAMASCUS OR HAMMER SHOTGUNS ARE VERY COLLECTIBLE IF ORIGINAL CONDITION IS HIGH. SPECIMENS IN 90% OR BETTER CONDITION WITH STRONG CASE COLORS CAN APPROXIMATE VALUES OF THE STEEL BARREL MODELS IF THE BORES ARE IN EXCELLENT CONDITION ALSO (NO PITTING). VALUES FOR UNDER 90% SPECIMENS FALL OFF RAPIDLY AND ARE NO LONGER COMPARABLE TO STEEL BARREL GUNS. AS AN EXAMPLE, A STEEL "D" GRADE (WITHOUT EJECTORS) MIGHT RANGE FROM $3,000 TO $700 (100%-10%) WITH A RATHER EVEN DOWNWARD PROGRESSION OF VALUES IN BETWEEN THE HIGH AND LOW VALUES. A 100% DAMASCUS "D" GRADE MIGHT RANGE FROM $3,000 TO $295 WITH THE 70% AND LOWER CONDITIONS BEING $800 DOWN TO $295 — NOT MUCH OF A SPREAD. REMEMBER — THE GUNS ARE NOT RARE BUT THEIR CONDITION IS.

SHOTGUNS: FLUID STEEL BARRELS

VALUES LISTED BELOW IN THE 95%-100% CONDITION COLUMNS CAN VARY IMMENSELY AS THERE IS ALMOST NO SUPPLY FOR THESE HIGH DEMAND ITEMS, ALWAYS A PREREQUISITE FOR UNPREDICTABLE PRICES. 95% OF THE ORIGINAL PARKERS BOUGHT AND SOLD EACH YEAR ARE IN 90% OR LESS CONDITION.

Note: Values are for non-ejector guns. Add 15% - 30% for vent ribs. Skeet model has beavertail forearm and single selective trigger valued at approximately 20% higher than values shown. Higher grade guns typically had ejectors, and will not make as much difference percentage-wise in the overall value as those lower grades with ejectors. Also, lower condition high grade models sometimes have their values established by the potential gain in refurbishing these specimens.

Due to the extremely high value of Parker Guns, extreme care should be taken in their purchase. There are many upgraded guns represented as original; expert advice should always be sought.

PARKER BROTHERS, cont.

100%	98%	95%	90%	80%	70%	60%	50%	40%	30%	20%	10%

Frame size on Parker shotguns is determined by the number on the bottom of the barrel lug on breech. Frame sizes (from largest to smallest) include 7, 6, 5, 4, 3, 2, 1½, 1, 0, 00, and 000. 8 ga. guns typically are framed 5, 6, or 7. 10 ga. guns typically are 3 or 4. 12 ga. guns typically range from 2 through 1. 20 and 16 ga.'s range from 2 through 0. 28 ga. guns typically are 2 through 0. .410 ga. shotguns are 0, 00, or 000.

The grade on Parker shotguns is a number or initials located on the water table of the frame. An alphabetical designation would indicate the grade immediately. For numerals, a "2" would indicate a GH, while an "8" would specify an A-1 Special. Interpolate for the others (numbers 3 through 7).

A NOTE ABOUT PARKER CONDITION: PERCENTAGES OF CONDITION INDICATE THE AMOUNT OF ORIGINAL CASE COLORS REMAINING ON THE FRAME. A PARKER IS NOT 60% IF THE BARREL BLUEING AND STOCK/FORARM VARNISH ARE 60% BUT CASE COLORS ARE ONLY 10%. TYPICALLY, A 60% CASE COLOR PARKER SHOTGUN WILL HAVE 90% + BLUE AND VARNISH, YET THIS DOES NOT MEAN THE GUN IS 90% OVERALL. SIMILARLY, A 20% CASE COLOR PARKER WILL PROBABLY HAVE 90% BARREL BLUEING REMAINING. STRONG, ORIGINAL CASE COLORS ARE THE KEY IN DETERMINING PARKER CONDITION AND SUBSEQUENT VALUES.

TROJAN—Parker's lowest-priced gun, single or double triggers, but no auto ejectors available, very rarely found in mint condition because they were used a lot, a genuine utility gun, approximately 48,000 produced.

12 ga.

100%	98%	95%	90%	80%	70%	60%	50%	40%	30%	20%	10%
$2,500	$2,000	$1,625	$1,400	$1,150	$995	$900	$825	$750	$675	$600	$500

16 ga.

$2,500	$2,000	$1,625	$1,400	$1,150	$995	$900	$825	$750	$675	$600	$500

20 ga.

$3,500	$3,000	$2,500	$2,175	$1,850	$1,625	$1,400	$1,150	$995	$900	$825	$750

VH—Parker's biggest selling model, offered with all options, the most commonly found Parker, approximately 60,000 produced. 10 ga. is very rare in this model.

12 ga.

$2,750	$2,200	$1,750	$1,450	$1,200	$1,000	$900	$825	$750	$675	$600	$500

16 ga.

$2,750	$2,200	$1,750	$1,450	$1,200	$1,000	$900	$825	$750	$675	$600	$500

20 ga.

$3,900	$3,350	$2,800	$2,400	$1,900	$1,700	$1,450	$1,150	$995	$900	$825	$750

28 ga.

$6,500	$5,750	$4,600	$3,220	$2,875	$2,645	$2,300	$2,075	$1,900	$1,750	$1,500	$1,350

.410 ga.

$16,100	$12,250	$10,000	$8,750	$7,900	$6,900	$6,250	$5,750	$5,350	$4,775	$4,250	$3,650

Add 33%-50% for ejectors (VHE Model).

PH—offered for a very short time, most had damascus barrels, prices here are for fluid steel barrels only, approximately 8,500 produced. No .410 ga.'s were produced. 10 ga. is very rare in this model.

12 ga.

$3,150	$2,600	$2,100	$1,625	$1,400	$1,150	$995	$900	$825	$750	$625	$525

16 ga.

$3,150	$2,600	$2,100	$1,625	$1,400	$1,150	$995	$900	$825	$750	$625	$525

20 ga.

$4,600	$4,000	$3,350	$2,600	$2,175	$1,850	$1,625	$1,400	$1,150	$995	$900	$825

28 ga.

$8,100	$6,950	$5,250	$4,675	$4,150	$3,750	$3,350	$2,600	$2,175	$1,850	$1,625	$1,400

Add 33%-50% for ejectors (PHE Model).

PARKER BROTHERS, cont.

	100%	98%	95%	90%	80%	70%	60%	50%	40%	30%	20%	10%

GH—very popular model, barrels marked Parker, special steel, engraved moderately with all options available, approximately 28,500 produced. 10 ga. is very rare in this model.

12 ga.

100%	98%	95%	90%	80%	70%	60%	50%	40%	30%	20%	10%
$3,950	$3,500	$3,150	$2,475	$1,850	$1,625	$1,400	$1,150	$950	$795	$695	$595

16 ga.

$4,250	$3,750	$3,350	$2,600	$2,175	$1,850	$1,575	$1,250	$950	$795	$695	$595

20 ga.

$4,600	$4,000	$3,350	$2,600	$2,175	$1,850	$1,625	$1,400	$1,150	$995	$875	$750

28 ga.

$7,000	$6,375	$5,750	$5,125	$4,550	$3,925	$3,375	$2,875	$2,645	$2,300	$2,075	$1,750

.410 ga.

$20,000	$17,250	$15,350	$12,850	$10,500	$8,525	$7,375	$6,600	$5,950	$5,300	$4,500	$3,850

Add 33% for ejectors (GHE Model).

DH—the most popular higher grade gun, very tastefully engraved and flawlessly finished, approximately 48,000 produced. 10 ga. is very rare in this model.

12 ga.

$5,500	$4,850	$4,100	$3,450	$2,675	$2,175	$1,850	$1,625	$1,400	$1,125	$925	$795

16 ga.

$5,800	$4,925	$4,200	$3,500	$2,675	$2,175	$1,850	$1,625	$1,400	$1,125	$925	$795

20 ga.

$6,375	$5,750	$5,125	$4,550	$3,925	$3,375	$2,875	$2,400	$2,075	$1,750	$1,350	$950

28 ga.

$10,500	$9,250	$8,175	$7,000	$6,375	$5,750	$5,125	$4,550	$3,925	$3,375	$2,875	$2,375

.410 ga.

$40,500	$35,250	$28,250	$22,000	$18,950	$16,350	$14,000	$12,750	$10,650	$9,100	$8,000	$7,250

Add 33% for ejectors (DHE Model).

CH—scarce because they were only slightly more decorative than the DHE, Acme steel barrels, approximately 5,000 produced. 10 ga. is very rare in this model.

12 ga.

$6,250	$5,575	$4,775	$4,000	$3,350	$2,600	$2,175	$1,850	$1,450	$1,100	$875	$750

16 ga.

$6,575	$5,700	$4,850	$4,050	$3,350	$2,600	$2,175	$1,850	$1,450	$1,100	$875	$750

20 ga.

$8,450	$7,425	$6,375	$5,550	$4,950	$4,300	$3,750	$3,100	$2,650	$2,175	$1,675	$1,000

28 ga.

$21,000	$17,500	$13,850	$10,500	$9,250	$8,175	$7,000	$6,375	$5,750	$5,125	$4,550	$3,895

.410 ga.

$49,500	$40,500	$35,250	$28,250	$23,250	$19,950	$17,250	$14,450	$12,950	$11,000	$9,950	$8,950

Add 33% for ejectors (CHE Model).

BH—quite popular and decorative, 4 styles of engraving available, Acme steel barrels, approximately 13,000 produced. 10 ga. is very rare in this model.

12 ga.

$9,500	$8,450	$7,425	$6,375	$5,550	$4,950	$4,300	$3,750	$3,100	$2,650	$2,075	$1,575

16 ga.

$9,950	$8,650	$7,600	$6,400	$5,550	$4,950	$4,300	$3,750	$3,100	$2,650	$2,075	$1,575

20 ga.

$17,500	$14,500	$12,000	$10,250	$9,300	$8,275	$7,100	$6,375	$5,650	$5,000	$4,550	$3,650

28 ga.

$32,500	$27,650	$21,000	$17,500	$13,850	$10,500	$9,250	$8,175	$7,000	$6,275	$5,350	$4,550

.410 ga.

$55,750	$47,500	$40,500	$35,250	$28,250	$23,250	$19,950	$16,000	$13,250	$10,500	$7,600	$5,250

Add 33% for ejectors (BHE Model).

100%	98%	95%	90%	80%	70%	60%	50%	40%	30%	20%	10%

AH—a scarce gun, extremely decorative and flawlessly executed, Acme steel barrels, approximately 5,500 produced. 10 ga. is very rare in this model.

12 ga.

100%	98%	95%	90%	80%	70%	60%	50%	40%	30%	20%	10%
$23,000	$19,550	$16,100	$12,250	$9,250	$8,000	$7,150	$6,250	$5,600	$4,950	$4,175	$3,450

16 ga.

$26,000	$21,000	$17,000	$13,000	$9,375	$8,100	$7,150	$6,250	$5,600	$4,950	$4,175	$3,450

20 ga.

$32,500	$27,650	$21,000	$17,500	$13,850	$10,500	$9,250	$8,175	$7,000	$6,400	$5,700	$5,100

28 ga.

$57,500	$49,750	$40,250	$31,500	$23,750	$18,975	$16,000	$14,000	$12,250	$10,750	$9,000	$8,250

.410 ga.

$70,000	$61,000	$51,750	$40,250	$30,475	$20,700	$18,975	$16,000	$14,000	$12,750	$11,350	$9,995

Add 25% for ejectors (AHE Model).

Grading			100%	98%	95%	90%	80%	70%	60%

AHE NEW MODEL—20 ga. only, 28 in. vent. rib barrels, single selective trigger, metal engraving and woodwork are the same as the older AHE Model, limited mfg. (50 guns).

Mfg.'s Sug. Retail			$12,750	$12,750	$10,000	$9,000	$8,400	$7,800	$7,200	$6,700

This new model has a color case hardened receiver and deluxe walnut stock and forearm — mfg. by Remington's Custom Shop.

100%	98%	95%	90%	80%	70%	60%	50%	40%	30%	20%	10%

AAH—very elaborate model, early AA's have Whitworth barrels, late ones have Peerless, approximately 340 produced.

12 ga.

$35,000	$28,500	$23,000	$19,550	$16,100	$12,250	$9,250	$8,000	$7,150	$6,250	$5,300	$4,950

16 ga.

$39,500	$30,000	$24,000	$20,000	$16,100	$12,250	$9,250	$8,000	$7,150	$6,250	$5,300	$4,950

20 ga.

$57,500	$51,750	$40,250	$31,050	$26,450	$19,550	$17,250	$15,000	$13,000	$11,250	$10,000	$9,250

28 ga.

$86,250	$74,750	$63,250	$53,475	$33,925	$28,175	$25,875	$21,750	$19,000	$17,000	$15,950	$14,000

Add 25% for ejectors (AAHE Model).

A-1 SPECIAL GRADE—100% engraved, all were special ordered, each one inspected by the company president before being shipped, approximately 320 produced.

12 ga.

$57,500	$51,750	$40,250	$31,050	$26,450	$19,550	$17,250	$15,000	$13,000	$11,250	$10,000	$9,250

16 ga.

$59,500	$53,750	$41,750	$31,050	$26,450	$19,550	$17,250	$15,000	$13,000	$11,250	$10,000	$9,250

20 ga.

$92,000	$80,000	$69,000	$58,000	$47,000	$36,650	$32,200	$26,000	$23,000	$20,000	$17,500	$15,000

28 ga.

$115,000	$92,000	$80,000	$70,000	$60,000	$51,750	$46,000	$40,250	$34,500	$30,000	$26,000	$22,000

SINGLE BARREL TRAP GUNS

12 ga. only, 30, 32, and 34 in. barrels, any boring is available, as is stock configuration, boxlock, auto ejector. The grades differ only in engraving, checkering and wood finish.

IT SHOULD BE NOTED THAT SINGLE BARREL TRAP GUNS CANNOT BE COMPARED TO THE SXS MODELS AS THEY ARE NOT AS DESIRABLE EVEN THOUGH THEY ARE RARER. MOST SIDE BY SIDE COLLECTORS ARE NOT THAT INTERESTED IN SINGLE BARREL TRAP MODELS AND VERY FEW COLLECTORS SPECIALIZE IN SINGLE BARRELS.

100%	98%	95%	90%	80%	70%	60%	50%	40%	30%	20%	10%

S.C. GRADE

| $2,275 | $1,850 | $1,625 | $1,400 | $1,150 | $995 | $900 | $825 | $750 | $675 | $600 | $475 |

S.B. GRADE

| $3,400 | $3,050 | $2,675 | $2,275 | $1,700 | $1,425 | $1,100 | $950 | $850 | $750 | $650 | $500 |

S.A. GRADE

| $4,750 | $3,875 | $3,050 | $2,675 | $2,275 | $1,700 | $1,425 | $1,100 | $950 | $850 | $750 | $650 |

S.A.A. GRADE

| $6,950 | $5,800 | $4,750 | $3,875 | $3,050 | $2,675 | $2,275 | $1,700 | $1,425 | $1,100 | $875 | $750 |

S.A.-1 SPECIAL GRADE

| $10,000 | $9,150 | $8,350 | $7,425 | $6,375 | $5,550 | $4,950 | $4,300 | $3,750 | $3,100 | $2,650 | $2,000 |

PARKER REPRODUCTIONS

IMPORTED BY THE PARKER REPRODUCTION DIVISION OF REAGENT CHEMICAL & RESEARCH, INC., LOCATED IN MIDDLESEX, NJ. DISTRIBUTED BY PARKER REPRODUCTIONS LOCATED IN WEBB CITY, MO. FIREARMS ARE MANUFACTURED IN JAPAN TO ORIGINAL PARKER SPECIFICATIONS BY WINCHESTER.

In 1984 Winchester was contracted by Reagent Chemical & Research, Inc. to manufacture a new Parker shotgun. The new SxS was a DHE model, available in 20 and 28 ga. initially. These models are being fabricated in Japan under to original Parker specifications, and the reproduction is so authentic that most parts are interchangeable with original Parker guns. New in 1984.

Later in 1989 this trademark may encounter some factory related supply problems due to possible relocation.

SHOTGUNS: SIDE BY SIDE

Grading	100%	98%	95%	90%	80%	70%	60%

D GRADE—12 (new in 1986), 20, or 28 (new in 1986) ga., boxlock action, ejectors, single selective or double triggers, beavertail or splinter forend, straight or pistol grip stock, skeleton steel butt plate, engraving in original DH style, case hardened frame, rust blued barrels. Supplied with leather trunk case, canvas and leather cover, and snap caps.

| *Mfg.'s Sug. Retail* | $2,970 | $2,850 | $2,100 | $1,850 | $1,650 | $1,500 | $1,400 | $1,300 |

Add $630 for extra set of barrels.

Add $150 for beavertail forend.

Add $150 for internal screw chokes.

A .410 ga. is available in limited quantities on a special small frame (size 0000). Also, a 28/.410 ga. combo is available with 2 forends and a 16/20 ga. combo on a 20 ga. frame with 2 forends is pending. The 16 ga. is lighter than the 20 ga.

DHE STEEL SHOT SPECIAL—similar to 12 ga. D Grade, except has stengthened No. 1½ barrels, 3 in. chambers, and 28 in. chrome lined barrels, 7¼-7½ lbs. New in 1987.

| *Mfg.'s Sug. Retail* | $3,100 | $3,100 | $2,600 | $2,100 | $1,700 | $1,500 | $1,400 | $1,300 |

Add $100 for beavertail forend.

This model is available at all authorized Parker Reproduction dealers.

B GRADE LIMITED EDITION—12, 20, 28, or .410 ga., original Parker BH specifications, single selective or double trigger(s), straight or pistol grip stock, engraved skeleton buttplate, bank note scroll engraving around game scenes, cased. Only 100 manufactured in each gauge — mfg. began in late 1987.

| *Mfg.'s Sug. Retail* | $3,970 | $3,750 | $2,900 | $2,500 | $2,150 | $1,850 | $1,650 | $1,500 |

Add $1,000 for extra set of barrels.

Add $150 for beavertail forend.

A .410 ga. is available in limited quantities on a special small frame (size 0000). Also, a 28/.410 ga. combo is available with 2 forends and a 16/20 ga. combo on a 20 ga. frame with 2 forends is pending. The 16 ga. is lighter than the 20 ga.

Grading	100%	98%	95%	90%	80%	70%	60%

A-1 SPECIAL—12, 20, 28 or .410 ga., original Parker A-1 specifications, single selective or double trigger(s), fine scroll engraving with game scenes, 32 lines/in. checkering, cased with accessories. Mfg. began in early 1988.

Mfg.'s Sug. Retail	$8,740	$8,500	$6,750	$6,000	$5,475	$4,800	$4,350	$3,800

Add $1,000 for extra set of barrels.

Add $200 for beavertail forend.

A .410 ga. is available in limited quantities on a special small frame (size 0000). Also, a 28/.410 ga. combo is available with 2 forends and a 16/20 ga. combo on a 20 ga. frame with 2 forends is pending. The 16 ga. is lighter than the 20 ga.

A-1 Special Custom Engraved—custom (per individual special order) engraving, available with two sets of barrels only, cased with accessories. Mfg. began in early 1988. Prices start at $10,500 and go up according to individualized special features.

Federal Duck Stamp Collector's Series—available in 12, 20, 28, .410, or 20/16 and 28/.410 combo ga., A-1 Special specifications, authorized by U.S. Department of Interior. Manufacture is limited to 10 per year. New in late 1988.

Mfg.'s Sug. Retail	$14,000	$14,000	$10,000	$8,000

This model includes special case and 2 barrels per buyers specifications.

PARKER-HALE LIMITED

MANUFACTURED IN BIRMINGHAM, ENGLAND. CURRENTLY IMPORTED BY PRECISION SPORTS, LOCATED IN CORTLAND, NY.

RIFLES: BOLT ACTION

Add $90 for hunting rifle set trigger option on models listed below.

Parker-Hale bolt action rifles utilize the Mauser K-98 action and are offered in a variety of configurations. A single set trigger option was introduced in 1984 on most models which allows either "hair trigger" or conventional single stage operation - add $85.

MODEL 81 CLASSIC—available in 11 cal.'s between .22-250 and 7mm Rem. Mag., 24 in. barrel, open sights, 4 shot mag., select checkered walnut with sling swivels, 7¾ lbs. New in 1985.

Mfg.'s Sug. Retail	$880	$725	$565	$475	$395	$340	$300	$280

Model 81 African—.375 H&H cal., similar specifications as Model 81 Classic and has engraved action. New in 1986.

Mfg.'s Sug. Retail	$1,150	$895	$700	$600	$500	$425	$360	$330

MODEL 84 TARGET—7.62mm, match rifle with special sights, adj. cheekpiece on stock.

Mfg.'s Sug. Retail	$1,300	$1,080	$875	$760	$680	$610	$530	$465

MODEL 85 SNIPER—similar to Model 84 Target, except is equipped with scope and bipod. Imported in 1986 only.

	$1,760	$1,440	$1,200	$995	$895	$820	$750

Last Mfg.'s Sug. Retail was $2,000.

MODEL 86 TARGET—7.62mm, 27½ in. barrel, 5 shot mag., stippled stock and forend, aperture front and rear sights, 11¼ lbs. Imported in 1986 only.

	$980	$830	$760	$690	$610	$530	$465

Last Mfg.'s Sug. Retail was $1,149.

MODEL 87 TARGET—.243, 6.5 x 55, .308, .30-06, and .300 Win. Mag. cal.'s, target stock, aperture sights. New in 1987.

Mfg.'s Sug. Retail	$1,300	$1,080	$875	$760	$680	$610	$530	$465

MODEL 1000 STANDARD—available in 9 cal.'s between .22-250 and .308 Win., 22 in. barrel, 4 shot mag., walnut stock with cheekpiece, 7¼ lbs. Disc. in 1988.

	$400	$330	$285	$255	$230	$215	$195

Last Mfg.'s Sug. Retail was $500.

Grading	100%	98%	95%	90%	80%	70%	60%

MODEL 1100 LIGHTWEIGHT—available in 9 cal.'s between .22-250 and .30-06, 22 in. barrel, open sights, 4 shot mag., 6½ lbs. New in 1985.

Mfg.'s Sug. Retail	$600	$495	$400	$350	$325	$285	$270	$255

Model 1100M—.375 H&H, .404 Jeffery, or .458 Win. Mag. cal., 24 in. barrel, 4 shot mag., 9½ lbs.

Mfg.'s Sug. Retail	$1,000	$825	$650	$575	$500	$450	$425	$400

MODEL 1200 SUPER—bolt action, Mauser type action, .22-250, .243, 6mm, .25-06, .270, .30-06, .300 Win. Mag., 7mm Rem., or .308 cal., 24 in. barrel, folding sight, skip checkered walnut stock, pad swivels, rosewood pistol grip cap and forend tip, made 1968-present.

Mfg.'s Sug. Retail	$700	$550	$450	$375	$330	$295	$275	$260

Model 1200 Super Clip—similar to Model 1200 Super, except has detachable 4 shot box mag.

Mfg.'s Sug. Retail	$760	$600	$500	$400	$350	$300	$280	$265

MODEL 1200P PRESENTATION—same as 1200, except .243 or .30-06 cal., scroll engraved, no sights, made 1969-1975.

	$495	$425	$395	$340	$315	$305	$275

MODEL 1200 SUPER VARMINT—same as 1200, except .22-250, 6mm, .25-06, or .243 cal., 24 in. heavy barrel, no sights. Disc. in 1988.

	$525	$425	$365	$325	$285	$270	$255

Last Mfg.'s Sug. Retail was $660.

MODEL 2100 MIDLAND (HYBRID ACTION)—available in 11 cal.'s between .22-250 and .300 Win. Mag. cal.'s, 22 in. barrel, 4 round mag., open sights, 7 lbs.

Mfg.'s Sug. Retail	$380	$305	$250	$225	$200	$190	$180	$170

Model 2100 Midland Magnum—.375 H&H, .404 Jeffery, or .458 Win. Mag. cal., 24 in. barrel, 4 shot mag., 9½ lbs. New in 1989.

Mfg.'s Sug. Retail	$430	$380	$325	$295	$270	$260	$250	$240

MODEL 2600 MIDLAND SPECIAL—.243 Win., .270 Win., .308 Win., or .30-06 cal., Midland Gun Co. action, iron sights. New in 1989.

Mfg.'s Sug. Retail	$330	$295	$250	$225	$200	$190	$180	$170

SHOTGUNS

MODEL 640E—12, 16, or 20 ga., boxlock action, double triggers, straight grip stock, splinter forend, concave rib, extractors, silver finished receiver. New in 1986.

Mfg.'s Sug. Retail	$565	$475	$415	$350	$295	$260	$230	$210

Add $70 for 28 or .410 ga.

The "E" suffix in this model designates English configuration.

Model 640A—same ga.'s as 640E, except has non-selective single trigger, pistol grip, beavertail forend, and raised matted rib. New in 1986.

Mfg.'s Sug. Retail	$665	$550	$450	$385	$330	$300	$275	$260

Add $70 for 28 or .410 ga.

The "A" suffix in this model designates American configuration (pistol grip stock and single trigger).

MODEL 640M—10 ga., 3½ in. chambers, 30 in. barrels bored full and full, DT's, recoil pad. New in 1989.

Mfg.'s Sug. Retail	$675	$555	$450	$385	$330	$300	$275	$260

MODEL 645E—12, 16, or 20 ga., boxlock action, double triggers, straight grip stock, moderate engraving, splinter forend, concave rib, ejectors, silver finished receiver. New in 1986.

Mfg.'s Sug. Retail	$715	$600	$475	$400	$345	$290	$270	$255

Add $70 for 28 or .410 ga.

Model 645E-XXV—available in all ga.'s, 25 in. barrels only, ejectors, moderately engraved, silver finished receiver. New in 1986.

Mfg.'s Sug. Retail	$745	$600	$495	$400	$350	$300	$275	$260

Add $70 for 28 or .410 ga.

Grading	100%	98%	95%	90%	80%	70%	60%

Model 645E Bi-Gauge—2 barrel set available in either 20/28 ga. or 28/.410 ga. combination. New in 1988.

Mfg.'s Sug. Retail $1,300 $1,075 $900 $775 $700 $600 $550 $500

MODEL 645A—same ga.'s as 645E, except has non-selective single trigger, pistol grip, beavertail forend, and raised matted rib. New in 1986.

Mfg.'s Sug. Retail $815 $675 $550 $475 $425 $375 $330 $300
     Add $70 for 28 or .410 ga.

Model 645A Bi-Gauge—2 barrel set available in either 20/28 ga. or 28/.410 ga. combination. New in 1988.

Mfg.'s Sug. Retail $1,400 $1,175 $950 $825 $750 $625 $575 $525

MODEL 670E—12, 16, and 20 ga.'s, sidelock action, 26, 27, or 28 in. barrels, ejectors, engraved silver finished receiver, double triggers, straight grip. New in 1986.

Mfg.'s Sug. Retail $3,100 $2,700 $2,275 $1,800 $1,550 $1,375 $1,200 $1,025
     Add $200 for 28 or .410 ga.

This model is available by custom order only.

MODEL 680E-XXV—similar to Model 670E, except has color case hardened sideplates and 25 in. barrels only.

Mfg.'s Sug. Retail $2,900 $2,500 $2,100 $1,650 $1,475 $1,300 $1,175 $1,025
     Add $200 for 28 or .410 ga.

This model is available by custom order only.

PEDERSEN CUSTOM GUNS
DIVISION OF O.F. MOSSBERG, NORTH HAVEN, CT. MANUFACTURED BETWEEN 1973-1975.

RIFLES
MODEL 3000—bolt action rifle, Mossberg Model 810 action, .270, .30-06, 7mm Mag., .338 Mag. cal.'s, 22 and 24 in. barrel, open sight, checkered Monte Carlo stock.

   Grade III—no engraving.

     $550 $495 $470 $440 $420 $385 $330

   Grade II—moderately engraved.

     $660 $580 $525 $495 $440 $420 $385

   Grade I—heavily engraved and inlaid, with silver select wood.

     $990 $770 $745 $690 $635 $560 $495

MODEL 4700—custom deluxe lever action, (Model 472 Mossberg), .30-30 and .35 Rem. cal.'s, 5 shot, tube mag., 24 in. barrel, open sight, black walnut stock.

     $250 $195 $165 $155 $145 $130 $120

SHOTGUNS
MODEL 4000 SLIDE ACTION SHOTGUN—custom Mossberg Model 500, 12, 20, and .410 ga.'s, 3 in. chamber, 26 in. imp. cyl. or skeet, 28 in. full or mod., 30 in. full, vent rib, floral engraved, checkered select walnut stock, made in 1975.

     $460 $375 $330 $305 $265 $230 $220

MODEL 4000 TRAP—same as 4000, except 12 ga., 30 in. full, Monte Carlo trap stock and pad, made 1975.

     $485 $395 $350 $325 $285 $255 $240

MODEL 4500—same as 4000, less engraving.

     $420 $330 $305 $275 $240 $200 $175

MODEL 4500 TRAP—same as 4000 Trap, less engraving.

     $440 $350 $310 $280 $240 $210 $200

MODEL 1500 O/U HUNTING GUN—12 ga., 2¾ or 3 in. chambers, 26 in. imp. cyl. and mod., 28 in. mod. and full, 30 in. mod. and full, boxlock, auto ejectors, selective or non-selective single trigger, checkered pistol grip stock, made 1973-1975.

     $700 $575 $500 $440 $415 $385 $365

Grading	100%	98%	95%	90%	80%	70%	60%

MODEL 1500 SKEET—same as Hunting Gun, except 27 in. skeet, skeet stock, made 1973-1975.

	100%	98%	95%	90%	80%	70%	60%
	$725	$600	$525	$450	$425	$400	$385

MODEL 1500 TRAP—same as Hunting Gun, except 30 and 32 in. full barrels, trap Monte Carlo stock, made 1973-1975.

	$650	$550	$475	$435	$410	$375	$350

MODEL 1000 O/U HUNTING GUN—12 or 20 ga., 26, 28, or 30 in. barrels, various chokes, boxlock, auto ejectors, SST, checkered select walnut stock, silver inlays, more engraving, made 1973-1975.

	100%	98%	95%	90%	80%	70%	60%
Grade I	$2,200	$1,980	$1,870	$1,700	$1,540	$1,460	$1,375
Grade II	$1,815	$1,540	$1,430	$1,265	$1,185	$1,100	$1,045

MODEL 1000 TRAP GUN—same as Hunting Gun, but 12 ga., 30 or 32 in. mod. and full barrels, Monte Carlo trap stock, made 1973-1975.

	100%	98%	95%	90%	80%	70%	60%
Grade I	$2,100	$1,800	$1,650	$1,500	$1,350	$1,200	$995
Grade II	$1,650	$1,500	$1,375	$1,200	$1,050	$900	$725

MODEL 1000 SKEET—same as Hunting Gun, except 26 or 28 in. barrels, bored skeet, made 1973-1975.

	100%	98%	95%	90%	80%	70%	60%
Grade I	$2,255	$2,145	$2,035	$1,870	$1,705	$1,625	$1,540
Grade II	$1,980	$1,705	$1,595	$1,430	$1,350	$1,265	$1,210

MODEL 200 S X S—12 or 20 ga., 26 in. imp. cyl. and mod., 28 in. mod. and full, 30 in. mod. and full, boxlock, auto ejectors, SST, made 1973-1974.

	100%	98%	95%	90%	80%	70%	60%
Grade I	$2,420	$2,175	$2,090	$1,955	$1,790	$1,705	$1,625
Grade II	$2,200	$1,955	$1,815	$1,735	$1,625	$1,540	$1,485

MODEL 2500 DOUBLE BARREL—12 and 20 ga., 26 in. imp. cyl. and mod., 28 in. mod. and full, auto ejectors, boxlock, checkered pistol grip stock and forearm.

	$470	$385	$360	$305	$275	$260	$240

PERAZZI

MANUFACTURED IN BRESCIA, ITALY. IMPORTED AND DISTRIBUTED BY PERAZZI USA, INC. LOCATED IN MONROVIA, CA. (PREVIOUSLY LOCATED IN ROME, NY.)

Note: Perazzi shotguns are manufactured in Brescia, Italy. They were formerly imported by both Winchester and Ithaca during the 60's and 70's. The company now has its own distribution network and its current model line-up is extensive.

Because of the devaluation of the U.S. dollar since 1984, Perazzi shotguns have gone up in value substantially. Importers or distributors that carry inventory over from year to year occasionally will sell guns less expensively than the 1988 values listed below. Since they purchased this older inventory at the previous pricing level, these savings could be passed on to the consumer.

SHOTGUNS: DISCONTINUED

COMPETITION ONE TRAP GRADE—single shot, 12 ga., auto ejector, vent rib, cased.

	$1,650	$1,540	$1,375	$1,100	$935	$825	$660

COMPETITION ONE O/U TRAP—same as Competition, except O/U double.

	$1,485	$1,375	$1,210	$935	$770	$660	$550

COMPETITION ONE SKEET

	$2,500	$2,400	$2,250	$1,600	$1,400	$1,200	$900

SINGLE BARREL TRAP—12 ga., 34 in. vent rib, full choke barrel, boxlock, auto ejector, checkered pistol grip stock, recoil pad, made 1971-1972.

	$1,430	$1,320	$1,265	$990	$880	$800	$660

LIGHT GAME MODEL O/U FIELD—12 ga., 27½ in. vent rib barrels, mod. and full or imp. cyl. and mod., boxlock, auto ejectors, field stock, made 1972-1974.

	$1,430	$1,320	$1,265	$990	$880	$800	$660

PERAZZI, cont.

MX-8—12 ga., trap grade, vent rib, auto ejector, non selective single trigger, 30 or 32 in. full and mod., barrels, trap stock, recoil pad, cased, made 1969-present.

	$4,150	**$3,300**	**$3,000**	**$2,600**	**$2,200**	**$2,000**	**$1,800**

MX-8 COMBO TRAP GRADE—same as MX-8, except single 32 or 34 in. full barrel, cased, made 1973-present.

	$6,155	**$4,900**	**$4,300**	**$3,750**	**$3,300**	**$2,900**	**$2,500**

MIRAGE TRAP GRADE—12 ga., same as MX-8, except tapered rib.

	$2,970	**$2,375**	**$2,050**	**$1,760**	**$1,650**	**$1,540**	**$1,375**

MIRAGE SKEET—12 ga., same as Trap, except 28 in. barrel with muzzle brakes, skeet choke.

	$2,970	**$2,375**	**$2,090**	**$1,870**	**$1,760**	**$1,650**	**$1,265**

MT-6 GRADE—12 ga., vent rib, auto ejector, cased, five interchangeable choke tubes. Discontinued in 1983.

	$3,510	**$2,800**	**$2,400**	**$1,900**	**$1,600**	**$1,430**	**$1,265**

CURRENTLY MANUFACTURED TRAP, SKEET, AND HUNTING SHOTGUNS

Rather than list 1989 prices individually (because of the recent devaluation of the U.S. dollar), ADD APPROXIMATELY 20% TO THE 95%-100% VALUES LISTED BELOW to ascertain 1989 Perazzi prices.

AMERICAN TRAP SHOTGUNS-SINGLE BARREL—12 ga. only, 32 or 34 in. barrel, high post rib, select walnut, more expensive models vary in the amount of engraving, grade of walnut, and other special order features.

MX 3—standard trap gun, no engraving, interchangeable trigger group and stock, blue only.

Mfg.'s Sug. Retail	**$3,550**	**$2,940**	**$2,475**	**$2,240**	**$2,000**	**$1,800**	**$1,600**	**$1,500**

Also available as MX 3 Special which includes selective adj. trigger - add $600.

TMX Special—same as MX 3, only very high rib.

Mfg.'s Sug. Retail	**$3,680**	**$3,130**	**$2,550**	**$2,385**	**$2,150**	**$1,920**	**$1,700**	**$1,600**

TM1 Special—similar to TMX, except has adj. trigger.

Mfg.'s Sug. Retail	**$3,680**	**$3,185**	**$2,560**	**$2,385**	**$2,150**	**$1,920**	**$1,700**	**$1,600**

MX 3L—same as MX 3, only light engraving.

Mfg.'s Sug. Retail	**$4,350**	**$3,620**	**$3,090**	**$2,760**	**$2,400**	**$2,200**	**$2,000**	**$1,800**

MX 8 Special—similar to MX 3, except has adj. selective trigger and better wood. New in 1986.

Mfg.'s Sug. Retail	**$4,900**	**$4,050**	**$3,400**	**$3,090**	**$2,760**	**$2,400**	**$2,200**	**$1,875**

Grand America Special—similar to MX 8 Special. New in 1986.

Mfg.'s Sug. Retail	**$4,900**	**$4,050**	**$3,400**	**$3,090**	**$2,760**	**$2,400**	**$2,200**	**$1,875**

MX3S SC3—moderately engraved. New in 1986.

Mfg.'s Sug. Retail	**$6,850**	**$5,500**	**$4,475**	**$3,930**	**$3,500**	**$3,150**	**$2,800**	**$2,450**

MX 3 SCO—extensive scroll engraving on coin finished receiver, gold trigger.

Mfg.'s Sug. Retail	**$10,100**	**$8,390**	**$7,160**	**$6,390**	**$5,960**	**$5,600**	**$5,200**	**$4,750**

Add 12% fo "S" suffix model.

TMXS SCO—very similar to MX 3 SCO.

Mfg.'s Sug. Retail	**$10,150**	**$8,400**	**$7,160**	**$6,390**	**$5,960**	**$5,600**	**$5,200**	**$4,750**

Add $650 for Model TM1S SCO.

MX 3 Gold—extensive game scene engraving on coin finish receiver with multiple gold inlays.

Mfg.'s Sug. Retail	**$11,350**	**$9,420**	**$8,040**	**$7,180**	**$6,600**	**$6,000**	**$5,600**	**$5,100**

Add 12% for "S" suffix model.

TMXS Gold—extensive scroll work engraving on coin finish receiver with multiple gold inlays.

Mfg.'s Sug. Retail	**$11,400**	**$9,430**	**$8,040**	**$7,180**	**$6,600**	**$6,000**	**$5,600**	**$5,100**

Add $600 for TM1S Gold Model.

PERAZZI, cont.

AMERICAN TRAP SHOTGUNS: OVER AND UNDER COMBINATION
SETS—12 ga. only, 32 or 34 in. single barrel and choice of 29½ or 31½ in. O/U barrels, high post rib, select walnut, more expensive models vary in the amount of engraving, grade of walnut, and other special order features.

Rather than list 1989 prices individually (because of the recent devaluation of the U.S. dollar), ADD APPROXIMATELY 20% TO THE 95%-100% VALUES LISTED BELOW to ascertain 1989 Perazzi prices.

MX 3 Combo—Standard Trap Gun, no engraving, interchangeable trigger group and stock, blue only.
Mfg.'s Sug. Retail $5,000 $4,145 $3,340 $2,950 $2,700 $2,350 $2,075 $1,800
Add 16% for MX 3 Special Model.

MX 3L Combo—same as MX 3, only light engraving, 2 sets of barrels.
Mfg.'s Sug. Retail $6,500 $5,405 $4,615 $4,120 $3,780 $3,500 $3,200 $2,980

MX 8 Special Combo—supplied with 2 separate detachable and interchangeable trigger groups.
Mfg.'s Sug. Retail $6,900 $5,565 $4,500 $3,930 $3,500 $3,150 $2,800 $2,450

Grand America Special Combo—adj. selective trigger.
Mfg.'s Sug. Retail $6,900 $5,565 $4,500 $3,930 $3,500 $3,150 $2,800 $2,450

DB 81 Combo—case hardened frame, extra high rib on both barrels, 2 trigger groupings.
Mfg.'s Sug. Retail $6,900 $5,565 $4,500 $3,930 $3,500 $3,150 $2,800 $2,450

MX3S SC3—New in 1986.
Mfg.'s Sug. Retail $8,800 $7,100 $5,800 $5,275 $4,615 $4,000 $3,600 $3,500

SC3S Combo—light scroll engraving on coin finished receiver.
Mfg.'s Sug. Retail $10,350 $8,345 $7,150 $6,600 $6,100 $5,600 $5,100 $4,600

DB81S SC3 Combo—very similar to SC3.
Mfg.'s Sug. Retail $10,350 $8,345 $7,150 $6,600 $6,100 $5,600 $5,100 $4,600

MX 3 SCO Combo—extensive game scene engraving on coin finish receiver.
Mfg.'s Sug. Retail $13,000 $10,800 $9,220 $8,230 $7,500 $6,750 $6,000 $5,500
Add 12% for "S" suffix model.

MX 3 Gold Combo—extensive game scene engraving on coin finish receiver with multiple gold inlays.
Mfg.'s Sug. Retail $14,300 $11,830 $9,020 $8,500 $7,750 $7,000 $6,500 $6,000
Add 13% for "S" suffix model.

SCOS Combo—extensive scroll work engraving on coin finish receiver. Add $200 for DB 81 Model.
Mfg.'s Sug. Retail $16,000 $13,500 $10,770 $9,250 $8,500 $8,000 $7,400 $6,750

SCOS Gold Combo—extensive game scene engraving on coin finish receiver with multiple gold inlays.
Mfg.'s Sug. Retail $17,600 $14,145 $11,950 $9,750 $8,500 $8,000 $7,400 $6,750

DB81S SCO Combo—elaborate game scene engraving. New in 1986.
Mfg.'s Sug. Retail $16,000 $13,500 $10,770 $9,250 $8,500 $8,000 $7,400 $6,750

DB81S Gold Combo—top-of-the-line combo model.
Mfg.'s Sug. Retail $17,600 $14,145 $11,950 $9,750 $8,500 $8,000 $7,400 $6,750

SCO Sideplates Combo—similar to SCO, except with sideplates. New in 1987.
Mfg.'s Sug. Retail $22,500 $19,400 $17,250 $15,750 $14,200 $13,000 $11,500 $10,200

SCO Gold Sideplates Combo—similar to SCO Sideplates Combo, except has multiple gold inlays. New in 1987.
Mfg.'s Sug. Retail $25,600 $21,950 $19,600 $17,000 $15,000 $13,000 $11,800 $10,750

SKEET SHOTGUNS: OVER AND UNDER—12 ga. only, 27⅝ in. separated barrels, select walnut, more expensive models vary in the amount of engraving, grade of walnut, and other special order features.

Rather than list 1989 prices individually (because of the recent devaluation of the U.S. dollar), ADD APPROXIMATELY 20% TO THE 95%-100% VALUES LISTED BELOW to ascertain 1989 Perazzi prices.

PERAZZI, cont.

MX 3—Standard Skeet Gun, no engraving, flat VR, muzzle brakes, blue only.

Mfg.'s Sug. Retail	$3,750	$3,120	$2,400	$2,100	$1,900	$1,700	$1,500	$1,325

MX 3L—same as MX 3, only light engraving. MX 3CL has 5 choke tubes - add $150.

Mfg.'s Sug. Retail	$4,550	$3,780	$2,950	$2,550	$2,250	$2,000	$1,800	$1,700

MX 3 Special—similar to MX 3, except has adjustable selective trigger. New in 1987. MX 3C Special has choke tubes - add $150.

Mfg.'s Sug. Retail	$4,400	$3,680	$2,885	$2,510	$2,225	$2,000	$1,800	$1,700

Mirage—new in 1986.

Mfg.'s Sug. Retail	$4,550	$3,780	$2,950	$2,550	$2,250	$2,000	$1,800	$1,700

MX 8—same as MX 3, only vent barrel assembly. Values are the same for the MX8 Special Model.

Mfg.'s Sug. Retail	$4,550	$3,780	$2,950	$2,550	$2,250	$2,000	$1,800	$1,700

MX3 BL—12 ga. only, same as MX 3B, except with light engraving. New in 1987.

Mfg.'s Sug. Retail	$4,550	$3,780	$2,950	$2,550	$2,250	$2,000	$1,800	$1,700

Add $150 for choke tubes.

MX 3S SC3—12 ga. only, moderate engraving with deluxe walnut stock and forearm. New in 1987.

Mfg.'s Sug. Retail	$7,200	$6,125	$5,400	$5,200	$4,880	$4,475	$3,995	$3,500

Add $150 for choke tubes.

Mirage SC3—new in 1986.

Mfg.'s Sug. Retail	$8,000	$6,000	$5,000	$4,560	$4,175	$3,800	$3,350	$3,000

SC 3—moderate scroll engraving with one game bird on coin finished receiver.

Mfg.'s Sug. Retail	$8,000	$6,000	$5,000	$4,560	$4,175	$3,800	$3,350	$3,000

MX1 SC3—12 ga. only, moderate engraving with 27⅝ in. barrels. New in 1987.

Mfg.'s Sug. Retail	$8,000	$6,000	$5,000	$4,560	$4,175	$3,800	$3,350	$3,000

MX 1B SC3 has flat rib - same values as MX1 SC3.

MX 3 SCO—extensive scroll engraving on coin finished receiver, gold trigger. MX 3C has choke tubes - add $150.

Mfg.'s Sug. Retail	$10,950	$9,055	$7,300	$6,700	$6,050	$5,400	$4,900	$4,400

Add $1,700 for MX 3S SCO variation.

MX 3B SCO has flat rib - same values as MX 3 SCO.

MX 3 Gold—extensive game scene engraving on coin finished receiver with multiple gold inlays. Choke tubes - add $150.

Mfg.'s Sug. Retail	$12,600	$10,150	$8,400	$7,555	$6,600	$6,100	$5,550	$5,000

Mirage SCO—new in 1986.

Mfg.'s Sug. Retail	$13,150	$10,400	$8,500	$7,555	$6,600	$6,100	$5,550	$5,000

SCO—extensive game scene coverage on coin finished receiver, gold trigger.

Mfg.'s Sug. Retail	$13,150	$10,400	$8,500	$7,555	$6,600	$6,100	$5,550	$5,000

MX1 SCO—12 ga. only, highly engraved with extra fancy walnut stock and forearm. New in 1987.

Mfg.'s Sug. Retail	$13,150	$10,400	$8,500	$7,555	$6,600	$6,100	$5,550	$5,000

MX 1B is flat rib variation of MX1 SCO.

MX 3S Gold—12 ga. only, deluxe boxlock action with multiple gold inlays. New in 1987.

Mfg.'s Sug. Retail	$14,400	$11,880	$9,045	$8,500	$7,750	$7,000	$6,500	$6,000

Add $150 for choke tubes.

Mirage Gold—new in 1986.

Mfg.'s Sug. Retail	$15,200	$11,815	$9,150	$8,500	$7,750	$7,000	$6,250	$5,750

SCO Gold—extensive game scene engraving on coin finished receiver with multiple gold inlays.

Mfg.'s Sug. Retail	$15,200	$11,815	$9,150	$8,500	$7,750	$7,000	$6,250	$5,750

Values listed for this model also pertain to the following gold inlaid models: DB 81, MX1, MX1B, MX2, MX2L.

Grading	100%	98%	95%	90%	80%	70%	60%

SKEET O/U SHOTGUNS: 4-GAUGE SET

Rather than list 1989 prices individually (because of the recent devaluation of the U.S. dollar), ADD APPROXIMATELY 20% TO THE 95%-100% VALUES LISTED BELOW to ascertain 1989 Perazzi prices.

MX 3—4 ga. Skeet set (12, 20, 28, and .410 ga.'s), otherwise same as MX 3. Choke tubes - add $1,000.

Mfg.'s Sug. Retail	$8,500	$7,035	$6,000	$5,500	$5,000	$4,550	$3,995	$3,500

MX 3 Special—similar to MX 3 set except has adj. selective trigger.

Mfg.'s Sug. Retail	$10,200	$8,390	$7,160	$6,390	$5,960	$5,600	$5,200	$4,750

MX 3L—similar to MX 3 set except has light engraving.

Mfg.'s Sug. Retail	$10,200	$8,390	$7,160	$6,390	$5,960	$5,600	$5,200	$4,750

Mirage—new in 1986.

Mfg.'s Sug. Retail	$11,200	$9,000	$7,300	$6,700	$6,050	$5,400	$4,900	$4,400

MX 3S SC3—moderate engraving with game scenes.

Mfg.'s Sug. Retail	$14,900	$12,200	$9,320	$8,675	$7,800	$7,000	$6,500	$6,000

MX 3 SCO—4 ga. Skeet set (12, 20, 28, and .410 ga.'s), standard SCO game scene engraving.

Mfg.'s Sug. Retail	$18,250	$15,120	$12,300	$10,750	$9,700	$8,800	$7,900	$7,400

MX 3 Gold—4 ga. Skeet set (12, 20, 28, and .410 ga.'s), standard SCO gold game scene engraving.

Mfg.'s Sug. Retail	$19,900	$16,485	$12,960	$11,400	$9,900	$9,000	$8,500	$8,000

MX 3S SCO—with elaborate scroll engraving.

Mfg.'s Sug. Retail	$20,250	$16,600	$13,250	$11,400	$9,900	$9,000	$8,500	$8,000

MX 3S Gold—elaborate game scene engraving with gold inlays.

Mfg.'s Sug. Retail	$22,300	$17,950	$14,000	$11,950	$10,250	$9,000	$8,500	$8,000

LIVE PIGEON SHOTGUNS: OVER AND UNDER

Rather than list 1989 prices individually (because of the recent devaluation of the U.S. dollar), ADD APPROXIMATELY 20% TO THE 95%-100% VALUES LISTED BELOW to ascertain 1989 Perazzi prices.

MX 3—12 ga. only, separated barrels, high post rib.

Mfg.'s Sug. Retail	$3,750	$3,120	$2,400	$2,100	$1,900	$1,700	$1,500	$1,325

MX 3B—same as MX 3, except flat vent rib. Same prices as MX 3.

MX 1—same as MX 3, only fixed choke borings. MX 1B has flat rib.

Mfg.'s Sug. Retail	$4,800	$3,935	$3,075	$2,600	$2,275	$2,000	$1,800	$1,700

MX 3L—same as MX 3, only light engraving. MX 3BL has flat rib.

Mfg.'s Sug. Retail	$4,550	$3,780	$2,950	$2,550	$2,250	$2,000	$1,800	$1,700

MX1 SC3—moderate engraving with single game scene on silver receiver. MX 1B has flat rib.

Mfg.'s Sug. Retail	$8,000	$6,725	$5,800	$5,400	$4,950	$4,500	$3,995	$3,500

MX 3 SCO—extensive scroll engraving on coin finished receiver, gold trigger.

Mfg.'s Sug. Retail	$10,950	$9,055	$7,300	$6,700	$6,050	$5,400	$4,900	$4,400

MX 1 SCO—extensive game scene engraving on coin finished receiver, gold trigger. MX 1B has flat rib.

Mfg.'s Sug. Retail	$13,150	$10,400	$8,500	$7,555	$6,600	$6,100	$5,550	$5,000

MX 3 Gold—extensive game scene engraving on coin finished receiver with multiple gold inlays.

Mfg.'s Sug. Retail	$12,600	$10,150	$8,400	$7,555	$6,600	$6,100	$5,550	$5,000

MX 1 Gold—extensive game scene engraving on coin finished receiver with multiple gold inlays. MX 1B has flat rib.

Mfg.'s Sug. Retail	$15,200	$11,815	$9,150	$8,500	$7,750	$7,000	$6,250	$5,750

SHO—extensive sidelock game scene engraving on coin finished receiver with multiple gold inlays.

Mfg.'s Sug. Retail	$27,400	$23,000	$20,250	$17,500	$15,250	$13,000	$11,800	$10,750

Grading	100%	98%	95%	90%	80%	70%	60%

SHO Gold—extensive sidelock game scene engraving on coin finished receiver with multiple gold inlays.

Mfg.'s Sug. Retail	$30,650	$25,250	$21,750	$18,400	$15,950	$13,450	$11,800	$10,750

LIVE PIGEON AND GAME SHOTGUNS: SIDE-BY-SIDE SIDELOCKS

Rather than list 1989 prices individually (because of the recent devaluation of the U.S. dollar), ADD APPROXIMATELY 20% TO THE 95%-100% VALUES LISTED BELOW to ascertain 1989 Perazzi prices.

DHO—extensive sidelock scroll engraving on coin finished receiver. Limited production-special order only.

Mfg.'s Sug. Retail	$28,700	$23,800	$20,750	$17,850	$15,500	$13,000	$11,800	$10,750

DHO Gold—extensive sidelock game scene engraving on coin finished receiver with multiple gold inlays.

Mfg.'s Sug. Retail	$32,000	$26,150	$22,325	$18,900	$16,150	$13,500	$11,800	$10,750

DHO Extra—top of the line s x s, special order only, any gauge, rare. Perhaps the most expensive new shotgun in the world.

Mfg.'s Sug. Retail	$56,700	$50,800	$45,360	$40,000	$34,500	$29,000	$25,000	$20,000

OLYMPIC AND AMERICAN TRAP SHOTGUNS: OVER AND UNDER—

12 ga. only, 29½ or 31½ in. barrels, all bored improved modified through extra-full. More expensive models differ in the amount of engraving and the quality of walnut.

Rather than list 1989 prices individually (because of the recent devaluation of the U.S. dollar), ADD APPROXIMATELY 20% TO THE 95%-100% VALUES LISTED BELOW to ascertain 1989 Perazzi prices.

MX 3—12 ga. only, separated barrels, high post rib.

Mfg.'s Sug. Retail	$3,750	$3,120	$2,400	$2,100	$1,900	$1,700	$1,500	$1,325

MX 3B—same as MX 3, except flat vent rib and vent barrels. Same prices as MX 3.

MX 8—same as MX 3, only vent barrel assembly.

Mfg.'s Sug. Retail	$4,550	$3,780	$2,950	$2,550	$2,250	$2,000	$1,800	$1,700

DB 81—vent barrels with extra high rib, case hardened receiver, high Monte Carlo stock with vent recoil pad.

Mfg.'s Sug. Retail	$4,800	$3,930	$3,050	$2,610	$2,300	$2,000	$1,800	$1,700

MX 2—same as MX 8, except has high rib and Monte Carlo stock. Model MX 2L has flat rib and separated barrels.

Mfg.'s Sug. Retail	$4,800	$3,930	$3,050	$2,610	$2,300	$2,000	$1,800	$1,700

MX 3L—same as MX 3, only light engraving. MX 3BL has flat rib.

Mfg.'s Sug. Retail	$4,550	$3,780	$2,950	$2,550	$2,250	$2,000	$1,800	$1,700

SC3—moderate engraving with single game scene on silver receiver. MX 1B has flat rib.

Mfg.'s Sug. Retail	$8,000	$6,725	$5,800	$5,400	$4,950	$4,500	$3,995	$3,500

DB 81 SC3—light scroll engraving on coin finished receiver.

Mfg.'s Sug. Retail	$8,000	$6,725	$5,800	$5,400	$4,950	$4,500	$3,995	$3,500

MX 2 SC3—light game scene engraving on coin finished receiver, gold trigger. MX 2L SC3 has flat rib.

Mfg.'s Sug. Retail	$8,000	$6,725	$5,800	$5,400	$4,950	$4,500	$3,995	$3,500

MX 3 SCO—extensive scroll work engraving on coin finished receiver.

Mfg.'s Sug. Retail	$10,950	$9,055	$7,300	$6,700	$6,050	$5,400	$4,900	$4,400

SCO—engraving with multiple game scenes on silver receiver. DB 81 has American dimensions.

Mfg.'s Sug. Retail	$13,150	$10,400	$8,500	$7,555	$6,600	$6,100	$5,550	$5,000

MX 2 SCO—extensive game scene engraving on coin finished receiver, gold trigger. MX 2L SCO has flat rib.

Mfg.'s Sug. Retail	$13,150	$10,400	$8,500	$7,555	$6,600	$6,100	$5,550	$5,000

DB 81 SCO—highly engraved variation of the DB 81. New in 1987.

Mfg.'s Sug. Retail	$13,150	$10,400	$8,500	$7,555	$6,600	$6,100	$5,550	$5,000

Grading	100%	98%	95%	90%	80%	70%	60%

MX 3 Gold—extensive game scene engraving on coin finished receiver with multiple gold inlays.

Mfg.'s Sug. Retail	$12,600	$10,150	$8,400	$7,555	$6,600	$6,100	$5,550	$5,000

SCO—engraving with multiple game scenes on silver receiver with gold inlays. DB 81 gold has American dimensions.

Mfg.'s Sug. Retail	$13,150	$10,400	$8,500	$7,555	$6,600	$6,100	$5,550	$5,000

MX 2 Gold—extensive game scene engraving on coin finished receiver with multiple gold inlays. MX 2L has flat rib.

Mfg.'s Sug. Retail	$15,200	$11,815	$9,150	$8,500	$7,750	$7,000	$6,250	$5,750

SCO Sideplate—extensive sidelock game scene engraving on coin finished receiver.

Mfg.'s Sug. Retail	$18,850	$15,625	$12,600	$10,900	$9,750	$8,800	$7,900	$7,400

SCO Gold Sideplate—extensive sidelock game scene engraving on coin finished receiver with multiple gold inlays.

Mfg.'s Sug. Retail	$21,650	$17,550	$12,775	$11,850	$10,250	$9,000	$8,500	$8,000

Extra—top-of-the-line over and under incorporating every refinement.

Mfg.'s Sug. Retail	$37,150	$30,250	$26,425	$22,750	$19,000	$15,950	$13,700	$11,850

GAME SHOTGUNS: OVER AND UNDER—12, 20, 28, or .410 ga., 26, 26⅜, or 27⅝ in. barrels only, choice of chokes.

Rather than list 1989 prices individually (because of the recent devaluation of the U.S. dollar), ADD APPROXIMATELY 20% TO THE 95%-100% VALUES LISTED BELOW to ascertain 1989 Perazzi prices.

MX 5—12 ga. only, boxlock, blued finish, top grade walnut. New in 1987.

Mfg.'s Sug. Retail	$3,150	$2,675	$2,100	$1,900	$1,700	$1,500	$1,325	$1,200

Add $150 for choke tubes.

MX 3—12 and 20 ga., separated barrels. MS 3C has 5 choke tubes — add $150. This model was developed in conjunction with Pachmayr.

Mfg.'s Sug. Retail	$3,750	$3,120	$2,400	$2,100	$1,900	$1,700	$1,500	$1,325

Add 17% for MX3 Special.

MX 12—similar to MX 3, except has better engraving and wood.

Mfg.'s Sug. Retail	$4,550	$3,780	$2,950	$2,550	$2,250	$2,000	$1,800	$1,700

Add $150 for choke tubes.

MX 20—20, 28, and .410 ga.'s, separated barrels. Imported in 1986 only. MX20C has choke tubes — add $110.

	$3,100	$2,650	$2,250	$2,025	$1,775	$1,600	$1,450

Last Mfg.'s Sug. Retail was $3,540.

SC3—moderate engraving with single game scene on silver receiver.

Mfg.'s Sug. Retail	$6,405	$5,700	$5,000	$4,560	$4,175	$3,800	$3,350	$3,000

MX 3S SC3—12 ga. only, medium engraving coverage. New in 1987.

Mfg.'s Sug. Retail	$7,200	$6,125	$5,400	$5,200	$4,880	$4,475	$3,995	$3,500

Add $150 for choke tubes.

MX 12 SC3—12 ga. only, similar to MX 3S SC3, except has better engraving and wood. New in 1987.

Mfg.'s Sug. Retail	$8,000	$6,725	$5,800	$5,400	$4,950	$4,500	$3,995	$3,500

Add $150 for choke tubes.

MX 20 SC3—20, 28, or .410 ga., 26 in. barrels, boxlock action with moderate engraving. New in 1987.

Mfg.'s Sug. Retail	$8,000	$6,725	$5,800	$5,400	$4,950	$4,500	$3,995	$3,500

Add $150 for choke tubes.

MX 3C SCO—extensive scroll work engraving on coin finished receiver, choke tubes (5) standard.

Mfg.'s Sug. Retail	$11,100	$9,130	$7,350	$6,725	$6,050	$5,400	$4,900	$4,400

Add 15% for "S" suffix model.

Grading	100%	98%	95%	90%	80%	70%	60%

MX 3C Gold—extensive game scene engraving on coin finished receiver with multiple gold inlays.

Mfg.'s Sug. Retail $12,750 $10,225 $8,450 $7,575 $6,600 $6,100 $5,550 $5,000
Add 15% for "S" suffix model.

Standard equipment includes 5 interchangeable choke tubes.

MX 12 SCO—12 ga. only, deluxe grade walnut with elaborate engraving. New in 1987.
Mfg.'s Sug. Retail $13,150 $10,400 $8,500 $7,555 $6,600 $6,100 $5,550 $5,000
Add $150 for choke tubes (20 ga. only).

MX 20 SCO—20, 28, or .410 ga., 26 in. barrels only, profusely engraved with deluxe walnut stock and forearm. New in 1987.
Mfg.'s Sug. Retail $13,150 $10,400 $8,500 $7,555 $6,600 $6,100 $5,550 $5,000
Add $150 for choke tubes (20 ga. only).

MX 12 Gold—12 ga. only, top-of-the-line boxlock model. New in 1987.
Mfg.'s Sug. Retail $15,200 $11,810 $9,150 $8,475 $7,750 $7,000 $6,250 $5,750
Add $150 for choke tubes.

MX 20 Gold—20, 28, or .410 ga., 26 in. barrels only, top-of-the-line smaller gauge boxlock without sideplates. New in 1987.
Mfg.'s Sug. Retail $15,200 $11,810 $9,150 $8,475 $7,750 $7,000 $6,250 $5,750
Add $150 for choke tubes.

SCO—20, 28, and .410 ga.'s, engraving with multiple game scenes on silver receiver. DB 81 has American dimensions.
Mfg.'s Sug. Retail $15,350 $11,895 $9,200 $8,500 $7,750 $7,000 $6,250 $5,750

SCO Gold—20, 28, and .410 ga.'s, engraving with multiple game scenes on silver receiver with gold inlays.
Mfg.'s Sug. Retail $17,100 $14,035 $12,550 $10,000 $9,000 $8,100 $7,450 $6,750

MX 12 SCO Sideplates—12 ga. only, elaborately engraved sideplates, extra deluxe walnut. New in 1987.
Mfg.'s Sug. Retail $18,850 $15,625 $12,600 $10,900 $9,750 $8,800 $7,900 $7,400
Add $150 for choke tubes.

SCO Sideplates—12, 20, 28, and .410 ga.'s, engraving with multiple game scenes on silver side plate receiver.
Mfg.'s Sug. Retail $18,850 $15,625 $12,600 $10,900 $9,750 $8,800 $7,900 $7,400

MX 12 Gold Sideplates—top-of-the-line boxlock with non-functional sideplates. New in 1987.
Mfg.'s Sug. Retail $21,650 $17,550 $12,775 $11,850 $10,250 $9,000 $8,500 $8,000
Add $150 for choke tubes.

SCO Gold Sideplates—12, 20, 28, and .410 ga.'s, engraving with multiple game scenes on silver receiver with gold inlays on side plates.
Mfg.'s Sug. Retail $21,650 $17,550 $12,775 $11,850 $10,250 $9,000 $8,500 $8,000

SHO—12 ga. only, true sidelock with extensive game scene engraving on coin finish receiver.
Mfg.'s Sug. Retail $27,400 $23,000 $20,250 $17,500 $15,250 $13,000 $11,800 $10,750

SHO Gold—12 ga. only, true sidelock with extensive game scene engraving with multiple gold inlays on coin finish receiver.
Mfg.'s Sug. Retail $30,650 $25,250 $21,750 $18,400 $15,950 $13,450 $11,800 $10,750

Extra—12, 20, 28, or .410 ga.'s, top-of-the-line model incorporating every refinement.
Mfg.'s Sug. Retail $37,150 $30,250 $26,425 $22,750 $19,000 $15,950 $13,700 $11,850

GAME SHOTGUNS: SIDE-BY-SIDE SIDELOCKS

Rather than list 1989 prices individually (because of the recent devaluation of the U.S. dollar), ADD APPROXIMATELY 20% TO THE 95%-100% VALUES LISTED BELOW to ascertain 1989 Perazzi prices.

Grading	100%	98%	95%	90%	80%	70%	60%

DHO—extensive sidelock scroll engraving on coin finished receiver. Limited production-special order only.

Mfg.'s Sug. Retail $28,700 $23,800 $20,750 $17,850 $15,500 $13,000 $11,800 $10,750

DHO Gold—extensive sidelock game scene engraving on coin finished receiver with multiple gold inlays.

Mfg.'s Sug. Retail $32,000 $26,150 $22,325 $18,900 $16,150 $13,500 $11,800 $10,750

DHO Extra—top of the line SXS, special order only, any gauge, rare. Perhaps the most expensive new shotgun in the world.

Mfg.'s Sug. Retail $56,700 $50,800 $45,360 $40,000 $34,500 $29,000 $25,000 $20,000

PERUGINI-VISINI

MANUFACTURED IN BRESCIA, ITALY. MODELS BOXLOCK EXPRESS, BOXLOCK MAGNUM, AND SIDELOCK SUPER EXPRESS WERE PREVIOUSLY IMPORTED AND DISTRIBUTED BY W.L. MOORE, LOCATED IN WESTLAKE VILLAGE, CA. ALL OTHER MODELS LISTED BELOW WERE IMPORTED AND DISTRIBUTED BY ARMES DE CHASSE LOCATED IN CHADDS FORD, PA, 19317 UNTIL 1988.

Due to the recent devaluation of the American dollar against foreign currencies, the values listed below could change substantially if there is further fluctuation in the exchange rate. Perugini-Visini rifles and shotguns are very limited production, and are mostly made on a custom order basis only.

RIFLES

STANDARD MODEL: BOLT ACTION—available in most U.S. and metric cal.'s, Mauser 98K action, 24 or 26 in. barrel, 3 shot mag.(non-detachable), matte finished European walnut, high polish bluing, no sights. Importation disc. in 1987.

   $4,250 $3,800 $3,400 $2,950 $2,500 $2,000 $1,800

Last Mfg.'s Sug. Retail was $4,250.

DELUXE MODEL: BOLT ACTION—similar to Standard Model, except has finely checkered oil finished walnut stock, sights, knurled bolt handle, and is cased. Importation disc. in 1987.

   $4,250 $3,800 $3,400 $2,950 $2,500 $2,000 $1,800

Last Mfg.'s Sug. Retail was $4,250.

MODEL EAGLE: SINGLE SHOT—available in most U.S. and metric cal.'s, Anson & Deeley type action, ejector, sights, adj. trigger, oil finished finely checkered European walnut stock, 24 or 26 in. Hammerli barrel. Importation disc. in 1987.

   $5,255 $4,500 $3,800 $3,400 $2,950 $2,500 $2,000

Last Mfg.'s Sug. Retail was $5,255.

MODEL VICTORIA SxS—.30-06, 7 x 65R, or 9.3 x 74 cal., Anson & Deeley type boxlock action, border engraving, ejectors, folding leaf rear sight, DT's, 24 or 26 in. barrels with chopper lumps, leather cased. Importation disc. in 1989.

   $6,400 $5,500 $4,700 $3,900 $3,375 $2,750 $2,400

Add $1,200 for full engraving coverage.

Last Mfg.'s Sug. Retail was $6,800.

Model Victoria Mag. SxS—similar to Model Victoria, except in .375 H&H or .458 Win. Mag. cal. Importation disc. in 1989.

   $14,750 $11,550 $9,150 $7,350 $6,725 $6,050 $5,400

Add $5,000 for full engraving coverage.

Last Mfg.'s Sug. Retail was $15,300.

MODEL SELOUS SxS—9.3 x 74R, 375 H&H, .458 Win. Mag., .470 N.E., and .500 3 in. N.E. cal.'s, H&H style detachable sidelock action, ejectors, folding leaf rear sight, border engraving with best quality checkered walnut, top-of-the-line model, leather cased. Importation disc. in 1989.

   $21,200 $16,750 $13,250 $10,750 $8,875 $7,000 $6,250

Add $5,000 for full engraving coverage.

Last Mfg.'s Sug. Retail was $21,800.

Grading	100%	98%	95%	90%	80%	70%	60%

BOXLOCK EXPRESS SxS—.444 Marlin or 9.3 x 74R cal.'s, Anson & Deeley boxlock action, ejectors, color case hardened frame, iron sights. Importation disc. in 1989.

	$3,150	$2,800	$2,500	$2,200	$1,950	$1,700	$1,475

Last Mfg.'s Sug. Retail was $3,500.

BOXLOCK MAGNUM O/U—.270 Win., .375 H&H, and .458 Win. Mag. cal.'s, Anson & Deeley boxlock action, ejectors, monoblock barrels, select walnut. Importation disc. in 1989.

	$5,500	$4,900	$4,300	$3,750	$3,100	$2,600	$2,200

Last Mfg.'s Sug. Retail was $6,100.

SIDELOCK SUPER EXPRESS SxS—choice of 9 different cal.'s including .470 Nitro Express, H&H patterned sidelocks, chopper lump barrels, third lever fastener, multi-leaf express sights, coin finished or case hardened receiver, engraving patterns optional. Importation disc. in 1989.

	$9,500	$8,400	$7,400	$6,850	$6,100	$5,600	$5,000

Last Mfg.'s Sug. Retail was $10,500.

SHOTGUNS

LIBERTY MODEL—12, 20, 28, or .410 ga., Anson & Deeley type engraved action, 28 in. chopper lump barrels, double Purdey-type lock, ejectors, leather cased. Importation disc. in 1989.

	$5,255	$4,500	$3,800	$3,400	$2,950	$2,500	$2,000

Last Mfg.'s Sug. Retail was $5,255.

CLASSIC MODEL—12 or 20 ga., H&H style scroll engraved sidelock action, 28 in. chopper lump barrels, double Purdey-type lock, best quality checkered walnut stock and forearm, top-of-the-line model, leather cased. Importation disc. in 1989.

	$10,970	$8,650	$7,500	$6,925	$6,200	$5,675	$5,050

Last Mfg.'s Sug. Retail was $10,970.

PHOENIX ARMS CO.

PREVIOUS IMPORTER LOCATED IN LOWELL, MA.

PHOENIX—.25 ACP cal., Belgium semi-auto, previously manufactured by Robar et DeKerkhove located in Liege, Belgium.

This trademark is rarely encountered - values would start at $350 and go up according to original condition.

PIOTTI

MANUFACTURER LOCATED IN BRESCIA, ITALY. CURRENTLY IMPORTED EXCLUSIVELY BY W.L. MOORE & CO. LOCATED IN WESTLAKE VILLAGE, CA.

Fratelli Piotti is one of Italy's premier gunmakers. These shotguns meet the highest British standards of craftsmanship and are made to customer specifications. Variety of gauges, engraving, styles, chokes, etc.

For the following models — add $375 for single trigger, $250 for hand-detachable locks, $2,500 for self-opening action, approx. $560 for leather case, $625-$1,250 for 28 or .410 ga. (depending on if boxlock or sidelock).

SHOTGUNS

PIUMA—12, 16, 20, 28, or .410 ga., Anson & Deeley boxlock ejector double with chopper double barrels, level file-cut rib, light scroll and rosette engraving, scalloped frame.

Mfg.'s Sug. Retail	$6,600	$5,300	$4,500	$3,500	$2,950	$2,500	$2,000	$1,800

Grading	100%	98%	95%	90%	80%	70%	60%

WESTLAKE—12, 16, 20, 28, or .410 ga., H&H sidelock action, moderate scroll engraving. Importation disc. in 1989.

	$7,500	$6,050	$5,300	$4,700	$4,200	$3,750	$3,000

Last Mfg.'s Sug. Retail was $8,400.

MONTE CARLO—12, 16, 20, 28, or .410 ga., best-quality H&H pattern sidelock ejector double with chopper lump barrels, Purdey style scroll and rosette engraving.

Mfg.'s Sug. Retail	$11,400	$9,100	$8,000	$7,100	$6,000	$5,000	$4,500	$4,000

KING NUMBER 1—12, 16, 20, 28, or .410 ga., best-quality H&H pattern sidelock ejector double with chopper lump barrels, level file-cut rib, very fine, full coverage scroll engraving with small floral bouquets, gold crest in forearm, gold crown in top lever, name in gold and finely figured wood.

Mfg.'s Sug. Retail	$13,500	$10,800	$9,100	$7,650	$6,600	$5,500	$4,500	$3,500

LUNIK—12, 16, 20, 28, or .410 ga., best-quality H&H pattern sidelock ejector double with lump (demi-bloc) barrels, level, file-cut rib, Renaissance style large scroll engraving in relief, gold crown in top lever, gold name, and gold crest in forearm, finely figured wood.

Mfg.'s Sug. Retail	$14,400	$11,500	$9,625	$8,950	$7,100	$6,000	$5,000	$4,500

KING EXTRA—12, 16, 20, 28, or .410 ga., best-quality H&H pattern sidelock ejector double with chopper lump barrels, level file-cut rib, choice of either bulino game scene engraving or game scene engraving with gold inlays, engraved and signed by a master engraver, exhibition grade wood.

This model ranges in price (retail) between $15,600-$20,000, depending on amount of engraving and other special orders. In 100% condition this model will range from $12,500-$16,000.

MONACO NUMBER 1 OR 2—12, 16, 20, 28, or .410 ga., best-quality H&H pattern sidelock ejector double with lump (demi-bloc) barrels, level, file-cut rib, Renaissance style large scroll engraving in relief, gold crown in top lever, gold name, and gold crest in forearm, finely figured wood.

Mfg.'s Sug. Retail	$17,700	$14,200	$12,000	$9,995	$8,900	$7,900	$6,900	$5,900

MONACO NUMBER 4—top-of-the-line model with every refinement incorporated. Custom order only and extremely rare.

Since this model is available on an individual custom order only basis, specimens have to be evaluated one at a time. The last retail price published was $22,000 in 1988.

POLY TECHNOLOGIES, INC.

DISTRIBUTED BY PTK INTERNATIONAL, INC. LOCATED IN ATLANTA, GA. IMPORTED BY KENG'S FIREARMS SPECIALTY, INC., LOCATED IN RIVERDALE, GA. MANUFACTURED IN CHINA BY POLY TECHNOLOGIES, INC.

Poly Technologies commercial firearms are made to Chinese military specifications and have excellent quality control.

POLY TECH AKS-762—7.62 x 39mm Soviet military, 16¼ in. barrel, semi-auto version of the Chinese AKM (Type 56) assault rifle, 8.4 lbs., wood stock. Importation began in 1988.

Mfg.'s Sug. Retail	$400	$365	$300	$250	$230	$210	$195	$180

Add $10 for side-fold plastic stock.

This model is also available with a downward folding stock at no extra charge.

CHINESE SKS—7.62 x 39mm Soviet military, 20‰₀ in. barrel, full wood stock, machine steel parts to Chinese military specifications, 7.9 lbs. Importation began in 1988.

Mfg.'s Sug. Retail	$200	$175	$140	$130	$120	$110	$105	$100

RUSSIAN AK-47/S—7.62 x 39mm Soviet military, 16⅜ in. barrel, semi-auto configuration of the original AK-47, 8.2 lbs. Importation began in 1988.

Mfg.'s Sug. Retail	$550	$480	$420	$385	$320	$295	$270	$255

The S suffix in this variation designates third model specifications.

U.S. M-14/S—.308 cal., semi-auto, 22 in. barrel, forged receiver, quality reproduction of the famous M-14, 9.2 lbs. Importation began in late 1988.

Mfg.'s Sug. Retail	$700	$620	$495	$420	$385	$360	$330	$295

POWELL, WILLIAM & SON LTD.

MANUFACTURED IN BIRMINGHAM, ENGLAND. LIMITED IMPORTATION BY JAQUAS, LOCATED IN FINDLEY, OH.

NUMBER 3 BOXLOCK EJECTOR—12, 16, 20, or .410 ga., chopper lump barrels, extra choice French walnut, many special orders available.

	100%	98%	95%	90%	80%	70%	60%
	$7,500	$6,000	$5,350	$4,900	$4,500	$4,000	$3,600
Model 4	$6,000	$5,000	$4,300	$3,500	$3,200	$2,750	$2,400
Model 6	$2,100	$1,750	$1,625	$1,500	$1,375	$1,250	$1,100

NUMBER 1 SIDELOCK EJECTOR—12, 16, 20, or .410 ga., chopper lump barrels, extra choice French walnut, many special orders available. Gold inlays, deep relief carved action fences, can be obtained in self opener.

100%	98%	95%	90%	80%	70%	60%
$18,000	$13,500	$12,000	$10,800	$9,500	$9,000	$8,500

PRANDELLI-GASPERINI

PREVIOUS MANUFACTURER LOCATED IN BRESCIA, ITALY. PREVIOUSLY IMPORTED BY RICHLAND ARMS LOCATED IN BLISSFIELD, MI.

Prandelli-Gasperini made both O/U and S X S shotguns in either sidelock or boxlock. Currently, older boxlock models start at approximately $1,250 (assuming 80% or better original condition). Sidelock models in similar condition usually start at $2,500, depending on gauge, embellishments, and condition.

Approximately 250 specimens of this trademark were imported during Richland Arms importation.

PREMIER

PREVIOUSLY MANUFACTURED IN ITALY AND SPAIN.

SHOTGUNS: SIDE-BY-SIDE

REGENT DOUBLE BARREL SHOTGUN—12, 16, 20, 28, or .410 ga., 26, 28, or 30 in. barrels, various chokes, checkered pistol grip stock and beavertail forearm, made 1955-discontinued.

100%	98%	95%	90%	80%	70%	60%
$275	$250	$220	$195	$140	$110	$100

REGENT MAGNUM EXPRESS—12 ga., 3 in. chambers only, 30 in. full, recoil pad, made 1957-discontinued.

100%	98%	95%	90%	80%	70%	60%
$305	$275	$250	$220	$165	$140	$110

REGENT 10 GAUGE MAGNUM—same as 12 ga. Mag., but 10 ga., 3½ in. chamber, 32 in. full and full, made 1975-discontinued.

100%	98%	95%	90%	80%	70%	60%
$330	$305	$275	$250	$195	$165	$140

BRUSH KING—12 or 20 ga., 22 in. imp. cyl. and mod. barrels, straight grip stock, made 1959-discontinued.

100%	98%	95%	90%	80%	70%	60%
$275	$250	$220	$195	$140	$110	$100

MONARCH SUPREME GRADE—12 or 20 ga., 26 or 28 in. barrels, various chokes, boxlock, auto ejectors, select stock, made 1959-discontinued.

100%	98%	95%	90%	80%	70%	60%
$440	$385	$360	$330	$275	$250	$200

PRESENTATION CUSTOM GRADE—custom made, gold and silver game scene, made 1959-discontinued.

100%	98%	95%	90%	80%	70%	60%
$1,100	$990	$880	$825	$715	$605	$495

AMBASSADOR MODEL—12, 16, 20, or .410 ga., 26 or 28 in. barrels, mod. and full choke, checkered pistol grip stock, made 1957-discontinued.

100%	98%	95%	90%	80%	70%	60%
$385	$360	$330	$305	$250	$220	$195

Note: The Premier is a trade name for guns that have been produced in both Spain and Italy for various importers.

PRINZ

MANUFACTURER OF BOLT ACTION RIFLES, SINGLE SHOT RIFLES, AND COMBINATION GUNS. IMPORTED AND DISTRIBUTED BY HELMUT HOFMANN INC. LOCATED IN PLACITAS, NM.

GRADE 1 BOLT ACTION—.243 Win., .30-06, .308 Win., .300 Win. Mag. or 7mm Rem. Mag. cal., single or double set trigger(s), oil finished walnut stock. Importation began in 1989.

No Mfg.'s Retail	$495	$440	$385	$360	$330	$275	$250

Grade 1 Carbine—similar to Grade 1 except has carbine barrel.

No Mfg.'s Retail	$570	$495	$435	$390	$360	$330	$275

GRADE 2 BOLT ACTION—similar to Grade 1 except has rosewood forend cap.

No Mfg.'s Retail	$545	$485	$425	$385	$360	$330	$275

TIP UP RIFLE—available in 8 cal.'s between .222 Rem. and .30-06, high quality and limited mfg. Importation began in 1989.

No Mfg.'s Retail	$2,175	$1,900	$1,675	$1,375	$1,100	$950	$775

PRINCESS MODEL 85—combination gun available in 12 ga. (2¾ in. chamber) and choice of 8 cal.'s between .222 Rem. and .30-06. Importation began in 1989.

No Mfg.'s Retail	$1,450	$1,275	$1,100	$925	$800	$775	$650

This model comes standard with a leather case.

PURDEY, JAMES & SONS, LTD.

MANUFACTURER LOCATED IN LONDON, ENGLAND. PURDEY HAS BEEN MAKING TOP QUALITY FIREARMS SINCE 1814.

Purdey guns have long been regarded as among the finest in the world. They were often custom made to customer specifications and as such should be regarded on an individual basis for purposes of evaluation. Value varies with gauge, barrel length, chamber length and age. We shall list the modern models and approximate values for reference purposes, but strongly recommend professional appraisal if purchase or sale is contemplated.

RIFLES

PURDEY DOUBLE RIFLE—various English Nitro Express cal.'s, 25½ in. barrels, folding leaf sight, checkered pistol grip stock, recoil pad, sidelock, auto ejectors, made pre-WWII and post-war. Prices are for more-popular calibers.

$25,000	$23,000	$22,000	$20,000	$18,000	$17,000	$16,500

MAGAZINE RIFLE—Mauser type bolt action, 7 x 57mm, .300 H&H Mag., 10¾ x 73mm cal.'s, 24 in. barrel, folding leaf sight, checkered pistol grip stock.

$5,750	$4,500	$3,800	$3,500	$3,000	$2,500	$2,000

Add a premium for large cal.'s.

SHOTGUNS

BEST QUALITY SIDE BY SIDE—12, 16, or 20 ga., 26-30 in. barrels, any choke and style of rib, checkered straight or pistol grip stock, made 1880-present, auto ejector gun, best quality only.

Mfg.'s Sug. Retail	$29,750	$29,750	$15,750	$12,750	$10,750	$9,950	$9,000	$8,250
Older mfg.			$14,750	$12,500	$10,000	$8,950	$8,000	$7,500	$7,000

Add 50% for 20 ga.
Add $1,750 for 28 or .410 ga. on new mfg.
Add 35%-50% for 28 or .410 ga. older mfg.
Add 10% if cased with accessories.
Add $1,000 for SST.

PURDEY, JAMES & SONS, LIMITED, cont.

Grading	100%	98%	95%	90%	80%	70%	60%

O/U GUN—12, 16, 20, or 28 ga., 26-30 in. barrel, any choke, sidelock, auto ejectors, checkered straight or pistol grip stock. Since WWII, Purdey has taken over the Woodward Company, and later guns have the Woodward O/U action. Very few early actions; early guns — ⅓ less. Perhaps the most desirable O/U shotgun ever manufactured.

Mfg.'s Sug. Retail	$39,400	$39,400	$20,000	$18,500	$16,500	$14,950	$13,000	$11,750
Older mfg.			$20,000	$17,000	$15,000	$13,500	$11,750	$10,000	$9,500

     Add $3,00 for Woodward action.
     Add 25% for 20 ga.
     Add 60% + for 28 ga.
     Add 10% for SST.

SINGLE BARREL TRAP GUN—12 ga. Purdey action only, same as O/U specifications, made prior to WWII.

	$11,250	$10,000	$8,750	$7,900	$7,200	$6,750	$5,950

NOTES

R

R.G. INDUSTRIES

IMPORTERS LOCATED IN MIAMI, FL. OPERATIONS CEASED IN JANUARY OF 1986.

HAND GUNS

R.G. Industries manufactured and imported plain utilitarian revolvers and semi-auto pistols. Unfortunately, because of the current product liability situation, R.G. Industries was litigated out of business. Whereas their models represent good values, they are not collectible, and a generalized listing is provided below.

Grading	100%	98%	95%	90%	80%	70%	60%

RG 14 S, RG 23, RG 31—prices vary from $61 to $100 retail.

RG 40, RG 74, & HIGHNOON S.A.—prices vary from $125 to $150 retail.

RG 26 SEMI-AUTO—.25 auto, 6 shot mag., 2¼ in. barrel, plastic grips, single action, 12 oz.

	100%	98%	95%	90%	80%	70%	60%
	$65	$55	$50	$40	$35	$30	$25

Last Mfg.'s Sug. Retail was $66.

RWS

RWS IS A TRADEMARK OF DYNAMIT NOBEL WHICH HAS BEEN MANUFACTURING FIREARMS IN NUREMBERG STADELN, W. GERMANY SINCE 1865. RWS IS CURRENTLY BEING IMPORTED BY DYNAMIT NOBEL OF AMERICA, INC. LOCATED IN NORTHVALE, NJ. OTHER TRADEMARKS CURRENTLY BEING DISTRIBUTED BY DYNAMIT NOBEL CAN BE LOCATED UNDER INDIVIDUAL HEADING NAMES IN THIS TEXT.

RIFLES: MATCH TARGET

MODEL 820 S—.22 LR only, 24 in. barrel, no. 75 aperture sight, oil polished stock for 3 position match, stippled pistol grip and forearm, recoil pad, adj. trigger, 10.3 lbs. Importation discontinued in 1986.

	100%	98%	95%	90%	80%	70%	60%
	$805	$725	$635	$550	$475	$420	$375

Last Mfg.'s Sug. Retail was $910.

Model 820 S—with Model 82 aperture sight.

	100%	98%	95%	90%	80%	70%	60%
	$895	$795	$650	$560	$480	$420	$375

Last Mfg.'s Sug. Retail was $995.

MODEL 820 SF—same as Model 820 S, except has heavy match barrel, 11 lbs. Importation discontinued in 1986.

	100%	98%	95%	90%	80%	70%	60%
	$815	$735	$640	$555	$475	$420	$375

Last Mfg.'s Sug. Retail was $925.

Model 820 SF—with Model 82 aperture sight.

	100%	98%	95%	90%	80%	70%	60%
	$905	$810	$660	$565	$480	$420	$375

Last Mfg.'s Sug. Retail was $1,010.

MODEL 820 K—.22 LR only, made for running boar competition, 24 in. barrel, stock similar to Model 820 SF, no sights, 9½ lbs. without barrel weight or scope. Importation discontinued in 1986.

	100%	98%	95%	90%	80%	70%	60%
	$780	$695	$615	$540	$470	$420	$375

Last Mfg.'s Sug. Retail was $870.

RADOM

POLISH ARSENAL, LOCATED IN RADOM, POLAND.

P-35 AUTOMATIC—9mm, 8 shot, 4¾ in. barrel, blue, fixed sights, plastic grips, made 1935-WWII.

POLISH EAGLE—dated 1936, 1937, 1938, 1939.

	100%	98%	95%	90%	80%	70%	60%
POLISH EAGLE	$850	$725	$600	$440	$260	$200	$160

POLISH EAGLE NAZI CAPTURE

	$1,000	$850	$715	$550	$400	$320	$250

NAZI TYPE I SLOTTED

	$450	$400	$350	$295	$230	$180	$150

NAZI TYPE II NO SLOT WITH TAKE-DOWN LEVER

	$300	$270	$230	$200	$185	$150	$130

NAZI TYPE III NO SLOT, NO TAKE-DOWN LEVER

	$260	$225	$200	$180	$160	$140	$120

NAZI TYPE III—parkerized with wood grips.

	$375	$325	$270	$235	$200	$170	$140

Note: Certain Radoms with German acceptance marks will bring a premium.

RANDALL FIREARMS COMPANY

PREVIOUSLY MANUFACTURED AND DISTRIBUTED IN SUN VALLEY, CA.
MANUFACTURED BETWEEN JUNE, 1983 AND MAY, 1985.

Before manufacturing ceased in May of 1985, 24 models with 12 variations in 3 different calibers had been produced. In some instances, production on certain models was very limited and premiums for these low volume niches are starting to develop. Between June of 1983 and December of 1985, 9,957 handguns were manufactured with 75% of all 9mm cal.'s being exported to Europe, and 35% of 9mm production employing a 10 groove barrel. Models manufactured after 1984 came equipped with an extended slide stop, long trigger and beavertail grip safety. Production ser. no.'s started at 02000 with various prefix/suffix letters being used during fabrication. Total mfg. for all models and variations was 9,957. Randall prototype serialization starts with a "T" — less than 45 were manufactured and these specimens command up to a 50% premium. In addition, 78 serial numbers under 2,000 were manufactured by special order.

Models below are generally described with values per specific variations listed afterward.

COMBAT MODEL—same size as Service Model, ribbed top fixed sight slide, Pachmayr grips on right hand model only, left hand models had Herret walnut grips. While this model was advertised as having a flat mainspring housing, it was never produced. The brochures of the time quoted $549 for mfg.'s sug. retail.

RAIDER/SERVICE MODEL-C—9mm or .45 ACP cal.'s, Colt Commander Model design, 4¼ in. barrel, 36 oz., total stainless steel construction. Add $130 for adj. sights/ribbed slide, available in either right-hand or left-hand (only 2 made) model. Roll-marked Service Model-C in 1983 and Raider in 1984.

Last Mfg.'s Sug. Retail was $460.

Raider/Service Model-C Featherweight—.45 ACP only, alloy receiver, 29 oz., stainless steel slide, roll-marked Service Model-C, disc. in 1984, only 4 manufactured. T-type serial numbers.

FULL SIZE SERVICE MODEL—.38 Super, 9mm, and .45 ACP cal.'s, Colt Model 1911 A1 design, 5 in. barrel, 38 oz., total stainless steel construction. Available in either right-hand or left-hand model. Add $130 for adj. sights and rib top slide.

Last Mfg.'s Sug. Retail was $460.

Grading	100%	98%	95%	90%	80%	70%	60%

CURTIS E. LeMAY 4-STAR MODEL—9mm or .45 ACP cal., Gen. Curtis E. LeMay design, 4¼ in. barrel, 35 oz., 6 (.45 ACP) or 7 (9mm) round mag., total stainless steel construction. Available in either right-hand or left-hand model, left hand models are a true mirror image with over 17 major parts changes. Add $10 for 9mm. Add $90 for adj. sight/ ribbed top slide.

Last Mfg.'s Sug. Retail was $533.

This model was ½ in. shorter in magazine well and had a cast, squared off trigger guard compared to the Colt 1911A1 design.

Curtis E. LeMay Featherweight Model—.45 ACP only, alloy receiver, 28 oz., stainless steel slide, T-type serial numbers, discontinued in 1984 (only one made).

RANDALL MATCHED SETS—.45 ACP only, each set consisted of a righthand and a lefthand Service Model with matching serial numbers. Only 4 sets were manufactured on a special order basis. A111/B111 model configuration.

Last Mfg.'s Sug. Retail was $1,250.

RANDALL VARIATIONS

IDENTIFYING RANDALL MODELS:

Randall pistols are denoted by a four-character model notation, starting with an alphabetical prefix followed by three digits. The alphabetical prefix will be either A, B, or C — A designates right-hand configuration only, B designates left-hand configuration only, and C designates right-hand lightweight model. The first digit will be 1, 2, or 3 — 1 denotes Service Model, 2 denotes Service Model-C or Raider, 3 represents the C.E. LeMay Model. The second digit again will be either 1, 2, or 3 — 1 designates round top and fixed sight slide, 2 denotes flat top fixed sight slide, and 3 represents adj. sights, flat top frame. The third digit again, is either 1, 2, or 3 — 1 denotes .45 ACP cal., 2 designates 9mm Para., and 3 represents .38 Super. Hence, if you had a left-hand Randall in the service model size with a flat top adj. sight slide, and in .45 ACP cal., your model would be a B131. These model codes are not marked on the pistols.

The following is a complete listing for Randall Firearms variations including production statistics. Values shown below represent recent aftermarket prices, but it should be noted regional interest can change these prices significantly. After only 5 years of discontinuance, Randall pistols are enjoying good demand.

A111—3429 mfg.

		$550	$475	$430			

A112—299 mfg.

		$700	$615	$550			

A121—1064 mfg.

		$550	$475	$430			

A122—12 mfg.

	$1,000	$875	$775				

A131—2080 mfg.

		$650	$565	$500			

A211—989 mfg.

		$550	$475	$430			

A212—75 mfg.

		$750	$675	$600			

A231—572 mfg.

		$625	$550	$490			

A232—2 mfg.

	$1,150	$1,000	$900				

A311—353 mfg.

		$675	$575	$525			

Most LeMay models (4¼ in. barrel) were shipped in gunrugs without a factory box. Original factory LeMay boxes are rare — add 10% premium. Beware of Randall LeMay model pistols made from parts kits — there were approx. 350-400 right-hand only pistols made from these parts kits and accordingly, values are lower on parts kit guns.

Grading	100%	98%	95%	90%	80%	70%	60%

A312—1 mfg.

Too rare to evaluate.

A331—293 mfg.

	$800	$710	$650				

The note appear above for the A311 model also applies to this variation.

A332—8 mfg.

	$1,100	$950	$850				

B111—289 mfg.

	$1,000	$875	$785				

B121—110 mfg.

	$1,200	$1,050	$950				

B122—2 mfg.

	$1,875	$1,550	$1,200				

B123—2 mfg.

	$1,875	$1,550	$1,200				

B131—225 mfg.

	$1,100	$975	$775				

B311—52 mfg.

	$1,050	$925	$820				

B311 w/9mm factory conversion.—1 mfg.

Rarity precludes accurate price evaluation.

B312—9 mfg.

	$1,900	$1,550	$1,400				

B321—1 mfg.

Rarity precludes accurate price evaluation. The B321 was the only factory 3-slide set. It was fitted with the 3 different LH LeMay slides available (B311, B321, & B331). This model was mirror polished, engraved, and had ivory grips with the Randall logo.

B331—45 mfg.

	$1,200	$1,075	$950				

B2/311—1 mfg.

Rarity precludes accurate price evaluation. This was the only factory model variation to leave Randall Firearms. This was a Lefthand Raider with the C.E. LeMay slide.

C331—1 mfg.

Too rare to evaluate.

Matched Sets—large premiums exist for different models with the same serial number if NIB condition.

1 set has recently sold for $3,950.

RAVELL

MANUFACTURER LOCATED IN BARCELONA, SPAIN. CURRENTLY, RAVELL HAS NO SINGLE U.S. IMPORTER AND VALUES BELOW REPRESENT GUNS PURCHASED DIRECTLY FROM SPAIN WITHOUT IMPORT DUTY/SHIPPING.

MAXIM DOUBLE RIFLE—.375 H & H or 9.3 X 74R cal., H & H type sidelock action with automatic extractor, Purdey scroll engraving, 23 in. barrels, deluxe walnut with full pistol grip and rubber buttplate, double articulated triggers.

Mfg.'s Sug. Retail	$4,310	$4,310	$3,750	$3,300	$2,950	$2,600	$2,300	$2,000

Add $400 for 9.3 X 74R cal.

RAVEN ARMS

MANUFACTURED AND DISTRIBUTED OUT OF INDUSTRY, CA.

P-25—.25 cal., single action semi-auto, 2⁷⁄₁₆ in. barrel, 6 round mag., 15 oz., walnut grips, available in nickel, blue, or chrome finish. Discontinued in 1984.

		$60	$50	$40	$35	$30	$25	$25

MP-25—same as Model P-25, except die-cast slide serrations are slightly different.

Mfg.'s Sug. Retail $70 $60 $50 $40 $35 $30 $25 $25

Walnut or ivory colored grips are available for this model.

In 1987, a new style safety was incorporated into manufacture.

RECORD-MATCH

MANUFACTURED BY ANSCHUTZ, LOCATED IN ZELLA-MEHLIS, GERMANY.

MODEL 210 FREE PISTOL—.22 LR, Martini action, 11 in. barrel, single shot, blue, carved and checkered walnut grips and forearm, set trigger (button release), micrometer rear sight, deluxe target pistol, pre-WWII.

$1,320 $1,265 $1,210 $1,100 $880 $745 $550

MODEL 210A—same as 210, but alloy frame.

$1,265 $1,210 $1,155 $1,045 $825 $690 $495

MODEL 200 FREE PISTOL—similar to 210, but less deluxe features and spur trigger guard, pre-WWII.

$990 $935 $770 $660 $525 $440 $360

REISING ARMS COMPANY

MANDUFACTURED ORIGINALLY IN NEW YORK, NY AND LATER IN HARTFORD, CT.

TARGET AUTOMATIC PISTOL—.22 LR, 12 shot, 6½ in. barrel, blue, hard rubber grips, hinged frame, outside hammer, made 1921-1924.

$385 $370 $340 $315 $265 $220 $195

This model was manufactured in New York, NY from serial number 1,001-4,000. The Hartford, CT address occurs in the serial range 10,000-12,000.

Warning: This pistol may crack the slide if modern high speed .22 ammo is used.

REMINGTON ARMS COMPANY

ORIGINALLY E. REMINGTON, HERKIMER, NY 1816-1831; MOVED TO ILION, NY IN 1831, MANUFACTURED AT ILION, NY TO DATE.

REMINGTON TRADEMARKS - 1856-PRESENT

1856-1888 — E. Remington & Sons.

1888-1910 — Remington Arms Co.

1910-1925 — Remington Arms U.M.C. Co.

1925 to date — Remington Arms Co.

REVOLVERS: EARLY MODELS

100%	98%	95%	90%	80%	70%	60%	50%	40%	30%	20%	10%

REMINGTON — BEALS 1ST MODEL POCKET—percussion, .31 cal., 5 shot non-fluted cylinder, 3 in. octagon barrel, blue, Gutta Percha grips, brass trigger guard, approx. 4,700 produced, 1857-1858.

$880	$750	$660	$605	$550	$495	$440	$415	$400	$360	$330	$305

100%	98%	95%	90%	80%	70%	60%	50%	40%	30%	20%	10%

2ND MODEL POCKET—similar to 1st Model, except spur trigger, checkered rubber grips and disc on outside of frame, 1,000 produced, 1858-1860.

| $4,200 | $3,850 | $3,520 | $3,080 | $2,530 | $2,365 | $2,200 | $2,090 | $1,980 | $1,925 | $1,815 | $1,650 |

3RD MODEL POCKET—larger version of 2nd Model, with loading lever, approx. 1,200 produced, 1859-1860.

| $1,250 | $1,100 | $990 | $910 | $825 | $770 | $745 | $715 | $660 | $605 | $550 | $495 |

REMINGTON — RIDER POCKET—.31 cal., percussion, 5 shot cylinder, blue or nickel with brass trigger guard, checkered rubber grips, 20,000 produced, 1860-1873.

| $665 | $625 | $550 | $440 | $415 | $385 | $360 | $340 | $315 | $305 | $290 | $270 |

.32 Rim Fire—cartridge conversion.

| $625 | $565 | $525 | $440 | $385 | $360 | $330 | $275 | $220 | $195 | $165 | $150 |

REMINGTON — BEALS ARMY MODEL—.44 cal., 6 shot unfluted cylinder, 8 in. octagon barrel, loading lever, blue, walnut grips, approx. 2,500 produced, 1860-1862.

| $3,000 | $2,650 | $2,175 | $1,870 | $1,760 | $1,650 | $1,595 | $1,540 | $1,430 | $1,320 | $990 | $825 |

Martially Marked—very scarce.

| $4,100 | $3,600 | $3,000 | $2,575 | $2,200 | $2,090 | $1,980 | $1,845 | $1,735 | $1,650 | $1,540 | $1,375 |

NAVY MODEL—slightly smaller than Army Model, .36 cal., 15,000 produced, 1860-1862.

| $1,050 | $940 | $850 | $800 | $745 | $715 | $690 | $660 | $605 | $550 | $495 | $440 |

Martially Marked—1,000 produced.

| $1,500 | $1,350 | $1,200 | $990 | $935 | $880 | $825 | $770 | $715 | $660 | $550 | $440 |

MODEL 1861 ARMY—.44 cal., percussion, 6 shot unfluted cylinder, 8 in. octagon barrel, blue, walnut grips, approx. 10,000 made, circa 1860.

| $1,600 | $1,300 | $1,050 | $875 | $740 | $660 | $605 | $550 | $525 | $495 | $440 | $385 |

Factory .46 Rim Fire—cartridge conversion.

| $700 | $650 | $550 | $495 | $440 | $385 | $360 | $330 | $305 | $275 | $250 | $195 |

MODEL 1861 NAVY—slightly smaller than Army Model, .36 cal.

| $1,600 | $1,300 | $1,050 | $880 | $825 | $800 | $770 | $715 | $660 | $605 | $550 | $495 |

.38 Cal.—cartridge conversion.

| $875 | $760 | $685 | $605 | $550 | $495 | $470 | $440 | $385 | $330 | $305 | $220 |

MODEL 1875 SINGLE ACTION ARMY—.44 Rem. cal., 6 shot fluted cylinder, 7½ in. round barrel, blue or nickel, walnut grips, 25,000 produced, 1875-1889.

Blue finish

| $6,000 | $5,100 | $4,200 | $3,400 | $2,950 | $2,420 | $1,980 | $1,650 | $1,100 | $880 | $660 | $550 |

Nickel finish

| $3,750 | $3,245 | $2,860 | $2,420 | $1,650 | $1,210 | $990 | $880 | $825 | $770 | $660 | $605 |

MODEL 1890 SINGLE ACTION ARMY—.44-40 cal., 6 shot fluted cylinder, 5½ or 7½ in. barrel, does not have web under barrel, blue or nickel, checkered rubber grips, 2,000 produced, 1891-1894.

Blue finish

| $6,500 | $5,500 | $4,625 | $3,960 | $3,300 | $3,025 | $2,420 | $1,980 | $1,650 | $1,100 | $880 | $660 |

Nickel finish

| $4,150 | $3,550 | $2,975 | $2,500 | $2,150 | $1,850 | $1,400 | $1,100 | $950 | $750 | $575 | $495 |

DERRINGER: EARLY MANUFACTURE

RIDER SINGLE SHOT—.17 cal., percussion, 3 in. barrel, all brass construction included, grips, silver plated, less than 1,000 produced, 1860-1863.

| $6,000 | $5,550 | $4,975 | $4,475 | $3,850 | $3,520 | $3,190 | $3,025 | $2,750 | $2,475 | $2,200 | $1,925 |

Note: Use caution, as many fakes have been noted.

ZIG ZAG—.22 short, 6 shot cluster barrels, 3³⁄₁₆ in. barrels, double action, concealed hammer, ring trigger, blue, hard rubber grips, less than 1,000 produced, 1861-1862.

| $3,000 | $2,350 | $2,000 | $1,700 | $1,375 | $1,265 | $1,100 | $1,045 | $990 | $935 | $825 | $715 |

ELLIOT .32 RIMFIRE AND .22 RIMFIRE—.22 cal. and .32 rimfire, 3⅜ in. barrels, 4 barrel (.32 cal.) or 5 barrel (.22 cal. - rare) pepperbox design, ring hammer, concealed hammer, 25,000 produced, 1863-1888.

| $1,150 | $975 | $850 | $740 | $625 | $550 | $495 | $440 | $385 | $360 | $330 | $275 |

Add 30% for .22 cal.

100%	98%	95%	90%	80%	70%	60%	50%	40%	30%	20%	10%

VEST POCKET PISTOL—.22 cal., 3¼ in. round barrel, hammer, spur trigger, blue or nickel, walnut grips, 25,000 produced, 1865-1888.

| $825 | $725 | $675 | $580 | $480 | $425 | $385 | $360 | $330 | $305 | $275 | $220 |

DOUBLE DERRINGER—.41 short rimfire, tip-up action, 3 in. O/U barrels, spur trigger, exposed hammer, blue or nickel, 150,000 produced, 1866-1935.

Numbers appearing on this model are assembly numbers (not serial numbers) and never go above 3 digits on early pistols.

Type I Early—no extractor, marked E. Remington & Sons, Ilion, NY, on one side of barrel, Elliot's Patent, December 12, 1865, on other side of barrel.

| $1,500 | $1,250 | $1,050 | $925 | $800 | $750 | $700 | $660 | $605 | $550 | $440 | $385 |

Type I Transitional—extractor, 1866.

| $1,650 | $1,350 | $1,100 | $960 | $825 | $800 | $745 | $690 | $660 | $605 | $495 | $440 |

Type I Late—same inscription, but on top of barrel and two lined, extractor, manufactured 1860's-1888.

| $650 | $550 | $495 | $450 | $395 | $350 | $310 | $275 | $250 | $225 | $190 | $150 |

Type II—marked Remington Arms Co., Ilion, N.Y., on top of barrel in one line, manufactured 1888-1911.

| $525 | $475 | $425 | $375 | $325 | $270 | $250 | $230 | $210 | $190 | $170 | $145 |

Type III—marked Remington Arms - U.M.C., CO., Ilion, N.Y., on top of barrel in one line, manufactured 1912-1935.

| $525 | $475 | $425 | $375 | $325 | $270 | $250 | $230 | $210 | $190 | $170 | $145 |

PISTOLS: SINGLE SHOT — EARLY MODELS

MODEL 1865 NAVY ROLLING BLOCK—.50 rimfire, 8½ in. round barrel, blue barrel, case hardened frame, walnut grips and forend, spur trigger, 6,500 produced, 1866-1870.

Martially Marked

| $2,500 | $2,150 | $1,800 | $1,625 | $1,375 | $1,265 | $1,155 | $1,100 | $1,045 | $990 | $935 | $880 |

Civilian Model

| $2,150 | $1,775 | $1,525 | $1,400 | $1,250 | $1,100 | $1,045 | $990 | $880 | $825 | $715 | $605 |

Centerfire Model—altered breech block.

| $2,150 | $1,775 | $1,525 | $1,400 | $1,250 | $990 | $935 | $880 | $825 | $770 | $660 | $550 |

MODEL 1867 NAVY ROLLING BLOCK—.50 centerfire, 7 in. barrel, standard guarded trigger, quantity unknown, ca. 1870's.

Navy marked

| $1,850 | $1,500 | $1,225 | $990 | $880 | $770 | $745 | $715 | $605 | $550 | $440 | $385 |

1867 Transitional—not martially marked.

| $2,450 | $1,825 | $1,600 | $1,425 | $1,275 | $1,150 | $1,045 | $990 | $935 | $880 | $825 | $715 |

1871 ARMY ROLLING BLOCK—.50 centerfire, 8 in. round barrel, blue with case hardened frame and trigger guard, 6,000 produced, 1872-1888.

| $1,900 | $1,650 | $1,250 | $1,000 | $875 | $780 | $715 | $660 | $605 | $550 | $495 | $440 |

1891 TARGET ROLLING BLOCK—.22, .25 Stevens, and .32 S&W cal.'s, 10 in. ½ octagon barrel, buckhorn rear sight, blue with case hardened frame, 116 produced, 1892-1898.

| $2,050 | $1,875 | $1,725 | $1,400 | $1,250 | $1,100 | $1,045 | $880 | $770 | $715 | $660 | $605 |

Note: Be wary of fakes.

1901 TARGET ROLLING BLOCK—.22 short and long, .25-10, and .44 S&W cal.'s, 10 in. ½ octagon barrel, blue finish overall, checkered forend and grips, 735 produced, 1901-1909.

| $2,050 | $1,875 | $1,725 | $1,400 | $1,250 | $1,100 | $1,045 | $880 | $770 | $715 | $660 | $605 |

Grading	100%	98%	95%	90%	80%	70%	60%

PISTOLS: MODERN

MODEL 51—.32 ACP and .380 cal.'s, semi-auto, 3½ in. barrel, 7 shot (.380 ACP) or 8 shot (.32 ACP) mag., blued, fixed sights, hard rubber grips, made 1918-1934. Add 15% for .32 ACP cal.

		100%	98%	95%	90%	80%	70%	60%
		$380	$340	$300	$265	$240	$220	$195

Date coded Model 51's in .380 ACP will bring a slight premium.

There are 2 types of the Model 51 in .380 ACP. Type I has no caliber marked on barrel and does not have Remington logo under ejection port in slide. Also, slide pulls are "U" shaped. Type II pistols have the caliber marked on barrel and also have the Remington logo under ejection port in slide. Also, they have "V" shaped slide pulls.

There are 3 types of the Model 51 in .32 ACP. Type I has "32 CAL" only on barrel (serial numbered 60,801-61,999). Type II guns have "32 CAL" over "7.65 M/M" on barrel (serial numbered 62,000-70,280). Type III pistols in 32 ACP are similar to Type II, except serial range is 90,501-92,626.

XP-100 VARMINT SPECIAL—bolt action pistol, .221 Rem. Fireball (disc. in 1985-10½ in. barrel) and .223 Rem. (new in 1986) cal.'s, 14½ in. barrel, adj. sights (.221 cal. only), drilled and tapped for scope, one piece nylon stock, made 1963-present.

Mfg.'s Sug. Retail	$373	$310	$280	$225	$195	$165	$150	$140

XP-SILHOUETTE—.35 Rem. (new in 1987), 7mm Rem., bench rest model, 15 in. barrel, comes without sights, nylon stock, drilled and tapped for for sight mounts.

Mfg.'s Sug. Retail	$380	$350	$320	$270	$220	$200	$180	$165

Add $13 for .35 Rem. cal.

XP-100 CUSTOM—.223 Rem. standard or HB (heavy barrel-new in 1987), .250 Savage standard or HB (new in 1989), 6mm BR standard or HB (new in 1989), 7mm BR standard or HB (new in 1989), 35 Rem. (standard barrel only), or 7mm-08 Rem. (HB new in 1989) cal., available through custom gun shop only, nylon or wood stock with contoured pistol grip, regular or shrouded barrel, ramp front sight. New in 1986.

Mfg.'s Sug. Retail	$907	$795	$750	$685	$600	$550	$500	$460

Also available, on special order only, is the .458 x 2 in. caliber

RIFLES: DISCONTINUED MANUFACTURE

100%	98%	95%	90%	80%	70%	60%	50%	40%	30%	20%	10%

REVOLVING PERCUSSION RIFLE—.36 and .44 cal.'s, 6 shot unfluted cylinder, 24 and 28 in. octagon barrel, walnut stock with crescent butt, scroll trigger guard, blue with case hardened frame, less than 1,000 produced, 1866-1879.

.36 Caliber

100%	98%	95%	90%	80%	70%	60%	50%	40%	30%	20%	10%
$3,500	$3,200	$2,900	$2,640	$2,475	$2,310	$2,200	$2,090	$1,980	$1,925	$1,815	$1,760

.44 Caliber—very rare.

$4,250	$3,850	$3,400	$3,150	$2,925	$2,650	$2,530	$2,420	$2,310	$2,200	$2,035	$1,925

MODEL 1862 "ZOUAVE RIFLE"—.58 cal., muzzle loading percussion, 33 in. round barrel, two barrel bands, blue barrel, case hardened lock, brass furniture, 12,501 produced, 1862-1865.

$1,500	$1,350	$1,200	$1,050	$935	$825	$715	$660	$550	$440	$385	$330

U.S. NAVY ROLLING BLOCK CARBINE—.50-70 cal., 23¼ in. barrel, open sight, blue with case hardened frame, bar and ring on frame, walnut straight grip stock, 5,000 produced, 1868-1869.

$1,400	$1,250	$1,075	$925	$795	$660	$635	$580	$525	$495	$440	$385

LONG RANGE "CREEDMOOR"—rolling block, .44-90, .44-100, .44-70, .50-45, .50-70 cal.'s, barrel ½ octagon, long range tang sight, globe front sight, checkered pistol grip stock, blue, approximately 2,000 produced, 1873-1890.

$3,250	$2,700	$2,400	$1,750	$1,375	$1,100	$990	$880	$770	$715	$605	$550

NO. 1 SPORTING RIFLE—rolling block, .40-50, .40-70, .44-70, .45-70, .50-45, and .50-70 cal.'s, 28 and 30 in. octagon barrels, folding leaf sight, straight grip stock, several thousand produced, 1868-1902.

$925	$850	$775	$680	$560	$440	$385	$360	$330	$275	$220	$195

100%	98%	95%	90%	80%	70%	60%	50%	40%	30%	20%	10%

LIGHT BABY CARBINE—rolling block, .44-40 cal., 20 in. lightweight round barrel with band, straight stock, few thousand produced, 1892-1902.

| $3,650 | $3,100 | $2,500 | $2,000 | $1,650 | $1,375 | $1,500 | $895 | $775 | $700 | $640 | $575 |

REMINGTON — HEPBURN NO. 3—falling block, single shot, side lever actuated, blue barrel, case hardened actions, patented 1879, first introduced 1880, many custom features were offered, variations as follows:

NO. 3 SPORTING & TARGET—various cal.'s from .22 Win. to .50-90 Sharps, 26, 28, and 30 in. round or octagon barrel, open sight, semi-pistol grip stock, made 1883-1907.

| $1,550 | $1,300 | $1,150 | $1,045 | $935 | $880 | $770 | $660 | $550 | $495 | $440 | $385 |

NO. 3 MATCH RIFLE A QUALITY—same as Sporting and Target, with target match sights (tang), and Schuetzen stock, less than 1,000 produced, 1883-1907.

| $1,700 | $1,550 | $1,400 | $1,150 | $1,045 | $960 | $880 | $825 | $715 | $605 | $550 | $495 |

B Quality—select grade wood.

| $2,150 | $1,975 | $1,825 | $1,525 | $1,200 | $1,045 | $935 | $880 | $770 | $715 | $605 | $550 |

NO. 3 LONG RANGE CREEDMOOR—.44 cal., 32 or 34 in. octagon barrel, tang sight, otherwise same as Target Model, a few hundred made, 1880-1907.

| $2,500 | $2,225 | $1,950 | $1,675 | $1,400 | $1,225 | $1,100 | $1,045 | $935 | $880 | $770 | $715 |

NO. 3 MID RANGE CREEDMOOR—same as Long Range, in .40-65 cal., 28 in. barrel.

| $2,150 | $1,975 | $1,825 | $1,525 | $1,200 | $1,045 | $935 | $880 | $770 | $715 | $660 | $605 |

N. 3 LONG RANGE MILITARY—same as Creedmoor, with 34 in. full musket stock, in .44-75-520 Rem. cal., military sights, 1880's.

| $3,375 | $2,950 | $2,625 | $2,250 | $1,925 | $1,700 | $1,540 | $1,430 | $1,320 | $1,100 | $990 | $825 |

NO. 3 SCHUETZEN MATCH—under lever actuated, 30 or 32 in. barrel, tang sight palm rest, target stock, very few known, perhaps the rarest single shot American rifle.

| $5,500 | $5,000 | $4,600 | $4,000 | $3,500 | $2,850 | $2,420 | $2,200 | $2,145 | $2,035 | $1,925 | $1,815 |

With False Muzzle

| $6,100 | $5,400 | $4,900 | $4,300 | $3,875 | $3,200 | $2,850 | $2,600 | $2,300 | $2,100 | $2,000 | $1,900 |

Grading		100%	98%	95%	90%	80%	70%	60%

REMINGTON KEENE MAGAZINE BOLT RIFLE— .45.-70 Gov't, .40, or .43 cal., manufactured 1880-1888. Approximately 5,000 made,

Frontier Model—made for U.S. Dept. of Interior (Indian Police), marked U.S.I.D.

| | | $1,325 | $950 | $800 | $600 | $500 | $400 | $350 |

Carbine Model—22 in. full stock.

| | | $1,100 | $850 | $750 | $550 | $450 | $350 | $300 |

Army Rifle—32½ in. barrel, full stock.

| | | $1,100 | $850 | $750 | $550 | $450 | $350 | $300 |

Sporter Rifle—½ oct. barrel, full or "BUTTON" mag. Add for pistol grip and select wood variations.

| | | $1,000 | $825 | $650 | $550 | $450 | $350 | $300 |

Navy Rifle—29½ in. barrel, full stock.

| | | $1,100 | $850 | $750 | $550 | $450 | $350 | $300 |

RIFLES: MODERN PRODUCTION 1906 TO DATE

MODEL 8 AUTOLOADING RIFLE—.25, .30, .32, and .35 Rem. cal.'s, 22 in. barrel, open sights, 5 round non-detachable box mag., plain stock, approx. 60,000 made 1906-1936. Also made in higher grades C through F — add premiums.

| | | $400 | $320 | $270 | $220 | $195 | $165 | $140 |

MODEL 8—same as 8 Autoloading Rifle, except .300 Savage cal. was also available, pistol grip stock, made 1936-1950.

| | | $375 | $300 | $265 | $220 | $195 | $165 | $140 |

Grading	100%	98%	95%	90%	80%	70%	60%

MODEL 12A SLIDE ACTION RIFLE—.22 S, L, and LR, hammerless, 22 in. barrel, open sights, tube mag., plain grip stock, made 1909-1936.

	$450	$400	$300	$200	$120	$95	$85

Originally designated Model 12.

MODEL 12B (GALLERY SPECIAL)—same as 12A, except .22 short, a few were made in octogon barrel

	$450	$400	$300	$200	$120	$95	$85

MODEL 12C—same as 12A, except 24 in. octagon barrel. Also mfg. in grades D, E, and F — add premiums.

	$550	$450	$350	$300	$220	$140	$110

MODEL 12C NRA TARGET—limited manufacture.

	$675	$550	$450	$350	$300	$220	$140

MODEL 12CS—same as 12C, chambered for .22 Rem. Spl. (.22 WRF).

	$450	$400	$300	$200	$120	$95	$85

MODEL 121A SLIDE ACTION RIFLE—hammerless, .22 S, L, or LR, 24 in. round barrel, tube mag., plain pistol grip stock, made 1936-1954.

	$350	$285	$225	$195	$165	$140	$110

Originally designated Model 121.

MODEL 121S—same as 121A, except chambered for .22 Rem. Spl. (rare).

	$450	$375	$315	$260	$215	$175	$140

MODEL 121B—same as 121A, except smooth bore for .22 short. 5 different chamberings and barrel markings.

	$450	$375	$300	$250	$200	$165	$140

Add 25% for Ruttledge smooth bore (Model 121SB).

MODEL 14/14A SLIDE ACTION—.25, .30, .32, and .35 cal.'s, 22 in. barrel, open sight, plain pistol grip stock, made 1912-1935.

	$350	$285	$230	$195	$165	$130	$110

MODEL 14R CARBINE—same as 14A, with 18½ in. barrel, straight grip stock.

	$400	$325	$285	$260	$220	$195	$165

MODEL 14½ RIFLE—same as 14A, with 22½ in. barrel, .38-40 and .44-40 cal.'s, made 1912-1922.

	$425	$365	$300	$200	$165	$130	$110

MODEL 14½R CARBINE—same as 14½, with 18½ in. barrel.

	$475	$415	$350	$250	$200	$175	$150

MODEL 141/141A SLIDE ACTION—.30, .32, and .35 Rem. cal.'s, 24 in. barrel, takedown, open sight, plain pistol grip stock, made 1936-1950.

	$395	$305	$250	$220	$195	$165	$140

MODEL 16/16A AUTOLOADING RIFLE—.22 autoloading cal., 22 in. barrel, open sight, tube mag. in buttstock, straight stock, made 1914-1928. Also mfg. in grades C, D, and F — add premiums.

	$295	$230	$195	$170	$140	$110	$90

MODEL 24/24A AUTOLOADING RIFLE—.22 S or LR, 19 in. barrel, open sights, Browning semi-auto design, bottom ejection, tube mag. through buttstock, takedown, plain pistol grip stock, made 1922-1935.

	$325	$240	$210	$170	$140	$110	$90

MODEL 241/241A SPEEDMASTER—.22 S or LR, 24 in. barrel, replaced the Model 24, open sights, takedown, tube mag. through stock, non-checkered walnut stock and forearm, approx. 56,000 mfg. 1935-1949.

	$360	$275	$250	$195	$150	$120	$100

This model was also available in a Special, Peerless, Expert, and Premier Grade - add premiums.

Grading	100%	98%	95%	90%	80%	70%	60%

MODEL 81 WOODSMASTER—.25, .30, .32, .35 Rem., or .300 Savage cal., semi-auto, 5 shot, non-detachable box mag., 22 in. round barrel, notched elevator rear sight. An improvement of the model 8 is available in 5 grades. Better grades bring higher prices. Made 1936-1950.

	$400	$350	$300	$250	$200	$175	$150

The .25 and .32 Rem. calibers were dropped after WWII and the .300 Savage was added.

MODEL 25/25A SLIDE ACTION—.25-30 or .32-20 cal., 24 in. barrel, open sight, tube mag., plain pistol grip stock, made 1923-1936.

	$330	$275	$220	$140	$85	$65	$55

MODEL 25R CARBINE—same as 25A, with 18 in. barrel and straight stock.

	$385	$330	$220	$195	$140	$100	$85

MODEL 550A AUTOLOADER—.22 S, L, or LR interchangeably, 24 in. barrel, open sight, tube mag., plain one piece pistol stock, approx. 220,000 mfg. made 1941-1971.

	$175	$140	$115	$95	$75	$65	$55

This model replaced the Model 241.

MODEL 550P—same as 550A, with aperture sight.

	$190	$150	$125	$105	$85	$75	$65

MODEL 55-2G—same as 550A, except shell deflector and screw eye for counter chain in shooting gallery.

	$175	$140	$115	$95	$75	$65	$55

MODEL 760 SLIDE ACTION RIFLE—.222, .223, 6mm, .243, .257 Roberts, .270, .280, .30-06, .300 Sav., .308 and .35 Rem. cal.'s, 22 in. barrel, detachable mag., checkered pistol grip stock, made 1952-1982.

	$250	$195	$175	$145	$130	$120	$110
.222 or .257 R	$650	$575	$525	$450	$400	$350	$300
.223 cal.	$950	$825	$695	$635	$560	$475	$400

A very few Model 760's were also mfg. in .244 cal. (before going to 6mm) — very rare with pricing unpredictable.

MODEL 760 CARBINE—.270, .280, .30-06, .308, or .35 Rem. cal., 18½ in. barrel.

	$280	$225	$180	$160	$145	$130	$120

Add 25% for .35 Rem. cal.

MODEL 760D PEERLESS GRADE—same as 760, with engraving and fancy wood, made 1953-1982.

	$1,100	$935	$825	$770	$690	$605	$525

MODEL 760F—same as 760, with extensive engraved game scenes, best grade wood.

	$2,420	$1,980	$1,760	$1,650	$1,485	$1,375	$1,100

Gold Inlaid Model

	$5,500	$4,675	$4,180	$3,960	$3,300	$2,750	$2,200

MODEL 760 150 YEAR ANNIVERSARY—.30-06 only, mfg. in 1966 only.

	$375	$300	$260	$200	$175	$150	$125

MODEL 760 BICENTENNIAL—same as 760, with commemorative inscription engraved on receiver, made 1976 only.

	$325	$265	$200	$165	$150	$130	$110

MODEL 760ADL—same as 760, with pistol grip and sling swivels, made 1953-1963.

	$260	$205	$180	$165	$150	$135	$125

MODEL 760BDL—same as 760, except .270, .30-06, and .308 cal.'s only, with basket weave checkering, Monte Carlo stock, black pistol grip and forend tip, made 1953-1982.

	$285	$225	$200	$180	$160	$150	$135

MODEL 76 SPORTSMAN SLIDE ACTION—.30-06 cal. only, 22 in. barrel, 4 shot mag., uncheckered hardwood stock and forearm, open sights, 7½ lbs. Mfg. 1985-1987.

	$255	$225	$195	$180	$170	$160	$150

Last Mfg.'s Sug. Retail was $319.

Grading	100%	98%	95%	90%	80%	70%	60%

MODEL 7600 SLIDE ACTION RIFLE—6mm Rem. (disc. in 1984), .243 Win., .270 Win., .280 Rem. (new in 1988), .30-06, .308 Win., and .35 Whelen (new in 1988) cal.'s, modified 760 action, 22 in. barrel, detachable mag., pressed checkered pistol grip stock and forearm, 7½ lbs., mfg. 1981 to date.

Mfg.'s Sug. Retail	$439	$380	$340	$275	$225	$205	$185	$165

Model 7600 Carbine—.38-06 cal. only, similar to Model 7600 Rifle, except has 18½ in. barrel, 7¼ lbs.

Mfg.'s Sug. Retail	$439	$380	$340	$275	$225	$205	$185	$165

The below listed engraved Model 7600's were introduced in 1988.

D Peerless Grade
Mfg.'s Sug. Retail	$2,291	$1,975	$1,870	$1,200

F Premier Grade
Mfg.'s Sug. Retail	$4,720	$4,150	$3,835	$2,650

F Premier Gold Grade—with gold inlays.
Mfg.'s Sug. Retail	$7,079	$6,420	$5,735	$4,000

MODEL SIX SLIDE ACTION—6mm Rem. (disc. in 1984), 243 Win., 270 Win., .30-06, and 308 Win. (discontinued in 1984) cal.'s, pump action, detachable sights, 4 shot mag., mfg. 1981-1987.

$400	$360	$290	$265	$235	$215	$195

Last Mfg.'s Sug. Retail was $439.

D Peerless Grade
$1,975	$1,870	$1,200

Last Mfg.'s Sug. Retail was $2,291.

F Premier Grade
$4,150	$3,835	$2,650

Last Mfg.'s Sug. Retail was $4,720.

F Premier Gold Grade—with gold inlays.
$6,420	$5,735	$4,000

Last Mfg.'s Sug. Retail was $7,079.

MODEL 740 & 740A AUTOLOADER—.30-06 and .308 cal.'s, 22 in. barrel, open sight, box mag., gas operated, plain pistol grip stock, made 1955-1960. Carbine version — add 15%.

$250	$205	$180	$160	$140	$120	$100

MODEL 740ADL—same as 740A, with checkered stock, grip cap and swivels, made 1955-1960. Carbine version - add 15%.

$275	$230	$200	$175	$155	$140	$110

MODEL 740BDL—same as 740ADL, with select wood. Carbine version - add 15%.

$290	$250	$215	$195	$165	$150	$140

MODEL 742 SEMI-AUTO—6mm Rem., .243, .280, .30-06, and .308 cal.'s, 22 in. barrel, open sights, 4 shot box mag., gas operated, checkered pistol grip stock, made 1960-1980.

$285	$260	$240	$220	$200	$175	$150

MODEL 742 CARBINE—same as 742, except .30-06 and .308 cal.'s only, 18½ in. barrel, made 1961-1980.

$325	$290	$260	$240	$220	$200	$180

MODEL 742BDL—same as 742, except .30-06 and .308 cal.'s only, Monte Carlo basket weave stock, black pistol grip cap and forend tip, made 1966-1980.

$315	$270	$240	$220	$200	$180	$160

MODEL 742D PEERLESS GRADE—same as 742, with scroll engraving and fancy wood, made 1961-1980.

$2,000	$1,870	$1,200

MODEL 742F PREMIER GRADE—same as 742, with extensive game scenes and scroll engraving, best grade wood.

$4,200	$3,860	$2,650

Grading	100%	98%	95%	90%	80%	70%	60%

MODEL 742 P PREMIER GRADE—gold inlaid model.

	$6,500	$5,785	$4,180				

MODEL 742 150 YEAR ANNIVERSARY—.30-06 only, mfg. in 1966 only.

	$350	$300	$250	$200	$175	$150	$125

MODEL 742 BICENTENNIAL—same as 742, with inscription on receiver, made 1976 only.

	$330	$240	$205	$180	$165	$150	$140

MODEL 74 SPORTSMAN SEMI-AUTO—.30-06 only, 22 in. barrel, 4 shot mag., uncheckered hardwood stock and forearm, open sights, 7½ lbs. Mfg. 1985-1987.

	$295	$260	$235	$210	$190	$175	$160

Last Mfg.'s Sug. Retail was $353.

MODEL 7400 SEMI-AUTO RIFLE—6mm Rem. (disc. in 1987), .243 Win., .270 Win., .280 Rem., .30-06, or .308 Win. cal., same action as 742, gas operation, 22 in. barrel, 4 shot detachable mag., pressed checkered walnut stock, 7½ lbs., mfg. 1982 to date.

Mfg.'s Sug. Retail	$459	$400	$355	$300	$255	$230	$210	$185

Model 7400 Carbine—.30-06 cal. only, similar to Model 7400 Rifle, except has 18½ in. barrel, 7¼ lbs. New in 1988.

Mfg.'s Sug. Retail	$459	$400	$355	$300	$255	$230	$210	$185

MODEL FOUR SEMI-AUTO—6mm Rem., .243 Win., .270 Win., .280 Rem., .30-06, or .308 Win. (discontinued in 1984) cal., gas operation with metering system, 22 in. barrel, 4 shot detachable mag., deluxe Monte Carlo stock and forend, detachable sights, mfg. 1982-1987.

	$435	$400	$330	$280	$255	$230	$205

Last Mfg.'s Sug. Retail was $475.

D Peerless Grade

	$1,975	$1,870	$1,200				

Last Mfg.'s Sug. Retail was $2,291.

F Premier Grade

	$4,150	$3,835	$2,650				

Last Mfg.'s Sug. Retail was $4,720.

F Premier Gold Grade—with gold inlays.

	$6,420	$5,735	$4,000				

Last Mfg.'s Sug. Retail was $7,079.

NYLON 66 AUTOLOADER—.22 LR, 19⅝ in. barrel, open sights, buttstock tube mag. holds 14 shells, 4 labs., made 1959 to date. Made from Zytel Plastic (stock) in black (Apache Model with chromed metal), brown, or green (1959-1961). Disc. in 1988.

	$110	$95	$85	$70	$60	$55	$50

This model was made in many configurations including an inexpensive Mohawk Model. Most prices are similar to those listed above.

Last Mfg.'s Sug. Retail was $124.

NYLON 66 BICENTENNIAL—inscription on receiver, manufactured in 1976 only, brown nylon stock only.

	$150	$110	$95	$75	$60	$55	$50

NYLON 77—same as Nylon 66, except with 5 shot clip mag., made 1970-1971 only.

	$105	$95	$85	$70	$55	$45	$30

This model is similar to the Remington 10-C.

NYLON 76 LEVER ACTION—similar appearance to Nylon 66, except short throw lever action, made 1962-1964 only.

	$140	$100	$85	$65	$55	$40	$30

NYLON 10 SINGLE SHOT—.22 S, L, or LR, bolt action, made 1962-1964.

	$100	$85	$55	$50	$45	$40	$35

REMINGTON ARMS COMPANY, cont.

Grading	100%	98%	95%	90%	80%	70%	60%

MODEL 11 NYLON—bolt action repeater, clip fed, 6 or 10 shot mag., 4½ lbs., made 1962-1964.

	$110	$85	$70	$55	$45	$40	$30

MODEL 12 NYLON—same as 11, with tube mag., made 1962-1964.

	$175	$140	$110	$85	$70	$55	$45

MODEL 30A BOLT ACTION RIFLE—Enfield M/1917 type action, 7mm, .30-06, .25, .30, .32, and .35 Rem. cal.'s, 22 in. barrel, checkered pistol grip stock, made 1921-1940.

	$360	$275	$250	$220	$195	$175	$150

MODEL 30R CARBINE—same as 30A, with 20 in. barrel.

	$360	$275	$250	$220	$195	$175	$150

MODEL 30S—deluxe version of Model 30A, .257 Robts., 7mm, and .30-06 cal.'s, 24 in. barrel, Lyman receiver sight, special stock, made 1930-1940.

	$440	$360	$330	$305	$275	$250	$220

RIFLES: INEXPENSIVE .22 CAL.

From 1930-1960 Remington produced a number of bolt action .22 cal. Rimfire rifles, both single shot and repeaters. They were good quality, serviceable weapons with many slight variations upon a basic design. The values for these rifles on today's market are essentially the same.

Add 10%-20% on the following models for either smooth bore, "P" models, Boy's Carbines and repeaters.

	100%	98%	95%	90%	80%	70%	60%
Model 33	$110	$90	$75	$65	$55	$40	$30
Model 33 NRA	$110	$90	$75	$65	$55	$40	$30

These models were mfg. 1931-1936.

Model 34	$110	$90	$75	$65	$55	$40	$30
Model 34 NRA	$110	$90	$75	$65	$55	$40	$30

These models were mfg. 1932-1936.

Model 341 A	$110	$90	$75	$65	$55	$40	$30
Model 341 P	$110	$90	$75	$65	$55	$40	$30
Model 341 SB	$110	$90	$75	$65	$55	$40	$30

These models were mfg. 1936-1940.

Model 41 A	$110	$90	$75	$65	$55	$40	$30
Model 41 AS	$110	$90	$75	$65	$55	$40	$30
Model 41 P	$110	$90	$75	$65	$55	$40	$30
Model 41 SB	$110	$90	$75	$65	$55	$40	$30

These models were mfg. 1936-1940.

Model 510 A	$110	$90	$75	$65	$55	$40	$30
Model 510P	$110	$90	$75	$65	$55	$40	$30
Model 510 SB	$110	$90	$75	$65	$55	$40	$30
Model 510 X	$110	$90	$75	$65	$55	$40	$30

These models were mfg. 1939-1962.

Model 511 A	$110	$90	$75	$65	$55	$40	$30
Model 511 P	$110	$90	$75	$65	$55	$40	$30
Model 511 X	$110	$90	$75	$65	$55	$40	$30

These models were mfg. 1939-1962.

Model 512 A	$110	$90	$75	$65	$55	$40	$30
Model 512 P	$110	$90	$75	$65	$55	$40	$30
Model 512 X	$110	$90	$75	$65	$55	$40	$30

These models were mfg. 1965-1967.

Model 514—produced 1948-1971.

	$110	$90	$75	$65	$55	$40	$30

Model 514 P—produced until 1971.

	$110	$90	$75	$65	$55	$40	$30

Model 514 BC—produced until 1971.

	$110	$90	$75	$65	$55	$40	$30

Grading	100%	98%	95%	90%	80%	70%	60%

MODEL 37 BOLT ACTION—.22 LR, 5 shot with single shot adapter, 28 in. barrel, target sight and scope bases, target stock, made 1937-1940.

	$385	$305	$275	$250	$220	$195	$165

MODEL 37 - 1940—improved trigger and stock design, made 1940-1954.

	$440	$360	$330	$305	$275	$220	$195

MODEL 511 SCOREMASTER—.22 cal., similar to Model 510, except has clip mag. and is a sporter. No serial numbers.

	$250	$225	$180	$140	$115	$95	$85

This model was the 1st Remington bolt action, clip magazine sporter.

MODEL 513TR BOLT ACTION—.22 LR, 27 in. barrel, Redfield aperture sight, target stock, 6 shot, sling swivels, made 1940-1969.

	$295	$250	$220	$180	$140	$115	$95

MODEL 513S—similar to 513TR, with Marbles open sight and checkered sporter stock, made 1941-1956.

	$400	$350	$320	$290	$260	$230	$210

MODEL 521TL JR. BOLT ACTION—.22 LR, 25 in. barrel, Lyman target sights, takedown, 6 shot mag., target stock, made 1947-1969.

	$245	$190	$160	$140	$120	$100	$90

MODEL 552A SPEEDMASTER—.22 S, L, or LR, 23 in. barrel, semi-auto open sight, tube mag., pistol grip stock, made 1957-disc.

	$160	$135	$120	$100	$85	$75	$65

Add $15 for BDL Deluxe.

MODEL 552C—same as 552A, with 21 in. barrel, made 1961-1977.

	$140	$110	$100	$90	$85	$70	$55

MODEL 552 SPEEDMASTER—.22 LR only, semi-auto, 21 in. barrel, walnut stock and forearm, tube mag., 5¾ lbs. Mfg. 1959 to 1988.

	$155	$135	$120	$100	$85	$75	$65

Last Mfg.'s Sug. Retail was $168.

Model 552 BDL Deluxe—same as Model 552, except with select wood and pressed checkering. Mfg. 1966 to date.

Mfg.'s Sug. Retail	$198	$175	$155	$140	$125	$105	$90	$75

MODEL 572A SLIDE ACTION—.22 S, L, or LR, 21, 24, or 25 in. barrel, open sight, tube mag., plain pistol grip stock, made 1955-disc.

	$160	$145	$125	$110	$100	$85	$75

Add $15 for BDL Deluxe.

MODEL 572 LIGHTWEIGHT—anodized alloy receiver and barrel, steel sleeved, 3 colors: tan, blue, and black, made 1958-1962.

	$225	$185	$150	$125	$110	$100	$90

MODEL 572SB—same as 572A, except smooth bore.

	$300	$250	$195	$160	$140	$120	$100

MODEL 572 FIELDMASTER—.22 LR only, slide action, 21 in. barrel, walnut stock and forearm, tube mag., 5½ lbs. Mfg. 1955 to 1988.

	$160	$145	$125	$105	$90	$75	$65

Last Mfg.'s Sug. Retail was $176.

Model 572 BDL Deluxe—same as Model 572, except with select wood and pressed checkering. Mfg. 1966 to date.

Mfg.'s Sug. Retail	$208	$180	$165	$150	$125	$105	$90	$75

MODEL 580 SINGLE SHOT—.22 S, L or LR, bolt action, 24 in. barrel, open sights, Monte Carlo stock, made 1968-1978.

	$95	$70	$55	$50	$40	$35	$30

MODEL 580BR—Boy's Model, 1 in. shorter stock, made 1971-1978.

	$105	$90	$85	$65	$55	$40	$35

Grading	100%	98%	95%	90%	80%	70%	60%

MODEL 581—.22 LR cal., bolt-action, 6 round clip mag., converts to single-shot, made 1967-1983.

	$150	$115	$110	$100	$90	$70	$60

MODEL 581-S—.22 LR cal., bolt action, 5 round clip mag., 24 in. barrel, hardwood uncheckered stock, 4¾ lbs. New in 1986.

Mfg.'s Sug. Retail	$184	$175	$160	$145	$125	$105	$90	$75

MODEL 582—same as 581, with tube mag., made 1967-1983.

	$150	$110	$100	$90	$70	$65	$60

MODEL 591 BOLT ACTION—5mm Rimfire Mag., 24 in. barrel, open sight, 5 shot clip mag., Monte Carlo stock, approx. 20,000 mfg. 1970-1973.

	$175	$160	$145	$130	$120	$110	$100

Original Remington 5mm ammo is selling for $25-$35 per box.

MODEL 592—same as 591, with tube mag. Approx. 7,000 mfg.

	$295	$260	$230	$200	$180	$160	$145

MODEL 541S CUSTOM—.22 S, L, or LR, bolt action, 24 in. barrel, no sights, 5 shot, scroll engraved receiver and trigger guard, checkered walnut stock with rosewood pistol grip cap and forend tip, made 1972-1984.

	$400	$350	$300	$275	$250	$225	$200

MODEL 541T—.22 LR only, 5 shot clip mag., 24 in. barrel, checkered American walnut stock with satin finish, barrel is drilled and tapped, 5⅞ lbs. New in 1986.

Mfg.'s Sug. Retail	$333	$295	$250	$225	$200	$180	$165	$150

MODEL 720A BOLT ACTION—Enfield type action, .257 Robts., .270, and .30-06 cal.'s, 22 in. barrel, open sights, 5 shot, checkered pistol grip stock.

	$1,200	$1,000	$850	$750	$675	$595	$535

This model is very rare as only 2,500 were mfg. during 1941 only.

MODEL 720R—same as 720A, with 20 in. barrel.

	$330	$250	$220	$195	$165	$140	$120

MODEL 721(A) BOLT ACTION—.264 Mag., .270, or .30-06 cal., 24 in. barrel, open sights, 4 shot, plain pistol grip stock, made 1948-1962.

	$295	$260	$220	$195	$165	$155	$145

MODEL 721ADL—same as Model 721A, except has deluxe checkered stock.

	$330	$275	$235	$200	$175	$165	$150

MODEL 721BDL—same as 721 ADL, except has extra select wood.

	$400	$350	$310	$280	$265	$245	$225

MODEL 721A MAGNUM—.300 H&H, 26 in. heavy barrel, recoil pad, 3 shot mag., 8¼ lbs.

	$400	$360	$320	$295	$275	$260	$245

MODEL 721ADL MAGNUM—same as 721A Mag., checkered.

	$450	$400	$350	$315	$290	$275	$260

MODEL 721BDL MAGNUM—same as 721ADL Mag., select wood.

	$525	$460	$420	$385	$360	$330	$300

MODEL 722(A)—short action version of 721A, .257 Roberts, .300 Savage, or .308 cal., 7 lbs., made 1948-1962.

	$325	$265	$220	$200	$165	$155	$145

MODEL 722ADL—same as Model 722A, except with deluxe checkered wood.

	$350	$285	$235	$210	$175	$165	$155

MODEL 722BDL—same as Model 722ADL, except features extra select wood.

	$425	$375	$325	$280	$265	$245	$225

MODEL 722(A)—.222 Rem., 26 in. barrel, 5 shot, made 1950-1962.

	$295	$250	$220	$210	$195	$175	$165
.222ADL	$335	$290	$260	$230	$220	$205	$185
.222BDL	$350	$315	$280	$250	$230	$220	$200

Grading	100%	98%	95%	90%	80%	70%	60%

MODEL 722A—.244 Rem., 4 shot, made 1955-1962.

	100%	98%	95%	90%	80%	70%	60%
	$295	$270	$235	$210	$195	$175	$165
.244BDL	$350	$315	$280	$250	$230	$220	$200

MODEL 725ADL BOLT ACTION—.222, .243, .244, .270,, .280, or .30-06 cal., 22 in. barrel, open sights, 4 shot, checkered Monte Carlo stock, made 1958-1961.

	100%	98%	95%	90%	80%	70%	60%
	$375	$325	$285	$250	$220	$200	$185
.222 cal.	$995	$800	$700	$600	$550	$500	$460

MODEL 725 KODIAK—.357 H&H Mag. or .458 Win. Mag. cal., 26 in. barrel, 3 shot, recoil reducer in muzzle, deluxe checkered Monte Carlo stock, black pistol grip cap and forend tip, made in 1961 only.

	100%	98%	95%	90%	80%	70%	60%
	$795	$675	$550	$495	$440	$385	$360

MODEL 600 BOLT ACTION—.222, .223 (very rare), 6mm, .243, .308, or .35 Rem. cal., 18½ in. vent rib barrel, dog leg bolt handle, checkered pistol grip stock, made 1964-1967.

	100%	98%	95%	90%	80%	70%	60%
Reg. cal.'s	$375	$295	$250	$210	$195	$175	$155
.222 cal.	$450	$395	$350	$320	$295	$270	$250
.35 Rem.	$550	$475	$425	$360	$320	$285	$250

Subtract 20% for Mohawk variation.

Approx. 312 Model 600's in .223 cal. were manufactured and large premiums are being asked for this rare caliber. There was also a Model 600 Montana Commemorative issued in limited numbers add a small premium.

MODEL 600 MAGNUM—6.5mm Rem. Mag. or .350 Rem. Mag. cal., laminated walnut/beech stock with recoil pad, made 1965-1967.

	100%	98%	95%	90%	80%	70%	60%
6.5mm Rem.	$595	$550	$500	$460	$440	$420	$395
.350 Rem. Mag.	$650	$580	$540	$500	$460	$430	$400

MODEL 660 BOLT ACTION—.222, 6mm, .243, or .308 cal., 20 in. barrel, open sight, dog leg bolt handle, checkered pistol grip stock, black pistol grip cap and forend tip, made 1968-1971.

	100%	98%	95%	90%	80%	70%	60%
	$495	$450	$400	$360	$330	$295	$260

Add 20% for .222 Rem. cal.

.223 cal.—rare and values can fluctuate greatly ($675 and up). This model was never listed in a Remington catalog.

MODEL 660 MAGNUM—6.5 Mag. and .350 Mag. cal.'s, laminated stock and recoil pad.

	100%	98%	95%	90%	80%	70%	60%
	$650	$575	$500	$450	$400	$350	$300
6.5 Mag.	$600	$525	$465	$420	$370	$325	$295

MODEL 78 SPORTSMAN BOLT ACTION—.223 Rem., .243 Win., .270 Win., .30-06, or .308 Win. cal., 22 in. barrel, 4 shot mag., uncheckered hardwood stock, open sights, 7 lbs. New in 1985.

	100%	98%	95%	90%	80%	70%	60%
Mfg.'s Sug. Retail	$333	$270	$235	$210	$190	$170	$160	$150

MODEL 700ADL DELUXE BOLT ACTION—.22-250, .222, .25-06, 6mm, .243, .270, .30-06, .308, or 7mm Mag. cal., 22 and 24 in. barrel, open sights, 4 shot mag., checkered Monte Carlo stock, made 1962-present, .222, and 6mm cal.'s are discontinued, also a few Model 700's were made in .222 Mag — rare.

	100%	98%	95%	90%	80%	70%	60%
Mfg.'s Sug. Retail	$392	$330	$295	$250	$210	$175	$165	$155

7mm Mag.

	100%	98%	95%	90%	80%	70%	60%
Mfg.'s Sug. Retail	$415	$360	$315	$260	$220	$205	$195	$165

Remington, in 1987, introduced a Model 700 Gun Kit that enables the owner to assemble the stock to the barreled action. All metal work is completely finished and wood finishing is all that is required. Available in most popular cal.'s - retail price is $333. Add $20 for 7mm Rem. Mag. cal.

Model 700ADL/LS—.243 Win. (new in 1989), .270 Win. (new in 1989), or .30-06 cal., laminate stock with checkering. New in 1988.

	100%	98%	95%	90%	80%	70%	60%
Mfg.'s Sug. Retail	$440	$375	$330	$275	$230	$210	$195	$165

Grading	100%	98%	95%	90%	80%	70%	60%

MODEL 700BDL CUSTOM DELUXE—similar to 700ADL Deluxe, except with hinged floorplate, cut skipline checkering, black pistol grip cap and forend tip, additional cal.'s in .17 Rem., .222 Rem., .223 Rem., .264 Mag. (disc.), 6mm Rem. Mag., 7mm Rem. Mag., 7mm-08 Rem., .300 Win. Mag., .338 Win. Mag. (new in 1988), and 8mm Mag. (disc.) cal.'s.

Mfg.'s Sug. Retail **$462** **$405** **$365** **$300** **$275** **$250** **$220** **$195**
Add $54 for left-hand model.
Add $23 for .17, 7mm Rem. Mag., .300 Win. Mag., .35 Whelen (new in 1989), or .338 Win. Mag. cal.'s.

MODEL 700 MOUNTAIN RIFLE—.243 Win. (new in 1988), .270 Win., 7mm-08 Rem. (new in 1988), .280 Rem., .30-06, or .308 (new in 1988) cal., 22 in. tapered barrel, checkered satin finished American walnut stock with cheekpiece and ebony forend, 4 shot mag., without sights, 6¾ lbs. New in 1986.

Mfg.'s Sug. Retail **$469** **$405** **$365** **$300** **$275** **$250** **$220** **$195**

MODEL 700 CUSTOM KS MOUNTAIN RIFLE—.270 Win., .280 Rem., .300 Win. Mag., .300 Wby. Mag. (new in 1989), .30-06, .338 Win. Mag. (new in 1986), .35 Whelen (new in 1989), 7mm Rem. Mag., 8mm Rem. Mag. (new in 1986), or .375 H&H Mag. cal., features extra lightweight Kevlar fiber-reinforced stock — available in either right or left-hand. New in 1986.

Mfg.'s Sug. Retail **$867** **$740** **$670** **$545** **$460** **$415** **$385** **$350**

This model is available from the Custom Shop only (special order).

MODEL 700BDL VARMINT SPECIAL—.22-250, .222, .223, .25-06 (disc.), 6mm, .243, .308 Win., or 7mm-08 cal., 24 in. heavy barrel, no sights, made 1967-present.

Mfg.'s Sug. Retail **$493** **$435** **$390** **$335** **$310** **$285** **$265** **$250**

MODEL 700 SAFARI GRADE—heavier 700BDL, in .375 H&H, 8mm Rem. Mag. (new in 1986), .416 Rem. Mag. (new in 1989), or .458 Mag. cal., 3 shot mag., 24 in. barrel, available with either classic or Monte Carlo stock configuration, made 1962-present.

Mfg.'s Sug. Retail **$871** **$750** **$660** **$525** **$440** **$415** **$385** **$330**

Model 700 Custom KS Safari Grade—8mm Rem. Mag., .375 H & H, .416 Rem. Mag., or .458 Win. Mag., stock made from extra lightweight Kevlar fiber, 24 in. barrel. New in 1989.

Mfg.'s Sug. Retail **$1,004** **$925** **$800** **$700**

MODEL 700 CLASSIC—similar to 700BDL, except classic straight stock, high polish bluing, has been offered in .22-250, .250 Savage (250/3000), 6mm, 7 x 57 Mauser, .243, .257 Roberts, .264 Win. Mag., .270, .300 Wby. Mag., .30-06, .338 Win. Mag., .350 Rem. Mag., .35 Whelen, .300 H&H, or .375 H&H cal.

Mfg.'s Sug. Retail **$485** **$410** **$355** **$300** **$265** **$250** **$220** **$195**

This model is produced in limited quantities of a different caliber each year. Add premiums for several older calibers in N.I.B. condition only (including 7 x 57 Mauser, .257 Roberts, .300 H&H, and .375 H&H).

The following is a partial list of calibers offered previously and year of manufacture: 7 x 57mm (1981), .257 Roberts (1982), .300 H&H (1983), .250 Savage (1984), .350 Rem. Mag. (1985), .264 Win. Mag. (1986), .338 Win. Mag. (1987), .35 Whelen (1988), and .300 Wby. Mag. (1989).

MODEL 700C GRADE—from custom shop, no engraving, deluxe checkered wood with rosewood forearm cap.

　　　　　　$850 **$775** **$695** **$635** **$510** **$440** **$400**

MODEL 700D PEERLESS GRADE—scroll engraving, best wood.

　　　　　　$1,320 **$1,100** **$880** **$825** **$690** **$660** **$550**

MODEL 700F PREMIER GRADE—elaborate engraving, best wood.

　　　　　　$2,750 **$2,420** **$2,200** **$2,035** **$1,870** **$1,760** **$1,650**

MODEL 700 AS—.22-250, .243 Win., .270 Win., .280 Rem., .30-06, .308 Win., or 7mm Rem. Mag., synthetic stock is made from Arylon resin, matte black finished stock and metal, 22 or 24 in. barrel, 6½ lbs. New in 1989.

Mfg.'s Sug. Retail **$479** **$410** **$365** **$300** **$275** **$250** **$220** **$195**
Add $20 for 7mm Rem. Mag. cal.

Grading	100%	98%	95%	90%	80%	70%	60%

MODEL 700 RS—.270 Win., .280 Rem., and .30-06 cal.'s, 22 in. polished blue barrel, gray or gray camo DuPont Rynite synthetic stock with smooth cheekpiece and solid recoil pad, iron sights, 7¼ lbs. Mfg. 1987-1988 only.

	$490	$440	$405	$370	$335	$310	$285

Last Mfg.'s Sug. Retail was $547.

MODEL 700 FS—.243 Win., .270 Win., .30-06, .308 Win., and 7mm Rem. Mag. cal.'s, 22 in. polished blue barrel, gray or gray camo Kevlar fiberglass stock with solid recoil pad, iron sights, 6¼ lbs. Mfg. 1987-1988 only.

	$530	$460	$415	$375	$335	$310	$285

Add $20 for 7mm Rem. Mag. cal. (24 in. barrel).

Last Mfg.'s Sug. Retail was $613.

MODEL 700 CUSTOM GRADE—special order only, grades differ in amount of engraving and type of walnut. Available as a custom order only through Remington.

Custom Grade Model I

Mfg.'s Sug. Retail	$1,263	$1,075	$925	$795

Custom Grade Model II

Mfg.'s Sug. Retail	$2,245	$1,925	$1,660	$1,295

Custom Grade Model III

Mfg.'s Sug. Retail	$3,508	$2,800	$2,100	$1,750

Custom Grade Model IV

Mfg.'s Sug. Retail	$5,475	$4,700	$4,000	$2,900

MODEL 788 BOLT ACTION—.222, .22-250, .223, 6mm, .243, .308, .30-30, 7mm-08, and .44 Mag. cal.'s, 22 and 24 in. barrel, open sight, plain pistol grip Monte Carlo stock, made 1967-1984.

	100%	98%	95%	90%	80%	70%	60%
Rifle	$325	$275	$225	$200	$180	$160	$140
Carbine (18 in. barrel)	$350	$300	$240	$210	$185	$160	$140

MODEL SEVEN BOLT ACTION—compact bolt action available in .223 Rem., .243 Win., 6mm Rem., 7mm-08 Rem., and .308 Win. cal.'s, 18½ in. barrel, 6¼ lbs., 4 or 5 round mag., individually test fired, oil finished American walnut, 1982-present.

Mfg.'s Sug. Retail	$440	$385	$335	$260	$225	$205	$180	$165

Model Seven FS—.243 Win., 7mm-08 Rem., and .308 Win. cal.'s, 18½ in. polished blue barrel, gray or gray camo Kevlar fiberglass stock, adj. rear sight, 5¼ lbs. New in 1987.

Mfg.'s Sug. Retail	$600	$525	$455	$415	$375	$335	$310	$285

Model Seven Custom KS—.223 Rem. (new in 1989), 7mm BR (new in 1989), 7mm-08 Rem. (new in 1989), .35 Rem. or .350 Rem. Mag., 20 in. barrel, synthetic Kevlar stock with solid recoil pad. New in 1987.

Mfg.'s Sug. Retail	$867	$785	$660	$530

This model is available from the Custom Shop only (special order).

TARGET RIFLES

MODEL 40X SPORTER—.22 LR only, sporterized version of the 40X Target Rifle, less than 700 mfg. 1969-1980, 5 shot clip, custom 700 stock, a special order only gun from the factory. Rare.

	$1,495	$1,200	$925	$800	$720	$650	$595

This model was last listed in the 1977 Remington catalog — retail was $525.

MODEL 40X TARGET RIFLE—bolt action single shot, .22 LR, 28 in. heavy barrel, Redfield Olympic sights, scope bases, target stock, rubber butt, 12¾ lbs., made 1955-1964.

	100%	98%	95%	90%	80%	70%	60%
	$495	$395	$325	$260	$220	$190	$175
No sights	$450	$360	$295	$240	$200	$180	$165

MODEL 40X STANDARD BARREL—same as 40X Target Rifle, with lighter barrel, 10¾ lbs.

	100%	98%	95%	90%	80%	70%	60%
	$475	$380	$310	$250	$220	$190	$175
No sights	$450	$360	$295	$240	$200	$180	$165

Grading	100%	98%	95%	90%	80%	70%	60%

MODEL 40X CENTERFIRE—similar to Model 40X Rim Fire, except in .222, .222 Mag., .30-06, and .308 cal.'s, made 1961-1964.

	100%	98%	95%	90%	80%	70%	60%
	$525	$440	$360	$320	$305	$275	$250
No sights	$495	$400	$330	$290	$275	$250	$220

MODEL 40XB RANGEMASTER RIMFIRE—.22 LR, bolt action single shot, 28 in. light or heavy barrel, no sights, target stock with guide rail, rubber butt, made 1964-1974.

	$525	$420	$335	$275	$220	$195	$165

MODEL 40XB RANGEMASTER CENTERFIRE—over 12 cal.'s, custom made, 27½ in. barrel (current model is stainless), test fired, made 1964-present.

Mfg.'s Sug. Retail	$983	$885	$775	$615	$500	$410	$370	$315

Add $69 for bench rest model.
Add $84 for repeater model.
Add $140 for 2 oz. trigger.

An International Free Rifle was also offered - only 107 were mfg. with premiums being paid.

MODEL 40XB KEVLAR STOCKED—.220 Swift, 27¼ in. bright finished stainless steel barrel, single shot, black finish Kevlar stock, no sights, 9¾ lbs. New in 1987.

Mfg.'s Sug. Retail	$1,123	$995	$825	$675

Add $84 for repeater model.
Add $140 for 2 oz. trigger.

MODEL 40XB REPEATER—same as 40XB Centerfire, with 5 shot mag. Discontinued.

	$870	$770	$625	$500	$420	$370	$315

MODEL 40-XC—7.62 Nato, National Match Course rifle, adj. trigger pull.

Mfg.'s Sug. Retail	$1,052	$930	$825	$675	$520	$450	$410	$370

Add $141 for Kevlar stock.

MODEL 40XR RIMFIRE—.22 LR, single shot bolt action, 24 in. heavy barrel, no sights, adj. buttplate and palm stop, target stock, made 1974-present.

Mfg.'s Sug. Retail	$983	$885	$775	$615	$500	$410	$370	$315

Add $140 for Kevlar stock.

MODEL 40XR CUSTOM SPORTER—.22 cal. only, single shot, available on special order from Remington's custom shop only, Grades I-IV increase by amount of engraving, quality of wood, and other special order options/features. New in 1986.

Custom Grade Model I
Mfg.'s Sug. Retail	$1,263	$1,075	$925	$795

Custom Grade Model II
Mfg.'s Sug. Retail	$2,245	$1,925	$1,660	$1,295

Custom Grade Model III
Mfg.'s Sug. Retail	$3,508	$2,800	$2,100	$1,750

Custom Grade Model IV
Mfg.'s Sug. Retail	$5,475	$4,700	$4,000	$2,900

MODEL 540X RIMFIRE—.22 LR, single shot bolt action, 26 in. heavy barrel, no sights, target stock, adj. butt, made 1969-1974.

	$360	$310	$260	$230	$200	$175	$150

MODEL 540XR—similar to 540X, with large position style stock, made 1974-1983.

	$395	$335	$285	$240	$210	$175	$150

SHOTGUNS

100%	98%	95%	90%	80%	70%	60%	50%	40%	30%	20%	10%

MODEL 1874 DOUBLE BARREL HAMMER—10 or 12 ga., 28 or 30 in. decarbonized or damascus barrels, top "thumb-lever" action activated by pushing forward on opening lever, rib top marked "E. REMINGTON & SONS, ILION. N.Y.", patented AUG.8.1871, APRIL 16.1872, made in various grades, pistol grip was optional. Mfg. 1874-1882.

$1,750	$1,500	$1,200	$995	$900	$800	$700	$600	$500	$425	$350	$275

There were also a very few double rifles and combination guns (shotgun/rifle barrel) made in this model - they are very rare. Above values represent standard model without extra options.

	100%	98%	95%	90%	80%	70%	60%	50%	40%	30%	20%	10%

MODEL 1882 DOUBLE BARREL—10, 12, or 16 ga., 28, 30, or 32 in. damascus barrels, exposed "circular" hammers, checkered pistol grip stock, made 1882-1889. Approximately 7,500 mfg. Higher grades will bring premiums.

Damascus Barrels

$1,700	$1,400	$1,150	$995	$900	$800	$700	$600	$500	$425	$350	$275

Steel Barrels

$1,950	$1,600	$1,250	$1,100	$975	$875	$775	$675	$575	$500	$450	$400

Auxiliary rifle barrel inserts were also available in this model — add 15%.

Models 1885 and 1887 were slightly improved Model 1882's available in 10, 12, or 16 ga. Sideplates are marked Remington. Values will approximate those listed above.

MODEL 1889 DOUBLE BARREL—10, 12 or 16 ga., 28, 30, or 32 in. damascus barrels, exposed hammers, checkered pistol grip stock, made 1889-1909. Approximately 30,000 manufactured. Higher grades bring premium.

Damascus Barrels

$1,400	$1,150	$995	$900	$800	$700	$600	$500	$425	$350	$275	$225

Steel Barrels

$1,650	$1,250	$1,100	$975	$875	$775	$675	$575	$500	$450	$400	$350

Grades range from No. 1 - No. 7, No. 7 being the highest. Values above assume No. 1 or 2 grade.

MODEL NO. 3 RIDER—10, 12, 16, 20, 24, and 28 ga.'s, single barrel, 30 or 32 in. barrels, top lever break open, plain pistol grip stock, made 1893-1903.

$325	$290	$260	$230	$200	$170	$140	$110	$85	$65	$50	$35

MODEL NO. 9 RIDER—same as No. 3, with auto ejector, made 1902-1910.

$375	$325	$290	$260	$230	$200	$170	$140	$110	$85	$65	$50

MODEL 1894 DOUBLE BARREL—10, 12, and 16 ga.'s, 26-32 in. "Ordnance" steel barrels, auto ejectors, hammerless, boxlock, double triggers, checkered pistol grip stock, made 1894-1910. Over 100,000 manufactured.

$600	$550	$520	$480	$440	$395	$360	$330	$295	$260	$220	$180

Grades offered range from "A" (lowest) to "E" and "Special" (highest). Large premiums exist for higher grade models in excellent condition. Trap model was named either "F.E." or "C.E.O.". Values above assume "A" model (most frequently encountered specimen).

MODEL 1900 DOUBLE BARREL—improved model 1894, made 1900-1910.

$660	$600	$550	$520	$480	$440	$395	$360	$330	$295	$260	$220

Grades ranged from "K", "K.E.", or damascus "K.D." or "K.E.D.". Both steel and damascus barrels were guaranteed for nitro powder.

MODERN SHOTGUNS

Grading	100%	98%	95%	90%	80%	70%	60%

MODEL 10A SLIDE ACTION—12 ga., 26-32 in. barrels, various chokes, takedown, plain pistol grip stock, made 1907-1929. Add 10% for 32 in. full choke barrel.

	$400	$330	$300	$275	$220	$165	$140

MODEL 11A AUTOLOADER 5-SHOT—12, 16, and 20 ga.'s, 26-32 in. barrels, takedown, various chokes, Browning type, checkered pistol stock, made 1911-1948. Approximately 300,000 manufactured.

	$330	$250	$220	$195	$165	$150	$120
Solid rib	$440	$330	$250	$220	$195	$165	$140
Vent rib	$440	$360	$335	$305	$275	$220	$165

This model was manufactured under "A - 5" patent agreements (including royalties) with Fabrique Nationale in Herstal, Belgium.

MODEL 11R RIOT GUN—same as Standard 11A, with 20 in. barrel.

	$330	$250	$220	$195	$165	$150	$120

MODEL 11B SPECIAL—higher grade wood, engraved.

	$525	$440	$385	$360	$305	$250	$195

Grading	100%	98%	95%	90%	80%	70%	60%

MODEL 11D TOURNAMENT

	100%	98%	95%	90%	80%	70%	60%
	$1,100	$880	$715	$550	$495	$470	$440

MODEL 11E EXPERT

	$1,540	$1,265	$990	$770	$660	$605	$550

MODEL 11F PREMIER

	$2,750	$2,200	$1,650	$1,100	$990	$935	$770

Note: Grades differ in quality, grade of wood, and amount of engraving.

SPORTSMAN SKEET MODEL—12, 16, and 20 ga.'s, 26 in. barrel, skeet choke, beavertail forend, made 1931-1949.

	100%	98%	95%	90%	80%	70%	60%
	$385	$305	$275	$250	$195	$165	$140
Solid rib	$470	$415	$330	$275	$220	$195	$165
Vent rib	$470	$415	$360	$330	$275	$250	$220

MODEL 17A SLIDE ACTION—20 ga., 26-32 in. barrels, various chokes, takedown, bottom ejection, 4 shot mag., plain grip stock, made 1917-1933. Approximately 48,000 manufactured.

	100%	98%	95%	90%	80%	70%	60%
Plain barrel	$330	$250	$220	$195	$165	$140	$110
Vent rib	$495	$440	$380	$335	$290	$250	$210

Grades range from A - F in suffix form, F being the highest. Large premiums are paid for mint condition, higher grade models.

MODEL 29A SLIDE ACTION—12 ga., 26-32 in. barrels, bottom ejection, various chokes, takedown, 5 shot mag., checkered pistol grip stock, made 1929-1933. Approximately 24,000 manufactured. Add 15% for solid rib, 25% for vent rib.

	100%	98%	95%	90%	80%	70%	60%
	$305	$220	$195	$165	$150	$120	$100

30 and 32 in. barrels

	$525	$475	$425	$350	$250	$200	$180

Grades range from A - C and TA - TF, lowest to highest. Premiums exist for finer condition upper grades. The Model 29 was similar in appearance to the Model 10.

MODEL 29S—"Trap Special" with trap style straight grip stock, matted rib.

	$385	$305	$275	$250	$195	$165	$140

MODEL 31A SLIDE ACTION—12, 16, and 20 ga.'s, side ejection, 2 or 4 shot mag., 26-32 in. barrels, various chokes, takedown, pistol grip stock, made 1931-1949. Approximately 160,000 manufactured.

	100%	98%	95%	90%	80%	70%	60%
	$415	$360	$320	$280	$240	$200	$160
Solid rib	$480	$400	$360	$320	$280	$240	$200
Vent rib	$515	$450	$395	$360	$320	$270	$235

Grades range from A - F suffixes. Higher grades will bring considerable premiums in excellent condition. TC suffix is Target Model.

MODEL 31R RIOT GUN—same as 31A, with 20 in. barrel.

	$330	$250	$200	$175	$150	$130	$110

MODEL 31 SPECIAL—higher grade wood and engraving.

	$650	$550	$440	$385	$360	$305	$275

MODEL 31 TOURNAMENT

	$1,100	$880	$715	$580	$525	$495	$470

MODEL 31E EXPERT

	$1,320	$1,100	$935	$880	$770	$660	$605

MODEL 31F PREMIER

	$2,420	$1,980	$1,760	$1,540	$1,320	$1,100	$880

Note: Grades differ in quality, grade of wood, and amount of engraving.

MODEL 31TC TRAP—same as 31A, with 12 ga. only, 30 or 32 in. barrel, vent rib, full choke, trap stock and beavertail forend, pad.

	$660	$550	$495	$470	$415	$385	$305

MODEL 31S TRAP—solid rib barrel, plainer wood.

	$495	$415	$385	$330	$275	$250	$220

Grading	100%	98%	95%	90%	80%	70%	60%

MODEL 31H HUNTER—same as 31S, with sporter stock.

	100%	98%	95%	90%	80%	70%	60%
	$470	$385	$360	$305	$250	$220	$195

MODEL 31 SKEET—same as 31A, with 26 in. skeet bored barrel, standard solid rib, beavertail forend.

	100%	98%	95%	90%	80%	70%	60%
	$495	$415	$385	$330	$275	$250	$220
Vent rib	$605	$495	$445	$415	$360	$305	$275

MODEL 870AP SLIDE ACTION—"Wingmaster", 12, 16, and 20 ga.'s, 26, 28, and 30 in. barrel, 5 shot, various chokes, plain pistol grip stock, made 1950-1963.

	100%	98%	95%	90%	80%	70%	60%
	$220	$195	$175	$165	$140	$120	$110
Matted top barrel	$230	$205	$185	$175	$150	$130	$120
Vent rib	$250	$220	$200	$195	$165	$150	$140

In 1959 "Sun Grain" blonde wood became an option.

MODEL 870DL—deluxe checkered version of 870AP, made 1950-1963.

	100%	98%	95%	90%	80%	70%	60%
	$250	$220	$200	$180	$165	$140	$120
Vent rib	$275	$250	$220	$210	$195	$165	$140

MODEL 870BDL—select walnut stock.

	100%	98%	95%	90%	80%	70%	60%
	$275	$250	$220	$200	$180	$165	$140
Vent rib	$305	$275	$250	$220	$210	$195	$165

SPORTSMAN PUMP—12 ga. only (3 in. chamber), 28 or 30 in. barrel, recoil pad, vent rib standard, hardwood stock and forearm, Model 870 type action, 7½ lbs. Manufactured in 1985-86 only. Add $35 for Rem. chokes.

	100%	98%	95%	90%	80%	70%	60%
	$225	$195	$180	$165	$150	$140	$130

Last Mfg.'s Sug. Retail was $270.

MODEL 870 EXPRESS—12 ga. only (3 in. chamber), 28 in. VR Rem. choked (supplied with Mod. choke) barrel, parkerized metal, matte finished hardwood stock and forearm, solid recoil pad, 7¼ lbs. New in 1987.

	100%	98%	95%	90%	80%	70%	60%
Mfg.'s Sug. Retail	$238	$210	$185	$165	$150	$140	$130	$125

Add $97 for Combo package (extra 20 in. IC barrel).

MODEL 870 FIELD WINGMASTER—same as 870AP, with checkering, incorporates twin slide rails. Add $56 for left-hand. 3 in. chambers became standard in 1985, Rem. chokes became standard in 1987. Made 1964 to present.

	100%	98%	95%	90%	80%	70%	60%
	$250	$225	$205	$190	$175	$160	$150

Vent rib—became standard in 1985.

	100%	98%	95%	90%	80%	70%	60%
Mfg.'s Sug. Retail	$439	$335	$265	$230	$200	$185	$170	$160

Subtract $45 without Rem. chokes.

MODEL 870 MAGNUM DUCK GUN—3 in. chamber, 12 and 20 ga.'s, 26, 28, or 30 in. full or mod. barrel, recoil pad, made 1964-present. 3 in. chambers are standard in all Model 870's starting in 1985. Rem. chokes became standard in 1987 (introduced in 1986 as $40 option).

	100%	98%	95%	90%	80%	70%	60%
Mfg.'s Sug. Retail	$439	$335	$265	$230	$200	$185	$170	$160

Subtract $45 without Rem. chokes.

870 Special Purpose Mag.—differs only in that metal parts are sand blasted and wood has low lustre finish. Add $40 for Rem. chokes (introduced in 1986).

	100%	98%	95%	90%	80%	70%	60%
Mfg.'s Sug. Retail	$439	$335	$265	$230	$200	$185	$170	$160

SMALL GAUGE MODEL 870—scaled down 870, in 28 and .410 ga.'s, 25 in. barrel, made 1969-present. Vent rib became standard in 1984. Subtract $40 if without vent rib.

	100%	98%	95%	90%	80%	70%	60%
Mfg.'s Sug. Retail	$465	$375	$325	$275	$235	$200	$185	$170

MODEL 870 LIGHTWEIGHT—20 ga. only, lighter and shorter mahogany stock, 23 in. barrel made 1972-1983.

	100%	98%	95%	90%	80%	70%	60%
	$270	$230	$210	$190	$175	$165	$155

Add $30 for vent rib.

Model 870 Youth—similar to Model 870 Lightweight, except has 1 in. shorter stock and 21 in. barrel only.

	100%	98%	95%	90%	80%	70%	60%
Mfg.'s Sug. Retail	$423	$295	$255	$220	$195	$180	$170	$160

Grading	100%	98%	95%	90%	80%	70%	60%

MODEL 870 SPECIAL FIELD—12 and 20 ga., lighter straight grip stock, 21 in. barrel.
New in 1984. Rem. chokes became standard in 1987 (introduced in 1986 as $40 option).

Mfg.'s Sug. Retail	$439	$365	$315	$260	$230	$210	$190	$175

MODEL 870 LIGHTWEIGHT MAGNUM—20 ga., 3 in. magnum, 26 or 28 in.
barrel, 6 lbs., made 1972-present. Rem. chokes became standard in 1987.

Mfg.'s Sug. Retail	$439	$365	$315	$250	$220	$195	$175	$160

Subtract $45 without Rem. chokes.
Subtract $40 without vent rib.

MODEL 870 RIOT—18 or 20 in. barrel, 12 ga. only.

Mfg.'s Sug. Retail	$326	$285	$255	$220	$200	$170	$150	$130

Add $23 for police rifle sights.

MODEL 870 STANDARD DEER GUN—12 or 20 ga., 20 in. imp. cyl. with rifle sights,
3 in. chamber standard for 1985.

Mfg.'s Sug. Retail	$386	$335	$290	$230	$210	$195	$185	$175

Add $28 for 12 ga. with Rem. choke.
Add $68 for left-hand model.

MODEL 870 DEER BRUSHMASTER—12 or 20 ga., 20 in. barrel, rifle sights,
checkered, recoil pad, 3 in. chamber standard for 1985. Disc. in 1988.

	$330	$295	$250	$230	$210	$200	$190

Add $40 for left-hand model (disc.).
Subtract $16 for 20 ga.

Last Mfg.'s Sug. Retail was $381.

MODEL 870 SPECIAL PURPOSE DEER GUN—12 ga. only, 3 in. chamber, 20 in.
Rem. choke barrel, satin finished stock and forearm, matte black metal, rifle sights, 7¼ lbs.
New in 1989.

Mfg.'s Sug. Retail	$414	$285	$245	$215	$190	$175	$170	$165

Add $62 for cantilever scope mount system.

MODEL 870 D-GRADE (TOURNAMENT)—custom order only, any gauge, made
1950 - present.

Mfg.'s Sug. Retail	$2,291	$1,975	$1,870	$1,200

MODEL 870 F-GRADE (PREMIER)—custom order only, any gauge, made 1950 -
present.

Mfg.'s Sug. Retail	$4,720	$4,150	$3,835	$2,650

MODEL 870 F-GRADE W/GOLD (GOLD PREMIER)—with gold inlay, custom
order only, made 1950 - present.

Mfg.'s Sug. Retail	$7,079	$6,420	$5,735	$4,000

Note: Grades differ in quality, grade of wood, and amount of engraving.

MODEL 870 DUCKS UNLIMITED—"DU" in serial number, disc.

	$335	$270	$195

Remington has offered many variations of the Model 870 specifically manufactured according to individual DU chapter specifications. The price of a DU 870 varies substantially from the "DU point of purchase" to real market conditions. When contemplating a DU gun it is always important to know how many of that particular variation were manufactured. The Remington factory normally has this information unless the special DU work was subcontracted elsewhere. While most DU guns are good vehicles for fund raising, their collectability to date has been minimal. Actual market conditions indicate that unless production is truly limited, most DU firearms sell very close to the model it was derived from. Also, any collectability that does exist is for 100% guns new in the box with warranty papers. Used DU guns have values comparable to the standard model from which they are derived.

In addition to regular DU guns, Remington has also produced special editions including the 1982 Mississippi Edition (dinner gun) and a 1974 DU (dinner gun — first 500 mfg.). These were rarer DU shotguns, and current values could vary significantly.

Grading	100%	98%	95%	90%	80%	70%	60%

MODEL 870 SKEET—12 ga., 26 in. vent rib skeet bore barrel, made 1950-1981.

	100%	98%	95%	90%	80%	70%	60%
	$295	$260	$230	$215	$200	$185	$170

MODEL 870 SKEET CASED SET—.410 and 28 ga.'s, 1,503 sets made in 1969 only.

	$850	$700	$650	$620	$575	$530	$475

MODEL 870TA TRAP—12 ga. trap model, deluxe walnut, vent rib. Add $15 for Monte Carlo stock. Discontinued in 1986.

	$365	$345	$280	$240	$220	$200	$180

Last Mfg.'s Sug. Retail was $430.

MODEL 870TB TRAP—same as 870, with 28 or 30 in. vent rib full choke barrel, trap stock, recoil pad, made 1950-1981.

	$395	$355	$285	$245	$220	$200	$185

MODEL 870TC TRAP—higher grade walnut and special VR, Rem. chokes became standard in 1987.

Mfg.'s Sug. Retail	$572	$475	$400	$315	$260	$240	$220	$200

Add $13 for Monte Carlo stock.
Subtract $13 if without Rem. chokes.

COMPETITION TRAP—12 ga. competition model, reduced recoil, special checkered walnut, vent rib. Discontinued in 1986.

	$575	$545	$390	$320	$280	$240	$210

Last Mfg.'s Sug. Retail was $680.

MODEL 870 ALL AMERICAN TRAP—30 in. full choke barrel, engraved receiver, trigger guard and barrel, deluxe trap stock, approx. 1,000 mfg. 1972-1976.

	$795	$700	$650	$605	$495	$440	$385

MODEL SPORTSMAN - 48 SEMI-AUTO—12, 16, and 20 ga.'s, 26, 28, and 32 in. barrels, 3 shot, mechanical (solid breech) ejection system, various chokes, rounded receiver, checkered pistol grip stock, made 1949-1959. Approximately 275,000 manufactured.

	100%	98%	95%	90%	80%	70%	60%
	$310	$250	$220	$200	$175	$165	$140
Matted top barrel	$320	$265	$240	$220	$200	$175	$150
Vent rib	$360	$305	$275	$255	$230	$195	$165

Differs from Model 11-48 in that forearm sides have longitudinal grooves and also has capped grips.

MODEL 48B SELECT

	$420	$360	$310	$290	$245	$220	$195

MODEL 48D TOURNAMENT

	$1,100	$825	$715	$660	$605	$440	$415

MODEL 48F PREMIER

	$2,420	$2,035	$1,540	$1,210	$990	$770	$715

MODEL 48A RIOT GUN—12 ga. only, 20 in. plain barrel.

	$275	$220	$195	$165	$150	$140	$110

MODEL 48SA SKEET—26 in. barrel, skeet bore, ivory bead, made 1949-1960.

	$305	$275	$255	$230	$210	$195	$165
With vent rib	$360	$310	$285	$260	$230	$210	$195

MODEL 48SC TARGET

	$385	$360	$330	$305	$275	$250	$220

MODEL 48SD TOURNAMENT

	$1,100	$825	$715	$660	$605	$440	$415

MODEL 48SF PREMIER

	$2,200	$1,925	$1,650	$1,210	$990	$770	$715

MODEL 11-48 SEMI-AUTO—12, 16, 20, 28 (introduced 1952), and .410 (introduced 1954) ga.'s, recoil operated action, walnut stock, manufactured 1949-1968. Approximately 429,000 manufactured.

	$280	$250	$215	$185	$175	$160	$150

Add 15% - 40% for 28 and .410 ga.'s, $40 for vent rib.

Grading	100%	98%	95%	90%	80%	70%	60%

MODEL 58ADL "SPORTSMAN - 58" SEMI-AUTO—12, 16, or 20 ga., 26, 28, and 30 in. barrel, gas operation, various chokes, 3 shot, checkered pistol grip stock, scroll game scene engraved, made 1956-1963. Approximately 271,000 manufactured.

	$305	$275	$250	$220	$195	$140	$120
With vent rib	$360	$305	$275	$250	$220	$165	$140

MODEL 58BDL—same as 58ADL, with select wood.

	$360	$330	$305	$275	$220	$195	$165
With vent rib	$415	$360	$330	$305	$275	$220	$195

MODEL 58SA SKEET GUN—same as 58ADL, with 26 in. skeet bore vent rib barrel, skeet stock.

	$360	$330	$305	$275	$220	$195	$165

MODEL 58SC TARGET

	$495	$440	$415	$385	$330	$305	$275

MODEL 58D TOURNAMENT

	$825	$715	$635	$580	$525	$470	$440

MODEL 58SF PREMIER

	$1,650	$1,375	$1,210	$1,045	$965	$880	$800

Note: Models differ in grade of wood, and amount of engraving.

MODEL 878A "AUTOMASTER"—12 ga. gas operated semi-auto, 26, 28, and 30 in. barrels, action similar to Model 58, made 1959-1962. Approximately 62,000 manufactured. Add 15% for vent rib.

	$250	$220	$195	$170	$160	$150	$135

Barrels on this model are interchangeable with those on the Model 58.

SPORTSMAN SEMI-AUTO—12 ga. only, 2¾ in. chamber, 28 or 30 in. barrel, Model 1100 style action, vent rib standard, hardwood stock and forearm, 7¾ lbs. Manufactured 1985-86 only. Add $40 for Rem. chokes (new in 1986).

	$300	$260	$220	$195	$170	$160	$150

Last Mfg.'s Sug. Retail was $405.

MODEL 1100 SEMI-AUTO FIELD—12 (disc. in 1987), 16 (disc.), or 20 ga., 26, 28, and 30 in. barrels, various chokes, gas operated, checkered pistol grip stock, made 1963-1988. Rem. chokes became standard in 1987 (introduced in 1986 as $40 option). In 1985, vent ribs became standard on this model. Prices below assume vent rib and Rem. chokes.

	$395	$320	$275	$255	$220	$200	$180

Subtract $40 if without vent rib.
Subtract $45 if without Rem. chokes.

Last Mfg.'s Sug. Retail was $545.

This model is currently produced only in a Lightweight or Mag. 20 (3 in. chamber), 28, or .410 ga., since the release of the Model 11-87.

MODEL 1100 SPECIAL FIELD—12 and 20 ga.'s, 21 in. VR barrel, various chokes, gas operated, checkered straight grip stock, vent rib standard. New in 1984. Rem. chokes became standard in 1987.

Mfg.'s Sug. Retail	$545	$430	$365	$320	$265	$230	$210	$180

Subtract $45 if without Rem. chokes.

MODEL 1100 SMALL GAUGE—28 and .410 ga.'s, 25 in. barrel, scaled down receiver, skeet and field chokes, vent rib standard, made 1969-present.

Mfg.'s Sug. Retail	$587	$435	$335	$285	$260	$225	$200	$180

MODEL 1100 LIGHTWEIGHT—same as 1100, 20 ga. only, with mahogany stock and lightened receiver, 21, 26, or 28 in. barrel, vent rib became standard in 1985, 6½ lbs.

Mfg.'s Sug. Retail	$545	$405	$320	$285	$260	$220	$200	$180

Subtract $40 if without vent rib.

Model 1100 Youth—similar to Model 1100 Lightweight, except stock is 1 in. shorter and 21 in. barrel only.

Mfg.'s Sug. Retail	$532	$350	$300	$275	$255	$220	$200	$180

Grading	100%	98%	95%	90%	80%	70%	60%

MODEL 1100 LIGHTWEIGHT MAGNUM—chambered with 3 in. 20 ga. Mag., vent rib standard, Rem. chokes became standard in 1987.

Mfg.'s Sug. Retail	$545	$420	$340	$300	$275	$230	$200	$180

Subtract $40 if without vent rib.

MODEL 1100 MAGNUM DUCK GUN—same as 1100, in 12 (disc. in 1987) or 20 ga., 3 in. chamber, recoil pad, vent rib became standard in 1984, made 1963-1988. Rem. chokes became standard in 1987.

	$400	$325	$280	$260	$220	$200	$180

Add $80 for left-hand model (disc.in 1986).
Subtract $40 if without vent rib.
Subtract $45 if without Rem. chokes.

Last Mfg.'s Sug. Retail was $533.

Model 1100 Magnum Special Purpose (SP)—12 ga. only, low lustre finish on stock and forearm, sand blasted metal parts. Manufactured in 1985-86 only. Add $40 for Rem. chokes (new in 1986).

	$365	$300	$275	$255	$220	$200	$180

Last Mfg.'s Sug. Retail was $550.

MODEL 1100 "1 OF 3,000" FIELD—12 ga. only, limited edition, serial numbered 1-3,000, deluxe walnut, gold washed etched hunting scenes on receiver, 28 in. modified vent rib barrel, made in 1980.

	$1,100	$900	$600	$500	$425	$350	$300

MODEL 1100 DEER GUN—12 (disc. in 1987) and 20 ga.'s, 20 (20 ga. only) or 22 in. imp. cyl. barrel with rifle sights.

Mfg.'s Sug. Retail	$492	$330	$290	$265	$245	$225	$200	$180

Add $80 for left-hand model (disc.in 1986).

Model 1100 Special Purpose Deer (SP)—similar to Model 1100 Deer Gun, except has low lustre finish on stock and forearm, sandblasted metal parts. Manufactured in 1986 only.

	$335	$295	$275	$255	$220	$200	$180

Last Mfg.'s Sug. Retail was $495.

MODEL 1100 TOURNAMENT SKEET—12 (disc. in 1987) or 20 ga., 26 in. skeet bored barrel, optional Cutts Compensator, made 1963-present.

Mfg.'s Sug. Retail	$618	$420	$325	$280	$255	$220	$200	$180

Add $40 for left-hand model (disc.in 1986).

MODEL 1100 SMALL GAUGE TOURNAMENT SKEET—20, 28 or .410 ga., 25 in. vent. rib barrel, 6½-7¼ lbs., made 1969-present.

Mfg.'s Sug. Retail	$618	$440	$355	$310	$285	$235	$215	$200

MODEL 1100 SKEET CASED SET—28 and .410 ga.'s, 5,067 cased Skeet sets were manufactured in 1969 and 1970 only, walnut stock and forearm.

	$995	$800	$725	$675	$630	$600	$575

MODEL 1100TA TRAP—12 ga., 30 in. barrel, recoil pad on regular stock, available in left or right-hand, made 1979-86.

	$410	$330	$295	$270	$230	$210	$190

Last Mfg.'s Sug. Retail was $570.
Add $15 for Monte Carlo stock.
Add $50 for left-hand model.

MODEL 1100TB TRAP—12 ga., 30 in. vent rib full choke barrel, special trap stock, select wood, made 1963-1981.

	$435	$350	$300	$270	$230	$210	$190
Monte Carlo stock	$450	$360	$310	$280	$235	$220	$195

MODEL 1100 TOURNAMENT TRAP—12 ga., 30 in. vent rib full choke barrel, special trap stock, extra select wood, made 1979-86.

	$540	$480	$390	$345	$295	$255	$210

Last Mfg.'s Sug. Retail was $675.
Add $15 for Monte Carlo stock.

Grading	100%	98%	95%	90%	80%	70%	60%

MODEL 1100 DUCKS UNLIMITED—"DU" in serial number.

Remington has offered many variations of the Model 1100 specifically manufactured according to individual DU chapter specifications. The price of a DU 1100 varies substantially from the "DU point of purchase" to real market conditions. When contemplating a DU gun it is always important to know how many of that particular variation were manufactured. The Remington factory normally has this information unless the special DU work was subcontracted elsewhere. While most DU guns are good vehicles for fund raising, their collectability to date has been minimal. Actual market conditions indicate that unless production is truly limited, most DU firearms sell very close to the model it was derived from. Also, any collectability that does exist is for 100% guns new in the box with warranty papers. Used DU guns have values comparable to the standard model from which they are derived.

In addition to regular DU guns, Remington has also produced special editions including the 1982 Atlantic Flyway (dinner gun) and a 1981 DU Lt. 20 ga. and 12 ga. (dinner gun — 2,400 mfg. each), and a 1973 dinner gun (600 mfg.). These were rarer DU shotguns, and current values could vary significantly.

MODEL 1100 D-GRADE (TOURNAMENT)—custom order only, any gauge, made 1963 - present.

Mfg.'s Sug. Retail   **$2,291 $1,975 $1,870 $1,200**

MODEL 1100 F-GRADE (PREMIER)—custom order only, any gauge, made 1963 - present.

Mfg.'s Sug. Retail   **$4,720 $4,150 $3,835 $2,650**

MODEL 1100 F-GRADE W/GOLD (GOLD PREMIER)—with gold inlay, custom order only, made 1963 - present.

Mfg.'s Sug. Retail   **$7,079 $6,420 $5,735 $4,000**

Note: Grades differ in quality, grade of wood, and amount of engraving.

MODEL 11-87 PREMIER—12 ga. only (3 in. chamber), 26, 28, or 32 in. VR Rem. choked barrel, gas compensating action adaptable to all loads, stainless steel magazine tube, polished blue finish, satin finished and checkered walnut stock and forearm, solid recoil pad, 8⅛-8⅜ lbs., successor to Model 1100. Introduced in 1987.

Mfg.'s Sug. Retail   **$559 $475 $400 $325 $280 $240 $220 $200**
Add $53 for left-hand action.

Note: Model 11-87 Premier barrels are not interchangeable with Model 1100 barrels.

MODEL 11-87 PREMIER SPECIAL PURPOSE—12 ga. only (3 in. chamber), 26 or 30 in. VR Rem. choked barrel, parkerized metal with matte finish stock and forearm, vent recoil pad, includes camouflaged nylon sling, 8¼ lbs. New in 1987.

Mfg.'s Sug. Retail   **$559 $475 $400 $325 $280 $240 $220 $200**

MODEL 11-87 SPECIAL PURPOSE DEER GUN—12 ga. only (3 in. chamber), 21 in. IC or Rem. choked barrel with rifle sights, parkerized metal with matte finished stock and forearm, vent recoil pad, includes camouflaged nylon sling, 7¼ lbs. New in 1987.

Mfg.'s Sug. Retail   **$543 $460 $380 $315 $270 $240 $220 $200**
Add $53 for cantilever scope mount system.
Subtract $30 if fixed choke barrel.

Rem. chokes became standard on this model in 1989.

MODEL 11-87 PREMIER SKEET—12 ga. only, 26 in. VR Rem. choked barrel, deluxe walnut with quality cut checkering, 7¾ lbs.. New in 1987.

Mfg.'s Sug. Retail   **$597 $495 $400 $325 $275 $240 $220 $200**
Subtract $15 if without Rem. chokes.

MODEL 11-87 PREMIER TRAP—12 ga. only, 30 in. raised VR Rem. choked barrel, deluxe walnut with quality cut checkering, 8¼ lbs. New in 1987.

Mfg.'s Sug. Retail   **$618 $500 $380 $300 $260 $230 $215 $195**
Add $15 for Monte Carlo stock.
Subtract $13 if without Rem. chokes.

Grading	100%	98%	95%	90%	80%	70%	60%

MODEL SP-10—10 ga., 3½ in. chamber, semi-auto stainless steel gas system operation, lighter recoil than most 12 ga. Mag.'s, 26 or 30 in. barrel with ⅜ in. VR and Rem. chokes (2), checkered stock and forearm with low gloss satin finish, metal is matte finished, crossbolt safety, recoil pad, supplied with camo sling, approx. 11 lbs.

Mfg.'s Sug. Retail	$1,265	$1,175	$1,000	$900	$800	$725	$650	$595

The first 5,000 SP-10's have been assigned special serialization and will no doubt command premiums shortly.

This model is NOT a re-designed Ithaca Mag-10 and the parts are NOT interchangeable. The SP-10 is a new design.

SHOTGUNS: OVER/UNDER

MODEL 32—12 ga., double lock action, SST, separated barrels,26, 28, or 30 in. barrels with no rib, SR, or VR, approx. 15,000 mfg. 1932-1942.

	$2,500	$2,150	$1,800	$1,600	$1,400	$1,300	$1,175

Add 15% for SST.
Add 15% for vent or solid rib.

MODEL 32D TOURNAMENT

	$3,600	$3,250	$2,875	$2,400	$2,100	$1,750	$1,400

MODEL 32E EXPERT

	$4,300	$3,750	$3,300	$2,640	$2,200	$1,875	$1,525

MODEL 32F PREMIER

	$7,000	$6,000	$5,000	$4,400	$3,520	$2,750	$2,420

Note: Grades differ in quality, grade of wood, and amount of engraving.

MODEL 32 SKEET—same as 32A, with 26-28 in. skeet bored barrel, SST, made 1932-1942.

	$2,800	$2,475	$2,100	$1,900	$1,700	$1,500	$1,325

Add 10% for vent rib.

MODEL 32TC TARGET—same as 32A, with 30-32 in. vent rib, full choke barrels, trap style stock, made 1932-1942. Add 10% for SST.

	$3,000	$2,575	$2,200	$1,975	$1,750	$1,525	$1,325

MODEL 3200 FIELD—12 ga., 26, 28, and 30 in. barrels, vent rib, various chokes, boxlock, auto ejectors, single selective trigger, checkered pistol grip stock, separated barrels, made 1973-1980.

	$825	$750	$680	$640	$560	$525	$495

MODEL 3200 MAGNUM—12 ga., 3 in. chambers, 30 in. barrels, made 1975-1980.

	$1,050	$900	$775	$675	$600	$560	$525

MODEL 3200 SKEET—same as 3200 Field, with 26 or 28 in. skeet bored barrels, skeet style stock, made 1973-1980.

	$825	$750	$680	$640	$560	$525	$500

Model 3200 Four Ga. Set—includes 12, 20, 28, and .410 ga.'s, cased.

	$4,800	$4,400	$4,000	$3,650	$3,400	$3,200	$2,950

MODEL 3200 COMPETITION SKEET—same as 3200 Skeet, with scroll engraved frame and trigger guard, select wood, made 1973-1980.

	$1,250	$1,000	$900	$820	$750	$675	$600

MODEL 3200 TRAP—same as 3200 Field, with 30 or 32 in. barrels, trap stock, made 1973-1980.

	$850	$795	$740	$680	$640	$575	$540

MODEL 3200 SPECIAL TRAP—same as 3200 Trap, except fancy wood, made 1973-1981.

	$995	$825	$750	$700	$650	$600	$560

MODEL 3200 COMPETITION TRAP—same as 3200 Trap, with scroll engraving, made 1973-1981.

	$1,250	$1,000	$900	$820	$750	$675	$600

Grading	100%	98%	95%	90%	80%	70%	60%

MODEL 3200 PREMIER—12 ga., sold through Remington's International Division, 500 mfg. in 1975 only, patterned after "One of 1000" series, regular or Monte Carlo stock, 116 were engraved in Germany — add 25% + .

	$2,200	$1,800	$1,600	$1,400	$1,250	$1,100	$875

MODEL 3200 "ONE OF 1000"—limited edition, elaborate engraving, fancy wood, supplied in case, made in both skeet and trap models, 1,000 produced of each model in 1973 only.

	$2,000	$1,800	$1,600	$1,400	$1,300	$1,200	$1,100

RENETTE, GASTINE

MANUFACTURER AND RETAILER LOCATED IN PARIS, FRANCE.

Currently being manufactured with limited importation and distribution. No manufacturers' list price is shown in this section.

RIFLES: BOLT ACTION

MAUSER ACTION
No Mfg.'s Retail

	$2,700	$2,000	$1,850	$1,580	$1,430	$1,260	$1,000

DELUXE MAUSER ACTION
No Mfg.'s Retail

	$4,900	$4,100	$3,325	$2,500	$2,175	$1,875	$1,580

SHOTGUNS SXS

MODEL 105—12 and 20 ga., Anson and Deeley type triple bolt action, ejectors, double triggers, case hardened frame, 6 lbs. 8 oz.

	$1,800	$1,400	$1,250	$1,125	$1,000	$900	$800

MODEL 98—12 and 20 ga., Purdey type triple bolt action, ejectors, double triggers, case hardened frame, 6 lbs. 8 oz.

	$2,500	$2,000	$1,850	$1,580	$1,430	$1,260	$1,000

MODEL 202—12 and 20 ga., Purdey type triple bolt action, sidelocks, fine English engraving, first grade French walnut, ejectors, double triggers, coin finished receiver, 6 lbs. 10 oz.

	$3,325	$2,500	$2,175	$1,875	$1,580	$1,200	$1,000

MODEL 353—12 and 20 ga., Purdey type triple bolt action, hand detachable sidelocks, Chopper lump barrels, fine English engraving, first grade French walnut, ejectors, double triggers, case hardened receiver, best quality, 6 lbs. 10 oz.

	$8,900	$6,700	$6,250	$5,780	$5,150	$4,600	$4,150

DOUBLE RIFLES

The models listed below are older, discontinued models.

STANDARD TYPE G—9.3 x 74R, 7.65R, .30-06, and .375 H&H cal.'s, double bolt action, ejectors, reinforced stock, 23¾ in. barrels, 7 lbs. 6 oz., bouquet style engraving with deluxe walnut stock and forearm.

	$2,270	$1,700	$1,560	$1,480	$1,340	$1,250	$1,125

DELUXE TYPE R—9.3 x 74R, 7.65R, .30-06, and .375 H&H cal.'s, double bolt action, true sideplates, ejectors, reinforced stock, 23¾ in. barrels, 7 lbs. 6 oz., animal engraving with deluxe walnut stock and forearm.

	$2,700	$2,050	$1,850	$1,700	$1,520	$1,390	$1,260

PRESIDENT TYPE PT—9.3 x 74R, 7.65R, .30-06, and .375 H&H cal.'s, double bolt action, true sideplates, ejectors, reinforced stock, 23¾ in. barrels, 7 lbs. 6 oz., light engraving with gold line inlays, best quality walnut.

	$3,160	$2,370	$2,060	$1,850	$1,690	$1,570	$1,400

RHODE ISLAND ARMS COMPANY

HOPE VALLEY, RI.

MORRONE O/U—12 and 20 ga.'s, 26 and 28 in. plain barrels, boxlock, extractors, single trigger, checkered straight or pistol grip stock, made 1949-1953, only 500 of these guns were produced, 450 in 12 ga., and 50 in 20 ga., very few with vent rib, they are quite rare although collector interest is not overwhelming.

		$1,100	$880	$770	$660	$550	$495	$440

Add 20% for 20 gauge.
Add 20% for vent rib.

RICHLAND ARMS COMPANY

PREVIOUS IMPORTER (UNTIL 1986) LOCATED IN BLISSFIELD, MI. BELOW LISTED SHOTGUNS WERE SPANISH MANUFACTURED.

SHOTGUNS

MODEL 80 LS SINGLE SHOT—12, 20, or .410 ga.'s, 26 or 28 in. full choke barrel. Manufactured in 1986 only.

		$140	$120	$110	$100	$90	$80	$70

Last Mfg.'s Sug. Retail was $162.

MODEL 711 MAGNUM SXS—10 ga., 3½ in. chamber, 12 ga., 3 in. chamber, 32 in. full and full, 30 in. full and full, 20, 28, and .410 ga.'s also available on special order, hammerless, boxlock, extractors, checkered, walnut stock, recoil pad, made 1963-1985 in Spain.

12 gauge	$340	$295	$265	$250	$230	$210	$190
20 gauge	$450	$340	$295	$260	$230	$210	$195

MODEL 707 DELUXE SXS—12 and 20 ga.'s, 3 in. chambers, 26, 28, and 30 in. barrels, various chokes, boxlock, extractors, double triggers, checkered stock and forend, made 1963-1972 in Spain.

		$330	$305	$290	$275	$250	$230	$210

MODEL 200 FIELD GRADE SXS—12, 16, 20, 28, and .410 ga.'s, 22, 26, and 28 in. barrels, various chokes, Anson & Deeley boxlock, extractors, double triggers, checkered stock, 6 lbs. 2 oz. - 7 lbs. 4 oz., made 1963-1985 in Spain.

		$320	$285	$255	$225	$195	$175	$150

Last Mfg.'s Sug. Retail was $379.

MODEL 202 ALL PURPOSE—same as Field, except 2 sets of barrels, 12 and 20 ga. only, made 1963-discontinued in Spain.

		$305	$260	$230	$220	$195	$165	$150

MODEL 41 ULTRA O/U—20, 28, and .410 ga.'s, 3 in. chambers (.410 ga. only), single non-selective trigger, 26 or 28 in. barrels, extractors, vent rib, engraved silver finished receiver, select checkered walnut stock and forearm, 6 lbs. 2 oz. Importation discontinued in 1986.

		$265	$220	$210	$200	$190	$180	$170

Last Mfg.'s Sug. Retail was $298.

MODEL 747 O/U—20 ga. only, 3 in. chambers, boxlock action, vent rib and barrels, SST, extractors. Importation discontinued in 1986.

		$420	$350	$325	$310	$295	$280	$265

Last Mfg.'s Sug. Retail was $464.

MODEL 757 O/U—12 ga., 3 in. chambers, boxlock action with Greener crossbolt, vent barrels and rib, double triggers, extractors, walnut stock and forearm, 7 lbs. 4 oz. New in 1986. Add $70 for multi-chokes (Model 7570). Importation discontinued in 1986.

		$290	$260	$230	$215	$200	$185	$170

Last Mfg.'s Sug. Retail was $325.

Grading	100%	98%	95%	90%	80%	70%	60%

MODEL 787 O/U—12 ga. only, 3 in. chambers, boxlock action with silver finish, single trigger, vent barrels and rib, extractors, walnut stock with recoil pad, is supplied with 5 interchangeable choke tubes, 7¼ lbs. Made in 1986 only.

	$435	$375	$340	$310	$295	$280	$265

Last Mfg.'s Sug. Retail was $471.

MODEL 808 O/U—12 ga., 26, 28, and 30 in. barrels, various chokes, boxlock, extractors, checkered stock, made 1963-1968 in Italy.

	$420	$360	$330	$315	$290	$270	$230

MODEL 828 O/U—20 ga., single non-selective trigger, extractors, engraved, only 250 imported.

	$695	$635	$575	$510	$460	$400	$350

RIEDL RIFLE COMPANY

SINGLE SHOT RIFLE—available in any caliber, 22-30 in. barrel, rack and pinion action, lever trigger guard activated, fully adj. trigger, select walnut stock, basically custom made.

	$495	$470	$440	$415	$385	$330	$305

Stainless barrel

	$560	$535	$505	$480	$450	$395	$370

RIGBY, JOHN & CO. (GUNMAKERS), LTD.

MANUFACTURE BEGAN IN DUBLIN, IRELAND IN 1735. THE FIRST LONDON BRANCH WAS OPENED IN 1865 AND THE DUBLIN PREMISES WERE CLOSED THREE YEARS LATER. THE FIRM BECAME A COMPANY IN 1900, AND HAS BEEN RESPONSIBLE FOR MANY OF THE LARGE CALIBER DEVELOPMENTS IN BOTH RIFLES AND AMMUNITION.

Rigby is one of the world's finest weapons makers. A good portion of the guns they manufacture were custom built to customer specifications. They were chambered for the large black powder express cartridges used for dangerous game in Africa and Asia. The modern Rigby guns follow this same tradition.

We will list the modern Rigby Guns with approximate values but strongly urge that if purchase or sale is contemplated, professional appraisal be utilized.

Due to the recent devaluation of the U.S. dollar, prices may fluctuate rapidly on this trademark. Current values are based on the exchange rates at this writing ($1.75 per pound).

RIFLES: BOLT ACTION & SIDE BY SIDE

RIGBY MAGAZINE RIFLE—Mauser action (pre-1939), bolt action, various standard cal.'s including .243 Win., .270, .275 Rigby, 7mm x 57mm, .30-06, .300 H&H, .300 Win. Mag., .308, 7mm Rem. Mag., and .375 H&H, 3-5 shot mag., 21-24 in. barrel, checkered half pistol grip stock, folding leaf sight.

Mfg.'s Sug. Retail	$4,375	$4,375	$3,700	$3,275	$2,850	$2,400	$2,000	$1,700

Add $350 for .375 H&H, .404 Rigby, or .458 Win. Mag. cal.

The .416 Rigby cal. is also available on special order only — prices start at $8,750.

Above values are minimums for the Standard Rigby bolt action rifle. The factory quotes a price range of $4,375-$8,750 depending on the grade of wood, engraving, telescopic sight, case, or other details.

LIGHTWEIGHT MAGAZINE RIFLE—similar to Standard, with 24 in. barrel.

Mfg.'s Sug. Retail	$4,375	$4,375	$3,700	$3,275	$2,850	$2,400	$2,000	$1,700

.416 RIGBY MAGAZINE RIFLE—similar to Standard Rigby rifle, except is available in .375 H&H, .404, .416 Rigby, .458 Win. Mag., and .505 cal.'s only, modified Brno square bridge magnum action, 4 shot mag., 21-24 in. barrel, approx. 10 lbs.

Mfg.'s Sug. Retail	$6,125	$6,125	$5,200	$4,300	$3,700	$3,000	$2,500	$1,995

Add $680 for .505 cal.

Grading	100%	98%	95%	90%	80%	70%	60%

.350 MAGNUM MAGAZINE RIFLE—.350 Magnum cal.

	100%	98%	95%	90%	80%	70%	60%
	$3,995	$3,400	$2,950	$2,600	$2,300	$2,000	$1,700

Values assume out of production models.

SINGLE SHOT FALLING BLOCK—Farquharson lever actuated action, various English and European cal.'s, 24 in. barrel, ejector, checkered pistol grip stock, deluxe finish and engraving.

	100%	98%	95%	90%	80%	70%	60%
	$4,100	$3,400	$2,800	$2,400	$2,000	$1,600	$1,250

BEST QUALITY SIDELOCK EJECTOR DOUBLE RIFLE—.275 Mag., .350 Mag., .416, .458 Win. Mag., .465, or .470 Nitro Express cal., 24-28 in. barrels, sidelocks, folding express rear sight, checkered pistol grip stock, deluxe finish and engraving.

	100%	98%	95%	90%	80%	70%	60%
Mfg.'s Sug. Retail $35,000	$35,000	$29,000	$24,000	$20,000	$17,500	$15,000	$12,750

Add $3,500 for .577 cal.

Subtract 35% without ejectors.

Rigby sidelock double rifles can instantly be recognized by their contoured sideplates.

John Rigby & Co. will also build a .600 Nitro Express — price available by quotation only.

SECOND QUALITY BOXLOCK EJECTOR DOUBLE RIFLE—same as Best Quality, with boxlock.

	100%	98%	95%	90%	80%	70%	60%
	$16,500	$13,000	$11,500	$9,500	$8,500	$7,500	$6,500

Subtract 35% without ejectors.

Values above are for larger calibers, smaller cal.'s could have less value than listed.

THIRD QUALITY BOXLOCK EJECTOR DOUBLE RIFLE—same as Second Quality, with plainer wood and less engraving.

	100%	98%	95%	90%	80%	70%	60%
	$12,750	$10,750	$9,750	$8,750	$7,350	$6,350	$5,000

Subtract 35% without ejectors.

Values above are for larger calibers, smaller cal.'s could have less value than listed.

SHOTGUNS

BOXLOCK DOUBLE BARREL SHOTGUN—all ga.'s, barrel lengths and chokes to order, checkered stock to order, auto ejectors, double triggers.

Chatsworth Grade

	100%	98%	95%	90%	80%	70%	60%
	$4,500	$3,500	$3,000	$2,500	$2,000	$1,600	$1,200

Sackville Grade—deluxe engraved.

	100%	98%	95%	90%	80%	70%	60%
	$5,900	$5,000	$4,500	$3,750	$3,100	$2,650	$2,200

20 gauge — add 20%.

28 gauge — add 40%.

.410 gauge — add 60%.

Boxlock Game Gun—12, 20, or 28 ga., traditional deep scroll engraving, current mfg.

	100%	98%	95%	90%	80%	70%	60%
Mfg.'s Sug. Retail $7,000	$7,000	$5,750	$5,000	$4,500	$3,750	$3,100	$2,650

This is John Rigby's only current production boxlock shotgun.

SIDELOCK DOUBLE BARREL SHOTGUN—all ga.'s, barrel lengths and chokes to specifications, double triggers, auto ejectors stocked to order.

Sandringham Grade

	100%	98%	95%	90%	80%	70%	60%
	$9,500	$7,500	$6,000	$5,000	$4,450	$3,775	$2,950

Regal Grade—deluxe engraved.

	100%	98%	95%	90%	80%	70%	60%
	$12,500	$10,000	$8,750	$7,500	$6,400	$5,250	$4,250

20 gauge — add 20%.

28 gauge — add 40%.

.410 gauge — add 60%.

Sidelock Game Gun—12 or 20 ga., engraving similar to Best Quality SxS rifle, current mfg.

	100%	98%	95%	90%	80%	70%	60%
Mfg.'s Sug. Retail $21,000	$21,000	$16,500	$13,000	$11,500	$9,400	$8,200	$6,950

Grading	100%	98%	95%	90%	80%	70%	60%

RIPAMONTI, GUY

MANUFACTURER LOCATED IN SAINT ETIENNE, FRANCE. SHOTGUNS IMPORTED AND DISTRIBUTED EXCLUSIVELY BY WES GILPIN LOCATED IN DALLAS, TX. RIFLES IMPORTED AND DISTRIBUTED EXCLUSIVELY BY MORTON'S LIMITED LOCATED IN LEXINGTON, KY.

DOUBLE RIFLES

For further information regarding Ripamonti double rifles, Morton's Ltd. should be contacted directly.

MODEL SE IX SIDE BY SIDE—9.3 X 74R cal., scalloped boxlock action with triple Purdey locks, iron sights, 23½ in. barrels, extensive engraving on coin finished receiver, DT's, English straight stock. Importation began in 1988.

Mfg.'s Sug. Retail **$13,939 $13,939 $10,000 $8,750 $7,800 $7,000 $6,400 $5,800**

MODEL SE VIII SIDE BY SIDE—similar to Model SE IX except has pistol grip stock and more elaborate engraving with gold inlays. Importation began in 1989.

Mfg.'s Sug. Retail **$15,238 $15,238 $12,000 $10,000 $8,750 $7,800 $7,000 $6,400**

MODEL SE VII SIDE BY SIDE—9.3 X 74R cal., scalloped rounded triple Helix action, 23½ in. barrels, DT's, extensive engraving on coin finished receiver, pistol grip Monte Carlo stock. Importation began in 1989.

Mfg.'s Sug. Retail **$11,238 $11,238 $8,750 $7,800 $7,000 $6,400 $5,800 $5,400**

JAEGER MODEL—specially manufactured for Paul Jaeger Inc. located in Grand Junction, TN.

Mfg.'s Sug. Retail **$9,413 $9,413 $7,000 $5,500 $4,750 $4,000 $3,400 $3,000**

MODEL SI IV OVER/UNDER—9.3 X 74R cal., reinforced boxlock action, 23½ in. barrels, DT's, extensive engraving. Importation began in 1989.

Mfg.'s Sug. Retail **$7,133 $7,133 $5,500 $4,750 $4,000 $3,400 $2,850 $2,300**

SHOTGUNS

Ripamonti shotguns are available in 12, 16, or 20 ga. in boxlock actions, 12 or 20 ga. in sidelock actions.

SHOTGUNS: SIDE BY SIDE—Ripamonti S X S shotguns start at $8,490 (Model SE V boxlock) and go up to $22,490 (Model JL sidelock) depending on embellishments and other special order features. Other models include Model SE IV and Model SE VI.

For further information regarding Ripamonti shotguns Wes Gilpin should be contacted directly.

RIZZINI

MANUFACTURED IN BRESCIA, ITALY. CURRENTLY IMPORTED BY W.L. MOORE & CO. LOCATED IN WEST LAKE VILLAGE, CA.

Rizzini shotguns are made by individual custom order only (about 25 are made a year). Prices below do not include engraving (prices range from $3,000-$7,500) and are subject to the fluctuation of the U.S. dollar.

Due to the recent devaluation of the U.S. dollar, prices may fluctuate rapidly on this trademark.

SHOTGUNS

BOXLOCK EJECTOR—12 or 20 ga., select walnut, inspection plate, various barrel lengths.

Mfg.'s Sug. Retail **$14,200 $11,800 $9,700 $8,850 $7,100 $6,200 $5,500 $4,750**

28 or .410 ga.—otherwise same as above.

Mfg.'s Sug. Retail **$15,700 $12,600 $10,750 $9,125 $7,950 $6,675 $6,000 $5,375**

SIDELOCK EJECTOR—12 or 20 ga., H&H patterned sidelocks, select circassian walnut, various barrel lengths.

Mfg.'s Sug. Retail **$22,500 $18,000 $15,700 $12,500 $10,400 $9,150 $7,500 $6,250**

28 or .410 ga.—otherwise same as above.

Mfg.'s Sug. Retail **$25,200 $20,200 $18,650 $15,750 $13,250 $11,250 $9,400 $8,000**

ROHM

WEST GERMANY

DERRINGER—.22 LR, blued, copy of Remington O/U derringer. Excellently made, but half-cock safety is old design and could fail if dropped. No longer imported.

		$150	$115	$95	$85	$75	$65	$55

ROSS RIFLE COMPANY

QUEBEC, CANADA.

CANADIAN 1907 MARK II—.303 Brit. cal., bolt action, straight pull, 28 in. barrel, pre-WWII.

		$295	$250	$200	$180	$160	$140	$120

MODEL 1910 SPORTING RIFLE—similar action as 1907, .280 Ross and .303 Brit. cal.'s, checkered Sporter stock, leaf sights, made 1910-1920.

		$275	$225	$200	$180	$160	$140	$120

Note: Many experts state this rifle is unsafe to fire.

ROSSI

MANUFACTURED BY AMADE ROSSI S.A., LOCATED IN S. LEOPOLDO, BRAZIL. CURRENTLY IMPORTED BY INTERARMS, LOCATED IN ALEXANDRIA, VA.

REVOLVERS: DOUBLE ACTION

MODEL 31—.38 Spl., 5 shot, 4 in. medium barrel, target trigger and hammer, 22 oz. Add $5 for nickel. Discontinued in 1985.

		$120	$105	$95	$85	$75	$70	$65

Last Mfg.'s Sug. Retail was $139.

MODEL 51—.22 LR, 6 shot, 6 in. barrel, blue only, adj. sights. Discontinued in 1985.

		$125	$110	$100	$90	$85	$80	$75

Last Mfg.'s Sug. Retail was $149.

Sportsman 511—.22 LR only, stainless steel, 4 in. barrel, with matted rib, adj. rear sight, 6 shot, 30 oz., hardwood stocks. New in 1986.

Mfg.'s Sug. Retail		$235	$190	$160	$125			

MODEL 68—.38 Spl., 5 round, 2 or 3 in. barrel.

Mfg.'s Sug. Retail		$180	$145	$120	$100	$90	$80	$70	$65

Add $15 for nickel.
Add $5 for 2 in. barrel.

MODEL 69—.32 S&W, 6 round, 3 in. barrel, walnut grips. Discontinued in 1985.

		$120	$105	$95	$85	$75	$70	$65

Add $5 for nickel.

Last Mfg.'s Sug. Retail was $139.

MODEL 70—.22 cal, 6 round, 3 in. barrel. Add $5 for nickel. Discontinued in 1985.

		$120	$105	$95	$85	$75	$70	$65

Last Mfg.'s Sug. Retail was $139.

MODEL 84 STAINLESS—.38 Spl., 6 shot, 3 or 4 in. solid raised rib barrel, standard service sights, checkered hardwood grips, 27½ oz. Imported 1985-86 only.

		$190	$155	$125				

Last Mfg.'s Sug. Retail was $205.

MODEL 851 STAINLESS—.38 Spl., 3 or 4 in. vent rib barrel, 6 shot, walnut grips, adj. rear sight, 27½ oz. New in 1985.

Mfg.'s Sug. Retail		$245	$200	$165	$135			

This model was previously the Model 85 Stainless.

ROSSI, cont.

MODEL 88 STAINLESS—.38 Spl., 5 shot, stainless steel construction, 2 or 3 in. barrel, hardwood grips, 21 oz.

	Mfg.'s Sug. Retail	$215	$175	$135	$110			

MODEL 89 STAINLESS—.32 S&W cal. only, 6 shot, 3 in. barrel. Imported 1985-86. Reintroduced in 1989.

Mfg.'s Sug. Retail $210 $170 $135 $115

MODEL 94—.38 Spl., 6 shot, 3 or 4 in. barrel, blued finish only, 27½ oz. Imported 1985-1988.

$160 $140 $120 $110 $95 $85 $75

Last Mfg.'s Sug. Retail was $185.

MODEL 951—.38 Spl., 6 shot, 3 or 4 in. vent. rib barrel, blued finish only, 27½ oz. New in 1985.

Mfg.'s Sug. Retail $225 $185 $155 $135 $120 $110 $100 $90

This model was previously the Model 95.

MODEL 971—.357 Mag., 4 in. solid rib barrel with internal ejector shroud, 6 shot, adj. rear sight, blue only, hardwood grips, 36 oz. Importation began in 1988.

Mfg.'s Sug. Retail $245 $200 $165 $145 $135 $125 $115 $105

Model 971 Stainless—.357 Mag., 4 or 6 in. solid rib barrel with full shroud, combat style rubber grips, adj. rear sight, 35.4 - 40.5 oz. Importation began in 1989.

Prices have yet to be announced on this model.

RIFLES

MODEL 92 SRC LEVER ACTION—.357 Mag, .44 Mag, and .44-40 cal.'s, copy of Win. Model 92, 16 (Model 92 SRS) or 20 in. round barrel, 5-5¾ lbs. Also available in matte blue finish at no extra charge.

Mfg.'s Sug. Retail $282 $225 $190 $150 $125 $110 $100 $90
   Add $15 for .44 Spl./.44 Mag./.44-40 (disc.) cal.

.44-40 and .44 Mag. cal.'s are Model 65 SRC's.

Blue Engraved—with etched engraving and special wood.

Mfg.'s Sug. Retail $327 $275 $225 $175

Gold or Chrome Engraved—either gold (disc. in 1987) or chrome (disc.) finish with special wood.

$280 $230 $185 $150 $130 $120 $110

Last Mfg.'s Sug. Retail was $330.

MODEL 62 SA SLIDE ACTION—.22 LR cal., copy of Win. 1890 "gallery" model, rifle (23 in. barrel) or carbine (16½ in. barrel) available, takedown action, round or octagonal barrel, 12 or 13 shot tube mag.

Mfg.'s Sug. Retail $195 $150 $130 $110 $95 $85 $80 $75
   Add $15 for nickel finish.
   Add $25 for octagonal barrel.

Model 62 SAC—similar to Model 62 SA, except has 16½ in. barrel with full length mag. tube (12 shot), 4¼ lbs. Importation began in 1988.

Mfg.'s Sug. Retail $195 $150 $130 $110 $95 $85 $80 $75
   Add $15 for nickel finish.

Model 62 SA Stainless—similar to regular model, except is stainless steel. Imported in 1986 only.

$165 $145 $120

Last Mfg.'s Sug. Retail was $192.

MODEL 59—.22 Mag. version of Model 62 SA, 10 shot mag., 5.5 lbs.

Mfg.'s Sug. Retail $240 $185 $155 $130 $120 $110 $100 $90

MODEL 65 SRC—.44 Spl./.44 Mag. cal., lever action carbine, 20 in. barrel, full tube mag. holding 10 rounds, iron sights, 5¾ lbs. Importation began in 1989.

Mfg.'s Sug. Retail $297 $240 $185 $160 $145 $135 $125 $115

ROSSI, cont.

Grading	100%	98%	95%	90%	80%	70%	60%

SHOTGUNS

OVERLUND SxS—12, 20, or .410 ga., exposed hammers, 20 (Coach Model), 26, or 28 in. barrels, double triggers. Importation disc. in 1988.

	$275	$230	$185	$155	$140	$125	$115

> Add $5 for .410 ga.

> Last Mfg.'s Sug. Retail was $332.

SQUIRE SxS—12, 20, or .410 ga., hammerless, 20, 26 or 28 in. barrels, double triggers, raised matted rib, beavertail forearm, pistol grip, hardwood stock, 3 in. chambers. Add $5 for .410 ga. New in 1985.

Mfg.'s Sug. Retail	$340	$300	$245	$195	$160	$150	$140	$130

> Add $5 for .410 ga.

ROTTWEIL

MANUFACTURED IN ROTTWEIL, WEST GERMANY. PREVIOUSLY IMPORTED BY DYNAMIT NOBEL OF AMERICA LOCATED IN NORTHVALE, NJ.

SHOTGUNS

MODEL 650 FIELD O/U—12 ga. only, 28 in. barrels with vent rib, ejectors, single trigger, select checkered walnut, multi-choked with 6 choke tubes, lightly engraved, coin finished receiver. Importation discontinued in 1986.

	$750	$650	$595	$550	$500	$460	$435

> Last Mfg.'s Sug. Retail was $850.

MODEL 72 FIELD O/U—12 ga. only, 28 in. vent barrels and rib, sand blasted receiver, select walnut with checkered stock and forearm, single trigger, ejectors. Importation disc. in 1987.

	$1,850	$1,650	$1,450	$1,200	$1,000	$850	$700

> Last Mfg.'s Sug. Retail was $2,295.

MODEL 72 AMERICAN SKEET O/U—12 ga. only, 26¾ in. barrels, vent rib, ejectors, select French walnut, marginal engraving on sand blasted receiver, single trigger, 7½ lbs. Importation disc. in 1987.

	$1,850	$1,650	$1,450	$1,200	$1,000	$850	$700

> Last Mfg.'s Sug. Retail was $2,295.

> This model was distributed exclusively by Paxton Arms, located in Dallas, TX.

MODEL 72 AAT SINGLE BARREL TRAP—12 ga. only, adj. American trap (AAT), barrel features adj. point of impact, 34 in. barrel bored full, high vent rib. Importation discontinued in 1986.

	$1,400	$1,200	$1,000	$850	$700	$650	$600

> Last Mfg.'s Sug. Retail was $2,295.

MODEL 72 AT O/U—12 ga. only, 32 in. IM & F barrels, vent rib and barrels, sand blasted receiver, checkered select walnut stock and forearm, non-adj. point of impact, single trigger ejectors. Importation disc. in 1987.

	$1,850	$1,650	$1,450	$1,200	$1,000	$850	$700

> Last Mfg.'s Sug. Retail was $2,295.

MODEL 72 AAT COMBINATION—12 ga. only, comes with 2 single barrels (32 and 34 in.) that have adj. impacts. Importation discontinued in 1986.

	$2,450	$2,100	$1,850	$1,600	$1,450	$1,250	$995

> Last Mfg.'s Sug. Retail was $2,850.

> **72 AAT Combination**—supplied with 1 single adj. barrel and 32 in. O/U barrels.

	$2,450	$2,100	$1,850	$1,600	$1,450	$1,250	$995

> Last Mfg.'s Sug. Retail was $2,850.

ROTTWEIL, cont.

Grading	100%	98%	95%	90%	80%	70%	60%

MODEL 72 AAT 3-BARREL SET—12 ga. only, supplied with 2 single barrels (32 and 34 in.) with adj. impact and 1 set of 32 in. O/U barrels bored IM & F. Importation discontinued in 1986.

	$2,850	$2,600	$2,300	$2,000	$1,800	$1,600	$1,400

Last Mfg.'s Sug. Retail was $3,250.

MODEL 72 INTERNATIONAL TRAP—12 ga. only, O/U 30 in. barrels bored IM & F with extra high rib. Importation disc. in 1987.

	$1,850	$1,650	$1,450	$1,200	$1,000	$850	$700

Last Mfg.'s Sug. Retail was $2,295.

MODEL 72 INTERNATIONAL SKEET—12 ga. only, 26¾ in. barrels, vent rib, select walnut stock and forearm. Importation disc. in 1987.

	$1,850	$1,650	$1,450	$1,200	$1,000	$850	$700

Last Mfg.'s Sug. Retail was $2,295.

ROYAL AMERICAN SHOTGUNS

PREVIOUSLY IMPORTED BY ROYAL ARMS INTERNATIONAL, LOCATED IN WOODLAND HILLS, CA.

SHOTGUNS

MODEL 100 O/U—12 or 20 ga., 2¾ in. chambers, double triggers, extractors, vent rib and barrels. Imported 1985-87 only.

	$325	$265	$240	$220	$200	$180	$170

Last Mfg.'s Sug. Retail was $390.

Add $40 for above model with 3 in. chambers, single trigger, and auto ejectors.

MODEL 600 BOXLOCK SxS—12, 20, 28, and .410 ga.'s, sideplates, silver finished receiver, 3 in. chambers, single trigger, auto ejectors. Imported 1985-87 only.

	$365	$295	$265	$235	$210	$195	$180

Last Mfg.'s Sug. Retail was $420.

Deduct 25% for double triggers and 2¾ in. chambers.

MODEL 800 SIDELOCK SxS—12, 20, 28, and .410 ga.'s, sidelocks with sideplates, silver finished receiver, 3 in. chambers, single trigger, checkered straight grip stock with select walnut, auto ejectors. Imported 1985-87 only.

	$775	$650	$595	$550	$500	$460	$435

Last Mfg.'s Sug. Retail was $899.

RUBY

MANUFACTURED IN EIBAR, SPAIN.

MILITARY TYPE—trade name for Spanish auto pistol fashioned after M1911 Colt's, cal. 7.65mm, mag. release at bottom of grip, fixed sights. No longer produced.

	$115	$85	$80	$75	$70	$65	$60

RUGER

SEE STURM, RUGER, & CO. SECTION IN THIS TEXT.

RUSSIAN SERVICE PISTOL AND RIFLE

TULA ARSENAL.

MODEL TT30 & TT33 TOKAREV AUTOMATIC—design borrowed from Colt 1911 Petter-type unitized trigger/hammer assembly, 7.62mm Russian, 8 shot, 4½ in. barrel, blue, made 1930-1954. Add 20% for TT30 model.

	100%	98%	95%	90%	80%	70%	60%
	$360	$335	$280	$225	$165	$145	$110
M.244ADL.	$330	$305	$250	$200	$150	$120	$95

NAGANT REVOLVER—7 shot, cylinder comes forward to seal barrel. Add 10% for pre-communist Imperial marked.

	100%	98%	95%	90%	80%	70%	60%
	$260	$225	$185	$165	$135	$115	$100

MAKAROV MD—9mm, clip fed double action, post-war manufacture.

	100%	98%	95%	90%	80%	70%	60%
	$1,075	$950	$850	$800	$750	$700	$650

TOKAREV M38 & M40 RIFLE—semi-auto Russian issue bolt action. Add 20% for M38, 100% for scoped sniper.

	100%	98%	95%	90%	80%	70%	60%
	$365	$310	$270	$250	$230	$210	$195

NOTES

S

S.A.C.M.
CHOLET, FRANCE.

Grading	100%	98%	95%	90%	80%	70%	60%

FRENCH MODEL 1935A—semi-auto, 7.65mm long, 8 shot, 4.3 in. barrel, blue, fixed sights, checkered stocks, used by French troops in WWII and Indo-China 1945-1954, made 1935-1945.

		100%	98%	95%	90%	80%	70%	60%
		$220	$205	$180	$165	$150	$140	$110

SAE
SPAIN AMERICA ENTERPRISES INC. (SAE) PREVIOUS IMPORTER OF FELIX SARASQUETA SHOTGUNS FROM SPAIN. SAE WAS LOCATED IN MIAMI, FL.

SHOTGUNS: O/U

MODEL 70—12 or 20 ga., 3 in. chambers, boxlock action, single trigger, ejectors, 26 in. VR barrel, European checkered walnut stock and forearm, standard finish is blue, Model 70 multi-choke has silver finished action with Florentine engraving and low gloss stock finish. Imported in 1988 only.

		100%	98%	95%	90%	80%	70%	60%
		$400	$275	$260	$245	$230	$215	$195

Add $120 for multi-chokes (27 in. barrel).

Last Mfg.'s Sug. Retail was $598.

MODEL 66C—12 ga. only, 26 in. Skeet or 30 in. F&M VR barrels, boxlock with engraved sideplates including 24Kt. inlays, Monte Carlo deluxe stock and beavertail forearm. Imported in 1988 only.

		100%	98%	95%	90%	80%	70%	60%
		$950	$725	$650	$575	$495	$450	$395

Last Mfg.'s Sug. Retail was $1,544.

SHOTGUNS: SxS

MODEL 210S—12, 20, or .410 ga., 3 in. chambers, boxlock action, double triggers, extractors, silver finished receiver with light engraving, approx. 7 lbs. Imported in 1988 only.

		100%	98%	95%	90%	80%	70%	60%
		$420	$280	$260	$245	$230	$215	$195

Last Mfg.'s Sug. Retail was $638.

MODEL 340X—12 or 20 ga., sidelock action, 26 in. barrels with 2¾ in. chambers, H&H bolt lock action, case hardened finish with moderate scroll engraving, straight grip select walnut stock and forearm with high gloss finish. Imported in 1988 only.

		100%	98%	95%	90%	80%	70%	60%
		$700	$550	$495	$460	$430	$395	$375

Last Mfg.'s Sug. Retail was $1,170.

MODEL 209E—12, 20, or .410 ga., H&H type sidelock action, 26 or 28 in. barrels with 2¾ in. chambers, hand engraved coin finished receiver, select checkered walnut stock and forearm, double triggers. Imported in 1988 only.

		100%	98%	95%	90%	80%	70%	60%
		$925	$700	$650	$575	$495	$450	$395

Last Mfg.'s Sug. Retail was $1,490.

S K B ARMS COMPANY
MANUFACTURED IN TOKYO, JAPAN. CURRENTLY IMPORTED AND DISTRIBUTED BY THE NEW SKB COMPANY U.S.A. LOCATED IN MANHEIN, PA. SKB HAS BEEN MANUFACTURING FIREARMS SINCE 1855.

Grading	100%	98%	95%	90%	80%	70%	60%

Formerly imported by Ithaca. In 1987, importation resumed on most SKB models. While the model numbers have changed, quality is similar to those models imported previously by Ithaca. In most cases, the newer models are derived closely from their previous counterparts. Listings below will differentiate older discontinued models from currently imported models.

SHOTGUNS: O/U AND SINGLE SHOT

MODEL 500—12, 20, 28, or .410 ga., field grade, vent rib, selective ejector, 26 in. imp. cyl. and mod., 28 in. full and mod., and 30 in. full and mod., checkered stock, made in Japan by SKB in 1966-1979.

	100%	98%	95%	90%	80%	70%	60%
	$525	$440	$395	$365	$330	$300	$275

Add 25% for 28 or .410 ga.
Add 15% for 20 ga.

Model 500 Magnum—12 ga., 3 in. Mag., field grade, same as 500, except 3 in. Mag. chambers.

	$625	$455	$410	$385	$355	$320	$290

MODEL 505 O/U—similar to Model 500, 3 in. chambers, 12 and 20 ga. barrels are supplied with choke tubes, single selective trigger, ejectors, checkered walnut stock with recoil pad and forearm.

No Mfg.'s Retail	$750	$675	$575	$500	$460	$420	$375

Add $455 for combo package.

The combo package includes either 12/20 ga. barrels with inter-chokes or 28/.410 ga. barrels.

Model 505 Trap O/U—12 ga., 30 or 32 in. fixed choke barrels with or without Monte Carlo stock, high rib.

No Mfg.'s Retail	$775	$650	$525	$475	$430	$395	$360

Add $370 for O/U Trap Combo.

The above Combo includes one set of O/U Trap barrels and a top single Trap barrel.

Model 505 Trap Single Barrel—12 ga., 32 or 34 in. barrel with multi-chokes, regular or Monte Carlo stock.

No Mfg.'s Retail	$775	$625	$495	$460	$420	$375	$345

Model 505 Skeet—12, 20, 28, or .410 ga., 28 in. barrels with multi-chokes.

No Mfg.'s Retail	$775	$690	$595	$525	$480	$440	$400

Model 505 3-Ga. Skeet Set—includes 20, 28, and .410 ga. extra Skeet barrels, aluminum case.

No Mfg.'s Retail	$1,850	$1,575	$1,300	$1,150	$1,000	$925	$850

Model 505 Sporting Clay—28 in. multi-choke barrels, dimensioned for Sporting Clay competition.

No Mfg.'s Retail	$775	$690	$595	$525	$480	$440	$400

MODEL 600 FIELD GRADE—same as 500, except silver plated frame and select wood.

	$700	$495	$465	$440	$375	$345	$325

Add 20% for 20 ga.

MODEL 600 MAGNUM—same as 600 Field, except chambered for 3 in. Mag., 12 ga., made 1969-1972 by SKB.

	$720	$510	$480	$455	$415	$390	$355

MODEL 600 TRAP GRADE—same as 600, except 12 ga. only, trap stock, recoil pad, select wood.

	$675	$555	$520	$485	$445	$410	$385

MODEL 600 DOUBLES GUN—same as 600 Trap, except choked for 21 yd. and 30 yd. targets, made 1973-1975.

	$675	$555	$520	$485	$445	$410	$385

MODEL 600 SKEET GRADE—12, 20, 28, and .410 ga.'s, 26 or 28 in. barrels, bored S&S, otherwise same as 600 Trap.

	$700	$540	$510	$475	$430	$400	$370

28 and .410 ga.'s

	$850	$740	$620	$560	$485	$440	$420

Grading	100%	98%	95%	90%	80%	70%	60%

MODEL 600 SKEET GRADE COMBO SET—same as 600 Skeet, except fitted with matched set of 20, 28, and .410 ga. barrels, in fitted case.

	$2,000	$1,430	$1,265	$1,155	$935	$770	$660

MODEL 605 FIELD—similar to Model 505 except has silver finished engraved receiver with better walnut.

No Mfg.'s Retail $900 $775 $675 $550 $475 $425 $375

Add $475 for extra set of barrels (Combo).

Model 605 Trap—12 ga., 30 or 32 in. fixed choke barrel with or without Monte Carlo stock, high rib.

No Mfg.'s Retail $900 $725 $625 $500 $450 $400 $360

Add $430 for O/U Trap Combo.

The above Combo includes one set of O/U Trap barrels and a top single Trap barrel.

Model 605 Trap Single Barrel—12 ga., 32 or 34 in. barrel with multi-chokes.

No Mfg.'s Retail $900 $700 $600 $475 $430 $400 $360

Model 605 Skeet—12, 20, 28, or .410 ga., 28 in. barrels with multi-chokes.

No Mfg.'s Retail $900 $800 $700 $595 $530 $480 $440

Model 605 3-Ga. Skeet Set—includes 20, 28, and .410 ga. extra Skeet barrels, aluminum case.

No Mfg.'s Retail $1,950 $1,650 $1,325 $1,175 $1,000 $900 $850

Model 605 Sporting Clay—28 in. multi-choke barrels, dimensioned for Sporting Clay competition.

No Mfg.'s Retail $900 $800 $700 $595 $530 $480 $440

MODEL 680 ENGLISH—same as 600 Field, except English style stock, select walnut and fine scroll engraving. Made from 1973 to 1976.

	$725	$640	$600	$555	$520	$495	$445

MODEL 700 TRAP GRADE—12 ga., same as 600 Trap, except more engraving, better grade wood, wide rib. Made from 1969 to 1975.

	$820	$770	$740	$685	$630	$595	$565

MODEL 700 DOUBLES GUN—12 ga., same as 700 Trap, except choked for 21 yd. and 30 yd. targets, made 1973-1975.

	$795	$770	$740	$685	$630	$595	$565

MODEL 700 SKEET GRADE—12 ga., same as 700 Doubles, only bored S&S, available in 12 and 20 ga.'s.

	$840	$770	$740	$685	$620	$585	$555

MODEL 800 TRAP GRADE—12 ga., same as 700 Trap, except more engraving, better grade wood, wide rib. Made from 1969 to 1975.

	$1,150	$875	$775	$675	$575	$500	$425

MODEL 800 SKEET GRADE—12 or 20 ga., skeet chokes, mfg. 1969-1975.

	$1,200	$1,000	$895	$795	$680	$595	$565

MODEL 880 CROWN GRADE—12, 20, 28, and .410 ga.'s, coin finish receiver, extensively engraved with sideplates, SST, ejectors, select walnut with fleur-de-lis scroll style checkering, double cross bolt action. Discontinued in 1980.

	$1,650	$1,300	$1,150	$975	$890	$835	$750

Add 25% for 28 or .410 ga.

MODEL 885—available in either Skeet or Trap configuration only, coin finished receiver featuring fine scroll engraving with game scenes, boxlock action with sideplates. Imported in 1988 only.

Model 885 Trap O/U—12 ga., 30 or 32 in. barrels with multi-chokes.

	$1,275	$995	$875	$800	$750	$700	$650

Add $400 for O/U Trap Combo.

The above Combo includes one set of O/U Trap barrels and a top single Trap barrel.

Last Mfg.'s Sug. Retail was $1,495.

Grading	100%	98%	95%	90%	80%	70%	60%

Model 885 Skeet—12, 20, 28, or .410 ga., 28 in. barrels with multi-chokes.

	$1,275	$995	$875	$800	$750	$700	$650

Last Mfg.'s Sug. Retail was $1,495.

Model 885 3-Ga. Skeet Set—includes 20, 28, and .410 ga. extra Skeet barrels, aluminum case.

	$2,300	$1,925	$1,600	$1,325	$1,175	$1,000	$900

Last Mfg.'s Sug. Retail was $2,650.

Model 885 Sporting Clay—28 in. multi-choke barrels, dimensioned for Sporting Clay competition.

	$1,275	$995	$875	$800	$750	$700	$650

Last Mfg.'s Sug. Retail was $1,495.

MODEL 5600—12 ga. only, available as Trap or Skeet model only, vent rib (Trap only) and barrels (Skeet only), no engraving, select walnut. Discontinued in 1980.

	$575	$495	$450	$420	$390	$360	$330

Model 5700—available as Trap or Skeet model only, light engraving, select walnut, vent rib. Discontinued in 1980.

	$750	$625	$540	$495	$460	$430	$400

Model 5800—available as Trap or Skeet model only, more deluxe engraving, select walnut. Discontinued in 1980.

	$950	$800	$695	$595	$500	$450	$425

SHOTGUNS: SIDE-BY-SIDE

Models 100, 150, 200, 280, 300, 400, 480 — 12 and 20 ga. only, 25-30 in. barrels, all boxlock actions, more expensive models differ in the amount of engraving, grade of walnut, and style of checkering. 6¼ - 7 lbs., beavertail forend. Discontinued in 1980.

MODEL 100—12 or 20 ga., Mag. model also, SST, AE, blue only.

	$485	$425	$380	$340	$310	$275	$250

MODEL 150—same as 100, except scroll engraving, beavertail forearm, made 1972-1974 by SKB.

	$520	$435	$385	$345	$310	$275	$250

MODEL 200—12 or 20 ga., Mag. model also, SST, AE, boxlock, scalloped frame, lightly engraved coin finish receiver.

	$550	$475	$410	$375	$340	$310	$280

MODEL 200 (NEW MFG.)—similar to original Model 200, SST, ejectors, recoil pad. Imported in 1987-1988 only.

	$725	$525	$425	$420	$375	$345	$325

Last Mfg.'s Sug. Retail was $895.

Model 200E (English)—similar to New Model 200, except has straight grip stock. Importation disc. in 1988.

	$725	$525	$425	$420	$375	$345	$325

Last Mfg.'s Sug. Retail was $895.

MODEL 280 ENGLISH—12 or 20 ga., Mag. model also, SST, AE, lightly engraved blue receiver, straight grip.

	$850	$775	$625	$525	$440	$410	$375

MODEL 300—12 or 20 ga., Mag. model also, SST, AE, lightly engraved coin finish receiver.

	$750	$650	$575	$485	$440	$410	$375

MODEL 400—12 or 20 ga., Mag. model also, boxlock, SST, AE, moderately engraved coin finish receiver with sideplates.

	$695	$600	$510	$460	$430	$410	$385

MODEL 400 (NEW MFG.)—similar to original Model 400, SST, ejectors, recoil pad. Imported 1987-1988 only.

	$975	$850	$780	$690	$595	$525	$475

Last Mfg.'s Sug. Retail was $1,195.

Grading	100%	98%	95%	90%	80%	70%	60%

Model 400E (English)—similar to New Model 400, except has engraved sideplates and straight grip stock. Importation disc. in 1989.

	$975	$850	$780	$690	$595	$525	$475

Last Mfg.'s Sug. Retail was $1,195.

MODEL 480 ENGLISH—12 or 20 ga., Mag. model also, SST, AE, moderately engraved coin finish receiver, straight grip.

	$1,250	$1,000	$825	$725	$625	$525	$475

SHOTGUNS: SEMI-AUTO

MODEL 300 STANDARD—12 and 20 ga.'s, 3 in. chamber, 26 in. imp. cyl., 28 in. mod. or full, 30 in. full, recoil operated, autoloading, checkered pistol grip stock, made 1968-1972.

	$295	$255	$205	$165	$155	$145	$140
Vent rib model	$320	$275	$220	$195	$165	$155	$150

MODEL 1300 UPLAND—12 or 20 ga., 3 in. chamber, 22, 26, or 28 in. VR barrel with multi-chokes, matte black receiver, checkered walnut stock and forearm. Importation resumed in 1988.

No Mfg.'s Retail	$450	$365	$330	$305	$285	$265	$250

Add $15 for 12 ga. Slug Gun with rifle sights.

This model was previously designated the Model 300. The new Model 1300 is also available in Slug configuration with 22 in. barrel/iron sights. New Model 1300's have a magazine cutoff system on front left side of frame.

XL 900 MR—12 ga. only, gas operated semi-auto, 26-30 in. barrels, 5 shot, alloy receiver, etched game bird scroll work on receiver, shoots both 2¾ and 3 in. shells by interchanging barrels. Discontinued in 1980.

	$325	$280	$260	$240	$225	$190	$175
XL 900—same as XL 900, only in 20 ga. and no recoil pad, 6¼ lbs.							
	$360	$315	$275	$250	$230	$190	$175

XL 900 TRAP GRADE—same as XL 900, 12 ga. only, scroll engraved black chrome receiver, 30 in. imp. mod. or full, trap style stock, straight or Monte Carlo, recoil pad, made 1972-present.

	$395	$350	$320	$305	$275	$265	$260

XL 900 SKEET GRADE—same as XL 900, except scroll engraved black chrome receiver, 26 in. barrel, skeet stock, made 1972-discontinued.

	$400	$350	$320	$305	$275	$265	$260

XL 900 SLUG GUN—same as XL 900, except 24 in. slug barrel, rifle sights, no rib, made 1972-discontinued.

	$350	$310	$280	$265	$250	$220	$200

MODEL 1900—12 or 20 ga., 3 in. chamber, 22, 26, or 28 in. VR barrel with multi-chokes, deluxe outdoor field scene etched on receiver, gold trigger.

No Mfg.'s Retail	$500	$425	$385	$345	$320	$300	$280

Add $25 for Trap model (2¾ in. chamber).

This model was previously designated the Model 900. The new Model 1900 is also available in Slug configuration with 22 in. barrel/iron sights. New Model 1900's have a magazine cutoff system on front left side of frame.

MODEL 3000—12 or 20 ga., 3 in. chamber, gas semi-auto (shoots both 2¾ and 3 in. shells interchangeably) with semi-squareback styling, elaborate game scenes etched on both sides of receiver, deluxe checkered walnut stock and forearm. Importation disc. in 1989.

	$465	$390	$350	$325	$300	$280	$255

Add $10 for Trap model (2¾ in. chamber).

This model has not previously been imported in this configuration.

Last Mfg.'s Sug. Retail was $585.

SHOTGUNS: SLIDE ACTION

MODEL 7300—12 or 20 ga., 2¾ and 3 in. chambers, blue only, French walnut stock-hand checkered, twin action slide bars. Discontinued in 1980.

	$295	$250	$225	$200	$180	$165	$150

MODEL 7900—trap or skeet variation of the Model 7300.

	$350	$310	$265	$235	$200	$180	$160

SKS

COMMUNIST MANUFACTURE

SKS—semi-auto rifle, 7.62 x 39mm Russian, Soviet designed, gas operated weapon, 10 round fixed mag., wood stock, permanently attached folding bayonet, tangent rear and hooded front sight.

Please refer to this model under those importers/distributors who import this model and are listed in this text.

SSK INDUSTRIES

MANUFACTURER/CUSTOMIZER LOCATED IN BLOOMINGDALE, OH.

SSK Industries uses Thompson Center flatside frames and puts on an industrial hard chrome finish. Receivers and barrels may be purchased separately — values below are for a complete assembled pistol with no scope rings (add $60).

SSK has also manufactured various limited editions including the Handgun Hunters International (HHI) Models 1, 2, and 3. Issue price on these guns varied from $1,100 (Model 3) to $1,300 (Model 1). Only 50 were manufactured total.

HAND CANNONS

SSK-CONTENDER—over 74 cal.'s available from .17 Bee to .588 JDJ, customized Thompson Center receiver and barrel, scope rings or iron sights are extra, basically a custom order gun.

Mfg.'s Sug. Retail $563 $525 $460 $395
   Add $10 for barrels under .22 cal.
   Add up to $25 for barrels over .41 cal.

This model includes barrel, frame, stocks, and sights as standard equipment.

Contender Models in cal.'s over .50 since BATF ruling have become very expensive. A .588 JDJ cal. gun can cost as much as $1,800.

SSK-XP100—various cal.'s between .17 and .50, includes TSOB mount and rings.
Mfg.'s Sug. Retail $650 $610 $550 $475

The .50 cal. XP100 (12.9 X 50.8 JDJ) comes with SSK muzzle brake, scope dyes and new reinforced fiberglass stock - retail price is $1,700.

S.W.D., INC.

MANUFACTURED IN ATLANTA, GA. SIMILAR MODELS HAVE PREVIOUSLY BEEN MANUFACTURED BY R.P.B. INDUSTRIES, INC. (1979-82), AND WERE MET WITH B.A.T.F. DISAPPROVAL BECAUSE OF CONVERTABILITY INTO FULLY AUTOMATIC OPERATION. "COBRAY" IS A TRADEMARK FOR THE M11/9 SEMI-AUTOMATIC PISTOL.

COBRAY PISTOLS

M-11/NINEmm SEMI-AUTO PISTOL—9mm, fires from closed bolt, 3rd generation design, stamped steel frame, 32 shot mag., parkerized finish, similar in appearance to Ingram Mac 10.

No Mfg.'s Retail $215 $175 $160 $150 $140 $135 $125

This model is also available in a fully-auto variation, class III transferable only.

CARBINES

SEMI-AUTO CARBINE—9mm, same mechanism as M11, 16¼ in. shrouded barrel, telescoping stock, various Mag.'s.

No Mfg.'s Retail $240 $195 $170 $160 $150 $140 $130

SHOTGUNS

TERMINATOR—12 or 20 ga., single shot assault shotgun with 18 in. cylinder bore barrel, parkerized finish, ejector. Mfg. in 1986-1988 only.

   $95 $80 $70 $60 $55 $50 $45

Last Mfg.'s Sug. Retail was $110.

SAFARI ARMS

MANUFACTURER/CUSTOMIZER LOCATED IN PHOENIX, AZ. M-S SAFARI ARMS WAS STARTED IN 1978 AND IS A DIVISION OF M-S SAFARI OUTFITTERS. IN 1987, SAFARI ARMS WAS ABSORBED BY OLYMPIC ARMS LOCATED IN OLYMPIA, WA. OLYMPIC ARMS IS CURRENTLY UTILIZING EXISTING PARTS OF OLDER SAFARI ARMS AND WILL BE MANUFACTURING PISTOLS WITH THEIR OWN TRADEMARK ONCE EXISTING INVENTORY PARTS HAVE BEEN DEPLETED.

Safari Arms manufactured single action, semi-auto pistols derived from the Browning M1911 design with modifications. Values below reflect previously mfg. pistols by Safari Arms. New models can be found under the Olympic Arms, Inc. section of this text.

DEFENSE PISTOLS

ENFORCER—.45 ACP, 3.9 in. barrel, 6 shot mag., shortened grip, available in stainless steel, blue, Armaloy, parkerized, electroless nickel or lightweight anodized finishes, flat or arched mainspring housing, adj. sights, neoprene or checkered walnut grips, 27 oz. Mfg. disc. in 1987.

		$680	$600	$525	$450	$400	$350

Last Mfg.'s Sug. Retail was $745.

Match Master—similar to the Enforcer, except has 5 in. barrel and 7 shot mag., 30 oz. Mfg. disc. in 1987.

		$680	$600	$525	$450	$400	$350

Last Mfg.'s Sug. Retail was $745.

Safari Arms also has made the Phoenix, Special Forces, Camp Perry, and Royal Order of Jesters commemoratives in various configurations and quantities. Prices average in the $1,500 range except for the Royal Order of Jesters ($2,000).

BLACK WIDOW—.45 ACP, 3.9 in. barrel, hand-contoured front grip strap, schrimshawed ivory Micarta grips with black widow emblem, 6 shot mag., 27 oz. Mfg. disc. in 1987.

		$680	$600	$525	$450	$400	$350

Last Mfg.'s Sug. Retail was $745.

TARGET PISTOLS

MODEL 81—.38 Spl. or .45 ACP, 5 in. barrel, hand-contoured front grip strap, 2 lbs. 10 oz. Mfg. disc. in 1987.

		$775	$695	$550	$440	$410	$375	$350

Add $50 for Deluxe Model (with Herrett adj. grips).

Last Mfg.'s Sug. Retail was $875.

Model 81L—.38 Spl. or .45 ACP, 6 in. barrel, 2 lbs. 13 oz. Mfg. disc. in 1987.

		$850	$775	$695	$550	$440	$410	$375

Add $50 for Deluxe Model (with Herrett adj. grips).

Last Mfg.'s Sug. Retail was $975.

Model 81 NM—.38 Spl. or .45 ACP, similar frame as Model 81, except has flat front grip strap, 5 in. barrel, 2 lbs. 5 oz. Mfg. disc. in 1987.

		$775	$695	$550	$440	$410	$375	$350

Last Mfg.'s Sug. Retail was $875.

Model 81BP—.38 Spl. or .45 ACP, 6 in barrel, contoured front grip strap, faster cycle time, 2 lbs. 9 oz. Mfg. disc. in 1987.

		$875	$775	$695	$550	$440	$410	$375

Last Mfg.'s Sug. Retail was $995.

Silueta—.45 ACP or .38/.45 Wildcat, 10 in. extended barrel, designed for silhouette shooting, 2 lbs. 14 oz. Mfg. disc. in 1987.

		$875	$775	$695	$550	$440	$410	$375

Last Mfg.'s Sug. Retail was $1,050.

ULTIMATE/UNLIMITED—various cal.'s, bolt-action target pistol, single shot, $14^{15}/_{16}$ in. barrel, black finished metal, laminate stock. Mfg. disc. in 1987.

		$850	$775	$695	$550	$440	$410	$375

Last Mfg.'s Sug. Retail was $975.

Grading	100%	98%	95%	90%	80%	70%	60%

RIFLES

COUNTER SNIPER RIFLE—.308 cal., bolt-action utilizing M-14 mag.'s, 26 in. heavy barrel, camo-fiberglass stock, 10½ lbs. Mfg. disc. in 1987.

	$1,100	$900	$775	$695	$550	$440	$410

Last Mfg.'s Sug. Retail was $1,225.

SURVIVOR I CONVERSION UNIT—.223 or .45 ACP cal., converts M1911 variations into carbine, bolt-action, collapsible stock, 16¼ in. barrel, 5 lbs.

	$275	$225	$195

This kit is also available for S&W and Browning High-Power models.

SAKO

MANUFACTURED IN RIIHIMAKI, FINLAND. CURRENT MODELS ARE PRESENTLY BEING IMPORTED BY STOEGER INDUSTRIES LOCATED IN SOUTH HACKENSACK, NJ.

Note: Prices below are for pre-Garcia (pre-1972) rifles unless stated otherwise. Post-1972 models will sell for approximately 25% less.

RIFLES: DISCONTINUED

DELUXE—various cal.'s, Monte Carlo stock, skipline checkering, long, medium, or short actions, contrasting P.G. Cap & Forearm, engraved floorplate.

	$775	$695	$550	$440	$410	$375	$350

STANDARD SPORTER—long, medium, and short actions.

	$600	$550	$475	$440	$410	$375	$350

HEAVY BARREL MODEL—long, medium, and short actions.

	$600	$550	$475	$440	$410	$375	$350

FULL STOCK MODELS—20 in. carbine barrel (all actions), 23½ in. barrel on rifle (short & medium actions).

Finnbear—long action.

	$795	$710	$560	$440	$410	$375	$350

Approximately 20 rifles in this Model were produced in .458 Win. Mag. cal., - values can exceed $1,500.

Forester—medium action.

	$795	$710	$560	$440	$410	$375	$350

Vixen—short action.

	$795	$710	$560	$440	$410	$375	$350

A limited quantity of rifles in 7.62 X 39mm Russian cal. was imported previously - large premiums exist.

MAUSER ACTION (FN)—.270 Win. and .30-06 cal.'s, long action, produced 1950-1957.

	$550	$500	$400	$345	$310	$280	$260

MAGNUM MAUSER (FN)—.300 H&H and .375 H&H cal.'s.

	$695	$635	$580	$495	$450	$410	$375

MODEL 74—various cal.'s.

	$560	$495	$440	$375	$340	$320	$290

FINNWOLF—lever-action, various cal.'s, 4 shot clip early model, 3 shot clip later model, made 1962-1974.

	$600	$550	$500	$440	$410	$375	$350

ANNIVERSARY MODEL—7mm Rem. Mag. only, 1,000 made. Price listed for N.I.B./ unfired condition, otherwise deduct 25%.

	$1,250	$925	$695

SAKO, cont.

RIFLES: RECENT MANUFACTURE

All Sako left-handed models are available in long action only.

SAKO HUNTER—available in short (AI), medium (AII), or long (AIII) action, .17 - .375 H&H Mag. cal.'s, 21¼, 21¾, or 22 in. barrel, classic styled stock with choice of oil or lacquer finish, finely checkered French walnut.

Mfg.'s Sug. Retail	$860	$710	$600	$540	$490	$460	$430	$410

Add $30 for long action.
Add $40-$75 for Mag. cal.'s.
Add $120 for left-hand action.
Add $40 for .17 Rem. cal.

Sako Carbine (Handy)—available in medium or long action only, 18½ in. barrel with iron sights, oil or lacquer finished deluxe walnut stock with checkering, about 7 lbs. New in 1986.

Mfg.'s Sug. Retail	$860	$710	$600	$540	$490	$460	$430	$410

Add $30 for long action.
Add $40-$75 for Mag. cal.'s.

Sako FiberClass—available in .25-06 through .375 H&H Mag. cal.'s, same as Standard Model, except has black fiberglass stock.

Mfg.'s Sug. Retail	$1,175	$1,025	$840	$765	$710	$630	$560	$510

Add $15 for long action.
Add $45 for Mag. cal.'s.
Add $80 for left-hand action.

Sako FiberClass Carbine (Handy)—available in medium or long action only, 18½ in. barrel with fiberglass stock. New in 1986.

Mfg.'s Sug. Retail	$1,175	$1,025	$840	$765	$710	$630	$560	$510

Add $15 for long action.
Add $45 for Mag. cal.'s.

SAKO LAMINATED—available in all actions (.17 Rem. to .375 H&H cal.'s) with laminated wood stock, new in 1988.

Mfg.'s Sug. Retail	$965	$830	$700	$600	$540	$490	$460	$430

Add $15 for long action.
Add $30-$55 for Mag. cal.'s.
Add $120 for left-hand action.

SAKO MANNLICHER CARBINE—available in .222 Rem.-.375 H&H cal.'s, either short (AI), medium (AII), or long (AIII) action, 18½ in. barrel, two-piece full Mannlicher style stock, open sights.

Mfg.'s Sug. Retail	$945	$780	$675	$585	$530	$475	$430	$400

Add $15 for long action.
Add $35-$75 for Mag. cal.'s.

SAKO PPC—22 PPC or 6 PPC cal., 21¾ or 23¾ (Benchrest Model) in. barrel, single shot in Benchrest Model, 4 shot mag. in Hunter or Deluxe Model, checkered walnut stock, Deluxe Model has rosewood pistol grip and forearm caps plus skip line checkering, matte lacquer finish on Hunter and Deluxe, oiled finish on Benchrest, 6¼ or 8¾ (Benchrest Model with heavy barrel) lbs. Importation began in 1989.

Mfg.'s Sug. Retail	$1,085	$925	$815	$700	$650	$590	$540	$500

Add $275 for Deluxe Hunter Model.

SAKO VARMINT (HEAVY BARREL)—available in short (AI) and medium (AII) actions, .222 Rem., .223 Rem., .22-250, .243 Win., and .308 Win. cal.'s, 22¾ in. barrel, no sights.

Mfg.'s Sug. Retail	$965	$815	$700	$600	$550	$525	$460	$420

Also available in single shot configuration (6mm PPC or .22 PPC only) — subtract $110.

SAKO CLASSIC GRADE—available in short (AI), medium (AII), or long (AIII) action, .17-7 mm Mag. cal.'s, classic styled stock, finely checkered French walnut. Disc. in 1985.

	$835	$715	$660	$600	$560	$510	$475

Add $50 for Mag. cal.'s.

Last Mfg.'s Sug. Retail was $954.

Grading	100%	98%	95%	90%	80%	70%	60%

SAKO DELUXE—available in short (AI), medium (AII), or long action (AIII), .223 Rem.-.375 H&H Mag. cal.'s, 21¼, 21¾, or 22 in. barrel, deluxe quality skipline checkered walnut stock with rosewood forend tip.

Mfg.'s Sug. Retail	$1,120	$925	$815	$700	$650	$590	$540	$500

Add $30 for long action.
Add $45-$75 for Mag. cal.'s.
Add $100 for left-hand action.
Add $50 for .17 Rem. cal.

SAKO SAFARI GRADE—available in long (AIII) action only, .300 Win. Mag., .338 Win. Mag., and .375 H&H Mag. cal.'s, deluxe walnut with sculptured cheekpiece, 22 in. barrel, 4 shot mag., open sights, sling swivels.

Mfg.'s Sug. Retail	$2,225	$1,875	$1,650	$1,425	$1,225	$1,030	$900	$795

SAKO SUPER DELUXE—a limited edition rifle available on special order only, various cal.'s are available in the short (AI), medium (AII), and long (AIII) actions, presentation grade walnut with both checkering and carving, rosewood forend tip.

Mfg.'s Sug. Retail	$2,225	$1,875	$1,650	$1,425	$1,225	$1,030	$900	$795

SAKO MODEL 78—.22 LR and .22 Hornet, clip mag., same size as short action Standard Model. Importation discontinued in 1986.

	$480	$395	$340	$310	$280	$265	$250

Add $30 for .22 Hornet cal.

Last Mfg.'s Sug. Retail was $647.

SAKO FINSPORT MODEL 2700—available in long (AIII) action only, .270 - .300 Win. Mag. cal.'s, select checkered walnut. Discontinued in 1985.

	$795	$680	$600	$560	$510	$475	$430

Last Mfg.'s Sug. Retail was $910.

PISTOLS

SAKO TRIACE—.22 Short, .22 LR or .32 S&W wadcutter cal.'s, target pistol incorporating unique action, competition walnut grips with thumb rest and adj. heel, blued finish with chrome accents. Imported 1985-86 only.

	$1,150	$1,045	$925	$810	$700	$600	$500

Last Mfg.'s Sug. Retail was $1,395.

Although discontinued, limited quantities remain at the distributor for this model.

Triace Pistol Kit—consists of Triace frame, .22 short, .22 LR, and .32 S&W barrels. Cased with accessories. Imported 1985-86 only.

	$2,050	$1,840	$1,625	$1,450	$1,300	$1,175	$1,025

Last Mfg.'s Sug. Retail was $2,385.

SAM INC.

MANUFACTURED BY SPECIAL SERVICE ARMS MFG., INC. LOCATED IN RESTON, VA.

MODEL 88 CROSSFIRE—combination gun (12 ga. over .308 Win.) in assault configuration featuring independent O/U shotgun/rifle operation, dual gas piston rotating bolts, slide activated first round followed by semi-auto operation thereafter, 3 position selector designates rifle, shotgun, or safe operation, twin box magazines (20 shot rifle and 7 shot shotgun), 20 in. barrels, composite construction, 9½ lbs. New in 1989.

Mfg.'s Sug. Retail	$1,177	$1,050	$925	$815	$700	$650	$590	$540

SAMCO GLOBAL ARMS, INC.

IMPORTER/DISTRIBUTOR LOCATED IN MIAMI, FL.

Samco Global Arms currently imports a variety of foreign and domestic surplus military rifles (including various contract Mausers, Loewe, Steyr, Hakim, Lee Enfield, etc.). Most of these guns are in the $60-$120 range and while they offer excellent values to the shooter, to date they have not been collectible. Samco also sells newly remanufactured sporting rifles (German or Spanish) in .308 Win. or 7 x 57mm cal. These sporters range in value from approx. $170-$200. Samco also imports BSA rifles which can be located in their own heading of this text.

SARDIUS

MANUFACTURED IN ISRAEL FOR ARMSCORP OF AMERICA, INC.

SD-9—9mm Para., semi-auto double action, compact design, 3.07 in. barrel, matte black finish, 6 shot mag., 3 dot sighting system, 1.54 lbs. Importation started in 1988.

Mfg.'s Sug. Retail	$350	$315	$280	$260	$240	$220	$200	$185

SARRIUGARTE, FRANCISO S.A.

MANUFACTURER LOCATED IN ELGOIBAR, SPAIN. CURRENTLY PART OF THE DIARM S.A. GROUP WHICH IS IMPORTED AND DISTRIBUTED BY AMERICAN ARMS, INC. LOCATED IN NORTH KANSAS CITY, MO.

Francisco Sarriugarte is now exporting shotguns as part of the Diarm S.A. conglomerate. Please refer to the Diarm S.A. heading in this text for information pertaining to current models.

SARASQUETA, FELIX

MANUFACTURED IN EIBAR, SPAIN. CURRENTLY IMPORTED AND DISTRIBUTED BY SAE (SPAIN AMERICA ENTERPRISES), INC. LOCATED IN MIAMI, FL.

Felix Sarasqueta firearms are currently being imported exclusively by SAE and can be found under that heading in this text.

SHOTGUNS

MODEL MERKE O/U—12 ga. only, boxlock action, 22 or 27 in. separated barrels, single non-selective trigger, blue only, extractors, recoil pad. Imported in 1986 only.

	$255	$215	$200	$190	$180	$170	$160

Last Mfg.'s Sug. Retail was $291.

SARASQUETA, J.J.

MANUFACTURED IN EIBAR, SPAIN. IMPORTED UNTIL 1984 BY AMERICAN ARMS, INC. LOCATED IN OVERLAND PARK, KS.

SHOTGUNS: SIDE-BY-SIDE

MODEL 107 E—12, 16, or 20 ga., ejectors, various barrel lengths, checkered walnut stock and forearm, double triggers.

	$360	$290	$270	$255	$240	$215	$200

Last Mfg.'s Sug. Retail was $435.

MODELS 119E-132E-1882E—more deluxe versions of Model 107E.

	$470	$375	$340	$315	$285	$255	$230

Last Mfg.'s Sug. Retail was $570.

MODEL 130 E—more deluxe version of Model 119 E.

	$800	$635	$590	$555	$515	$480	$450

Last Mfg.'s Sug. Retail was $960.

MODEL 131 E—action similar to Model 107 E, except has deluxe engraving.

	$1,050	$845	$770	$710	$665	$620	$585

Last Mfg.'s Sug. Retail was $1,250.

MODEL 1882 E LUXE—double triggers, moderate engraving, otherwise similar to Model 107 E.

	$825	$660	$615	$565	$520	$480	$450

Last Mfg.'s Sug. Retail was $990.

Model 1882 E Luxe w/gold inlays—SST, extensive engraving.

	$1,120	$920	$850	$790	$740	$695	$650

Last Mfg.'s Sug. Retail was $1,320.

Grading	100%	98%	95%	90%	80%	70%	60%

Model 1882 E Luxe w/silver inlays—SST, extensive engraving.

	100%	98%	95%	90%	80%	70%	60%
	$1,055	$855	$795	$740	$700	$660	$630

Last Mfg.'s Sug. Retail was $1,260.

MODEL 150 E—12 or 16 ga., single trigger, ejectors, select walnut and extensive engraving.

	$1,285	$1,035	$960	$895	$835	$770	$695

Last Mfg.'s Sug. Retail was $1,500.

Model 150 E Trap—same as Model 150 E, except trap dimensions on stock.

	$1,360	$1,125	$1,010	$940	$875	$790	$720

Last Mfg.'s Sug. Retail was $1,600.

SARASQUETA, VICTOR

PREVIOUSLY MANUFACTURED IN EIBAR, SPAIN. TRADEMARK IS CURRENTLY OWNED BY DIARM S.A.

SHOTGUNS

MODEL 3 SXS—12, 16, and 20 ga.'s, all standard barrel lengths and chokes, boxlock, double triggers, checkered English style stock and forend.

Auto ejectors

	$580	$505	$480	$440	$380	$365	$345

HAMMERLESS SIDELOCK—12, 16, or 20 ga., s x s, barrel length and choke to order, straight English style stock, models differ as to amount of engraving, grade of wood, and overall quality as follows:

MODEL 4—extractors.

	$620	$550	$525	$495	$450	$415	$360

MODEL 4E—auto ejectors.

	$680	$605	$580	$550	$505	$470	$415

MODEL 203—extractors.

	$650	$570	$545	$515	$475	$435	$380

MODEL 203E—auto ejectors.

	$710	$625	$600	$570	$530	$490	$435

MODEL 6E

	$800	$715	$690	$660	$615	$580	$525

MODEL 7E

	$855	$770	$745	$715	$670	$635	$580

MODEL 10E

	$1,735	$1,595	$1,485	$1,405	$1,320	$1,240	$1,100

MODEL 11E

	$1,870	$1,680	$1,595	$1,515	$1,430	$1,350	$1,265

MODEL 12E

	$2,145	$1,900	$1,790	$1,705	$1,570	$1,430	$1,375

SAUER, J.P. & SOHN

MANUFACTURED SINCE 1751 IN GERMANY. PREVIOUSLY LOCATED IN SUHL - CURRENTLY HEADQUARTERED IN ECKERNFORDE, W. GERMANY. PRESENTLY IMPORTED BY SIGARMS, INC. LOCATED IN TYSONS CORNER, VA. IN 1972, J.P. SAUER & SOHN FORMED A COOPERATION WITH THE SIG SWISS INDUSTRIAL COMPANY WHICH IS PRESENTLY THE PARENT HOUSE OF SAUER & SOHN.

PISTOLS

MODEL 1913 POCKET AUTOMATIC—.32 auto, 7 shot, 3 in. barrel, fixed sights, blue, black rubber grips, made 1913-1930.

	$250	$220	$185	$165	$155	$145	$135

Grading	100%	98%	95%	90%	80%	70%	60%

MODEL 1913 25 AUTOMATIC—.25 auto, 7 shot, 2½ in. barrel, fixed sights, blue, black rubber grips, made 1913-1930.

	$275	$240	$200	$175	$150	$140	$135

MODEL 28—.25 ACP, 7 shot, 3 in. barrel, fixed sights, blue, black rubber grips, made 1930-1938.

	$260	$210	$185	$170	$155	$145	$135

BEHORDEN (SERVICE) MODEL—.32 ACP, 3 in. barrel, blue only, black plastic grips.

	$275	$240	$200	$175	$150	$145	$135

MODEL 38 H DOUBLE ACTION AUTOMATIC—.25 and .32 auto, and 3¼ in. barrel, fixed sights, blue, plastic grips, made 1938-1945. Add 10% for Waffenamt, 50% for .25 cal., 10% for Waffenamt or police proofs, 60% for alloy frame.

	$300	$275	$240	$205	$185	$165	$150

RIFLE

SAUER MAUSER BOLT ACTION RIFLE—most popular European cal.'s and .30-06, 22 or 24 in. barrel, raised solid rib, Krupp steel, double set triggers, folding 3 leaf express sight, checkered sporter stock, made pre-WWII.

	$715	$550	$495	$440	$360	$330	$305

RIFLES: DRILLINGS — O/U COMBINATION GUNS

MODEL 200 BOLT ACTION—available in 9 cal.'s between .243 Win. and 9.3 x 62, short and medium actions only, 23.62 in. unique interchangeable barrels, 6 lug bolt, easily detachable stock and forearm, optional set trigger, detachable mag. with hidden release button, 7.7 lbs. Importation disc. in 1987.

	$600	$550	$500	$465	$435	$400	$375

    Add $100 for 7mm Rem. Mag. or .300 Win. Mag. cal.

    Add $235 for extra interchangeable barrel.

Last Mfg.'s Sug. Retail was $875.

Model 200 Lightweight—same as Model 200, only with alloy receiver, 6.6 lbs. Importation disc. in 1987.

	$575	$525	$480	$450	$425	$395	$370

    Add $85 for left-hand version.

Last Mfg.'s Sug. Retail was $875.

Model 200 Lux—similar to Model 200, except has deluxe walnut, rosewood forend tip and pistol grip cap, marmorized bolt and gold trigger. Importation disc. in 1987.

	$675	$600	$560	$520	$480	$440	$400

Last Mfg.'s Sug. Retail was $1,075.

American 200 Lux—similar to Model 200 Lux, except has high gloss Monte Carlo stock, 24 in. barrel, jeweled bolt, and gold trigger. Imported 1987-1988 only.

	$775	$675	$600	$550	$500	$465	$430

    Add $95 for left-hand action.

Last Mfg.'s Sug. Retail was $1,175.

European 200 Lux—similar to Model 200 Lux, except has European configured stock with Schnabel forearm, 26 in. barrel. Importation disc. in 1988.

	$775	$675	$600	$550	$500	$465	$430

    Add $95 for left-hand action.

Last Mfg.'s Sug. Retail was $1,175.

Model 200 Carbon Fiber—similar to Model 200, except has carbon fiber stock. Imported 1987-88 only.

	$800	$700	$625	$565	$500	$465	$430

Last Mfg.'s Sug. Retail was $1,200.

Grading	100%	98%	95%	90%	80%	70%	60%

MODEL 90 BOLT ACTION—available in 17 cal.'s between .222 Rem. and .458 Win. Mag., short, medium and long actions, 22.44 or 26 in. barrel, 3 or 4 shot detachable mag., deluxe checkered walnut stock, approx. 7½ lbs.(except .458 Win. Mag.). Importation disc. in 1989.

	$775	$675	$600	$550	$500	$465	$430

Add $35 for Mag. cal.'s.

Last Mfg.'s Sug. Retail was $1,175.

Model 90 Stutzen—Mannlicher style full stock, not available in European or Mag. cal.'s. Importation disc. in 1989.

	$800	$700	$600	$550	$500	$465	$430

Last Mfg.'s Sug. Retail was $1,225.

Safari Model—.458 Win. Mag, 23.62 in. barrel, 10½ lbs. Imported 1986-1988 only.

	$1,250	$950	$850	$750	$650	$575	$500

Last Mfg.'s Sug. Retail was $1,675.

MODEL 90 LUX—similar to Model 90, except has better walnut stock with rosewood forearm tip and pistol grip cap, gold trigger.

Mfg.'s Sug. Retail	$1,325	$1,200	$1,020	$900	$795	$585	$465	$430

Add $50 for Mag. cal.'s.

Model 90 Stutzen Lux—Mannlicher style full stock, not available in European or Mag. cal.'s.

Mfg.'s Sug. Retail	$1,325	$1,200	$1,020	$900	$795	$585	$465	$430

Safari Model Lux—.458 Win. Mag., 23.62 in. barrel, 10½ lbs. Imported 1986-87 only.

	$1,650	$1,400	$1,100	$940	$775	$680	$600

Last Mfg.'s Sug. Retail was $1,825.

Add 45% for grade I engraving, 65% for grade II engraving, 80% for grade III, and 100% for grade IV engraving on this model. A left-handed stock is also available - add $135.

MODEL 90 SUPREME—similar to Model 90 Lux, except has high gloss stock, jeweled bolt, and gold trigger. New in 1987.

Mfg.'s Sug. Retail	$1,475	$1,290	$1,085	$935	$800	$600	$465	$430

Add $50 for Mag. cal.'s.

SAUER MODEL 3000 DRILLING—available in either 16 ga./6.5 x 57R, 7 x 57R, 7 x 65R or 12 ga./.222 Rem., .243 Win., .30-06, 6.5 x 57R, 7 x 57R, 7 x 65R, 9.3 x 74R, Greener cross-bolt and double barrel lug locking, cocking indicators, front set trigger, automatic sight, walnut pistol grip stock with hog-back and cheekpiece, light scroll engraving, 7¼ lbs.

Mfg.'s Sug. Retail	$3,325	$2,700	$2,200	$2,060	$1,760	$1,565	$1,380	$1,250

Luxury Grade—same as Model 3000 standard, except select root timber and extensive engraving featuring two animals.

	$3,000	$2,650	$2,350	$2,000	$1,785	$1,600	$1,475

Last Mfg.'s Sug. Retail was $2,920.

COMBO BBF 54 O/U—standard grade combination gun, 16 ga./.222 Rem., .243 Win., 6.5 x 57R, 7 x 57R, 7 x 65R, and .30-06 cal.'s, ejectors, double triggers with front set trigger, moderate engraving on coin finished receiver, Greener cross-bolt with double barrel lugs, 6 lbs. Importation discontinued in 1986.

	$2,200	$2,060	$1,760	$1,565	$1,380	$1,250	$1,125

Last Mfg.'s Sug. Retail was $2,495.

This model is still available in 1987 from the distributor in limited quantities.

Luxury Grade—same as BBF 54, except game scene engraved and deluxe crotch walnut.

	$2,450	$2,200	$2,000	$1,785	$1,600	$1,475	$1,300

Last Mfg.'s Sug. Retail was $2,745.

LUFTWAFFE SURVIVAL DRILLING—12 ga. x 65 mm SxS over 9.3 x 74 R, 28 in. barrels, large Eagle swastika on stock and breech end of right barrel. Originally mfg. for Luftwaffe pilots during WWII. Add 20% for original aluminum case and accessories.

	$4,500	$4,000	$3,600	$3,200	$2,600	$2,400	$2,200

SAUER MODEL 3000E DRILLING—see listing under Colt Sauer Drilling.

SNIPER RIFLE—very accurate, special order only Sniper Rifle, built to customer specifications.

	$4,845	$3,655	$3,200	$2,850	$2,500	$2,275	$2,000

SHOTGUNS

MODEL 60—various ga.'s, boxlock action, DT, extractors, checkered walnut stock and forearm, this model was the standard model of its period.

	$715	$550	$495	$440	$360	$330	$305

ROYAL DOUBLE BARREL SHOTGUN—12 and 20 ga.'s, 26, 28, and 30 in. barrels, various chokes, boxlock, scalloped engraved frame, cocking indicators, SST, auto ejectors, Krupp steel barrel, checkered pistol grip stock, made 1955-1977.

	$1,650	$1,375	$1,210	$1,100	$880	$770	$660

20 ga. — add 20%.

ARTEMIS—12 ga., 28 in. barrels, mod. and full choke, H&H type sidelock, SST, auto ejector, Krupp steel, checkered pistol grip stock, made 1966-1977.

Grade I—fine line engraved.

	$5,500	$4,620	$3,850	$3,520	$3,080	$2,640	$2,200

Grade II—extensive engraving.

	$6,600	$5,500	$4,840	$4,235	$3,850	$3,300	$3,080

MODEL 66 O/U FIELD GUN—12 ga., 28 in. mod. and full, Krupp steel barrels, H&H type sidelocks, SST, auto ejectors, checkered pistol grip stock, made 1966-1975, available in three grades of engraving.

Grade I	$2,200	$1,760	$1,540	$1,320	$1,100	$880	$770
Grade II	$3,080	$2,420	$1,980	$1,650	$1,430	$1,210	$990
Grade III	$3,850	$3,300	$2,860	$2,420	$1,980	$1,650	$1,320

MODEL 66 O/U SKEET GUN—same as Field Gun, with 26 in. vent rib skeet bored barrel and vent forearm, made 1966-1975.

MODEL 66 O/U TRAP GUN—same as 66 Skeet, with 30 in. barrels, full and full, or mod. and full choke, trap style stock.

Grade I	$2,090	$1,760	$1,540	$1,320	$1,100	$880	$770
Grade II	$3,080	$2,420	$1,980	$1,650	$1,430	$1,210	$880
Grade III	$3,850	$3,300	$2,860	$2,420	$1,980	$1,650	$1,320

SAUER/FRANCHI STANDARD GRADE O/U—12 ga. only, double triggers, checkered walnut stock and forearm, SST, blued finish only, sling swivels, VR. Importation discontinued in 1986.

	$375	$340	$315	$290	$275	$260	$245

Last Mfg.'s Sug. Retail was $785.

Regent Grade—similar to Standard grade, except has single trigger and lightly engraved silver finished receiver. Importation discontinued in 1986.

	$475	$395	$350	$310	$290	$275	$265

Last Mfg.'s Sug. Retail was $825.

Favorit Grade—similar to Regent Grade, except has elaborate scroll engraving on coin finished receiver, gold plated trigger. Importation discontinued in 1986.

	$550	$495	$450	$420	$385	$350	$300

Last Mfg.'s Sug. Retail was $875.

Diplomat Grade—similar to Favorit Grade, except has more elaborate scroll engraving and with model name gold filled on receiver sides and barrel, extra grain French walnut, cased.

	$875	$750	$625	$550	$495	$460	$435

Last Mfg.'s Sug. Retail was $1,520.

Grading	100%	98%	95%	90%	80%	70%	60%

SAUER/FRANCHI SPORTING S O/U—12 ga. only, 28 in. barrels, ejectors, SST, select European walnut with checkered stock and forearm, 10mm vent rib, plain silver finished receiver with model name gold filled on both sides. Importation discontinued in 1986.

	100%	98%	95%	90%	80%	70%	60%
	$800	$700	$600	$500	$450	$420	$395

Last Mfg.'s Sug. Retail was $1,375.

SAUER/FRANCHI MODEL TRAP O/U—similar to Sporting S, except has 29 in. barrels, trap chokes and stock dimensions. Importation discontinued in 1986.

	$875	$750	$625	$550	$495	$460	$435

Last Mfg.'s Sug. Retail was $1,375.

SAUER/FRANCHI MODEL SKEET O/U—similar to Sporting S, except has skeet chokes. Importation discontinued in 1986.

	$875	$750	$625	$550	$495	$460	$435

Last Mfg.'s Sug. Retail was $1,375.

SAVAGE INDUSTRIES, INC.

INITIALLY MANUFACTURED IN UTICA, NY, LATER MANUFACTURED IN CHICOPEE FALLS, MA, CURRENTLY MANUFACTURED IN WESTFIELD, MA SINCE 1959.

This company originally started in Utica, NY in 1895. The Model 1895 was initially manufactured by Marlin between 1895-1899. The company was renamed Savage Arms Co. in 1899. After WWI, the name was again changed to the Savage Arms Corporation. Savage moved to Chicopee Falls, MA in the 1946 circa (to it's J. Stevens Arms Co. plants). In the Mid-1960'S the company became The Savage Arms Division of American Hardware Corp., which later became The Emhart Corporation. This division was sold in September 1981, and became Savage Industries, Inc. located in Westfield, MA (since the move in the 1959 circa).

PISTOLS

MODEL 1907 AUTO PISTOL—.32 auto, 10 shot, .380 auto, 9 shot, $3^{13}/_{16}$ (.32 ACP) or $4^{5}/_{16}$ (.380 ACP) in. barrel, blue, fixed sights, hard rubber grips, exposed hammer, made 1910-1917. Add 15% for .380.

	$270	$220	$175	$150	$125	$115	$100

Add 80% for factory nickel finish (rare).

MODEL 1915 HAMMERLESS—same as 1907, with grip safety and no visible hammer, made 1915-1917. Add 15% for .380.

	$325	$290	$210	$190	$170	$150	$130

MODEL 1917 AUTOMATIC—same as 1907, with spur hammer and trapezoidal grips, made 1920-1928. Add 15% for .380

	$250	$225	$175	$145	$130	$110	$100

U.S. ARMY TEST TRIAL .45 ACP—.45 ACP, large version of 1910, exposed hammer, approx. 400 produced during 1907-1910 for military trials.

	$4,500	$3,800	$3,300	$2,800	$2,400	$2,000	$1,800

Some of these models were repurchased from the government, reconditioned (many reblued), and resold to the public as commercial models.

MODEL 101 SINGLE SHOT—single action, .22 cal., 5½ in. barrel, adj. sight, swing out barrel, blue, wood grips, made 1960-1968.

	$150	$120	$95	$80	$70	$60	$50

RIFLES

Savage Industries announced in early 1988 that they will no longer publish retail prices for currently manufactured firearms.

SAVAGE INDUSTRIES, INC., cont.

MODEL 1895—.303 Savage only, lever action, mfg. in either carbine (22 in.), rifle (26 in.), or musket (30 in.) variations, closed top, solid breech, side ejecting, 5 shot rotating box mag., unfired shots indicator, originally mfg. by Marlin, marked "Savage Repeating Arms Co. Utica, N.Y. U.S.A. Pat. Feb. 7, 1893.", approx. 6,000 mfg. 1895-1899, early models had hole in top of bolt — latter ones were smooth.

	$1,500	$1,250	$995	$880	$770	$660	$495

Values assume rifle configuration — add premiums for the carbine (rare) and musket.

MODEL 1899—.25-35, .30-30, .303 Savage, .32-40, or .38-55 cal., improvement of Model 1895, 20 in. round (carbine), 22 in. (round), or 26 in. (round, half-oct. or full oct.) barrel marked "Savage Arms Company, Utica, N.Y. Pat. Feb. 7.1893.", over 75,000 mfg. 1899-1917, approx. 7½ lbs. Older "perch-belly stocks" and high-gloss blueing will command premiums on this variation.

	$695	$575	$500	$450	$375	$300	$225

Add 25% for takedown (added 1909).

In 1905 Savage broadened the variety of this model and added the 1899A2, CD, BC, AB, Excelsior, Leader, Crescent, Victor, Rival, Premier, and Monarch (top-of-the-line model). Prices at the time ranged from $21 to $250 — quite a range of prices. Any factory engraved Savage 99 is rare (less than 1,000 total have been made to date) with values having to be computed one gun at a time. Above values assume standard rifle with no engraving options (Grades A through G).

MODEL 99A—.30-30, .250-3000, .300 Sav. and .303 Sav. cal.'s, lever action, 24 in. barrel, open sight, hammerless, straight grip stock, crescent butt, made 1920-1936.

	$550	$440	$330	$275	$180	$165	$150

MODEL 99A RECENT—similar to original, with .243, .250 Sav., .300 Sav., or .308 Sav. cal., 20 or 22 in. barrel, tang. safety, conventional butt, made 1971-1981.

	$375	$340	$310	$275	$250	$225	$200

MODEL 99B—takedown version of original 99A, made 1920-1936.

	$880	$770	$660	$495	$330	$250	$195

MODEL 99H CARBINE—.250-3000, .30-30, or .300 Sav. cal., solid frame, carbine type stock, made 1931-1942.

	$440	$330	$275	$220	$180	$165	$150

MODEL 99E—.22 Hi Power, .250-3000, .30-30, .300 Sav., and .303 Sav. cal.'s, 22 in. barrel, made 1920-1936.

	$880	$770	$660	$550	$440	$275	$220

MODEL 99E CARBINE—.243, .250 Sav., .300 Sav., and .308 Win. cal.'s, 22 in. barrel, checkered pistol grip stock, 5 shot rotary mag., made 1960-1982.

	$320	$260	$230	$200	$180	$165	$150

Last Mfg.'s Sug. Retail was $343.

MODEL 99F FEATHERWEIGHT—same as pre-war 99E, except takedown and ½ pound lighter, made 1920-1942.

	$440	$330	$275	$220	$195	$175	$160

MODEL 99F—.243, .300 Sav., or .308 Win. cal., solid frame, checkered pistol grip stock. Discontinued 1970.

	$350	$310	$285	$260	$230	$210	$190

This model had the receiver marked "99M".

MODEL 99G—same as 99E pre-war, with checkered stock and takedown, made 1920-1942.

	$660	$550	$440	$275	$220	$165	$150

MODEL 99EG—same as 99G, with solid frame and no checkering, made 1936-1941.

	$550	$440	$330	$260	$230	$210	$190

MODEL 99EG POST-WAR—.243, .250 Sav., .300 Sav., .308, and .358 cal.'s, checkered stock, made 1946-1960.

	$350	$310	$285	$260	$230	$210	$190

MODEL 99R PRE-WAR—.250-3000 and .300 Sav. cal.'s, 22 or 24 in. barrel, large pistol grip stock and forearm, made 1936-1942.

	$495	$440	$305	$275	$250	$220	$195

Grading	100%	98%	95%	90%	80%	70%	60%

MODEL 99R POST-WAR—same as Pre-War, .300 Sav., .308, .358, and .243 cal.'s, 24 in. barrel only, swivel studs, made 1946-1960.

	$350	$310	$285	$260	$230	$210	$190

MODEL 99RS PRE-WAR—same as 99R Pre-War, with Lyman aperture sight, swivels and sling, made 1936-1942.

	$605	$550	$440	$330	$275	$250	$220

MODEL 99RS POST-WAR—same as 99R Post-War, with Redfield receiver sight, made 1946-1958.

	$350	$330	$285	$250	$225	$200	$180

MODEL 99T—20 or 22 in. barrel, solid frame, lightweight, checkered pistol grip stock, made 1936-1942.

	$440	$330	$275	$205	$180	$165	$150

MODEL 99K—engraved receiver and fancy wood stock, Lyman aperture sight and folding middle sight, made 1931-1942.

	$2,200	$1,870	$1,210	$880	$770	$550	$440

MODEL 99DL—.243 and .308 cal.'s, Monte Carlo stock and sling swivels, post-war, made 1960-1973.

	$350	$310	$285	$260	$230	$210	$185

MODEL 99C—same as 99F Post-War, available in .243, .284 Win. (discontinued), 7mm-08 (discontinued), or .308 cal., 22 in. barrel, Monte Carlo stock with cut checkering and recoil pad, top tang safety, cocking indicator, open sights, detachable 4 shot mag., 8 lbs., made 1965-present.

No Mfg.'s Retail

	$525	$430	$365	$300	$260	$230	$200

MODEL 99CD—same as 99C, with Monte Carlo cheekpiece stock, made 1980-1981.

	$370	$330	$280	$245	$215	$195	$165

MODEL 99-358—.358 Win. cal., recoil pad, made 1977-1980.

	$375	$335	$285	$250	$220	$200	$175

MODEL 99PE—elaborately engraved and plated receiver, tang. and lever, fancy wood with hand cut checkering, mfg. 1966-1970.

	$1,320	$990	$740	$500	$375	$300	$260

This model had the receiver marked "99M".

MODEL 99DE CITATION—similar to Model 99PE, except with less engraving and pressed checkering, made 1968-1970.

	$885	$660	$495	$330	$250	$220	$195

This model had the receiver marked "99M".

MODEL 99M—while the receivers on models 99F, 99PE, and 99DE were marked "99M" this is not a model designation. Rather, the "M" barrel designation indicated Monte Carlo stock.

SAVAGE 1895 ANNIVERSARY—a replica of the original M1895, .308 cal., 24 in. octagon barrel, engraved receiver, brass plated lever, straight stock, Schnabel forend, medallion in stock, brass crescent butt plate, 9,999 produced, issued 1970 only, to commemorate Savage's 75th year.

	$385	$275	$220	$195	$165	$150	$140

MODEL 1903 SLIDE ACTION—.22 S, L, or LR, 24 in. barrel, open sights, box mag., pistol grip stock, made 1903-1921.

	$275	$220	$110	$90	$75	$65	$45

MODEL 1909 SLIDE ACTION—similar to 1903, with 20 in. round barrel, made 1909-1915.

	$220	$140	$110	$90	$75	$65	$45

MODEL 1904 SINGLE SHOT—.22 S, L, or LR, bolt action, 18 in. barrel, straight stock, made 1904-1917.

	$140	$85	$55	$45	$35	$30	$30

MODEL 1905 SINGLE SHOT—similar to 1904, except 24 in. barrel, takedown, made 1905-1919.

	$140	$85	$55	$45	$35	$30	$30

Grading	100%	98%	95%	90%	80%	70%	60%

MODEL 1912 AUTOLOADER—.22 LR, 20 in. barrel, takedown, straight stock, made 1912-1916.

	$330	$275	$195	$110	$90	$75	$65

MODEL 1914 SLIDE ACTION—.22 S, L, and LR, 24 in. octagon barrel, plain pistol grip stock, made 1914-1924.

	$275	$250	$195	$110	$90	$75	$65

MODEL 19 NRA BOLT ACTION—.22 LR, 25 in. barrel, adj. aperture sight, 5 shot military stock, approx. 50,000 mfg. 1919-1937.

	$220	$140	$110	$100	$90	$75	$65

Between 1943-1945 approx. 6,000 Model 19's were made under military contract — add 15%.

MODEL 10 BOLT ACTION TARGET—.22 LR, 25 in. barrel, speed lock, adj. aperture sight, target stock, made 1933-1946.

	$250	$165	$140	$110	$100	$90	$70

MODEL 19L—same as 19, with Lyman receiver sight, made 1933-1942.

	$330	$275	$195	$140	$120	$110	$100

MODEL 19M—same as 19, with 28 in. heavy barrel and scope bases, made 1933-1942.

	$330	$275	$195	$165	$140	$120	$110

MODEL 19H—same as 19, except .22 Hornet, made 1933-1942.

	$550	$495	$330	$220	$175	$165	$155

MODEL 1920 BOLT ACTION—Mauser type action, .250-3000 and .300 Sav. cal.'s, 22 or 24 in. barrel, open sights, 5 shot, checkered pistol grip, Schnabel forend, made 1920-1926.

	$330	$250	$220	$200	$175	$165	$155

MODEL 1920-1926—same as 1920, with 24 in. barrel, Lyman aperture sight, made 1926-1927.

	$330	$250	$220	$200	$175	$165	$155

MODEL 23A BOLT ACTION RIFLE—.22 LR, 23 in. barrel, open sights, plain pistol grip stock, Schnabel forend, made 1923-1933.

	$220	$165	$140	$110	$95	$85	$70

MODEL 23AA—improved version of 23A, with speedlock and checkered stock, made 1933-1942.

	$275	$195	$165	$130	$110	$100	$85

MODEL 23B—same configuration as 23A, with .25-20 cal., 25 in. barrel, full forearm, made 1923-1942.

	$220	$140	$110	$100	$90	$75	$65

MODEL 23C—same as 23B, with .32-20, made 1923-1942.

	$220	$140	$110	$100	$90	$75	$65

MODEL 23D—same as 23B, with .22 Hornet, made 1933-1947.

	$305	$250	$220	$195	$165	$140	$110

MODEL 25 SLIDE ACTION—.22 S, L, or LR, 24 in. octagon barrel, open sight, takedown, hammerless, tube mag., plain pistol grip stock, made 1925-1929.

	$330	$275	$220	$140	$110	$75	$65

MODEL 40 BOLT ACTION RIFLE—.250-3000, .300 Sav., .30-30, and .30-06 cal.'s, 22 or 24 in. barrel, open sight, 4 shot mag., plain pistol grip stock, Schnabel forend, made 1928-1940.

	$330	$220	$195	$165	$155	$140	$120

MODEL 45 SUPER—same as 40, with Lyman receiver sight and checkered stock, made 1928-1940.

	$385	$275	$250	$200	$175	$165	$140

MODEL 29 SLIDE ACTION—.22 S, L, or LR, 22 in. barrel, octagon until 1940, round on post-WWII, open sights, checkered pistol grip stock on pre-war, plain on late model, made 1929-1967.

	$275	$220	$165	$100	$90	$75	$65
Pre-war	$330	$275	$195	$120	$110	$100	$90

Grading	100%	98%	95%	90%	80%	70%	60%

MODEL 3 SINGLE SHOT—.22 S, L, or LR, bolt action, 26 in. barrel, 24 in. barrel on post-war, open sights, plain grip stock, made 1933-1952.

	$85	$65	$55	$40	$30	$30	$30

MODEL 3S—same as 3, with aperture sight, made 1933-1942.

	$100	$85	$70	$55	$40	$30	$30

MODEL 3ST—same as 3S, with swivels and sling, made 1933-1942.

	$110	$90	$85	$70	$45	$35	$30

MODEL 4 BOLT ACTION REPEATER—.22 S, L, or LR, 24 in. barrel, open sight, takedown, 5 shot, checkered pistol grip stock on pre-war, plain stock on post-war, made 1933-1965.

	$110	$85	$70	$55	$40	$30	$30
Pre-war	$120	$95	$85	$65	$50	$40	$30

MODEL 4S—same as 4, with aperture sight, made 1933-1942.

	$120	$90	$75	$65	$55	$40	$30

MODEL 4M—same as 4, except .22 WRM.

	$110	$85	$70	$55	$45	$30	$30

MODEL 5—same as 4, with tubular mag., made 1936-1961.

	$110	$85	$70	$55	$45	$30	$30

MODEL 5S—same as 5, with aperture sight, made 1936-1942.

	$120	$95	$85	$65	$55	$40	$30

MODEL 6 AUTOLOADER—.22 S, L, or LR, 24 in. barrel, tubular mag., takedown, checkered pistol grip stock on pre-war, plain stock on post-war, made 1938-1968.

	$140	$110	$95	$85	$65	$55	$40
Pre-war	$150	$120	$105	$95	$75	$65	$50

MODEL 6S—same as 6, with aperture sight, made 1938-1942.

	$150	$120	$105	$95	$75	$65	$45

MODEL 7 AUTOLOADER—same as 6, with box mag., made 1939-1951.

	$140	$110	$95	$65	$55	$55	$40
Pre-war	$150	$120	$105	$95	$75	$65	$50

MODEL 7S—same as 7, with aperture sight, made 1938-1942.

	$150	$120	$105	$95	$75	$65	$45

MODEL 60 AUTOLOADER—.22 LR, 20 in. barrel, leaf sight, tubular mag., checkered Monte Carlo stock, made 1969-1972.

	$95	$85	$70	$55	$45	$35	$30

MODEL 90 AUTOLOADING CARBINE—same as 60, with 16½ in. barrel, plain carbine stock, with barrel band.

	$95	$85	$70	$55	$45	$35	$30

MODEL 88 AUTOLOADER—same as 60, except has walnut finished hardwood stock, made 1969-1972.

	$85	$65	$55	$45	$40	$35	$30

MODEL 63K SINGLE SHOT—.22 S, L, or LR, bolt action, 18 in. barrel, open sights, trigger locks with key, full length pistol grip stock, made 1970-1972.

	$80	$65	$55	$45	$40	$35	$30

MODEL 63KM—same as 63K, except .22 WRM.

	$90	$70	$65	$55	$45	$40	$35

MODEL 219 SINGLE SHOT—.22 Hornet, .25-20, .32-20, and .30-30 cal.'s, 26 in. barrel, open sight, hammerless, break open, top lever, plain pistol grip stock, made 1938-1965.

	$100	$85	$70	$55	$45	$35	$30

MODEL 219L—same as 219, with side lever, made 1965-1967.

	$100	$85	$70	$55	$45	$35	$30

MODELS 221, 222, 223, 227, 228, AND 229—single barrel, same as 219, only supplied with additional shotgun barrel, interchangeable, different model numbers are for different cal.'s, ga.'s, and barrel lengths, all have been discontinued.

	$130	$100	$85	$65	$55	$45	$30

Grading	100%	98%	95%	90%	80%	70%	60%

SAVAGE/STEVENS MODEL 65—please refer to listing under Stevens section.

MODEL 34M—same as 34, chambered for .22 WRM, made 1969-1973.

	$90	$70	$55	$45	$35	$30	$30

MODEL 35—.22 LR, bolt action, 22 in. barrel, 5 shot clip mag., open sights, hardwood Monte Carlo stock. Discontinued in 1985.

	$90	$80	$65	$50	$35	$30	$30

Last Mfg.'s Sug. Retail was $100.

MODEL 46—same as 34, with tubular mag., made 1969-1973.

	$90	$70	$55	$45	$35	$30	$30

MODEL 65M—same as 65, in .22 WRM.

	$95	$75	$65	$55	$45	$35	$30

SAVAGE/STEVENS MODEL 72 "CRACKSHOT"—please refer to listing under Stevens section.

SAVAGE/STEVENS MODEL 89 SINGLE SHOT—please refer to listing under Stevens section.

MODEL 340 BOLT ACTION—.22 Hornet, .222 Rem., .223 Win., and .30-30 cal.'s, 22 and 24 in. barrel, open sights, 4 or 5 shot mag., 7½ lbs., plain pistol grip stock, made 1950-1985.

	$225	$195	$170	$160	$150	$140	$130

Last Mfg.'s Sug. Retail was $257.

EL 340C—same as 340, with aperture sight, checkered stock and sling swivels, made 1952-1960.

	$235	$205	$180	$165	$155	$145	$135

MODEL 340V—.225 Win., varmint configuration, 24 in. barrel, limited mfg. in late 1960's.

	$295	$265	$235	$205	$180	$165	$150

MODEL 340S DELUXE—same as 340, with aperture sight, checkered stock, sling swivels, made 1952-1960.

	$260	$225	$205	$190	$175	$160	$150

MODEL 342 AND 342S—same as 340, .22 Hornet designation, made 1950-1955.

	$250	$215	$200	$185	$170	$160	$150

MODEL 110 SPORTER—.243, .270, .308, and .30-06 cal.'s, 22 in. barrel, open sight, 4 shot, checkered pistol grip stock, made 1958-1963.

	$175	$145	$120	$110	$95	$85	$55

MODEL 110-MC—same as 110, with Monte Carlo stock, made 1959-1969.

	$195	$160	$140	$120	$110	$95	$85

MODEL 110-M—same as 110MC, except 7mm Mag., .264 Mag., .300 Win. Mag., and .338 Mag. cal.'s, recoil pad, made 1963-1969.

	$275	$220	$195	$150	$140	$125	$110

MODEL 110-D—.22-250 (discontinued), .223, .243, .25-06 (discontinued), .270, .308 (discontinued), .30-06, 7mm Mag., .300 Win. Mag. (discontinued), and .338 Win. Mag. cal.'s, similar to Model 110B, push button detachable mag., checkered walnut stock, removable and adj. rear sight, 7½ lbs., made 1966-1988.

	$340	$290	$260	$240	$215	$190	$170

Add $80 for left-hand version.

Last Mfg.'s Sug. Retail was $409.

MODEL 110-E—.22-250, .223, .243, .270, 7mm Rem. Mag., .308 Win., and .30-06 cal.'s, 22 or 24 (Mag. only) in. barrel, open sights, uncheckered hardwood Monte Carlo stock, push button detachable 5 shot mag., 7 lbs., made 1963-1988.

	$260	$230	$190	$175	$165	$155	$145

Subtract $16 without sights.

Last Mfg.'s Sug. Retail was $325.

MODEL 110-F—available in 8 cal.'s between .22-250 and .300 Win. Mag., 22 or 24 (Magnum) in. barrel, black DuPont Rynite stock with swivel studs and recoil pad, adj. rear sight, drilled and tapped for scope mounts, 4 or 5 shot mag., 6¾ lbs. New in 1989.

No Mfg.'s Retail	$400	$340	$300	$275	$250	$225	$200

SAVAGE INDUSTRIES, INC., cont.

Grading	100%	98%	95%	90%	80%	70%	60%

MODEL 110-FX—similar to Model 110-F except is without sights and has integral Weaver type scope bases. New in 1989.

No Mfg.'s Retail — $385 $330 $290 $260 $230 $200 $185

MODEL 110-G—available in 8 cal.'s between .22-250 and .300 Win. Mag., top loading internal box mag., 22 or 24 in. barrel, checkered hardwood stock, approx. 7 lbs. New in 1989.

No Mfg.'s Retail — $330 $275 $230 $215 $200 $190 $180

Add $60 for left-hand action (.30-06, .270, or 7mm Rem. Mag. only).

MODEL 110-GX—similar to Model 110-G except has no sights and includes integral Weaver type scope bases. New in 1989.

No Mfg.'s Retail — $350 $285 $240 $220 $200 $190 $180

Add $60 for left-hand action (.30-06, .270, or 7mm Rem. Mag. only).

MODEL 110-K—.243, .270, and .30-06 cal.'s, incorporates laminated camouflage stock. Mfg. 1986-1988.

$335 $280 $240

Last Mfg.'s Sug. Retail was $399.

MODEL 110-S—.308 Win. & 7mm-08 Rem. (discontinued) cal.'s, silhouette model, 22 in. heavy barrel, Wundhammer swell pistol grip with stipling, no sights, 4 round mag., 8 lbs. 10 oz. Discontinued in 1985.

$340 $290 $255 $225 $205 $190 $175

Last Mfg.'s Sug. Retail was $385.

MODEL 110-V—.22-250 or .223 cal.'s only, varmint model, 26 in. heavy barrel, no sights, 5 shot mag., stippled walnut Wundhammer pistol grip stock, 9¼ lbs. Disc. in 1989.

$370 $315 $265 $230 $205 $190 $175

Last Mfg.'s Sug. Retail was $439.

MODEL 110-GV—.22-250 or .223 Rem. cal., 24 in. medium barrel, no sights, checkered hardwood stock with rubber rifle pad, drilled and tapped for scope, 8¼ lbs. New in 1989.

No Mfg.'s Retail — $375 $300 $250 $235 $210 $190 $180

MODEL 110-B—same as 110E, select stock and pistol grip cap on previous manufacture, made 1976-1979. Reintroduced in 1989 with laminate stock.

1976-1979 mfg. — $360 $300 $265 $235 $205 $190 $175

Model 110-B Laminate—includes .300 Win. Mag. cal., brown laminate stock with iron sights, approx. 7½ lbs. New in 1989.

No Mfg.'s Retail — $385 $330 $290 $260 $230 $200 $185

MODEL 110-P PREMIER GRADE—similar to 110B, with select French walnut stock, skip checkered, rosewood forend and pistol grip cap, sling swivels, 7mm Mag. has recoil pad, made 1964-1970.

| | $440 | $330 | $310 | $275 | $250 | $220 | $195 |
| 7mm Mag. | $460 | $350 | $330 | $305 | $275 | $240 | $220 |

MODEL 110-PE PRESENTATION GRADE—same as 110P, with engraved receiver, floorplate and trigger guard, made 1968-1970.

| | $660 | $550 | $525 | $470 | $440 | $415 | $385 |
| 7mm Mag. | $690 | $580 | $550 | $495 | $470 | $440 | $415 |

MODEL 111 CHIEFTAIN ACTION—.243, .270, 7 x 57mm, 7mm Mag., and .30-06 cal.'s, 22 in. barrel, 24 in. barrel on Mag., leaf sight, 4 shot detachable mag., checkered walnut Monte Carlo stock, pistol grip cap, sling swivels, made 1974-1978.

| | $330 | $275 | $240 | $220 | $195 | $165 | $155 |
| Magnum | $315 | $285 | $265 | $240 | $220 | $195 | $165 |

MODEL 112V VARMINT RIFLE—single shot, bolt action, .220 Swift, .222 Rem., .223 Rem., .22-250, .243, and .25-06 cal.'s, 26 in. heavy barrel, no sights, heavy select walnut stock, checkered, swivels, made 1975-1978.

$305 $275 $250 $230 $210 $175 $155

MODEL 112 R—.22-250, .25-06, or .243 cal., similar to Model 112V, except has 4 shot mag. Disc. in 1980.

$340 $305 $275 $250 $230 $210 $175

Grading	100%	98%	95%	90%	80%	70%	60%

MODEL 170 PUMP RIFLE—.30-30 and .35 Rem. cal.'s, 22 in. barrel, folding leaf sight, 3 shot tube mag., checkered pistol grip stock, made 1970-1981.

	$180	$155	$140	$110	$90	$65	$55

MODEL 170C—same as 170, .30-30 only, 18½ in. barrel. Made 1974-1981.

COMBINATION GUNS

Savage Industries announced in early 1988 that they will no longer publish retail prices for their currently manufactured firearms.

MODEL 24 O/U COMBINATION GUN—.22 over .410, 24 in. separated barrels, open rifle sight, visible hammer, break open, plain pistol grip stock, made 1950-1965.

	$130	$110	$100	$85	$70	$55	$40

MODEL 24S—same as 24, with 20 ga. or .410 barrel, sidelever, dovetail for scope, made 1965-1971.

	$155	$135	$120	$100	$90	$80	$75

MODEL 24MS—same as 24S, with .22 WRM barrel, made 1965-1971.

	$140	$120	$110	$90	$85	$70	$55

MODEL 24DL—same as 24S, with top lever, satin chrome frame and checkered stock, made 1965-1969.

	$140	$120	$110	$90	$85	$70	$55

MODEL 24MDL—same as 24DL, with .22 WRM barrel, made 1965-1969.

	$145	$125	$115	$95	$85	$70	$55

MODEL 24FG—same as 24S, with top lever, made 1972-discontinued.

	$130	$110	$90	$85	$65	$55	$40

MODEL 24 FIELD—.22 LR or .22 Mag. over 20 or .410 ga., lightweight field version, 24 in. separated barrels, 3 in. chambers, 6¾ lbs. Disc. in 1989.

	$175	$145	$120	$100	$85	$80	$70

Last Mfg.'s Sug. Retail was $209.

MODEL 24F—choice of .222 Rem., .223 Rem., or .30-30 cal. over 12 or 20 ga., 3 in. chamber, stocked in wood or matte black DuPont Rynite synthetic, hammer block safety, DT's, approx. 7½ lbs. New in 1989.

No Mfg.'s Retail	$350	$300	$265	$230	$200	$175	$150

Add $20 for shotgun choke tube.
Add $35 for Camo Rynite stock.

MODEL 24V—simiar to 24, with .22 Hornet (discontinued in 1984), .222, .223, .30-30, .357 Max., or .357 Mag.(disc.), over 24 in. 20 ga. (3 in.) barrel, single trigger, 7 lbs., made 1971-present.

No Mfg.'s Retail	$300	$265	$230	$200	$175	$150	$130

MODEL 24D—.22 LR or .22 Mag. over .410 or 20 ga., black or case hardened frame, game scene decoration was eliminated in 1974, forearm not checkered after 1976.

	$210	$160	$130	$115	$105	$100	$95

MODEL 24C CAMPER'S COMPANION—nickel finish, .22 LR over 20 ga., 20 in. barrel cylinder bore, buttplate stores 11 cartridges, carrying case, made 1972-1988.

	$200	$165	$130	$115	$105	$95	$80

Last Mfg.'s Sug. Retail was $239.

MODEL 24 VS CAMPER'S COMPANION—same as 24CS, only .357 Mag. over 20 ga., nickel finish.

	$250	$210	$185	$160	$145	$135	$120

SHOTGUNS

MODEL 389—12 ga. over choice of .308 Win. or .222 Rem., choke tubes standard, double trigger, checkered walnut stock and forearm with recoil pad. New in 1988.

Prices have yet to be established on this model at this writing.

MODEL 420 O/U—12, 16, and 20 ga.'s, 26-30 in. barrel, various chokes, boxlock, double trigger, extractors, plain pistol grip stock made 1938-1942.

	$385	$305	$275	$250	$210	$195	$155
Single trigger	$440	$360	$330	$305	$265	$220	$195

Grading	100%	98%	95%	90%	80%	70%	60%

MODEL 430—same as 420, with checkered stock and solid rib, recoil pad.

	100%	98%	95%	90%	80%	70%	60%
	$440	$360	$305	$275	$240	$220	$195
Single trigger	$495	$415	$360	$320	$285	$265	$220

MODEL 220 SINGLE BARREL—12, 16, 20, and .410 ga.'s, 26-32 in. barrel, various chokes, hammerless, plain pistol grip stock, made 1938-1965.

	$90	$65	$55	$45	$35	$30	$30

MODEL 220P—same as 220, with poly choke, not made in .410.

	$90	$65	$55	$45	$35	$30	$30

MODEL 220 AC—same as 220, with Savage adj. choke.

	$100	$85	$65	$55	$45	$35	$30

MODEL 220L—same as 220, with sidelever, made 1965-1972.

	$90	$65	$55	$45	$35	$30	$30

MODEL 720 AUTOLOADER STANDARD—12 and 16 ga.'s, Browning A-5 style action, 26-32 in. barrels, various choke, checkered pistol grip stock, made 1930-1949.

	$275	$195	$165	$155	$140	$120	$110

MODEL 726 UPLAND SPORTER—same as 720, except 2 shell mag., made 1931-1949.

	$275	$195	$165	$155	$140	$120	$110

MODEL 740C SKEET GUN—same as 726, with Cutts Compensator and skeet stock, 24½ in. barrel, made 1936-1949.

	$305	$230	$200	$175	$155	$140	$120

MODEL 745 LIGHTWEIGHT—same as 720, with alloy receiver, 12 ga. only, 28 in. barrel, made 1940-1949.

	$275	$195	$165	$155	$140	$120	$110

MODEL 755 STANDARD SEMI-AUTO—12 and 16 ga.'s, 26, 28, and 30 in. barrel, various chokes, rounded off receiver, checkered pistol grip stock, made 1949-1958.

	$265	$180	$160	$150	$140	$120	$110

MODEL 755SC—same as 755, with Savage Super Choke.

	$275	$195	$165	$155	$140	$120	$110

MODEL 775 LIGHTWEIGHT—same as 755, with alloy receiver, made 1950-1965.

	$275	$195	$180	$165	$150	$140	$120

MODEL 775SC—same as 775, with Savage Super Choke.

	$285	$205	$195	$175	$160	$150	$130

MODEL 750 SEMI-AUTO—12 ga., Browning patterned semi-auto, 26 and 28 in. barrels, various chokes, checkered pistol grip stock, made 1960-1967.

	$275	$195	$165	$155	$140	$120	$110

MODEL 750SC—same as 750, with Savage Super Choke.

	$285	$205	$175	$165	$150	$130	$120

MODEL 750AC—same as 750, with poly choke.

	$285	$205	$175	$165	$150	$130	$120

MODEL 30 SLIDE ACTION—12, 16, 20, and .410 ga.'s, 26, 28, and 30 in. barrels, various chokes, VR, plain pistol grip stock, made 1958-1970.

	$220	$175	$155	$140	$120	$100	$85

Checkered Late Model

	$230	$185	$165	$150	$130	$110	$95

MODEL 30AC—same as 30, with adj. choke, 12 ga. only, made 1959-1970.

Checkered.	$240	$200	$175	$160	$145	$120	$100

MODEL 30T TRAP AND DUCK GUN—same as 30, with 30 in. full, 12 ga. only, Monte Carlo stock and pad, made 1963-1970.

	$230	$185	$165	$150	$130	$110	$90

MODEL 30FG TAKEDOWN ACTION—12, 20, and .410 ga.'s, 26, 28, and 30 in., barrel, various chokes, checkered pistol grip stock, made 1970-1975.

	$175	$155	$130	$110	$95	$85	$70

MODEL 30T TAKEDOWN TRAP—12 ga. only, 30 in. full, Monte Carlo stock with pad, made 1970-1973.

	$195	$175	$155	$140	$110	$100	$85

Grading	100%	98%	95%	90%	80%	70%	60%

MODEL 30AC TAKEDOWN—same as 30FG, with adj. choke, 12 and 20 ga., 26 in. barrel, made 1971-1972.

| | $200 | $180 | $165 | $150 | $120 | $110 | $90 |

MODEL 30 TAKEDOWN SLUG GUN—same as 30FG, with 32 in. cylinder bore barrel, rifle sights, made 1971-discontinued.

| | $195 | $175 | $160 | $140 | $110 | $100 | $85 |

MODEL 30D TAKEDOWN—same as 30FG, with VR, engraved receiver and pad, made 1971-discontinued.

| | $200 | $180 | $165 | $150 | $120 | $110 | $90 |

MODEL 67 SLIDE ACTION—see listing under Stevens Section.

FOX MODELS B, B-SE, AND STEVENS 311—see listing under Stevens Section.

MODEL 242 SXS—.410 ga., exposed hammers, single trigger, full chokes, made 1977-1981.

| | $155 | $130 | $110 | $100 | $90 | $75 | $70 |

MODEL 440 O/U—12 and 20 ga.'s, 26, 28, and 30 in. barrels, various chokes, boxlock, SST, extractors, checkered pistol grip stock, vent rib, imported from Italy 1968-1972.

| | $495 | $440 | $415 | $385 | $330 | $305 | $250 |

MODEL 440T—same as Model 440, 12 ga., 30 in. only, imp mod. or full choke, wide vent rib, trap style stock, pad, made 1969-1972.

| | $550 | $470 | $440 | $415 | $385 | $360 | $330 |

MODEL 444 DELUXE—same as Model 440, with auto ejectors, select walnut, made 1969-1972.

| | $550 | $470 | $440 | $415 | $385 | $360 | $330 |

MODEL 550 SXS—12 and 20 ga.'s, 26, 28, and 30 in. barrels, various chokes, boxlock, auto ejectors, single trigger, checkered pistol grip stock, made 1971-1973.

| | $275 | $220 | $195 | $165 | $150 | $130 | $110 |

MODEL 330 O/U—12 and 20 ga.'s, 26, 28, and 30 in. barrels, various chokes, boxlock, SST, extractors, checkered pistol grip stock, made by Valmet between 1969-1980.

| | $495 | $440 | $385 | $335 | $275 | $250 | $220 |

MODEL 333T—same as 330, with 30 in. vent rib, imp. mod. and full choke, trap stock with pad, made by Valmet between 1972-1980.

| | $550 | $470 | $415 | $385 | $360 | $305 | $275 |

MODEL 333 O/U—12 and 20 ga.'s, 26, 28, and 30 in. barrels, various chokes, boxlock, SST, auto ejectors, checkered pistol grip stock, made by Valmet between 1973-1980.

| | $580 | $525 | $470 | $440 | $400 | $375 | $330 |

MODEL 2400 O/U COMBINATION GUN—12 ga. full choke barrel over .222 or .308 rifle barrel, 23½ in. barrels, folding leaf sight, solid rib, dovetailed for scope mount, checkered Monte Carlo stock, made by Valmet between 1975-1980.

| | $605 | $550 | $525 | $495 | $440 | $415 | $385 |

SCHALL

MANUFACTURED IN HARTFORD, CT.

REPEATING HANDGUN—.22 LR only, target pistol, mag. fed manual repeating action. Unusual.

| | $425 | $360 | $320 | $270 | $220 | $180 | $150 |

SCHULTZ & LARSEN

MANUFACTURED IN OTTERUP, DENMARK SINCE 1911.

NO. 47 MATCH RIFLE—.22 LR, bolt action, single shot, 28 in. heavy barrel, target sights, set trigger, free rifle stock.

| | $660 | $550 | $495 | $440 | $385 | $360 | $330 |

M61 MATCH RIFLE—.22 LR, bolt action, single shot, 28 in. heavy barrel, target sights, set trigger, free rifle stock, palm rest.

| | $895 | $825 | $740 | $680 | $600 | $550 | $500 |

Grading	100%	98%	95%	90%	80%	70%	60%

M62 MATCH RIFLE—various cal.'s, bolt action, single shot, 28 in. heavy barrel, target sights, set trigger, free rifle stock, palm rest.

	$995	$875	$780	$700	$620	$550	$500

MODEL 54 FREE RIFLE—any American centerfire standard caliber, plus 6.5 x 55mm, 27 in. heavy barrel, target sights, free rifle stock.

	$825	$745	$690	$605	$550	$495	$440

MODEL 54J SPORTING RIFLE—.270, .30-06, 7 x 61 Sharpe and Hart cal.'s, bolt action, 3 shot, 24 in. barrel, checkered Monte Carlo stock, no sights.

	$650	$550	$470	$415	$360	$330	$300

MODEL 68 DL—.22-250, .243 Win., 6mm Rem., .264 Win. Mag., .270, .30-06, .308 Win., 7 x 61 S&H, 7 mm Rem. Mag., 8 x 57 JS, 300 Win. Mag., .308 Norma Mag., .338 Win. Mag., .358 Norma Mag., .458 Win. Mag. cal.'s, bolt action, 24 in. barrel, Bofors Steel receiver, bolt has 4 rear locking lugs, select French walnut, adj. trigger, no sights except for .458 Mag.

	$725	$650	$575	$525	$495	$460	$430

SCOTT, W.C., LTD.

MANUFACTURED SINCE 1834 IN BIRMINGHAM, ENGLAND. PREVIOUSLY DISTRIBUTED BY L. JOSEPH RAHN, INC., MANCHESTER, MI. W.C. SCOTT, LTD. HAS BEEN ABSORBED BY HOLLAND & HOLLAND AND ALL NEW GUNS ARE BEING SOLD THROUGH THE AUSPICES OF H&H LOCATED IN LONDON, ENGLAND.

Because of the devaluation of the American dollar recently, prices could differ substantially from values listed below (computed at $1.75/pound).

SHOTGUNS: SIDE-BY-SIDE

KINMOUNT—12, 16, 20, and 28 ga.'s, double barrel boxlock action, ejectors, deluxe checkered walnut, scroll engraving, current mfg.

Mfg.'s Sug. Retail $5,690 $5,690 $3,950 $3,300 $2,785 $2,450 $2,250 $2,000
Add $790 for 28 or .410 ga.
Add $790 for single non-sel. trigger.

BOWOOD—12, 16, 20, and 28 ga.'s, double barrel boxlock action, ejectors, deluxe checkered walnut, extensive scroll engraving, current mfg.

Mfg.'s Sug. Retail $6,560 $6,560 $5,690 $4,750 $3,650 $2,785 $2,350 $2,050
Add $790 for 28 or .410 ga.
Add $790 for single non-sel. trigger.

CHATSWORTH—12, 16, 20, and 28 ga.'s, top-of-the line boxlock action, ejectors, deluxe checkered walnut, extensive scroll engraving, currently mfg.

Mfg.'s Sug. Retail $8,310 $8,310 $7,100 $6,000 $4,950 $3,750 $2,785 $2,350
Add $790 for 28 or .410 ga.
Add $790 for single non-sel. trigger.

BLENHEIM—12 bore only, upgraded models, custom made to individual specifications, priced per individual order.

SECURITY INDUSTRIES

LITTLE FERRY, NJ.

MODEL PSS 38 DOUBLE ACTION—.38 Spl. 5 shot cylinder, 2 in. barrel, stainless steel, fixed sights, wood grips, made 1973-1978.

	$175	$150	$140	$130	$125	$110	$100

MODEL PM357—similar to PSS 38, except .357 Mag., 2½ in. barrel, made 1975-discontinued.

	$225	$175	$165	$150	$140	$125	$110

MODEL PPM 357—.357 Mag., 5 shot, 2 in. barrel, spurless hammer until 1977, new models have spur, made 1965-discontinued.

	$225	$175	$165	$150	$140	$125	$110

SEDCO INDUSTRIES INC.

MANUFACTURER LOCATED IN LAKE ELSINORE, CA.

MODEL SP-22—.22 LR cal., semi-auto single action, 2½ in. barrel, rotary safety, serrated slide, nickel or black metal finish, simulated pearl grips, 11 oz. New in 1989.

Mfg.'s Sug. Retail	$69	$60	$55	$50	$45	$40	$35	$35

SEDGLEY, R.F., INC.

PHILADELPHIA, PA.

SPRINGFIELD SPORTING RIFLE—'03 Springfield bolt action, .220 Swift, .218 Bee, .22-3000, .22-4000, .22 Hornet, .25-35, .250-3000, .257 Roberts, .270, 7mm, and .30-06 cal.'s, 24 in. barrel, Lyman receiver sight, checkered pistol grip stock, pre-WWII.

	$550	$470	$415	$360	$315	$275	$250

SPRINGFIELD CARBINE SPORTER—same as Rifle, with 20 in. barrel, and full length stock.

	$605	$525	$470	$415	$360	$330	$295

SEECAMP, L.W. CO.,INC.

MANUFACTURED AND DISTRIBUTED IN MILFORD, CT.

All Seecamp pistols are hand machined and hand fitted from stainless steel. Manufacture has always emphasized quality over quantity - this explains why values often exceed the company's retail prices. There is simply more demand than supply. Currently, approximately 100 pistols (LWS 32 Model) per month are being fabricated.

LWS .25 ACP MODEL—.25 ACP, double action, semi-auto, 2 in. barrel, 7 shot mag., stainless steel, matte finish, 12 oz., approx. 5,000 mfg. 1982-1985.

	$340	$295	$260	$235	$220	$210	$200

Last Mfg.'s Sug. Retail was $275.

LWS 32 MODEL—.32 ACP Silvertip, double action, semi-auto, 2 in. barrel, stainless steel, 6 shot mag., 12 ½ oz., limited mfg.

Mfg.'s Sug. Retail	$330	$440	$385	$360	$330	$310	$295	$280

This model is available in either a matte or polished finish. The polished finish carries a slight premium.

MATCHED PAIR—includes both .25 ACP and .32 ACP pistols with the same serial number, approx. 200 sets were mfg. before the BATF stopped this practice.

	$950	$800	$700

This set contains a matte finished .25 ACP and a polished .32 ACP.

SEITZ

SINGLE BARREL TRAP GUN—12 ga. only, single barrel, various barrel lengths, pull or release trigger, only 45 guns manufactured.

	$13,000	$10,000	$8,500	$7,700	$6,950	$6,200	$5,400

SEMMERLING

MANUFACTURED AND DISTRIBUTED BY AMERICAN DERRINGER CORP. LOCATED IN WACO, TX.

Grading	100%	98%	95%	90%	80%	70%	60%

LM-4 PISTOL—9mm (new in 1986) or .45 ACP cal.'s, 2 in. barrel, blue, smallest .45 ACP repeater available, slide is worked manually with thumb on serrated slide-top, extremely high quality, hand fit and finished, a special purpose weapon, very limited production with 14-24 month waiting period.

Mfg.'s Sug. Retail $1,250 $3,000 $2,650 $2,000 $1,600 $1,250 $1,100 $1,000

Because of the limited supply (approx. 100 guns are mfg. yearly), used LM-4's are selling for considerably over their retail price. The original U.S. Army contract pistol sold for $5,000. Earlier production specimens will also command premiums above values listed above.

Stainless Steel—matte finish stainless steel variation of the LM-4, limited mfg. (approx. 100 guns per year). New in 1986.

Mfg.'s Sug. Retail $1,500 $3,350 $2,850 $2,200

SHARPS, CHRISTIAN

MANUFACTURED IN WINDSOR, VT UNDER SHARPS RIFLE MANUFACTURING COMPANY BETWEEN 1851-1855. MANUFACTURED IN HARTFORD, CT UNDER SAME NAME BETWEEN 1855-1874. REORGANIZED AS SHARPS RIFLE COMPANY IN 1876 WITH PRODUCTION RESUMING IN HARTFORD (1876 ONLY) AND BRIDGEPORT, CT. FROM 1877-1881.

REVOLVER, PERCUSSION—made 1850's in Philadelphia, production about 2000, 3 in. octagonal tip-up barrel with rib, .25 caliber, 6 shot.

$900 $850 $800 $750 $675 $600 $500

PEPPERBOX PISTOL—also marked Sharps and Hankins, 4-shot breech-loading, .32, .30, .22 rimfire cal.'s, firing pin rotates, brass frame with silver plating, or case-hardening on iron frame.

First model—5 variations. Scarcer variations can be worth up to 150% more.

$375 $350 $300 $250 $200 $175 $125

Second model—5 variations. Scarcer variations can be worth up to 150% more.

$425 $400 $375 $325 $250 $200 $150

Third model—Sharps and Hankins markings, .32 rimfire short, 4 variations. Premium for scarcer variations.

$375 $350 $325 $275 $225 $175 $150

Fourth model—4 variations, bird's-head grip, .32 rimfire long. Premium for scarcer variations.

$385 $360 $330 $275 $220 $195 $140

RIFLES: BREECH LOADING

The Model 1863 Carbine was one of the highest production rifles of the Civil War with production totaling over 100,000. During a period after the Civil War, the Model 1874 was loosely dubbed "Buffalo Rifle" because of its involvement on the western plains.

MODEL 1851 CARBINE—.52-caliber percussion, breech-loading, Maynard tape primer, U.S. military markings. Deduct 40% for non-martial sporting rifle version.

$3,000 $2,650 $2,500 $2,000 $1,500 $1,350 $1,000

MODEL 1852 CARBINE—slanting Breech, made 1853-1855, about 4500 produced, caliber .52 with Sharps' patented pellet primer built into lockplate. Add 50% for U.S. martial markings. Also sporting rifles in .52, .44, and .36 cal.

$925 $900 $850 $750 $650 $550 $425

MODEL 1853 CARBINE—made 1854-1858 in quantity of some 10,350, caliber .52 with Sharps' patented pellet primer feed. Deduct 10% for sporting-rifle version.

$900 $850 $800 $750 $700 $625 $500

MODEL 1855 CARBINE—U.S. martial model in .52 caliber, breech-loading, Maynard tape primer system, sling ring is mounted on left side.

$1,750 $1,675 $1,600 $1,500 $1,200 $1,000 $800

Grading	100%	98%	95%	90%	80%	70%	60%

STRAIGHT-BREECH RIFLES AND CARBINES, 1859, 1863, 1865.—breech-loading caliber .52 with Sharps patented pellet-priming system in lockplate. (Prices listed are for models that are original and have not been converted). The Model 1859 is worth a slight premium.

		$1,200	$1,150	$1,100	$1,000	$800	$650	$400

Over 32,000 carbines (majority) and rifles were converted to .50-70 centerfire. Can be detected by additional "DFC" ribbon cartouche on left center of stock. These converted specimens (mostly Model 1863's) are worth approximately 50% of values listed above.

COFFEE-MILL MODEL—built-in coffee-grinding mill for cavalry use. Easy to fake.

	$8,500	$8,000	$7,500	$6,000	$5,000	$4,500	$4,000

MODEL 1874 RIFLE—produced from 1871 until 1881, known as the "Buffalo Rifle" in its day. Many variations, cal.'s, and accessories. Research should be done before purchasing.

SPORTING RIFLE—.50, .45, .44, .40 cal.'s. Heavier barrels worth more. Some 6,500 made.

	$2,000	$1,800	$1,600	$1,250	$1,000	$900	$800

MILITARY RIFLE—mostly in .50-70 and .45-70 cal.'s, 30 in. barrel with three bands. Production about 1700.

	$1,400	$1,300	$1,200	$1,000	$850	$750	$650

MILITARY CARBINE—mostly .50-70 cal. Fewer than 500 made.

	$1,750	$1,650	$1,500	$1,150	$850	$750	$675

CREEDMOOR, MID-RANGE, LONG-RANGE, AND BUSINESS RIFLE—these have a basically common look, though there are many differences and variations among them. (Price range is quite general).

	$2,500	$2,350	$2,000	$1,600	$1,350	$1,000	$750

SCHUETZEN RIFLE—.40-50 cal., 30 in. octagonal barrel. Only 70 made.

	$2,255	$2,000	$1,800	$1,500	$1,250	$1,000	$900

SHERIDAN PRODUCTS INCORPORATED

RACINE, WI.

PISTOL

KNOCKABOUT—.22 S or L, single shot, 5 in. barrel, checkered plastic grips, fixed sights, made 1953-1960.

	$110	$100	$85	$75	$60	$50	$40

SHILEN RIFLES, INCORPORATED

ENNIS, TX.

RIFLES: BOLT ACTION

DGA SPORTER—.17 Rem., .223 Rem., .22-250, .220 Swift, 6mm Rem., .243 Win., .250 Savage, .257 Roberts, .284 Win., .308 Win., and .358 Win. cal.'s, 3 shot mag., 24 in. barrel, no sights, claro walnut stock.

	$580	$560	$530	$495	$440	$415	$385

DGA VARMINTER—same as Sporter, except 25 in. medium heavy barrel.

	$580	$560	$530	$495	$440	$415	$385

DGA SILHOUETTE RIFLE—same as Varminter, .308 only.

	$580	$560	$530	$495	$440	$415	$385

DGA BENCHREST RIFLE—single shot, choice of cal.'s, 26 in. heavy barrel or medium barrel, no sights, choice of fiberglass or walnut stock, thumbhole available.

	$690	$670	$635	$580	$525	$475	$430

SHILOH RIFLE MFG. CO., INC.

MANUFACTURED AND DISTRIBUTED IN BIG TIMBER, MT.

The Shiloh Arms Company is currently manufacturing replicas of Sharps rifles and carbines. They are available in black powder cartridge rifles in the following cal.'s: .45-70, .45-90, .45-120, .50-70, .50-90, and .50-140. They are also available in .54 cal. breech loading Percussion Rifles. They are high quality reproductions. The models and values are as follows:

Grading		100%	98%	95%	90%	80%	70%	60%
RIFLES: BLACK POWDER CARTRIDGE								
MODEL 1874 LONG RANGE EXPRESS								
Mfg.'s Sug. Retail	**$850**	**$775**	**$640**	**$550**	**$475**	**$410**	**$350**	**$320**
MODEL 1874 NO. 1 SPORTING								
Mfg.'s Sug. Retail	**$820**	**$695**	**$550**	**$475**	**$410**	**$350**	**$320**	**$295**
MODEL 1874 NO. 2 SPORTING		**$605**	**$520**	**$440**	**$380**	**$320**	**$285**	**$270**
MODEL 1874 NO. 3 SPORTING								
Mfg.'s Sug. Retail	**$725**	**$640**	**$520**	**$440**	**$380**	**$320**	**$295**	**$270**
MODEL 1874 BUSINESS RIFLE								
Mfg.'s Sug. Retail	**$725**	**$640**	**$500**	**$420**	**$360**	**$310**	**$290**	**$265**
MODEL 1874 HUNTER'S RIFLE		**$480**	**$440**	**$400**	**$340**	**$300**	**$280**	**$260**
MODEL 1874 MILITARY RIFLE								
Mfg.'s Sug. Retail	**$845**	**$765**	**$640**	**$550**	**$475**	**$410**	**$350**	**$320**
MODEL 1874 MILITARY CARBINE								
Mfg.'s Sug. Retail	**$725**	**$620**	**$510**	**$425**	**$360**	**$310**	**$290**	**$265**
MODEL 1874 SADDLE RIFLE								
Mfg.'s Sug. Retail	**$790**	**$700**	**$550**	**$475**	**$410**	**$350**	**$320**	**$295**
MODEL 1874 ROUGHRIDER								
Mfg.'s Sug. Retail	**$725**	**$650**	**$550**	**$475**	**$410**	**$350**	**$320**	**$295**
Add $85 for semi-fancy walnut.								
MODEL 1874 JAEGER HUNTING RIFLE—hunting rifle with lightweight half-octagon/half-round barrel. New in 1987.								
Mfg.'s Sug. Retail	**$795**	**$700**	**$550**	**$475**	**$410**	**$350**	**$320**	**$295**
RIFLES: PERCUSSION								
MODEL 1863 NO. 1 SPORTING								
Mfg.'s Sug. Retail	**$740**	**$600**	**$520**	**$440**	**$380**	**$320**	**$295**	**$270**
MODEL 1863 NO. 2 SPORTING		**$550**	**$470**	**$415**	**$360**	**$300**	**$275**	**$250**
MODEL 1863 NO. 3 SPORTING		**$525**	**$440**	**$385**	**$340**	**$290**	**$270**	**$250**
MODEL 1863 MILITARY RIFLE								
Mfg.'s Sug. Retail	**$850**	**$775**	**$640**	**$550**	**$475**	**$410**	**$350**	**$320**
MODEL 1863 MILITARY CARBINE								
Mfg.'s Sug. Retail	**$740**	**$625**	**$545**	**$425**	**$360**	**$310**	**$290**	**$265**
MODEL 1859 MILITARY CARBINE		**$440**	**$360**	**$305**	**$275**	**$220**	**$165**	**$140**
MODEL 1862 ROBINSON CONFEDERATE CARBINE								
Mfg.'s Sug. Retail	**$800**	**$650**	**$520**	**$440**	**$380**	**$320**	**$295**	**$270**
MONTANA CENTENNIAL RIFLE SERIES—mfg. to commemorate Montana's 100th Centennial (1889-1989), limited manufacture, mfg. began in 1988.								
Creedmoor Rifle—.45-70 cal., extra fancy rifle with engraving, 32 in. barrel, 100 mfg. only ser. numbered 1-101, walnut cased.								
Mfg.'s Sug. Retail	**$3,750**	**$3,750**	**$2,500**	**$1,950**				

Grading	100%	98%	95%	90%	80%	70%	60%

Hartford Rifle—.45-70 cal, 30 in. barrel, serial numbered 102-902, case colored receiver, 12 lbs.

Mfg.'s Sug. Retail **$1,375 $1,375 $995 $750**

Bridgeport Rifle—.45-70, 30 in. barrel, similar to Hartford rifle without Pewter forearm cap, 12 lbs.

Mfg.'s Sug. Retail **$1,075 $1,075 $775 $575**

SIG

MANUFACTURED BY SIG SWISS INDUSTRIAL COMPANY SINCE 1860 IN NEUHAUSEN, SWITZERLAND. PREVIOUSLY IMPORTED AND DISTRIBUTED BY SIGARMS LOCATED IN TYSONS CORNER, VA.

PISTOLS

Mandall Shooting Supplies, Inc. located in Scottsdale, AZ still has limited quantities of this model and should be contacted directly regarding prices and availability.

In 1987, SIG announced that the Model 210 and variations would no longer be imported into the U.S. This has resulted in demand surpassing supply for the short term, and as a result, P210's are very sought after currently.

P 210—9mm or 7.65 parabellum, single action, 4¾ in. barrel, 8 shot mag., standard weapon of the Swiss Army, 2 lbs.

Originally manufactured in 1947, this pistol was first designated the SP 47/8 and became the standard military pistol of the Swiss Army in 1949. Later designated the P 210, this handgun has been manufactured continuously for over 40 years.

P 210-1—polished finish, wood grips, special hammer, micrometer sights. Importation discontinued in 1986.

$1,700 $1,550 $1,375 $1,195 $995 $900 $800

Last Mfg.'s Sug. Retail was $1,861.

P 210-2—matte finish, field sights, plastic grips. Importation disc. in 1987.

$1,350 $1,150 $975 $860 $750 $625 $550

Last Mfg.'s Sug. Retail was $1,350.

P 210-5—matte finish, micrometer sights, 150mm or 180mm (rare) extended barrel, walnut grips, special order only, very limited mfg. Importation disc. in 1987.

$1,850 $1,475 $1,325 $1,150 $950 $875 $760

Last Mfg.'s Sug. Retail was $1,795.

P 210-6—matte finish, micrometer sights, 120mm barrel, walnut grips. Importation disc. in 1987.

$1,495 $1,310 $1,200 $1,050 $900 $850 $740

Last Mfg.'s Sug. Retail was $1,595.

P 210 Deluxe Models—various models differ in the amount of engraving, gold inlays, carved wooden grips, presentation cases, and other special order features available from the factory. Prices start at $3,500 and can go up to $5,500, depending on the amount of special orders executed.

Conversion kits can be special ordered converting to either 7.65 Luger or .22 LR cal. Add $630 for conversion kit with field sights or $781 for conversion kit with micrometer sights.

RIFLES

PE-57—7.5 Swiss cal. only, semi-auto version of the Swiss military rifle, 24 in. barrel, includes 24 round mag., leather sling, bipod and maintenance kit. Importation disc. in 1988.

$1,675 $1,445 $1,325 $1,150 $950 $875 $760

The PE-57 was previously distributed in limited quanities by Osborne's located in Cheboygan, MI.

Last Mfg.'s Sug. Retail was $1,745.

Grading	100%	98%	95%	90%	80%	70%	60%

SIG-AMT SEMI-AUTO RIFLE—semi-auto version of SG510-4 auto assault rifle, roller delayed blowback action, .308 Win., 5, 10, and 20 shot mag.'s, 18¾ in. barrel, wood stock, folding bipod, made 1960-present. Importation disc. in 1988.

	$1,700	$1,465	$1,330	$1,150	$950	$875	$760

This model is available in very limited quantities through Osborne's located in Cheboygan, MI.

Last Mfg.'s Sug. Retail was $1,795.

SG 550/551—.223 cal. with heavier bullet, Swiss Army's semi-auto version of its newest assault rifle (SIG 90), 20.8 (SG 550) or 16 in. (SG 551 Carbine) barrel, some synthetics used to save weight, 20 round mag., diopter night sights, built-in folding bipod, 7.7 or 9 lbs.

Mfg.'s Sug. Retail	$1,950	$1,750	$1,375	$1,100	$950	$850	$750	$675

Add $250 for case.

SIG-HAMMERLI

MANUFACTURED BY HAMMERLI LTD. IN LENZBURG, SWITZERLAND. PREVIOUSLY IMPORTED BY OSBORNE'S LOCATED IN CHEBOYGAN, MI.

P240 TARGET PISTOL—.32 S&W Long wadcutter and .38 (discontinued) cal.'s, single action, 5 shot mag., 5.9 in. barrel, blued finish, thumb rest walnut grips, adj. sights and trigger, 3 lbs. Add $100 for Morini adj. grips. Importation discontinued in 1986.

	$1,250	$1,100	$985	$870	$770	$715	$660

Last Mfg.'s Sug. Retail was $1,350.

.22 CONVERSION UNIT

	$550	$495	$400

Last Mfg.'s Sug. Retail was $595.

SIG SAUER

MANUFACTURED IN W. GERMANY BY SAUER. CURRENTLY IMPORTED BY SIGARMS LOCATED IN HERNDON, VA.

PISTOLS: SEMI-AUTO

MODEL P210—refer to listing under SIG pistols.

MODEL P220—double action, .22 LR (disc.), .38 Super, 7.65mm (disc.), 9mm Luger, and .45 ACP cal.'s, 7 (.45 ACP) or 9 shot mag., 4.4 in. barrel, decocking lever safety, matte blue, lightweight alloy frame, black plastic grips, (action is same as Browning BDA), values are for .45 ACP cal. and assume side mag. release (standard in 1986), 28.2 oz., made 1976-present.

Mfg.'s Sug. Retail	$720	$595	$495	$440	$395	$350	$310	$265

Add $100 for Siglite night sights.
Add $170 for electroless nickel finish (supplied with Siglite sights).
Add $680 for .22 LR conversion kit (disc.).
Subtract $25 for "European" Model (bottom mag. release - includes 9mm and .38 Super cal.'s).

MODEL P225—9mm, double action, similar to P220, shorter dimensions, 3.85 in. barrel, 8 shot, thumb actuated button release mag., fully adj. sights, 28.8 oz.

Mfg.'s Sug. Retail	$750	$615	$510	$450	$400	$350	$310	$265

Add $100 for Siglite night sights.
Add $170 for electroless nickel finish (supplied with Siglite sights).

MODEL P226—9mm, double action compact model, 15 or 20 shot mag., 4.4 in. barrel, alloy frame, high contrast sights, 29.9 oz. New in 1983.

Mfg.'s Sug. Retail	$780	$630	$535	$475	$415	$360	$310	$265

Add $70 for electroless nickel finish (disc. in 1987).
Add $35 for K-Kote (Polymer) finish (special order only).
Add $100 for Siglite night sights.

Grading	100%	98%	95%	90%	80%	70%	60%

MODEL P230—double action, .22 LR (discontinued), 10 shot, .32 auto, 8 shot, .380 auto and 9mm Ultra (discontinued), 7 shot, 3.6 in. barrel, blue, wood grips, made 1976-present, 17.6 oz.

Mfg.'s Sug. Retail	$495	$390	$350	$300	$270	$240	$215	$190

Model P230 SL—same as Model P230, except stainless steel construction, 22.4 oz.

Mfg.'s Sug. Retail	$575	$450	$410	$350

RIFLES

MODEL SSG 2000—available in .223, 7.5mm Swiss, .300 Wby. Mag., and .308 (standard) cal.'s, bolt action, 4 shot mag., no sights, deluxe sniper rifle featuring thumb hole style walnut stock with stippling and thumbwheel adj. cheekpiece, 13 lbs. Importation discontinued in 1986.

	$2,480	$2,260	$1,950	$1,700	$1,500	$1,300	$1,100

Last Mfg.'s Sug. Retail was $2,850.

This model was available in .223, .300 Wby. Mag., and 7.5mm cal.'s by special order only.

SIRKIS INDUSTRIES, LTD.

MANUFACTURED IN RAMAT-GAN, ISRAEL. PREVIOUSLY IMPORTED AND DISTRIBUTED BY ARMSCORP OF AMERICA, INC. LOCATED IN BALTIMORE, MD.

PISTOLS: SEMI-AUTO

S.D. 9—9mm parabellum, double action mechanism, frame is constructed mostly of heavy gauge sheet metal stampings, 3.07 in. barrel, parkerized finish, chamber indicator, 7 shot mag., plastic grips, 24½ oz. Imported under this trademark between 1986-1988.

	$300	$250	$225	$200	$190	$180	$170

Last Mfg.'s Sug. Retail was $330.

This pistol is now listed under the Sardius heading in this section.

RIFLES

MODEL 35 MATCH RIFLE—.22 LR only, single shot bolt action, 26 in. full floating barrel, select walnut, match trigger, micrometer sights. Discontinued 1985.

	$650	$625	$595	$550	$510	$460	$420

Last Mfg.'s Sug. Retail was $690.

MODEL 36 SNIPER RIFLE—7.62mm only, gas operated action, carbon fiber stock, 22 in. barrel, flash supressor, free range sights. Discontinued in 1985.

	$670	$580	$520	$475	$430	$390	$350

Last Mfg.'s Sug. Retail was $760.

SMITH, L.C.

MANUFACTURED FROM 1880-1888 IN SYRACUSE, NY. MANUFACTURED IN FULTON, NY 1890-1945 BY HUNTER ARMS COMPANY.

The L.C. Smith shotgun was made from 1890-1945 by the Hunter Arms Company in Fulton, New York. In 1946, the company was acquired by Marlin Firearms Company. Production continued until 1951 when it ceased for a period of 17 years. In 1968, Marlin brought the L.C. Smith back to life for a period of 5 years. Production stopped in 1973. The L.C. Smith is one of the finest American made shotguns and collector interest is very high. All values shown are for hammerless shotguns.

SMITH, L.C., cont.

HAMMERLESS SHOTGUNS 1890-1913

All prices listed below are for guns with fluid steel barrels (except A-1 grade).

IT IS IMPORTANT TO NOTE THAT DAMASCUS BARRELED GUNS IN 90% ORIGINAL CONDITION OR BETTER ARE VERY COLLECTIBLE AND VALUES CAN APPROXIMATE THOSE OF STEEL BARREL MODELS IF THE BORE IS EXCELLENT WITH NO PITTING. DAMASCUS SPECIMENS BELOW 90% CONDITION ARE NOT AS COLLECTIBLE, HOWEVER, AND VALUES FALL OFF RAPIDLY IF UNDER 90%. PRICES SHOWN BELOW FOR 90% AND UP CONDITION ARE VERY DIFFICULT TO EVALUATE AND ARE MEANT AS A GUIDE ONLY — L.C. SMITH SHOTGUNS ARE RARE AND HARD TO EVALUATE IF OVER 95% CONDITION IN THE HIGHER GRADES.

OO GRADE—12, 16, and 20 ga.'s, production totaled appx. 60,000.

	100%	98%	95%	90%	80%	70%	60%
	$1,500	$1,200	$800	$500	$400	$350	$300

Auto ejectors — add 33%.
20 ga. — add 50%.

O GRADE—10, 12, 16, and 20 ga.'s, production totaled appx. 30,000.

	100%	98%	95%	90%	80%	70%	60%
	$1,600	$1,400	$1,000	$700	$500	$400	$350

Auto ejectors — add 33%.
20 ga. — add 50%.

NO. 1 GRADE—10, 12, 16, and 20 ga.,s, production totaled appx. 10,000.

	100%	98%	95%	90%	80%	70%	60%
	$2,400	$1,950	$1,425	$995	$650	$450	$400

Auto ejectors — add 33%.
20 ga. — add 50%.
SST — add $200.

NO. 2 GRADE—10, 12, 16, and 20 ga.'s, production totaled appx. 13,000.

	100%	98%	95%	90%	80%	70%	60%
	$2,900	$2,275	$1,700	$1,200	$825	$650	$500

Auto ejectors — add 33%.
20 ga. — add 75%.
SST — add $200.

NO. 3 GRADE—10, 12, 16, and 20 ga.'s, production totaled appx. 4,000.

	100%	98%	95%	90%	80%	70%	60%
	$3,475	$2,950	$2,400	$1,800	$1,325	$900	$675

Auto ejectors — add 25%.
20 ga. — add 75%.
SST — add $200.

PIGEON GRADE—10, 12, 16, and 20 ga.'s, production totaled appx. 1,200.

	100%	98%	95%	90%	80%	70%	60%
	$3,475	$2,950	$2,400	$1,800	$1,325	$900	$675

Auto ejectors — add 25%.
20 ga. — add 75%.
SST — add $200.

NO. 4 GRADE—10, 12, 16, and 20 ga.'s, production totaled appx. 500, seldomly encountered.

	100%	98%	95%	90%	80%	70%	60%
	$10,000	$8,000	$5,750	$4,500	$3,500	$2,450	$1,875

Auto ejectors — add 25%.
20 ga. — add 75%.
SST — add $200.

A-1 GRADE—10, 12, and 16 ga.'s, production totaled appx. 700. Damascus barrels only.

	100%	98%	95%	90%	80%	70%	60%
	$4,850	$3,700	$2,900	$2,100	$1,750	$995	$750

Auto ejectors — standard.
SST — add $200.

NO. 5 GRADE—10, 12, 16, and 20 ga.'s, production totaled appx. 500.

	100%	98%	95%	90%	80%	70%	60%
	$9,000	$7,000	$4,950	$3,750	$2,600	$2,200	$1,900

Auto ejectors — standard.
SST — add $200.
20 ga. — add 75%, extremely rare.

Grading	100%	98%	95%	90%	80%	70%	60%

MONOGRAM GRADE—10, 12, 16, and 20 ga.'s, production totaled appx. 100.

	$10,750	$9,475	$7,200	$6,000	$5,000	$4,500	$4,000

Auto ejectors — standard.
20 ga. — add 50%, extremely rare.

A-2 GRADE—10, 12, 16, and 20 ga.'s, production totaled appx. 200.

	$15,000	$11,000	$8,000	$7,000	$5,500	$4,500	$4,000

Auto ejectors — standard.
20 ga. — only 6 manufactured.

A-3 GRADE—10, 12, 16, and 20 ga.'s, production totaled appx. 20. Rarity precludes acurate pricing on this model.

Auto ejectors — standard.
20 ga. — only 2 manufactured.

SHOTGUNS: 1914-1951 MFG.

Fulton trademarked shotguns mfg. by Hunter Arms Co. were inexpensive, utilitarian shotguns designed for a price point rather than quality. Models Fulton and Fulton Special were supplied in 12, 16, or 20 ga. When encountered today, values usually are in the $100-$300 range. The Hunter Special, although not a L.C. Smith shotgun, did employ the rotary locking bolt system. This was also a low priced gun in its day and prices today are usually in the $125-$350 range. These models had nothing in common with the L.C. Smith shotguns of the circa.

L.C. SMITH DOUBLE BARREL SHOTGUN—12, 16, 20, and .410 ga.'s, any choke, sidelock, auto ejectors standard from Crown Grade up, extractors on lower grades, double or single triggers, straight, ½ pistol grip, or pistol grip stock, grade specifications differ in grade of wood, degree of engraving, and overall quality.

STANDARD FIELD GRADE

	$1,250	$1,000	$775	$575	$415	$385	$330

Auto ejector — add 33%.
SST — add $200.
20 ga. — add 30%.
.410 — add 300%.

IDEAL GRADE STANDARD

	$1,400	$1,175	$895	$650	$575	$500	$440

Auto ejectors — add 33%.
SST — add $200.
20 ga. — add 30%.
.410 — add 400%.

TRAP GRADE

	$1,550	$1,300	$1,050	$795	$650	$570	$475

Auto ejectors — add 33%.
SST — add $200.
20 ga. — add 50%.
.410 — add 400%.

SPECIALTY GRADE

	$2,950	$2,450	$1,475	$850	$750	$650	$550

SST — add $200.
20 ga. — add 50%.
.410 — add 400%.
Auto ejectors — add 33%.

EAGLE GRADE

	$4,750	$4,250	$3,500	$2,900	$2,300	$1,800	$1,295

SST — add $200.
20 ga. — add 50%.

Grading	100%	98%	95%	90%	80%	70%	60%

SKEET SPECIAL GRADE

	$3,100	$2,575	$1,625	$950	$825	$725	$600

    20 ga. — add 50%.
    .410 — add 400%.
    Auto ejectors — add 33%.
    SST — add $200.

PREMIER SKEET GRADE

	$3,100	$2,575	$1,625	$950	$825	$725	$600

    20 ga. — add 50%.
    .410 — add 400%.
    Auto ejectors — add 33%.
    SST — add $200.

CROWN GRADE

	$5,750	$4,725	$3,850	$3,300	$2,420	$2,100	$1,795

    SST — add $200.
    20 gauge — very rare.
    .410 — rare and very expensive, only 6 manufactured.

MONOGRAM GRADE

	$12,000	$9,750	$7,650	$6,475	$5,200	$4,500	$3,950

    20 ga. — add 50%.

PREMIER GRADE—very limited mfg., rarity precludes accurate pricing on this model.

DELUXE GRADE—very limited mfg., rarity precludes accurate pricing on this model.

SINGLE BARREL TRAP GUN—12 ga. only, 32 or 34 in. vent rib barrel, boxlock, auto ejector, checkered pistol grip stock, recoil pad, approx. 2,650 mfg. 1917-1951.

Olympic Grade

	$1,650	$1,320	$1,100	$990	$770	$715	$605

Specialty Grade

	$1,950	$1,650	$1,375	$1,210	$990	$935	$825

Crown Grade

	$3,450	$3,300	$2,750	$2,200	$1,980	$1,650	$1,320

Monogram Grade

	$6,000	$5,000	$4,000	$3,500	$2,900	$2,200	$1,750

Premier Grade

	$9,750	$8,150	$6,200	$4,900	$3,400	$2,950	$2,500

Deluxe Grade

	$13,950	$12,250	$9,995	$7,850	$5,650	$4,500	$3,500

1968 SXS MODEL—12 ga., 28 in. vent rib barrel, full and mod. choke, sidelock, extractors, double triggers, checkered pistol grip stock, made 1968-1973 by Marlin.

	$715	$605	$550	$495	$415	$330	$275

1968 SXS DELUXE MODEL—same as Standard, with Simmons floating rib, beavertail forearm, made 1971-1973 by Marlin.

	$995	$820	$730	$600	$480	$385	$330

SMITH & WESSON

MANUFACTURED IN SPRINGFIELD, MASSACHUSETTS 1857 TO DATE. S & W BECAME A SUBSIDIARY OF BANGOR-PUNTA BETWEEN 1957-1983. BETWEEN 1983-1987 SMITH & WESSON WAS OWNED BY THE LEAR SIEGLER CO. ON MAY 22, 1987 SMITH & WESSON WAS SOLD TO R.L. TOMPKINS, AN ENGLISH PLUMBING CO.

100%	98%	95%	90%	80%	70%	60%	50%	40%	30%	20%	10%

REVOLVERS: EARLY MODELS

MODEL NO. 1 FIRST ISSUE—single action, .22 short, 7 shot non-fluted cylinder, $3\frac{3}{16}$ in. octagon barrel, bottom break, spur trigger, silver plated brass frame, blue barrel and cylinder, square rosewood grips, 11,671 produced, 1857-1860.

First Type—serial range 1-200.

100%	98%	95%	90%	80%	70%	60%	50%	40%	30%	20%	10%
$4,950	$4,400	$4,125	$3,850	$3,575	$3,300	$2,975	$2,600	$2,200	$1,650	$1,375	$990

Second Type—serial range 200-1130.

$3,025	$2,500	$2,200	$1,975	$1,775	$1,575	$1,320	$1,100	$880	$715	$550	$415

Third Type—serial range 1130-3000.

$2,200	$1,825	$1,600	$1,450	$1,300	$1,155	$1,045	$935	$880	$825	$770	$660

Fourth Type—serial range 3000-4200.

$2,200	$1,825	$1,600	$1,450	$1,300	$1,155	$1,045	$935	$880	$825	$770	$660

Fifth Type—serial range 4200-5500.

$2,200	$1,825	$1,600	$1,450	$1,300	$1,155	$1,045	$935	$880	$825	$770	$660

Sixth Type—serial range 5500-11,671.

$1,925	$1,600	$1,425	$1,300	$1,200	$1,100	$990	$880	$770	$715	$660	$495

MODEL NO. 1 SECOND ISSUE—similar to First Issue, except flat sided frame and irregular shaped sideplate, 117,000 produced, 1860-1868.

$360	$305	$275	$220	$195	$180	$165	$150	$140	$120	$110	$100

Second Quality—marked, 4402 revolvers.

$715	$605	$550	$495	$440	$415	$385	$360	$330	$275	$250	$225

MODEL NO. 1 THIRD ISSUE—similar to Second Issue, except fluted cylinder and birds head grip, 131,163 produced, 1868-1881.

$3\frac{3}{16}$ in. barrel model

$305	$250	$220	$195	$165	$150	$140	$120	$110	$100	$90	$80

$2\frac{7}{11}$ in. barrel model

$415	$360	$310	$275	$250	$220	$200	$175	$165	$140	$120	$110

MODEL NO. 1½ FIRST ISSUE—.32 rimfire, single action, 3½ and 4 in. octagon barrel, 5 shot non-fluted cylinder, bottom break, spur trigger, blue or nickel, rosewood grips, 26,300 produced, 1865-1868.

$440	$360	$330	$275	$250	$220	$200	$180	$165	$150	$120	$110

MODEL NO. 1½ SECOND ISSUE—similar to First Issue, with birds head grips and round barrel, 100,700 produced, 1868-1875.

3½ in. barrel model

$385	$330	$275	$220	$200	$175	$165	$150	$140	$120	$110	$100

2½ in. barrel model

$495	$440	$385	$330	$310	$290	$250	$220	$195	$165	$140	$125

Transitional Model—serial range 27,200-28,800.

$1,210	$1,045	$935	$880	$825	$770	$660	$550	$495	$440	$385	$340

MODEL NO. 1½ SINGLE ACTION—.32 S&W, similar to Second Issue, except top break, rebounding hammer, auto extraction, 97,574 produced, 1878-1892.

Early Model—without strain screw, serial range 1-6500.

$415	$360	$330	$275	$250	$220	$195	$165	$140	$110	$95	$85

Later Model—with strain screw, remainder of serial range.

$415	$330	$250	$220	$195	$165	$150	$125	$110	$100	$90	$80

8 and 10 in. barrel model.

$770	$550	$440	$330	$310	$305	$290	$275	$265	$250	$220	$200

MODEL NO. 2 ARMY—.32 rimfire long, similar in appearance to No. 1½ First Issue, except 6 shot cylinder, different barrel lengths, used as a sidearm during Civil War, 77,155 produced, 1861-1874.

5 or 6 in. Early Model—serial range 1-3000.

$550	$475	$420	$385	$360	$330	$305	$275	$220	$165	$140	$125

5 or 6 in. Standard Model—remainder of serial range.

$525	$460	$395	$350	$315	$275	$250	$195	$165	$145	$120	$115

100%	98%	95%	90%	80%	70%	60%	50%	40%	30%	20%	10%

4 in. barrel model

100%	98%	95%	90%	80%	70%	60%	50%	40%	30%	20%	10%
$1,045	$935	$880	$770	$715	$660	$580	$495	$440	$385	$330	$285

Note: Watch for fakes on 4 in. model.

FIRST MODEL .32 DOUBLE ACTION—.32 S&W, 5 shot fluted cylinder, 3 in. round barrel, blue or nickel, black rubber grips, one of the rarest of all S&W's, only 30 produced, 1880.

| $3,245 | $2,750 | $2,350 | $1,980 | $1,760 | $1,650 | $1,540 | $1,375 | $1,175 | $1,025 | $935 | $865 |

SECOND MODEL .32 DOUBLE ACTION—similar to First Model, except irregular shaped sideplate, 22,142 produced, 1880-1882.

| $330 | $280 | $230 | $195 | $180 | $165 | $150 | $140 | $110 | $100 | $90 | $80 |

THIRD MODEL .32 DOUBLE ACTION—similar to Second Model, except no groove around cylinder, 22,232 made, 1882-1883.

| $330 | $280 | $230 | $195 | $180 | $165 | $150 | $140 | $110 | $100 | $90 | $80 |

FOURTH MODEL .32 DOUBLE ACTION—similar to Third Model, except rounded trigger guard, 239,600 produced, 1883-1909.

| $250 | $200 | $165 | $140 | $120 | $110 | $100 | $90 | $85 | $80 | $75 | $70 |

FIFTH MODEL .32 DOUBLE ACTION—similar to Fourth Model, except integral front sight, 44,641 produced, 1909-1919.

| $275 | $250 | $220 | $195 | $165 | $150 | $140 | $120 | $110 | $95 | $85 | $55 |

MODEL 320 REVOLVING RIFLE—.320 S&W, 6 shot cylinder, 16, 18, and 20 in. round barrel, hard rubber grips, detachable shoulder stock, blue or nickel finish, 977 produced, 1879-1887.

16 or 20 in. barrel model—239 - 16 in., and 224 - 20 in. produced.

| $8,500 | $6,600 | $5,500 | $4,400 | $3,575 | $3,300 | $3,135 | $2,750 | $2,640 | $2,420 | $2,200 | $1,925 |

18 in. barrel model—514 produced.

| $8,500 | $6,600 | $5,500 | $4,400 | $3,300 | $3,025 | $2,750 | $2,585 | $2,310 | $2,145 | $1,925 | $1,650 |

MODEL NO. 3 FIRST MODEL AMERICAN—.44 S&W and .44 rimfire Henry cal.'s, single action, 6 shot fluted cylinder, 8 in. round barrel, blue or nickel, walnut grips, 8000 produced, 1870-1872.

Standard Model—vent hole in extractor housing, first 1500 produced.

| $2,750 | $2,200 | $1,925 | $1,650 | $1,375 | $1,100 | $990 | $880 | $850 | $775 | $675 | $600 |

Standard Model—without hole in extractor.

| $2,475 | $2,000 | $1,705 | $1,430 | $1,100 | $880 | $825 | $770 | $715 | $605 | $525 | $440 |

Transitional Model—shorter cylinder, serial range 6700-8000.

| $3,025 | $2,525 | $2,225 | $1,950 | $1,775 | $1,650 | $1,375 | $1,210 | $990 | $935 | $825 | $660 |

.44 Rim Fire Henry—100 produced.

| $3,850 | $3,300 | $2,975 | $2,750 | $2,475 | $2,310 | $2,200 | $1,980 | $1,815 | $1,650 | $1,485 | $1,210 |

U.S. Marked—200 produced.

| $3,300 | $2,675 | $2,375 | $2,100 | $1,875 | $1,650 | $1,540 | $1,430 | $1,265 | $1,100 | $990 | $825 |

MODEL NO. 3 SECOND MODEL—similar to First Model, except bump on bottom of frame and steel front sight instead of German silver, 20,735 produced, 1872-1874.

Standard Model

| $2,475 | $2,000 | $1,675 | $1,485 | $1,275 | $1,100 | $990 | $880 | $770 | $660 | $550 | $500 |

MODEL NO. 3 SECOND MODEL

.44 Rim Fire Henry—3014 produced.

| $3,245 | $2,750 | $2,300 | $1,925 | $1,815 | $1,650 | $1,485 | $1,210 | $1,045 | $825 | $715 | $650 |

MODEL 3 RUSSIAN FIRST MODEL—.44 S&W Russian, 6, 7, and 8 in. barrels, Russian contract 8 in., blue or nickel, walnut grips, looks similar to First and Second Model American, 5165 commercial and 20,014 Russian Contract produced, 1871-1874.

Commercial Version—4665 produced.

| $2,200 | $1,725 | $1,430 | $1,100 | $935 | $855 | $825 | $770 | $715 | $580 | $550 | $440 |

Reject Russian Contract—500 produced.

| $2,200 | $1,725 | $1,430 | $1,100 | $935 | $855 | $825 | $770 | $715 | $580 | $550 | $440 |

Russian Contract—20,000 produced, rare, most sent to Russia.

| $3,025 | $2,915 | $2,750 | $2,420 | $1,925 | $1,815 | $1,540 | $1,320 | $1,210 | $1,045 | $935 | $770 |

SMITH & WESSON, cont.

100%	98%	95%	90%	80%	70%	60%	50%	40%	30%	20%	10%

NEW MODEL NO. 3 FRONTIER—.44-40 cal., single action, 4, 5, and 6½ in. barrel, blue or nickel, walnut or hard rubber grips, 2072 produced, 1885-1908.

Standard Model—.44-40.

100%	98%	95%	90%	80%	70%	60%	50%	40%	30%	20%	10%
$1,650	$1,265	$1,045	$935	$825	$740	$660	$605	$550	$495	$440	$385

Japanese Purchase—786 conv. to .44 Russian.

$2,200	$1,650	$1,100	$880	$770	$715	$660	$550	$495	$415	$330	$275

FIRST MODEL SCHOFIELD—.45 S&W, single action, 7 in. barrel, 6 shot fluted cylinder, blue finish, nickel rare, walnut grips, 3035 produced, 1875.

U.S. Issue—3000 produced.

$2,475	$2,000	$1,725	$1,540	$1,375	$1,155	$1,045	$990	$880	$770	$715	$605

Commercial Model-35 produced without U.S. markings.

$3,025	$2,550	$2,145	$1,925	$1,650	$1,430	$1,320	$1,100	$1,045	$990	$880	$770

Wells Fargo and Company

$2,750	$2,175	$1,800	$1,540	$1,375	$1,210	$1,100	$1,045	$990	$935	$825	$605

SECOND MODEL SCHOFIELD—improved version of First Model.

Standard Model—U.S. on butt.

$2,750	$2,200	$1,800	$1,650	$1,375	$1,210	$1,045	$990	$880	$770	$660	$605

Commercial Model—650 produced.

$2,200	$1,750	$1,525	$1,375	$1,155	$1,045	$935	$825	$715	$660	$605	$495

Wells Fargo and Company

$2,200	$1,750	$1,540	$1,375	$1,210	$1,100	$1,045	$990	$935	$825	$715	$650

PISTOLS: SINGLE SHOT, EARLY MODELS

FIRST MODEL—.22 LR, .32 S&W, and .38 S&W cal.'s, 6, 8, and 10 in. barrel blue or nickel, hard rubber grips, 1251 produced, 1893-1905.

.22 LR—862 produced.

$660	$550	$440	$305	$275	$250	$230	$220	$205	$195	$165	$140

.32 S&W—229 produced.

$770	$660	$550	$440	$385	$360	$330	$310	$290	$275	$250	$220

.38 S&W—160 produced.

$880	$770	$660	$440	$385	$360	$330	$310	$290	$275	$250	$220

SECOND MODEL .22 LR—similar to First Model, but will not accommodate a revolver cylinder, 10 in. barrel only, 4,617 produced, 1905-1909.

$550	$440	$385	$330	$275	$250	$220	$200	$175	$165	$150	$140

THIRD MODEL .22 LR—similar to Second Model, but trigger is centered in guard, 6,949 produced, 1909-1923.

$550	$440	$385	$330	$275	$250	$220	$200	$175	$165	$150	$140

REVOLVERS: MODERN, OUT OF PRODUCTION

Grading	100%	98%	95%	90%	80%	70%	60%

MODEL 1 HAND EJECTOR—.32 S&W long, first solid frame swingout cylinder, 3¼, 4¼, and 6 in. barrel, fixed sights, blue or nickel, round butt, rubber grips, made 1896-1903.

	100%	98%	95%	90%	80%	70%	60%
	$440	$415	$385	$360	$275	$220	$175

LADYSMITH (MODEL M HAND EJECTOR)—originally chambered for .22 S&W (same as .22 Long), 7 shot fluted cyliner, small frame, available in blue or nickel finish, dubbed "Ladysmith" because many women (including Ladies of the night) liked them as a personal defense weapon due to the diminutive size. Over 26,000 manufactured between 1902-1921.

First Model—.22 L, 2¼, 3, or 3½ in. barrel length, serial numbered 1-4,575, checkered hard rubber grips, round butt, manufactured in 1902-1906.

	100%	98%	95%	90%	80%	70%	60%
	$1,350	$1,125	$1,025	$875	$725	$600	$475

Besides serialization, First Models are identifiable by frame mounted cylinder release lever.

Grading	100%	98%	95%	90%	80%	70%	60%

Second Model—.22 L, 3 or 3½ in. barrel, serial numbered 4,576-13,950, manufactured 1906-1910, distinguishable from first model in that cylinder locking device was placed on barrel bottom - locking at both ends.

	$1,200	$1,075	$975	$850	$725	$600	$475

Third Model—.22 L, 2½, 3, 3½, and 6 in. barrel lengths, serial numbered 13,951-26,154, manufactured 1910-1921, smooth walnut grips with S&W medallion inlays, square butt, ivory or pearl grips will command a premium.

	$1,200	$1,075	$975	$850	$725	$600	$475

The 6 in. barrel length will command a premium - this barrel length was also available with target sights.

MODEL 30 HAND EJECTOR—.32 S&W long, 6 shot, 2, 3, 4, and 6 in. barrel, blue or nickel, fixed sights, walnut or rubber grips, made 1908-1976.

	$275	$220	$165	$140	$110	$105	$100

SAFETY HAMMERLESS MODEL (LEMON SQUEEZER)—.32 and .38 cal.'s, 5 shot revolver, rear grip safety, break open tip up action, either blue or nickel finish, barrel lengths range from 2 to 6 in., made 1887-1940, black rubber grips.

	$550	$475	$425	$380	$330	$295	$240
Nickel finish	$600	$495	$400	$350	$300	$275	$240

NEW CENTURY "TRIPLE LOCK"—.44 S&W, .450 Eley, .455 Mark II cal.'s, 6 shot, 4, 5, 6½, and 7½ in. barrel, fixed sights, blue or nickel, walnut grips, has third lock at crane, made 1907-1915.

	$1,175	$875	$750	$700	$650	$495	$440

.22-32 TARGET-MODEL 35 (BEKEART MODEL)—"Bekeart Model", .22 LR revolver made on .32 hand ejector frame, 6 shot, 6 in. barrel, adj. sights, blue, checkered walnut extended grips, named after San Francisco gun dealer Phillip Bekeart, who originally contracted S&W to manufacture this revolver, made 1911-1953.

	$500	$425	$400	$230	$210	$180	$165

1911 production—292 manufactured, Bekeart's original contract.

	$750	$650	$525	$495	$440	$385	$330

.44 HAND EJECTOR SECOND MODEL—similar to new Century, except triple lock feature eliminated, .44 S&W, .44-40, .45 Colt cal.'s, made 1915-1937.

	$650	$600	$450	$385	$330	$275	$230

MODEL 1917 ARMY—.45 Auto Rim or .45 ACP in half moon clip, 6 shot, 5½ in. barrel, fixed sights, satin on military, blue gloss on commercial, smooth walnut on military, checkered walnut on commercial.

Military—175,000 produced, 1917-1919.

	$360	$340	$320	$275	$220	$195	$165

Commercial—made 1919-1941.

	$440	$420	$395	$370	$320	$285	$230

REGULATION POLICE TARGET—similar to Regulation Police, but target sight, .32 S&W, 6 in. barrel only, blue, made 1917-1940.

	$300	$250	$195	$165	$130	$110	$90

MODEL 31 REGULATION POLICE—.32 S&W, 6 shot, .38 S&W, 5 shot, 2, 3, 4, and 6 in. barrel in .32 cal., 4 in. barrel in .38 cal. (Model 33), square butt, walnut grips, fixed sights, blue or nickel, made 1917-present.

MODEL 31-1	$275	$220	$180	$160	$130	$110	$85
PRE-1960 MANUFACTURE	$325	$275	$225	$170	$145	$135	$125

MODEL 44 1926 TARGET—target sight, blue only, otherwise same as 1926 Model 44, made 1926-1941.

	$1,400	$1,150	$1,000	$850	$700	$585	$475

MODEL 35 TARGET—See .22-.32 Target (Bekeart) Model on previous page.

MODEL 45 M & P—.22 LR only, originally manufactured as training gun between 1948-1957, also 500 made in 1963.

	$550	$450	$375	$300	$280	$270	$260

Grading	100%	98%	95%	90%	80%	70%	60%

38/44 HEAVY DUTY—.38 and .44 cal.'s, 6 shot, 4, 5, and 6½ in. barrel lengths, fixed sights, walnut grips, blue or nickel, walnut grips, manufactured 1930-1941 and reintroduced in 1946 (with S prefix starting at serial 62,940). The 38/44 Heavy Duty became the Model 20 in 1957.

	100%	98%	95%	90%	80%	70%	60%
	$350	$285	$260	$220	$195	$160	$145
Pre-War (.44 cal.)	$595	$490	$450	$415	$385	$340	$300

MODEL 20—.38 Spl. and .44 cal.'s, 6 shot, 4, 5, and 6½ in. barrel, fixed sights, blue or nickel, checkered walnut grips, made 1957-1967.

	$350	$285	$260	$220	$195	$145	$125

MODEL 23 .38-44 OUTDOORSMAN—similar to Model 20 in .38-44 Heavy Duty, but adj. sights, blue only, made 1930-1967.

	$450	$365	$330	$300	$275	$250	$225

Add approx. 50% for older 5 screw model.

MODEL 44 1926 MILITARY—.44 S&W, 6 shot, 4, 5, and 6½ in. large frame, blue, walnut grips, fixed sights, made 1926-1941.

	$490	$400	$360	$300	$275	$250	$225

MODEL 51—.22 Mag. only, .22/32 kit gun, 3 in. barrel, 6 shot, adj. rear sight, blue or nickel, walnut stocks. Discontinued.

	$400	$350	$300	$275	$250	$225	$200

MODEL 32 TERRIER—.38 S&W, 5 shot, 2 in. barrel, walnut or rubber grips, blue or nickel, fixed sights, built on .32 frame, made 1936-1974.

	$330	$220	$175	$150	$135	$125	$115

K-22 OUTDOORSMAN—K frame, .22 LR, 6 shot, 6 in. barrel, blue, adj. target sights, walnut grips, made 1931-1940.

	$495	$375	$330	$285	$250	$210	$185

K-22 MASTERPIECE—similar to K-22 Outdoorsman, but improved sight, short action, made 1940.

	$500	$400	$350	$300	$250	$200	$175

K-32 MODEL 16—.32 S&W long, 6 in. barrel, adj. sights, checkered walnut, blue, only 3630 produced, 1947-1974.

	$700	$540	$400	$380	$330	$275	$230

MODEL .22-32 KIT GUN—same as Model 35 1953 .22-32 Target, except 4 in. barrel, round butt, made 1935-1953.

	$300	$255	$185	$165	$130	$120	$110

.22/32 KIT GUN, 1935—4 in. barrel, 21 oz., grip butt rounded. Discontinued in 1953.

	$325	$230	$200	$175	$160	$150	$140

.22-32 KIT GUN MODEL 43, 1955—3½ in. barrel, grip butt square, 15-oz. alloy frame. Discontinued 1974.

	$350	$260	$230	$180	$165	$150	$140

MODEL 13 LIGHTWEIGHT, USAF—.38 Spl., aluminum cylinder and frame. Most were destroyed by the Government.

	$800	$725	$675	$525	$475	$425	$350

MODEL 24 1950 .44 TARGET—post-war 1926 Model .44 Target, redesigned hammer, ribbed barrel, micrometer sights, made 1950-1967.

	$750	$625	$550	$500	$430	$400	$350

MODEL 21 1950 .44 MILITARY—post-war version of Model 1926, same but redesigned hammer, made 1950-1967.

	$1,400	$1,200	$1,150	$1,000	$900	$800	$700

MODEL 22—.45 auto rim or ACP, same specifications as 1917 Army, except redesigned hammer, fixed sights, made 1950-1967.

	$770	$660	$550	$440	$275	$200	$150

MODEL 26 1950 TARGET .45 ACP—adj. sights, thin barrel.

	$770	$660	$550	$440	$275	$200	$150

MODEL 29 S-PREFIX—.44 mag, 6½, or 8⅜ in. barrels. Discontinued.

	$650	$550	$500	$400	$300	$275	$250

Subtract $40 if without case.

SMITH & WESSON, cont.

Grading	100%	98%	95%	90%	80%	70%	60%

MODEL 29-4 SCREW—.44 Mag., 4 screw, 3 exposed screws on right sideplate, mfg. began
in 1957 after approx. ser. no. S175,000.

	$995	$850	$750	$500	$450	$400	$325

MODEL 29-5 SCREW—.44 Mag. 5 screw, 4 exposed screws on right sideplate, approx.
6,500 mfg. during 1956-1957. Subtract $50 if no box. Discontinued.

	$1,050	$850	$800	$650	$525	$425	$375

MODEL 31 REGULATION POLICE—.32 S&W, fixed sights, 2, 3, and 4
(discontinued) in. barrels, blue only. Early flatlatch models - add 25%.

	$275	$240	$230	$225	$200	$185	$160

MODEL 40 CENTENNIAL—.38 Spl., 2 in. barrel double action only, hammerless, grip
safety, checkered walnut grips, blue or nickel, made 1953-1974.

	$425	$345	$290	$260	$240	$220	$180

MODEL 42 CENTENNIAL AIRWEIGHT—same as Model 40 Centennial, but alloy
frame.

	$575	$440	$395	$360	$330	$300	$275

MODEL 43—.22 LR, 4 in. barrel, kit gun, aluminum frame, round or square butt, adj. sights.

	$425	$340	$290	$260	$240	$220	$200

MODEL 50—Chief Special Target, .38 Spl., mfg. from 1955 in 2 and 3 in. barrels, target sights,
most were unmarked for model number. Others were Model 36's.

	$385	$350	$300	$250	$225	$200	$190

MODEL 53 .22 REM. JET—.22 S, L, and LR inserts, 6 shot, 4, 6, and 8⅜ in. barrel, blue,
walnut grips, adj. sights, made 1960-1974.

	$715	$605	$550	$470	$385	$360	$330

> Add 10% for 8⅜ in. barrel.
> Add 25% for early 4 screw Model (pre-1960).
> Add 15% for later 3 screw Model (post-1960).

MODEL 58—.41 Mag, M&P, fixed sights, 4 in. barrel, blue or nickel finish. Add $25 for nickel
finish. Discontinued.

	$385	$340	$315	$290	$260	$220	$200

MODEL 35 1953 .22-32 TARGET—same as .22-32 Target, except micrometer rear sight,
magna target grips, made 1953-1974.

	$425	$300	$265	$230	$200	$180	$160

MODEL 520—.357 mag., N frame, originally ordered for N.Y. State Police but never
purchased, approx. 1,000 mfg. with "N.Y.S.P." on frame, 4 in. barrel, fixed sights.

	$300	$250	$240	$210	$185	$175	$165

.357 MAGNUM FACTORY REGISTERED—This model was made 1935-1938. It
could be custom ordered with any barrel length from 3½ - 8 in. The gun was hand fitted
and registered to the buyer by a number found on the inside of the yoke. This practice was
discontinued in 1938 due to the tremendous demand for the .357 Mag. revolver, adj.
sights, checkered walnut grips.

	$1,150	$995	$850	$675	$575	$500	$450

> Distinguishable by "REG" prefix.

.357 MAGNUM PRE-WAR—same as above, but not registered.

	$660	$525	$470	$385	$330	$300	$275

REVOLVERS: RECENT PRODUCTION

> Add 10% for those models listed below that are pinned and recessed (pre-1978
> mfg.).

*To determine which variation a particular revolver is in the following section, simply swing
the cylinder out to the loading position and notice the model number inside the yoke. A two digit
number followed by a dash and another number designates which engineering change was
underway when the gun was manufactured. Hence, a 48-3 is a Model 48 in its 3rd improvement
(i.e. 3rd engineering update). Usually, earlier variations are the most desirable to collectors unless
a particular improvement is rare. The same rule applies to semi-auto pistols and the model
designation is usually marked on the outside of the gun.*

502

Grading	100%	98%	95%	90%	80%	70%	60%

The prices listed below are for original factory finished guns with no extra engraving. The listings below show 1989 factory engraving costs. These prices should be added to the cost of each engraved production gun to determine the correct value.

CLASS "C" ENGRAVING-⅓ METAL COVERAGE
For J Frames — add $624.
2-5 in. KLN Frames — add $805.
6-8⅜ in. KLN Frames — add $916.
10⅝ in. N Frames — add $916.
Automatics — add $790.

CLASS "B" ENGRAVING — ⅔ METAL COVERAGE
For J Frames — add $1,019.
2-5 in. KLN Frames — add $1,053.
6-8⅜ in. KLN Frames — add $1,140.
10⅝ in. N Frames — add $1,140.
Automatics — add $1,032.

CLASS "A" ENGRAVING — FULL COVERAGE
For J Frames — add $1.070.
2-5 in. KLN Frames — add $1,293.
6-8⅜ in. KLN Frames — add $1,368.
10⅝ in. N Frames — add $1,368.
Automatics — add $1,255.

SPECIAL ENGRAVING—Also available: inlays, seals, game scenes, lettering, prices quoted on request at $5.25 per quotation.

MODEL 10 M & P—.38 Spl., 6 shot, round or square butt, fixed sights, 2, 3, 4, 5, and 6 in. barrels. Nickel finish — add $11.

Mfg.'s Sug. Retail	$323	$250	$205	$150	$140	$130	$115	$100

The Model 10 is currently available in 2 or 4 in. barrel only.

MODEL 12 M & P AIRWEIGHT—same as Model 10, only alloy frame, 2 or 4 in. barrel. Nickel finish - add $40 (discontinued). Discontinued in 1986.

		$280	$245	$210	$200	$185	$175	$150

Last Mfg.'s Sug. Retail was $320.

MODEL 13 M & P—.357 Mag., heavy barrel, fixed sights, square butt, 3 or 4 in. barrel. Nickel finish - add $22(disc.in 1986).

Mfg.'s Sug. Retail	$329	$250	$205	$155	$145	$135	$125	$120

MODEL 13 LIGHTWEIGHT, USAF—.38 Spl., aluminum cylinder and frame, 6 shot, only 14⅜ oz. Most were destroyed by the Government.

		$800	$750	$675				

This model was purchased in large quantities during 1953 and early 1954 only. While S&W never assigned a model number to this variation, M 13 is marked on the top strap and thus retains the Model 13 designation. In 1954, a conventional steel cylinder replaced the aluminum cylinder because of cracking.

MODEL 14 K-38—.38 Spl., target model. For 6 in. barrels single action — add $20. Discontinued in 1981.

		$294	$250	$215	$200	$185	$175	$160

MODEL 15 COMBAT MASTERPIECE—.38 Spl., adj. sights, 6 shot, 2, 4, 6, or 8⅜ in. barrel (6 and 8⅜ new in 1986). Add $31 for TT or TH, $23 for nickel finish (disc. in 1987).

Mfg.'s Sug. Retail	$350	$275	$230	$205	$190	$180	$160	$150

Add $11 for 8⅜ in. barrel (disc.).

MODEL 17 K-22 MASTERPIECE—.22 LR, blue only, 4 (new in 1986), 6 or 8⅜ in. barrel. Add $13 for long barrel (8⅜ in.), $46 for TT, TH, and TS (available in 6 or 8⅜ in. barrel only).

Mfg.'s Sug. Retail	$368	$290	$255	$230	$215	$200	$185	$175

Grading	100%	98%	95%	90%	80%	70%	60%

MODEL 18 .22 COMBAT MASTERPIECE—.22 LR, combat style adj. sights, 4 in. barrel, blue only. Add $30 for TT and TH. Discontinued in 1985.

	100%	98%	95%	90%	80%	70%	60%
	$305	$270	$225	$200	$180	$175	$165

Last Mfg.'s Sug. Retail was $352.

MODEL 19 .357 COMBAT MAGNUM—K frame, .357 Mag., adj. sights, 2½, 4, or 6 in. barrel, bright blue or nickel finish. Add $28 for TT, TH, & TS.

Mfg.'s Sug. Retail	$346	$280	$240	$200	$190	$180	$170	$160

Add $11 for nickel finish.

Model 19 Oregon State Police Commemorative—boxed with belt buckle.

	$895	$750	$650

Model 19 Texas Ranger Commemorative

	$750	$625	$495

MODEL 24—44 Spl., 4 or 6½ in. barrel, blue finish only. TS-TT-TH — add $30. Made 1983 and 1984 only.

	$300	$275	$240	$225	$205	$190	$175

Last Mfg.'s Sug. Retail was $359.

MODEL 25-2 .45 ACP—N frame, blue or nickel, target grips, 4, 6, or 8⅜ in. barrel. Add $14 for nickel, $50 for presentation case. Discontinued.

	$340	$300	$235	$200	$190	$180	$160

Last Mfg.'s Sug. Retail was $347.

Model 25-5 125th Anniversary—.45 LC, presentation cased.

	$450	$300	$250

MODEL 25-5—.45 Long Colt cal., 4, 6, or 8⅜ in. barrel, blue or nickel finish (no extra charge - disc. in 1987). Add $7 for 8⅜ in. barrel.

Mfg.'s Sug. Retail	$429	$335	$285	$225	$210	$200	$190	$180

MODEL 27—.357 Mag., N frame, 4, 6, or 8⅜ in. barrel, blue or nickel (disc. in 1987) finish. Add 10% for wood case, $28 for outlined sights.

Mfg.'s Sug. Retail	$423	$345	$285	$235	$220	$205	$190	$180

3½ and 5 in. barrel—discontinued.

	$400	$350	$275	$265	$240	$230	$180

50th Year .357 Mag. Commemorative—presentation cased.

	$475	$325	$300

MODEL 28 HIGHWAY PATROLMAN—.357 Mag., "Highway Patrol" utility model, dull finish, adj. sights, standard grips, blue only, 4 or 6 in. barrel. Add $20 for TS. Discontinued in 1986.

	$270	$235	$210	$200	$190	$180	$150

Last Mfg.'s Sug. Retail was $306.

MODEL 29—.44 Mag., same as 25, except .44 Mag., 4, 6, or 8⅜ in. barrel. Add $11 for 8⅜ in. barrrel, blue or nickel finish (add $11). Add $58 for wood case.

Mfg.'s Sug. Retail	$481	$385	$325	$285	$265	$255	$245	$210

Note: It must be noted that collectors will often pay a 50% premium for the older 5 screw versions of these current production guns. First year of production Model 29 can bring $1500 if condition warrants. Original boxes are extremely desirable! When examining S&W's for purchase, be aware of these factors.

Discontinued Model 29's appear under the previous subheading: Revolvers, modern, out of production.

MODEL 29 SILHOUETTE—.44 Mag., 10⅝ in. barrel, adj. front and rear sights, bright blue only, Goncalo Alves target stocks. New in 1983.

Mfg.'s Sug. Retail	$535	$445	$370	$300	$290	$280	$270	$260

MODEL 629 STAINLESS STEEL—.44 Mag., same as Model 29. Has 4, 6, and 8⅜ in. barrels. Add $17 for 8⅜ in. barrel, $78 for wood case.

Mfg.'s Sug. Retail	$510	$435	$370	$300

Grading	100%	98%	95%	90%	80%	70%	60%

MODEL 31 REGULATION POLICE—.32 S&W long, fixed sights, 2, 3 or 4 (discontinued) in. barrel, blue only. Early flatlatch models — add 25%.

Mfg.'s Sug. Retail	$354	$285	$235	$195	$185	$175	$165	$150

MODEL 34 - 1953 .22/32 KIT GUN—.22 LR or .32 cal. (disc.), adj. sights, J frame, 6 shot, 2 or 4 in. barrel, round or square butt, blue or nickel. Add $25 for nickel (disc.in 1986).

Mfg.'s Sug. Retail	$355	$295	$235	$195	$185	$175	$165	$150

Early flatlatch models — add 25%

MODEL 36 CHIEF'S SPECIAL—.38 Spl., 5 shot, J frame, round or square butt, 2 or 3 in. (heavy) barrel, blue or nickel finish. Add $11 for nickel.

Mfg.'s Sug. Retail	$328	$250	$210	$175	$165	$155	$150	$145

MODEL 37 CHIEF'S SPECIAL AIRWEIGHT—same as 36 Chief's Special, except alloy frame. Add $14 for nickel finish.

Mfg.'s Sug. Retail	$348	$260	$225	$195	$185	$175	$165	$150

MODEL 38 BODYGUARD AIRWEIGHT—.38 S&W Spl., 5 shot, alloy frame, round butt, shrouded hammer, 2 in. barrel, blue or nickel finish. Add $13 for nickel.

Mfg.'s Sug. Retail	$368	$290	$240	$205	$190	$180	$170	$150

MODEL 40 GRIP SAFETY BODYGUARD—38 S&W Spl. Discontinued. Add $20 for airweight.

	$425	$395	$325	$300	$265	$240	$200

Model 40 Centennial—2 in. barrel, blue finish only.

	$400	$275	$250

MODEL 48 K-22 MASTERPIECE—.22 Mag, 4, 6 or 8⅜ in. barrel, blue only. Add $15 for 8⅜ in. barrel, $15 for TT., TH, & TS (discontinued). Discontinued in 1986.

	$275	$245	$200	$185	$175	$165	$150

Last Mfg.'s Sug. Retail was $320.

MODEL 49 BODYGUARD—same as Model 38, only steel frame, blue or nickel. Add $25 for nickel finish (disc.).

Mfg.'s Sug. Retail	$348	$265	$220	$180	$170	$160	$150	$145

MODEL 649 STAINLESS BODYGUARD—same as Model 49 Bodyguard, except in stainless steel. New in 1986.

Mfg.'s Sug. Retail	$397	$310	$235	$195

MODEL 57—.41 Mag., same as Model 29, except for cal., 4, 6 or 8⅜ in. barrel, blue or nickel finish. Add $58 for wood case, $15 for 8⅜ in. barrel. Nickel finish is no extra charge (disc.).

Mfg.'s Sug. Retail	$427	$325	$245	$220	$205	$190	$175	$165

MODEL 657 STAINLESS—.41 Mag., 4, 6, or 8⅜ in. barrel. New in 1986. Add $15 for 8⅜ in. barrel.

Mfg.'s Sug. Retail	$455	$370	$300	$260

MODEL 58—.41 Mag., M&P, fixed sights, 4 in. barrel, blue or nickel finish. Add $25 for nickel finish. Discontinued.

	$385	$340	$315	$290	$260	$220	$200

MODEL 544 COMMEMORATIVE—.44-40 cal. only, 6 shot, 5 in. barrel, bright blue finish, adj. sights, 7,800 mfg. in 1986 to commemorate the Texas Sesquicentennial (1836-1986). Special markings on frame and barrel, smooth Goncalo commemorative grips, ser. no. TWT001 - TWT7800 (estimated). Made 1986 only.

	$495	$375	$350

Last Mfg.'s Sug. Retail was $600.

MODEL 547 M & P—9mm, 3 or 4 in. heavy barrel, 6 shot, round (3 in. barrel) or square (4 in. barrel) butt, blue only, 32 oz. Discontinued in 1985.

	$275	$240	$210	$195	$185	$175	$165

Last Mfg.'s Sug. Retail was $317.

Grading	100%	98%	95%	90%	80%	70%	60%

MODEL 581—.357 Mag., L-Frame, 4 in. barrel, 6 shot, blue or nickel finish, 38 oz. Add $20 for nickel (disc. in 1987).

	100%	98%	95%	90%	80%	70%	60%
	$275	$225	$180	$170	$160	$150	$145

This model was discontinued in 1985-86, and reintroduced in 1987-1988.

Last Mfg.'s Sug. Retail was $335.

MODEL 586—.357 Mag., L-Frame, 4, 6, or 8⅜ in. barrel, blue or nickel finish. Add $12 for white outlined sights, $27 for 8⅜ in. barrel, $53 for adj. front sight (6 in. barrel only — new in 1986).

Mfg.'s Sug. Retail	$381	$300	$250	$205	$195	$185	$175	$165

Add $12 for nickel finish.

1985 Model 586 Iowa Highway State Patrol—mfg. to commemorate 50th anniversary, gold etching, 4 in. barrel.

Mfg.'s Sug. Retail	$375	$250	$225

REVOLVERS: STAINLESS STEEL

MODEL 60 CHIEF'S SPECIAL—.38 Spl., stainless version of Chief's Special, 2 in. barrel.

Mfg.'s Sug. Retail	$375	$290	$230	$195

Note: 1st models with high polish blue and diamond grips will bring premiums when mint in original box.

MODEL 63 .22/32 KIT GUN—.22 LR/.32, stainless kit gun, 4 in. barrel, 19 oz.

Mfg.'s Sug. Retail	$390	$310	$230	$195

MODEL 64 M & P—.38 S&W, stainless Model 10, has 2, 3, or 4 in. barrel. 3 and 4 in. barrels are heavy.

Mfg.'s Sug. Retail	$351	$270	$205	$185

MODEL 65—.357 Mag., stainless version of Model 13, has 3 or 4 in. heavy barrels. Add $35 for TT, TH, and TS (disc.).

Mfg.'s Sug. Retail	$357	$275	$205	$185

MODEL 66—.357 Mag., stainless version of model 19, has 2½, 4, or 6 in. barrel. Add $12 for white outlined sights, $52 for TT, TH, and TS.

Mfg.'s Sug. Retail	$385	$325	$230	$195

Note: Several models of the Model 66 were made — such features as all stainless steel rear sight and recessed cylinder will bring a premium only when N.I.B.

Model 66 Missouri Highway Patrol Commemorative—cased, with Bowie knife and badge. Discontinued.

	$850	$600	$500

Model 66 Montana Highway Patrol Commemorative—4 in. barrel, commemorates 44 years of service, 213 mfg.

	$650	$525	$425

Model 66-1 Chicago Police Commemorative—4 in. barrel, presentation cased.

	$375	$300	$260

MODEL 67 COMBAT MASTERPIECE—.38 S&W, stainless version of Model 15, has 4 in. barrel. Discontinued in 1988.

	$295	$220	$195

Last Mfg.'s Sug. Retail was $360.

MODEL 624 .44 TARGET—.44 S&W Spl., 6 shot, 4 or 6½ in. barrel, 42 oz. Mfg. 1986-87 only. Add $14 for 6½ in. barrel.

	$340	$250	$225

Last Mfg.'s Sug. Retail was $449.

MODEL 629—.44 Mag, same action as Model 29, has 4, 6, or 8⅜ in. barrel. Add $17 for 8⅜ in. barrel, $78 for wood case.

Mfg.'s Sug. Retail	$510	$435	$370	$300

MODEL 649 STAINLESS BODYGUARD—same as Model 49 Bodyguard, except in stainless steel with combat trigger. New in 1986.

Mfg.'s Sug. Retail	$397	$310	$235	$195

Grading	100%	98%	95%	90%	80%	70%	60%

MODEL 650—.22 Mag., service kit gun, 3 in. heavy barrel, J-Frame, fixed sights. Mfg. 1983-87.

	$250	$200	$185				

Last Mfg.'s Sug. Retail was $305.

MODEL 651—.22 Mag., target kit gun, 4 in. barrel, J-Frame, adj. sights (same as old Model 51). Mfg 1983-87.

	$280	$210	$190				

Last Mfg.'s Sug. Retail was $345.

MODEL 657—.41 Mag., 4, 6, or 8⅜ in. barrel. New in 1986. Add $15 for 8⅜ in. barrel.

Mfg.'s Sug. Retail	$433	$360	$295	$260			

MODEL 681 DISTINGUISHED SERVICE—.357 Mag., distinguished service Magnum, 4 in. barrel, L-Frame. Discontinued in 1988.

	$285	$200	$185				

Last Mfg.'s Sug. Retail was $362.

MODEL 686 DISTINGUISHED COMBAT—.357 Mag., same as Model 586, except 4, 6, or 8¾ in. barrel, target sights, L-Frame. Add $28 for 8⅜ in. barrel, $12 for white outline sights, $37 for adj. front sight (new in 1986).

Mfg.'s Sug. Retail	$410	$335	$245	$225			

1984 Model 686 Lew Horton Edition—2½ in. barrel only, limited mfg.

	$450	$275	$225				

PISTOLS: SEMI-AUTO & SINGLE SHOT, MODERN & OUT OF PRODUCTION

MODEL 35 SEMI-AUTO—.35 S&W Auto cal., 7 shot, 3½ in. barrel, blue or nickel, fixed sights, plain walnut grips, made 1913-1921.

	$625	$420	$370	$330	$275	$250	$225

A slight premium might exist for the first model (up to ser. no. 3,125).

MODEL 32 SEMI-AUTO—.32 auto, similar to Model 35, very limited production, made 1924-1937.

	$1,200	$900	$820	$760	$700	$650	$500

MODEL 10-6—.357 Mag., 4 in. barrel, blued, fixed sights. The first 1200 of the Model 10-6's were actually Model 13's (these were purchased by the N.Y. State Police and are so marked. All 1200 were recalled by S&W and exchanged for Model 28's).

	$375	$300	$250	$200	$175	$150	$140

STRAIGHT LINE TARGET—.22 LR, single shot, 10 in. barrel, sideswing barrel, blue, target sights, smooth walnut grips, shaped like an autoloader, made 1925-1936.

	$635	$560	$495	$440	$415	$365	$350

MODEL 39 EARLY STEEL FRAME—9mm parabellum, 8 shot, 4 in. barrel, walnut stocks, blue, adj. sights, double action M41 without the fine finish and walnut grips, 927 pistols produced, 1954-1966.

	$995	$750	$700	$675	$600	$500	$425

First commercially produced 9mm double action semi-auto in the U.S.

MODEL 39—double action, 9mm, 8 shot mag., 4 in. barrel, checkered walnut grips, adj. sight, alloy frame. Discontinued 1982. Add $25 for nickel finish.

	$360	$325	$260	$240	$220	$200	$195

MODEL 59—similar to Model 39, except has 14 shot mag., larger grips. Discontinued 1981. Add $25 for nickel finish.

	$370	$335	$270	$250	$225	$215	$200

MODEL 41—.22 LR, match target pistol, single action, adj. sights, walnut grips, 5½ or 7 in. barrel, blue only, made 1957-present.

Mfg.'s Sug. Retail	$550	$365	$305	$255	$240	$225	$200	$195

Earlier variations (A series guns with cocking indicator, Model 41-1, etc.) will command substantial premiums over values listed above.

Note: there are several discontinued barrels on the Model 41. They are the 5 in. standard weight w/extended sight, 7⅜ in. with muzzle brake, and 5½ in. heavy barrel with extended sight. Add $60 for 5 or 5½ in. barrels with extended sight and add $35 for 7⅜ in. with muzzle brake.

Grading	100%	98%	95%	90%	80%	70%	60%

MODEL 46 .22 AUTOMATIC—.22 LR, 5, 5½, and 7 in. barrel, blue, nylon grips, adj. sights, 4000 produced, 1957-1966.

	$450	$335	$300	$260	$225	$200	$195

This model is the same as a Model 41 without high polish bluing.

MODEL 61 ESCORT POCKET—.22 LR, 5 shot, semi-auto, blue or nickel, 2½ in. barrel, plastic grips.

	100%	98%	95%	90%	80%	70%	60%
Blue finish	$250	$210	$165	$150	$140	$110	$95
Nickel finish	$275	$230	$165	$150	$140	$110	$95

MODEL 52-A—.38 Spl., similar action to Model 39, 5 in. barrel, originally manufactured for U.S. Army Marksman Training Unit, less than 90 mfg.

	$2,500	$2,200	$1,950	$1,600	$1,300	$1,000	$850

MODEL 52—.38 Spl. wadcutter only, similar action to Model 39, except incorporates a set screw locking out the double action, 5 in. barrel, 5 shot mag., approx. 3,500 mfg. 1961-1963.

	$650	$560	$450	$395	$360	$330	$300

MODEL 52-1—.38 Spl. wadcutter only, 5 shot mag., 5 in. barrel, single action trigger and hammer, bright blue only. Mfg. 1963-1971.

	$500	$460	$385	$350	$325	$300	$295

MODEL 52-2—.38 Spl. wadcutter only, single action semi-auto, 5 in. barrel, adj. sights, checkered walnut grips, 5 round mag. Mfg. 1971-present.

Mfg.'s Sug. Retail	$712	$510	$465	$385	$350	$325	$300	$295

MODEL 422 FIELD—.22 LR, single action, 4½ or 6 in. barrel, aluminum frame with steel slide, 10 shot mag., fixed sights, black plastic grips, matte blue finish, 22 oz. New in 1987.

Mfg.'s Sug. Retail	$200	$165	$140	$115	$110	$105	$100	$95

Model 422 Target—.22 LR, single action, 4½ or 6 in. barrel, aluminum frame with steel slide, 10 shot mag., adj. rear sight, checkered walnut grips, matte blue finish, 22 oz. New in 1987.

Mfg.'s Sug. Retail	$250	$205	$165	$120	$115	$110	$105	$95

MODEL 439—9mm, double action, 4 in. barrel, blue or nickel finish, alloy frame, 8 shot mag., checkered walnut grips, 30 oz. Add $34 for nickel (disc.in 1986), $26 for adj. sights. Disc. in 1988.

	$385	$315	$255	$240	$225	$210	$200

Last Mfg.'s Sug. Retail was $472.

MODEL 459—9mm, 15 shot version of Model 439, checkered nylon stocks. Add $26 for adj. sights. $44 for nickel finish (disc.in 1986). Disc. in 1988.

	$410	$345	$290	$270	$255	$240	$210

Last Mfg.'s Sug. Retail was $501.

MODEL 469 "MINI"—9mm, double action, alloy frame, 12 shot finger extension mag., short frame, bobbed hammer, 3½ in. barrel, sandblast blue finish, amibidextrous safety standard (1986), molded Delrin black grips, 26 oz. Disc. in 1988.

	$370	$320	$265	$250	$235	$220	$210

Last Mfg.'s Sug. Retail was $478.

MODEL 539—9mm, double action, steel frame, 8 shot, 4 in. barrel, blue or nickel. Add $30 for nickel. Discontinued in 1983.

	$388	$375	$350	$325	$300	$275	$210

MODEL 559—9mm, double action, steel frame, 12 shot, 4 in. barrel, blue or nickel. Add $30 for nickel. Discontinued in 1983.

	$442	$420	$375	$275	$250	$225	

THIRD GENERATION SEMI-AUTOMATICS

MODEL 3904—9mm Para., double action semi-auto, aluminum alloy frame, 4 in. barrel with fixed bushing, 8 shot mag., Delrin one piece wraparound grips, ambidextrous safety, beveled magazine well, extended squared off trigger guard, adj. fixed rear sight, 3 dot sighting system, 25½ oz. New in 1989.

Mfg.'s Sug. Retail	$495	$430	$375	$350	$325	$300	$280	$265

Add $25 for adj. rear sight.

SMITH & WESSON, cont.

MODEL 3906—stainless steel variation of the Model 3904, 34 oz. New in 1989.
Mfg.'s Sug. Retail $545 $475 $425 $375
   Add $27 for adj. rear sight.

MODEL 5904—similar to Model 3904 except has 14 shot mag., 26 oz. New in 1989.
Mfg.'s Sug. Retail $526 $450 $390 $360 $330 $300 $280 $265
   Add $27 for adj. rear sight.

MODEL 5906—stainless steel variation of the Model 5904, 34½ oz. New in 1989.
Mfg.'s Sug. Retail $579 $495 $440 $390
   Add $29 for adj. rear sight.

MODEL 6904—compact variation of the Model 5904, 3½ in. barrel, 12 shot mag., fixed rear sight, finger extension mag., 23½ oz. New in 1989.
Mfg.'s Sug. Retail $502 $435 $380 $350 $325 $300 $280 $265

MODEL 6906—stainless steel variation of the Model 6904, 23½ oz. New in 1989.
Mfg.'s Sug. Retail $553 $480 $425 $375

MODEL 4506—.45 ACP, double action semi-auto, total stainless steel construction, 5 in. barrel, 8 shot mag., 36 oz. New in 1989.
Mfg.'s Sug. Retail $653 $565 $495 $400
   Add $33 for adj. rear sight.

PISTOLS: DOUBLE ACTION SEMI-AUTO STAINLESS

MODEL 639—9mm, same as Model 439-only stainless steel, 8 shot mag., ambidextrous safety became standard in 1986, 36 oz. Add $27 for adj. sights. Disc. in 1988.
$420 $300 $275

   Last Mfg.'s Sug. Retail was $523.

MODEL 645—.45 ACP only, 5 in. barrel, 8 shot mag., squared off trigger guard, black molded nylon grips, ambidextrous safety, 37½ oz., fixed sights. New in 1986. Add $27 for adj. sight. Disc. in 1988.
$475 $365 $300

   Last Mfg.'s Sug. Retail was $622.

MODEL 659—9mm, same as Model 459-only stainless steel, 14 shot mag., ambidextrous safety became standard in 1986, 39½ oz. Add $27 for adj. sights. Disc. in 1988.
$445 $335 $300

   Last Mfg.'s Sug. Retail was $553.

MODEL 669—9mm, smaller version of Model 659 with 12 shot finger extension mag., 3½ in. barrel, fixed sights, molded Delrin grips, ambidextrous safety standard, 26 oz. Mfg. 1986-1988 only.
$425 $305 $275

   Last Mfg.'s Sug. Retail was $522.

MODEL 745 IPSC—.45 ACP, single action, 5 in. barrel, stainless steel frame with steel slide hammer and trigger, checkered walnut stocks, target sights, 38¾ oz. New in 1987.
Mfg.'s Sug. Retail $699 $575 $440 $335

RIFLES

S&W in 1984 discontinued importation of all Howa manufactured rifles. Mossberg continued importation utilizing both leftover S&W parts in addition to fabricating their own.

MODEL A BOLT ACTION RIFLE—.22-250, .243, .270, .308, .30-06, 7mm Mag., .300 Win. Mag. cal.'s, 23¾ in. barrel, folding leaf sight, checkered Monte Carlo stock with rosewood forend tip and pistol grip cap, made 1969-1972.
$385 $330 $305 $275 $220 $195 $165

MODEL B—same as A, in .243, .270, and .30-06 cal.'s, 20¾ in. barrel, Schnabel forend.
$425 $305 $275 $250 $195 $165 $140

MODEL C—same as B, with cheekpiece.
$425 $305 $275 $250 $195 $165 $140

MODEL D—same as C, with full length stock.
$550 $385 $360 $305 $250 $220 $195

SMITH & WESSON, cont.

MODEL E—same as D, with no cheekpiece.

	100%	98%	95%	90%	80%	70%	60%
	$550	$385	$360	$305	$250	$220	$195

Note: These rifles were made for S&W by Husqvarna in Sweden.

MODEL 1500 MOUNTAINEER—.222 Rem., .22-250, 223 Rem, .243 Win, .25-06 Rem, .270 Win, .30-06, and .308 Win. cal.'s, bolt-action, 22 in. barrel 5-6 round mag., no sights, about 7 lbs. 10 oz. Walnut stock and forend. Add $15 for Mag. models, (7mm Rem. & 300 Win.), $27 for sights. New in 1983.

	$300	$250	$245	$210	$195	$175	$160

MODEL 1500 DELUXE—same cal.'s as standard 1500, Monte Carlo stock, skip-line checkering, select walnut, no sights. Add $20 for 7mm Mag. and .300 Win. Mag. New in 1983.

	$350	$300	$260	$220	$200	$180	$160

MODEL 1500 DELUXE VARMINT—.222 Rem, .22-250, .223 Rem-heavy cal.'s, 24 in. barrel, skip-line checkering, no sights. Add $15 for parkerized finish. New 1983.

	$350	$275	$315	$275	$215	$195	$170

MODEL 1700 LS "CLASSIC HUNTER"—.243 Win, 270 Win, .30-06 cal.'s, 22 in. barrel, removable 5 round mag., solid recoil pad, no sights, Schnabel forend, finely checkered. New in 1983.

	$400	$350	$315	$265	$240	$220	$195

SHOTGUNS

S&W in 1984 discontinued importation of all Howa manufactured shotguns. Mossberg continued importation utilizing both leftover S&W parts in addition to fabricating their own.

MODEL 916 SLIDE ACTION SHOTGUN—12, 16, and 20 ga.'s, 20, 26, 28, and 30 in. barrels, various chokes, plain pistol grip stock, solid frame, made 1972-discontinued.

	$120	$155	$145	$140	$120	$110	$100

Vent rib and pad

	$150	$195	$165	$155	$140	$120	$110

MODEL 916T SLIDE ACTION—same as 916, except barrels can be interchanged.

	$135	$165	$155	$150	$130	$120	$110

Vent rib and pad

	$160	$200	$175	$165	$150	$130	$120

MODEL 96 SLIDE ACTION—various cal.'s, ga.'s, discontinued.

	$125	$110	$100	$90	$75	$70	$65

MODEL 1000 P SLIDE ACTION—12 ga, various barrel lengths, chokes, vent rib.

	$350	$305	$270	$230	$210	$190	$170

This model is the same as the Model 3000.

MODEL 3000 SLIDE ACTION—12 and 20 ga.'s, 3 in. chambers, 22-30 in. barrels. Add $30 for multi-choke insertion tubes, subtract $40 for slug gun (rifle sights on 22 in. barrel), walnut stock and forend, 6¼-7½ lbs.

	$350	$305	$270	$230	$210	$190	$170

MODEL 3000 POLICE—12 ga. only, blue or parkerized finish, many combinations of finishes, stock types, and other combat accessories are available for this model, 18 or 20 in. barrel. Add $70 for folding stock.

	$332	$255	$215	$185	$170	$155	$140

MODEL 1000 AUTOLOADER—12 and 20 ga.'s, 22-30 in. barrels, various chokes, gas operated, vent rib, engraved alloy receiver, checkered pistol grip stock, made 1972-present. Add $30 for multi-choke tubes.

	$350	$386	$320	$290	$260	$240	$220

12 and 20 gauge—Magnum 28 or 30 in. barrel, steel receiver.

	$350	$420	$360	$310	$270	$260	$250

Model 1000 Super 12—handles all loads interchangeably, top of the line model during its circa.

	$525	$470	$420	$360	$330	$300	$280

Add $50 for multi-choke.

SMITH & WESSON, cont.

Grading	100%	98%	95%	90%	80%	70%	60%

MODEL 1100 TARGET—12 and 20 ga., skeet, super skeet and trap models available. Super skeet has 15 barrel muzzle vents to reduce recoil. Trap model has multi-choke tubes, Monte Carlo select walnut stock and forend. Both alloy and steel receivers available in Skeet model, Trap is steel only.

	100%	98%	95%	90%	80%	70%	60%
Skeet	$400	$390	$335	$260	$235	$215	$190
Super skeet-steel frame	$450	$535	$460	$390	$355	$320	$285
Trap	$450	$460	$370	$310	$285	$255	$225

Note: Shotguns made for S&W by Howa Machinery, Ltd., Japan.

SNAKE CHARMER

MANUFACTURED AND DISTRIBUTED BY SPORTING ARMS MANUFACTURING, INC. LOCATED IN LITTLEFIELD, TX.

SNAKE CHARMER II—.410 ga. only, stainless steel, break open single shot, molded plastic stock and forend, shell holder in stock, 3½ lbs., also available as Night Charmer (add $9) and Sea Charmer (add $18.)

Mfg.'s Sug. Retail	$140	$120	$100	$85

Add $10 for black carbon steel barrel (New Generation Model).

SOCIETA SIDERURGICA GLISENTI

MANUFACTURED IN BRESCIA, ITALY.

GLISENTI MODEL 1910—9mm Glisenti, 7 shot, 4 in. barrel, fixed sights, blue, checkered wood, rubber or plastic grips, Italian service pistol, made 1910-WWII.

Warning: While some Glisentis may chamber and fire the 9mm Luger cartridge, it is extremely dangerous to do so.

$210	$200	$180	$170	$140	$125	$100

SODIA, FRANZ

MANUFACTURED IN FERLACH, AUSTRIA.

Sodia arms are superb and are often excellently engraved and inlaid. Professional appraisal should be sought before purchase, since prices are high. Sodia is famous for double-barrel shotguns as well as two- and three-barrel combinations of rifles and shotguns.

BOCHDRILLING—various cal.'s, top quality worksmanship.

$7,000	$6,500	$6,000	$5,000	$4,000	$3,000	$2,500

DOPPLEBUSCHE—various cal.'s, top quality worksmanship.

$5,000	$4,500	$4,000	$3,000	$2,000	$1,800	$1,600

RIFLE, OVER/UNDER—various cal.'s, top quality worksmanship.

$4,500	$4,250	$4,000	$3,500	$3,000	$2,000	$1,800

TRAP SHOTGUN—12 ga. only, boxlock action, various degrees of engraving and ornamentation.

$2,500	$1,850	$1,475	$1,100	$900	$750	$600

SOKOLOVSKY CORPORATION SPORT ARMS (SCSA)

MANUFACTURED AND DISTRIBUTED IN SUNNYVALE, CA.

SOKOLOVSKY .45 AUTOMASTER—.45 ACP only, stainless steel, single action, 6 in. barrel, 6 shot mag., adj. millet sights, 55 oz., unique action, is free of external devices. Manufactured since 1984.

Mfg.'s Sug. Retail	$3,300	$2,700	$2,200	$1,850

Total production on this model is 50 pistols.

SPRINGFIELD ARMORY

AMERICA'S FIRST FEDERAL ARMORY LOCATED IN SPRINGFIELD, MA. PRODUCTION BEGAN IN 1795 AND AN ACT OF CONGRESS MADE IT AN OFFICIAL FEDERAL ARSENAL IN 1872. NOT ASSOCIATED WITH THE PRIVATE FIRM OF THE SAME NAME LOCATED IN GENESEO, IL.

In recent years collectors have realized that military specimens in 98%-100% original condition are very rare and desirable in most cases. Since the supply of these guns is so limited, values listed below for these condition factors may not be indicitive of current market conditions. As always, many collectors agree that it is hard to overpay for a mint, original, military specimen.

MODEL 1870 ROLLING-BLOCK RIFLE, U.S.N.—.50 cal. centerfire, 32⅝ in. barrel, not serial numbered, 22,013 made.

	100%	98%	95%	90%	80%	70%	60%
	$700	$650	$600	$550	$450	$400	$350

MODEL 1871 ROLLING-BLOCK RIFLE, U.S.A.—.50 cal. centerfire, 36 in. barrel, not serial numbered, 10,001 made.

	$700	$650	$600	$550	$450	$400	$350

MODEL 1873 RIFLE "TRAPDOOR"—.45-70, 32 ⅝ in. barrel, 2 bands, approximately 73,000 mfg. between 1873-1877. Deduct 20% if stock cartouche faint or absent.

	$650	$525	$420	$360	$320	$295	$260

MODEL 1884 RIFLE "TRAPDOOR"—.45-70, 32 ⅝ in. barrel, 2 bands, approximately 232,000 mfg. between 1885-1890. Deduct 20% if stock cartouche faint or absent.

	$595	$500	$420	$360	$320	$295	$260

MODEL 1873 CARBINE—22 in. barrel, half stock, single barrel band/stacking swivel, 20,000 made, but semi-scarce. Pre-Custer serial numbers below 43,700 made, add up to 50%. (Pre-1876 mfg.).

	$1,750	$1,675	$1,600	$1,400	$1,100	$900	$800

MODEL 1873 CADET RIFLE—29½ n. barrel, stacking swivel, no sling swivels. Deduct $100 for variation with sling-swivels.

	$700	$600	$500	$425	$375	$325	$300

MODEL 1875 OFFICER'S RIFLE FIRST TYPE—477 made between 1875 and 1886, 26 in. barrel, single barrel band. Not serial numbered, some dated, non-issue.

	$5,750	$5,500	$5,000	$4,500	$4,000	$3,500	$3,000

SECOND AND THIRD TYPE—deduct 15-20%.

MODEL 1877 RIFLE—3943 made.

	$900	$800	$700	$600	$550	$500	$450

MODEL 1877 CARBINE—22 in. barrel, "C" rear sight to 1,200 yards, 2946 made.

	$2,000	$1,900	$1,800	$1,600	$1,300	$1,000	$850

MODEL 1877 CADET RIFLE—29½ in. barrel, 1,050 made.

	$1,000	$950	$900	$800	$700	$600	$550

MODEL 1879 RIFLE—some 140,000 made.

	$500	$450	$400	$350	$300	$275	$250

MODEL 1879 CARBINE—no stacking swivel, about 15,000 made.

	$750	$700	$650	$550	$500	$450	$400

MODEL 1879 CADET RIFLE—stacking swivel but no sling swivels, 5,000 made.

	$575	$525	$475	$425	$375	$325	$300

MODEL 1880—combination triangular, bayonet-ramrod, sliding-type, 1,001 made.

	$1,000	$950	$900	$800	$700	$600	$550

U.S. MODEL 1892-1895-1896-1898 KRAG JORGENSEN—.30-40 Krag, bolt action, made until 1904.

	$395	$320	$280	$240	$220	$200	$165

1898 CARBINE—same as 1898 Krag Jorgenson, with 22 in. barrel. Add 20% for Model 1899 Carbine.

	$595	$525	$460	$420	$385	$350	$320

1898 KRAG NRA CARBINE—Carbine stock and hardware, shortened rifle (22 in.) barreled action, identifiable by full band front sight.

	$440	$360	$330	$250	$220	$200	$165

Grading	100%	98%	95%	90%	80%	70%	60%

U.S. MODEL 1903 SPRINGFIELD—.30-06, bolt action, 24 in. barrel, made 1903-1930. Deduct 20% if reworked for WWII.

	$265	$215	$190	$160	$135	$110	$95

Serial numbers between 800,000 - 1,275,767—double heat treated receiver.

	$275	$220	$195	$165	$140	$110	$95

Serial numbers over 1,275,767—nickel steel receiver.

	$330	$275	$250	$220	$180	$160	$140

U.S. MODEL 1903 MARK I—same as 1903, except altered for the Pedersen device, a slot is milled into the left side of receiver to act as an ejection port for use of the semi-auto bolt insert, value without device.

	$330	$275	$250	$220	$180	$160	$140

1903 A1—same as 1903, except type C pistol grip stock, made 1930-1939, in 1941 Remington produced approximately 350,000.

	$385	$305	$260	$230	$195	$165	$140

Remington produced

	$330	$275	$230	$210	$180	$155	$120

1903-A3—similar to 1903, with production modifications, aperture rear sight, no finger groove in forestock, lower quality finish, stamped floorplate and barrel band, made WWII by Remington and Smith Corona.

	$275	$220	$195	$165	$140	$110	$100

1903-A3 NATIONAL MATCH—200 made, known as the "unmatched" match rifle.

	$850	$760	$700	$600	$500	$420	$375

1903-A4 SNIPER—.30-06 with M73B1 or M84 scope in Redfield mount, no front sight.

	$575	$450	$420	$380	$360	$335	$320

1903 NRA NATIONAL MATCH—similar to 1903, with hand selected and custom fit parts, produced for target shooting. "NRA" and flaming bomb proofed on trigger guard. 1915 date.

	$550	$470	$440	$385	$360	$330	$275

1903 SPORTER—same as National Match, with sporter stock and Lyman sight.

	$605	$525	$470	$415	$385	$360	$305

1903 MATCH STYLE T—same as Sporter, with heavy barrel, globe sight, target bases, 26, 28, or 30 in. barrel.

	$715	$635	$580	$525	$495	$470	$415

1903 FREE RIFLE TYPE A—same as Type T, with 28 in. barrel, and Swiss hook butt.

	$770	$690	$635	$580	$525	$470	$385

1903 FREE RIFLE TYPE B—same as Type A, with double set triggers, cheekpiece stock, modified firing pin.

	$1,045	$965	$880	$825	$745	$660	$580

MODEL 192-M1—.22 Target Rifle and .22 LR, 5 shot mag., 24 in. barrel, modified 1903, Lyman receiver sight, sporter stock, issued 1927.

	$550	$440	$415	$360	$305	$275	$250

M2 .22 TARGET RIFLE—similar to 1922 M1, except improved lock time, adj. head space, bolt design.

	$635	$550	$495	$440	$360	$305	$275

SPRINGFIELD ARMORY, GENESEO, IL.

PRIVATE MANUFACTURER LOCATED IN GENESEO, IL.

The Springfield Armory manufactures commercial reproductions of older military handguns and rifles. Prices shown below are for current manufactured models. In addition to the semi-auto rifles listed below, Springfield Armory also makes fully automatic versions of the M-60 and Browning .50 cal. machine guns, besides the SAR-48, M1-A, and Beretta BM-59 rifle models. While these rifles are currently available, they are not listed in this text. For availability and prices, contact the Springfield Armory.

Grading	100%	98%	95%	90%	80%	70%	60%

COMBINATION GUNS

M6 SCOUT—.22 LR, .22 Mag., or .22 Hornet/.410 O/U Survival Gun, 14 or 18 in. barrels, Add $4 for .22 Hornet cal. Disc. in 1989.

Mfg.'s Sug. Retail	$100	$90	$80	$70	$60	$50	$40

Last Mfg.'s Sug. Retail was $120.

PISTOLS

OMEGA—.38 Super, 10mm Norma, or .45 ACP, single action, ported slide, 5 or 6 in. Polygon interchangeable ported or unported barrel, Pachmayr grips, adj. rear sight. New in late 1987.

Mfg.'s Sug. Retail	$849	$775	$650	$575	$495	$425	$360	$295

Add $663 for interchangeable conversion units.

Add $336 for interchangeable 6 in. barrels (including fact. install.)

MODEL 1911-A1 STANDARD MODEL—.38 Super (special order only), 9mm, or .45 ACP cal., copy of Colt's military M1911-A1, 5.04 (standard) or 3.63 (Officer's Model) in. barrel, 6 shot (Officer's Model), 7 shot (.45 ACP), or 8 shot (9mm) mag.'s, walnut stocks, blued (add $21) or parkerized finish, 35.6 oz. New in late 1985.

Mfg.'s Sug. Retail	$420	$385	$350	$325	$300	$280	$260	$240

This model is also available with a .22 LR or 9mm conversion kit - add $175 for 9mm, $483 for .22 LR.

Defender Model—.45 ACP only, similiar to Standard Model, except has fixed combat sites, extended thumb safety, lowered ejection port, walnut grips, and two stainless steel magazines. Mfg. in 1988.

Mfg.'s Sug. Retail	$535	$470	$420	$365	$320	$300	$280	$260

Add $20 for blued finish.

Combat Commander—.45 ACP only, 4¼ in. barrel, bobbed hammer, walnut grips. New in mid-1988.

Mfg.'s Sug. Retail	$479	$430	$380	$320	$280	$260	$240	$230

Add $20 for blued finish.

Custom Carry Gun—.38 Super (special order only), 9mm, or .45 ACP cal., similiar to Defender Model, except has tuned trigger pull, heavy recoil spring, extended thumb safety, and other features. New in 1988.

Mfg.'s Sug. Retail	$750	$660	$535	$460	$420	$385	$360	$340

National Match Model—.38 Super (special order only), 9mm, or .45 ACP cal., National Match barrel and bushing, specially fitted frame and slide, heavy duty adj. sights, walnut grips. New in 1988.

Mfg.'s Sug. Retail	$838	$740	$625	$550	$500	$440	$375	$325

Competition Grade—.38 Super (special order only), 9mm, or .45 ACP cal., competition model which includes low profile combat sights, ambidextrous safety, long match trigger, bobbed hammer, Pachmayr wraparound grips. New in 1988.

Mfg.'s Sug. Retail	$1,033	$925	$815	$750	$695	$650	$575	$495

Master Grade Competition Pistol "A"—.38 Super (special order only), 9mm, or .45 ACP cal., similiar to Custom Carry Gun, except has National Match barrel and bushing, commander hammer, and two stainless steel mag.'s. New in 1988.

Mfg.'s Sug. Retail	$1,683	$1,450	$1,225	$1,025	$950	$890	$850	$800

Master Grade Competition Pistol "B-1"—similiar to Pistol "A", except has barrel compensator, "pin gun" configuration for USPSA/IPSC shooters, many options available. New in 1988.

Mfg.'s Sug. Retail	$2,073	$1,850	$1,425	$1,225	$1,025	$950	$890	$850

Subtract $130 for B Model.

RIFLES: MILITARY DESIGN

M1 GARAND STANDARD RIFLE—.30-06 Springfield, .270 (disc. in 1987), or .308 cal., semi-auto, 24 in. barrel, gas operated, 8 shot mag., adj. sights, 9½ lbs.

Standard Model—add $240 for Kevlar stock (discontinued), or $38 for folding stock.

Mfg.'s Sug. Retail	$761	$670	$570	$495	$440	$360	$305	$275

Subtract $65 if with GI stock.

Grading	100%	98%	95%	90%	80%	70%	60%

National Match—walnut stock, match barrel and sights. Add $240 for Kevlar stock (discontinued).

Mfg.'s Sug. Retail	$897	$750	$650	$550	$500	$440	$375	$325

Ultra Match—match barrel and sights, glass bedded stock, walnut stock standard. Add $240 for Kevlar stock (discontinued).

Mfg.'s Sug. Retail	$1,033	$845	$725	$660	$610	$550	$500	$450

M1-D Sniper Rifle—limited quantities, with original M84 scope, prong type flash suppressor, leather cheek pad and slings, .30-06 only.

Mfg.'s Sug. Retail	$1,033	$845	$725	$660	$610	$550	$500	$450

M1 Tanker Rifle—same as T-26 authorized by Gen. MacArthur at the end of WWII, 18¼ in. barrel, .30-06 or .308 cal., GI stock standard. Add $23 for walnut full stock.

Mfg.'s Sug. Retail	$797	$670	$575	$500	$460	$380	$335	$295

BM 59—7.62mm (.308 Win.), original Beretta conversion of the U.S. M1 Rifle, 20 shot box mag., 19.32 in. barrel, 9½ lbs.

Standard Italian Rifle—with grenade launcher, winter trigger, tri-compensator, and bipod.

Mfg.'s Sug. Retail	$1,373	$1,200	$1,000	$895	$850	$800	$740	$680

Alpine Rifle—with Beretta pistol grip type stock. Add $190 for folding stock (Paratrooper model).

Mfg.'s Sug. Retail	$1,580	$1,340	$1,200	$1,000	$925	$860	$820	$760

Nigerian Rifle—same as BM 59, except has Beretta pistol grip type stock.

Mfg.'s Sug. Retail	$1,502	$1,300	$1,125	$900	$850	$795	$750	$700

E Model Rifle

Mfg.'s Sug. Retail	$1,385	$1,195	$1,040	$900	$850	$800	$740	$680

BM 59 M-1 GARAND—with original Beretta M1 receiver, only 200 imported into the U.S.

Mfg.'s Sug. Retail	$1,665	$1,425	$1,225	$1,000	$945	$890	$850	$800

M1A RIFLES—7.62mm (NATO), or .243 (optional - disc. in 1987) cal., original GI M14 wood or fiberglass stock, semi-auto, 22 in. barrel, fiberglass handguard, 9 lbs. Add $60 for walnut stock, $120 for heavy composition stock, $323 for Kevlar stock, $314 for fancy burl walnut stock, $75 for folding stock on Standard Model.

Standard Model—above specifications.

Mfg.'s Sug. Retail	$884	$740	$625	$540	$500	$460	$400	$350
.243 Win.		$745	$650	$590	$550	$495	$450	$400

Last Mfg.'s Sug. Retail was $842 for the .243 Win. cal.

M1A E-2—add $31 for walnut stock, $119 for Shaw stock with Harris bipod, standard stock is birch.

Mfg.'s Sug. Retail	$842	$745	$650	$590	$550	$495	$505	$460

National Match—National Match sights, barrel, mainspring guide, flash suppressor, and gas cylinder, special glass bedded oil finished match stock, tuned trigger, 9 lbs. Add $120 for heavy composition stock, $242 for Kevlar stock, $257 for fancy burl stock, $25 for Shaw stock, $50 for Shaw stock with Harris bipod, no extra charge for E-2.

Mfg.'s Sug. Retail	$998	$880	$765	$690	$630	$580	$530	$475

.243 cal. was also available until 1987 at no extra charge.

Super Match—same as National Match, except has air-gauged Douglas or Hart heavy barrel and modified operating rod guide, about 10 lbs. with standard folding stock. Add $54 for heavy composition walnut stock, add $246 for Kevlar stock, add $257 for fancy burle walnut stock, add $25 for standard Shaw stock, $50 for Shaw stock with Harris bipod, no extra charge for E-2.

Mfg.'s Sug. Retail	$1,329	$1,125	$925	$800	$680	$625	$560	$510

.243 cal. is also available at no extra charge.

M1A "GOLD SERIES"—.308 cal., heavy walnut competition stock, gold metal grade heavy Douglas barrel. Add $126 for Kevlar stock, add $390 for special Hart stainless steel barrel, add $516 for Hart stainless steel barrel with Kevlar stock. Mfg. in 1987 only.

	$1,750	$1,375	$1,150	$975	$850	$740	$650

Last Mfg.'s Sug. Retail was $1,944.

Grading	100%	98%	95%	90%	80%	70%	60%

M1A-A1 BUSH RIFLE—7.62mm only, 18¼ in. shrouded barrel, 8 lbs. 12 oz., GI fiberglass stock standard. Add $53 for walnut stock, $68 for folding stock, $312 for fancy walnut stock, $320 for oversize fiberglass competition stocks, $53 for E-2.

Mfg.'s Sug. Retail	$806	$695	$610	$540	$500	$460	$400	$350

Add $192 for National Match variation.

Add $425 for Super Match variation.

M-14 VIETNAM COMMEMORATIVE—7.62mm, limited reproduction of the U.S. Military M-14 including gold plated small parts, medallion in stock, 1,500 each mfg. of both the Army and Marine Corps models. Mfg. 1987 only.

$1,495　$1,125　$850

Last Mfg.'s Sug. Retail was $1,595. This commemorative was marketed by The American Historical Foundation located in Richmond, VA.

SAR-48—.308 cal., authentic model of the Browning semi-auto LAR rifle, 21 in. barrel, adj. gas operation, 20 shot mag., adj. sights, supplied with two 20 shot mag.'s, bayonet and scabbard, sling, and mag. loader. New in 1985.

Mfg.'s Sug. Retail	$899	$795	$695	$640	$595	$550	$500	$460

Add $70 for Paratrooper model with folding stock.

This model can also be converted to .22 LR - add $454 for conversion kit in new condition.

SAR-48 Bush Rifle—similiar to standard model, except has 18 in. barrel.

Mfg.'s Sug. Retail	$899	$795	$695	$640	$595	$550	$500	$460

SAR-48 .22 Cal.—.22 LR variation of the standard model.

Mfg.'s Sug. Retail	$760	$660	$595	$540	$495	$450	$400	$350

RIFLES: SPORTING

MAUSER M98—7 x 57mm, surplus rifles with standard military dimensions and features.

Hunting/Utility Grade

Mfg.'s Sug. Retail	$75	$70	$50	$45	$45	$40	$40	$35

Collector Grade

Mfg.'s Sug. Retail	$116	$105	$90	$80	$70	$60	$50	$40

Premium Grade

Mfg.'s Sug. Retail	$194	$170	$150	$130	$115	$100	$90	$80

M-1 CARBINE, GARAND, ENFIELD, AND OTHERS

SEE U.S. MILITARY SECTION IN THIS BOOK.

STANDARD ARMS COMPANY

WILMINGTON, DELAWARE

MODEL G AUTOLOADER—.25-35, .30-30, .25 Rem., .30 Rem., and .35 Rem. cal.'s, bottom loading box mag., 22 in. barrel, open sight, straight stock. This was the first gas operated rifle in U.S.A. Gas port can be closed and gun will function as a slide action, made 1910.

	$400	$300	$275	$250	$225	$175	$150

A variation that was slide action only (Model M) also was mfg. — subtract 35% from values listed above.

STAR, BONIFACIO ECHEVERRIA

MANUFACTURED IN EIBAR, SPAIN. CURRENTLY IMPORTED BY INTERARMS LOCATED IN ALEXANDRIA, VA.

Grading	100%	98%	95%	90%	80%	70%	60%

PISTOLS: SEMI-AUTO

MODEL 1—.32 ACP, 9 shot, 4¾ in. barrel, blue, fixed sights, plastic grips, made 1934-1936.

	$165	$155	$140	$120	$100	$85	$70

MODEL 1N—.380 ACP, 8 shot, 4¾ in. barrel, blue, same as 1.

	$170	$160	$145	$125	$105	$90	$75

MODEL M (MILITARY)—a modification of Government Colt, available in 9mm Bergman, 9mm Luger, and .38 Super cal.'s, 8 shot, and .45 ACP, 7 shot, 5 in. barrel, blue, fixed sights, checkered wood grips.

	$250	$230	$200	$165	$150	$140	$120

MODEL HN—.380 auto, 6 shot, 2¾ in. barrel, blue, fixed sights, plastic grips, made 1934-1941.

	$165	$155	$140	$120	$100	$90	$75

MODEL H—same as HN, except 7.65mm, 7 shot.

	$165	$155	$140	$120	$100	$90	$75

SUPER STAR—improved Model M, .38 Super and 9mm Luger, 8 shot, 5 in. barrel, checkered wood grips, loaded chamber indicator, Spanish service pistol, 1946.

	$275	$265	$250	$210	$175	$165	$145

SUPER STAR TARGET MODEL—same as Super Star, but target sights.

	$305	$290	$265	$230	$200	$180	$160

MODEL 1920—9mm BB and .38 Super cal.'s, easily identified by unusual safety located on left rear slide.

	$350	$315	$295	$240	$185	$150	$120

MODEL 1921—9mm BB and .38 Super cal.'s, predecessor to the later Model A, this model was fit with a grip safety that was later dropped when standardizing the Model A production.

	$325	$285	$240	$215	$180	$145	$115

MODEL 1922—designation for the early Model A.

	$325	$285	$240	$215	$180	$145	$115

MODEL A—modified Government Colt, .38 Super, 5 in. barrel, no grip safety, blue, checkered wood grips, made 1934-present but not currently imported.

	$250	$230	$200	$165	$145	$130	$110

MODEL A CARBINE—usually 7.63mm, unusual variation, slotted with tangent rear sight and extended barrel. Add $250 for original stock.

	$1,500	$1,250	$1,050	$825	$700	$575	$450

MODEL B CARBINE—same as Model A, but 9mm Luger, made 1934-1975.

	$255	$235	$205	$170	$150	$140	$115

MODEL P CARBINE—same as Model A, except .45 ACP, 7 shot mag., made 1934-1975.

	$260	$240	$210	$175	$155	$145	$120

MODELS SUPER A, B, AND P—same as Models A, B, and P, except loaded chamber indicator, mag. safety and easier takedown feature, made 1946-present.

Mfg.'s Sug. Retail	$340	$275	$260	$240	$210	$175	$160	$140

MODEL MB—9mm parabellum, late production Model M cut for shoulder stock, mag. safety. Add $250 for shoulder stock.

	$875	$795	$675	$565	$450	$365	$250

MODEL MMS—7.63mm, late production Model M cut for shoulder stock, mag. safety. Add $250 for original stock.

	$600	$520	$460	$400	$325	$260	$200

MODEL S1—.32 auto, 8 shot, 4 in. barrel, blue, no grips safety, small version of Government .45 in appearance, plastic grips, made 1941-1965.

	$200	$190	$160	$135	$115	$100	$80

MODEL S—same as S1, except .380, 7 shot, made 1941-1965.

	$230	$220	$200	$175	$150	$125	$110

MODELS SUPER S1 AND S—same as S, with Super Star improvements, made 1946-1972.

	$240	$230	$210	$195	$165	$140	$120

Grading	100%	98%	95%	90%	80%	70%	60%

MODEL SUPER SM—same as Super S, except adjustable sight and wood grips, made 1973-1981.

	$250	$235	$220	$200	$175	$145	$125

MODEL CO POCKET—.25 auto, 2¾ in. barrel, blue, fixed sights, plastic grips, made 1941-1957.

	$165	$155	$140	$110	$100	$90	$85

MODEL CU STARLET—.25 auto, 2⅜ in. barrel, alloy frame, fixed sights, plastic grips, blue, or chrome slide, frame anodized in black, blue, green, gray, or gold, made 1957-present, no longer imported as 1968 GCA.

	$195	$180	$165	$145	$120	$110	$90

MODEL DK (STARFIRE)—.380 auto, 3⅛ in. barrel, fixed sights, plastic stocks, finished in same color availability as Model CU, made 1957-present, U.S. import ceased with 1968-GCA.

	$275	$255	$225	$180	$155	$130	$115

MODEL HK LANCER—similar to Starfire, except .22 LR, made 1955-1968.

	$210	$200	$180	$160	$140	$120	$110

MODEL F—.22 LR, 10 shot, 4 in. barrel, fixed sights, blue, plastic grips, made 1942-1967.

	$165	$155	$140	$110	$95	$85	$55

MODEL FS—same as F, except 6 in. barrel, adj. sights, made 1942-1967.

	$175	$165	$150	$120	$100	$90	$65

MODEL F OLYMPIC RAPID FIRE—.22 short, 9 shot, 7 in. barrel, adj. sight, aluminum slide, barrel weights and muzzle brake, blue, plastic grips, made 1942-1967.

	$250	$230	$210	$175	$155	$140	$130

MODEL FR—restyled Model F, adj. sight and slide stop, made 1967-1972.

	$175	$165	$150	$120	$100	$90	$65

MODEL FRS—same as FR, only 6 in. barrel, available in chrome, made 1967-present.

	$175	$165	$150	$120	$100	$90	$65

MODEL FM—same as FR, except heavier frame, web ahead of trigger guard, 4½ in. barrel, made 1972-present.

	$175	$165	$150	$120	$100	$90	$65

MODEL BKS STARLIGHT—9mm parabellum, 8 shot, 4¼ in. barrel, plastic grips, made 1970-1981.

	100%	98%	95%	90%	80%	70%	60%
Blue.	$250	$230	$210	$180	$160	$145	$130
Chrome.	$260	$240	$220	$195	$170	$155	$145

MODEL BM SEMI-AUTO—9mm, single action, 8 shot mag., 4 in. barrel, steel frame, Colt 1911 action, blue or chrome finish, plastic grips, 35 oz. Add $63 for chrome.

Mfg.'s Sug. Retail	$332	$260	$220	$195	$180	$165	$155	$145

MODEL BKM—similar to BM, except lightweight duraluminum frame, blued finish only, 26 oz.

Mfg.'s Sug. Retail	$375	$290	$235	$205	$190	$180	$165	$160

MODEL PD—.45 ACP, 6 shot mag., single action, 4 in. barrel, adj. rear sight, blue finish only, walnut grips, alloy frame, 25 oz., made 1975-present.

Mfg.'s Sug. Retail	$415	$310	$270	$240	$215	$195	$170	$160

MODEL 28—9mm, double action, 15 shot mag., 4¼ in. barrel, 40 oz., blue finish only, advanced design, made in 1983 and 1984 only.

	$414	$310	$325	$275	$250	$225	$200

Note: Model 28 is interesting since no screws are used in its manufacture. Hammer assembly (including spring, cocking lever, sear, disconnector and ejector) is housed under removable backstrap.

MODEL 30M—9mm only, successor to the Model 28, double action, 4.33 in. barrel, 15 shot mag., blued finish only, adj. rear sight, checkered wrap around plastic grips, steel frame, 40 oz. New in 1985.

Mfg.'s Sug. Retail	$535	$425	$350	$315	$295	$270	$250	$225

MODEL 30/PK DURAL—same as Model 28, except duraluminum frame, 3.86 in. barrel, 30 oz.

Mfg.'s Sug. Retail	$535	$425	$350	$315	$295	$270	$250	$225

STEEL CITY ARMS, INC.

MANUFACTURED AND DISTRIBUTED OUT OF PITTSBURGH, PA.

DOUBLE DEUCE—.22 LR only, double action semi-auto, matte finish stainless steel, 2½ in. barrel, 7 shot mag., uncheckered rosewood grips, 18 oz. New in 1984.

Mfg.'s Sug. Retail $290 $265 $230 $200

Various select hardwood stocks are also available at extra cost ($20-100).

STERLING

PREVIOUSLY MANUFACTURED IN GASPORT, NY. DISCONTINUED IN 1983.

PISTOLS

Rather than list individual models, the following generalizations will help in ascertaining values for this trademark. Models 300, 302 and 402 will average between $75 and $150 if in 70% + condition, Models 283, 284, 285 (Husky), and 286 (Trapper) are semi-auto .22 cal. pistols with various barrel lengths — values will range between $90-$150. Models 400 (.380 ACP), PPL (.380 ACP short barrel), and 450 (.45 ACP) usually range in the $150-$275 range.

STERLING ARMAMENT, LTD.

MANUFACTURED IN ENGLAND SINCE 1900. CURRENTLY IMPORTED AND DISTRIBUTED BY CASSI INC. LOCATED IN COLORADO SPRINGS, CO.

CARBINES

STERLING MK 6—9mm, blowback semi-auto with floating firing pin, shrouded 16.1 in. barrel, side mounted mag., folding stock, 7½ lbs.

Mfg.'s Sug. Retail $650 $565 $495 $450 $410 $375 $340 $315

PISTOLS

PARAPISTOL MK 7 C4—9mm, 4 in. barrel, semi-auto assault pistol, crinkle finish, same action as MK. 6 Carbine, fires from closed bolt, 10, 15, 20, 30, 34 or 68 round mag., 5 lbs.

Mfg.'s Sug. Retail $600 $500 $435 $375 $350 $325 $295 $265

PARAPISTOL MK 7 C8—9mm, similar to C4, except has 7.8 in. barrel, 5¼ lbs.

Mfg.'s Sug. Retail $620 $525 $450 $390 $365 $330 $300 $275

STEVENS, J., ARMS COMPANY

J. STEVENS ARMS COMPANY WAS FOUNDED IN 1864 AT CHICOPEE FALLS, MA AS J. STEVENS & CO. IN 1866 THE NAME WAS CHANGED TO J. STEVENS ARMS AND TOOL CO. IN 1916, THE PLANT BECAME NEW ENGLAND WESTINGHOUSE, AND TOOLED UP FOR BOTH BROWNING MACHINE GUNS AND MOISON-NAGANT RIFLES. IN 1920, THE PLANT WAS SOLD TO THE SAVAGE ARMS CORP. AND MANUFACTURED GUNS WERE MARKED "J. STEVENS ARMS CO.". THIS DESIGNATION WAS DROPPED IN THE LATE 1940'S, AND ONLY THE NAME "STEVENS" HAS BEEN USED UP TO THE PRESENT DATE.

Savage Industries announced in early 1988 that they will no longer publish retail prices for their new firearms. The retail values on models currently being manufactured reflect 1987 data and are included to give the reader a reference point for current values.

RIFLES

NO. 10 TARGET SINGLE SHOT—.22 LR, 8 in. barrel, blue, adj. sights, rubber grips, squared off like an automatic pistol, tip up action, made 1919-1939.

   $220 $200 $185 $165 $140 $120 $100

NO. 35 TARGET SINGLE SHOT—.22 LR, 6, 8, 10, and 12¼ in. barrel, blue, walnut grips, made 1907-1939.

   $220 $200 $185 $165 $140 $120 $100

Grading	100%	98%	95%	90%	80%	70%	60%

NO. 35 "OFFHAND" AUTOSHOT—.410 (actually a pistol-length shotgun). Class Three — must be registered with BATF. Introduced 1931, discontinued 1935.

	$300	$250	$200	$150	$100	$75	$60

MODEL 44 IDEAL SINGLE SHOT—.22 LR through .44-40 cal.'s, rolling block, lever action, takedown, 24 or 26 in. barrels, straight grip stock and forearm, mfg. 1894-1932.

	$465	$420	$375	$330	$290	$250	$220

MODEL 44½ IDEAL SINGLE SHOT—.22 LR through .44-40 cal.'s, falling block, lever action, takedown, 24 or 26 in. barrels, straight grip stock and forearm, action redesigned in 1903, otherwise basically same as Model 44, mfg. 1903-1916.

	$465	$420	$375	$330	$290	$250	$220

MODELS 45-54 SINGLE SHOTS—.22 LR through .44-40 cal.'s, rolling and falling block receivers, lever action, takedown, deluxe versions of the Models 44 and 44½, many special order features, including double set triggers, types of finish, engraving, length and weight of barrels, stock configuration could be special ordered. The higher grade Schuetzens and Stevens-Pope are very collectible and command premiums. These models have to be taken one at a time for determining value. Therefore, no prices are shown. Mfg. 1896-1916.

NO. 414 ARMORY MODEL—.22 LR or .22 short only, lever action, 26 in. barrel, single shot, Lyman aperture sight, made 1912-1932.

	$450	$400	$375	$330	$290	$250	$220

MODEL 416—bolt action, .22 LR, 25 in. medium barrel, 5 shot mag. Discontinued.

	$140	$120	$110	$100	$90	$80	$70

This model was also manufactured as a U.S. military training rifle. Can be denoted by "U.S. Property" on rear of bolt housing. Healthy premiums exist for this variation.

NO. 417 WALNUT HILL MODEL—.22 LR, .22 short, and .22 Hornet, lever action, 28 or 29 in. extra heavy barrel, target stock with full pistol grip, beavertail forend, made in 0-3 suffix variations (different sights), manufactured 1932-1947.

	$595	$525	$475	$440	$395	$360	$330

NO. 417½ WALNUT HILL MODEL—Same as No. 417, except available in .25 rimfire also, manufactured 1932-1940.

	$595	$525	$475	$440	$395	$360	$330

NO. 418 WALNUT HILL MODEL—.22 LR or .22 short only, 26 in. barrel, pistol grip stock, semi beavertail forearm, manufactured 1932-1940.

	$325	$290	$260	$230	$200	$180	$160

STEVENS' FAVORITE NO.'S 17-29—.22 LR, .25 RF and .32 RF cal.'s, 24 in. barrel most common, other lengths available, Rocky Mountain front sight, straight grip stock, small tapered forearm, manufactured 1894-1935. Octagonal barrels command a 33% premium.

	$225	$175	$150	$130	$115	$100	$90

STEVENS' MODEL 65—bolt action, 20 in. barrel, open sights, 5 shot mag., checkered walnut stock, made 1969-discontinued.

	$90	$70	$55	$45	$35	$30	$30

NO. 70 "VISIBLE LOADING" SLIDE ACTION RIFLE—.22 LR-L-S, exposed hammer, 22 in. barrel, open sights, straight grip stock, tube mag., grooved slide handle. Other variations with different barrel lengths and sights will command slight premiums.

	$250	$175	$150	$130	$115	$100	$90

MODEL 71 "STEVENS' FAVORITE"—replica of original, .22 LR, 22 in. octagon barrel, plain straight stock, medallion inlaid, crescent butt, 10,000 produced in 1971.

	$200	$175	$160	$145	$135	$115	$95

MODEL 72 CRACKSHOT—single shot falling block action, .22 cal., 22 in. octagon barrel, open sights, color case hardened frame, straight stock, made 1972-present.

Mfg.'s Sug. Retail	$165	$125	$105	$85	$70	$60	$50	$40

MODEL 987—.22 LR only, semi-auto, 15 shot tube mag., 20 in. barrel, hardwood Monte Carlo stock, adj. rear sight, 6 lbs.

Mfg.'s Sug. Retail	$119	$95	$80	$70	$60	$50	$40	$45

MODEL 89 LEVER ACTION—.22 LR, single shot, 18½ in. barrel, Martini type action, Western style lever, straight stock, made 1976-discontinued.

	$85	$65	$60	$50	$45	$40	$35

STEVENS, J., ARMS COMPANY, cont.

SHOTGUNS

Savage Industries announced in early 1988 that they will no longer publish retail prices for their new firearms. The retail values on models currently being manufactured reflect 1987 data and are included to give the reader a reference point for current values.

SHOTGUN MODEL 520 PUMP

	100%	98%	95%	90%	80%	70%	60%
	$190	$180	$150	$125	$95	$85	$75

MODEL 520 TRENCH GUN—12 ga., six-round, field grade for military use, 20 in.

	$290	$280	$250	$225	$175	$150	$100

MODEL 620—an improved version of the Model 520 with streamline receiver.

	$325	$290	$250	$225	$175	$150	$100

MODEL 67 SLIDE ACTION—12, 20, and .410 ga.'s, all are 3 in. chambered, steel receiver, 5 shot, 6¼ - 7½ lbs., upper receiver safety, recent production - made by Stevens. Disc. in 1989.

	$200	$180	$170	$155	$145	$135	$125

Add $30 for choke tubes (with VR).
Add $10 for VR only.

Last Mfg.'s Sug. Retail was $229.

Model 67 VTR-K Camo—12 or 20 ga., 28 in. vent rib barrel with choke tubes, laminated camo stock. Mfg. 1986-1988.

	$250	$220	$190	$170	$155	$145	$135

Last Mfg.'s Sug. Retail was $295.

Slug Model—12 ga. only, 21 in. barrel, rifle sights. Discontinued in 1989.

	$200	$165	$140	$110	$100	$90	$80

Last Mfg.'s Sug. Retail was $245.

Model 67 VRT-Y—20 ga. only, 22 in. vent rib barrel with choke tubes, youth model with smaller stock dimensions. Mfg. 1987-1988.

	$205	$170	$140	$110	$100	$90	$80

Last Mfg.'s Sug. Retail was $259.

MODEL 675—12 ga. only, 24 in. vent rib multi-choked barrel with iron sights (including removable rear ramp), hardwood stock with recoil pad, 6½ lbs. Mfg. 1987-1988.

	$250	$220	$190	$170	$155	$145	$135

Last Mfg.'s Sug. Retail was $295.

MODEL 69-RXL—12 ga. only, slide action law enforcement version of the Model 67, 18¼ in. cylinder bore barrel with recoil pad, 6½ lbs. Disc. in 1989.

	$200	$165	$140	$110	$100	$90	$80

Last Mfg.'s Sug. Retail was $245.

MODEL 311—12, 20, and .410 ga.'s, 3 in. chambers, double triggers, extractors, vent rib, current production.

Mfg.'s Sug. Retail	$309	$245	$205	$185	$150	$140	$125	$115

Model 311-R—12 ga. only, similar to Model 311, except has 18¼ in. cylinder bore barrels for law enforcement use, 3 in. chambers, 6¾ lbs.

Mfg.'s Sug. Retail	$309	$245	$205	$185	$150	$140	$125	$115

FOX/STEVENS MODEL B—12, 20 and .410 ga.'s, double triggers, VR, extractors, 26, 28, or 30 in. barrels, 7 lbs. Discontinued in 1986.

	$315	$280	$240	$220	$200	$180	$160

Add 25% for BDE Model (with ejectors).

Last Mfg.'s Sug. Retail was $369.

FOX/STEVENS MODEL B-SE—12, 20, and .410 ga.'s, single trigger, selective ejectors, vent. rib, beavertail forend, select walnut, current production.

Mfg.'s Sug. Retail	$525	$415	$370	$325	$280	$240	$210	$180

MODEL 94—12, 16, 20, and .410 ga.'s, single shot breakopen, inertia firing pin design (intro. in 1979 disc. in 1987),open hammer, 6¼ lbs. Discontinued.

	$80	$70	$65	$55	$50	$45	$40

Last Mfg.'s Sug. Retail was $92.

STEYR AUSTRIAN MILITARY

MANUFACTURED IN STEYR, AUSTRIA.

MODEL 95 RIFLE—straight pull bolt action, 8 x 50R Mannlicher, 30 in. barrel, adj. sights, military full stock.

$140	$110	$100	$85	$65	$55	$40

MODEL 90 CARBINE—same as Model 95, except 19½ in. barrel.

$155	$125	$110	$95	$85	$65	$45

STEYR DAIMLER PUCH A.G.

STEYR, AUSTRIA. 1911 TO DATE.

ARGENTINE MODEL 1905—7.65mm, Argentine crest on left panel is usually machined off, values assume matching numbers but removed crest.

$385	$340	$300	$255	$220	$185	$150

POCKET AUTO—.25 ACP and .32 cal.'s, tip up barrel, mag. fed. Discontinued.

$220	$180	$165	$150	$140	$130	$120

ROTH STEYR AUTO (MODEL 1907)—8mm Steyr cal.

$350	$315	$270	$225	$180	$160	$140

Add 30% for "Budapest" markings.

STEYR-HAHN MODEL 1911 AUTOMATIC—9mm Steyr, 8 shot, 5.1 in. barrel, fixed magazine top loaded by stripper clip, blue, checkered wood grips,made 1911-1919. In 1938, the Germans confiscated and converted about 250,000 Steyr Hahns to 9mm parabellum. "08" was stamped on the left side of these guns.

$305	$285	$275	$230	$195	$165	$140

Add 50% if marked "Budapest", "08", or with Rumanian Crest.

STEYR MANNLICHER

MANUFACTURED BY STEYR-DAIMLER-PUCH IN AUSTRIA. FOUNDED BY FERDINAND RITTER VON MANNLICHER AND OTTO SCHOENAUER IN 1903. CURRENTLY IMPORTED AND DISTRIBUTED BY GUN SOUTH, INC. LOCATED IN TRUSSVILLE, AL.

Note: also see Mannlicher Schoenauer in the M section for pre-WWII models.

PISTOLS

MODEL GB—9mm, double action, 18 shot mag, gas delayed blowback action, non-glare checkered plastic grips, 5¼ in. barrel with Polygon rifling, matte finish, steel construction, 2 lbs. 6 oz. Importation disc. in 1988.

Commercial	$485	$375	$335	$300	$280	$260	$240
Military	$425	$335	$300	$280	$260	$240	$220

Last Mfg.'s Sug. Retail was $514.

This model had its action originally derived from the Rogak Pistol. In 1987, Steyr mfg. a military variation of the Model GB - 937 were exported into the U.S.

RIFLES: POST-WW II

MODEL 1950—.257 Roberts, .270 Win., and .30-06 cal.'s, bolt action, 5 shot rotary mag., 24 in. barrel, low bolt handle, half length stock, ebony forearm, made 1950-1952.

$795	$725	$650	$575	$500	$460	$420

MODEL 1950 CARBINE—same as 1950, except 20 in. barrel, full length stock, made 1950-1952.

$1,000	$875	$770	$675	$580	$525	$440

STEYR MANNLICHER, cont.

Grading	100%	98%	95%	90%	80%	70%	60%

MODEL 1950 CARBINE 6.5—same as 1950 Carbine, except 6.5 x 54mm cal., 18½ in. barrel, made 1950-1952.

	$1,000	$875	$770	$675	$580	$525	$440

IMPROVED MODEL 1952—same specifications as 1950, except swept back bolt handle, made 1952-1956.

	$795	$725	$650	$575	$500	$460	$420

IMPROVED MODEL 1952 CARBINE—.257 Roberts, .270 Win., 7 x 57mm, and .30-06 cal.'s, swept back handle, otherwise same as 1950 Carbine.

	$1,000	$875	$770	$675	$580	$525	$440

IMPROVED MODEL 1952 6.5 CARBINE—same as 1952 Carbine, except 6.5mm, 18½ in. barrel, made 1952-1956.

	$1,000	$875	$770	$675	$580	$525	$440

MODEL 1956 RIFLE—similar to 1952, except .243 and .30-06 cal.'s, new high comb. stock design, 22 in. barrel, half length stock, made 1956-1960.

	$795	$725	$650	$575	$500	$460	$420

MODEL 1956 CARBINE—similar to 1956 Rifle, except .243, 6.5 x 53mm, .257 Roberts, .270, 7mm, .30-06, and .308 cal.'s, 2 in. barrel, full length stock, made 1956-1960.

	$1,000	$875	$770	$675	$580	$525	$440

MODEL 1961 MCA RIFLE—same as Model 1956, except Monte Carlo stock, made 1961-1971.

	$795	$725	$650	$575	$500	$460	$420

MODEL 1961 MCA CARBINE—same as 1956 Carbine, except Monte Carlo stock, made 1961-1971.

	$1,000	$875	$770	$675	$580	$525	$440

MODEL M72 L/M RIFLE—M72 bolt action, .243, .308, .270, .30-06, 7 x 57, and 7 x 64 cal.'s, 23 in. barrel, single or double set triggers, made 1972-1980.

	$795	$725	$650	$575	$500	$460	$420

RIFLES: CURRENT MANUFACTURE

Current production guns are now called Steyr-Mannlicher models.

Prices below reflect the recent devaluation of the U.S. dollar against some foreign currencies. While the manufacturer's suggested retails have gone up considerably, prices for used specimens (98% or less original condition) have not increased proportionately, and in some cases, have changed very little.

The below listed models have 4 different action lengths and model designations stand for the following: SL = Super Light, L = Light, M = Medium, S = Magnum, S/T = Magnum with heavy barrel. All sporting rifles are available with left-hand stock - add $75 and with either single set or double set triggers - add $108.

MODEL SL—.222 Rem. and Mag., .223 Rem., .22-250 Rem., and 5.6 x 50 Mag. cal.'s, bolt-action, 23.6 in. barrel, double set triggers, rotary mag. Available in full-stock (Carbine), half stock (rifle), or varmint version (vent square forearm).

Mfg.'s Sug. Retail	$1,812	$1,625	$775	$675	$600	$540	$495	$440

Carbine Model—skip line checkered full stock, 20 in. barrel.

Mfg.'s Sug. Retail	$1,939	$1,680	$800	$700	$625	$540	$495	$440

Varmint Rifle—.222 R., .22-250, .243 Win., and .308 Win. cal.'s, 26 in. heavy barrel, stippled pistol grip, vent forearm, no sights.

Mfg.'s Sug. Retail	$1,939	$1,680	$800	$700	$625	$540	$495	$440

MODEL L—5.6 x 57, .243 Win., or .308 Win. cal.'s, available in .22-250 and 6mm Rem. on special order only, otherwise same general specifications as Model SL.

Mfg.'s Sug. Retail	$1,812	$1,625	$775	$675	$600	$540	$495	$440

Carbine Model—skip-line checkered full stock, 20 in. barrel.

Mfg.'s Sug. Retail	$1,939	$1,680	$800	$700	$625	$540	$495	$440

Varmint Rifle—.222 R., .22-250, .243 Win. cal.'s, 26 in. heavy barrel, stippled pistol grip, vent forearm, no sights.

Mfg.'s Sug. Retail	$1,939	$1,680	$800	$700	$625	$540	$495	$440

Model L Luxus—5.6 x 57, .243 Win., or .308 Win. cal.'s, full or half stock only, .22-250 and 6mm Rem. available on special order, 3 shot mag.

Mfg.'s Sug. Retail	$2,364	$2,100	$1,050	$850	$750	$675	$625	$575

Grading	100%	98%	95%	90%	80%	70%	60%

Model L Luxus Carbine—similar to L Luxus rifle, except has full stock and 20 in. barrel.

Mfg.'s Sug. Retail	$2,495	$2,150	$1,095	$895	$750	$675	$625	$575

MODEL M—6.5 x 57, 7 x 64, .270 Win., .30-06, and 9.3 x 62, cal.'s, bolt action, full stock or half stock, rotary mag., double set triggers. Add $551 for left hand action on Professional Models only.

Mfg.'s Sug. Retail	$1,812	$1,625	$775	$675	$600	$540	$495	$440

Carbine Model—skip-line checkered full stock, 20 in. barrel.

Mfg.'s Sug. Retail	$1,939	$1,680	$800	$700	$625	$540	$495	$440

Professional Rifle—.270 Win., 7 x 57, 7 x 64, and .30-06 cal.'s, 23.6 in. barrel, Cycolac synthetic stock, 7½ lbs.

Mfg.'s Sug. Retail	$1,532	$1,375	$725	$660	$600	$540	$495	$440

This variation is also available in .270 Win. or .30-06 cal. with half stock and 20 in. barrel.

Model M Luxus—6.5 x 57, 7 x 64, .270 Win., and .30-06 cal.'s, special order in 6.5 x 55 and 7.5 Swiss.

Mfg.'s Sug. Retail	$2,364	$2,100	$1,050	$850	$750	$675	$625	$575

Model M Luxus Carbine—same as Model M Luxus, except with full stock and 20 in. barrel.

Mfg.'s Sug. Retail	$2,495	$2,150	$1,095	$895	$750	$675	$625	$575

Carbine - 1000 Year Commemorative—1984 only, .30-06 cal.

	$4,200	$3,620	$2,835

MODEL S & S/T—6.5 x 68, 8 x 68S, .300 Win. Mag., .338 Win. Mag., 7mm Rem. Mag. cal.'s, half-stock, 26 in. barrel, bolt action. Model S/T is only available in 9.3 x 64, .375 H & H and .458 Win. Mag. cal.'s in heavy barrel - add $224.

Mfg.'s Sug. Retail	$1,952	$1,680	$825	$725	$625	$540	$495	$440

Tropical Rifle—.375 H&H and .458 Win. Mag. cal.'s, 26 in. heavy barrel. Discontinued in 1985.

	$1,150	$900	$810	$730	$660	$600	$550

Last Mfg.'s Sug. Retail was $1,332.

Luxus S—available in 6.5 x 68, 8 x 68S, 7mm Mag., .300 Win. Mag. cal.'s, 26 in. barrel, half stock only, 3 shot mag., 8 lbs.

Mfg.'s Sug. Retail	$2,567	$2,195	$1,125	$900	$750	$675	$625	$575

MODEL SSG—.243 Win. and .308 Win cal.'s, for competition or law-enforcement use. Marksman has regular sights, rotary mag., teflon coated bolt with heavy duty locking lugs, synthetic stock has removeable spacers, parkerized finish. Match version has heavier target barrel and "match" bolt carrier, can be used as single shot. Extremely accurate.

Marksman—26 in. barrel, 3 shot mag., black or green ABS Cycolac synthetic stock. Add $397 for walnut stock.

Mfg.'s Sug. Retail	$1,598	$1,400	$750	$660	$600	$540	$495	$440

Match—.308 Win. only, 26 in. heavy barrel, brown Cycolac stock, Walther Diopter sights, 8.6 lbs. Add $250 for walnut stock.

Mfg.'s Sug. Retail	$1,875	$1,625	$795	$700	$625	$540	$495	$440

PII Sniper Rifle—.243 or .308 Win. cal.'s, 26 in. heavy barrel, no sights, black synthetic Cycolac stock, modified bolt handle, choice of single or set triggers.

Mfg.'s Sug. Retail	$1,682	$1,450	$775	$675	$600	$540	$495	$440

Match UIT—.308 Win. only, 10 shot steel mag., special single set trigger, free floating barrel, Diopter sights, raked bolt handle, 10.8 lbs.

Mfg.'s Sug. Retail	$2,350	$1,940	$1,435	$1,210	$995	$900	$820	$760

UIT stands for Union Internationale de Tir.

AUG S.A.—.223 Rem./5.56mm, semi-auto assault rifle, design incorporates use of advanced plastics, integral Swarovski scope, 20 in. barrel, bullpup configuration, 7.9 lbs.

Mfg.'s Sug. Retail	$1,362	$975	$725	$625	$560	$530	$500	$470

Add $432 for special receiver mfg. with Stanag.

MODEL MAADI AKM—7.62 x 39 Russian, semi-auto, copy of Soviet AKM assault rifle, 30 round mag., open sights.

	$995	$800	$730	$675	$620	$575	$525

STOCK, FRANZ

GERMANY.

SEMI-AUTO PISTOL—.22 LR. Made in Germany 1920-1940.

	100%	98%	95%	90%	80%	70%	60%
	$275	$250	$225	$175	$125	$100	$75

SEMI-AUTO PISTOL—.25 ACP, .32 ACP. Made in Germany 1920-1940.

	100%	98%	95%	90%	80%	70%	60%
	$220	$200	$175	$150	$100	$90	$80

STREET SWEEPER

MANUFACTURED BY SALES OF GEORGIA, INC. LOCATED IN ATLANTA, GA.

STREET SWEEPER—12 ga. only, 12 shot rotary mag., assualt configuration with 18 in. barrel, double action, folding stock, 9¾ lbs. New in 1989.

Mfg.'s Sug. Retail	$595	$525	$450	$375	$325	$300	$275	$250

STURM, RUGER, & COMPANY

MANUFACTURED IN SOUTHPORT, CT. 1949 TO DATE. P-85'S ARE BEING MANUFACTURED AT RUGER'S NEW FACILITY IN PRESCOTT, AZ (1986).

ALL VALUES FOR 100% CONDITION RUGERS ASSUME N.I.B. CONDITION — SUBTRACT 5% - 10% WITHOUT BOX AND ACCESSORIES.

PISTOLS: SEMI-AUTO

STANDARD MODEL—.22 LR, 9 shot, 4¾ in. or 6 in. barrel, blue, fixed sights, checkered wood or rubber grips, made 1951-1982.

	$140	$125	$115	$105	$95	$85	$75

Standard Model was also available in a refined version called the Mark I. Barrel lengths were 5¼, 5½, and 6⅞ in.

"RED EAGLE"—made 1949-1952, approximately 25,600 manufactured, most production occurred prior to Alexander Sturm's death (1951).

	$550	$500	$450	$375	$325	$275	$225

Distinguishable by recessed red enamel eagle in grips. Produced until early 1952. Serialized approximately 12,000 - 34,000 with Mark I Auto occupying blocks from 15,000 17,000 and 25,000 - 30,000.

Stainless Steel 1 of 5,000

	$450	$390	$325

MARK I TARGET—same as Standard, but 5½ in. heavy barrel, or 7 in. heavy tapered barrel, adj. rear sights, target sight, made 1951-1982.

	$190	$175	$160	$150	$140	$130	$120

For factory installed muzzle brake - add $100.

MARK II STANDARD—.22 LR, 4¾ or 6 in. barrel, checkered composition panels, 10 round mag., mfg. 1982 to date.

Mfg.'s Sug. Retail	$208	$165	$140	$120	$110	$105	$100	$95

Stainless Steel—otherwise same as Mark II Standard.

Mfg.'s Sug. Retail	$277	$225	$190	$165

Serial numbers start approximately at 18-00001.

MARK II TARGET—.22 LR, 5½, 6⅞, or 10 in. bull barrel, single action, 42 oz.

Mfg.'s Sug. Retail	$260	$200	$170	$150	$135	$120	$110	$100

Stainless Steel—otherwise same as Mark II Target.

Mfg.'s Sug. Retail	$329	$265	$220	$180

Government Model (MK678G)—government training model without "U.S." markings, 6⅞ in. bull barrel, adj. rear sight, blue finish, black plastic grips, 46 oz. New in 1987.

Mfg.'s Sug. Retail	$300	$250	$210	$175

Grading	100%	98%	95%	90%	80%	70%	60%

P-85—9mm, double action, 4½ in. barrel, aluminum frame with steel slide, 3-dot fixed sights, 15 shot mag., ambidextrous safety, oversized trigger, synthetic Xenoy grips, matte black finish, 2 lbs. New in 1987.

Mfg.'s Sug. Retail	$325	$290	$265	$235	$215	$200	$185	$175

Add $30 if cased with extra mag.

This model was introduced during 1987 and until recently, very limited manufacture has resulted in substantial premiums being paid to obtain an early production specimen. Currently, approximately 4,000 P-85's are being produced per month in the Prescott, AZ plant.

REVOLVERS: SINGLE ACTION

Note: Some of the following Rugers are known as "Old Models" (made 1963-1973) and are instantly recognized by the three screws through the frame and the four clicks emitted upon cocking. They are now actively sought by collectors and some shooters who desire the smoother operation they afford.

SINGLE SIX REVOLVER—.22 LR, 4⅝, 5½, 6½, or 9½ in. barrel, fixed sights, rubber or wood grips, blue, made 1953-1972.

	$275	$200	$175	$130	$120	$110	$100

This model will command a premium with either a 4⅝ in. or 9½ in. barrel.

Flat loading gate—5½ in. barrel only, approx. 61,000 mfg. from 1953-1956. Four variations.

	$300	$250	$200	$175	$165	$160	$150

.22 Mag.—6½ in. barrel only, manufactured only three years, serial numbered between 300,000 - 340,000. Frame stamped Mag. only. Add 40% for extra .22 LR cylinder.

	$300	$250	$200	$175	$165	$160	$150

Approximately 250 factory engraved Single Six models have been manufactured. Seldomly seen and among the rarest of Ruger revolvers, prices have been reported at over $1,500.

SINGLE SIX CONVERTIBLE—same as Single Six, except .22 LR and .22 WMR interchangeable cylinders, 4⅝, 5½, 6½, and 9½ in. barrels with 4⅝ and 9½ in. being the rarest.

	$275	$200	$175	$150	$140	$115	$100

LIGHTWEIGHT SINGLE SIX—same as Single Six, except alloy frame, 4⅝ in. barrel, made 1956-1958. Should be in 200,000 - 212,000 serial range, can have alloy or steel cylinder.

	$300	$250	$175	$170	$165	$160	$150

SUPER SINGLE SIX CONVERTIBLE—same as Single Six Convertible, except adj. sights, made 1964-1972.

	$275	$250	$200	$155	$140	$120	$105

BLACKHAWK SINGLE ACTION—.357 Mag., .41 Mag., or .45 LC cal.'s, this model is the 1962 variation, hooded rear sight, 4⅝ or 6½ in barrel, a few were produced with brass grip frames.

	$350	$300	$250	$215	$180	$160	$140

This model was also available in .30 carbine with a 7½ in. barrel — add 10%. Beware of non-factory grip frames on this model.

BLACKHAWK SINGLE ACTION "FLAT-TOP"—.357 Mag., 6 shot, 4⅝, 6½, and 10 in. barrel, flat top cylinder strap, adj. sight, blue, walnut grips, made 1955-1963. Approximately 45,000 manufactured.

	$400	$350	$300	$250	$210	$200	$175

6½ in. barrel — add 60%.
10 in. barrel — add 150%.

BLACKHAWK CONVERTIBLE—same as Blackhawk, with extra cylinder, .357 and 9mm, and .45 Colt and .45 ACP cal.'s.

	$300	$265	$240	$220	$180	$150	$130

Add $50 for .45 LC/.45 ACP combination.

Grading	100%	98%	95%	90%	80%	70%	60%

BLACKHAWK FLAT-TOP .44 MAGNUM—similar to Blackhawk Flat-Top, except heavier frame and cylinder, .44 Mag., 6½, 7½, and 10 in. barrels, made 1956-1963.

	$550	$485	$415	$360	$305	$230	$210

7½ in. barrel — add 25%.
10 in. barrel — add 50%.

Distinguishable by fluted cylinder and rounded trigger guard.

SUPER BLACKHAWK—.44 Mag., 6½ (rare) or 7½ in. barrel, larger frame and improved trigger guard, unfluted cylinder, adj. sights, walnut grips, made 1959-1972.

	$300	$250	$200	$195	$190	$185	$175

Rare early models in wood case will command 300-400% premium. White cardboard boxed Super Blackhawks will command a 200-300% premium. 6½ in. barrel will command a 50% + premium.

BEARCAT—.22 cal., 6 shot, 4 in. barrel, alloy frame, brass trigger guard, blue, wood grips with medallion, 17 oz., made 1958-1973.

	$240	$220	$195	$180	$165	$150	$135

Several variations exist within this model incorporating production changes.

SUPER BEARCAT—same as Bearcat, except steel frame, made with brass trigger guard (early model), or blued steel guard, 25 oz., made 1971-1973.

	$275	$240	$225	$200	$180	$165	$150

HAWKEYE SINGLE SHOT—.256 Mag., single shot, cylinder replaced by rotating breech block, 8½ in. barrel, blue, walnut grips, adj. sight, very rare, approximately 3,300 manufactured, made 1963-1964.

	$1,175	$1,000	$ 875	$ 700	$ 580	$ 475	$ 400

NEW MODEL REVOLVERS

The following single actions are known as "New Models". They have 2 pins through the frame and cock without the clicks associated with the single action. The change over occurred as a result of desire for safety features. The "New Models" have a transfer bar similar to those found on modern double action revolvers and do not accidentally discharge if dropped. Manufacture started in 1973.

During certain years of manufacture, Rugers' changes in production on certain models (cal.'s, barrel markings, barrel lengths, etc.) have created rare variations that are now considered premium niches. These areas of low manufacture will add premiums to the values listed below on standard models.

SUPER SINGLE SIX CONVERTIBLE—.22 LR, with interchangeable .22 WMR cylinder, 4⅝, 5½, 6½, or 9½ in. barrel, similar to old Super Single Six, except has new interlocking mechanism previously described, adj. rear sight, made 1973-present.

Mfg.'s Sug. Retail	$255	$205	$175	$150	$130	$120	$110	$100

Subtract 15% if without extra .22 Mag. cylinder.

Stainless steel—similar to Super Single Six, except stainless steel and is supplied with extra .22 Mag. cylinder, 5½ or 6½ in. barrel only.

Mfg.'s Sug. Retail	$321	$255	$215	$180

Colorado Centennial Super Single Six—15,000 mfg. in 1975 only, includes walnut case with medallion insert, stainless steel grip frame, 6½ in. barrel, issue price was $250.

	$295	$245	$200

This model was a Bicentennial gun as well as the Colorado Centennial Pistol. Most specimens do not have the Bicentennial statement on the barrel and are rarer with that stamping.

SINGLE SIX SSM—.32 H&R Mag. cal., 4⅝, 5½, 6½ or 9½ in. barrel, blue only, 32 oz. with 5½ in. barrel.

Mfg.'s Sug. Retail	$245	$200	$165	$145	$135	$125	$115	$105

BLACKHAWK—similar to Blackhawk, with new interlocking mechanism, 30 Carbine, .357 Mag., .41 Mag., and .45 LC cal.'s available, 4⅝, 6½, or 7½ in. (.30 Carbine and .45 LC only) barrel, made 1973-present. Add $13 for extra 9mm cylinder (convertible with .357 Mag.).

Mfg.'s Sug. Retail	$297	$235	$195	$170	$155	$145	$135	$125

Subtract $11 for .30 Carbine cal.

Grading	100%	98%	95%	90%	80%	70%	60%

Stainless steel—.357 Mag. only, 4⅝ or 6½ in. barrel.
Mfg.'s Sug. Retail $366 $305 $250 $210

New Model Blackhawks are serial numbered 32-00001 on up.

BLACKHAWK-SRM—same as New Model Blackhawk, except is chambered for .357 Rem. maximum, 7½ or 10½ in. barrels available, target sights, 53 oz., made in limited quantities in 1984 only - taken off the market because metallurgy was not perfected.

	$340	$300	$275	$250	$225	$200	$180

BLACKHAWK CONVERTIBLE—same as New Model Blackhawk, except interchangeable cylinders, .357/9mm (current), or .45 Colt/.45 ACP (discontinued in 1985).
Mfg.'s Sug. Retail $312 $255 $210 $185 $170 $160 $150 $140

BISLEY MODEL—.22 LR, .32 H&R Mag., .357 Mag., .41 Mag., .44 Mag., and .45 LC cal.'s, incorporates Bisley features (flat-top frame, raked hammer, longer grip frame), 6½ or 7½ in. barrel, fixed or adj. sights, available with fluted/unfluted or roll-marked/unmarked cylinders, satin blue finish only, Goncalo Alves smooth grips. New in 1986. Add $56 for .357 Mag.-.45 LC cal.'s (available with 7½ in. barrel only).
Mfg.'s Sug. Retail $298 $250 $205 $180 $170 $160 $150 $140

SUPER BLACKHAWK—.44 Mag., 5½ (new in 1987), 7½ or 10½ in. barrel, blued finish, walnut grips, similar to old model in appearance, but has new action, made 1973-present. The new model started with serial number 81-00001.
Mfg.'s Sug. Retail $343 $270 $225 $200 $180 $170 $160 $150

Stainless steel—otherwise same as Super Blackhawk.
Mfg.'s Sug. Retail $375 $320 $270 $220

Note: In 1976, Ruger stamped "Made in the 200th year of American Liberty" on the side of all of the guns they produced for this one year only. These Bicentennial or "Liberty Model" guns will bring a $50 - $75 premium from collectors interested in acquiring them. In most cases this is only true of 100% guns, unfired with the original box and papers.

REVOLVERS: DOUBLE ACTION

During certain years of manufacture, Rugers' changes in production on certain models (cal.'s, barrel markings, barrel lengths, etc.) have created rare variations that are now considered premium niches. These areas of low manufacture will add premiums to the values listed below on standard models.

SPEED SIX (MODELS 207, 208 and 209)—.38 Spl., .357 Mag., or 9mm cal.'s, 2¾ or 4 in. barrel, fixed sights, checkered walnut grips, round butt, blued finish, some guns have factory speed hammer (no hammer spur), made 1973-present. Add $35 for 9mm (Model 209-discontinued in 1984). Model 207 and 208 disc. in 1988.

	$255	$220	$205	$190	$170	$160	$150

Last Mfg.'s Sug. Retail was $292.

Models 737 and 738—stainless steel versions of Models 207 and 208, .357 Mag and .38 Spl. cal.'s, 2¾ or 4 in. barrel. Disc. in 1988.
$280 $245 $220

Last Mfg.'s Sug. Retail was $320.

Model 739—stainless steel, 9mm. Discontinued in 1984.
$300 $250 $230

SECURITY SIX MODEL 117—.357 Mag. cal., 6 shot, 2¾, 4 (heavy), or 6 in. barrel, adj. sights, checkered walnut grips, square butt. Add $15 for target grips. Manufactured 1970-1985.
$270 $235 $210 $195 $185 $160 $150

Last Mfg.'s Sug. Retail was $309.

500 of this model were manufactured for the California Highway Patrol in 1983. They are distinguishable by a C.H.P. marking. Premiums might exist in certain regions for this derivative.

Model 717—stainless steel version of Model 117. Discontinued in 1985.
$295 $255 $230

Last Mfg.'s Sug. Retail was $338.

Grading	100%	98%	95%	90%	80%	70%	60%

POLICE SERVICE SIX—.357 Mag., .38 Spl., and 9mm cal.'s, blued finish only, square butt, fixed sights, checkered walnut grips.

Model 107—.357 Mag, 2¾ or 4 in. barrel, fixed sights. Disc. in 1988.

	$250	$220	$200	$190	$180	$170	$165

Last Mfg.'s Sug. Retail was $287.

Model 108—.38 Spl., 4 in. barrel, fixed sights. Disc. in 1988.

	$250	$220	$200	$190	$180	$170	$165

Last Mfg.'s Sug. Retail was $287.

Model 109—9mm, 4 in. barrel, fixed sights. Discontinued in 1984.

	$275	$230	$205	$195	$185	$180	$175

POLICE SERVICE SIX STAINLESS—stainless construction, 4 in. barrel only, fixed sights, checkered walnut grips.

Model 707—.357 Mag., square butt. Disc. in 1988.

	$270	$235	$210

Last Mfg.'s Sug. Retail was $310.

Model 708—.38 Spl., square butt. Disc. in 1988.

	$270	$235	$210

Last Mfg.'s Sug. Retail was $310.

GP-100—.357 Mag. or .38 Spl. cal., 4 (heavy) or 6 in. barrel, strengthened design intended for constant use with all .357 Mag. ammunition, rubber cushioned grip panels with polished Goncalo Alves wood inserts, adj. sights with white outlined rear and interchangeable front, 6 shot, 41 oz. New in 1986.

Mfg.'s Sug. Retail	$360	$315	$265	$240	$220	$200	$185	$170

Add $15 for adj. rear sight.

GP-100 Stainless—same as GP-100, except is stainless steel. New in 1987.

Mfg.'s Sug. Retail	$390	$335	$275	$250

Add $15 for adj. rear sight.

SP-101 STAINLESS—.38 Spl., small frame variation of the GP-100 Stainless, 5 shot, fixed sights, 2¼ or 3⁹⁄₁₆ in. barrel, 25 oz. New in 1989.

Mfg.'s Sug. Retail	$370	$315	$260	$240

RED HAWK—.357 Mag. (discontinued in 1985), .41 Mag., and .44 Mag. cal.'s, this is a redesigned stainless steel-large frame handgun, 5½ and 7½ in. barrel only, square butt. Add $33 for scope rings.

Mfg.'s Sug. Retail	$397	$345	$300	$275	$240	$215	$180	$165

Red Hawk Stainless—stainless steel construction. Add $35 for stainless scope rings.

Mfg.'s Sug. Retail	$447	$385	$330	$300

Note: The "Liberty Models" also appear in Ruger Double Action handguns that were made in 1976, and the same premium applied.

SUPER REDHAWK STAINLESS—.44 Mag., 7½ or 9½ barrel, adj. rear sight, cushioned grip panels (GP-100 style), 53 oz. Delivery began in late 1987.

Mfg.'s Sug. Retail	$510	$440	$350	$285

OLD ARMY PERCUSSION REVOLVER—.44 cal., black powder, 6 shot, 7½ in. barrel, blued finish, walnut grips.

Mfg.'s Sug. Retail	$290	$240	$195	$165	$150	$135	$120	$110

Stainless Steel

Mfg.'s Sug. Retail	$370	$300	$255	$200

RIFLES: SEMI-AUTO

During certain years of manufacture, Rugers' changes in production on certain models (cal.'s, barrel markings, barrel lengths, etc.) have created rare variations that are now considered premium niches. These areas of low manufacture will add premiums to the values listed below on standard models.

10/22 STANDARD CARBINE—.22 LR, 10 shot rotary mag., 18½ in. barrel, birch stock, folding rear sight, made 1964-present. Add $20 for walnut stock (new in 1987), $42 for deluxe checkered walnut stock.

Mfg.'s Sug. Retail	$183	$145	$125	$95	$80	$70	$60	$55

10/22 SPORTER—same as Standard, except Monte Carlo stock and beavertail forearm, made 1964-1971.

	$160	$150	$140	$130	$120	$110	$100

Grading	100%	98%	95%	90%	80%	70%	60%

10/22 STANDARD CARBINE—walnut stock. Discontinued.

	$140	$130	$120	$110	$100	$90	$80

10/22 CANADIAN CENTENNIAL—limited production. Discontinued.

	$375	$350	$325	$275	$250	$225	$180

10/22 SP DELUXE SPORTER—same as Standard, except checkered walnut stock with flat butt plate, made 1971-present.

	$163	$135	$125	$110	$100	$90	$80

10/22 INTERNATIONAL—same as Standard, except full stock Mannlicher style, made 1964-1971.

	$475	$425	$350	$330	$300	$250	$225

MODEL 44 STANDARD CARBINE—.44 Mag., 4 shot mag., 18½ in. barrel, gas operated, folding sight, curved butt, made 1961-1985.

	$325	$275	$250	$220	$195	$185	$175

Last Mfg.'s Sug. Retail was $332.

Deerstalker Model—approx. 2,000 mfg. with "Deerstalker" marked on rifle until Ithaca discontinued manufacture (1962).

	$425	$350	$285	$250	$220	$195	$185

25th Year Anniversary Model—made in 1985 only, limited production, engraved.

	$400	$350	$310				

Last Mfg.'s Sug. Retail was $495.

MODEL 44RS—same as 44, but has aperture sight and swivels.

	$295	$275	$250	$230	$210	$195	$175

MODEL 44 SPORTER DELUXE—stocked version of 44 Standard, made until 1971.

	$350	$320	$280	$255	$225	$205	$190

MODEL 44 INTERNATIONAL—same as Standard, except full length Mannlicher style stock, made until 1971.

	$660	$550	$400	$350	$325	$300	$275

MINI 14—.223 Rem. or .222 (discontinued) cal.'s, 5, 10, or 20 shot mag., 18½ in. barrel, gas operated, aperture rear sight, military style stock, made 1976-present. Add $78 for folding stock.

Mfg.'s Sug. Retail	$422	$355	$300	$265	$240	$215	$185	$170

K Mini 14—mini stainless steel version. Add $70 for folding stock.

Mfg.'s Sug. Retail	$465	$375	$320	$280			

MINI 14 RANCH RIFLE—.223 cal., 15⅛ in. barrel, folding rear sight, receiver cut for factory rings, similar to Mini 14, supplied with scope rings.

Mfg.'s Sug. Retail	$454	$385	$330	$300	$280	$260	$245	$230

Stainless Ranch Rifle—stainless steel construction. Add $65 for folding stock. New in 1986.

Mfg.'s Sug. Retail	$498	$415	$355	$310			

MINI-THIRTY—7.62 x 39mm Russian, 18½ in. barrel, 5 shot detachable mag.,hardwood stock, includes scope rings, 7 lbs. 3 oz. New in 1987.

Mfg.'s Sug. Retail	$454	$385	$330	$300	$280	$260	$245	$230

XGI—.243 or .308 Win. cal.'s , similar to Mini 14, 20 in. barrel, 5 shot mag., 8 lbs. Made 1985-86 only.

	$370	$325	$300	$280	$260	$245	$230

Last Mfg.'s Sug. Retail was $425.

RIFLES: SINGLE SHOT

Note: All Ruger Rifles, except Stainless Mini-14, were made in 1976 "Liberty" version. Add $50 - $75 when in 100% in the original box condition.

During certain years of manufacture, Rugers' changes in production on certain models (cal.'s, barrel markings, barrel lengths, etc.) have created rare variations that are now considered premium niches. These areas of low manufacture will add premiums to the values listed below on standard models.

Grading	100%	98%	95%	90%	80%	70%	60%

NO. 1-A & B STANDARD—falling block action with curved Farquharson lever, some cal.'s include .22-250, .220 Swift, .223, .257 Roberts, .243, 6mm, .25-06, .270, .280, .30-06, 7mm Mag., and .300 Win. Mag., .338 Win. Mag. cal.'s, 22 or 26 in. barrel, quarter rib with integral scope bases, supplied with rings and no sights, checkered stock and semi beavertail forearm, made 1966-present.

Mfg.'s Sug. Retail	$575	$415	$360	$320	$260	$220	$205	$195

The "A" suffix designates an Alexander Henry classic forearm with light barrel and is available in .243, .270, 7 x 57mm, and .30-06 cal.'s only. The "B" suffix designates semi beavertail forearm with medium barrel and is available in all cal.'s under .375 H&H.

NO. 1-RSI—same cal.'s as No. 1-A Standard, 20 in. barrel with full length Mannlicher stock, includes swivels, 7¼ lbs.

Mfg.'s Sug. Retail	$595	$435	$375	$330	$265	$220	$205	$195

NO. 1-V VARMINT—similar to No. 1-B Standard, except .22-250, 220 Swift, .223, .243 (discontinued), .25-06, 6mm and .280 (discontinued) cal.'s, 24 in. heavy barrel, no rib, target scope blocks, 9 lbs., made 1966-present.

Mfg.'s Sug. Retail	$575	$415	$360	$320	$260	$220	$205	$195

NO. 1-A LIGHT SPORTER—same as Standard, .243, .270, 7 x 57, .30-06 cal.'s, 22 in. barrel, folding sight on quarter rib, ramp front sight, no rings, Alexander Henry forearm, front swivel in barrel band, made 1966-present.

Mfg.'s Sug. Retail	$575	$415	$360	$320	$260	$220	$205	$195

NO. 1-S MEDIUM SPORTER—same as Light Sporter, only 7mm, .338 Win. Mag. and .300 Win. Mag. cal.'s, 26 in. medium barrel.

Mfg.'s Sug. Retail	$575	$415	$360	$320	$260	$220	$205	$195

.45-70 cal.—with 22 in. barrel.

Mfg.'s Sug. Retail	$575	$415	$360	$320	$260	$220	$205	$195

NO. 1-H TROPICAL RIFLE—similar to Medium Sporter, except 24 in. heavy barrel, .375 H&H and .458 Win. Mag. cal.'s only.

Mfg.'s Sug. Retail	$575	$425	$370	$325	$260	$220	$205	$195

NO. 1 INTERNATIONAL—.243 Win., .30-06, .270 Win., and 7 x 57mm cal.'s, lightweight 20 in. barrel, Mannlicher style forearm. Discontinued.

	$425	$325	$300	$260	$230	$205	$195

NO. 3 CARBINE—same basic action as No. 1, except simpler lever design, stock uncheckered and very similar to .44 Carbine, made in .22 Hornet, .30-40 Krag, .45-70 (only cal. available in 1986), .223, .44 Mag., and .375 Win. cal.'s, 22 in. barrel, folding sight, made 1972-1987.

	$250	$215	$200	$180	$165	$145	$130

Last Mfg.'s Sug. Retail was $284.

RIFLES: BOLT ACTION

Note: All Ruger Rifles, except Stainless Mini-14, were made in 1976 "Liberty" version. Add $50 - $75 when in 100% in the original box condition.

During certain years of manufacture, Rugers' changes in production on certain models (cal.'s, barrel markings, barrel lengths, etc.) have created rare variations that are now considered premium niches. These areas of low manufacture will add premiums to the values listed below on standard models.

Earlier flat-bolt models (pre-1972) are desirable in the rarer cal.'s and will command premiums if 98% + condition.

MODEL 77/22—.22 LR only, 10 shot rotary mag., 20 in. barrel, all steel construction, checkered walnut stock, 5¾ lbs., non-adj. trigger. New in 1984. Available with scope rings or open sights - add $20 for both.

Mfg.'s Sug. Retail	$364	$300	$275	$250	$230	$210	$190	$175

Model 77/22 Synthetic Stock—similar to Model 77/22 except has matte black synthetic stock, approx. 6 lbs. New in 1989.

Mfg.'s Sug. Retail	$300	$260	$220	$200	$185	$175	$165	$155

Add $20 for scope rings.

Grading	100%	98%	95%	90%	80%	70%	60%

Model 77/22 Stainless/Synthetic—similar to Model 77/22 except has stainless steel metal with matte black synthetic stock. New in 1989.

Mfg.'s Sug. Retail	$360	$300	$275	$250			

Add $20 for scope rings.

MODEL 77R—.22-250, .220 Swift, 6mm, .243, .257 Roberts .25-06, .270, 7 x57, 7mm-08, 7mm Rem. Mag., 280 Rem., .308, .30-06, .300 Win. Mag., or .338 Win Mag. cal.'s, 5 shot mag., 3 shot in Mag., 22, 24, or 26 in. barrel, available with integral bases or round top, some models supplied with sights, stock is checkered walnut with red rubber butt plate, made 1968-present.

Mfg.'s Sug. Retail	$483	$400	$335	$285	$265	$245	$200	$200

Add 10% for .284 cal.

This model is encountered with or without the "R" suffix.

Model 77 RL—ultra light, 6 lbs., black forearm tip, various cal.'s.

Mfg.'s Sug. Retail	$513	$425	$355	$290	$270	$250	$225	$205

Model 77 RS—same as Model 77R, except has open sights.

Mfg.'s Sug. Retail	$533	$440	$370	$305	$280	$260	$230	$210

Model 77 RS African—similar to Model 77R, except in .458 Win. Mag. cal.

Mfg.'s Sug. Retail	$618	$510	$440	$395	$360	$335	$315	$300

This model is supplied standard with a steel trigger guard and steel floor plate.

Model 77 RLS—.243, .270, .30-06, and .308 cal.'s, ultra light, 18½ barrel, open sights, 6 lbs. New in 1987.

Mfg.'s Sug. Retail	$513	$430	$370	$305	$280	$260	$230	$210

Model 77 RSI—international Mannlicher (full length stock) with 18½ in. barrel and open sights.

Mfg.'s Sug. Retail	$540	$450	$380	$310	$280	$260	$230	$210

.250-3000—discontinued.

	$400	$365	$325	$270	$250	$220	$200

MODEL 77V VARMINT RIFLE—same as Standard, except .22-250, .220 Swift, .243, 6mm, .25-06, and .308 cal.'s, 24 in. heavy barrel (26 in. on .220 Swift), drilled and tapped for target bases, made 1968-present.

Mfg.'s Sug. Retail	$497	$410	$345	$295	$265	$245	$210	$200

SHOTGUNS

RED LABEL O/U—12 or 20 ga., 3 in. chambers, various barrel lengths and choke (including skeet) combinations, boxlock, SST, VR, auto ejectors, checkered pistol grip stock, stainless steel frame became standard on 12 ga. in 1985 (not available in 20 ga.), made 1977-present. Choke tubes became optional in 1988.

Mfg.'s Sug. Retail	$920	$750	$650	$575	$525	$480	$445	$410

Add $130 for choke tubes.

Earlier all-steel 12 ga. models with short field tubes could command 35% + premiums over values listed above to collectors interested in acquiring this variation. 20 ga. models are blue only.

SUNDANCE INDUSTRIES, INC.

MANUFACTURER LOCATED IN NORTH HOLLYWOOD, CA.

DERRINGER

MODEL D-22M—.22 LR or .22 Mag., 4.6 in., aluminum and steel construction, double barrel design, bright chrome or black finish, simulated pearl or black grips, approx. 12 oz. New in 1989.

Please contact Sundance Industries, Inc. directly for prices.

T

TANNER, ANDRÉ

MANUFACTURED IN SWITZERLAND. PREVIOUSLY IMPORTED BY OSBORNE'S LOCATED IN CHEBOYGAN, MI.

Tanner rifles are noted for their superior accuracy and limited production - less than 150 are mfg. each year.

Prices below reflect the recent devaluation of the U.S. dollar against some foreign currencies. While the manufacturer's suggested retails have gone up considerably, prices for used specimens (98% or less original condition) have not increased proportionally, and in some cases, have changed very little.

Grading	100%	98%	95%	90%	80%	70%	60%

MODEL 300 FREE—7.5 Swiss and 7.62mm cal.'s only, single shot, top of the line 300 meter match rifle incorporating all match shooting features including deluxe palm rest, aperture sights. Add $100 for adj. cheekpiece. Importation disc. in 1988.

| | $3,300 | $2,700 | $2,250 | $1,900 | $1,700 | $1,500 | $1,300 |

A repeating model is also available with similar features — subtract $190.

Last Mfg.'s Sug. Retail was $3,635.

MODEL 300 S—similar to Model 300 F, except is without palm rest and adj. Swiss buttplate, 10 shot mag., aperture sights. Add $100 for adj. cheekpiece. Importation disc. in 1988.

| | $3,000 | $2,625 | $2,225 | $1,975 | $1,760 | $1,560 | $1,350 |

This variation is the U.I.T. Model (single shot).

Last Mfg.'s Sug. Retail was $3,354.

MODEL 50 F—.22 LR only, 50 meter free rifle, deluxe palm rest, adj. buttplate, thumbhole stock. Add $100 for adj. cheekpiece. Importation disc. in 1988.

| | $2,450 | $2,050 | $1,850 | $1,700 | $1,560 | $1,350 | $1,175 |

Last Mfg.'s Sug. Retail was $2,685.

TAURUS INTERNATIONAL MANUFACTURING, INC.

MANUFACTURED IN PORTO ALEGRE, BRAZIL. CURRENTLY IMPORTED BY TAURUS INTERNATIONAL MANUFACTURING, INC. LOCATED IN MIAMI, FL.

REVOLVERS: CURRENT MANUFACTURE

MODEL 65—.357 Mag./.38 Spl., double action, 6 shot, 3 or 4 in. barrel, 34 oz., checkered walnut grips.

| *Mfg.'s Sug. Retail* | $228 | $185 | $150 | $125 | $115 | $100 | $90 | $85 |

Add $12 for satin nickel finish.

MODEL 66—.357 Mag./.38 Spl., double action, 6 shot, 3, 4, and 6 in. barrels, 35 oz., checkered walnut grips, adj. sights.

| *Mfg.'s Sug. Retail* | $248 | $200 | $160 | $135 | $125 | $115 | $100 | $90 |

Add $11 for satin nickel finish.

Model 66 Stainless—similar to Model 66, but in stainless steel. New in 1987.

| *Mfg.'s Sug. Retail* | $315 | $265 | $215 | $185 |

MODEL 669—similar to Model 66 except has fully shrouded barrel, 4 or 6 in. barrel, 37 oz.

| *Mfg.'s Sug. Retail* | $257 | $210 | $170 | $145 | $125 | $115 | $100 | $90 |

Model 669 Stainless—similar to Model 669, but in stainless steel.

| *Mfg.'s Sug. Retail* | $324 | $275 | $225 | $190 |

Grading	100%	98%	95%	90%	80%	70%	60%

MODEL 73—.32 long only, double action, 6 shot, 3 in. heavy barrel only, 20 oz., checkered walnut grips.

| *Mfg.'s Sug. Retail* | $204 | $170 | $150 | $125 | $115 | $105 | $95 | $85 |

Add $18 for satin nickel finish.

MODEL 80—.38 Spl. only, double action, 6 shot, 3 or 4 in. barrel, 30 oz., checkered walnut grips.

| *Mfg.'s Sug. Retail* | $198 | $165 | $135 | $115 | $105 | $95 | $85 | $80 |

Add $12 for satin nickel finish.

MODEL 82—.38 Spl. only, double action, 6 shot, 3 or 4 in. heavy barrel, 34 oz., checkered walnut grips.

| *Mfg.'s Sug. Retail* | $198 | $165 | $135 | $115 | $105 | $95 | $85 | $80 |

Add $12 for satin nickel finish.

MODEL 83—.38 Spl. only, double action, 6 shot, 4 in. heavy barrel, 34½ oz., checkered walnut grips, adj. sights.

| *Mfg.'s Sug. Retail* | $208 | $170 | $140 | $125 | $115 | $105 | $95 | $80 |

Add $11 for satin nickel finish.

MODEL 85—.38 Spl. only, double action, 5 shot, 2 or 3 in. heavy barrel, 21 oz., checkered walnut grips.

| *Mfg.'s Sug. Retail* | $217 | $175 | $145 | $125 | $115 | $105 | $95 | $85 |

Add $16 for satin nickel finish.

Model 85 Stainless—stainless construction, otherwise same as Model 85.

| *Mfg.'s Sug. Retail* | $275 | $225 | $185 | $150 | | | | |

MODEL 86 TARGET MASTER—.38 Spl. only, double action, 6 shot, 6 in. barrel, 34 oz., checkered walnut grips, adj. rear sight, blue only.

| *Mfg.'s Sug. Retail* | $277 | $225 | $185 | $160 | $150 | $140 | $130 | $120 |

MODEL 94—.22 LR, double action, 9 shot, 4 in. barrel, blue finish, adj. rear sight, target featues, 25 oz. New in 1989.

| *Mfg.'s Sug. Retail* | $230 | $185 | $150 | $135 | $120 | $105 | $95 | $85 |

MODEL 96 TARGET SCOUT—.22 LR only, double action, 6 shot, 6 in. barrel, 34 oz., checkered walnut grips, same features as Model 86.

| *Mfg.'s Sug. Retail* | $277 | $225 | $185 | $160 | $150 | $140 | $130 | $120 |

PISTOLS: SEMI-AUTO

PT-58—.380 ACP, similar to PT-99AF, except in .380 ACP cal. and 13 round mag. New in 1988.

| *Mfg.'s Sug. Retail* | $388 | $315 | $270 | $235 | $215 | $200 | $190 | $180 |

Add $7 for satin nickel finish.

PT-92AF—9mm Para., semi-auto double action, design similar to Beretta Model 92 SB-F, exposed hammer, 4.92 in. barrel, 15 shot mag., 34 oz., smooth Brazilian walnut grips, blue only, fixed sights.

| *Mfg.'s Sug. Retail* | $425 | $345 | $295 | $250 | $225 | $200 | $190 | $180 |

Add $12 for satin nickel finish.

PT-99AF—same as Model PT 92, except has adj. rear sight.

| *Mfg.'s Sug. Retail* | $460 | $375 | $310 | $265 | $235 | $210 | $200 | $190 |

Add $15 for satin nickel finish.

Action similar to Beretta Model 92SB-F.

TERRIER ONE

FOREIGN MANUFACTURE. PREVIOUSLY DISTRIBUTED (1984-85) BY SOUTHERN GUN DISTRIBUTORS, MIAMI, FL.

TERRIER ONE—.32 S&W revolver, double action, 2¼ in. barrel, 5 shot, nickel plated, 17 oz. Mfg. 1984-87.

| | $45 | $35 | $30 | $25 | $25 | $25 | $25 |

Last Mfg.'s Sug. Retail was $55.

TEXAS GUNFIGHTERS

Grading	100%	98%	95%	90%	80%	70%	60%

IMPORTER LOCATED IN IRVING, TX.

SHOOTIST EDITION SINGLE ACTION—.45 LC, patterned after the Colt SAA, 4¾ in. barrel, nickel plated blackpowder frame, one-piece walnut grips, mfg. by A. Uberti of Italy. New in 1988.

Standard Model—1,000 total mfg., cased.

Mfg.'s Sug. Retail	$649	$649	$525	$440

1 of 100 Edition—100 total mfg., fully engraved, genuine mother-of-pearl one piece grips, cased.

Mfg.'s Sug. Retail	$1,395	$1,395	$1,050	$775

This model is also supplied with an extra set of walnut grips.

TEXAS LONGHORN ARMS, INC.

MANUFACTURED AND DISTRIBUTED IN RICHMOND, TX.

REVOLVERS

SINGLE-ACTION—various cal.'s, patterned after Colt's S.A.A., except the ejection port has been moved to left side of frame enabling left-hand loading, mfg. from 4140 steel, Pope rifled barrels, 1 piece grips, adj. trigger, case-hardened and blued, entirely hand-made, supplied with lifetime warranty. 1,000 mfg. of each model.

Texas Border Special—.44 Spl. and .45 LC cal.'s, 3½ in. barrel, 1 piece birdshead grip.

Mfg.'s Sug. Retail	$1,500	$1,500	$1,300	$1,000

South Texas Army—.357 Mag., .44 Spl., and .45 LC cal.'s, 4¾ in. barrel, 1 piece regular walnut stock.

Mfg.'s Sug. Retail	$1,500	$1,500	$1,300	$1,000

West Texas Target—.32-20, .357 Mag., .44 Mag./Spl., and .45 LC cal.'s, flat top frame, 7½ in. barrel.

Mfg.'s Sug. Retail	$1,500	$1,500	$1,300	$1,000

Grover's Improved Number Five—.44 Mag. only, 5½ in. target barrel, 1,200 mfg. serial numbered K1-K1200. This variation incorporates Elmer Keith's 1926 designs including No. 5 lockwork, base pin and latch, and grip straps. New in 1988.

Mfg.'s Sug. Retail	$985	$985	$725	$595

Special Edition—includes 10 sets, one of each model listed above, matching cal.'s (.44 Spl. and .45 LC only), matching ser. no.'s divisible by 100 to 1,000 only. Includes carrying case.

Mfg.'s Sug. Retail	$5,750	$5,750	$4,950	$4,200

Engraved Special Edition—each set includes 3 guns that are factory engraved.

Mfg.'s Sug. Retail	$7,650	$7,650	$6,800	$5,950

Texas Sesquicentennial Commemorative—.45 LC, 4¾ in. barrel, one-piece elephant ivory grips, 75% engraved in Nimschke style, walnut presentation case, 150 manufactured in 1987 only.

Mfg.'s Sug. Retail	$2,500	$2,500	$1,950	$1,500

Mason Commemorative—.45 LC, 4¾ in. barrel, one-piece extra-grained walnut grips, engraved 18 Kt. Mason insignia, oak presentation case, serial numbered BL-1 on up. New in 1987.

Mfg.'s Sug. Retail	$1,500	$1,500	$1,300	$1,000

PISTOLS

JEZEBEL MODEL—.22 LR or .22 Mag., single shot, tip-up action, stainless steel, 6 in. barrel, walnut stock and forearm, 17 oz., right or left hand action. New in 1987.

Mfg.'s Sug. Retail	$200	$200	$160	$135

THOMPSON CARBINES

See Auto Ordnance section of this book.

THOMPSON/CENTER ARMS

MANUFACTURED AND DISTRIBUTED IN ROCHESTER, N.H. 1967 TO DATE.

PISTOL: SINGLE SHOT

Caution: older and newer TC components do not interchange safely. Although parts will fit they may not function properly. Special ordering of barrels, frames, and calibers started in 1988.

CONTENDER—.22 LR, .22 WMR, 5mm Rem., .218 Bee, .22 Hornet, .22 Jet, .221 Fireball, .222, .25-35, .256 Mag., .30 Carb., .30-30, .385 Spl., .357 Mag., .17 Ackley Bee, .17 Bumblebee, .17 Hornet, 17K Hornet, .30 Herrett, .357 Herrett, .357-44 B&D, 7 x 30 Waters, .32 H&R Mag., .32-20 Win., 9mm, and 6mm TCU cal.'s, barrels are interchangeable, 8¾ (discontinued), 10, or 14 in. barrel, hinged break open, trigger guard, action lever, blue, .44, .357 Mag., and .45 Colt available with detachable choke for hot shot cartridges, vent rib, 10 in. barrel available, 10 in. bull barrel, adj. sights, checkered walnut grip and forearm.

The Contender action is in its third variation and a wide variety of changes have been made to grips, stocks, sights, etc. since 1967. These production variances do not necessarily add premiums to values listed below.

Octagon barrel—.22 LR, .22 Mag., .22 Hornet, .222 Rem., or .357 Mag. cal.'s, 10 in. barrel.

Mfg.'s Sug. Retail	$335	$280	$230	$190	$180	$170	$160	$150

Bull barrel—available in 15 cal.'s between .22 LR and .44 Mag., 10 in. round barrel only.

Mfg.'s Sug. Retail	$335	$280	$230	$190	$180	$170	$160	$150

Add $20 for .44 Mag/.45 Colt with internal chokes.

Armour Alloy II Bull Barrel—7 cal.'s between .22 LR and .30-30, similar to regular Bull Barrel, except has Armour Alloy II satin finish which is harder than stainless steel. New in 1986.

Mfg.'s Sug. Retail	$415	$320	$285	$230

Add $5 for .45 Colt/.410 ga. internal choke.

Vent Rib—.357 Mag.(discontinued), .44 Mag.(discontinued) or .45 Colt/.410 cal.'s, 10 in. VR barrel only, adj. front and flip up rear sight, internal choke became standard in 1985.

Mfg.'s Sug. Retail	$355	$295	$240	$200	$190	$180	$165	$155

Extra barrels (14 available) without vent rib — $145, or with vent rib — $130.

Armour Alloy Vent Rib—.45/.410 internal choke, has Armour Alloy II satin finish which is harder than stainless steel. New in 1986.

Mfg.'s Sug. Retail	$435	$350	$295	$230

CONTENDER SUPER—13 cal.'s available from .22 LR - .45 Win. Mag. (discontinued), 14 in. bull barrel only, special grips, beavertail forearm, adj. sight, 3½ lbs.

Mfg.'s Sug. Retail	$345	$290	$245	$200	$190	$180	$165	$155

Extra barrels - $155. Thompson Center will also make special order guns in different cal.'s other than those listed above. If factory work, these pistols will be worth a premium.

Armour Alloy II Super Contender—5 cal.'s between .22 LR and 7mm, similar to regular Super Contender, except has Armour Alloy II satin finish which is harder than stainless steel. New in 1986.

Mfg.'s Sug. Retail	$425	$355	$295	$240

Extra Armour Alloy II Bull Barrels are available for $195 + .

RIFLES

CONTENDER CARBINE—available in 9 cal.'s between .22 LR and .44 Rem. Mag., also .410 ga. (3 in.), Contender action with pistol grip full stock and forearm, 21 in. interchangeable barrel, drilled for scope mounts, iron sights standard. New in 1986.

Mfg.'s Sug. Retail	$375	$310	$270	$235	$210	$190	$175	$160

Add $20 for .410 ga. barrel.
Subtract $30 for Youth Model (16¼ in. barrel).

Extra barrels are available at $150 each.

Grading	100%	98%	95%	90%	80%	70%	60%

HUNTER MODEL—single shot, top lever break open action w/interchangeable barrels, .22 Hornet, .223, .22-250, .243, .270, 7mm, .30-06, and .308 Win. cal.'s. 23 in. barrel, 6 lbs. 14 oz., checkered walnut stock, choice of medium or light sporter weight barrel. New in 1983 and improved in 1987.. Available in left-hand at no extra charge.

Mfg.'s Sug. Retail	$425	$365	$320	$285	$260	$240	$220	$200

A 12 ga. (field or slug with 3 in. chamber) or 10 ga. (3½ in.) barrel is available for this model at no extra charge (steel shot approved).

TRC '83 ARISTOCRAT—same as Hunter Model, except stock has cheekpiece and forearm is checkered, stainless steel double set triggers. Discontinued in 1986.

		$425	$370	$345	$320	$300	$280	$260

Add $175 for each additional barrel(s) (including 12 ga. slug).

Last Mfg.'s Sug. Retail was $475.

TIKKA

MANUFACTURED BY OY TIKKAKOSKI AB, OF TIKKAKOSKI FINLAND. CURRENTLY IMPORTED BY STOEGER INDUSTRIES LOCATED IN SOUTH HACKENSACK, NJ.

Also see listings under Ithaca LSA for older models.

BOLT-ACTION RIFLE—.223, .243, .270, .30-06, 7mm Rem. Mag, or .338 Win. Mag. cal., 3 shot mag

Mfg.'s Sug. Retail	$720	$660	$600	$550	$500	$450	$400	$360

TIPPMAN ARMS CO.

PREVIOUSLY MANUFACTURED AND DISTRIBUTED IN FORT WAYNE, IN.

Tippman Arms manufactured 1/2 scale semi-auto working models of famous machine guns. All models were available with an optional hardwood case, extra ammo cans, and other accessories. Mfg. 1986-1987 only.

MODEL 1919 A-4—.22 LR only, copy of Browning 1919 A-4 Model, belt fed, closed bolt operation, 11 in. barrel, 10 lbs. Includes tripod.

		$1,195	$1,045	$950	$870	$800	$750	$695

Last Mfg.'s Sug. Retail was $1,325.

MODEL 1917—.22 LR only, copy of Browning M1917, watercooled, belt fed, closed bolt operation, 11 in. barrel, 10 lbs. Includes tripod.

		$1,650	$1,445	$1,285	$1,140	$995	$895	$795

Last Mfg.'s Sug. Retail was $1,830.

MODEL .50 HB—.22 Mag. only, copy of Browning .50 cal. machine gun, belt fed, closed bolt operation, 18¼ in. barrel, 13 lbs. Includes tripod.

		$1,750	$1,525	$1,350	$1,200	$1,050	$950	$850

Last Mfg.'s Sug. Retail was $1,929.

TOKAREV

SEE RUSSIAN MILITARY HEADING.

TRADEWINDS

Grading	100%	98%	95%	90%	80%	70%	60%

TACOMA, WA IMPORTERS.

HUSKY MODEL 5000—.22-250, .243, .270, .308, and .30-06 cal.'s, bolt action, 23¾ in. barrel, adj. sight, removable mag., hand checkered walnut stock.

	$325	$310	$290	$250	$225	$200	$175

MODEL 311-A—.22 LR, bolt action, 5 shot, 22½ in. barrel, folding leaf rear sight, walnut checkered stock.

	$180	$170	$150	$130	$120	$100	$85

MODEL 260-A—.22 LR, semi-auto, 5 shot, 22½ in. barrel, 3 leaf folding sight, checkered walnut stock.

	$200	$190	$175	$150	$130	$120	$100

MODEL H-170—12 ga., auto shotgun, 2¾ in. chamber, 26 in. mod. or 28 in. full, recoil operated action, alloy receiver, 5 shot, tube mag., vent rib, checkered walnut stock.

	$275	$265	$250	$225	$200	$180	$150

U

USAS 12

MANUFACTURED UNDER LICENSE BY DAEWOO PRECISION INDUSTRIES, LTD. IN SOUTH KOREA. IMPORTED AND DISTRIBUTED IN THE U.S. BY GILBERT EQUIPMENT CO., INC. LOCATED IN MOBILE, AL.

Grading	100%	98%	95%	90%	80%	70%	60%

USAS 12—12 ga. only, gas operated action available in either semi or fully auto versions, 18¼ in. cylinder bore barrel, synthetic stock and forearm, carrying handle, 10 round box or 20 drum mag., 2¾ in. chamber only, parkerized finish, 10 lbs. New in 1987.

Mfg.'s Sug. Retail	$695	$620	$550	$495	$460	$425	$390	$360

Values above are for a semi-auto model. Add $50 for fully auto version (Class III only). This model previously has been saleable to military or law enforcement agencies because of BATF rulings. Potential manufacture in the U.S. would allow this gun to be owned by individual citizens.

U.S. ARMS COMPANY

RIVERHEAD, NY

REVOLVERS: SINGLE ACTION

ABILENE .357 MAG.—6 shot, 4⅝, 5½, and 6½ in. barrel, adj. sights, transfer bar ignition, smooth walnut grips, blue finish only, made 1976-1983.

$225	$200	$180	$165	$150	$140	$120

ABILENE .357 MAG. STAINLESS STEEL—same as Abilene, only in stainless steel.

$300	$275	$250

ABILENE .44 MAG.—7½ and 8½ in. barrel, unfluted cylinder blue finish only, otherwise similar to .357 Mag.

$265	$240	$220	$200	$165	$150	$120

ABILENE .44 MAG. STAINLESS STEEL—same as Abilene .44 Mag., only stainless steel.

$330	$290	$260

UBERTI USA, INC.

IMPORTER/DISTRIBUTOR LOCATED IN NEW MILFORD, CT, 06776.. BOTH BLACK POWDER AND MODERN FIREARMS ARE IMPORTED BY UBERTI USA, INC. AND ARE MANUFACTURED BY ALDO UBERTI OF PONTE ZANANO, ITALY.

A. Uberti also manufactures firearms for Cimarron Arms which are marked differently from those firearms imported by Uberti USA, Inc.

REVOLVERS & CARBINES: SINGLE ACTION REPRODUCTIONS

Can be ordered with either black powder or modern configured frames. Factory engraving and other embellishments can be special ordered by contacting the importer directly.

CATTLEMAN VARIATIONS—available in .45 LC, .44-40, .44 S&W Spl. (new in 1989), .38-40 (new in 1989) .38 Spl., .357 Mag., .32-20 (new in 1989), .22 LR, and .22 Mag cal.'s, 4¾, 5½, and 7½ in. barrel lengths, brass or steel backstraps and trigger guard.

Quick Draw Model

Mfg.'s Sug. Retail	$330	$315	$235	$190	$175	$160	$150	$135

Add $27 for steel backstrap and trigger guard.
Add $64 for stainless steel construction.

Grading	100%	98%	95%	90%	80%	70%	60%

Sheriff's Model—.44-40 and .45 LC cal.'s, 3 in. barrel, brass backstrap.

Mfg.'s Sug. Retail	$330	$270	$235	$190	$175	$160	$150	$135

Add $27 for steel backstrap and trigger guard.

Target Model—same as standard Cattleman model, only fully adj. rear blade sight, brass backstrap.

Mfg.'s Sug. Retail	$350	$325	$240	$200	$185	$170	$150	$135

Add $26 for steel backstrap and trigger guard.

Add $60 for stainless steel construction.

CATTLEMAN BUNTLINE—.45 LC and .357 Mag. cal.'s, 18 in. barrel, brass backstrap cut for shoulder stock.

Mfg.'s Sug. Retail	$360	$335	$250	$210	$185	$175	$165	$150

Add $23 for target sights.

Add $23 for steel backstrap and trigger guard.

Buntline Carbine—similar cal.'s as Cattleman Buntline, 18 in. barrel, includes non-detachable shoulder stock with brass hardware and lanyard ring.

Mfg.'s Sug. Retail	$440	$415	$285	$230	$200	$185	$180	$175

Add $34 for target sights.

Add $34 for .22 LR/.22 Mag. combo.

Add $122 for detachable shoulder stock.

BUCKHORN—.44 Mag., .44 Spl., and .44-40 cal.'s, various barrel lengths, brass backstap, Buntline and revolving carbine models also available in the Buckhorn series — add approximately $32.

Quick Draw Model

Mfg.'s Sug. Retail	$337	$300	$210	$205	$190	$180	$170	$160

Add $30 for steel backstrap and trigger guard.

Add $30 for convertible cylinder.

Add $30 for Target Model.

Buckhorn Carbine—.44-40 or .44 Mag. cal., 18 in. barrel, includes non-detachable shoulder stock with brass hardware and lanyard ring.

Mfg.'s Sug. Retail	$450	$360	$285	$230	$200	$185	$180	$175

Add $34 for target sights.

Add $38 for extra .44-40 cylinder combo.

Add $122 for detachable shoulder stock.

STALLION 1873 COLT—.22 LR/.22 Mag. combo only, 4¾, 5½, or 6½ in. barrel, case hardened frame, 1-piece walnut grip, 2.4 lbs.

Mfg.'s Sug. Retail	$325	$300	$210	$195	$170	$155	$140	$120

Add $27 for steel backstrap and trigger guard.

Add $26 for Target Model.

Stainless Stallion—similar to standard Stallion, except is stainless steel.

Mfg.'s Sug. Retail	$425	$370	$275	$225	$200	$185	$180	$175

"OUTLAW" 1875 REMINGTON—available in .45 LC, .44-40, and .357 Mag. cal.'s, 7½ barrel.

Mfg.'s Sug. Retail	$350	$315	$225	$195	$170	$155	$140	$120

Add $41 for nickel plating.

Model 1875 Carbine—same cal.'s as Outlaw 1875, 18 in. barrel, includes non-detachable shoulder stock with brass hardware and lanyard ring.

Mfg.'s Sug. Retail	$440	$425	$285	$230	$200	$185	$180	$175

Add $111 for nickel plating.

1890 REMINGTON—available in .45 LC, .44-40, and .357 Mag. cal.'s, 5½ barrel. Mfg. in 1986-87 only.

Mfg.'s Sug. Retail	$340	$325	$220	$190	$175	$155	$140	$120

Add $40 for nickel plating.

PHANTOM MODEL—.357 and .44 Mag. only, 10½ in. barrel for silhouette use. New in 1985.

Mfg.'s Sug. Retail	$509	$475	$395	$325	$290	$260	$230	$215

Grading	100%	98%	95%	90%	80%	70%	60%

REVOLVERS: DOUBLE ACTION

INSPECTOR MODEL—.32 S&W and .38 Sp. cal.'s, 3, 4, and 6 in. barrels, double action, blued or chrome finish. New in 1985.

Mfg.'s Sug. Retail	$406	$390	$295	$245	$210	$170	$145	$125

Add $37 for target sights.

Add $28 for chrome plating.

TARGET PISTOLS

1871 ROLLING BLOCK TARGET PISTOL—available in .357 Mag., .22 LR, .22 Mag., and .22 Hornet cal.'s, 9½ in. barrel. Also available in carbine model (22 in. barrel) — add $55.

Mfg.'s Sug. Retail	$289	$265	$205	$175	$150	$135	$120	$100

RIFLES: REPRODUCTIONS

HENRY RIFLE/CARBINE—.44-40 cal., brass frame, 24½ in. barrel on rifle, 22½ in. barrel on carbine.

Mfg.'s Sug. Retail	$756	$725	$580	$490	$415	$360	$320	$260

Can also be special ordered with Grade A engraving ($234 extra), Grade B engraving ($412 extra), and Grade 3 (C) engraving ($635 extra).

Henry 1 of 1,000—discontinued several years ago, premiums are slightly higher than a C engraved gun.

1866 CARBINE—.44-40, .38 Spl., .22 Mag., and .22 LR cal.'s, brass receiver, 19 in. round barrel. "Indian" model — add $40.

Mfg.'s Sug. Retail	$587	$545	$420	$340	$285	$260	$235	$210

1866 Trapper Carbine—.22 LR, .38 Spl., or .44-40 cal., 16 or 18½ in. barrel.

Mfg.'s Sug. Retail	$686	$650	$475	$395	$340	$285	$260	$235

1866 Yellowboy Indian Carbine—.22 LR, .22 Mag., .38 Spl., or .44-40 cal., 19 in. barrel.

Mfg.'s Sug. Retail	$660	$555	$475	$385	$310	$275	$240	$220

Subtract $20 without brass tacks.

Red Cloud Commemorative Carbine—same cal.'s, special engraving and brass tacks in forearm and stock.

Mfg.'s Sug. Retail	$660	$625	$475	$385	$310	$275	$240	$220

1866 RIFLE—brass receiver, same cal.'s as the carbine, 24¼ in. oct. barrel.

Mfg.'s Sug. Retail	$624	$595	$445	$370	$300	$260	$235	$210

1866 Yellowboy Indian Rifle—.22 LR, .22 Mag., .38 Spl., or .44-40 cal., 19 in. barrel.

Mfg.'s Sug. Retail	$674	$645	$475	$385	$310	$275	$240	$220

This model comes without brass tacks.

1873 CARBINE—.44-40, .357 Mag., .22 Mag., and .22 LR cal.'s, steel receiver, 19 in. round barrel.

Mfg.'s Sug. Retail	$708	$660	$525	$450	$395	$360	$320	$280

Add $95 for nickel plating.

1873 Trapper Carbine—.44-40 cal. only, 16 in. barrel.

Mfg.'s Sug. Retail	$708	$660	$525	$450	$395	$360	$320	$280

1873 RIFLE—case hardened receiver, same cal.'s as the carbine, 24¼ in. oct. barrel.

Mfg.'s Sug. Retail	$742	$700	$535	$460	$400	$360	$320	$280

This model will also be available in .45 LC cal. later this year in addition to a pistol grip stock.

ULTIMATE

PLEASE REFER TO CAMEX-BLASER USA IN THE C SECTION OF THIS TEXT.

ULTRA LIGHT ARMS, INC.

MANUFACTURED AND DISTRIBUTED IN GRANVILLE, WV.

RIFLES: BOLT ACTION

ULTRA LIGHT RIFLE—caliber to customer spec.'s, various actions, stock lever safety, Timney trigger, Douglas 22 or 24 in. barrel, no sights, graphite reinforced stock with recoil pad, matte finish standard, other finishes at extra cost. Many special order features and services are available on these models - contact the manufacturer for prices, 4¾-5¾ lbs. New in 1986.

Model 20—18 cal.'s available, short action, Kevlar stock.

Mfg.'s Sug. Retail	$2,000	$1,800	$1,450	$1,150	$925	$800	$700	$640

Add $100 for left-hand action.

Model 24—.25-06, .270 Win., .30-06, and 7mm Exp. cal.'s, long action, Kevlar stock.

Mfg.'s Sug. Retail	$2,100	$1,850	$1,500	$1,200	$950	$800	$700	$640

Add $100 for left-hand action.

Model 28 Magnum—.264 Win. Mag., .300 Win., .338 Win. Mag., or 7mm Rem. Mag. cal.'s, Kevlar stock.

Mfg.'s Sug. Retail	$2,500	$2,225	$1,800	$1,400	$1,150	$900	$700	$600

Add $100 for left-hand action.

PISTOLS: BOLT-ACTION

MODEL 20 HUNTERS PISTOL—various cal.'s, 14 in. Douglas heavy barrel, 5-shot mag., Kevlar graphite reinforced stock in choice of 4 colors, Timney trigger, left-hand or right-hand bolt, approx. 4 lbs. New in 1987.

Mfg.'s Sug. Retail	$1,300	$1,175	$1,000	$900	$800	$700	$640	$575

UNIQUE

MANUFACTURED IN HENDAYE, FRANCE. PREVIOUSLY IMPORTED BY BEEMAN PRECISION ARMS LOCATED IN SANTA ROSA, CA.

PISTOLS: SEMI-AUTO

KREIGS MODEL L—7.65mm, 9 shot, 3.2 in. barrel, blue, plastic grips, fixed sights, made 1940-1945, during German occupation of France, has German acceptance marks.

	$325	$250	$220	$200	$180	$160	$140

MODEL RR—post-war commercial version of Kreigsmodell, higher quality finish, made 1951-discontinued. Add 15% for .22 LR

	$180	$170	$155	$130	$120	$110	$90

MODEL B/CF—7.65mm, 9 shot, and .380 auto cal.'s, 8 shot, 4 in. barrel, blue, plastic thumbrest grips, made 1954-discontinued.

	$205	$195	$175	$155	$145	$130	$110

MODEL D6—.22 LR, 10 shot, 6 in. barrel, adj. sights, blue, plastic grips, made 1954-discontinued.

	$300	$250	$200	$160	$145	$135	$120

MODEL D2—same as D6, except 4½ in. barrel.

	$300	$250	$200	$160	$145	$135	$120

MODEL L—.22 LR, 10 shot, 7.65mm, 7 shot, and .380 auto, 6 shot, 3.3 in. barrel, fixed sights, steel and alloy frame offered, plastic grips, made 1955-discontinued.

	$250	$200	$150	$130	$115	$100	$90

MODEL MIKROS POCKET—.22 short and .25 auto, 6 shot, fixed sights, blue, plastic grips, steel or alloy frame, made 1957-discontinued.

	$200	$155	$140	$120	$100	$90	$75

MODEL DES/69 STANDARD MATCH—.22 LR, 5 shot mag., 5.9 in. barrel, adj. rear sight, adj. target, stippled stocks, blue finish only, imported 1969-1988.

	$950	$795	$695	$625	$550	$490	$445

Add $60 for left-hand model.

Last Mfg.'s Sug. Retail was $1,065.

Grading	100%	98%	95%	90%	80%	70%	60%

MODEL DES/823-U RAPID FIRE MATCH—.22 short, 5 shot, 6 in. barrel, adj. sight, adj. trigger, adj. walnut target grips, squared barrel assembly, dry fire mechanism, imported 1974-1988.

	$1,100	$850	$725	$625	$550	$490	$445

> Add $60 for left-hand model.

> Last Mfg.'s Sug. Retail was $1,300.

MODEL DES/2000-U—.22 LR target pistol, wrap around grips, adj. features. Imported 1986-1988.

	$995	$850	$725	$625	$550	$490	$445

> Add $62 for left-hand model.

> Last Mfg.'s Sug. Retail was $1,198.

RIFLE

T66 MATCH RIFLE—.22 LR, single shot, bolt action, 25½ in. barrel, micro rear globe front, full target stock, made 1966-discontinued.

	$425	$410	$390	$350	$300	$280	$250

MODEL F 11—.22 LR, military trainer, adj. sights, target walnut stock.

Mfg.'s Sug. Retail	$695	$560	$435	$350	$285	$260	$240	$220

UNITED SPORTING ARMS, INC.

PREVIOUSLY MANUFACTURED AND DISTRIBUTED IN TUCSON, AZ. MANUFACTURE CEASED IN EARLY 1986.

> All the below models were discontinued in early 1986.

SEVILLE—.357 Mag., .41 Mag., .44 Mag., and .45 Colt cal.'s, single action revolver, 4⅝, 5½, 6½, and 7½ in. barrels, adj. sights, smooth walnut grips.

	$395	$350	$315	$280	$260	$240	$220

> Last Mfg.'s Sug. Retail was $435.

Stainless steel—otherwise same as above.

	$395	$350	$315

> Last Mfg.'s Sug. Retail was $435.

Silver Seville—same as Seville, except has blue barrel, and high polish stainless steel grip frame.

	$425	$370	$330

> Last Mfg.'s Sug. Retail was $460.

Stainless .357 Maxi—available in 5½ or 7½ in. barrel only.

	$575	$475	$395

> Last Mfg.'s Sug. Retail was $465.

Stainless .375 USA—only in 7½ in. barrel.

	$625	$525	$425

> Last Mfg.'s Sug. Retail was $490.

Stainless .454 Mag.—only in 7½ in. barrel, 5 shot.

	$700	$600	$500

> Last Mfg.'s Sug. Retail was $595.

> Note: In late 1986, some .454 Mag.'s were made up from parts purchased from the manufacturer. Unfortunately, while the exterior appearance might seem normal, they were not involved with any type of factory quality control program. As a result, shooting these non-factory revolvers could be dangerous, and careful inspection should be made before purchasing/shooting this particular specimen.

SILVER SEVILLE SILHOUETTE—.357 Mag., .41 Mag., or .44 Mag. cal.'s, single action revolver, 10½ in. barrel, adj. sights, Pachmayr grips, blued barrel finish with stainless grip frame.

	$445	$370	$330	$295	$270	$250	$230

> Last Mfg.'s Sug. Retail was $485.

Grading	100%	98%	95%	90%	80%	70%	60%

Stainless steel—otherwise same as above.

	$425	$370	$330				

Last Mfg.'s Sug. Retail was $460.

Stainless .357 Maxi—available in 10½ in. barrel only.

	$575	$475	$395				

Last Mfg.'s Sug. Retail was $480.

Stainless .375 USA—available in 10½ in. barrel only.

	$625	$525	$425				

Last Mfg.'s Sug. Retail was $515.

Stainless .454 Mag.—available in 10½ in. barrel only, 5 shot.

	$700	$600	$500				

Last Mfg.'s Sug. Retail was $620.

Note: In late 1986, some .454 Mag.'s were made up from parts purchased from the manufacturer. Unfortunately, while the exterior appearance might seem normal, they were not involved with any type of factory quality control program. As a result, shooting these non-factory revolvers could be dangerous, and careful inspection should be made before purchasing/shooting this particular specimen.

SHERIFF MODEL—.357 Mag., .38 Spl., .44 Spl., .44 Mag., or .45 Colt cal.'s, single action revolver, 3½ in. barrel, adj. sights, smooth walnut grips.

	$395	$350	$315	$280	$260	$240	$220

Last Mfg.'s Sug. Retail was $435.

Stainless steel—otherwise same as Sheriff Model

	$395	$350	$315				

Last Mfg.'s Sug. Retail was $435.

UNITED STATES HISTORICAL SOCIETY

AN ORGANIZATION WHICH MARKETS HISTORICALLY SIGNIFICANT FIREARMS REPRODUCTIONS. LOCATED IN RICHMOND, VA. FIREARMS ARE MANUFACTURED BY THE WILLIAMSBURG FIREARMS MANUFACTORY AND THE VIRGINIA FIREARMS MANUFACTORY.

PISTOLS

H. DERINGER PISTOL SET—.41 cal., percussion, reproduction of H. Deringer's famous pistol. Available with sterling silver mounts (1,000 pair manufactured — issue price $1,900), 14Kt. gold mounted (100 pair made-$2,700 issue price), precious gem stone mounted (only 5 pair made — $25,000 issue price). Manufactured in 1978.

Silver mounted

	$2,500	$1,750	$1,000

14Kt. gold mounted

	$7,500	$5,000	$3,000

18Kt. jewel mounted—too limited a supply for price evaluation.

ROBERT E. LEE MODEL 1851 NAVY—.36 cal. only, reproduction of the 1851 Navy Colt, extensive gold etching, cylinder scene portrays historical Civil War events, walnut stocks with Robert E. Lee medallion, cased with accessories, 41 oz., 2,500 manufactured.

	$2,400	$1,900	$1,450

Issue price is $2,400.

SAM HOUSTON WALKER—.44 cal., reproduction of the Colt Walker, 9 in. barrel, extensive gold etching on highly polished blued surface, smooth walnut stocks with S. Houston medallions, cased with accessories. 2,500 manufactured.

	$2,300	$2,000	$1,575

Issue price was $2,300.

Grading	100%	98%	95%	90%	80%	70%	60%

BUFFALO BILL CENTENNIAL MODEL 1860 ARMY—.44 cal., reproduction of the Colt Model 1860, bonded ivory stocks, extensive gold etchings portraying various wild west scenes, bonded ivory powder flask, brass accessories, cased. 2,500 manufactured in 1983.

$1,950 $1,450 $1,100

Issue price is $1,950.

U.S. CAVALRY MODEL 1860 ARMY—.44 cal., reproduction of the Colt Model 1860, stag grips, gold etched cylinder scene, cased with brass buckle. 975 manufactured starting in 1988.

Mfg.'s Sug. Retail   **$1,450 $1,450 $1,050 $800**

TEXAS PATERSON EDITION—reproduction of the famous Colt folding trigger model made in Paterson, NJ, engraved, cased. 1,000 manufactured starting in 1988. Cased with accessories.

Mfg.'s Sug. Retail   **$2,500 $2,500 $1,900 $1,450**

This model is an exact reproduction of the original Colt Paterson ser. no. 755, Model 5.

STONEWALL JACKSON PISTOL—.36 cal., reproduction of Colt's Model 1851 Navy, elaborate gold etching on frame and barrel, walnut grip with medallion, cased with sterling medallion and silver plated powder flask. 1988 release. 2,500 total mfg.

Mfg.'s Sug. Retail   **$2,100 $2,100 $1,650 $1,250**

SECRET SERVICE MUSEUM EDITION—500 manufactured starting in 1988.

Mfg.'s Sug. Retail   **$2,750 $2,750 $2,000 $1,600**

Secret Service Investigator's Edition—1,000 manufactured starting in 1988.

Mfg.'s Sug. Retail   **$1,250 $1,250 $875 $500**

ANDREW JACKSON

Silver Edition—2,500 manufactured.

$2,100 $1,750 $1,400

Issue price was $2,100.

Gold Edition—100 manufactured.

$5,500 $3,995 $2,750

Issue price was $5,500.

PITCAIRN—900 manufactured.

$2,950 $2,300 $1,750

Issue price was $2,950.

THOMAS JEFFERSON—1,000 manufactured, issue price was $1,900.

$3,500 $2,750 $1,995

HAMILTON — BURR DUALING PISTOLS—1,200 manufactured, issue price was $2,100.

$3,500 $2,750 $1,995

GEORGE WASHINGTON—975 manufactured, issue price was $2,500.

$4,250 $3,400 $2,450

MINIATURE REVOLVER SERIES

1851 NAVY PRESIDENTIAL EDITION—miniature reproduction of 1851 Navy Colt, color case hardened receiver, all parts operational, mother-of-pearl grips, full coverage engraving, cased. 1,500 manufactured starting in 1988.

Mfg.'s Sug. Retail   **$1,575 $1,575 $1,100 $825**

1851 Classic Edition—Similar to Presidential Edition, except has walnut grips and cylinder is roll-engraved, cased. 3,500 manufactured starting 1986.

Mfg.'s Sug. Retail   **$525 $525 $400 $295**

1860 ARMY PRESIDENTIAL EDITION—miniature reproduction of 1860 Army Colt, color case hardened engraved receiver and barrel, roll-engraved cylinder scene, all parts operational, ivory grips, cherry cased. 1,500 manufactured starting in 1988.

Mfg.'s Sug. Retail   **$1,250 $1,250 $875 $500**

1860 Classic Edition—similar to Presidential Edition without engraving, except has rosewood grips, cased. 3,500 manufactured starting in 1988.

Mfg.'s Sug. Retail   **$525 $525 $400 $295**

Grading	100%	98%	95%	90%	80%	70%	60%

SA ARMY PRESIDENTIAL EDITION—miniature reproduction of 1873 SAA Colt, nickel plated receiver and barrel with scroll engraving, gold plated cylinder, hammer, trigger, and ejector rod housing, one-piece ivory grips, cherry cased. 1,500 manufactured starting in 1988.

Mfg.'s Sug. Retail   **$1,550 $1,550 $1,100 $825**

This miniature is an exact replica of Serial No. 114 SAA (earliest known gold engraved SAA). All features are the same, only on a miniature basis.

SA Army Classic Edition—similar to Presidential Edition without engraving, except has color case hardened receiver and blued metal parts, one-piece rosewood grips. 1,500 manufactured starting in 1988.

Mfg.'s Sug. Retail   **$575 $575 $425 $300**

The Classic Edition is miniaturized, exact reproduction of Colt Serial No. 1 (includes pinched frame, slanted barrel address marking, donut ejector rod head, knurled hammer spur, etc.). All are serial numbered 1.

UNIVERSAL FIREARMS

UNIVERSAL FIREARMS BECAME A DIVISION OF IVER JOHNSON'S ARMS, INC. IN 1982. FORMERLY IMPORTED OUT OF HIALEAH, FL. CURRENTLY MANUFACTURED IN JACKSONVILLE, AR.

RIFLES: SEMI-AUTO CARBINE

1000 MILITARY—.30 cal., "G.I." copy, satin blue, birch stock, 18 in. barrel. Discontinued.

	$229	$180	$170	$160	$150	$135	$125

MODEL 1003—16, 18, or 20 in. barrel, .30 M1 copy, blued finish, adj. sight, birch stock, 5½ lbs. Add $45 for 4X scope. See current listing under Iver Johnson. Discontinued.

	$180	$160	$140	$120	$110	$100	$85

Last Mfg.'s Sug. Retail was $203.

Model 1010—nickel finish, discontinued.

	$299	$265	$240	$210	$180	$155	$120

Model 1015—gold electroplated, discontinued.

	$325	$275	$250	$215	$185	$160	$130

1005 DELUXE—.30 cal., custom Monte Carlo walnut stock, high polish blue, oil finish on wood.

	$246	$200	$180	$170	$150	$140	$130

1006 STAINLESS—.30 cal., stainless steel construction, birch stock, 18 in. barrel, 6 lbs. Discontinued.

	$205	$190	$170

Last Mfg.'s Sug. Retail was $234.

1020 TEFLON—.30 cal., Dupont Teflon-S finish on metal parts, black or grey color, Monte Carlo stock.

	$279	$259	$240

1256 "FERRET"—.256 Win. Mag. cal., M1 Action, satin blue, birch stock, 18 in. barrel, 5½ lbs. Discontinued.

	$200	$175	$165	$155	$145	$135	$125

Last Mfg.'s Sug. Retail was $219.

2200 LEATHERNECK—.22 cal., recoil operated action, birch stock, satin blue, 18 in. barrel, 5½ lbs.

	$240	$190	$180	$170	$160	$145	$135

MODEL 3000 ENFORCER PISTOL—11¼ in. barrel, .30 M1 Carbine, walnut stock, 17¾ in. overall, 1,15, and 30 shot, made 1964-1983. Add $50 for Teflon-S finish. See current listing under Iver Johnson.

	100%	98%	95%	90%	80%	70%	60%
Blued finish	$235	$200	$185	$170	$160	$150	$140
Nickel plated	$289	$235	$220	$200	$185	$165	$145
Gold plated	$328	$235	$220	$200	$185	$165	$145
Stainless	$312	$280	$260				

Grading	100%	98%	95%	90%	80%	70%	60%

5000 PARATROOPER—.30 cal., metal folding extension, walnut stock, 16 or 18 in. barrel. Discontinued. See current listing under Iver Johnson.

	$215	$185	$170	$160	$150	$140	$130

Last Mfg.'s Sug. Retail was $234.

5006 PARATROOPER STAINLESS—same as 5000, only stainless with 18 in. barrel only. Discontinued.

	$255	$235	$205

Last Mfg.'s Sug. Retail was $281.

1981 COMMEMORATIVE CARBINE—.30 cal., "G.I Military" model, cased with accessories, made for 40th Anniversary 1941-1981.

	$650	$490	$400

SHOTGUNS

All Universal shotguns were discontinued after 1982.

MODEL 7312 O/U—12 ga., 30 in. full and mod., vent rib barrel, boxlock, vent barrel spacer, SST, auto ejectors, barrels ported to reduce recoil, engraved, color case hardened receiver, trap or skeet style, checkered select stock.

	$1,650	$1,540	$1,485	$1,430	$1,320	$1,210	$1,045

MODEL 7412 O/U—similar to 7312, without ejectors, blue and silver receiver.

	$1,430	$1,210	$1,155	$1,100	$9,900	$880	$825

MODEL 7712 O/U—12 ga., 26 and 28 in. barrel, vent rib, non-selective single trigger, extractors, light engraving, checkered pistol grip stock.

	$440	$415	$385	$360	$330	$275	$220

MODEL 7812 O/U—same as 7712, with auto ejectors and more engraving.

	$605	$580	$550	$525	$470	$415	$385

MODEL 7912 O/U—same as 7812, with selective single trigger and gold damascene engraving.

	$1,210	$1,155	$1,100	$1,045	$965	$880	$825

MODEL 7112 DOUBLE BARREL—12 ga., 26 and 28 in. barrels, various chokes, boxlock, extractors, engraved case hardened frame, checkered pistol grip stock.

	$330	$305	$275	$250	$195	$165	$140

DOUBLE WING—10, 12, 20, and .410 ga.'s, 26, 28, and 30 in. barrels, various chokes, double triggers, boxlock, extractors, checkered pistol grip stock.

	$330	$305	$275	$250	$195	$165	$140
10 gauge.	$385	$360	$330	$305	$250	$220	$165

MODEL 7212 SINGLE BARREL TRAP—12 ga., 30 in. full, Simmons type vent rib, engraved case colored frame, vent barrel to reduce recoil, boxlock, auto ejector, select checkered trap style stock.

	$1,100	$990	$935	$880	$770	$715	$605

U.S. MILITARY

SEE LISTINGS UNDER COLT, SPRINGFIELD ARMORY, AND WINCHESTER.

U.S. M1 CARBINE

VARIOUS MAKERS

U.S. M1 CARBINE—semi-auto, .30 cal., 18 in. barrel, 15 or 30 round box mag., wood stocked, two or four position aperture rear, blade front sight with protective ears, with or without bayonet lug. This weapon was designed by Winchester for the U.S. government, over 6 million were produced by 10 different companies. It is a gas operated lightweight carbine that was also used by other countries' armed forces. Makers and values as follows. Values are for original, unmodified carbines, with proper parts makers and stock cartouches. Deduct 10% - 20% if modified for bayonet or adj. rear sight.

Grading	100%	98%	95%	90%	80%	70%	60%
Underwood	$330	$305	$250	$220	$195	$165	$150
S.G. Saginaw	$330	$305	$250	$220	$195	$165	$150
Quality Hardware	$360	$330	$275	$250	$220	$195	$185
Nat'l Postal Meter	$360	$330	$275	$250	$220	$195	$185
IBM	$360	$330	$275	$250	$220	$195	$185
Standard Products	$360	$330	$275	$250	$220	$195	$185
Inland	$330	$305	$250	$220	$195	$165	$150
SG Grand Rapids	$425	$350	$320	$290	$270	$250	$240
Winchester	$430	$390	$350	$320	$295	$265	$255
Irwin Pedersen	$1,100	$880	$800	$760	$700	$640	$580
Rockola	$375	$340	$320	$270	$260	$250	$240

M1 A1 PARATROOPER CARBINE—.30 cal., mfg. by Inland — WWII production, folding stock, crossed cannon proofed on bottom, 110,000 mfg. between 1942-1945. Stock folds to 26½ in. overall.

	$375	$335	$250	$220	$195	$165	$150

M1 GARAND—.30-06 cal., semi-auto, 8 shot en bloc clip fed, gas operated, adj. aperture sight, wooden stock. Made 1937-1957 by Springfield, Winchester, H&R, and International Harvester. Add 10% for WWII date, deduct 40% if rewelded, 20% if mismatched.

	$775	$600	$525	$475	$430	$400	$375

M1-C or M1-D Sniper—with scope and mounts (be wary of fakes and rewelds).

	$1,650	$1,455	$1,200	$1,060	$900	$780	$650

M1 NATIONAL MATCH—target version of the Garand, using National Match barrel and sights, glass bedding, etc. Should have serialized N.M. paperwork for premium.

	$1,250	$1,000	$900	$700	$500	$460	$425

U.S. MODEL 1917 ENFIELD RIFLE—.30-06, bolt action, 5 shot, 26 in. barrel, adj. sights, military stock, derived from English P14 Enfield, over two million produced in 1917 and 1918.

	$300	$240	$190	$150	$110	$95	$85

UZI

MANUFACTURED BY ISRAEL MILITARY INDUSTRIES (IMI). CURRENTLY IMPORTED BY ACTION ARMS, LTD., LOCATED IN PHILADELPHIA.

UZI CARBINE MODEL B—9mm, .41 Action Express (new in 1987), and .45 ACP (new in 1987) cal.'s, semi-auto carbine, 16.1 in. barrel, parkerized finish, 20, 25, 32 shot clip or 50 round snail drum mag. (9mm), metal folding stock, 8.4 lbs., includes molded case and carrying sling.

Mfg.'s Sug. Retail	$698	$535	$495	$430	$370	$330	$300	$275

Add $125 for .22 cal. conversion kit (new in 1987).

UZI MINI-CARBINE—9mm or .45 ACP cal., similar to Carbine except has 19¾ in. barrel, swing-away metal stock, scaled down version of the regular carbine, 7.2 lbs. New in 1987.

Mfg.'s Sug. Retail	$698	$535	$495	$430	$370	$330	$300	$275

UZI PISTOL—9mm or .45 ACP cal., semi-auto pistol, 4½ in. barrel, parkerized finish, 20 round mag., 3.8 lbs., supplied with molded carrying case.

Mfg.'s Sug. Retail	$579	$450	$420	$380	$350	$330	$300	$280

V

VALMET, INC.

MANUFACTURED IN JYVASKYLA, FINLAND. CURRENTLY IMPORTED BY STOEGER, INC. LOCATED IN SOUTH HACKENSACK, NJ.

Grading	100%	98%	95%	90%	80%	70%	60%

LION O/U SHOTGUN—12 ga., 26, 28, and 30 in. barrels, various chokes, boxlock, SST, checkered stock, made 1947-1968.

	$415	$370	$340	$320	$305	$275	$240

M-625 ASSAULT RIFLE—semi-auto version of Finn M-62, 7.62 x 39 Russian, 15 and 30 round mag., 16⅝ in. barrel, gas operated, rotary bolt, adj. rear sight, tube steel or wood stock, made 1962-discontinued.

	$770	$715	$635	$605	$550	$530	$495

Wood stock — add $50.

M-715—same as M-625, except .223, reinforced resin or wood stock.

	$635	$550	$415	$385	$370	$340	$325

Wood stock — add $50.

CURRENT PRODUCTION
Add $100 for sythetic stock

MODEL 412 O/U SHOOTING SYSTEM—interchangeable barrel assemblies permit a double rifle, shotgun/rifle, and O&U shotgun configuration, user installed interchangeable barrels, monobloc locking, rifle barrel positioning by adjustment, SST, extractors or ejectors checkered walnut stock and forend, cocking indicators, blued finish.

Model 412S Field Grade—12 ga. only, auto ejectors, screw-in choke tubes, matte nickel finish. New in 1986.

Mfg.'s Sug. Retail	$999	$855	$670	$580	$540	$475	$440	$400

Model 412S Field and Target—12 ga. only, 2¾ and 3 in. chambers, ejectors. Disc. in 1988.

	$775	$660	$580	$540	$475	$440	$400

Last Mfg.'s Sug. Retail was $874.

Model 412ST Trap and Skeet—12 ga., Monte Carlo stock on Trap model, 28 in. barrels on Skeet model, screw-in chokes standard.

Mfg.'s Sug. Retail	$1,215	$1.040	$875	$695	$650	$580	$540	$475

Model 412ST Premium Grade Target—similar to Model 412ST Trap and Skeet, except has better walnut and checkering. New in 1987.

Mfg.'s Sug. Retail	$1,550	$1,355	$1,050	$865	$750	$640	$580	$515

Model 412S Combination Gun—combination, 12 ga./3 in. chamber over choice of .222, .223, .243, .30-06, or .308 cal.'s, extractors.

Mfg.'s Sug. Retail	$1,165	$1,025	$850	$675	$600	$550	$475	$440

Model 412S Double Rifle—.243 (disc. in 1987), .30-06, .308 (disc. in 1987), .375 H&H (disc. in 1987), or 9.3 x 73 R cal., extractors, 24 in. barrels.

Mfg.'s Sug. Retail	$1,275	$1,060	$895	$725	$650	$580	$540	$475

Add $100 for 9.3 x 74 R cal. or .375 H&H cal.

This model in .30-06 cal. has extractors only while in 9.3 x 74 R cal. ejectors are standard.

Model 412K Double Rifle—.30-06 and .308 cal.'s only, 24 in. separated barrels, extractors. Importation discontinued in 1986.

	$800	$660	$580	$540	$475	$440	$400

Last Mfg.'s Sug. Retail was $899.

Grading	100%	98%	95%	90%	80%	70%	60%

Model 412 Engraved—satin finish, receiver extensively bank note engraved in choice of 4 patterns, select Triple-X wood hand checkered — choice of field or target, available in any Valmet model. Add $85 for shotgun rifle, $320 for double rifle.

This model has limited availability and prices are on request from the manufacturer. Last Mfg.'s Sug. retail was $2,499.

Extra Barrel Assemblies (Model 412 O/U)—$505 - $605 each for shotgun (includes screw-in chokes), $579 each for shotgun/rifle combo, $660 each for double rifle (add $100 for ejectors).

RIFLES

HUNTER MODEL—.223, .243, or .308 cal.'s, gas operated semi-auto, Kalashnikov action, 20½ in. barrel, checkered walnut stock and forearm, matte finished metal, 5, 9, or 20 round mag.'s, 8 lbs. New in 1986.

Mfg.'s Sug. Retail	$795	$625	$495	$450	$420	$380	$350	$315

This model will have limited availability in 1989.

MODEL 76—.223, 7.62 x 39mm, and .308 cal.'s, gas operated semi-auto assault rifle, 16¾ in. or 20½ (.308 only) in. barrel, 15 or 30 (7.62 x 39mm only) shot mag., parkerized finish.

Mfg.'s Sug. Retail	$740	$610	$515	$475	$450	$415	$385	$360

Add $95-$125 for synthetic or folding stock.

MODEL 78—.308 cal. only, similar to Model 76, except has 24½ in. barrel, wood stock and forearm, and barrel tripod, 11 lbs. New in 1987.

Mfg.'s Sug. Retail	$1,060	$875	$700	$600	$530	$475	$440	$400

VARNER SPORTING ARMS, INC.

MANUFACTURED AND DISTRIBUTED IN MARIETTA, GA.

VARNER FAVORITE HUNTER—.22 LR, patterned after J. Stevens Favorite Model, ½ round - ½ octagon 21½ in. take down barrel, blued frame, walnut stock and forearm, aperture rear sight, 5 lbs., new 1988.

Mfg.'s Sug. Retail	$369	$325	$270	$220	$185	$150	$130	$110

Hunter Deluxe—similar to Field Grade, except has case colored frame and lever, and deluxe walnut. New in 1988.

Mfg.'s Sug. Retail	$500	$450	$375	$285	$225	$175	$150	$135

Presentation Grade—includes target hammer and trigger, AAA quality checkered stock and forearm, includes take down case. New in 1988.

Mfg.'s Sug. Retail	$569	$480	$400	$310	$250	$195	$170	$155

PRESENTATION ENGRAVED—available in a No. 1 Grade for $649, a No. 2 for $779, or a No. 3 for $1,09.9

VERNEY-CARRON

VENTURA IMPORTS.

O/U SHOTGUN—12 ga., 26 and 28 in. vent rib barrel, boxlock, auto ejectors, SST, choked to specifications, checkered French walnut straight or pistol grip stock, made 1978-discontinued.

	$990	$880	$825	$770	$715	$660	$605

SKEET GUN—12 ga., same as Field, with 28 in. skeet and skeet barrel, skeet style pistol grip stock.

	$1,045	$935	$880	$825	$770	$715	$660

VICKERS LIMITED
MANUFACTURED IN CRAYFORD/KENT, ENGLAND.

JUBILEE SINGLE SHOT TARGET RIFLE—Martini type action, .22 LR, 28 in. heavy barrel, target sights, one piece pistol grip, target stock, pre-WWII.

	$440	$330	$305	$275	$250	$220	$165

EMPIRE MODEL—similar to Jubilee, with 27 or 30 in. barrel, straight grip stock.

	$415	$310	$285	$260	$220	$195	$150

VICTORY ARMS CO. LIMITED

MANUFACTURED BY VICTORY ARMS CO. LIMITED LOCATED IN NORTHHAMPTON, ENGLAND. DISTRIBUTED BY MAGNUM RESEARCH INC. LOCATED IN MINNEAPOLIS, MN.

PISTOL: SEMI-AUTO

MODEL MC5—9mm Para., .38 Super, .41 Action Express, 10mm, or .45 ACP cal., double action, 4⅜ (standard), 5⅞, or 7½ in. interchangeable barrel, decocking lever, 10 shot mag. in .45 ACP cal. (17 for 9mm/.38 Super, 12 for 41 AE cal.), stippled wooden grips, 3 dot sighting system, 45 oz. empty weight. New in 1989.

Mfg.'s Sug. Retail	$499	$440	$385	$350	$300	$275	$255	$240

    Add $100 per individual barrel.
    Add $59 for adj. Millett sights.

Converting this model from 9mm to .38 Super requires a barrel change only - magazines are interchangeable. Converting from .38 cal. to over .40 also requires a different mag. and vise versa.

VOERE

PREVIOUSLY MANUFACTURED IN KUFSTEIN, AUSTRIA. IN 1987, MAUSER-WERKE ABSORBED VOERE WITH ALL FURTHER PRODUCTION OCCURING IN OBERNDORF, W. GERMANY.

    Voere type actions are now utilized on the Titan series of bolt actions currently manufactured by Mauser and trademarked by KDF. Please refer to the KDF section in this text.

RIFLES
BOLT-ACTION MODEL—various cal.'s, no longer imported.

	$325	$250	$225	$200	$175	$125	$100

.22 SEMI-AUTO—.22 LR, open or closed bolt design, clip mag., checkered hardwood stock, adj. rear sight.

	$225	$195	$165	$145	$130	$120	$95

VIRGINIAN
THIS TRADEMARK CAN BE LOCATED UNDER THE INTERARMS SECTION IN THIS TEXT.

VOLUNTEER ENTERPRISES
PREVIOSLY MANUFACTURED IN KNOXVILLE, TENNESSEE.

    Volunteer Enterprizes became Commando Arms after 1978.

COMMANDO MARK III CARBINE—semi-auto, blowback action, .45 ACP, 16½ in. barrel, aperture sight, stock styled after "Tommy Gun", made 1969-1976.

	$350	$315	$280	$225	$195	$160	$145

Grading	100%	98%	95%	90%	80%	70%	60%

COMMANDO MARK III CARBINE
Vertical grip $365 $320 $280 $225 $195 $160 $145

COMMANDO MARK 9—same as Mark III in 9mm.
     $350 $315 $280 $225 $195 $160 $145
Vertical grip $365 $320 $280 $225 $195 $160 $145

	100%	98%	95%	90%	80%	70%	60%
COMMANDO MARK III CARBINE							
Vertical grip	$365	$320	$280	$225	$195	$160	$145
COMMANDO MARK 9—same as Mark III in 9mm.							
	$350	$315	$280	$225	$195	$160	$145
Vertical grip	$365	$320	$280	$225	$195	$160	$145

VOUZELAUD

MANUFACTURED IN FRANCE. IMPORTED BY WAVERLY ARMS CO. LOCATED IN SUFFOLK, VA 23433.

SHOTGUNS: SIDE-BY-SIDE

MODEL 315 E—12, 16 or 20 ga., boxlock, 28 in. barrels, auto ejectors, straight grip French walnut stock, double triggers, case colored receiver, light engraving. Importation disc. in 1987.

Prices generally range between $4,000-$10,000 and can vary substantially due to the exchange rate.

MODEL 315 EL—same as Model 315 E, except has satin finish receiver engraved with bouquets of fine English scroll work, trigger guard and forearm also engraved. Importation disc. in 1987.

Prices on this model are available upon request from importer listed above.

This model was also available by special order in 28 and .410 ga.'s (Model 315 EL-S) - add $1,100.

MODEL 315 EGL—12, 16 or 20 ga., sidelock, 28 in. barrels, selective ejectors, double triggers, extensive scroll engraving on coin finish receiver, English style stock of extra fancy French walnut. Importation disc. in 1987.

Prices on this model are available upon request from importer listed above.

MODEL 315 EGL-S—same general features as the Model 315 EGL, except monobloc barrel construction, extensive game scene engraving, and grand deluxe walnut stock and forearm with extra fine hand checkering. Importation disc. in 1987.

     $5,350 $4,720 $4,260 $3,850 $3,400 $3,020 $2,680

Last Mfg.'s Sug. Retail was $5,895.

W

WALTHER

PREVIOUSLY MANUFACTURED IN ZELLA-MEHLIS (NOW SUHL, E. GERMANY) 1886
TO 1945. CURRENT PRODUCTION IS IN ULM, W. GERMANY, 1953 TO DATE.
CURRENTLY IMPORTED BY INTERARMS LOCATED IN ALEXANDRIA, VA.

SEMI-AUTO PISTOLS, PRE-WAR

Grading	100%	98%	95%	90%	80%	70%	60%

MODEL 1—.25 auto, 2.1 in. barrel, fixed sights, blue, checkered hard rubber grips, pre-WWI, made 1908.

	$450	$350	$300	$250	$200	$150	$125

MODEL 2—.25 auto, 2.1 in. barrel, fixed sights, blue, rubber grips, made 1909, pop-up rear sight on early models, fixed on late models.

	$425	$390	$325	$225	$175	$120	$100

This model can usually be distinguished by its knurled barrel ring.

Early Model—differentiated by its pop-up rear sight.

	$1,050	$925	$875	$750	$675	$550	$400

MODEL 3—.32 auto (7.65mm), 2.6 in. barrel, blue, fixed sights, rubber grips, made 1910. Ejection port on left side.

	$1,350	$1,050	$950	$750	$550	$500	$400

MODEL 4—7.65mm, 8 shot, 3½ in. barrel, blue, rubber grips, made 1910-1918, ejection port on left side. Add 10% for WWI "Eagle" proofs.

	$365	$275	$200	$150	$125	$100	$ 80

MODEL 5—better quality version of 2, made 1913, fixed rear sight.

	$375	$315	$250	$200	$145	$115	$100

MODEL 6—9mm Parabellum, 4¾ in. barrel, blue, hard rubber grips, made 1915-1917, ejection port on right side. Some are Imperial proofed.

	$4,200	$3,800	$3,000	$2,300	$1,500	$1,050	$800

MODEL 7—.25 auto, 3 in. barrel, blue, fixed sights, rubber grips, made 1917-1918, ejector port on right side.

	$575	$450	$375	$325	$250	$200	$125

MODEL 8—.25 auto, 2⅞ in. barrel, blue, fixed sights, plastic grips, made 1920-1945. Add 25% for engraved slide.

	$400	$340	$290	$265	$200	$150	$125

Add 10% for "Eagle N" proofing.

MODEL 9 VEST POCKET—.25 auto, 2 in. barrel, blue, fixed sights, plastic grips, made 1921-1945. Add 40% for engraved slide, 20% for nickel, 100% for gold engraved.

	$425	$385	$325	$275	$200	$160	$140

MODEL PP DOUBLE ACTION AUTOMATIC "POLICE PISTOL"—.22 LR, .25 auto, .32 auto, .380 auto cal.'s, 3⅞ in. barrel, blue, fixed sights, plastic grips, made 1929-1945. Crown N proof until 1939. Eagle N Nazi commercial proof until 1945.

Add 20% for nickel finish.
Add 15% for alloy frame.

	100%	98%	95%	90%	80%	70%	60%
.22 caliber	$750	$675	$625	$525	$385	$320	$250
.25 caliber	$2,400	$2,200	$1,900	$1,500	$1,200	$1,000	$750
.32 caliber	$400	$375	$350	$275	$225	$200	$160
.380 caliber	$900	$825	$775	$725	$650	$500	$425

.32 Bottom Release Magazine—90 degree safety

	$800	$700	$625	$600	$525	$425	$395

WALTHER, cont.

.380 Bottom Release Magazine—90 degree safety.

	100%	98%	95%	90%	80%	70%	60%
	$1,050	$950	$875	$800	$700	$600	$500

Pre-War Persian proofed—9mm Kurz BMR.

	$2,000	$1,800	$1,600	$1,450	$1,250	$995	$825

Pre-War Verchromt .32 cal.—add 50% for .380 cal.

	$1,200	$1,000	$800	$750	$675	$485	$395

Pre-War Stoeger—.32 cal. only.

	$1,200	$1,050	$925	$800	$600	$425	$325

Nairobi—Chas. Heyer.

	$1,100	$950	$800	$700	$575	$400	$300

Aluminum frame—90 degree safety.

	$650	$600	$500	$400	$275	$235	$200

Allemagne—French Comm.

	$1,050	$950	$825	$720	$600	$425	$325

MODEL PP WARTIME PRODUCTION—made 1940-1945, "Eagle N" Proof (Nazi commercial nitro proof after April 1940) or "Crown N" proof (German commercial proof mark used to April, 1940) found on pre-WWII military production. Variations are listed either by proof marks or frame/slide markings.

Add 20% for nickel.

Late war PP's are sometimes encountered with Walther marked walnut grips - add 20%.

"Waffenamt" Proofed—.32 cal., "Eagle N", military acceptance marking. Add 60% for .380 cal.

	$500	$400	$350	$300	$250	$220	$200

Eagle N Proofed—.22 or .32 cal., with lanyard loop.

	100%	98%	95%	90%	80%	70%	60%
.32 cal.	$450	$395	$350	$300	$250	$200	$150
.22 cal.	$750	$700	$625	$550	$495	$450	$395

Eagle C Marked—.32 cal., "Eagle N", for Nazi Police units.

	$575	$500	$440	$400	$360	$315	$260

Eagle F Marked—.32 cal., "Eagle N", for rural Nazi units or Forestry Police.

	$650	$600	$550	$500	$450	$380	$300

RFV Marked—.32 cal., "Crown N", made for Reich Finance Administration.

	$700	$625	$575	$500	$400	$325	$225

RJ Marked—.32 cal, "Crown N", made for Reich Justice Ministry.

	$800	$750	$700	$575	$450	$325	$225

SA Marked—.22 and .32 cal, "Crown N", made for SA (storm troops) of the Nazi party. Add 10% for .22 LR.

	$1,450	$1,350	$1,050	$925	$725	$600	$425

NSKK Marked—.32 cal, "Crown N or Eagle N" proofed, made for Nazi Party Transport Corps, rare.

	$1,550	$1,450	$1,250	$1,025	$875	$700	$550

RRZ proofed—7.65mm "Reich Rundfunk Zenhale", for German Radio Broadcasting - only 3 known.

	$3,500	$3,000	$2,500				

PDM Marked—.32 cal, "Crown N", Branch of Postal Service.

	$850	$775	$700	$625	$525	$450	$360

AC Marked—.32 cal., replaced Walther Banner during 1945, "Eagle N".

	$300	$275	$250	$225	$175	$150	$125

Czech. Contract—stamped Rampant Lion.

	$850	$825	$775	$700	$600	$500	$400

Panagraphed

	$825	$750	$695	$630	$550	$385	$275

Danish Rplt.

	$975	$925	$825	$775	$700	$625	$400

Grading	100%	98%	95%	90%	80%	70%	60%

MODEL PP LIGHTWEIGHT—aluminum alloy version.

Add 20% to Standard Model prices, 20% for nickel plate.

MODEL PPK PRE-WAR PRODUCTION—Police Pistol Kriminal, for use by detectives, .22 LR, .25 auto, .32 auto, and .380 auto cal.'s, 3¼ in. barrel, blue, fixed sights, plastic grips, made 1931-1940.

.22 caliber	$995	$800	$750	$700	$650	$525	$400
.25 caliber	$3,850	$3,500	$3,000	$2,200	$1,600	$1,250	$800
.32 caliber	$485	$425	$375	$275	$200	$180	$160
.380 caliber	$1,800	$1,675	$1,400	$1,100	$800	$600	$500

On .32 cal. - add 60% for bottom release Mag.

MODEL PPK WARTIME PRODUCTION—made 1940-1945, "Eagle N" proofed after April 1940, "Crown N" proofs appear on pre-1940 production with frame/slide markings. Variations are listed either by proof marks, frame/slide markings, or type of finish. Eagle N proofed PPK's are slightly more desirable than Crown N proofed Walthers.

Commercial "Eagle N" Proofed—.22, .32, 7.65mm or .380 cal., Nazi Eagle over N (standard Nazi commercial acceptance proof).

.22 cal.	$850	$750	$675	$595	$525	$460	$420
	$495	$425	$350	$300	$200	$180	$160
.380 cal.	$1,000	$900	$800	$700	$600	$500	$400

This variation is normally encountered with unpolished exterior metal showing milling marks.

Waffenamt Proofed — high polish

	$850	$650	$575	$500	$425	$330	$275

Add 70% if .380 or .22 cal.

Eagle C Marked—.32 cal., "Crown N - Eagle C", Nazi Police designation.

	$600	$550	$475	$400	$300	$250	$200

Add 25% for high polish.

Eagle F Marked—.32 cal., "Crown N - Eagle F", Nazi rural units or Forestry Police.

	$700	$600	$525	$450	$375	$300	$250

Eagle L Marked—.32 cal., "Crown N", made for Nazi Provincial Police.

	$795	$740	$690	$630	$525	$450	$350

RZM Marked—.32 cal., "Crown N", proof marking for Nazi Party Purchasing Office - distributed to SS and SA (storm troopers).

	$850	$750	$625	$450	$350	$275	$225

Party Leader—.32 cal., named because grips (brown or black plastic) have the German eagle holding a Swastika, either "Crown N or Eagle N" proofed, honor weapon awarded 3rd Reich political leaders, rare. Be very wary of fake grips.

	$3,000	$2,800	$2,500	$2,000	$1,400	$1,100	$1,000

RZM Party Leader—.32 cal., RZM marked, "Crown N" proofed.

	$3,200	$2,950	$2,650	$2,200	$1,300	$1,200	$1,100

RFV Marked—.32 cal., "Crown N", made for Reich Finance Administration.

	$975	$900	$825	$750	$800	$700	$675

PDM Marked—.32 cal., "Crown N", made for Branch Postal Service.

	$975	$900	$825	$750	$600	$500	$395

POM—aluminum frame — BMR.

	$900	$825	$750	$650	$525	$500	$475

DRP Marked—.32 cal, "Crown N", made for Postal Service.

	$800	$675	$575	$500	$420	$350	$260

Panagraph Slide

	$800	$675	$625	$525	$450	$375	$300

Verchrompt (Ultra)—.32 or 9mm K cal.'s, differentiated by dull silver satin type finish, add 25% for 9mm K.

	$1,550	$1,400	$1,200	$1,000	$800	$650	$500

"K" suffix—"K" beneath ser. no.

	$625	$525	$475	$375	$300	$275	$250

Grading	100%	98%	95%	90%	80%	70%	60%

"W" suffix—.32 cal., "Crown N" proofed, W-suffix ser. no.

	$825	$750	$650	$575	$500	$450	$375

Early 90 degree safety

	$650	$575	$475	$425	$325	$260	$195

Early bottom release Mag.

	$950	$850	$750	$650	$500	$475	$375

PPK marked PP

	$2,500	$2,150	$1,850	$1,600	$1,400	$1,180	$900

7-digit ser. no.

	$725	$700	$650	$600	$550	$400	$300

Dural frame—.22, .32, or .380 cal.'s, chrome finish, "Eagle N". Add 25% for .380 cal. or .22 cal.

	$650	$600	$575	$525	$400	$325	$275

Stoeger Contract—.32 cal., marked "A. F. Stoeger Inc. New York" on left center of slide.

	$850	$700	$550	$425	$300	$225	$200

Heyer Contract—.32 cal., marked "Chas. A. Heyer and Co., Nairobi" on top left of slide.

	$1,200	$1,050	$900	$775	$675	$550	$400

Czech. Contract—Rampant Lion stamped.

	$950	$875	$750	$625	$550	$425	$325

Danish Rplt.

	$950	$875	$750	$625	$550	$425	$325

Allemagne—French Commercial — rare.

	$950	$875	$750	$625	$550	$425	$325

MODEL PPK LIGHTWEIGHT—aluminum alloy version.

Worth 20% additional to Standard Model.

PRESENTATION PPK—soft gold aluminum version, not made to be fired.

	$1,750	$1,650	$1,520	$1,400	$1,150	$800	$500

SPORT MODEL 1926—.22 S and LR (known as Standard Model in Germany) cal.'s. Winner in 1932 Olympics.

	$1,050	$900	$800	$675	$595	$550	$495

1932 OLYMPIA MODEL—.22 LR and short, 10 shot, 6 and 9 in. barrel, target sights, one piece grip. Introduced 1928. Used in 1932 Olympics — Gold Medal Winner. Marketed by Stoeger and Chas. Heyer-Nairobi.

	$825	$750	$650	$575	$495	$440	$395

OLYMPIA SPORT MODEL—.22 LR, 4 in. barrel, adj. target sights, blue, wood grips, 4 barrel weights available. Made 1936-1940. Add 20% for weight set.

	$795	$725	$625	$550	$475	$420	$375

1936 OLYMPIA "JAGERSCHAFTS" HUNTING MODEL—same as Sport, with 4 in. barrel. Made 1936-1940. Also seen with Eagle N proofs.

	$750	$675	$625	$550	$495	$440	$360

OLYMPIA RAPID FIRE MODEL—.22 short only, 7.4 in. barrel, blue, adj. sight, wood grip, has alloy side. Made 1936-1940.

	$850	$785	$700	$600	$520	$460	$380

1936 OLYMPIA FUNFKAMPF MODEL—.22 LR, 9¼ in. barrel, blue, adj. sight, wood grips, barrel weights. Made 1936, gold medal winner in 1936 Olympics

	$1,050	$895	$775	$650	$575	$500	$440

MODEL HP COMMERCIAL DOUBLE ACTION—pre-war version of P-38, 9mm, 5 in. barrel, fixed sight, blue, wood or plastic grips. Made 1937-1944. Many variations, including several different finishes.

See German WWII Military Pistols for values on this model.

Grading	100%	98%	95%	90%	80%	70%	60%

PISTOLS: SEMI-AUTO, POST-WAR

In 1983, Carl Walther from West Germany announced the discontinuance of models PP and PPK/S from the American market. These guns are attracting more collector interest as their production records are now complete. Manurhin of France no longer imports into the U.S. and guns imported between 1984-86 will not have the Interarms logo or Walther trademark.

Prices below reflect the recent devaluation of the U.S. dollar against some foreign currencies. While the manufacturer's suggested retails have gone up considerably, prices for used specimens (98% or less original condition) have not increased proportionately, and in some cases, have changed very little.

MODEL PP DOUBLE ACTION—.22 LR, .32 ACP, and .380 ACP cal's specifications similar to pre-war PP, 3⅞ in. barrel, made 1963-1987. W. German manufacture.

.380 cal.

Mfg.'s Sug. Retail	$875	$525	$425	$350	$320	$295	$275	$250

.32 cal.

Mfg.'s Sug. Retail	$850	$475	$335	$295	$270	$245	$200	$160

.22 LR cal. only.

Mfg.'s Sug. Retail	$875	$600	$425	$375	$350	$325	$230	$275

Blue Engraved—.22 LR(disc.) or .380 ACP cal.

Mfg.'s Sug. Retail	$1,550	$1,250	$1,100	$950

Add 5% for .22 LR cal.

Chrome Engraved—.22 LR or .380 ACP cal.

Mfg.'s Sug. Retail	$1,600	$1,250	$1,100	$950

Add $50 for .22 LR cal.

Silver Engraved—.22 LR or .380 ACP cal.

Mfg.'s Sug. Retail	$1,700	$1,300	$1,150	$1,000

Add $50 for .22 LR cal.

Gold Engraved—.22 LR or .380 ACP cal.

Mfg.'s Sug. Retail	$1,850	$1,500	$1,350	$1,150

Add $50 for .22 LR cal.

Manurhin PP—.22 LR, .32 ACP, and .380 ACP cal.'s.

	$350	$310	$285	$225	$180	$165	$150

Add 10% for .380 ACP cal.
Deduct 30% in .32 cal. for 98% or less condition.

Model PP 50th Anniversary Commemorative—.22 LR or .380 ACP, gold-plated parts, hand carved grips, presentation case, 500 imported to U.S. in 1979.

Mfg.'s Sug. Retail	$1,700	$1,075	$800	$750

Add $100 for 22 cal.

PP SPORT—double action, thumbrest grips, round hammer with spur, adj. rear sight, long barrel, made 1953-1970.

Note: Add $75 for barrel weight, $100 for factory case, 20% for factory nickel, 5% for single action.

Manurhin manufacture	$650	$625	$600	$525	$475	$400	$325
Mark II (made 1955-1957)	$725	$680	$625	$575	$520	$480	$425
Walther manufacture	$775	$725	$700	$575	$520	$475	$400

Deduct 10% if not marked.

PP Sport "C" Model—made for competition shooting, single action, 7⅝ in. barrel, spur hammer.

	$750	$725	$675	$625	$525	$475	$400

WALTHER, cont.

Grading	100%	98%	95%	90%	80%	70%	60%

MODEL PPK—similar to pre-war PPK, .22, .32, and .380 cal.'s, 3.31 in. barrel, made 1963-present, U.S. import stopped by GCA 68 on W. German and French production. 100% column assumes NIB condition - if not boxed deduct 15%.

.32 cal.	$450	$400	$350	$325	$295	$270	$250
.22 LR.	$680	$600	$525	$500	$400	$320	$280
.380 cal.	$600	$550	$480	$440	$400	$325	$275
Blue engraved	$1,400	$1,100	$900				
Silver engraved	$1,650	$1,200	$1,000				
Gold engraved	$2,000	$1,350	$1,075				

MODEL PPK LIGHTWEIGHT—same as Standard, with dural frame, .22 LR and .32 auto.

	100%	98%	95%	90%	80%	70%	60%
	$600	$550	$500	$440	$400	$360	$330

Add 20% for .22 LR.

MODEL PPK-1986 U.S. MFG.—.380 ACP only, 3.2 in. barrel, similar specifications as previous W. German and French manufacture, 6 shot finger extension mag., black plastic grips, 21 oz. Made in the U.S. Introduced in 1986.

Mfg.'s Sug. Retail	$529	$440	$370	$330	$310	$290	$275	$260

Manufacture in the U.S. is under an exclusive licensing agreement with Walther of W. Germany.

PPK Stainless—stainless steel construction. New in 1986.

Mfg.'s Sug. Retail	$529	$430	$360	$340	

MODEL PPK/S—.22, .32, and .380 cal's, similar to PPK, except has larger PP frame to meet import requirements of 1968, 3¼ in. barrel, production in W. Germany (now discontinued), Manurhin of France (disc.in 1986), and in the U.S. (made under license from Walther by Interarms). 7 or 8 shot, double action, fixed sights.

American PPK/S—.380 only, blue finish, 7 shot finger extension mag.

Mfg.'s Sug. Retail	$529	$435	$350	$330	$310	$290	$275	$260

W. German PPK/S—.22 and .380 cal. Discontinued in 1982.

	$575	$500	$450	$350	$270	$260	$225

Add 10% for .22 cal.

Stainless PPK/S—.380 only, American manufacture, introduction July of 1983.

Mfg.'s Sug. Retail	$529	$450	$375	$320	

American PPK/S—blue engraved. Discontinued in 1985.

	$875	$850	$800

Last Mfg.'s Sug. Retail was $990.

American PPK/S Gold-Engraved Commemorative—500 total manufacture. Disc. in 1987.

	$1,000	$850	$675

Last Mfg.'s Sug. Retail was $1,200.

American PPK/S Gold-Engraved—discontinued in 1985.

	$975	$800	$675

Last Mfg.'s Sug. Retail was $1,070.

W. German PPK/S Blue Engraved

Mfg.'s Sug. Retail	$1,550	$1,195	$925	$775

W. German PPK/S Chrome Engraved

Mfg.'s Sug. Retail	$1,600	$1,275	$975	$800

W. German PPK/S Silver Engraved—discontinued in 1988.

Mfg.'s Sug. Retail	$1,400	$1,050	$850

Last Mfg.'s Sug. Retail was $1,700.

W. German PPK/S Gold Engraved—discontinued in 1985.

	$1,600	$1,150	$875

Last Mfg.'s Sug. Retail was $1,800.

Grading	100%	98%	95%	90%	80%	70%	60%

PPK/S Durgarde (Manurhin mfg.)—same as above, only with bonded brushed chrome finish. Add $10 for .22 LR cal.

| Under Walther license | $395 | $310 | $290 | $265 | $245 | $210 | $195 |

MANURHIN PPK/S—see listings under Manurhin section.

MODEL PP SUPER—9 x 18mm, (Police) and .380 cal.'s, 3.6 in. barrel, fixed sights, plastic grips, blue, made 1975-1981.

| | $550 | $475 | $395 | $345 | $275 | $250 | $235 |

Deduct 25% if in 9 x 18mm cal.

PP Super-Cutaway

| | $650 | $600 | $550 | | | | |

MODEL TP—.22 LR, 25 auto, updated version of Model 9, concealed hammer, made 1962-1970.

| .22 cal. | $675 | $600 | $435 | $350 | $300 | $260 | $210 |
| .25 cal | $495 | $425 | $360 | $300 | $250 | $220 | $185 |

MODEL TPH—.22 LR, .25 auto, double action 2.8 in. barrel, alloy frame, blue, fixed sights, plastic grips, made 1969-present in W. Germany, U.S. import stopped by GCA 6800 100% price assumes NIB condition.

| .22 cal. | $625 | $560 | $495 | $425 | $300 | $275 | $220 |
| .25 cal. | $675 | $625 | $550 | $475 | $350 | $300 | $250 |

Deduct 10% on the 100% values if not boxed with all accessories.

AMERICAN MODEL TPH—.22 LR only, stainless steel double action, black plastic grips, 6 shot mag., 2¼ in. barrel, 14 oz. Introduced in 1987.

| *Mfg.'s Sug. Retail* | $399 | $350 | $300 | $250 | | | |

MODEL P.38—Post-war version of P.38 Military, .22 LR, .30 Luger (discontinued), or 9mm Luger cal.'s, 5 in. barrel, alloy frame, matte black finish, 28 oz. W. German manufacture. See German WWII Military Pistols for wartime listings.

Note: Due to the release of large numbers of W. German police and Army trade-ins of P 38 9mm and PP 32 Models, the actual value of these models has only recently gone down. The two models most affected are the P-1 variation of the P 38, and the German PP in .32 cal.

| *Mfg.'s Sug. Retail* | $995 | $675 | $500 | $400 | $360 | $295 | $245 | $190 |

.22 LR only.

| *Mfg.'s Sug. Retail* | $1,050 | $740 | $525 | $440 | $365 | $305 | $255 | $200 |

Steel Frame P.38—9mm, similar to regular P 38, except has steel frame, 34 oz. New in 1987.

| *Mfg.'s Sug. Retail* | $1,400 | $975 | $675 | $500 | $435 | $360 | $295 | $245 |

P.38 100th Year Commemorative—alloy frame, presentation engraved with deluxe walnut presentation case. New in 1987.

| *Mfg.'s Sug. Retail* | $995 | $750 | $560 | $425 | | | |

Blue Engraved—9mm.

| *Mfg.'s Sug. Retail* | $1,750 | $1,200 | $1,050 | $900 | | | |

Chrome Engraved—9mm.

| *Mfg.'s Sug. Retail* | $1,850 | $1,300 | $1,075 | $925 | | | |

Silver Engraved—9mm.

| *Mfg.'s Sug. Retail* | $1,950 | $1,350 | $1,115 | $960 | | | |

Gold Engraved—9mm. Disc. in 1987.

| | $1,550 | $1,300 | $1,000 | | | | |

Last Mfg.'s Sug. Retail was $2,050.

P.38 IV—modernized variation of the original P.38, 4½ in. barrel, 8 shot mag., updates include reinforced steel slide and alloy frame, includes decocking lever and automatic safeties, adj. rear sight, 29 oz. Importation disc. in 1982.

| | $595 | $525 | $450 | $350 | $300 | $250 | $200 |

MODEL P.38K—short 2.8 in. barrel, version of P.38, front sight on slide, made 1974-1980.

| | $595 | $525 | $450 | $350 | $300 | $250 | $200 |

Grading	100%	98%	95%	90%	80%	70%	60%

MODEL P-5—9mm Luger, double action, alloy frame, slide mounted decocking lever, 3½ in. barrel, adj. rear sight, blue finish only, 8 shot mag., auto safeties, 28 oz.

Mfg.'s Sug. Retail	$825	$750	$540	$495	$465	$425	$380	$340

P-5 Compact—compact variation of P-5.

Mfg.'s Sug. Retail	$1,100	$875	$625	$550	$500	$465	$425	$380

P-5 100th Year Commemorative—elaborate engraving with presentation walnut case. New in 1987.

Mfg.'s Sug. Retail	$2,700	$2,000	$1,425	$1,025

MODEL P-88—9mm, double action, alloy frame, 4 in. barrel, 15 shot side release mag., ambidextrous decocking lever, matte finish, adj. rear sight, internal safeties, loaded chamber indicator, black synthetic grips, 31½ oz. New in 1987.

Mfg.'s Sug. Retail	$1,150	$975	$850	$650	$575	$535	$490	$450

TARGET PISTOLS

MODEL GSP TARGET—.22 LR, 4½ in. barrel, single action, 5 shot mag., adj. sights, blue finish, walnut target grips, 49.4 oz., supplied with carrying case.

Mfg.'s Sug. Retail	$1,400	$1,150	$925	$750	$650	$530	$425	$375

Model GSP Junior—slimmer barrel design, smaller walnut grips, less weight.

Mfg.'s Sug. Retail	$1,400	$1,100	$875	$750	$650	$530	$425	$375

Model GSP-C—same as Model GSP Target, except in .32 S&W wadcutter, 42.3 oz.

Mfg.'s Sug. Retail	$1,650	$1,295	$925	$800	$675	$550	$450	$400

.22 short conversion unit for GSP-C — $875.

.22 LR conversion unit for GSP-C — $875.

.32 S&W Wadcutter converison unit for GSP-C — $1,050.

MODEL OSP RAPID FIRE—similar to GSP, in .22 short, made 1968-present, for international competition (meets ISU and NRA reg.'s), 4½ in. barrel, 44.4 oz., supplied with case.

Mfg.'s Sug. Retail	$1,550	$1,275	$925	$770	$670	$550	$450	$400

FREE PISTOL—.22 LR single shot, electronic trigger, 11.7 in. heavy barrel, advanced target design with fully adj. grips and sights, 48 oz.

Mfg.'s Sug. Retail	$1,850	$1,500	$1,100	$950	$820	$700	$575	$495

P.38—see German Military for breakdown.

HAMMERLI-WALTHER—see Hammerli.

RIFLES: DISCONTINUED

MODEL B—.30-06 bolt action, post-war mfg., 22 in. barrel. Add 20% for double set triggers. Discontinued.

	$450	$420	$380	$340	$300	$275	$250

OLYMPIC SINGLE SHOT—.22 LR, bolt action, 26 in. heavy barrel, target sights, checkered pistol grip, full beavertail forearm, palm rest, adj. butt, pre-war.

	$935	$825	$770	$715	$605	$550	$440

MODEL 1—Carbine model, clip fed.

	$395	$350	$310	$295	$270	$250	$200

MODEL 2 AUTOLOADING—may be used as bolt action, autoloader or single shot, .22 LR, 24½ in. barrel, tangent sight, checkered sporter stock, pre-war.

	$495	$440	$385	$330	$275	$220	$165

MODEL 2 LIGHTWEIGHT—20 in. barrel, lighter stock.

	$495	$440	$385	$330	$275	$220	$165

MODEL V SINGLE SHOT—.22 LR, bolt action, 26 in. barrel, open sight, plain pistol grip stock, pre-war.

	$385	$360	$330	$305	$275	$250	$195

MODEL V CHAMPION—same as Standard, with micrometer adj. sight and checkered pistol grip stock.

	$470	$440	$415	$385	$330	$305	$250

Grading	100%	98%	95%	90%	80%	70%	60%

MODEL KKM INTERNATIONAL MATCH—.22 LR, single shot bolt action, 28 in. heavy barrel, adj. aperture sight, adj. hook butt, thumbhole stock, accessory rail, post-war production.

	$880	$770	$715	$660	$550	$495	$440

MODEL KKM-S—same as KKM, with adj. cheekpiece.

	$935	$825	$770	$715	$605	$550	$495

MODEL KKJ SPORTER—.22 LR, bolt action, 5 shot, 22½ in. barrel, open sight, checkered sporter stock, post-war. Add 20% for double set triggers.

	$550	$500	$450	$385	$330	$250	$200

MODEL KKW—.22 LR, single shot, military stock, tangent sight, pre-war manufacture.

	$540	$490	$420	$300	$260	$220	$195

MODEL KKJ-MA—.22 WMR.

	$550	$495	$440	$385	$305	$250	$220

MODEL KKJ-HO—.22 Hornet. Add 20% for double set triggers.

	$725	$675	$625	$580	$540	$480	$440

MODEL SSV VARMINT—.22 LR, single shot bolt action, 25½ in. barrel, no sights, Monte Carlo pistol grip stock, post-war.

	$605	$550	$525	$495	$415	$360	$330
.22 Hornet.	$660	$605	$580	$550	$470	$415	$385

MODEL PRONE 400—similar to UIT Match, with Prone style competitive stock and no sights. Discontinued.

	$750	$635	$580	$525	$415	$360	$305

RIFLES: CURRENT MFG.

Prices below reflect the recent devaluation of the U.S. dollar against some foreign currencies. While the manufacturer's suggested retails have gone up considerably, prices for used specimens (98% or less original condition) have not increased proportionately, and in some cases, have changed very little.

MODEL UIT BV UNIVERSAL—.22 LR, single shot bolt action, 25½ in. heavy barrel, adj. aperture sight, target stock with palm rest, adj. butt, meets IUS reg.'s, 16 lbs.

Mfg.'s Sug. Retail	$1,700	$1,325	$1,050	$850	$700	$635	$580	$530

This model was previously known as the Model UIT Special.

MODEL UIT MATCH—same as UIT Special, except with improved stock design which includes fully stippled lower forearm and pistol grip, 13 lbs.

Mfg.'s Sug. Retail	$1,300	$1,075	$900	$800	$660	$610	$555	$510

Model UIT-E—electronic trigger, 25½ in. barrel, 9 lbs. Discontinued in 1986.

	$1,350	$940	$860	$770	$670	$630	$560

Last Mfg.'s Sug. Retail was $1,250.

GX 1—similar to UIT Match, 25½ in. barrel with fully adj. free rifle stock, all accessories included, 16½ lbs.

Mfg.'s Sug. Retail	$2,200	$1,795	$1,325	$1,125	$985	$860	$775	$680

MODEL KK/MS SILHOUETTE—.22 LR only, designed for silhouette shooting with no sights, thumbhole stock with adj. butt, fully stippled forend and stock grip, front barrel weight, 25½ in. barrel, 8¾ lbs. New in 1984.

Mfg.'s Sug. Retail	$1,100	$935	$780	$625	$560	$495	$435	$395

RUNNING BOAR MODEL 500—similar to KK/MS, no sights, thumbhole stock with adj. butt and cheekpiece, 23½ in. barrel, 10¼ lbs.

Mfg.'s Sug. Retail	$1,300	$1,025	$825	$640	$570	$500	$435	$395

MODEL WA-2000—.300 Win. Mag. or .308 Nato cal.'s, ultra-deluxe bolt action, special order only. Discontinued in 1988.

	$6,400	$4,800	$4,500	$4,000	$3,500	$3,000	$2,500

Grading	100%	98%	95%	90%	80%	70%	60%

SHOTGUNS: SIDE-BY-SIDE

MODEL SF—12 or 16 ga., double barrel, checkered walnut stock, double triggers, boxlock, sling swivels. Discontinued.

	$500	$450	$395	$325	$275	$240	$200

MODEL SFD—12 or 16 ga., double barrel, cheekpiece, checkered walnut stock, double triggers, boxlock, sling swivels. Discontinued.

	$625	$575	$500	$425	$375	$340	$300

WALTHER, FRENCH-MADE BY MANURHIN

MANUFACTURED IN MULHOUSE, FRANCE. PREVIOUSLY IMPORTED 1984-86 BY MATRA-MANURHIN INTERNATIONAL, INC., ALEXANDRIA, VA.

PISTOLS: SEMI-AUTO

Manufacture of these Walther pistols commenced in France in 1951. They were marked MANURHIN on slide until 1954. Since then they were designated Walther MKII. They were imported into the USA by Interarms up to 1983. In 1984, Manurhin was imported directly with no Interarms logo or Walther trademark appearing on Models PP and PPK/S. Importation was discontinued in 1986.

MODEL PP—.22 LR, .32 ACP, and .380 ACP cal.'s, 3⅞ in. barrel, 10 round mag.-.22 LR, 8 round mag.-.32 ACP, 7 round mag.-.380 ACP, blue only, 24 oz., all steel construction, double action with positive steel block safety. Add $10 for .22 LR cal., $46 for durgarde finish.

	$360	$320	$275	$230	$205	$185	$170

Last Mfg.'s Sug. Retail was $419.

Collector Model—blue finish, special engraving. New in 1986.

	$465	$415	$350				

Last Mfg.'s Sug. Retail was $529.

Presentation Model—blue finish, special ornamentation. New in 1986.

	$720	$650	$500				

Last Mfg.'s Sug. Retail was $819.

Also available with various engraving options in either blue, nickel, or gold finish - prices range from $222 - $540.

Interarms import	$350	$325	$285	$230	$205	$180	$160

PP SPORT—.22 LR cal. only, double action, 6.1 or 8.1 in. barrel, blue finish only, 25 oz., precision adj. sights, contoured plastic grips with thumb rest. New Manurhin design for 1985.

	$545	$485	$430	$385	$325	$290	$270

Last Mfg.'s Sug. Retail was $635.

PP Sport-C—same as PP Sport, except is single action.

	$540	$475	$415	$370	$310	$280	$260

Last Mfg.'s Sug. Retail was $635.

MODEL PPK—.22 LR, .32 ACP, and .380 ACP cal.'s, 3¼ in. barrel, 10 round mag.-.22 LR, 8 round mag.-.32 ACP, 7 round mag.-.380 ACP, blue only, 23 oz., all steel construction, double action with positive steel block safety. Add 10% for .22 LR cal.

	$600	$495	$425	$375	$350	$325	$300

MODEL PPK/S—.22 LR, .32 ACP, and .380 ACP cal.'s, 3¼ in. barrel, 10 round mag.-.22 LR, 8 round mag.-.32 ACP, 7 round mag.-.380 ACP, blue only, 23 oz., all steel construction, double action with positive steel block safety. Add $10 for .22 LR cal.

	$360	$320	$275	$230	$205	$185	$170

Last Mfg.'s Sug. Retail was $419.

Grading	100%	98%	95%	90%	80%	70%	60%

PPK/S Durgarde—same as above, only with bonded brushed chrome finish. Add $14 for .22 LR cal.

	100%	98%	95%	90%	80%	70%	60%
	$410	$365	$325	$290	$265	$250	$240

Last Mfg.'s Sug. Retail was $465.

Collector Model—blue finish, special engraving. New in 1986.

	$465	$415	$350

Last Mfg.'s Sug. Retail was $529.

Presentation Model—blue finish, special ornamentation. New in 1986.

	$720	$650	$500

Last Mfg.'s Sug. Retail was $819.

Interarms import

	$395	$340	$300	$275	$250	$235	$210

Also available with various engraving options in either blue, nickel, or gold finish — prices range from $222 - $540.

WARNER ARMS CORPORATION

NORWICH, CT.

INFALLIBLE POCKET AUTO PISTOL—.32 auto, 7 shot, 3 in. barrel, fixed sights, rubber grips, made 1917-1919.

	$300	$200	$175	$150	$125	$100	$90

WEATHERBY

MANUFACTURER/IMPORTER LOCATED IN SOUTH GATE, CALIFORNIA, 1945 TO DATE.

Weatherby is an importer of long arms. Earlier production was from Germany and Italy and German mfg. is usually what is collectible. Current production is from Japan. Workmanship in all instances is quite good. Weatherby is well known for their high-velocity proprietary rifle calibers.

Early Weatherby rifles used a Mathieu Arms action in the 1950's - primarily since it was available in left hand action. Right handed actions were normally manufactured from the FN Mauser type.

SILOUETTE PISTOL

WEATHERBY SILOUETTE PISTOL—.22-250 or .308 cal., mfg. in Japan during late 1970's, 14½ in. barrel, Lyman sights, fitted case. Only 50 were made in .22-250 and 150 in .308 cal.

	$3,750	$3,300	$2,750	$2,450	$2,100	$1,850	$1,650

RIFLES - BOLT ACTION

For German rifle manufacture, add 15% to 25% for calibers under .35.

MARK V DELUXE—.240 Wby. Mag., .257 Wby. Mag., .270 Wby. Mag., 7 mm Wby. Mag., .30-06, and .300 Wby. Mag. cal.'s, bolt action, 3-5 round mag., 24 or 26 in. barrel, deluxe skip line checkered pistol grip walnut stock with rosewood tipped forearm and pistol grip, no sights, 8 lbs. Left hand actions available at no extra charge.

Mfg.'s Sug. Retail	$991	$865	$695	$605	$510	$475	$450	$410

Add $16 for 26 in. barrel.

Mark V .340 Weatherby Magnum—26 in. barrel only, 8½ lbs.

Mfg.'s Sug. Retail	$1,011	$875	$715	$615	$525	$480	$455	$425

Mark V .378 Weatherby Magnum—26 in. barrel only, 8½ lbs.

Mfg.'s Sug. Retail	$1,165	$995	$830	$730	$655	$580	$520	$480

Add 100% if in .375 Wby. Mag. and W. German mfg. (95% or better condition only).

Grading	100%	98%	95%	90%	80%	70%	60%

Mark V .416 Weatherby Magnum—first new caliber (introduced in 1989) since the .240 Mag. was released in 1965.

| *Mfg.'s Sug. Retail* | $1,270 | $1,075 | $895 | $780 | $670 | $630 | $590 | $550 |

Add $20 for 26 in. barrel.

Mark V .460 Weatherby Magnum—24 or 26 in. barrel, includes custom stock, internal muzzle break, 10 lbs., no extra charge for left-hand.

| *Mfg.'s Sug. Retail* | $1,330 | $1,135 | $940 | $830 | $670 | $630 | $590 | $550 |

Add $20 for 26 in. barrel.

Add 120% for this cal. if in 95% or better condition.

This model includes custom stock, customized action, and integral muzzle break.

MARK V ULTRAMARK—available in .240 through .378 cal.'s, fancy American walnut, individually hand-bedded, high lustre finish, customized action, 24 or 26 in. barrel, basket weave checkering (including pistol grip). New in 1989.

| *Mfg.'s Sug. Retail* | $1,250 | $1,075 | $895 | $780 | $670 | $630 | $590 | $550 |

Add $25 for 26 in. barrel.

Add $220 for .378 Wby. Mag. cal. (26 in. barrel only).

Add $325 for .416 Wby. Mag. cal. (26 in. barrel only).

MARK V VARMINT—.22-250 and .224 Varmintmaster cal.'s, 24 or 26 in. barrel, 6½ lbs.

| *Mfg.'s Sug. Retail* | $971 | $855 | $680 | $585 | $510 | $475 | $450 | $410 |

Not available in left-hand action. Add $16 for 26 in. barrel.

MARK V EUROMARK—available in all cal.'s, except .22-250 and .224 Varmintmaster, differs from Mark V in that it has an oil finished, hand checkered, deluxe American claro walnut pistol grip cap stock with ebony forend tip, low lustre bluing, and solid black recoil pad. New in 1986.

Rather than list individual prices, add approximately 5% to the values shown in Mark V Deluxe.

MARK V LAZERMARK—available in the same calibers and barrel lengths as the Mark V Deluxe (including Varmint Model), differs only in that stock and forearm have been laser carved. New in 1985.

Rather than list individual prices, add approximately 11% to the values shown in Mark V Deluxe.

MARK V FIBERMARK—available in .240, .257, .270, 7mm, .300 and .340 Wby. Mag.'s, and .30-06 cal., black non-glare fiberglass with wrinkle finish stock, metal has non-glare matte finish, 24 or 26 in. barrel, 7¼ lbs.

| *Mfg.'s Sug. Retail* | $1,123 | $880 | $720 | $615 | $525 | $480 | $455 | $425 |

Add $20 for 26 in. barrel or .340 Mag. cal.

1984 MARK V OLYMPIC COMMEMORATIVE—.257 WM, 270 WM, 7mm WM, or .300 WM cal.'s, special gold accenting, extra-fancy walnut stock with "star in motion" inlay, 1,000 mfg. in 1984 only at $2,000 retail.

| $2,195 | $1,750 | $1,350 |

MARK V 35TH ANNIVERSARY COMMEMORITIVE—limited mfg. in 1980, 1,000 produced total.

| $1,250 | $925 | $700 |

SAFARI GRADE CUSTOM—.300 Wby. Mag. through .460 Wby. Mag. cal.'s only, custom order only, various options available, 8-10 month delivery.

| *Mfg.'s Sug. Retail* | $2,866 | $2,460 | $2,000 | $1,750 | $1,600 | $1,450 | $1,300 | $1,175 |

Add approx. $200 for .378 and larger cal.'s.

CROWN MODEL CUSTOM—custom order only, engraved barrel receiver and scope mount, top-of-the-line model.

| *Mfg.'s Sug. Retail* | $4,320 | $3,750 | $3,060 | $2,525 | $2,175 | $1,825 | $1,550 | $1,350 |

Subtract $1,200 without Crown engraving option.

Grading	100%	98%	95%	90%	80%	70%	60%

VANGUARD VGX—.22-250, .243 Win., .25-06, .270 Win., 7mm Rem. Mag., .30-06, and 300 Win. Mag. cal.'s, bolt action, checkered deluxe walnut stock with rosewood tip forearm and pistol grip, 24 in. barrel, no sights, 5 shot mag.(except 3 shot for .300 Win. Mag.), high luster bluing, about 8 lbs. Discontinued in 1988.

	$525	$425	$365	$330	$300	$275	$255

Not available in left-hand action.

Last Mfg.'s Sug. Retail was $600.

VANGUARD VGS—same cal.'s as Vanguard VGX, bolt action, checkered satin finished walnut stock, 24 in. barrel, no sights, about 8 lbs. Discontinued in 1988.

	$415	$355	$295	$265	$245	$220	$200

Not available in left-hand action.

Last Mfg.'s Sug. Retail was $467.

VANGUARD VGL—.223 Rem., .243 Win., .270 Win., 7mm Rem. Mag., .30-06, and 308 Win. cal.'s, lightweight bolt action, checkered walnut stock, 5 shot mag.(6 on .223 Rem.), 20 in. barrel, no sights, 6½ lbs. Discontinued in 1988.

	$415	$355	$295	$265	$245	$220	$200

Not available in left-hand action.

Last Mfg.'s Sug. Retail was $467.

VANGUARD FIBERGUARD—.223 Rem., .243 Win., .270 Win., 7 mm Rem Mag., .30-06, and 308 Win. cal.'s, 20 in. barrel, green fiberglass stock, 3 to 6 shot mag.'s, no sights, blued metal parts, about 6½ lbs. Discontinued in 1988.

	$500	$450	$395	$355	$285	$255	$220

Not available in left-hand action.

Last Mfg.'s Sug. Retail was $560.

RIFLES - SEMI-AUTO

MARK XXII CLIP MAG—.22 LR, mag.-feed, skip line checkered walnut stock with rosewood forearm and pistol grip caps, 10 shot mag., 24 in. barrel, open sights, 6 lbs.

Mfg.'s Sug. Retail	$454	$395	$320	$265	$245	$215	$195	$180

The Mark XXII clis was originally manufactured in Italy - a slight premium might be asked.

VANGUARD CLASSIC I—.223 Rem., .243 Win., .270 Win., 7mm/08 Rem., 7mm Rem. Mag., .30-06 or .308 Win. cal., checkered walnut stock with satin finish, black butt pad, 24 in. barrel, 3 (7mm Rem. Mag.) or 5 shot mag., No. 1 barrel contour, approx. 7 lbs. 5 oz. New in 1989.

Mfg.'s Sug. Retail	$465	$410	$375	$330	$300	$280	$260	$240

This model is th replacement for the Vanguard VGS and VGL.

VANGUARD WEATHERGUARD—same cal.'s as Classic I, replacement for Fiberguard, wrinkle black finished synthetic stock, entry level Weatherby, similar spec.'s as Classic I, approx. 8 lbs. New in 1989.

Mfg.'s Sug. Retail	$399	$360	$330	$300	$280	$265	$250	$235

VANGUARD CLASSIC II—.22-250, .243 Win., .270 Wby. Mag., .270 Win., 7mm Rem. Mag., .30-06, .300 Win. Mag., .300 Wby. Mag., or .358 Win. Mag. cal., 24 in. barrel, 3 or 5 shot mag., custom checkered deluxe walnut stock with pistol grip cap and black forend cap, solid black recoil pad, matte finished metal, approx. 7¾ lbs. New in 1989.

Mfg.'s Sug. Retail	$600	$550	$500	$460	$425	$395	$360	$330

VANGUARD VGX DELUXE—similar to Vanguard Classic II except has Monte Carlo stock, high gloss wood and metal, and 60% cut forend cap. New in 1989.

Mfg.'s Sug. Retail	$600	$550	$500	$460	$425	$395	$360	$330

MARK XXII TUBE MAG—.22 LR, same general specifications as above model, except tube-feed, 15 shot, 6 lbs.

Mfg.'s Sug. Retail	$454	$395	$320	$265	$245	$215	$195	$180

Grading	100%	98%	95%	90%	80%	70%	60%

SHOTGUNS: OVER AND UNDER

REGENCY FIELD GRADE—20 ga. Mag. and 12 ga., checkered stock, vent rib, engraved side plates, SST, imported from Italy 1972-1980.

	$900	$800	$700	$600	$550	$500	$475

REGENCY TRAP GRADE—12 ga., checkered trap stock, engraved, vent rib, SST, imported from Italy

	$900	$800	$700	$600	$550	$500	$475

OLYMPIAN STANDARD—12 ga. only, lightly engraved sideplates. Discontinued 1980.

	$850	$775	$725	$625	$525	$450	$400

OLYMPIAN SKEET—26 or 28 in. barrel.

	$885	$775	$725	$625	$525	$450	$400

OLYMPIAN TRAP—30 or 32 in. barrel, vent rib.

	$850	$775	$725	$625	$525	$440	$400

ATHENA GRADE IV—12, 20, 28 (new in 1989), or .410 (new in 1989) ga., 3 in. chambers, boxlock with Greener Crossbolt, SST, ejectors, high luster finish on hand checkered claro walnut, engraved sideplates with satin nickel finish, vent barrels and rib, introduced 1982, 7-8½ lbs. Multi-chokes became standard (except 28 and .410 ga.) in 1986 — if without tubes, subtract $60.

Mfg.'s Sug. Retail	$1,590	$1,375	$1,120	$995	$850	$700	$595	$525

This model became the Grade IV in 1989.

Skeet & Trap Models—12 (Trap only) and 20 ga., special stock dimensions, target sights.

Mfg.'s Sug. Retail	$1,601	$1,380	$1,125	$995	$850	$700	$595	$525

Skeet models are available in fixed choke only.

Single Trap Grade IV—12 ga., 32 or 34 in. barrel with multi-choke feature.

Mfg.'s Sug. Retail	$1,601	$1,375	$1,050	$950	$825	$750	$675	$600

Trap Combo—12 ga., includes a set of O/U barrels and oversingle barrel with multi-choke feature.

Mfg.'s Sug. Retail	$2,100	$1,850	$1,575	$1,350	$1,150	$900	$775	$650

Master Skeet Set—12 ga., includes 6 fitted full length Briley tubes with integral extractors (20, 28, and .410 ga.), cased. New in 1988.

Mfg.'s Sug. Retail	$3,200	$2,750	$2,375	$2,000	$1,850	$1,725	$1,600	$1,500

ATHENA GRADE IV—12 or 20 ga., 3 in. chambers, similar to Grade IV except has more elaborate engraving and better walnut. New in 1989.

Mfg.'s Sug. Retail	$2,000	$1,775	$1,600	$1,375	$1,100	$900	$775	$650

ORION GRADE I—12 or 20 ga., 3 in. chambers, 26 or 28 in. VR barrels with multi-chokes, SST, ejectors, entry level O/U with no engraving, checkered walnut stock and forearm. New in 1989.

Mfg.'s Sug. Retail	$850	$775	$700	$625	$550	$495	$450	$400

ORION GRADE II—12 and 20 ga.'s, 3 in. chambers, boxlock with Greener Crossbolt, SST, ejectors, walnut with high-gloss finish, blue only, light engraving.

Mfg.'s Sug. Retail	$1,000	$885	$750	$625	$560	$495	$475	$455

Add $11 for Skeet grade (fixed chokes only).

Add $51 for Trap grade.

Subtract $60 if without tubes.

Multi-chokes became standard in 1986.

This model was designated Grade II in 1989.

ORION GRADE III—similar to Grade II except has silver grey receiver with custom engraving including mallard and pheasant game scenes. New in 1989.

Mfg.'s Sug. Retail	$1,100	$965	$825	$700	$600	$525	$475	$455

Grading	100%	98%	95%	90%	80%	70%	60%

SHOTGUNS: SEMI-AUTO

CENTURION FIELD GRADE—12 ga., vent rib, checkered stock, gas operation, walnut full pistol grip stock. 1972-1981.

	100%	98%	95%	90%	80%	70%	60%
	$300	$280	$250	$240	$230	$210	$190

CENTURION TRAP GRADE—12 ga., checkered stock, vent rib.

	$335	$300	$250	$240	$230	$210	$190

CENTURION DE LUXE—12 ga., vent rib, checkered stock, lightly engraved, fancy wood ($200-250).

	$375	$350	$310	$275	$250	$235	$210

Centurion DU—mfg. in 1980 for DU chapters.

	$550	$375	$325				

MODEL 82—12 ga. only, 2¾ or 3 in. chamber, gas operation, alloy receiver, vent rib, deluxe walnut. New in 1983. Subtract $20 if not multi-choke barrel (multi-chokes became standard in 1985), $30 for Trap Grade (discontinued in 1984).

Mfg.'s Sug. Retail	$500	$440	$375	$340	$310	$290	$275	$250

Model 82 Buckmaster—22 in. barrel choked skeet, rifle sights, 7½ lbs.

Mfg.'s Sug. Retail	$500	$440	$375	$340	$310	$290	$275	$250

SHOTGUNS: SLIDE ACTION

PATRICIAN FIELD GRADE—12 ga., checkered stock, vent rib 1972-1981.

	$290	$260	$240	$210	$190	$180	$170

PATRICIAN TRAP GRADE—12 ga., checkered stock, vent rib.

	$310	$285	$265	$215	$190	$180	$170

PATRICIAN DE LUXE—12 ga., checkered stock, lightly engraved, fancy wood, vent rib.

	$360	$340	$320	$285	$260	$250	$240

MODEL 92—12 ga. only, 2¾ and 3 in. chambers, ultra-short slide action w/twin rails, 26-30 in. vent rib barrels, engraved black alloy receiver, checkered pistol grip walnut stock and forearm. New in 1983. Subtract $30 for Trap grade (discontinued in 1984), $20 if fixed choke (multi-chokes became standard in 1985) barrel. Disc. in 1987.

	$345	$285	$260	$240	$220	$200	$185

Last Mfg.'s Sug. Retail was $400.

Model 92 Buckmaster—22 in. skeet bore barrel rifle sights, 7½ lbs. Disc. in 1987.

	$345	$285	$260	$240	$220	$200	$185

Last Mfg.'s Sug. Retail was $400.

WEAVER ARMS CORPORATION

MANUFACTURED AND DISTRIBUTED IN ESCONDIDO, CA SINCE 1984.

NIGHTHAWK CARBINE—9mm parabellum, closed bolt semi-auto assault carbine, fires from closed bolt, 16.1 in. barrel, retractable shoulder stock, 25, 32, 40, or 50 shot mag. (interchangeable with Uzi), 6½ lbs., ambidextrous safety, parkerized finish.

Mfg.'s Sug. Retail	$575	$440	$360	$330	$300	$275	$250	$230

NIGHTHAWK ASSAULT PISTOL—9mm, closed bolt semi-auto, 10 or 12 in. barrel, alloy upper receiver, ambidextrous safety, black finish, 5 lbs. New in 1987.

Mfg.'s Sug. Retail	$475	$410	$340	$320	$295	$275	$250	$230

WEBLEY & SCOTT, LIMITED

MANUFACTURED IN LONDON AND BIRMINGHAM, ENGLAND. 1898 TO 1981. SHOTGUNS ARE CURRENTLY IMPORTED BY NEW ENGLAND ARMS CO. LOCATED IN KITTERY POINT, ME.

PISTOLS

MARK III M&P REVOLVER—double action, .38 S&W, 6 shot, 3 in. and 4 in. barrel, hinged top break, blue, fixed sights, wood service or competition grips, made 1897-1945.

	$350	$295	$255	$220	$195	$165	$140

Grading	100%	98%	95%	90%	80%	70%	60%

MARK IV M&P REVOLVER—same as Mark III, except 3 in., 4 in., and 5 in. barrel, improved hammer and grip design, made 1929-1957.

	$350	$295	$255	$220	$195	$165	$140

MARK IV .22 TARGET REVOLVER—same as Mark IV, except .22 LR, 6 in. barrel, target sights, production ceased 1945.

	$450	$385	$330	$285	$235	$200	$165

NO. 1 MARK VI BRITISH SERVICE REVOLVER—.455 Webley, 4 in., 6 in., and 7½ in. barrel, top break, blue, fixed sights, wood service or competition grips, made 1915-1947.

	$195	$140	$110	$90	$75	$65	$45

MARK VI .22 TARGET REVOLVER—same as Mark VI, except .22 LR, target sights, produced until 1945.

	$220	$165	$140	$110	$90	$85	$70

MARK V REVOLVER—.455 calibre. Many were military-modified for .45 Colt or .45 ACP; many were civilian-modified. Round butt, top-break.

	$225	$200	$175	$150	$125	$105	$85

BULLDOG OR RIC MODEL—double action, .455 Webley, 5 shot, 2½ in. barrel, solid frame, blue, fixed sights, made for Royal Irish Constabulary.

	$195	$140	$110	$100	$90	$65	$55

WEBLEY-FOSBERY AUTOMATIC REVOLVER—.455 Webley, 6 shot, 6 in. barrel, top break, recoil revolves cylinder and cocks hammer, blue, fixed sights, walnut grips, made 1901-1939.

	$550	$440	$385	$330	$220	$195	$165

8 shot—extremely rare, .38 Colt Auto cal.

	$1,100	$935	$825	$660	$550	$440	$330

HAMMER MODEL .25 AUTOMATIC—.25 auto, 6 shot mag., 2 in. barrel, no sights, blue, composition grips, made 1906-1940.

	$220	$165	$110	$90	$75	$65	$55

HAMMERLESS MODEL .25—.25 auto, same as Hammer Model .25, except no exposed hammer and fixed sights, made 1909-1940.

	$220	$165	$110	$90	$75	$65	$55

SINGLE SHOT TARGET PISTOL—.22 LR, 10 in. barrel, top break, blue, fixed sights on early models, made 1909-present.

	$250	$195	$120	$110	$100	$90	$75

METROPOLITAN POLICE AUTOMATIC—.32 auto and .380 auto, 7 or 8 shot, 3½ in. barrel, blue, fixed sights, composition grips, made 1906-1940.

	$220	$165	$110	$100	$90	$75	$65

SEMI-AUTO SINGLE SHOT—.22 long, 4¼ and 9 in. barrel, adj. sights, blue, composition grips, empty case is ejected and hammer cocked as in a semi-auto, then it is loaded singly and slide closed, made 1911-1927.

	$330	$275	$165	$120	$110	$100	$85

9MM M&P AUTOMATIC—9mm Browning Long, 8 shot, 5 in. barrel, blue, fixed sights, made 1909-1930.

	$275	$220	$165	$100	$90	$75	$65

MARK I .455 AUTO PISTOL—.455 Webley, 7 shot, 5 in. barrel, blue, fixed sights, made 1912-1945.

	$440	$385	$330	$220	$165	$110	$90

MARK I NO. 2—same as Mark I, except adj. sights, modified safety.

	$385	$330	$275	$165	$150	$140	$110

SHOTGUNS

MODEL 700 SIDE-BY-SIDE DOUBLE BARREL—12 and 20 ga.'s, boxlock, case hardened receiver, minimum engraving, single trigger. Deduct $50 for double trigger.

	$1,700	$1,625	$1,500	$1,400	$1,000	$750	$600

Grading	100%	98%	95%	90%	80%	70%	60%

MODEL 701—same as 700 but fanciest walnut, most engraving. Deduct $100 for double trigger.

	100%	98%	95%	90%	80%	70%	60%
	$3,150	$2,500	$2,100	$1,800	$1,400	$1,150	$925

MODEL 702—same as 700 but middle grade. Deduct $75 for double trigger.

	$2,650	$2,200	$1,800	$1,500	$1,250	$950	$750

WEIHRAUCH, HANS-HERMANN

MANUFACTURED IN W. GERMANY. IMPORTED AND DISTRIBUTED IN THE U.S. BY BEEMAN PRECISION ARMS, INC. LOCATED IN SANTA ROSA, CA, AND HELMUT HOFFMAN LOCATED IN PLACITAS, NM.

MODEL HW 60M—.22 LR, match rifle featuring adj. sights, 26¾ in. barrel, single shot, match walnut stock, and other match features, 10.8 lbs.

Mfg.'s Sug. Retail	$675	$560	$475	$385	$325	$285	$250	$215
Add $50 for lefthand action.								

HW 66 RIFLE—.22 Hornet or .222 Rem. cal., match grade bolt-action rifle, importation started in 1989.

Mfg.'s Sug. Retail	$590	$540	$465	$425	$385	$340	$300	$260
Add $57 for stainless steel barrel (.22 Hornet).								
Add $64 for double set triggers.								
Add $82 for .222 Rem. cal.								

This model is imported exclusively by Helmut Hoffman.

WESSON ARMS, DAN

MANUFACTURED AND DISTRIBUTED IN MONSON, MASSACHUSETTS.

REVOLVERS: DOUBLE ACTION

MODEL 11—.357 Mag., 6 shot, 2½, 4, and 6 in. interchangeable barrels, fixed sights, blue, interchangeable grips, exposed barrel nut, made 1970-1971.

	$200	$175	$160	$150	$140	$130	$120
Extra barrels	$60	$50	$35				

MODEL 12—same as 11, with adj. sights, made 1970-1971.

	$245	$200	$175	$160	$150	$140	$130

MODEL 14—same as 11, with recessed barrel nut, made 1971-1975.

	$225	$185	$170	$160	$150	$140	$130

MODEL 8—same as 14, except .38 Spl.

	$200	$170	$155	$145	$135	$125	$115

MODEL 15—same as 14, with adj. sights, made 1971-1975.

	$245	$200	$155	$145	$135	$125	$115

MODEL 9—same as 15, except .38 Spl., made 1971-1975.

	$245	$200	$155	$145	$135	$125	$115

REVOLVERS: CURRENT MANUFACTURE

Dan Wesson revolvers are manufactured with solid rib barrels as standard equipment.

MODEL 22—.22 LR, double action, 6 shot, adj. sights, 2½, 4, 6, 8, or 10 in. (disc. in 1987) barrel, current production. Add $20 for vent rib, $48 for heavy vent rib, $8 for each additional longer barrel length.

Mfg.'s Sug. Retail	$337	$280	$225	$200	$190	$180	$170	$160

Model 22 Pistol Pac—includes 2½, 4, 6, and 8 in. barrel assemblies, extra grip, 4 additional front sight blades, and aluminum case.

Mfg.'s Sug. Retail	$615	$495	$395	$360	$330	$300	$275	$260
Add $100 for full shroud VR barrels.								
Add $190 for heavy full shroud VR barrels.								

Grading	100%	98%	95%	90%	80%	70%	60%

MODEL 22M—.22 Mag., otherwise same as Model 22.

Mfg.'s Sug. Retail $349 $290 $230 $200 $190 $180 $170 $160

Model 22M Pistol Pac—includes 2½, 4, 6, and 8 in. barrel assemblies, extra grip, 4 additional front sight blades, and aluminum case.

Mfg.'s Sug. Retail $637 $500 $400 $360 $330 $300 $275 $260

Add $100 for full shroud VR barrels.

Add $190 for heavy full shroud VR barrels.

MODEL 32—.32 H&R Mag., 2½, 4, 6, or 8 in. barrel, adj. rear sight, interchangeable colored front sight blades, blue finish, checkered target grips. New in 1986. Add $20 for VR barrel shroud (Model 32-V), add $43 for VR heavy barrel shroud (Model 32-VH). Also add approx. $8 for each additional barrel length over 2½ in.

Mfg.'s Sug. Retail $337 $280 $225 $200 $190 $180 $170 $160

Model 32 Pistol Pac—includes 2½, 4, 6, and 8 in. barrel assemblies, extra grip, 4 additional front sight blades, and aluminum case.

Mfg.'s Sug. Retail $615 $495 $395 $360 $330 $300 $275 $260

Add $100 for full shroud VR barrels.

Add $190 for heavy full shroud VR barrels.

MODEL 14-2—.357 Mag., 4, 6, and 8 in. interchangeable barrels, fixed sights, blue, made 1975-present. Add $8 for each additional longer barrel length.

Mfg.'s Sug. Retail $267 $215 $170 $150 $140 $130 $120 $110

Model 14-2 Pistol Pac—includes 2½, 4, and 6 in. barrel assemblies, extra grip and aluminum case.

Mfg.'s Sug. Retail $456 $385 $325 $300 $275 $260 $245 $230

MODEL 8-2—same as 14-2, except .38 Spl. cal.

Mfg.'s Sug. Retail $267 $215 $170 $150 $140 $130 $120 $110

This model is also available in a Pistol Pac - same specifications and values as the Model 14-2 Pistol Pac.

MODEL 15-2—same as 14-2, except adj. sights, available with 2, 4 , 6, 8, 10, 12, and 15 in. barrels. Add approx. $9 for each additional barrel length over 2 inches, $20 for VR barrel (Model 15-2V), or $44 for VR heavy barrel shroud (Model 15-2HV).

2 in. barrel

Mfg.'s Sug. Retail $337 $280 $225 $200 $190 $180 $170 $160

Model 15-2 Pistol Pac—includes 2½, 4, 6, and 8 in. barrel assemblies, extra grip, 4 additional front sight blades, and aluminum case.

Mfg.'s Sug. Retail $615 $495 $395 $360 $330 $300 $275 $260

Add $100 for full shroud VR barrels.

Add $190 for heavy full shroud VR barrels.

MODEL 15 GOLD SERIES—.357 Mag., 6 or 8 in. VR heavy slotted barrel, "Gold" stamped shrould with Dan Wesson signature, smoother action (8 lb. double action pull), 18 kt. gold plated trigger, white triangle rear sight with orange dot patridge front sight, exotic hardwood grips. New in 1989.

Mfg.'s Sug. Retail $544 $475 $420 $380 $340 $300 $260 $225

MODEL 9-2—same as 15-2, except .38 Spl. Use same add-ons as in Model 15-2.

Mfg.'s Sug. Retail $337 $280 $225 $200 $190 $180 $170 $160

This model is also available in a Pistol Pac - same specifications and values as the Model 9-2 Pistol Pac.

MODEL 375V SUPERMAG—.375 Super Mag., 6, 8, or 10 in. VR barrel, adj. rear sight, interchangeable front and rear sight blades, bright blue finish, smooth target grips. New in 1986. Add approx. $15 for each barrel length after 6 in., $26 for slotted shroud (Model 375-V8S, 8 in. barrel only), $12 for VR heavy shroud (Model 375 -VH).

Mfg.'s Sug. Retail $508 $410 $335 $285 $260 $240 $230 $225

MODEL 40V (.357 SUPERMAG)—.357 Super Mag. (.357 Max.), double action, 6 shot, 6, 8, or 10 in. barrel vent rib. Add $26 for slotted barrel shroud (8 in. barrel only), $12 for heavy VR barrel, $15 for each additional barrel length.

Mfg.'s Sug. Retail $508 $410 $335 $285 $260 $240 $230 $225

Grading	100%	98%	95%	90%	80%	70%	60%

MODEL 41V—.41 Mag., double action, 6 shot, 4, 6, 8, or 10 in. barrel vent rib. Add $21 for heavy barrel, $11 for each additional barrel length.

Mfg.'s Sug. Retail	$413	$345	$290	$270	$255	$240	$230	$225

Model 41V Pistol Pac—includes 6 and 8 in. VR barrel assemblies, extra grip, 2 additional front sight blades, and aluminum case.

Mfg.'s Sug. Retail	$615	$495	$395	$360	$330	$300	$275	$260

Add $50 for ventilated shroud VR barrels.

MODEL 44V—.44 Mag., double action, same as Model 41V, adj. sights. Add $21 for heavy barrel, $11 for each additional barrel length.

Mfg.'s Sug. Retail	$431	$365	$300	$265	$250	$230	$215	$200

Model 44V Pac—includes 6 and 8 in. VR barrel assemblies, extra grip, 4 additional front sight blades, and aluminum case.

Mfg.'s Sug. Retail	$707	$585	$425	$380	$330	$300	$275	$260

Add $50 for ventilated shroud VR barrels.

MODEL 45V—.45 Long Colt, 4, 6, 8, or 10 in. VR barrel, same frame as Model 44V, blued finish. Add $11 for each additional barrel length. New in 1988.

Mfg.'s Sug. Retail	$431	$365	$300	$265	$250	$230	$215	$200

Model 45V Pistol Pac—includes 6 and 8 in. VR barrel assemblies, extra grip, 2 additional front sight blades, and aluminum case.

Mfg.'s Sug. Retail	$707	$585	$425	$380	$330	$300	$275	$260

Add $50 for ventilated shroud VR barrels.

REVOLVERS: STAINLESS STEEL

MODEL 722—stainless version of Model 22, use same add-ons for various barrel options.

Mfg.'s Sug. Retail	$366	$315	$250	$205

This model is also available in a Pistol Pac including 2½, 4, 6, and 8 in. solid rib barrel assemblies, extra grip, 4 additional sight blades, and fitted carrying case - Mfg.'s Suggested Retail is $689. Add $100 for VR barrels, $200 for full shroud heavy VR barrels.

MODEL 722M—.22 Mag, otherwise same as Model 722, use same add-ons for various barrel options.

Mfg.'s Sug. Retail	$390	$320	$270	$230

This model is also available in a Pistol Pac including 2½, 4, 6, and 8 in. solid rib barrel assemblies, extra grip, 4 additional sight blades, and fitted carrying case - Mfg.'s Suggested Retail is $723. Add $100 for VR barrels, $200 for full shroud heavy VR barrels.

MODEL 708—.38 Spl., same as Model 8-2. Add $6 for each additional barrel length.

Mfg.'s Sug. Retail	$311	$260	$200	$170

This model is also available in a Pistol Pac including 2½, 4, and 6 in. solid rib barrel assemblies, extra grip and fitted carrying case - Mfg.'s Suggested Retail is $517.

MODEL 709—.38 Spl., target revolver, adj. sights. Add $9 for each additional longer barrel length, $20 for vent rib, $45 for heavy vent rib. Also available in special order 10, 12, or 15 barrel lengths (add approx. $100 for 10 in.).

Mfg.'s Sug. Retail	$366	$305	$250	$205

This model is also available in a Pistol Pac including 2½, 4, 6, and 8 in. solid rib barrel assemblies, extra grip, 4 additional sight blades, and fitted carrying case - Mfg.'s Suggested Retail is $689. Add $100 for VR barrels, $200 for full shroud heavy VR barrels.

MODEL 714—.357 Mag., same as Model 14-2. Add $6 for each additional barrel length.

Mfg.'s Sug. Retail	$311	$260	$200	$170

This model is also available in a Pistol Pac including 2½, 4, and 6 in. solid rib barrel assemblies, extra grip and fitted carrying case - Mfg.'s Suggested Retail is $517.

MODEL 715—.357 Mag., target revolver, adj. sights. Add $20 for vent rib, $45 for heavy vent rib.

Mfg.'s Sug. Retail	$366	$305	$250	$205

This model is also available in a Pistol Pac including 2½, 4, 6, and 8 in. solid rib barrel assemblies, extra grip, 4 additional sight blades, and fitted carrying case - Mfg.'s Suggested Retail is $689. Add $100 for VR barrels, $200 for full shroud heavy VR barrels.

Grading	100%	98%	95%	90%	80%	70%	60%

MODEL 732—.32 H&R Mag., same as Model 32, except is stainless steel. New in 1986. Add $20 for VR barrel shroud (Model 732-V), $44 for VR heavy barrel shroud (Model 732-VH). Also add approx. $9 for each additional barrel length over 2½ in.

Mfg.'s Sug. Retail	$366	$305	$250	$205			

This model is also available in a Pistol Pac including 2½, 4, 6, and 8 in. solid rib barrel assemblies, extra grip, 4 additional sight blades, and fitted carrying case - Mfg.'s Suggested Retail is $689. Add $100 for VR barrels, $200 for full shroud heavy VR barrels.

MODEL 740V - .357 SUPERMAG—.357 Max., 6, 8, or 10 in. barrel, adj. rear sight with interchangeable front and rear blades, high polished finish, smooth target grips. New in 1986. Add approx. $20 for each additional barrel length after 6 in., $27 for slotted shroud (only avail. with 8 in. barrel), $15 for VR heavy barrel shroud (Model 740-VH).

Mfg.'s Sug. Retail	$569	$455	$350	$315			

MODEL 741V—.41 Mag., same as Model 41V. Add $23 for heavy vent rib, $11 for each barrel length over 4 in.

Mfg.'s Sug. Retail	$462	$385	$315	$270			

This model is also available in a Pistol Pac including 6 and 8 in. VR barrel assemblies, extra grip, 2 additional sight blades, and fitted carrying case - Mfg.'s Suggested Retail is $690. Add $49 for ventilated shroud VR barrels.

MODEL 744V—.44 Mag., same as Model 44V. Add $21 for heavy vent rib, $10 for each barrel length over 4 in.

Mfg.'s Sug. Retail	$507	$420	$340	$285			

This model is also available in a Pistol Pac including 6 and 8 in. VR barrel assemblies, extra grip, 2 additional sight blades, and fitted carrying case - Mfg.'s Suggested Retail is $814. Add $53 for ventilated shroud VR barrels.

Model 744 Commemorative—limited mfg.

		$595	$475	$325			

MODEL 745V—.45 Long Colt, same as Model 45V, except in stainless steel. Add $23 for heavy full shroud VR barrels, $11 for each additional barrel length.

Mfg.'s Sug. Retail	$507	$420	$340	$285			

This model is also available in a Pistol Pac including 6 and 8 in. VR barrel assemblies, extra grip, 2 additional sight blades, and fitted carrying case - Mfg.'s Suggested Retail is $814. Add $53 for ventilated shroud VR barrels.

WESSON, FRANK

WORCESTER, MA 1854 TO 1865, SPRINGFIELD, MA 1865-1875.

PISTOLS: SINGLE SHOT

100%	98%	95%	90%	80%	70%	60%	50%	40%	30%	20%	10%

SMALL FRAME FIRST MODEL—.22 cal., tip up action, 3½ in. ½ octagon barrel, brass frame, spur trigger, rosewood grips, round frame, irregular sideplate, 2500 produced, 1859-1862.

$605	$550	$495	$440	$385	$330	$275	$220	$195	$165	$140	$110

SMALL FRAME SECOND MODEL—same as First Model, with flat sided frame and circular sideplate, 12,000 produced, 1862-1880.

$550	$495	$440	$385	$330	$305	$250	$195	$165	$110	$105	$85

MEDIUM FRAME FIRST MODEL—.30 S or L, .32 S rimfires, 4 in. ½ octagon barrel, iron frame, same as Small Frame in other respects, narrow hinge and short trigger, 1000 produced, 1859-1862.

$525	$470	$415	$360	$305	$275	$220	$195	$165	$110	$105	$85

MEDIUM FRAME SECOND MODEL—same as First Model, with wider hinge and longer trigger, 1000 produced, 1862-1870.

$495	$440	$385	$330	$275	$250	$220	$195	$165	$110	$105	$85

100%	98%	95%	90%	80%	70%	60%	50%	40%	30%	20%	10%

RIFLES

NO. 1 LONG RANGE—side hammer, falling block lever actuated, .44-100 and .45-100 standard, 34 in. octagon barrel, tang. sight, select checkered pistol grip stock, less than 50 produced, ca. 1870-1880.

100%	98%	95%	90%	80%	70%	60%	50%	40%	30%	20%	10%
$4,950	$4,675	$4,400	$3,850	$3,575	$3,080	$2,860	$2,475	$2,200	$2,035	$1,760	

NO. 2 HUNTING RIFLE—similar to No. 1, with finger loop lever, less than 100 produced.

$4,400	$4,180	$3,850	$3,520	$3,025	$2,750	$2,420	$2,255	$2,035	$1,925	$1,760	$1,540

NO. 1 SPORTING RIFLE—similar to No. 2, with center hammer, .38-100, .40-100, .45-100, less than 25 produced.

$4,400	$4,180	$3,850	$3,520	$3,025	$2,750	$2,420	$2,255	$2,035	$1,925	$1,760	$1,540

POCKET RIFLES

SMALL FRAME TIP UP—.22 rimfire, 6 in. ½ octagon barrel, brass frame, spur trigger, rosewood grips, approximately 500 produced, 1865-1875.

$605	$550	$525	$495	$470	$440	$415	$360	$330	$275	$220	$165

If without stock - deduct 25%.

MEDIUM FRAME TIP UP—.22, .30, and .32 rimfire cal.'s, 10 or 12 in. barrel, same as small frame, with exceptions noted and larger frame, approximately 1000 produced, 1862-1870.

$605	$550	$525	$495	$470	$440	$415	$360	$330	$275	$220	$165

If without stock - deduct 25%.

MODEL 1870 SMALL FRAME FIRST TYPE—similar to Small Frame Tip Up, except barrel rotates on its axis to load, detachable stock, approximately 3000 produced, 1870-1890.

$550	$495	$470	$440	$415	$385	$360	$305	$275	$220	$195	$165

If without stock - deduct 25%.

MODEL 1870 SMALL FRAME SECOND TYPE—full octagon barrel.

$525	$470	$440	$415	$385	$360	$330	$275	$250	$195	$165	$140

MODEL 1870 SMALL FRAME THIRD TYPE—iron frame, push button ½ cock.

$495	$440	$415	$385	$360	$330	$305	$250	$220	$165	$140	$110

MODEL 1870 MEDIUM FRAME FIRST TYPE—same as Small Frame, except in size and availability of .32 cal., 5000 produced, 1870-1893.

$525	$495	$470	$440	$415	$385	$360	$305	$275	$250	$195	$165

If without stock — deduct 25%.

MODEL 1870 MEDIUM FRAME SECOND TYPE—external push half cock and iron frame.

$440	$415	$385	$330	$305	$275	$220	$195	$165	$140	$110	$90

If without stock — deduct 25%.

MODEL 1870 MEDIUM FRAME THIRD TYPE—has three screws in frame, iron frame.

$440	$415	$385	$330	$305	$275	$220	$195	$165	$140	$110	$90

If without stock, deduct 25%.

MODEL 1870 LARGE FRAME FIRST TYPE—.32, .38, .42, and .44 rimfire cal.'s, 15-24 in. barrels, similar to smaller frame models, auto extractor, approximately 500 produced, 1870-1880.

$825	$770	$715	$660	$605	$550	$525	$495	$440	$385	$305	$275

If without stock — deduct 25%.

MODEL 1870 LARGE FRAME SECOND TYPE—same as First Type, with standard sliding extractor.

$825	$770	$715	$660	$605	$550	$525	$495	$440	$385	$305	$275

If without stock — deduct 25%.

WESTERN ARMS COMPANY

ITHACA, NEW YORK.

WESTERN LONG RANGE DOUBLE BARREL SHOTGUN—12, 16, 20, and
.410 ga.'s, 26-32 in. barrels, mod. and full choke, boxlock, extractors, double or single
trigger, plain pistol grip stock, Western Arms Co. was a division of Ithaca Gun, made
1929-1946.

$275	$225	$200	$175	$150	$125	$100

Single trigger

$325	$275	$250	$225	$200	$150	$125

WESTERN FIELD

TRADEMARK USED ON MONTGOMERY WARDS RIFLES AND SHOTGUNS.

The Western Field trademark has appeared literally on hundreds of various models
(shotguns and rifles) sold through the Montgomery Wards retail network. Most of these models
were manufactured through subcontracts with both domestic and international firearms
manufacturers. Typically, they were "spec." guns made to sell at a specific price to undersell the
competition. Most of these models were derivatives of existing factory models with less expensive
wood and perhaps missing the features found on those models from which they were derived. To
date, there has been very little interest in collecting Western Field guns, regardless of rarity. Rather
than list J.C. Higgins' models, a general guideline is that values generally are under those of their
"1st generation relatives". As a result, prices are ascertained by the shooting value of the gun, rather
than its' collector value.

WESTLEY RICHARDS & CO. LTD.

ORIGINALLY WILLIAM WESTLEY RICHARDS LOCATED IN BIRMINGHAM, ENGLAND.
CURRENTLY MANUFACTURED BY WESTLEY RICHARDS AND CO., LTD. LOCATED ON
GRANGE ROAD, BIRMINGHAM, ENGLAND (B296AR). MANUFACTURED 1821 TO
DATE. CURRENTLY IMPORTED BY NEW ENGLAND ARMS CO. LOCATED IN KITTERY
POINT, ME, OR DIRECTLY FROM FACTORY.

Note: Westley Richards guns are essentially custom ordered. They make many weapons
that are impossible to list and evaluate, except on an individual basis. Professional appraisal is
necessary upon purchase or sale.

Due to the recent devaluation of the U.S. dollar, prices could fluctuate significantly from
values listed below. To obtain a quotation for a new Westley Richards shotgun, an inquiry
should be submitted to the manufacturer at the above address.

SHOTGUNS

OVUNDO O/U—12 ga., barrel length and choke to order, hand detachable boxlock with
dummy sideplates, SST, checkered straight or pistol grip stock, pre-WWII.

$18,000	$15,000	$13,000	$11,000	$9,750	$8,500	$7,250

MODEL E SxS—12, 16, and 20 ga.'s, barrel length and choke to order, boxlock, extractors,
double triggers, checkered pistol grip or straight stock.

$1,960	$1,675	$1,450	$1,275	$1,100	$975	$875

20 gauge — add 20%.
Auto ejectors — add 33%.

CONNAUGHT MODEL SxS—12, 20, or 28 ga., Anson & Deeley scalloped boxlock
action, scroll engraving, 26 or 28 in. barrels, ejectors, about 6½ lbs.

Mfg.'s Sug. Retail							
	$7,250	$7,250	$6,100	$5,300	$4,600	$3,995	$3,300	$2,650

Add $240 for 20 or 28 ga.

Grading	100%	98%	95%	90%	80%	70%	60%

BEST QUALITY BOXLOCK SxS—12, 16, and 20 ga.'s, barrel lengths and chokes to order, detachable locks with hinged cover, checkered straight or pistol grip stock, auto ejectors.

	100%	98%	95%	90%	80%	70%	60%
	$7,250	$6,100	$5,500	$4,950	$4,400	$3,950	$3,300

    20 gauge — add 20%.
    SST — add $1,000.

DELUXE BOXLOCK—same as Best Quality, with higher grade wood and more engraving.

	100%	98%	95%	90%	80%	70%	60%
	$10,750	$8,950	$7,850	$6,900	$6,000	$5,500	$4,750

    20 gauge — add 20%.
    SST — add $1,000.

BEST QUALITY SIDELOCK—12, 16, 20, 28, and .410 ga.'s, barrel length and choke to order, hand detachable sidelocks, auto ejectors, checkered straight or pistol grip stock.

	100%	98%	95%	90%	80%	70%	60%
	$12,000	$10,550	$8,750	$8,000	$7,275	$6,600	$5,375

    20 gauge — add 20%.
    28 gauge — add 40%.
    .410 gauge — add 60%.
    SST — add $1,000.

WILLIAM BISHOP SIDELOCK MODEL—current mfg., best quality sidelock, made to individual customer specifications.

Mfg.'s Sug. Retail	100%	98%	95%	90%	80%	70%	60%
	$19,295	$19,295	$14,750	$12,200	$10,250	$8,975	$7,875	$6,800

    Add $105 - $205 for 20 or 28 ga.

CARLTON DETACHABLE SIDELOCK—12 or 20 ga., current mfg., detachable sidelocks, top of the line shotgun custom made per customer specifications, elaborate game scene engraving. Many options upon request.

Mfg.'s Sug. Retail							
	$21,450	$21,450	$17,750	$14,750	$12,200	$10,250	$8,975	$7,875

DELUXE SIDELOCK—same as Best Quality, with higher grade wood and elaborate custom engraving.

	100%	98%	95%	90%	80%	70%	60%
	$14,700	$12,200	$10,250	$8,975	$7,875	$7,000	$6,250

    20 gauge — add 20%.
    28 gauge — add 40%.
    .410 gauge — add 60%.
    SST — add $1,000.

RIFLES

BEST QUALITY DOUBLE RIFLE—auto ejectors, boxlock, hammerless, various English calibers and .30-06, folding leaf rear sight, hooded front sight, engraved with quality French walnut stock, horn forend tip. Values will vary according to caliber.

	100%	98%	95%	90%	80%	70%	60%
	$25,000	$18,500	$13,750	$11,000	$9,950	$9,000	$8,000

Values will vary greatly on this model depending on caliber and type/style of engraving.

DETACHABLE LOCK DOUBLE RIFLE—available in most cal.'s, boxlock with detachable locks, ejectors, colored case hardened frame, cased.

Mfg.'s Sug. Retail							
	$35,100	$35,100	$21,000	$16,500	$14,700	$12,200	$10,250	$8,975

STALKER MAGAZINE RIFLE—.243 Win., .270 Win., .30-06, .300 H&H, .375 H&H, or .458 Win. Mag. cal., bolt action, Mauser action, 22, 24, and 25 in. barrel, leaf rear and hooded front sight, engraved with French walnut stock, horn forend tip. Current mfg.

Mfg.'s Sug. Retail							
	$6,015	$6,015	$4,500	$3,850	$3,250	$2,875	$2,425	$2,000

    Add $322 for mag. cal.'s.

WHITNEY FIREARMS COMPANY

MANUFACTURED BETWEEN 1956-1959 IN HARTFORD, CT.

PISTOL: SEMI-AUTO

WOLVERINE OR LIGHTNING—.22 auto, unique futuristic appearance, 10 shot, 4⅝ in. barrel, plastic grips, aluminum alloy frame and barrel shroud, blue model is more common (approx. 13,000 mfg.), nickel is rare (approx. 900 mfg.). Made 1955-1962.

	100%	98%	95%	90%	80%	70%	60%
Blue finish	$400	$350	$300	$260	$230	$200	$175
Nickel finish	$525	$450	$375	$300	$260	$230	$200

WHITWORTH

THIS TRADEMARK CAN BE FOUND IN THE INTERARMS SECTION OF THIS TEXT.

WICHITA ARMS, INC.

MANUFACTURED AND DISTRIBUTED IN WICHITA, KS.

PISTOLS

WICHITA INTERNATIONAL PISTOL (WIP)—available in 8 cal.'s between .22 LR and .357 Mag., single shot, break open action, stainless steel, adj. sights, 10½ or 14 in. barrel, adj. sights or scope mounts, smooth walnut stocks and forearm.

Mfg.'s Sug. Retail	**$485**	**$445**	**$385**	**$340**			

WICHITA CLASSIC PISTOL—assorted cal.'s to .308 Win., 11¼ in. barrel, action has left-hand bolt for shooting with right-hand, 3 lbs. 15 oz., deluxe walnut, custom made.

Mfg.'s Sug. Retail	**$2,950**	**$2,950**	**$2,400**	**$2,100**	**$1,850**	**$1,575**	**$1,265**	**$1,000**

Wichita Classic Engraved—similar to Wichita Classic, except is extensively engraved.

Mfg.'s Sug. Retail	**$4,850**	**$4,850**	**$3,500**	**$2,750**			

WICHITA SILHOUETTE PISTOL (WSP)—.308 Win. or 7mm/HMSA cal., adj. trigger and sights, 14¹⁵⁄₁₆ in. barrel, center grip walnut stock, 4½ lbs. Left-hand action for shooting with right-hand.

Mfg.'s Sug. Retail	**$1,100**	**$1,100**	**$900**	**$750**	**$600**	**$525**	**$460**	**$400**

WICHITA MK40—.308 Win. and 7mm/HMSA, fiberthane (disc. in 1987) or walnut (new in 1988) stock, 13 in. barrel, adj. trigger, multi-range sights, 4½ lbs.

Mfg.'s Sug. Retail	**$1,100**	**$1,100**	**$900**	**$750**	**$600**	**$525**	**$460**	**$400**

Add $225 for stainless steel barrel.

RIFLES

WICHITA CLASSIC RIFLE (WCR)—17-222, 17-222 Mag., .222 Rem, 222 Mag., 223 Rem., 6x47, and other cal.'s up to and including .308 cal., bolt action, single shot, select walnut, 21 in. octagon barrel, Canjar trigger, no sights, 7 lbs.

Mfg.'s Sug. Retail	**$2,950**	**$2,950**	**$2,400**	**$2,100**	**$1,850**	**$1,575**	**$1,265**	**$1,000**

Add P.O.R. for blind box mag.
Add $175 for left-hand action.

Wichita Varmint Rifle (WVR)—similar to WCR, except available only in Varmint cal.'s (up to and including .308) and round barrel.

Mfg.'s Sug. Retail	**$1,975**	**$1,975**	**$1,600**	**$1,325**	**$1,100**	**$950**	**$800**	**$750**

Add P.O.R. for blind box mag.
Add $175 for left-hand action.

Wichita Silhouette Rifle (WSR)—available in most cal.'s, gray fiberthane stock, 24 in. match grade barrel, 2 oz Canjar trigger, no sights, 9 lbs.

Mfg.'s Sug. Retail	**$2,150**	**$2,150**	**$1,700**	**$1,375**	**$1,140**	**$975**	**$825**	**$750**

Add $175 for left-hand action.

Wichita Magnum—Mag. cal.'s. Disc. in 1984.

	$1,725	**$1,300**	**$1,175**	**$1,100**	**$1,000**	**$925**	**$875**

WICKLIFFE RIFLES

TRIPLE S DEVELOPMENT, OHIO.

RIFLES - SINGLE SHOT

MODEL 76 STANDARD—falling block action, most popular cal.'s, 22 or 26 in. barrel, no sights, select walnut pistol grip, 2 piece stock, made 1976-discontinued.

	$370	**$320**	**$305**	**$275**	**$250**	**$220**	**$165**

MODEL 76 DELUXE GRADE—same as Standard, in .30-06 only, 22 in. barrel, fancy wood, silver pistol grip cap.

	$460	**$415**	**$385**	**$360**	**$320**	**$290**	**$250**

WICKLIFFE RIFLES, cont.

Grading	100%	98%	95%	90%	80%	70%	60%

MODEL 76 COMMEMORATIVE—same as Deluxe, except etched receiver, U.S. silver dollar inlaid in stock, presentation case, 100 produced, 1976.

	$1,100	$825	$550	$495	$440	$330	$305

STINGER—similar to 76, .22 in. Hornet or .223, lightweight 22 in. barrel.

	$370	$320	$305	$275	$250	$220	$165

STINGER DELUXE—same as 76 Deluxe, in .22 Hornet or .223, lightweight 22 in. barrel.

	$460	$415	$385	$360	$325	$290	$250

TRADITIONALIST—same as Standard 76, in .30-06 and .45-70, 24 in. barrel.

	$370	$320	$305	$275	$250	$220	$165

KODIAK COMMEMORATIVE—similar to Deluxe, .338 Mag., 26 in. barrel, etched receiver.

	$605	$495	$440	$415	$360	$330	$275

WILDEY FIREARMS CO., INC.

ORIGINALLY MANUFACTURED BY I.F.D. INC., IN CHESHIRE, CT. LATER MANUFACTURE WAS IN NEW BURG, NY. NEW MANUFACTURE IS IN BROOKFIELD, CT.

WILDEY AUTO PISTOL—.45 Win. Mag., 9mm Win. Mag., .357 Peterbuilt, or .475 Wildey Mag., gas operated, 5, 6, 7, 8, or 10 in. vent rib barrel, selective single shot or semi-auto, 3 lug rotary bolt, stainless steel construction, double action adj. sights, wood grips, designed to fire two new cartridges specifically for this gun - 9mm Win. Mag. (never mfg.) or .45 Win. Mag., 64 oz. with 5 in. barrel.

Older Mfg.—.45 Win. Mag. cal. only, Cheshire, CT addressed, serial numbered 1-2,489 with 3 character prefix, priced by ser. no., 7, 8, or 10 in. barrel is most desirable. These pistols are older mfg. but a few dealers have limited inventory (including Wildey in Brookfield, CT.).

SERIAL NO. 1-200.

Mfg.'s Sug. Retail	$1,980	$1,750	$1,550	$1,400

Add $120 for 8 or 10 in. barrel.

SERIAL NO. 201-400.

Mfg.'s Sug. Retail	$1,780	$1,650	$1,375	$1,250

Add $20 for 8 or 10 in. barrel.

SERIAL NO. 401-600.

Mfg.'s Sug. Retail	$1,580	$1,450	$1,200	$1,000

Add $20 for 8 or 10 in. barrel.

SERIAL NO. 601-800.

Mfg.'s Sug. Retail	$1,380	$1,250	$1,050	$900

Add $20 for 8 or 10 in. barrel.

SERIAL NO. 801-1,000.

Mfg.'s Sug. Retail	$1,180	$1,050	$895	$795

Add $20 for 8 or 10 in. barrel.

SERIAL NO. 1,001-2,489.

Mfg.'s Sug. Retail	$1,080	$975	$850	$725

Add $20 for 8 or 10 in. barrel.

Survivor Model - New Mfg.—9mm Win. Mag., .357 Peterbuilt, .45 Win. Mag., or .475 Win. Mag. cal., mfg. in Brookfield, CT.

Mfg.'s Sug. Retail	$1,080	$975	$850	$725

Last Mfg.'s Sug. Retail was $1,295.

Presentation Model—same specifications as above model, except is engraved with hand checkered stocks.

	$2,500	$2,000	$1,600

Last Mfg.'s Sug. Retail was $2,000.

WILKINSON ARMS

DIANE AUTOMATIC PISTOL—.25 ACP, 6 shot, 2⅛ in. barrel, fixed sight, matte blue, plastic grips.

	100%	98%	95%	90%	80%	70%	60%
	$125	$110	$90	$80	$65	$55	$50

"TERRY" CARBINE—blowback action, 9mm parabellum, 30 shot mag., 16³⁄₁₆ in. barrel, closed breech, adj. sights.

	100%	98%	95%	90%	80%	70%	60%
With black P.V.C. stock	$325	$310	$300	$275	$230	$210	$180
With maple stock	$350	$340	$325	$300	$260	$230	$200

WINCHESTER

MANUFACTURED IN NEW HAVEN, CT FROM 1866 TO DATE. ALSO INCLUDES U.S. REPEATING ARMS FORMED IN 1981 WITH LICENSING AGREEMENT FROM OLIN CORP. TO MANUFACTURE SHOTGUNS AND RIFLES DOMESTICALLY USING THE WINCHESTER TRADEMARK. OLIN CORP. PREVIOUSLY MANUFACTURED SHOTGUNS AND RIFLES BEARING THE WINCHESTER HALLMARK AT THE OLIN KADENSHA PLANT (NOW CLOSING) LOCATED IN TOCHIGI, JAPAN AND ALSO IN EUROPEAN COUNTRIES.

RIFLES: LEVER ACTIONS — 1860-1895.

Note: Winchester Rifles are a field in themselves. Models Henry, 1866, 1873, 1876, 1885, 1886, 1892, 1894, and 1895 all were produced with a multitude of special order options. Special orders included front and rear special sights, half or ⅔ magazines, takedown, various barrel lengths, configurations, and weights, special metal finishes, deluxe wood (either checkered or carved) in a variety of finishes, an impressive range of engraving options, different buttplates, etc. All of these special orders act independently and interdependently to determine the correct value of a particular Winchester. Some of the finest rifles ever made are special order Winchesters engraved by the Ulrich's, G. Young, L.D. Nimschke, and others. For these reasons a Model 92 Winchester can range in price from $200 to over $250,000 - quite a price range for one model alone! When contemplating a purchase on the higher dollar range, qualified and professional opinions should be secured, preferably from at least 2 sources. Unfortunately many fakes and upgraded (non-original) guns have surfaced in the last 10 years with the sudden increase in prices. Winchesters shown in this section are priced assuming a standard model with no special orders. Any special orders will further add to the prices shown. Caliber rarities must also be considered. Many of the early Winchesters are broken down by year of manufacture. Refer to the "Model Serialization" section in this book.

A factory letter specifying original shipping information by serial number will certainly help solidify values shown on older out of production Winchester rifles and shotguns. A listing has been provided below by model number with serialization range which can be historically researched by the Winchester Museum now located in Cody, WY. To use this outstanding service, make sure the model and its serial number fall within the range listed below. If so, send $25 per serial number needing research payable to the Buffalo Bill Historical Center, P.O. Box 1000 in Cody, WY, 82414. Information received back will include specimen caliber, barrel length, any special orders or finishes, return(s) to the factory, as well as any additional provenance contained within Winchesters' factory shipping ledgers. I would recommend a trip to the Buffalo Bill Historical Center as it contains the most comprehensive collection of projectile arms (including Chinese specimens that date back 2,000 years) and Americana housed under one roof in this country.

A NOTE ON WINCHESTER FINISHES: Values below are for original finish with the percentage of bright blue ascertaining the current price. It is very important to understand that there is a big value difference between a Model 1873 with 90% bright blue as opposed to a gun that has 90% patina finish (turning brown). Even though it is true that both guns are 90%, the bright blue specimen might be worth 50% + more because it is closer to the way it originally left the factory — with bright bluing. For this reason, the type of finish remaining becomes as important as the amount of finish. "Brown" guns are simply not as desirable as bright guns that show little discoloration. Because of this, much consideration must be given as to what type of finish a specimen has, and if shiny or mostly brown, value has to be taken away from prices listed below accordingly.

WINCHESTER, cont.

Model 1886 Lever Action Rifle — ser. no. range 124,995-170,101.

Model 1873 Lever Action Rifle — ser. no. range 1-720,496.

Model 1876 Lever Action Rifle — ser. no. range 1-63,871.

Model 1883 Bolt Action Rifle (Hotchkiss Repeater) — ser. no. range 1-84,555.

Model 1885 Single Shot Rifle or Shotgun — ser. no. range 1-109,999.

Model 1886 Lever Action Rifle — ser. no. range 1-156,599.

Model 1887 & 1901 Lever Action Shotguns — ser. no. range 1-72,999.

Model 1890 Slide Action Rifle — ser. no. range 1-329,999.

Model 1892 Lever Action Rifle — ser. no. range 1-379,999.

Model 1893 Slide Action Shotgun — ser. no. range 1-34,050.

Model 1894 Lever Action Rifle — ser. no. range 1-353,999.

Model 1895 Lever Action Rifle — ser. no. range 1-59,999.

Model "Lee" Bolt Action Rifle — ser. no. range 1-19,999.

Model 1897 Lever Action Shotgun — ser. no. range 34,051-377,999.

Model 1903 Semi-Auto .22 Cal. Rifle — ser. no. range 1-39,999.

Model 1905 Semi-Auto Rifle — ser. no. range 1-29,078.

Model 1906 Semi-Auto Rifle — ser. no. range 1-79,999.

Model 1907 Semi-Auto Rifle — ser. no. range 1-9,999.

HENRY RIFLE—.44 twin rimfire, 15 shot, 24 in. barrel with integral slotted tube mag. and loading, blued barrel, brass frame, approximately 13,000 total production, manufactured 1860-1866.

Iron Frame Model—frame made of iron, round type buttplate, no lever latch, adj. sporting type rear leaf sight, serial numbers are in three digits only, total production is believed to be less than 300.

100%	98%	95%	90%	80%	70%	60%	50%	40%	30%	20%	10%
$16,500	$15,400	$13,750	$11,000	$9,350	$7,700	$6,600	$6,050	$5,280	$4,400	$3,740	

Early Model—approximately 1,500 manufactured, serialized below 2,500, with or without lever latch.

100%	98%	95%	90%	80%	70%	60%	50%	40%	30%	20%	10%
$12,100	$11,000	$9,350	$7,150	$5,795	$4,675	$4,180	$3,960	$3,740	$3,575	$2,750	$2,150

Martial Marked—contracted by U.S. military for Civil War use, denoted by "C.G.C." inspector markings on upper barrel breech and stock, approximately 1,900 with serialization scattered.

100%	98%	95%	90%	80%	70%	60%	50%	40%	30%	20%	10%
$13,200	$12,100	$10,450	$8,250	$7,100	$6,400	$5,200	$4,400	$4,070	$3,850	$3,080	$2,200

This rifle was the most revolutionary shoulder weapon introduced in the Civil War.

Late Model—similar to early model, except buttplate heel has pointed profile, lever latch became standard, most commonly encountered Henry, over 8,000 manufactured.

100%	98%	95%	90%	80%	70%	60%	50%	40%	30%	20%	10%
$12,100	$11,000	$9,350	$7,150	$5,795	$4,675	$4,180	$3,960	$3,500	$3,300	$2,500	$2,000

MODEL 1866 RIFLE—.44 twin rimfire or centerfire (4th Model only), 24 in. barrel, blued barrel with brass frame, differs from Henry in that it has a wood forearm, frame cartridge loading port (King's improvement), and separate tube mag., total production reached 170,101 for all models, manufactured 1866-1898.

Model 1866 First Model Rifle—"Improved Henry" action, .44 cal. twin rimfire, two screws on upper tang, no forend cap, serialization is concealed on lower tang inside butt stock, serial range is from mid 12,000 to mid 15,000 (which includes a number of Henry's).

100%	98%	95%	90%	80%	70%	60%	50%	40%	30%	20%	10%
$15,400	$14,300	$11,550	$9,900	$7,700	$6,820	$6,270	$5,500	$5,060	$4,675	$3,960	$3,300

Model 1866 Carbine First Model—same action as Rifle, only with 20 in. barrel, 2 barrel bands and saddle ring.

100%	98%	95%	90%	80%	70%	60%	50%	40%	30%	20%	10%
$9,900	$8,800	$7,040	$6,160	$5,775	$4,675	$3,740	$3,025	$2,420	$2,145	$1,650	$1,100

Model 1866 Rifle Second Model—"New Model" with redesigned frame, one screw on upper tang, and serial numbered outside lower tang beneath lever (approx. after serial number 20,000) and outside lower tang beneath lever.

100%	98%	95%	90%	80%	70%	60%	50%	40%	30%	20%	10%
$9,900	$8,800	$7,480	$6,160	$4,675	$3,850	$3,135	$2,640	$2,200	$1,650	$1,100	$825

100%	98%	95%	90%	80%	70%	60%	50%	40%	30%	20%	10%

Model 1866 Carbine Second Model—frame and other changes similar to Second Model Rifle.

| $8,800 | $7,700 | $6,160 | $4,840 | $4,125 | $3,080 | $2,200 | $1,815 | $1,320 | $1,100 | $825 | $550 |

Model 1866 Rifle Third Model—block style serial numbers usually located behind trigger, improved frame. Serial numbered approx. 25,000-149,000.

| $8,800 | $7,700 | $6,160 | $4,840 | $4,125 | $3,080 | $2,200 | $1,925 | $1,650 | $1,430 | $1,210 | $1,045 |

Model 1866 Carbine Third Model—same changes as Model 1866 Third Model Rifle, 20 in. barrel with 2 bands.

| $8,250 | $6,930 | $5,720 | $4,510 | $3,575 | $3,025 | $2,475 | $1,980 | $1,540 | $1,100 | $770 | $550 |

Model 1866 Musket Third Model—27 in. round barrel, 24 in. magazine, 3 barrel bands.

| $6,050 | $4,840 | $4,125 | $3,520 | $3,025 | $2,530 | $2,145 | $1,760 | $1,375 | $990 | $715 | $495 |

Model 1866 Rifle Fourth Model—.44 cal., twin rimfire and centerfire, script style serial number on lower tang near lever latch, improved frame, serial range approx. 149,000-170,101.

| $8,250 | $6,820 | $5,830 | $4,840 | $3,850 | $3,080 | $2,530 | $2,090 | $1,705 | $1,320 | $1,045 | $715 |

Model 1866 Carbine Fourth Model—same changes as Model 1886 Rifle Fourth Model, 20 in. barrel with 2 bands.

| $7,975 | $6,600 | $5,500 | $4,400 | $3,300 | $2,750 | $2,090 | $1,650 | $1,320 | $1,045 | $770 | $605 |

Model 1866 Musket Fourth Model—same changes as Model 1886 Rifle Fourth Model, 27 in. round barrel with 3 bands.

| $5,775 | $4,730 | $3,960 | $3,300 | $2,750 | $2,310 | $1,925 | $1,595 | $1,265 | $990 | $715 | $495 |

MODEL 1873 RIFLE—.32-20, .38-40, and .44-40 centerfire cal.'s, iron frame (changed to steel in 1884) with sideplates, frame loading port, 24 in. round or octagon barrel, tube mag., blued finish with case hardened parts, oil finished stock, serial numbered on lower tang, 720,610 manufactured between 1873-1919, guns produced after serial number 525,923 are modern firearms.

Deluxe Model 1873's had color case hardened frames and will add at least 50% to the values listed below for standard models.

Model 1873 First Model Rifle—serial numbered approx. 1-28,000, distinguishable by 2 screws in frame above trigger and separate thumbrest affixed to grooved dust cover.

| $4,850 | $2,750 | $2,420 | $1,980 | $1,650 | $1,375 | $1,100 | $880 | $770 | $660 | $440 | $305 |

Model 1873 Carbine First Model—20 in. round barrel with 2 bands. Distinctive curved buttplate, with saddle ring.

| $5,400 | $3,740 | $3,300 | $3,025 | $2,750 | $2,200 | $1,980 | $1,595 | $1,375 | $990 | $770 | $495 |

Late First Model 1873 Rifle—serial numbers from 28,000-31,000. Can be determined by thumbrest checkered on dust cover and trigger pin below the 2 frame screws.

| $5,125 | $3,300 | $2,750 | $2,200 | $1,925 | $1,595 | $1,320 | $1,100 | $880 | $715 | $495 | $275 |

Late First Model 1873 Carbine—same changes as Late First Model Rifle.

| $5,675 | $3,850 | $3,575 | $3,300 | $3,025 | $2,420 | $2,145 | $1,870 | $1,595 | $1,320 | $1,100 | $715 |

Late First Model 1873 Musket—30 in. round barrel, 27 in. mag. with 3 barrel bands.

| $4,850 | $3,300 | $2,750 | $2,420 | $2,200 | $1,980 | $1,760 | $1,650 | $1,485 | $1,320 | $1,100 | $715 |

Model 1873 Rifle Second Model—improved dust cover featuring slides on center rail on rear section of frame top, serial range 31,000-90,000.

| $4,025 | $2,750 | $2,200 | $1,925 | $1,650 | $1,320 | $1,100 | $880 | $660 | $440 | $330 | $260 |

Model 1873 Carbine Second Model—changes similar to 1873 Second Model Rifle, with 20 in. round barrel and 2 barrel bands.

| $4,850 | $3,300 | $3,025 | $2,750 | $2,475 | $2,200 | $1,815 | $1,595 | $1,045 | $660 | $440 | $305 |

Model 1873 Musket Second Model—changes similar to 1873 Second Model Rifle, with 30 in. barrel and 3 barrel bands.

| $2,750 | $2,475 | $2,200 | $1,925 | $1,650 | $1,320 | $1,100 | $880 | $715 | $550 | $330 | $260 |

Model 1873 Rifle Third Model—dust cover rail integral with frame, improved action with rear frame screws (2), serial 90,000-end of production.

| $3,995 | $2,750 | $2,200 | $1,925 | $1,650 | $1,320 | $1,100 | $880 | $660 | $440 | $330 | $260 |

100%	98%	95%	90%	80%	70%	60%	50%	40%	30%	20%	10%

Model 1873 Carbine Third Model—changes similar to 1873 Rifle Third Model, with 20 in. barrel and 2 barrel bands.

$4,850	$3,300	$3,025	$2,750	$2,475	$2,200	$1,815	$1,595	$1,045	$660	$440	$305

Model 1873 Musket Third Model—changes similar to 1873 Rifle Third Model, with 30 in. round barrel and 3 barrel bands.

$3,750	$2,475	$2,200	$1,925	$1,650	$1,320	$1,100	$880	$715	$550	$330	$220

Model 1873 .22 Rim Fire Rifle—.22 short and long, 24 or 26 in. barrel, no loading gate, the first .22 caliber repeater, 19,552 produced, manufactured 1884-1904. Made in rifle configuration only.

$4,025	$2,200	$1,925	$1,375	$1,045	$990	$880	$825	$660	$605	$440	$275

Model 1873 "1 of 1000"—special care taken in manufacture to guarantee better accuracy, markings on top of breech designate model, deluxe walnut, best model, extremely rare, 136 produced. Original cost was $100.

Values are not listed because too few original specimens are bought or sold to accurately establish pricing. A factory letter is a must for any "1 of 1,000;" Winchester.

Note: Rarity of the "1 of 1,000" and the "1 of 100" models makes upgrading to this model fairly common. Use extreme caution in purchasing.

Model 1873 "1 of 100"—similar to "1 of 1000" only rarer, 8 produced. Sold new for $20 over the list price of a similarly equipped Model 1873.

Values are not listed because too few original specimens are bought or sold to accurately establish pricing. A factory letter is a must for any "1 of 100" Winchester.

MODEL 1876 RIFLE—.40-60, .45-60, .45-75 (first caliber offered), and .50-95 Express cal.'s, 26 or 28 in. round or octagon barrel, similar but larger frame than Model 1873, tube mag., crescent butt, blued finish, straight grip stock, 63,871 produced, manufactured between 1876-1897.

The Model 1876 was also called the Centennial Model since its introduction coincided with the U.S. Centennial Exposition held in Philadelphia, PA in 1876. Popularity for this model decreased ten years later when the more powerful and advanced Model 1886 was introduced.

Deluxe Model 1876's had color case hardened frames and will add at least 50% to the values listed below for standard models. Deluxe Model 1876's with 90% + original case colors are very rare, desirable, and expensive.

Model 1876 Rifle First Model—serial numbered approx. 1-3,000, distinguishable by no dust cover on frame top.

$4,850	$3,300	$3,025	$2,200	$1,925	$1,650	$1,375	$1,100	$990	$825	$550	$385

Model 1876 Carbine First Model—22 in. round barrel, one barrel band, saddle ring, provision for bayonet attachment.

$5,400	$3,850	$3,300	$2,750	$2,475	$2,200	$2,035	$1,815	$1,375	$1,045	$825	$550

Model 1876 Musket First Model—32 in. round barrel with 1 band, scarce model because no foreign military contracts.

$7,600	$6,050	$5,500	$4,400	$4,125	$3,575	$3,300	$3,025	$2,750	$2,475	$2,035	$1,650

Model 1876 Rifle Early Second Model—"Thumbprint" dust cover with guide screwed to receiver added, serial range 3,000-7,000.

$4,245	$3,025	$2,750	$2,200	$1,925	$1,375	$1,100	$990	$825	$715	$550	$385

Model 1876 Carbine Second Model—changes similar to Model 1876 Rifle Early Second Model, with 22 in. round barrel and distinctive forend cap.

$5,125	$3,520	$3,300	$3,025	$2,750	$2,420	$1,980	$1,650	$1,100	$825	$605	$440

Model 1876 Musket Early Second Model—changes similar to Model 1876 Rifle Early Second Model, with 32 in. round barrel and carbine forend tip.

$7,050	$5,225	$4,400	$3,850	$3,575	$3,300	$3,025	$2,750	$2,420	$2,035	$1,650	$1,375

Model 1876 Rifle Late Second Model—improved dust cover lacking oval thumbprint, serial range 7,000-30,000.

$4,850	$3,300	$3,025	$2,200	$1,925	$1,650	$1,375	$1,100	$990	$825	$605	$385

Model 1876 Carbine Late Second Model—frame similar to Model 1876 Rifle Late Second Model, with 22 in. barrel.

$5,400	$3,850	$3,300	$2,750	$2,475	$2,200	$2,035	$1,815	$1,375	$1,045	$825	$550

100%	98%	95%	90%	80%	70%	60%	50%	40%	30%	20%	10%

Model 1876 Musket Late Second Model—frame similar to Model 1876 Rifle Late Second Model, with 32 in. round barrel.

100%	98%	95%	90%	80%	70%	60%	50%	40%	30%	20%	10%
$7,600	$6,050	$5,500	$4,400	$4,125	$3,575	$3,300	$3,025	$2,750	$2,475	$2,035	$1,650

Model 1876 Rifle Third Model—dust cover rail integral with frame, serial range 30,000-end of production.

$4,025	$2,750	$2,475	$2,035	$1,815	$1,595	$1,320	$1,100	$825	$605	$440	$275

Model 1876 Carbine Third Model—frame similar to Model 1876 Rifle Third Model, with 22 in. round barrel.

$4,850	$3,300	$3,025	$2,750	$2,475	$2,200	$1,815	$1,375	$935	$715	$550	$415

Model 1876 Musket Third Model—frame similar to Model 1876 Rifle Third Model, with 32 in. round barrel.

$6,500	$4,400	$3,850	$3,300	$3,025	$2,750	$2,475	$2,200	$2,090	$1,925	$1,650	$1,320

Model 1876 "1 of 1000"—special care taken in manufacture to guarantee better accuracy, markings on top of breech designate model, deluxe walnut, best model, extremely rare, 54 produced. Original cost was $100.

Values are not listed because too few original specimens are bought or sold to accurately establish pricing. A factory letter is a must for any "1 of 1,000" Winchester.

Note: Rarity of the "1 of 1,000" and the "1 of 100" models makes upgrading to this model fairly common. Use extreme caution in purchasing.

Model 1876 "1 of 100"—similar to "1 of 1000" only rarer, 8 produced. Sold new for $20 over the list price of a similarly equipped Model 1876.

Values are not listed because too few original specimens are bought or sold to accurately establish pricing. A factory letter is a must for any "1 of 100" Winchester.

Model 1876 Northwest Mounted Police Carbine—.45-75 cal. only, 22 in. barrel, "NWMP" stamped on butt stock, serial range 23,801-24,100 and 43,900-44,400.

$6,225	$4,400	$3,850	$3,300	$3,025	$2,750	$2,475	$2,200	$1,980	$1,650	$1,320	$1,100	$825

MODEL 1886 RIFLE—.33 WCF, .38-56 WCF, .38-70 WCF, .40-65 WCF, .40-70 WCF, .40-82 WCF, .45-70, .45-90, .50-110 Express, and .50-100-450 cal.'s available, Brownings' first high power lever action design distinguishable by vertical locking bars, .45-70 most popular cal., 26 in. round or octagon barrel, tube mag., steel forend cap, straight grip stock. Approx. 159,990 manufactured between 1886-1935.

The Model 1886 had case hardening standard on the frame, buttplate, and forend cap until 1901 (approx. 122,000 serial range) when the standard finish became blue.

Model 1886 Rifle—same as above.

$3,750	$2,420	$2,200	$1,760	$1,595	$1,375	$1,100	$990	$910	$825	$605	$385

Add 20% and more if .45-70 or .50-100/110 cal.'s. Original bright case colors will also bring premiums over values shown above.

Model 1886 Carbine—same general specifications as Rifle, except 22 in. round barrel and saddle ring.

$9,250	$7,150	$6,600	$5,775	$4,950	$4,400	$3,850	$3,300	$2,475	$1,925	$1,650	$1,320

Model 1886 Full Stock Carbine—same as regular carbine, except forearm extends almost to end of barrel (similar to Model 1876 Carbine).

$10,350	$8,250	$7,700	$7,150	$5,500	$4,950	$4,400	$3,850	$3,025	$2,475	$1,925	$1,650

Model 1886 Musket—30 in. round barrel, one barrel band, military sights, only 350 produced, very rare.

$14,200	$11,000	$9,350	$8,250	$7,150	$6,050	$5,500	$4,675	$3,850	$3,245	$2,750	$2,200

Model 1886 Lightweight Rifle—.45-70 and .33 WCF cal.'s only, 22 in. round nickel steel tapered barrel, half mag., rubber shotgun buttplate.

.33 caliber

$2,650	$1,375	$1,100	$825	$605	$550	$495	$470	$440	$415	$305	$220

.45-70 caliber

$4,025	$2,475	$2,200	$1,925	$1,705	$1,375	$1,100	$990	$770	$550	$440	$305

Model 1886 Takedown—magazine unscrews from frame allowing disassembly forward of breech.

Add 10% - 15% premium on rifles only.

100%	98%	95%	90%	80%	70%	60%	50%	40%	30%	20%	10%

RIFLES: 1890-1944 MANUFACTURE

MODEL 1890 SLIDE ACTION—See listing under RIFLES - SLIDE ACTION: DISCONTINUED in this section.

MODEL 1892 LEVER ACTION RIFLE—.218 Bee, .25-20, .32-20, .38-40, and .44-40 cal.'s, 24 in. round or octagon barrel, blue, tube mag., forend cap, crescent butt, 1,004,067 manufactured between 1892-1941.

| $2,650 | $1,775 | $1,300 | $935 | $825 | $675 | $575 | $475 | $395 | $335 | $275 | $225 |

Add 25% for .218 Bee caliber (manufactured 1936-1938, not advertised - special order only). Model 92's are also seen with barrels marked Model 65.

Model 1892 Takedown Rifle—magazine unscrews at frame allowing barrel/magazine takedown.

Add 20% + premium.

MODEL 1892 CARBINE—20 in. round barrel, two bands and saddle ring.

| $2,535 | $1,800 | $1,600 | $1,375 | $1,100 | $905 | $785 | $670 | $560 | $450 | $350 | $250 |

Manufactured in 13, 14, 15, 16, 18, and 20 in. barrel lengths in both carbines and rifles for the South American rubber industry.

MODEL 1892 TRAPPER'S CARBINE—same as Carbine, with 14, 15, 16, or 18 in. barrels. So called because was handy for trappers who had to carry a powerful but lightweight repeating rifle.

| $3,250 | $2,420 | $1,980 | $1,870 | $1,650 | $1,375 | $1,125 | $900 | $740 | $600 | $475 | $350 |

Note: Check federal laws on legality of 14 and 15 in. models.

MODEL 1892 MUSKET—30 in. round barrel, 3 barrel bands, military sights. Modified shotgun style buttplate.

| $4,350 | $3,575 | $3,200 | $2,950 | $2,600 | $2,200 | $1,900 | $1,600 | $1,200 | $900 | $675 | $450 |

MODEL 1894 LEVER ACTION RIFLE—.25-35, .30-30, .32-40, .32 Spl., and .38-55 cal.'s, most common (and popular) is .30-30 cal., tube mag., 26 in. octagon barrel, blue, straight grip stock, over 5,000,000 produced to date, manufactured 1894-present, currently available - see Modern Section.

Antique Model—ser. no.'s before 111,454.

| $2,500 | $1,400 | $995 | $825 | $700 | $575 | $450 | $400 | $360 | $340 | $320 | $300 |

1899-1936 Mfg.—model 94's built post 1898-1936.

| $1,495 | $1,200 | $850 | $750 | $650 | $525 | $425 | $360 | $325 | $300 | $275 | $250 |

The Model 1894 Winchester has the distinction of being the world's most popular rifle. Add 20% for .25-35 caliber (discontinued in 1936). Deluxe models or takedown variations will command substantial premiums over values listed above.

Model 1894 Takedown Rifle—magazine unscrews at frame allowing barrel/magazine takedown.

Add 20% + premium.

MODEL 94 TRAPPER'S CARBINE—same as Carbine, with 14, 16, or 18 in. barrel.

| $2,970 | $2,500 | $2,200 | $1,975 | $1,760 | $1,475 | $1,100 | $975 | $850 | $750 | $650 | $550 |

Note: Check federal laws on legality of 14 in. barrel. 70%-100% variations are almost never encountered in this model.

MODEL 94 SADDLE RING CARBINE—20 in. round barrel, deduct 10-20% for .30-30 and .32 Special cal.'s.

| $1,100 | $950 | $800 | $600 | $500 | $450 | $400 | $360 | $330 | $300 | $260 | $220 |

Without saddle ring—manufactured until 1940.

| $680 | $580 | $480 | $435 | $380 | $340 | $320 | $300 | $280 | $260 | $240 | $220 |

Post-War Carbine—1945-1964 mfg. without saddle ring.

| $450 | $395 | $375 | $350 | $325 | $310 | $290 | $270 | $250 | $230 | $210 | $190 |

.32-40, .32 Special, and .38-55 cal.'s will command premiums ($50-$100).

100%	98%	95%	90%	80%	70%	60%	50%	40%	30%	20%	10%

MODEL 1895 LEVER ACTION—.30-03, .30-06, .30-40 Krag, .303 Brit., .35 Win., .38-72, .40-72, .405 Win., .762 Russian cal.'s, 24-28 in. barrel, blued action, box mag., straight grip stock, 425,881 produced, manufactured from 1896-1931. Add 15% for .30-06 and .405 cal.'s.

| $2,050 | $1,375 | $1,100 | $935 | $825 | $675 | $575 | $475 | $400 | $350 | $290 | $250 |

The Model 1895 was a Browning design incorporating the first box type mag. in a lever action repeating rifle. A large Russian military contract was secured in 1915 with chambering for the 7.62mm Russian cartridge (over 293,000 manufactured or over 66% of total production). A very few were made with color case hardened frames (Winchesters last large frame rifle to have case colors) and are very rare and expensive.

Model 1895 Takedown Rifle—disassembles at breech.

Add 15% + premium.

MODEL 1895 RIFLE FLATSIDE—early model, distinguishable in that frame does not have fluting or ridge contouring, serial range approx. 1-5000.

| $2,750 | $2,000 | $1,800 | $1,600 | $1,375 | $1,100 | $905 | $785 | $670 | $560 | $450 | $350 |

MODEL 1895 CARBINE—.30-03, .30-06, and .303 Brit. cal.'s, 22 in. round barrel, one barrel band, with or without saddle ring, escalloped frame sides.

| $2,500 | $900 | $800 | $600 | $500 | $450 | $400 | $360 | $330 | $300 | $260 | $220 |

Model 1895 Government Carbine—with government markings.

| $2,800 | $1,650 | $1,400 | $1,200 | $995 | $825 | $700 | $575 | $450 | $360 | $330 | $300 |

MODEL 1895 FLATSIDE MUSKET—early models have serial range under 5000, no flutes on frame, .30-40 Krag only.

| $4,850 | $3,575 | $3,300 | $3,000 | $2,750 | $2,475 | $2,100 | $1,870 | $1,500 | $1,250 | $995 | $600 |

MODEL 1895 MUSKET—.30-03, .30-06, and .30-40 Krag cal.'s, 28 in. round barrel, two bands, hand guard over barrel, military sights.

| $2,400 | $1,200 | $995 | $825 | $700 | $575 | $450 | $360 | $330 | $300 | $260 | $220 |

U.S. GOVT. MODEL 1895 MUSKET—.30-40 Krag, "U.S." marked on frame.

| $2,650 | $1,400 | $1,200 | $995 | $825 | $700 | $575 | $450 | $360 | $330 | $300 | $260 |

U.S. ARMY NRA MUSKET 1895—same as Standard, with 30 in. barrel, 1901 Krag, rear sight. NRA approved for official NRA competition.

| $2,400 | $1,200 | $995 | $825 | $700 | $575 | $450 | $360 | $330 | $300 | $260 | $220 |

Also available in Models 1903 and 1906 which designated .30-30 and .30-06 cal.'s respectively.

MODEL 1895 RUSSIAN MUSKET—7.62mm Russian cal., over 293,000 produced for Imperial Russian Govt., manufactured 1915-1916, various Russian Ordnance stamps should be present.

| $2,100 | $950 | $800 | $600 | $500 | $450 | $400 | $360 | $330 | $300 | $260 | $220 |

MODEL 53 LEVER ACTION—.25-20, .32-20, and .44-40 cal.'s, 22 in. round barrel, ½ tube mag. holding 6 cartridges, blued finish, pistol grip or straight grip stock, 24,916 produced, manufactured between 1924-1932.

| $1,900 | $1,200 | $995 | $825 | $700 | $575 | $450 | $410 | $360 | $330 | $300 | $275 |

MODEL 53 TAKEDOWN RIFLE—magazine unscrews at frame allowing barrel to come apart at breech.

Add 5-15% premium.

MODEL 65 LEVER ACTION RIFLE—.218 Bee (introduced in 1939), .25-20, and .32-20 cal.'s, 22 in. round barrel (except 218 Bee 24 in.), ½ tube mag. holding 7 cartridges, blue with pistol grip stock, 5704 produced, manufactured between 1933-1947.

| $2,500 | $1,800 | $1,600 | $1,375 | $1,100 | $980 | $880 | $820 | $770 | $700 | $640 | $550 |

The Model 65 was a design evolving from the Model 53.

MODEL 55 LEVER ACTION RIFLE—.25-35, .30-30, and .32 Win. Spl. cal.'s, lever action designed, solid frame and takedown, 24 in. round barrel, shotgun style butt stock with checkered steel buttplate, tube mag., holds 3 cartridges, approx. 20,500 manufactured between 1924-1932. Serial numbered independently to approx. 2,865, then serialized with Model 1894 production on underside of receiver. Simply could not compete with the Model 1894.

| $1,295 | $750 | $680 | $580 | $480 | $435 | $380 | $340 | $310 | $285 | $250 | $225 |

100%	98%	95%	90%	80%	70%	60%	50%	40%	30%	20%	10%

MODEL 71 RIFLE STANDARD—.348 Win. cal., ⅔ tube mag. holding 4 cartridges, improved Model 1886 frame, blued metal with pistol grip stock, 20 or 24 in. barrel, 47,254 manufactured between 1935-1957.

$850	$700	$640	$600	$560	$520	$480	$440	$400	$360	$330	$300

Model 71 — 20 in. barrel—barrels mfg. during 1936-1937 only, model mfg. 1937-1947, very rare and desirable.

$3,600	$2,250	$2,000	$1,800	$1,600	$1,375	$1,100	$905	$785	$670	$560	$450

MODEL 71 RIFLE DELUXE—same as Standard, with higher grade wood and checkering.

$1,490	$900	$800	$750	$690	$640	$600	$560	$520	$480	$440	$400

MODEL 64 RIFLE—.219 Zipper, .25-35, .30-30, and .32 Win. Spl. cal.'s, 20, 24, or 26 in. round barrel, blued metal, pistol grip stock, 66,783 manufactured between 1933-1957 and 1972-1973 (over 8,250 manufactured in .30-30 cal. only these last two years with minor changes). Add 15% for .25-35 cal.

$1,050	$500	$460	$425	$395	$370	$350	$330	$310	$290	$270	$250

.219 Zipper.—manufactured 1938-1941 only.

$1,550	$990	$900	$800	$750	$690	$640	$600	$560	$520	$480	$440

The Model 64 was basically revamped Model 55.

RIFLES: SINGLE SHOT

MODEL 1885—most popular cal.'s available from .22-.50, falling block trigger guard activated action, John Browning's first high power single shot rifle design, many variations were made and we will list the standard types, over 139,725 manufactured between 1885-1920.

This design was originally manufactured as the Model 1878 by the Browning Brothers in Ogden, UT in the early 1880's. Fewer than 600 were made - see the Browning section for values.

Sporting Rifle Low Wall—28 in. round or octagon barrel, open sights, solid frame, standard trigger.

$2,250	$1,275	$1,000	$825	$700	$575	$450	$360	$315	$250	$175	$125

Sporting Rifle High Wall—30 in. barrel, standard trigger, open sights, solid frame. Available in various size and weight barrels numbered (in front of forearm) from numeric 1, 2, 3, 3½ (introduced 1910), 4, and 5, lightest to heaviest. Case hardened frames standard until 1901 when bluing became standard, three different frames depending on caliber. Heavier barrels in rare calibers will bring a premium.

$2,450	$1,475	$1,275	$1,000	$825	$700	$575	$450	$360	$315	$250	$215

Takedown frame — add 20%.

20 ga. High Wall Shotgun—chambered for 3 in., 26 in. full choke nickel steel barrel standard, receiver has matting on top. Also available with matted ribs (rare). Solid frame or takedown. Introduced in 1914.

$2,645	$1,675	$1,475	$1,275	$1,000	$825	$700	$575	$450	$385	$335	$300

Deluxe Grade High Wall—same as Standard, with fancy walnut and checkering.

$3,200	$2,100	$1,870	$1,650	$1,400	$1,200	$995	$825	$700	$575	$450	$400

Schuetzen Rifle—high wall, 30 in. octagon barrel, double set triggers, spur lever, aperture sight, Schuetzen style stock, adj. palm rest and buttplate.

$4,750	$3,500	$3,150	$2,675	$2,100	$1,870	$1,650	$1,400	$1,200	$995	$850	$725

POINT

Takedown frame — add 20%.

Winder Musket—low wall, 3rd model, .22 short or LR, 28 in. barrel, standard trigger and lever, military style stock and sights, grooved forearm, one barrel band.

$400	$370	$350	$330	$310	$290	$270	$250	$220	$190	$160	$130

Takedown frame — add 20%.

RIFLES: BOLT ACTION

MODEL 1883 (HOTCHKISS REPEATER)—.45-70 cal., designed by Benjamin D. Hotchkiss, unique tube mag. located in butt stock attached to receiver, up-turn/pull-back bolt action, 26 in. round or octagon standard on rifle. Over 84,000 manufactured between 1879-1889. Also available in carbine configuration (24 in. round barrel with one band), and musket (32 in. round barrel with cleaning rod and two barrel bands) — subtract 25%. Carbine extremely rare in Third Model (20 in. barrel).

100%	98%	95%	90%	80%	70%	60%	50%	40%	30%	20%	10%

First Style—approximately 6,419 manufactured with magazine cut off and safety control incorporated into one unit.

$1,100	$950	$800	$600	$500	$450	$400	$360	$330	$300	$260	$220

Second Style—approximately 16,102 manufactured, magazine cut off on right receiver top, safety on left side.

$950	$800	$600	$500	$450	$400	$360	$330	$300	$260	$220	$200

Third Style—most commonly encountered Hotchkiss, approximately 62,034 manufactured 1883-1899.

$880	$825	$575	$450	$400	$360	$330	$300	$260	$220	$200	$180

The Model 1883 Hotchkiss was the first bolt action designed for the U.S. military .45-70 cartridge. On the First and Second models inspect wood directly below bolt and left frame side for cracks, breaks or older repairs as it is frequently encountered on these early models with thin wrists.

LEE STRAIGHT PULL RIFLE—6mm Lee (.236 U.S.N. cal.), 5 shot non-detachable box mag., 24 (Sporting Rifle) or 28 (Musket) in. barrel, folding leaf sight, blue metal, military style full stock, manufactured 1897-1902, Navy Issue Model is the Musket with "236 U.S.N." on barrels. Approx. 20,000 manufactured (including 15,000 Muskets for the U.S. Navy military contract) between 1895-1902 with parts clean up occurring in 1916.

U.S.N. Military Musket

$880	$825	$575	$450	$400	$360	$330	$300	$260	$220	$200	$180

Lee Sporting Rifle—same as Musket, with 24 in. barrel, sporter style stock, approx. 1,700 made 1897-1902.

$950	$800	$600	$500	$450	$400	$360	$330	$300	$260	$220	$200

This design was originally patented by James Paris Lee and assigned to the Lee Arms Company. Winchester obtained manufacturing rights to produce this model for the U.S Navy military contract 1895-1902.

MODEL 1900 SINGLE SHOT—.22 S and L cal., 18 in. round barrel, blued metal, open sights, one piece straight grip stock without fitted buttplate, takedown, not serial numbered, approx. 105,000 manufactured between 1899-1902.

$400	$370	$350	$330	$310	$290	$270	$250	$220	$185	$140	$110

MODEL 1902 SINGLE SHOT—same as 1900, with minor improvements. Distinguishable by special shaped extended trigger guard. Not serial numbered. Approx. 640,299 manufactured between 1902-1931.

$175	$125	$110	$100	$90	$80	$70	$60	$55	$50	$45	$40

Chambering included .22 cal. Extra Long in 1914 (interchangeable with S&L).

THUMB TRIGGER MODEL 99—same as 1902, with button behind cocking piece used to fire with thumb instead of trigger, not serial numbered, approx. 75,433 were manufactured between 1904-1923.

$650	$575	$500	$400	$325	$290	$270	$250	$220	$185	$140	$110

MODEL 1904 SINGLE SHOT—improved version of 1902, 21 in. round barrel, chambering included .22 Extra Long in 1914, not serial numbered, approx. 302,859 manufactured between 1904-1931.

$175	$125	$110	$100	$90	$80	$70	$60	$55	$50	$45	$40

Model 1904-A—introduced in 1927 with new sear bar and chambered for .22 LR.

$200	$160	$125	$110	$100	$90	$80	$70	$60	$55	$50	$45

MODEL 43—.218 Bee, .22 Hornet, .25-20, .32-20 cal.'s, dubbed "Poor Man's Model 70", 24 in. round tapered barrel, box type mag., approx. 62,617 manufactured between 1949-1957. Add $50 for Special Grade, $50 for .22 Hornet cal.

$595	$520	$475	$440	$400	$360	$320	$290	$260	$240	$220	$200

Add 10% for Deluxe Model.

Grading	100%	98%	95%	90%	80%	70%	60%

ON MODELS 52, 54, 56, 57, 58, 59, 60, 60A, 67, 677, 68, 69, 69A, 697, AND 70 VALUES IN 50% OR LESS ORIGINAL CONDITION HAVE BEEN OMITTED SINCE VALUES IN THOSE CONDITIONS WILL APPROXIMATE THE 60% PRICE. THIS REFLECTS THE FACT THAT WHILE THESE LOWER CONDITION SPECIMENS ARE NOT AS DESIRABLE TO COLLECTORS, THEY ARE STILL SOUGHT AFTER AS SHOOTERS.

MODEL 52 TARGET—.22 LR cal., 5 shot mag., 28 in. standard barrel, target sights and target style stock, approx. 125,233 Model 52's in all variations were manufactured between 1919-1979.

	100%	98%	95%	90%	80%	70%	60%
	$440	$415	$375	$345	$315	$290	$265
With speedlock	$495	$470	$415	$375	$335	$310	$290

Model 52A Target—similar to Model 52, except has slow lock mechanism. Values are similar to above.

MODEL 52 HEAVY BARREL—same as Standard Target, with heavy barrel.

	$660	$605	$550	$525	$470	$415	$330

MODEL 52-B TARGET—extensively redesigned action, improved stock design, offered with a variety of sights, made 1935-1947.

	$605	$550	$495	$470	$415	$360	$305

MODEL 52-B HEAVY BARREL—same as 52-B, with heavy barrel.

	$660	$605	$550	$525	$470	$415	$330

MODEL 52-B BULL GUN—extra heavy weight barrel.

	$690	$635	$580	$550	$495	$440	$360

MODEL 52 SPORTER (SPORTING RIFLE)—24 in. round lightweight barrel with front sight cover, sporting type select walnut stock with cheekpiece, hard rubber pistol grip cap, black plastic tipped forearm, checkered steel buttplate, about 7¼ lbs., manufactured 1934-1958. The Models 52 and 52B are not generally factory drilled for scopes, as the receiver was specially designed for aperture rear sights, be cautious of "factory" drilled and tapped receivers on all model 52's.

Model 52—introduced in 1920, original slowlock time model changed to speedlock in 1929.

	$2,350	$1,875	$1,500	$1,400	$1,275	$1,150	$975

Model 52A—introduced in 1932, receiver and locking lug were strengthened.

	$2,350	$1,875	$1,500	$1,400	$1,275	$1,150	$950

Model 52B—introduced in 1935 with adj. sling swivel assembly and single shot adapter.

	$2,350	$1,700	$1,400	$1,200	$1,100	$1,000	$900

Model 52C—introduced in 1947 with adj. micro motion trigger.

	$2,500	$1,875	$1,500	$1,400	$1,275	$1,150	$950

MODEL 52-C TARGET—"Micro Motion" trigger and "Marksman" stock, otherwise same as 52-B, made 1947-1961.

	$700	$625	$550	$525	$470	$415	$330

MODEL 52-C STANDARD—same as Target, with standard sporter barrel.

	$625	$550	$490	$470	$415	$360	$305

MODEL 52-C BULL GUN—extra heavy barrel model of Target 52-C, made 1952-1961.

	$775	$675	$580	$550	$495	$440	$360

MODEL 52-D TARGET—improved version of 52-C with free floating barrel and adj. bedding device, made 1961-discontinued.

	$625	$550	$495	$440	$385	$360	$275

MODEL 52 INTERNATIONAL MATCH—same as 52-D, with free rifle stock, accessory rail and lead lapped barrel, made 1969-discontinued.

	$750	$675	$605	$550	$495	$470	$385

MODEL 52 INTERNATIONAL PRONE—similar International Match, with prone style stock, made 1975-discontinued.

	$750	$675	$605	$550	$495	$470	$385

Grading	100%	98%	95%	90%	80%	70%	60%

MODEL 54 HIGH POWER SPORTER—.270, 7 x 57mm, .30-30, .30-06 cal.'s, 5 shot mag., 24 in. barrel, open sights, checkered pistol grip stock, made 1925-1930. Approx. 50,145 Model 54's were manufactured in all variations between 1925-1936.

	$525	$450	$385	$330	$305	$275	$220

MODEL 54 CARBINE—introduced in 1927, same as Rifle, with 20 in. barrel, plain stock.

	$650	$550	$495	$440	$385	$360	$275

MODEL 54 IMPROVED SPORTER—.22 Hornet, .220 Swift, .250-3000, .257 Robts., .270, 7 x 57mm, .30-06 cal.'s, 5 shot mag., 24 or 26 in. barrel, one piece firing pin, checkered pistol grip stock, made 1930-1936.

	$525	$470	$415	$360	$330	$275	$220

MODEL 54 CARBINE IMPROVED—same as Rifle, with 20 in. barrel.

	$650	$575	$525	$470	$440	$385	$330

MODEL 54 SUPER GRADE—introduced in 1934, same as Sporter, with better wood and black forend tip and pistol grip cap.

	$700	$625	$550	$525	$495	$440	$385

Rare calibers will command considerable premiums (i.e. this variation in 7 x 57mm cal. will sell for $2,500 in mint condition).

MODEL 54 SPORTING SNIPER'S RIFLE—introduced in 1929, same as Sporter, with 26 in. heavy barrel, .30-06 only, aperture sight.

	$750	$660	$605	$580	$550	$495	$440

MODEL 54 NATIONAL MATCH—introduced in 1935, same as Standard, with Lyman sights and Marksman stock.

	$750	$660	$605	$580	$550	$495	$440

MODEL 56 SPORTER—.22 S or LR cal., 5 or 10 shot mag., 22 in. round barrel, open sights, plain pistol grip stock, approx. 8,297 manufactured between 1926-1929.

	$500	$425	$400	$350	$300	$250	$200

The .22 cal. Short was discontinued in 1929.

MODEL 57 TARGET—same as Model 56, with aperture sight and heavier target stock, approx. 18,600 were manufactured between 1926-1936.

	$475	$375	$300	$260	$220	$200	$180

MODEL 58 SINGLE SHOT—similar to Models 1902 and 1904, .22 LR cal., 18 in. round barrel, open sights, takedown, approx. 38,992 manufactured between 1928-1931.

	$250	$225	$200	$175	$150	$125	$120

MODEL 59 SINGLE SHOT—improved Model 58 with 23 in. round barrel and pistol grip stock with butt plate, approx. 9,200 manufactured between 1930-1931.

	$450	$425	$400	$350	$300	$250	$200

This model was discontinued due to lack of sales.

MODEL 60—improved Model 59, 23 in. round barrel increased to 27 in. in 1933, approx. 160,754 manufactured between 1930-1934.

	$175	$130	$95	$80	$70	$60	$50

MODEL 60A TARGET—similar to Model 60 with Lyman 55W aperture rear sight, heavier target stock, and 27 in. round tapered barrel, approx. 6,118 were manufactured between 1932-1939.

	$650	$525	$450	$375	$300	$260	$230

MODEL 64—.25-35 (rare), .30-30, .32 Win. Spl., or .219 Zipper (rare), revamped Model 55 action with increased mag. capacity, approx. 66,700 mfg. 1933-1957 and 1972-1973.

	$575	$475	$375	$300	$260	$230	$200

Deluxe Model

	$675	$525	$450	$375	$300	$260	$230

MODEL 67—.22 LR and .22 WRF (authorized in 1935) cal.'s, 20 in. (Junior Rifle), 24 (miniature target boring), and 27 in. (sporting or smooth bore) round barrels, same basic action as the Model 60, not serial numbered, approximately 383,000 manufactured between 1934-1963.

	$175	$130	$95	$80	$70	$60	$50

Grading	100%	98%	95%	90%	80%	70%	60%

MODEL 677—same basic specifications as Model 67, except no iron sights or sight cuts in barrel, not serial numbered. Approximately 2,240 manufactured between 1937-1939.

	100%	98%	95%	90%	80%	70%	60%
	$400	$350	$320	$250	$200	$150	$100
In .22 WRF cal. (rare)	$1,200	$1,000	$800	$600	$400	$300	$250

MODEL 68—.22 cal, bolt action single shot, similar to Model 67, walnut stock, approx. 100,000 manufactured between 1934-1946 no ser. no.'s on gun.

	100%	98%	95%	90%	80%	70%	60%
	$175	$130	$95	$80	$70	$60	$50

MODEL 69 & 69A—.22 LR and RF cal.'s, 5 or 10 shot repeater, 25 in. barrel, aperture or open rear sight, not serial numbered, approximately 355,000 manufactured between 1935-1963. Add $50 for Target version.

	100%	98%	95%	90%	80%	70%	60%
	$200	$150	$110	$95	$85	$75	$70

The Model 69 was cocked by the closing motion of the bolt, whereas the 69A was cocked by the opening motion of the bolt.

MODEL 697—same general specifications as the Model 69, except no iron sights or sight cuts in barrel and no ramp or sight cover. Telescope bases attached to barrel were standard.

	100%	98%	95%	90%	80%	70%	60%
	$175	$80	$70	$60	$55	$50	$45
.22 WRF cal.	$350	$320	$230	$180	$140	$120	$100

MODEL 70 STANDARD GRADE BOLT ACTION—.22 Hornet, .220 Swift, .243, .250-3000, .257 Robts., .264 Mag., .270, 7 x 57mm, 300 Sav., .30-06, .308, .300 Mag., 7.65, 338 Mag., 35 Rem., .358, 375 H&H, & 9mm, and .300 H&H cal.'s, 5 shot mag., 4 shot mag. on Magnums, 24, 25, and 26 in. barrels, open sights, checkered walnut pistol grip stock, made 1937-1963.

Values listed below assume original, unaltered specimens — modifications/alterations to either the metal or wood surfaces can reduce prices by large amounts.

Standard Calibers—.243, .270, .30-06, or .308.

	100%	98%	95%	90%	80%	70%	60%
	$775	$700	$625	$550	$425	$375	$350

Rarer Calibers

	100%	98%	95%	90%	80%	70%	60%
.22 Hornet or Swift	$925	$800	$750	$675	$550	$475	$400
.257 Roberts	$925	$800	$750	$675	$550	$475	$400
.300 Win. Mag.	$1,000	$895	$795	$740	$675	$550	$475
.338 Win. Mag.	$1,200	$1,000	$895	$795	$740	$675	$550
.375 H&H	$1,495	$1,250	$1,100	$995	$925	$850	$795
.250-3000 Savage	$1,750	$1,625	$1,500	$1,300	$1,100	$975	$850
7 x 57mm	$2,950	$2,600	$2,200	$1,800	$1,500	$1,300	$1,100

ADD APPROX. 80% FOR CARBINE VARIATIONS (MFG. 1936-1946 WITH 20 IN. BARREL IN .22 HORNET, .250-3000, .257 ROBERTS, .270, 7MM, and .30-06).

Rare cal.'s such as the .35 Rem., .300 Savage, and 9mm are seldomly encountered and their scarcity precludes accurate price determination.

MODEL 70 SUPER GRADE—same as Standard, with deluxe wood, black pistol grip cap and forend tip. Discontinued in 1960. A general rule for Super Grades is that if you add 80% to the standard grade in similar calibers, values should be rather close. For large cal.'s, values are listed below.

	100%	98%	95%	90%	80%	70%	60%
.375 H&H	$2,750	$2,350	$1,950	$1,675	$1,450	$1,200	$1,000
.458 Win. Mag.	$3,200	$2,900	$2,500	$2,200	$1,995	$1,750	$1,650

MODEL 70 FEATHERWEIGHT—lightened version of Standard, .243, .264 Mag., .270, .308, .30-06, .358 cal.'s, 22 in. barrel, aluminum trigger guard and floorplate, made 1952-1963.

Standard Calibers—.243, .30-06, .270, or .308

	100%	98%	95%	90%	80%	70%	60%
	$825	$740	$675	$550	$475	$425	$395

Other Calibers

	100%	98%	95%	90%	80%	70%	60%
.264 Mag.	$925	$795	$740	$675	$550	$475	$400
.358 Mag.	$1,595	$1,250	$1,000	$895	$775	$650	$525

ADD 100% FOR SUPER GRADE MODELS IN THE FEATHERWEIGHT.

MODEL 70 NATIONAL MATCH—same as Standard, with target stock and scope bases, .30-06 only. Discontinued 1960.

	100%	98%	95%	90%	80%	70%	60%
	$1,100	$825	$770	$715	$660	$550	$525

Grading	100%	98%	95%	90%	80%	70%	60%

MODEL 70 TARGET—same as 70 Standard, in .243 and .30-06 cal.'s, 24 in. medium weight barrel and target stock. Discontinued in 1963.

| | $1,100 | $825 | $770 | $715 | $660 | $550 | $525 |

MODEL 70 BULL GUN—same as Standard Model 70, with 28 in. heavy barrel, .300 H & H and .30-06 cal.'s only.

| | $1,750 | $1,400 | $1,000 | $800 | $660 | $550 | $525 |

MODEL 70 VARMINT—same as Standard Model 70, in .220 Swift and .243 cal.'s, 26 in. heavy barrel, scope bases, varmint style stock, made 1956-1963.

| | $900 | $770 | $715 | $605 | $550 | $440 | $385 |

MODEL 70 WESTERNER—same as Standard Model 70, with 26 in. barrel, .264 Win. Mag.

| | $900 | $825 | $770 | $660 | $550 | $440 | $375 |

MODEL 70 ALASKAN—same as Standard Model 70, in .338 Win. Mag. and .375 H&H Mag. cal.'s, 25 in. barrel, recoil pad, made 1960-1963.

| | $1,450 | $1,250 | $995 | $825 | $715 | $605 | $495 |

MODEL 72—.22 LR and Gallery Model (.22 short only), tube mag., bolt action, 25 in. round, tapered barrel, not serial numbered, over 161,000 manufactured between 1938-1959.

| | $225 | $180 | $160 | $140 | $115 | $100 | $90 |

MODEL 75 TARGET—.22 LR, 5 or 10 shot mag., 28 in. barrel, target sights, slight variation used by Government in WWII, about 88,715 Model 75 Target and Model 75's were manufactured between 1938-1958.

| | $500 | $450 | $400 | $370 | $330 | $275 | $200 |

MODEL 75 SPORTER—same as Target except 24 in. barrel, non-target sights and select checkered walnut.

| | $625 | $550 | $500 | $450 | $375 | $300 | $270 |

RIFLES: DISCONTINED SEMI-AUTO

ON MODELS 1903, 1905, 1907, 1910, 55, 63, 74, AND 77 VALUES IN 50% OR LESS ORIGINAL CONDITION HAVE BEEN OMITTED SINCE VALUES IN THOSE CONDITIONS WILL APPROXIMATE THE 60% PRICE. THIS REFLECTS THE FACT THAT WHILE THESE LOWER CONDITION SPECIMENS ARE NOT AS DESIRABLE TO COLLECTORS, THEY TEND TO BOTTOM OUT AT THE 60% PRICE.

MODEL 1903—.22 Win. Auto rimfire, 10 shot tube mag., 20 in. round barrel, open sights, straight grip stock cut out for partial magazine filling, approx. 126,000 manufactured 1903-1932.

| | $625 | $500 | $400 | $300 | $265 | $215 | $175 |

First U.S. semi-auto rifle designed for .22 rimfire cartridges.

MODEL 1905—.32 Win. and .35 Win. cal.'s, 5 or 10 shot box mag., 22 in. round barrel, open sights, plain pistol grip stock, approx. 29,113 manufactured between 1905-1920.

| | $650 | $550 | $425 | $350 | $275 | $200 | $175 |

MODEL 1907—.351 Win., 5 or 10 shot box mag., 20 in. round barrel, open sights, plain pistol grip stock, an improved version of the Model 1905, approx. 58,490 manufactured between 1907-1957.

| | $450 | $375 | $330 | $305 | $250 | $195 | $140 |

MODEL 1910—.401 Win., 4 shot box mag., 20 in. barrel, open sight, plain pistol grip stock, made 1910-1936, 20,786 manufactured.

| | $600 | $500 | $400 | $350 | $275 | $220 | $165 |

Add 10-15% for Fancy Sporting Rifle (special checkered walnut).

MODEL 55—.22 cal. only, top loading single shot, bottom ejection, 22 in. round barrel, open sporting sights, not serial numbered, over 45,000 manufactured between 1958-1961.

| | $275 | $225 | $175 | $140 | $120 | $100 | $80 |

WINCHESTER, cont.

Grading	100%	98%	95%	90%	80%	70%	60%

MODEL 63—.22 LR, styling similar to Model 1903, 10 shot tube mag., 20 (discontinued in 1936) or 23 in. barrel, open sights, plain pistol grip stock, approximately 174,692 manufactured between 1933-1958.

	100%	98%	95%	90%	80%	70%	60%
	$575	$480	$435	$370	$330	$290	$235

Add 50%-100% for 20 in barrel depending on condition.

The Model 63 was introduced to take advantage of the new .22 LR cartridge, which the older Model 1903 couldn't chamber. Add a slight premium for grooved receiver variation.

MODEL 74—.22 rimfire, tubular mag. in stock, pop-out bolt assembly, approximately 406,574 manufactured between 1939-1955. Distinguishable by squared off rear receiver.

	$200	$175	$150	$120	$100	$85	$75

MODEL 77—.22 rimfire, detachable box mag. or tubular mag. under barrel. Over 217,000 manufactured between 1955-1962. Add $15 for tubular mag.

	$150	$125	$100	$85	$75	$60	$50

RIFLES: DISCONTINUED SLIDE ACTION

100%	98%	95%	90%	80%	70%	60%	50%	40%	30%	20%	10%

MODEL 1890 SLIDE ACTION—.22 S, L, LR, or WRF rimfire, cal.'s were non-interchangeable, visible hammer, solid-frame (first 15,000) or takedown, 24 in. octagonal barrel, case hardened receivers until 1901. Made from 1890 until 1932, approx. 849,000 manufactured.

Blued Finish—post 1901 manufacture.
Add 20% premium for .22 LR cal.

100%	98%	95%	90%	80%	70%	60%	50%	40%	30%	20%	10%
$1,200	$775	$600	$495	$450	$400	$360	$330	$300	$260	$220	$195

Color casehardened receiver—discontinued in 1901, takedown feature was added in 1892 after over 15,000 solid frames had been made.

100%	98%	95%	90%	80%	70%	60%	50%	40%	30%	20%	10%
$3,600	$2,750	$2,100	$1,700	$1,000	$675	$495	$390	$350	$300	$275	$250

Deluxe models or solid frames will bring premiums over values listed above. There were also a limited amount of guns mfg. with stainless steel barrels which will add to values of post-1901 mfg.

The Model 1890 was Winchester's first slide action repeating rifle. It replaced the Model 1873 .22 cal. It was an excellent and inexpensive .22 rifle that rapidly became the universal firearm used in shooting galleries. Even though production reached approx. 849,000 units, most guns were heavily used and specimens existing today in 98% + condition are rare.

MODEL 1906—.22 S, L, or LR, 20 in. round barrel, tube mag., visible hammer, open sights, straight stock with shotgun butt plate, approximately 848,000 manufactured between 1906-1932.

100%	98%	95%	90%	80%	70%	60%	50%	40%	30%	20%	10%
$1,000	$800	$600	$495	$450	$400	$360	$330	$300	$260	$210	$165

Grading	100%	98%	95%	90%	80%	70%	60%

MODEL 61 HAMMERLESS—.22 S, L, or LR, 24 in. round or octagonal barrel, tube mag., open sights, plain grip stock, approximately 342,000 manufactured between 1932-1963.

	$500	$420	$375	$330	$300	$250	$225

Pre-war manufacture has small forearm. Add 15% for single caliber barrel marking. Pre-war octagon barrel in S or L cal.'s will command a 100% premium. "WRF" marked round barrel is rare - front of receiver must be marked "W.R.F.".

MODEL 61 MAGNUM—same as Standard 61, but chambered for .22 Win. Mag., made 1960-1963.

	$550	$450	$400	$350	$300	$250	$225

591

Grading	100%	98%	95%	90%	80%	70%	60%

MODEL 62 — 62A VISIBLE HAMMER—modern version of 1890, 23 in. round tappered barrel, over 409,000 made between 1932-1958.

	$425	$395	$360	$330	$250	$195	$165

Pre-war model is 62, distinguishable by small forearm. Add 30% for pre-war. The Model 62-A was introduced in 1940 at serial number 99,200 with minor changes. Model 62A single cal. barrel markings do not add premiums. Gallery variations of these models will command a large premium.

RIFLES: LEVER ACTION - POST 1964 MFG.

MODEL 94 STANDARD RIFLE—lever action, .30-30, 7-30 Water (new in 1989), or .44 Mag. (mfg. in 1984 and 1985 only) cal.'s, 6 or 7 (24 in. barrel only) shot tube mag., 20 or 24 (mfg. 1987-88 only) in. round barrel, open sights, straight walnut stock, barrel band on forearm, made 1964-present. Angled ejection became standard in 1982, 6½ lbs. Add $16 for .44 Mag. cal. (disc.in 1986).

Mfg.'s Sug. Retail $283 $230 $200 $180 $165 $150 $140 $135
Add $15 for 24 in. barrel.

Model 94 Deluxe—similar to Standard Rifle, except has checkered walnut stock and forearm. New in 1988.

Mfg.'s Sug. Retail $299 $240 $205 $160 $145 $135 $120 $105
Add $43 for 1.5 - 4.5x scope with low mounts.

Model 94 Ranger—.30-30 only, 20 in. barrel, uncheckered hardwood stock and forearm, 5 shot mag., 6½ lbs. New for 1985.

Mfg.'s Sug. Retail $251 $210 $180 $160 $150 $140 $130 $120
Also available with mounted scope - add $36.

Win-Tuff Rifle—similar to Model 94 Rifle, except has laminated hardwood stock and forearm with checkering. New in 1987.

Mfg.'s Sug. Retail $299 $240 $205 $160 $145 $135 $120 $105

MODEL 94 XTR—.30-30 and 7-30 Waters (new in 1985) cal.'s, 20 or 24 (7-30 Waters only) in. barrel, checkered select walnut, hooded front sight (except 7-30 Waters which has dovetailed front blade), 6½ lbs. Disc. in 1988.

	$260	$225	$205	$185	$160	$150	$140

For 7-30 Waters cal. rifle - add $26.

Last Mfg.'s Sug. Retail was $285.

Model 94 XTR Deluxe—.30-30 cal. only, deluxe American walnut stock and lengthened forearm with fancy checkering, 20 in. barrel with deluxe script, rubber butt pad. Mfg. 1987-1988 only.

	$370	$310	$270	$235	$210	$190	$160

Last Mfg.'s Sug. Retail was $426.

MODEL 94 TRAPPER—.30-30, .45 Colt (new in 1985), or .44 Mag./Spl. cal.'s, 16 in. barrel, walnut stock, 5 or 9 round tube mag., case colored receiver, dovetailed front sight, 6 lbs.

Mfg.'s Sug. Retail $283 $245 $210 $180 $160 $150 $140 $130
Add $16 for .45 Colt or .44 Mag. cal.'s.

The .44 Mag. cal. was introduced in 1985.

MODEL 94 .44 MAG. S.R.C.—.44 Mag., top eject, 20 in. barrel, SRC, mfg. late 60's.

	$325	$275	$250	$225	$200	$175	$150

MODEL 94 CLASSIC SERIES—.30-30 cal., 20 or 26 in. barrel, approx. 47,000 mfg. 1967-70.

	$275	$225	$200	$185	$160	$150	$140

MODEL 94 ANTIQUE CARBINE—same as Standard, with scroll on receiver, case hardened, gold-plated saddle ring, made 1964-1983.

	$250	$225	$200	$175	$160	$150	$140

MODEL 94 WRANGLER—.32 Win. Special, top ejection, only 7,947 made. Discontinued.

	$350	$310	$270	$235	$210	$190	$160

Grading	100%	98%	95%	90%	80%	70%	60%

MODEL 94 WRANGLER II—.32 Win. Special (disc. in 1984) or .38-55 Win. cal.'s, angle ejection, 16 in. barrel, oversized hoop-shaped lever, roll-engraved receiver, 5 shot mag., 6⅛ lbs. Made 1983-1985 only.

	$245	$220	$200	$185	$165	$150	$140

Last Mfg.'s Sug. Retail was $275.

MODEL 94 XTR BIG BORE—.307, .356, or .375 (disc. in 1987) Win. cal.'s, angled ejection port provides scope mounting, walnut Monte Carlo stock with recoil pad, 20 in. barrel, 6 round mag., 6½ lbs., sling swivels. New in 1983.

Mfg.'s Sug. Retail	$299	$250	$205	$190	$175	$160	$150	$140

Also mfg. in a top eject (pre-USRA).

MODEL 9422 XTR STANDARD—.22 LR or Mag., takedown, 20½ in. round barrel, 15 round (LR) mag., checkered straight grip, high gloss walnut stock and forearm, 6¼ lbs., 1972-present.

Mfg.'s Sug. Retail	$323	$275	$235	$210	$190	$175	$160	$145

.22 Mag. cal.

Mfg.'s Sug. Retail	$331	$280	$245	$220	$200	$180	$170	$160

This model is also available with a satin finished pistol grip, uncheckered walnut stock and forearm. New in 1988.

Model 9422 Win-Cam—similar to 9422 XTR Standard, except has greenish laminated hardwood stock and forearm. New in 1987.

Mfg.'s Sug. Retail	$342	$285	$240	$210	$190	$175	$160	$145

Model 9422 Win-Tuff—.22 LR or .22 Mag., laminated brown hardwood stock and forearm with wraparound checkering. New in 1988.

Mfg.'s Sug. Retail	$335	$280	$240	$210	$190	$175	$160	$145

Add $10 for .22 Mag. cal.

MODEL 9422 XTR CLASSIC—same general specifications as Model 9422 XTR Standard, except has 22½ in. barrel and non-checkered, satin finished, pistol grip walnut stock and extended forearm, stock also has fluted comb with crescent steel butt plate, curved finger lever, 6½ lbs. Mfg. 1985-1987.

	$285	$255	$230	$205	$185	$175	$160

Last Mfg.'s Sug. Retail was $301.

MODEL 64 1972-1974 MODEL—.30-30, lever action, 5 shot, ⅔ tube mag., 24 in. barrel, open sight, plain pistol grip stock, made 1972-1974.

	$220	$195	$165	$140	$110	$90	$70

RIFLES: BOLT ACTION - POST 1964 MFG.

MODEL 52D BOLT ACTION TARGET RIFLE—.22 LR, single shot, free floating standard or heavy barrel, scope bases, target stock with palm stop, made 1961-1980. Total production on all variations is approximately 125,233.

	$435	$415	$385	$360	$305	$275	$220

MODEL 52 INTERNATIONAL MATCH—similar to 52-D Heavy Barrel, with special free rifle stock, hooked butt.

	$495	$470	$440	$415	$330	$305	$250

MODEL 52 INTERNATIONAL PRONE—similar to 52-D, with prone stock, removable roll over cheekpiece, made 1975-1980.

	$495	$470	$440	$415	$330	$305	$250

MODEL 70 STANDARD—.22-250, .222, .225, .242, .270, .308, and .30-06 cal.'s, 5 shot, 22 in. barrel, open sight, Monte Carlo stock, swivels, made 1972-1980.

	$350	$330	$310	$285	$220	$200	$175

MODEL 70 XTR FEATHERWEIGHT—.22-250, .223 Rem., .243 Win., .257 Robts. (disc.), .270 Win., .280 Rem., 7mm Mauser (disc.), .30-06, or .308 cal., bolt action, both short and medium action, 5 round mag., 22 in. barrel, checkered walnut stock, no sights, around 6½ lbs. New in 1981.

Mfg.'s Sug. Retail	$472	$390	$355	$325	$300	$280	$260	$240

In 1981 during U.S.R.A. takeover transition guns were built distinguishable by the U.S.R.A. trademark on the recoil pad. Some collectors will pay a premium for Win. marked pads. Cal.'s .257 Robts and 7mm Mauser were discontinued in 1985.

Grading	100%	98%	95%	90%	80%	70%	60%

Model 70 XTR Win-Cam Featherweight (Lightweight)—.270 Win. or .30-06 cal., greenish laminated hardwood stock with checkering, 22 in. barrel. New in 1987.

Mfg.'s Sug. Retail	$442	$375	$325	$300	$280	$260	$240	$220

This model was redesignated Lightweight in 1989.

MODEL 70 XTR EUROPEAN FEATHERWEIGHT—6.5 x 55 Swedish Mauser cal., 22 in. barrel, 5 shot mag., rifle sights, 6¾ lbs. Made in 1986 only.

	$390	$365	$330	$305	$280	$260	$240

Last Mfg.'s Sug. Retail was $460.

MODEL 70 50TH ANNIVERSARY MODEL—.300 Win. Mag., 24 in. barrel, deluxe walnut stock, engraving and special motifs on metal surfaces, serial numbered 50 ANV 1 - 50 ANV 500, 7¾ lbs. 500 mfg. in 1987 only.

	$1,000	$840	$725

Last Mfg.'s Sug. Retail was $939.

MODEL 70 CUSTOM GRADE—various cal.'s, old style Model 70 action, semi-fancy American walnut checkered stock, engine turned bolt and follower, hand honed internal parts. New in 1988.

Mfg.'s Sug. Retail	$1,172	$1,172	$900	$750

MODEL 70 EXHIBITION GRADE—various cal.'s, fancy checkered American walnut stock with hardwood forend tip. New in 1988.

Mfg.'s Sug. Retail	$2,192	$2,192	$1,600	$1,000

MODEL 70 XTR FEATHERWEIGHT ULTRA GRADE—.270 Win., bolt action, extensively engraved, finely checkered deluxe French walnut, with mahogany presentation case.

	$1,875	$1,200	$950

Last Mfg.'s Sug. Retail was $5,000.

MODEL 70 LIGHTWEIGHT CARBINE—.22-250, .223 Rem., .243 Win., .250 Savage (new in 1986), .308 Win., .270 Win., and .30-06 cal.'s, bolt action, 5 round mag., both short and medium action, 20 in. barrel, checkered walnut stock, no sights, around 6 lbs. Mfg. 1984-86. Add $15 for open sights.

	$355	$320	$285	$255	$230	$210	$190

Last Mfg.'s Sug. Retail was $395.

MODEL 70 LIGHTWEIGHT RIFLE—.22-250, .223 Rem., .243 Win., .270 Win., .280 Rem. (new in 1988), .30-06, or .308 Win. cal., 22 in. barrel, checkered walnut stock, no sights, 6½ lbs. New in 1987.

Mfg.'s Sug. Retail	$430	$370	$315	$285	$255	$230	$210	$190

Model 70 Win-Tuff Lightweight Rifle—.22-250 (new in 1988), .223 (new in 1989), .243 Win. (new in 1988), .270 Win. .30-06 or .308 Win. (new in 1989) cal., similar to Model 70 Lightweight Rifle, except has laminated brown hardwood stock with checkering. New in 1987.

Mfg.'s Sug. Retail	$442	$375	$320	$290	$260	$230	$210	$190

Model 70 Win-Tuff Featherweight Rifle—similar to Model 70 Lightweight Rifle, except has wraparound, checkered stock with Schnabel forend, pistol grip cap,. Not available in .22-250 cal. New in 1988.

Mfg.'s Sug. Retail	$476	$400	$340	$310	$275	$250	$230	$210

MODEL 70 XTR SPORTER—.22-250 (new in 1989), .223 (new in 1989), .243 (new in 1989), .25-06 Rem. (mfg. 1985-87), .270 Win., .300 H&H (new in 1989), .270 Wby. Mag. (new in 1989), .300 Wby. Mag. (new in 1989), .30-06 or .308 Win. (new in 1986) cal.'s, 24 in. barrel, 5 round mag., custom Sporter styling, Monte Carlo cheekpiece, detachable sling swivels, 7¾ lbs. Add $15 for iron sights.

Mfg.'s Sug. Retail	$472	$400	$350	$315	$295	$275	$255	$235

MODEL 70 XTR SPORTER MAGNUM—same general specifications as standard Sporter, 7mm Mag., .264 Mag., .270 Wby. Mag. (new in 1988), .300 Wby. Mag., .300 Win. Mag., and .338 Mag. cal.'s, reinforced stock, 3 round mag., 24 in. barrel, 7¾ lbs., made 1972-present. Add $14 for rifle sights.

Mfg.'s Sug. Retail	$451	$390	$345	$315	$295	$275	$255	$235

Grading	100%	98%	95%	90%	80%	70%	60%

Model 70 XTR Super Express Mag.—.375 H&H and .458 Win. Mag. cal.'s, 3 round mag., 22 or 24 in. (.375 H&H only) barrel, 8½ lbs.

Mfg.'s Sug. Retail	$792	$690	$575	$525	$495	$460	$430	$400

MODEL 70 XTR VARMINT—same general specifications as standard Sporter, .22-250, .223, and .243 Win. cal.'s, 24 in. heavy barrel, no sights, 5 shot mag., target scope bases, 7¾ lbs., made 1972-present.

Mfg.'s Sug. Retail	$482	$410	$350	$315	$295	$280	$260	$240

MODEL 70 WINLIGHT—.270, .280 Rem. (new in 1987), .30-06, 7mm Rem. Mag., and .338 Win. Mag. cal.'s, fiberglass stock, thermoplastic receiver bedding, blued metal parts, 22 or 24 (Mag. cal.'s only) in. barrel, 3 or 4 shot mag., no sights, about 6½ lbs. New in 1986.

Mfg.'s Sug. Retail	$637	$555	$490	$440	$395	$350	$310	$280

RANGER RIFLE—.270 Win., .30-06, and 7mm Rem. Mag. (discontinued in 1985) cal.'s, bolt action, 22 or 24 in. barrel, 3 (7mm Rem. Mag.) or 4 round mag., plain hardwood stock with no checkering, open sights, 7⅛ lbs.

Mfg.'s Sug. Retail	$387	$310	$260	$215	$200	$180	$165	$155

RANGER YOUTH CARBINE—.223 Rem. or .243 Win. cal., 20 in. barrel, 4 or 5 (.223 Rem.) shot mag., youth hardwood stock dimensions, 5¾ lbs.

Mfg.'s Sug. Retail	$396	$320	$270	$215	$185	$170	$160	$150

MODEL 70 DELUXE—.243, .270, .30-06, and .300 Win. Mag. cal.'s, 22 in. barrel, open sight, hand checkered, black forend tip, became standard in 1972, made 1964-1971.

		$400	$340	$320	$285	$220	$180	$140

MODEL 70 TARGET RIFLE 1964-1971—.308 and .30-06 cal.'s, 24 in. heavy barrel, no sights, target bases, heavy target style stock with hand stop, made 1972-discontinued.

		$630	$550	$495	$440	$360	$330	$275

MODEL 70 INTERNATIONAL ARMY MATCH 1971—.308 cal., 5 shot, 24 in. heavy barrel, no sights, adj.rigger, ISU stock with forearm, accessory rail, adj. butt, made 1973-discontinued.

		$715	$660	$605	$550	$470	$440	$385

MODEL 70 MANNLICHER 1969-1971—.243, .270, .30-06, or .308 Win. cal., 19 in. barrel, open sight, full length Monte Carlo stock with steel forend cap. Discontinued in 1972.

		$550	$440	$385	$360	$305	$275	$250

MODEL 70A—economy version of 1972 type Model 70, same cal.'s, no hinged floorplate or forend tip, made 1972-1978.

			$325	$285	$265	$230	$200	$165	$140

MODEL 70A MAGNUM—same as Standard in Mag. cal.'s, not .375 H&H or .458, made 1972-1978.

			$340	$310	$275	$250	$220	$195	$165

MODEL 670 BOLT ACTION RIFLE—another economy version of the model 70, .225, .243, .270, .308, and .30-06 cal.'s, 22 in. barrel, open sights, no hinged floorplate, pistol grip stock, made 1967-1973.

			$300	$250	$220	$195	$175	$165	$140

MODEL 670 CARBINE—same as 670, with 19 in. barrel, not available in .308, made 1967-1970.

			$300	$250	$220	$195	$175	$165	$140

MODEL 670 MAGNUM—same as 670, with reinforced stock, .264 Mag., 7mm Mag., and .300 Win. Mag. cal.'s, made 1967-1970.

			$330	$275	$255	$220	$205	$195	$165

MODEL 770 BOLT ACTION—.22-250, .222, .243, .270, and .30-30 cal.'s, 22 in. barrel, open sights, no floorplate or forend tip, made 1969-1971.

			$325	$285	$275	$260	$250	$220	$195

MODEL 770 MAGNUM—same as Standard, in .264 Mag., 7mm Mag., and .300 Win. Mag. cal.'s, recoil pad, made 1969-1971.

			$350	$310	$285	$275	$265	$250	$220

Grading	100%	98%	95%	90%	80%	70%	60%

MODEL 88 LEVER ACTION CARBINE—.243, .284, and .308 cal.'s, 19 in. barrel, pistol gripped, one piece stock, barrel band, made 1968-1973.

.308 cal.

	100%	98%	95%	90%	80%	70%	60%
	$500	$400	$300	$250	$225	$200	$175

For .243 cal. — add 25%.

For .284 cal. — add 50-75%.

MODEL 88 RIFLE—.243, .284, .308, and .358 cal.'s, 22 in. barrel, basket weave checkering, no barrel band, almost 284,000 made 1955-1973.

	100%	98%	95%	90%	80%	70%	60%
.308 cal.	$375	$325	$300	$250	$225	$200	$175
.243 cal.	$450	$380	$350	$325	$275	$250	$225

Pre-1964 production — add $50.

.284 cal.	$700	$585	$500	$450	$400	$300	$200

Pre-1964 production — add 50%.

.358 cal.	$850	$775	$700	$500	$400	$300	$250

Available between 1956-1962 only.

MODEL 100 AUTOLOADING RIFLE—.243, .284, and .308 cal.'s, 4 shot detachable mag., open sights, gas operated, one piece basket weave stock, pistol grip cap, over 262,000 made 1961-1973.

	100%	98%	95%	90%	80%	70%	60%
	$375	$320	$285	$265	$240	$220	$200

Pre-1964 production

For .243 cal. — add $25.

For .284 cal. — add $50.

MODEL 100 CARBINE—same as rifle, with 19 in. barrel, plain pistol grip stock, barrel band, made 1967-1973.

	100%	98%	95%	90%	80%	70%	60%
	$475	$375	$300	$260	$235	$215	$200

For .243 cal. — add $25.

For .284 cal. — add $50.

MODEL 121 SINGLE SHOT RIFLE—.22 rimfire, bolt action, 20¾ in. barrel, open sights, plain pistol grip stock, made 1967-1973.

	100%	98%	95%	90%	80%	70%	60%
	$115	$85	$70	$55	$45	$35	$30

MODEL 121Y SINGLE SHOT RIFLE—same as 121, with shorter stock.

	$115	$85	$70	$55	$45	$35	$30

MODEL 121 DELUXE—same as 121, with ramp front sight and sling swivels.

	$125	$90	$75	$60	$50	$40	$35

MODEL 131 REPEATING RIFLE—.22 rimfire, bolt action, 7 shot, 20¾ in. barrel, plain Monte Carlo stock, made 1967-1973.

	$135	$100	$85	$70	$60	$50	$40

MODEL 141 REPEATER—same as 131, with tube mag. in butt stock, made 1967-1973.

	$135	$100	$90	$75	$65	$55	$45

MODEL 310 SINGLE SHOT—.22 rimfire, bolt action, 22 in. barrel, open sights, checkered pistol grip stock, swivels, made 1972-1975.

	$200	$175	$140	$100	$80	$70	$60

MODEL 320 REPEATING RIFLE—same as 310, with 5 shot clip, made 1972-1974.

	$375	$325	$275	$225	$165	$140	$100

MODEL 250 LEVER ACTION—.22 rimfire, 20½ in. barrel, tube mag., hammerless, checkered pistol grip stock made 1963-1973.

	$110	$95	$70	$60	$50	$40	$30

MODEL 255—same as 250, in .22 WMR, made 1964-1970.

	$135	$115	$90	$70	$60	$50	$40

MODEL 250 DELUXE—same as 250, with select wood and sling swivels, made 1965-1971.

	$150	$125	$90	$75	$60	$50	$45

MODEL 255 DELUXE—.22 WMR, with select wood and swivels, made 1965-1973.

	$175	$140	$110	$90	$80	$70	$60

Grading	100%	98%	95%	90%	80%	70%	60%

MODEL 270 SLIDE ACTION—.22 rimfire, tube mag., 20½ in. barrel, checkered pistol grip stock, made 1963-1973.

	100%	98%	95%	90%	80%	70%	60%
	$115	$90	$75	$60	$50	$40	$35

Plastic stock version

	$85	$75	$50	$40	$30	$20	

MODEL 275—same as 270, in .22 WMR.

	$135	$110	$100	$90	$80	$70	$65

MODEL 270 DELUXE—same as 270, with select wood, Monte Carlo stock, made 1965-1973.

	$135	$110	$90	$80	$70	$60	$50

MODEL 275 DELUXE—same as 270 Deluxe, in .22 WMR.

	$165	$140	$110	$90	$80	$70	$60

MODEL 290 DELUXE RIFLE—same as 290, with select Monte Carlo stock, made 1965-1973.

	$135	$115	$100	$90	$75	$65	$55

MODEL 490 AUTOLOADING RIFLE—.22 rimfire, 5 shot clip mag., 22 in. barrel, folding sight, checkered one piece stock, made 1975-1980.

	$250	$215	$185	$155	$145	$130	$110

DOUBLE RIFLE—.30-06, 7x65R, 9.3x74R, .257 Roberts, or .270 Win. cal., 23½ in. O&U barrels, iron sights with claw scope mounts, ejectors, fully engraved satin finish receiver, walnut specially hand checkered, sling swivels, 8½ lbs. Discontinued in 1986.

	$1,750	$1,495	$1,250	$1,125	$1,000	$875	$750

Last Mfg.'s Sug. Retail was $2,995.

SHOTGUNS: 1879-1964

ON MODELS BREECHLOADING, 1887, 1893, 1897, 1901, 1911, AND 36 VALUES IN 50% OR LESS ORIGINAL CONDITION HAVE BEEN OMITTED SINCE VALUES IN THOSE CONDITIONS WILL APPROXIMATE THE 60% PRICE. THIS REFLECTS THE FACT THAT WHILE THESE LOWER CONDITION SPECIMENS ARE NOT AS DESIRABLE TO COLLECTORS, THEY TEND TO BOTTOM OUT AT THE 60% PRICE.

BREECH LOADING SXS—10 or 12 ga., imported from England for sales through the Winchester New York City office only, exposed hammers, available in 5 grades ranging from Class D - Class A and Match gun (lowest to highest). Higher grades were manufactured by W.C. Scott & Sons, about 10,000 were imported between 1879-1884. Prices vary greatly due to condition and grade. Prices can range from $300 (poor condition Class D) to over $4,000 (95% + condition specimen in Class A or Match gun).

This side by side model was the first shotgun bearing the Winchester name sold in the U.S. Identifiable by "Winchester Repeating Arms Co., New Haven, Connecticut, U.S.A." marking on barrel rib top.

MODEL 1887 LEVER ACTION—10 and 12 ga.'s, 4 shot tube mag., 30 and 32 in. full choke barrels, plain pistol grip stock, first Browning patent shotgun manufactured by Winchester, made 1887-1901 with approximately 64,855 produced.

	$900	$750	$600	$575	$500	$425	$375

Standard frame finish on this model was color case hardening. Premiums exist for original bright case colored specimens. 10 ga. began production with serial number 22148. Also manufactured in Riot configuration (20 in. cylinder bore barrel). Gauges were chambered for 2⅝ in. (12 ga.) and 2⅞ in. (10 ga.). First lever action repeating shotgun domestically manufactured.

Model 1887 Deluxe—damascus barrel, checkered stock, and other special order features.

	$1,350	$1,100	$850	$700	$600	$500	$450

MODEL 1893 SLIDE ACTION—12 ga., 30 (standard) and 32 in. barrel, black powder only. First Winchester shotgun with sliding forearm action, first Browning slide action patent, discontinued 1897 after run of some 34,050. Note: chambered for 2⅝ shells only, damascus barrels were available at extra cost, as were fancy stocks.

	$850	$600	$425	$350	$300	$225	$175

This gun had limited sales because mechanical weaknesses developed when shooting smokeless powder.

Grading	100%	98%	95%	90%	80%	70%	60%

MODEL 1897 SLIDE ACTION—12 and 16 ga.'s (introduced in 1900), improved Model 1893 action, 26-32 in. barrels, visible hammer, various chokes, takedown or solid frame, plain pistol grip stock, made 1897-1957, over 1,024,700 manufactured.

	$675	$400	$325	$275	$240	$200	$175

First Winchester shotgun chambered for 2¾ in. smokeless ammunition.

MODEL 1897 RIOT GUN—same as Standard, with 20 in. cylinder bore barrel, 12 ga. only, made 1898-1935.

	$600	$475	$450	$400	$375	$300	$200

MODEL 1897 TRENCH GUN—same as Riot Gun, with hand guard and bayonet, issued for U.S. Army for trench warfare in WWI, also manufactured post-WWI, manufactured 1916-1935.

	$675	$575	$525	$480	$450	$425	$400

MODEL 1897 TRAP—higher grade version of Standard, sometimes encountered with special order ebony diamond inlay in stock pistol grip. Manufactured 1897-1931.

	$750	$700	$660	$480	$385	$330	$275

MODEL 1897 PIGEON—higher grade version of Standard 97. Manufactured 1897-1939.

	$990	$880	$770	$495	$440	$385	$330

MODEL 1901—10 ga. only, strengthened Model 1887 action to accept smokeless powder, lever action, standard barrel 32 in., blued barrel and frame, 5 shot mag., manufactured between 1901-1920, 13,500 manufactured starting with serial number 64,856. Fancy grade - add 25%.

	$1,300	$950	$750	$600	$500	$450	$400

This shotgun was chambered for 2⅞ in. smokeless powder ammunition.

MODEL 1911 AUTOLOADER—12 ga., recoil operated, 26 or 28 in. barrel, various chokes, pistol grip laminated birch stock, made 1911-1925, 82,774 produced, action had design problems.

	$500	$375	$300	$250	$195	$165	$110

The Model 1911 was Winchester's first semi-auto shotgun. It did not prove to be satisfactory partly because the design had to be exclusive of the patents for Browning's famous A-5 model, interestingly enough a design which Winchester originally had helped Browning patent.

MODEL 36 SINGLE SHOT—9mm long shot, short shot, and ball, 18 in. round barrel, single shot bolt action, guns were not serial numbered, one piece plain stock and forearm, special shaped trigger guard, 2¾ lbs. appx. 20,000 mfg. between 1920-1927.

	$350	$250	$200	$175	$150	$125	$100

MODEL 12 STANDARD SLIDE ACTION—12, 16, 20, and 28 ga.'s, 26-32 in. barrels, 6 shot, various chokes, hammerless, plain pistol grip walnut stock, 1912-1976.

The following add-ons do not apply to the 28 ga.

    Add $100 if in original unremarked box (N.I.B. only).

    Add $75 for Win. special VR (offset barrel proofmark).

    Add $150 for Win. solid rib.

    Add 75% for Win. milled VR.

    Extra barrel(s) — add 50% of specimens value/set.

Special order features on field guns have captured much collector interest in recent years. Combinations of these features can add a considerable percentage to the base values listed below. Rare special orders on rare variations are very desirable and prices can double and more if the combination is right.

GAUGE CAN BE DETERMINED BY REMOVING THE BUTT STOCK AND OBSERVING THE GAUGE MARKING ON THE STOCK SCREW BOSS.

12 ga.

	$550	$475	$395	$360	$330	$295	$250

16 ga.

	$525	$450	$375	$340	$310	$275	$250

20 ga.

	$725	$625	$525	$450	$395	$375	$350

Grading	100%	98%	95%	90%	80%	70%	60%

28 ga.

	$3,500	$3,200	$2,750	$2,450	$2,000	$1,750	$1,500

Subtract 40% if with factory Cutts compensator.

In the past several years many non-original, re-stamped barrels have been added to 16 or 20 ga. frames "creating" a more desirable (and expensive) gun to unsuspecting buyers. Roll die markings are getting better and better so be very cautious when considering a non-Cutts 28 ga. (as in get a receipt specifying originality).

Note: The Model 12 Winchester was produced continuously, from 1912-1980. Over 2,027,500 were produced both in standard and deluxe (Pigeon) grades. Pigeon grades were first listed in 1914 and discontinued during the war (1941). Reintroduced in 1948, they were discontinued permanently in 1964, after which the Super Pigeon Grade became available only on a custom order basis from Winchester's Custom Gun Shop. These guns are worth 50-300% premiums depending on guage, barrel lengths, stock options, engraving patterns, etc. With an attrition rate of 33%, Model 12's with rare features 50 years ago will only be much rarer today (and expensive). 28 ga. guns were built between 1934 and 1960. Gauge rarity in increasing order is 12 ga, 16 ga, 20 ga, .410 (Model 42), and 28 ga. Serialization breakdown by year of manufacture is provided under the "Model Serialization" section of this book. When collecting Model 12's, ser. no.'s on the underside of receiver (forward end), should match ser. no. on bottom rear of Mag. tube. Stainless steel barrel Model 12's were mostly manufactured in the late 1920's. Values typically range between $1,000-$2,500.

"Y" prefix appears on Model 12's built 1964-1980 — see listing under Post-64 Models.

MODEL 12 FEATHERWEIGHT—same as Standard, with alloy guard, made 1959-1962. "F" suffix after ser. no.

	$475	$400	$350	$275	$250	$200	$175

MODEL 12 RIOT GUN—12 ga., 20 in. cylinder bore barrel, made 1918-1963.

	$450	$395	$350	$300	$250	$225	$200

MODEL 12 MILITARY TRENCH GUN—12 ga., vent hand guard on barrel, bayonet lug, takedown or solid frame, must have parkerized finish and flaming bomb proofs on frame and barrel. Discontinued.

	$700	$625	$550	$500	$450	$375	$300

Note: barrel must not be drilled for front bead sight.

MODEL 12 HEAVY DUCK GUN—12 ga., 3 in. chamber, 30 or 32 in. barrel, solid rubber recoil pad, ½ in. shorter pull than regular Model 12, manufactured 1935-1963.

	$675	$525	$450	$400	$350	$325	$300

Solid rib — add 40%.

Vent. rib—2 different styles manufactured by Simons, notice barrel proof marking - rare. 32 in. barrel — add 15%.

MODEL 12 SKEET GUN—12, 16, 20, and 28 ga.'s, 26 in. barrel, skeet choke, checkered pistol grip stock, pre-WWII. 1933-1976.

	$850	$750	$700	$600	$550	$500	$450

Solid rib — add 25%.
Win. Special VR — add $75.
Win. milled VR — add $175.
Factory-Cutts compensator — subtract 50%.
16 gauge — rarity will command a premium.
20 gauge — add 20%.
28 gauge — add 400%.

MODEL 12 TRAP GUN—various ga.'s, full choke barrel, deluxe trap styled stock, solid recoil pad, manufactured 1938-1964.

	$895	$795	$695	$650	$500	$435	$400

Add $100 for white or brown plastic Hydrocoil stock. While plain barrelled variation is rare, it is not as desirable.

MODEL 12 PIGEON GRADE—finer and more deluxe version of Model 12, all variations, manufactured 1914-1941 and 1948-1964, usually with engraved pigeon on bottom rear of mag. tube. Add $500 or more if N.I.B.

	$1,900	$1,500	$1,175	$850	$800	$775	$700

Vent rib — add $150.

MODEL 20—.410 bore, hammer, boxlock, 26 in. full choke, 6 pounds. Made 1919-1924, 23,616 manufactured.

	$400	$300	$250	$175	$140	$110	$85

Winchester Junior Trap Shooting Outfit—includes shotgun, midget hand trap, 150 .410 ga. shells, 100 clay targets and accessories, cased.

	$600	$475	$400	$365	$330	$295	$250

MODEL 21

Approximately 35,000 manufactured since 1931.

The Winchester Model 21 is a boxlock side by side double barrelled shotgun. After years in the design stage, production began in 1929 with guns being shipped to the warehouse in 1930 and first offered in Winchester's 1931 price list. Regular production continued for thirty years, through 1959.

The early guns were plain, standard 12 gauge models with double triggers and extractors. Later in 1931, 16 and 20 gauge chamberings became available as did selective single triggers and automatic ejectors.

By the end of 1933 the Model 21 skeet gun had been introduced as had Tournament, Trap and Custom Built grades. By about this time options included fancier wood, beavertail or semi-beavertail fore-ends, checkered butts (standard on skeet guns) skeleton or solid steel butt plates, recoil pads and almost any variation the customers might desire. Metal finishes on a Model 21 are unusual in that they have salt blued frames and rust blued barrels — this explains the difference in coloration between these metal surfaces.

The Tournament Grade was dropped in 1936 and the Trap Grade in 1940. A Standard Grade Trap Gun was added in 1941. The early Custom Built Grade was dropped in 1942 and the Deluxe Grade was added. This grade included as standard many of the previously available extra cost options.

Relatively few guns were produced in chamberings smaller than 20 gauge. 28 gauge first appeared in the 1936 catalog, although a few were probably produced before that. Winchester records are unclear as to the total but it is generally believed that fewer than 200 original factory guns were made. In addition, a number of original 20 gauge guns have been modified at the factory or elsewhere with factory 28 gauge barrels. These latter guns are of considerably less value to most collectors than the original factory guns. Authenticity of the original guns should be established by factory letter.

.410 bore guns were first listed in 1955 but again some had been produced earlier, one having been built for John Olin in 1950. Throughout Winchester history all the rules seem to have had exceptions and nowhere is this more apparent than with respect to the Model 21 which, after all, has been pretty much a custom gun from the very beginning. Factory records and tallies among dealers indicate the existence of from 40 to 50 original factory guns. As in the case of the 28 gauge, extra barrels were available and at least some of those have been added to original 20 gauge guns.

The 3 inch Magnum 12 gauge Duck gun (stamped "Duck" on floor plate) was offered in Winchester catalogs from 1940 through 1952. Selective single triggers and automatic ejectors were standard as were the solid red Winchester recoil pads and 30" or 32" barrels. Some cases of non-factory upgrading of 2¾ or 3 inch Magnum guns have been reported. If authenticity is important to the buyer, a factory letter should be requested.

With respect to such letters, in cases where records may be missing or incomplete, the resultant letters may be less conclusive than desired. In some instances, consultation with, or a written appraisal from an authoritative collector arms dealer might be helpful.

Six standard patterns of engraving and several stock checkering and carving styles evolved during the production years. Values added by these and other embellishments such as precious metal inlays are beyond the scope of this work.

Grading	100%	98%	95%	90%	80%	70%	60%

The following retail prices are for a standard field gun with average wood, beavertail forearm, ejectors, and single selective trigger with no alterations.

12 ga.

	100%	98%	95%	90%	80%	70%	60%
	$2,500	$2,175	$1,900	$1,750	$1,650	$1,550	$1,400

16 ga.

	100%	98%	95%	90%	80%	70%	60%
	$3,500	$3,150	$2,675	$2,350	$2,125	$1,950	$1,850

20 ga.

	100%	98%	95%	90%	80%	70%	60%
	$3,750	$3,250	$2,750	$2,450	$2,125	$1,950	$1,850

Add $400-$550 for VR.

Double triggers w/extractors — deduct approx. 33%.

If double triggers with ejectors, subtract 15%-25%. Normally DT, extractor guns have splinter forearms.

Skeet Gun—available in Standard, Tournament, and Trap grades, introduced in 1933, add 20-50% depending on grade.

Trap Gun—introduced in 1940, Trap Grade discontinued same year, unaltered specimens will bring premium — add 10-25%.

3 Inch Duck Gun—introduced in 1940, must be so stamped(observe the 3 in. marking very carefully — add 20% or more.

As can be seen, values are partly based on a certain interdependence between options. A vent rib, for example, would have much less value on plain extractor barrels. Higher grade guns, of course, will bring somewhat higher prices although much of their increased value results from many "options" being included as standard features.

Buyers or sellers with limited experience should always seek expert advice or appraisals in dealing with a Model 21. This is especially true with regard to higher grade guns and those with extra ornamentation.

.410 BORE:

Retail prices for original guns may be expected to range between $20,000 and $35,000 for mechanically sound guns depending on quality of finish. These prices take into consideration the reported sale of a plain standard gun in recent years for $34,500. Non-original guns with add-on factory barrels would probably be reduced by half.

28 GAUGE:

Factory original guns will probably bring from $7,500 to $12,000 and, as with the 410's, 20 gauge guns modified to 28 gauge with factory barrels would be worth about 50% less.

Refinishing or Restoration: There is disagreement as to the effects of refinishing a Model 21. Many shooters and at least some collectors prefer a well refinished gun to a badly worn one. Higher grade guns restored by a master craftsman may approach factory original guns in value.

MODEL 21: CURRENT PRODUCTION—since 1960 Model 21 production has been limited to high grade, built from special order, U. S. Repeating Arms currently offers the Model 21 in 12, 16 or 20 ga.

Standard Custom guns (12 ga.) are currently trading in the $5,750 range if NIB.

Custom Built—standard model with no engraving.
Mfg.'s Sug. Retail $8,100 $8,100 $5,000 $3,750

Custom Grade—includes No. 6 engraved reciever and vent rib.
Mfg.'s Sug. Retail $11,080 $11,080 $7,250 $5,500

Grand American Grade—includes 2 sets of barrels with forearms, No. 6 engraved with gold inlays, cased.
Mfg.'s Sug. Retail $22,745 $22,745 $15,000 $11,500

Grand American Small Gauge—28 or .410 ga.
Mfg.'s Sug. Retail $34,460 $34,460 $25,000 $17,500
Add 10% for 28/.410 ga. combo.

Grading	100%	98%	95%	90%	80%	70%	60%

MODEL 24 DOUBLE-BARREL—12, 16, and 20 ga.'s, boxlock, hammerless, double triggers. Introduced in 1940, discontinued in 1957 after about 116,280 produced. Add 10% for 20 ga.

	$595	$525	$475	$400	$325	$250	$190

MODEL 25 SLIDE ACTION—12 ga. only, non-takedown version of the Model 12, 26 or 28 in. barrel, made 1949-1954, 87,937 manufactured.

	$450	$375	$350	$275	$250	$200	$175

MODEL 37 SINGLE-SHOT—12, 16, 20, 28 and .410 ga.'s, .410 bore, top-lever break-open action. Made 1936-1963. Not serial-numbered. Over 1,015,000 manufactured.

	$150	$125	$105	$85	$75	$55	$50

Add 30-300% for rare gauges, "Red Letter" models will bring 10% + premiums. Subtract 10-15% for post-64 models. 28 ga. is most desirable.

MODEL 40 SEMI-AUTO—12 ga. only, long recoil action, 28 or 30 in. barrel, walnut stock, skeet model also, poorly designed, many recalled by Winchester, made 1940-1941, around 12,000 made.

	$650	$495	$425	$350	$300	$275	$250

MODEL 42 SLIDE ACTION—the first pump specifically made for the .410 ga., hammerless, 2½ (introduced in 1935) or 3 in. chamber, 26 or 28 in. barrel, plain walnut pistol grip stock with circular grooved forearm (modified in 1947). Manufactured from 1933-1963. About 160,000 produced.

Special order features on field guns have captured much collector interest in recent years. Combinations of these features can add a considerable percentage to the base values listed below. Rare special orders on rare variations are very desirable and prices can double and more if the combination is right.

Standard Grade

	$775	$625	$525	$460	$420	$375	$330

Add 75% for solid rib.

Skeet or Trap Grade—has solid matted rib, fancy wood.

	$1,650	$1,450	$1,350	$1,100	$1,000	$900	$800

Deluxe Grade—fanciest grade, value is affected by wood and finish. Factory special orders can bring prices up to $10,000.

	$1,850	$1,650	$1,600	$1,500	$1,400	$1,200	$1,000

Factory vent rib barrels were never made available on the Model 42. Older catalogs list the Winchester special vent rib which were ribs installed by Simmons.

MODEL 50 SEMI-AUTO—12 or 20 ga., 3 shot, recoil-operated (non-recoiling barrel), 26-30 in. barrels, vent rib optional, feather weight model introduced 1958, all steel construction, made 1954-1961 with over 196,000 manufactured starting with serial number 1,000.

	$425	$360	$295	$280	$265	$240	$220

Vent rib (Simmons installed) — add $50.
20 ga. — add $50.
Trap & Skeet Model — add 15%.
Pigeon Grade — add 200-350%.

MODEL 59 SEMI-AUTO—12 ga. only, 3 shot, short recoil operation, Win-lite (steel and fiberglass) ribless barrels, 26-30 in. barrel lengths, alloy receiver inscribed with hunting scenes, Versalite (first interchangeable choke tubes) option introduced 1961, 6½ lbs., made 1960-1965, 82,085 manufactured.

	$525	$460	$420	$370	$340	$310	$260

Inspect carefully for either cracked receiver (by bolt handle cutout), or separating fiberglass on end of barrel.

Pigeon Grade—manufactured 1962-1965, add 200-350% (rare).

Winchester also manufactured 20 and 14 ga.'s experimentally in this model, extremely rare and expensive.

Grading	100%	98%	95%	90%	80%	70%	60%

SHOTGUNS: POST-1964

MODEL 370 SINGLE BARREL—12, 16, 20, 28 and .410 ga.'s, 28-32 in. full choke plain barrel, replaced the Model 37, top lever break open, exposed hammer, plain pistol grip stock, made 1968-1973. Approx. 221,578 manufactured. Add 20-60%+ for .28 ga. and .410 ga.

| | $120 | $100 | $90 | $85 | $80 | $75 | $70 |

The Model 370 was manufactured in Winchester's Canadian plant in Cobourg, Ontario.

MODEL 370 YOUTH—same as 370, with 26 in. barrel, 12½ in. stock, with recoil pad.

| | $145 | $110 | $95 | $85 | $80 | $75 | $70 |

MODEL 37A SINGLE BARREL—replaced the Model 370, roll engraved receiver, gold trigger, approximately 391,168 manufactured between 1973-1980 in the Winchester plant in Cobourg, Ontario.

| | $140 | $110 | $95 | $85 | $75 | $65 | $55 |

36 in. goose barrel — add 10%.
For 28 ga. or .410 ga. — add 20-60%.

MODEL 37A YOUTH—same as 37A, except 20 ga. only with 12½ in. pull stock.

| | $100 | $85 | $70 | $55 | $40 | $30 | $20 |

MODEL 12 SUPER PIGEON GRADE—12 ga., slide action, 26, 28, or 30 in. barrel, vent rib, any choke, hand honed action, engine turned breech block and loading flap, "B" checkering and No. 5 engraving, custom order grade walnut stock, limited production between 1964-1972.

| | $2,995 | $2,500 | $2,250 | $2,100 | $1,750 | $1,500 | $1,300 |

An additional 380 Super Pigeon Grades were manufactured in 1984-85.

MODEL 12 FIELD GRADE—12 ga., slide action, 26, 28, or 30 in. vent rib barrel, various chokes, jeweled bolt, hand checkered, checkered select walnut stock, made 1972-1976, "Y" Serial No. Prefix.

| | $675 | $550 | $525 | $495 | $450 | $400 | $350 |

In 1984 Y series Model 12's were once again available through a private contract with U.S.R.A. Co. which included engraving on Grades 1A-1C, and 2-5. These guns were available in either Field, Trap, or Skeet configurations. Since there was no manufacturers' suggested retail, Model 12 values shown below are established by analyzing the sales of the two private contractors - no more of these variations are available.

Grades 1-A, 1-B, & 1-C—light engraving depicting dogs or ducks. Discontinued.

| | $1,300 | $1,195 | $1,000 | $875 | $785 | $695 | $600 |

Last Mfg.'s Sug. Retail was $1,375.

Grades 2 & 3—engraving features large duck and dog game scenes on receiver flats. Discontinued.

| | $1,600 | $1,495 | $1,295 | $1,075 | $950 | $830 | $725 |

Last Mfg.'s Sug. Retail was $1,695.

Grade 4—more elaborate game scene engraving than Grades 2 & 3. Discontinued.

| | $1,850 | $1,695 | $1,450 | $1,225 | $1,075 | $950 | $850 |

Last Mfg.'s Sug. Retail was $1,995.

Grade 5—elaborate game scene engraving with style B checkering. Discontinued.

| | $2,195 | $1,995 | $1,725 | $1,500 | $1,225 | $1,095 | $950 |

Also available with gold inlays - add $1,000 to values shown above. Last Mfg.'s Sug. Retail was $2,450.

3 Barrel Set—grade 5 engraving with gold inlays and two extra barrels. Discontinued.

| | $5,500 | $4,995 | $4,350 | $3,750 | $3,325 | $2,750 | $2,300 |

Last Mfg.'s Sug. Retail was $6,000.

MODEL 12 SKEET GRADE—same as Field Grade, with 26 in. vent rib skeet bore barrel, skeet style stock, with recoil pad, made 1972-1975.

| | $725 | $575 | $525 | $495 | $450 | $425 | $350 |

See listings under Model 12 Field Grade for engraved values.

Grading	100%	98%	95%	90%	80%	70%	60%

MODEL 12 TRAP GRADE—same as Field grade, with 30 in. vent rib full choke barrel, trap style stock, straight or Monte Carlo, recoil pad, made 1972-1980.

	$675	$550	$525	$495	$450	$400	$350

See listings under Model 12 Field Grade for engraved values.

MODEL 1200 SLIDE ACTION FIELD GRADE—12, 16, and 20 ga.'s, 26, 28, or 30 in. barrel, alloy receiver, various chokes, checkered pistol grip stock, pad, made 1964-1981.

	$220	$200	$180	$165	$140	$110	$100
Vent rib	$240	$220	$205	$195	$165	$140	$110
Win. choke	$260	$240	$215	$200	$190	$180	$160

For Hydro-coil recoil system — add 33%.

MODEL 1200 MAGNUM—same as 1200, chambered for 12 and 20 ga., 3 in. magnum shells, made 1964-1980.

	$230	$200	$175	$165	$140	$110	$100
Vent rib	$275	$225	$200	$185	$150	$140	$110

MODEL 1200 SKEET GUN—same as 1200, 12 and 20 ga., 26 in. vent rib barrel, skeet bore, 2 shot mag. and select style stock, made 1965-1974.

		$300	$275	$250	$220	$195	$165	$140

MODEL 1200 TRAP GUN—same as 1200, with 12 ga., vent rib, 30 in. full choke barrel, select trap style stock, made 1965-1974.

	$300	$275	$250	$220	$195	$165	$140
Winchoke	$360	$330	$305	$275	$250	$220	$165

MODEL 1200 DEER GUN—same as 1200, with 22 in. barrel, rifle sights, 12 ga. only, made 1965-1974.

	$220	$195	$165	$140	$110	$100	$85

MODEL 1300 XTR SLIDE ACTION—12 and 20 ga.'s, 3 in. chamber, takedown, 5 shot, plain or vent rib., Winchoke tubes, walnut stock, alloy frame, 1978-present.

Mfg.'s Sug. Retail	$338	$285	$260	$230	$195	$175	$160	$145

Subtract $30 without vent rib.
Add $6 for Youth Model (new in 1989).

MODEL 1300 FEATHERWEIGHT—12 and 20 ga., 3 in. chamber, 22 in. barrel, Winchoked, checkered walnut stock and grooved forearm, roll-engraved, recoil pad, 6⅜ lbs. Mfg. 1984-1988 only.

	$275	$260	$230	$195	$175	$160	$145

Last Mfg.'s Sug. Retail was $324.

MODEL 1300 WATERFOWL—12 ga. only, 3 in. chamber, 30 in. vent rib barrel, matte finished metal, low luster walnut stock and forearm, roll-engraved, recoil pad, Winchokes standard, 7 lbs. New in 1984.

Mfg.'s Sug. Retail	$338	$285	$265	$235	$200	$180	$165	$150

Add $11 for Win-Tuff laminate stock (new in 1988).

MODEL 1300 TURKEY GUN—12 ga. only, 3 in. chamber, 22 in. vent rib barrel, Winchoked, walnut stock and forearm with low luster finish, metal surfaces have matte finish, supplied with camouflaged fabric sling, 6⅜ lbs. Mfg. 1985-1988 only.

	$290	$265	$235	$200	$180	$165	$150

Last Mfg.'s Sug. Retail was $348.

Model 1300 Win-Cam Turkey Gun—similar to Model 1300 Turkey Gun, except has greenish laminated hardwood stock and forearm. New in 1987.

Mfg.'s Sug. Retail	$368	$310	$280	$245	$200	$180	$165	$150

Add $19 for Win-Tuff camo stock.

MODEL 1300 COMBO PACK WIN-CAM—12 ga., supplied with 22 and 30 in. VR non-glare finished barrels, greenish laminated hardwood stock and forearm, camo sling, matte finished metal. Mfg. 1987-1988 only.

	$360	$320	$290	$260	$230	$200	$185

Last Mfg.'s Sug. Retail was $425.

Grading	100%	98%	95%	90%	80%	70%	60%

MODEL 1300 DEER GUN—12 ga. only, 22 in. rifle barrel with iron sights, checkered stock and forearm, satin finish. New in 1988.

Mfg.'s Sug. Retail	$367	$310	$285	$240	$200	$180	$165	$150

Add $11 for laminate stock.
Subtract $40 for smooth bore (new in 1989).

MODEL 1300 RANGER SLIDE ACTION—12 and 20 ga.'s, 3 in. chamber, 24⅛ (deer barrel), 28 or 30 in. barrel, alloy receiver. New in 1983. Subtract $18 without VR, add $14 for Winchokes.

Mfg.'s Sug. Retail	$261	$215	$175	$150	$135	$120	$110	$ 95

This model is also available in a deer combination package which includes a deer and regular Winchoke barrel in either 12 or 20 ga. — add 25% to values listed above.

Ranger Youth Model—20 ga. only, 3 in. chamber, 22 in. barrel, youth stock dimensions - 13 in. length of pull.

Mfg.'s Sug. Retail	$257	$210	$185	$155	$135	$125	$110	$100

Add $31 for Winchoke and vent rib.

MODEL 1300 STAINLESS SECURITY—12 and 20 ga., available in Police, Marine, and Defender variations, 18 in. barrel, 7 or 8 shot mag., 5½ - 7 lbs. Add $150 for pistol grip stock.

Mfg.'s Sug. Retail	$244	$205	$175	$150			

MODEL 1400 SEMI-AUTO—12, 16, and 20 ga.'s, 26, 28, or 30 in. barrels, alloy receiver, various chokes, gas operated, checkered pistol grip stock, made 1964-1981.

	$275	$250	$220	$200	$175	$155	$140
Vent rib	$315	$265	$240	$220	$195	$165	$150

For Hydro-coil recoil system — add 33%.

NEW MODEL 1400 WALNUT SEMI-AUTO—12 or 20 ga., 2¾ in. chamber, 22 or 28 (12 ga. only) in. VR barrel, checkered walnut stock and barrel, Winchokes standard, rotary bolt system, 7-7½ lbs. New in 1989.

Mfg.'s Sug. Retail	$399	$340	$300	$275	$250	$225	$195	$165

MODEL 1400 SKEET GRADE—same as 1400, in 12 and 20 ga.'s, with 26 in. vent rib barrel, skeet bore, select skeet style stock, made 1965-1973.

	$360	$330	$305	$275	$220	$195	$165

MODEL 1400 TRAP GRADE—same as 1400, with 30 in. full choke vent rib barrel, select trap style stock, made 1965-1973.

	$360	$330	$305	$275	$220	$195	$165

MODEL 1400 DEER GUN—same as 1400, with 22 in. barrel, rifle sights, 12 ga. only, made 1965-1974.

	$265	$240	$220	$200	$175	$165	$140

Note: In 1968 the model 1400 series was modified. The action release was improved and the checkering redesigned. From 1968-1972, they were designated MKII, which was then dropped. The values for the later guns made from 1968-1973 may run approximately 10% higher; values shown are for guns made from 1965-1968.

MODEL 1500 XTR SEMI-AUTO—12 and 20 ga.'s, 2¾ inch only, 28 inch barrel, plain or vent rib, Winchoke tubes, gas operation, made 1978-1982.

	$300	$260	$240	$220	$200	$180	$160

MODEL 1400 RANGER SEMI-AUTO—12 and 20 ga.'s, gas operation, alloy receiver, 28 in. Winchoke barrel, new in 1983, vent rib became standard in 1985, 7¼ lbs. Add $70 for deer combination (includes 24⅛ in. deer and regular Winchoke barrels).

Mfg.'s Sug. Retail	$333	$265	$225	$200	$180	$160	$140	$120

SUPER X MODEL 1 SEMI-AUTO—12 ga., 26, 28, and 30 in. vent rib barrel, various chokes, steel receiver, gas operated - self compensating, checkered pistol grip stock and forearm, made 1974-1981.

	$395	$365	$345	$315	$295	$275	$240

SUPER X MODEL 1 SKEET—same as Standard, with 26 in. skeet bore barrel, select skeet style stock, made 1974-1981.

	$440	$425	$400	$385	$330	$305	$275

Grading	100%	98%	95%	90%	80%	70%	60%

SUPER X MODEL 1 TRAP—same as Standard, with 30 in. barrel, imp. mod. or full choke, select trap style stock.

	$385	$360	$335	$310	$275	$250	$225

SUPER X MODEL 1 CUSTOM TRAP OR SKEET—12 ga. only, limited production from the Custom Shop, deluxe checkered walnut stock and forearm, extensive scroll engraving on receiver, built to custom order. New in 1987.

Mfg.'s Sug. Retail **$1,295 $1,295 $850 $650**

Add $700 for factory gold inlays (8 flying ducks).

SHOTGUNS: RECENT MANUFACTURE OVER AND UNDER

In November of 1987 Olin/Winchester discontinued the Model 101. Classic Doubles (listed separately in this text) is now importing this model under their own trademark.

MODEL 101 FIELD GRADE O/U—12, 20, and .410 ga.'s, 26, 28, and 30 in. barrels, various chokes, boxlock, auto ejectors, SST, engraved receiver, checkered American walnut pistol grip stock, made 1963-present. Values below assume Winchokes (standard since 1983) - subtract $60 if without.

Older production—checkered walnut stock and forearm, ejectors, SST, blued metal with light engraving on receiver.

	$725	$640	$595	$550	$500	$475	$440

Add 40% for 28 ga.

Add 55% for .410 ga.

Field Special—12 or 20 ga., 3 in. chambers, vent rib, 27 in. barrels with Winchokes, blued receiver with scroll engraving ejectors, 7 lbs. Discontinued in 1987.

	$995	$840	$775	$695	$600	$500	$450

Last Mfg.'s Sug. Retail was $1,185.

Lightweight Field—12 or 20 ga., similar to regular Field Grade, except has coin finished receiver, vent barrels, and solid rubber recoil pad, 6½ - 7 lbs. Discontinued in 1987.

	$1,285	$1,030	$965	$895	$800	$700	$600

Last Mfg.'s Sug. Retail was $1,425.

Waterfowl Model—12 ga. only, 3 in. chambers, 30 or 32(disc.) in. Winchoked barrels, vent rib, matte blued receiver with moderate engraving, low gloss walnut stock with vent recoil pad, 7 ¾ lbs. Disc. in 1987.

	$1,410	$1,175	$995	$895	$800	$700	$600

Last Mfg.'s Sug. Retail was $1,570.

Model 101 Field Grade 2 Barrel Hunting Set—12 and 20 ga. barrels, both with Winchokes, 26 in. barrels - 20 ga., 28 in. barrels - 12 ga., scroll engraved, blued receiver with game scene engraving and borders, cased, mfg. 1984-1987.

	$2,020	$1,825	$1,550	$1,375	$1,220	$1,050	$975

Last Mfg.'s Sug. Retail was $2,345.

Quail Special—12, 20 (disc.in 1984), 28 (new in 1987) and .410 (new in 1987) ga 's, 25½ in. Winchoke barrels, 6¾ lbs. - 12 ga., straight grip stock, vent barrels and rib, coin finished receiver with game scene engraving. Imported 1984-1987.

	$1,475	$1,245	$1,100	$1,000	$900	$825	$750

Add $120 for 28 or .410 ga.

Last Mfg.'s Sug. Retail was $1,950.

National Wild Turkey Federation Commemorative—only 300 mfg.

	$1,350	$1,100	$950				

American Flyer Live Bird—12 ga. only, 28 or 29½ (new in 1988) in. separated barrels with special competition VR, blued frame with gold wire borders and pigeon inlay, 8 - 8½ lbs. Imported 1987 only.

	$2,595	$2,275	$1,950	$1,775	$1,600	$1,425	$1,300

Add $925 for Combo Model (extra set of 29½ in. barrels).

Add $265 for 29½ in. barrel with WT4 choke tubes.

Last Mfg.'s Sug. Retail was $2,910.

Grading	100%	98%	95%	90%	80%	70%	60%

MODEL 101 MAGNUM O/U—same as 101 Field, in 12 and 20 ga.'s, 3 in. Mag. chambering, recoil pad, 30 in. barrels, full and mod., or full and full choke, made 1966-1981.

	$775	$715	$660	$605	$550	$500	$460

MODEL 101 SKEET GRADE—same as 101 Field, with 26 in. skeet bored barrels, skeet style stock, made 1966-1984.

	$1,000	$825	$770	$700	$650	$595	$540

MODEL 101 THREE GAUGE SKEET SET—same as Skeet 101, with 20 and 28 ga.'s, and .410 barrels, cased, made 1974-1984.

	$1,980	$1,650	$1,430	$1,320	$1,100	$935	$825

MODEL 101 TRAP GRADE—12 ga. only, 30 or 32 in. barrels, imp. mod. and full or full and full choke, trap style stock, made 1966-1984.

	$1,320	$1,100	$935	$825	$715	$660	$605

MODEL 101 SINGLE BARREL TRAP—similar to O/U Trap, with 32 or 34 in. full choke barrel, Monte Carlo trap style stock, made 1967-1971.

	$880	$660	$550	$495	$385	$360	$330

MODEL 101 PIGEON GRADE—12, 20, 28 or .410 (disc. in 1986) ga. deluxe engraved silver receiver version of 101, select checkered wood, made 1974-present.

Lightweight Field Model—lightweight variation, Winchokes standard, 6½ - 7 lbs. Discontinued in 1987.

	$1,575	$1,375	$1,120	$940	$785	$675	$600

Last Mfg.'s Sug. Retail was $1,950.

This model was previously available without Winchokes in 28 ga. only - deduct 5%.

Lightweight two barrel set—includes 28 and .410 ga. 27 in. barrels, 28 ga. has Winchokes; .410 ga. has fixed M/F chokes. Discontinued in 1986.

	$2,275	$1,950	$1,775	$1,600	$1,425	$1,300	$1,100

Last Mfg.'s Sug. Retail was $2,500.

Featherweight—12 or 20 ga., English straight stock, 25½ in. barrels bored IC/IM, 6½ - 6¾ lbs. Disc. in 1987.

	$1,325	$1,175	$975	$850	$750	$675	$600

Last Mfg.'s Sug. Retail was $1,580.

Skeet Grade—12 or 20 ga.

	$1,100	$1,045	$990	$880	$770	$715	$660

Trap Grade—12 ga. only, vent barrels and rib, coin finish receiver with fine scroll engraving, engraved pigeon on floorplate, Winchoke standard, 8¼ lbs. Discontinued in 1985.

	$1,300	$1,180	$990	$880	$770	$715	$660

Last Mfg.'s Sug. Retail was $1,475.

Super Pigeon Grade—12 ga. only, blued receiver with elaborate engraving including multiple gold inlays, extra select walnut with fleur-de-lis checkering on stock and forearm, Winchoke standard, 7½ lbs. Imported 1985-1987 only.

	$4,025	$3,625	$3,225	$2,835	$2,500	$2,150	$1,920

Last Mfg.'s Sug. Retail was $4,590.

101 DIAMOND GRADE—Trap or Skeet O/U, 12 (Trap only), 20, 28, and .410 ga.'s, vent barrels and rib, Winchoke standard on Trap — add $75 on Skeet model (disc.in 1986), select hand checkered walnut, engraved satin-finish receiver. Trap model has extra high vent rib. Skeet model has raised rib and muzzle vents.

Standard Trap—12 ga. only, 30 or 32 in. vent barrels, 8¾ - 9 lbs. Discontinued in 1987.

	$1,620	$1,440	$1,230	$1,075	$900	$780	$640

Last Mfg.'s Sug. Retail was $1,860.

Unsingle Trap—12 ga. only, lower single barrel, 32 or 34 in. barrel, extended rib. Add $60 for Winchoke. Discontinued in 1986.

	$1,575	$1,430	$1,200	$995	$895	$830	$740

Last Mfg.'s Sug. Retail was $1,760.

Grading	100%	98%	95%	90%	80%	70%	60%

Oversingle Trap—12 ga. only, Winchokes, 34 in. upper barrel only, 8½ lbs. Imported 1986-1987 only.

| | $1,985 | $1,695 | $1,545 | $1,395 | $1,200 | $995 | $895 |

Last Mfg.'s Sug. Retail was $2,145.

Oversingle Combo—includes one set of O/U barrels and an oversingle barrel, cased. Imported 1987 only.

| | $3,075 | $2,750 | $2,525 | $2,300 | $2,000 | $1,750 | $1,625 |

Last Mfg.'s Sug. Retail was $3,550.

Trap Combo—12 ga. only, includes a set of 30 or 32 in. vent O/U barrels and a 32 or 34 in. high ribbed unsingle (lower) barrel, standard or Monte Carlo stock, approx. 9 lbs. Discontinued in 1987.

| | $2,570 | $2,320 | $1,975 | $1,800 | $1,600 | $1,400 | $1,200 |

Add $275 for ATA Trap set.

Last Mfg.'s Sug. Retail was $2,940.

Standard Skeet—12, 20, 28, and .410 ga.'s, 27½ in. vent barrels and competition rib, 6½ - 7¼ lbs. Discontinued in 1987.

| | $1,650 | $1,465 | $1,240 | $1,075 | $900 | $780 | $640 |

Last Mfg.'s Sug. Retail was $1,950.

Four gauge Skeet set—includes 12, 20, 28, and .410 ga. 27½ in. separated barrel assemblies, cased. Imported 1985-1987 only.

| | $4,600 | $3,975 | $3,600 | $3,200 | $2,800 | $2,500 | $2,150 |

Last Mfg.'s Sug. Retail was $5,025.

Sporting Clays Grade—12 ga. only, 28 or 30 in. barrels with Winchokes, designed for Sporting Clay competition. Discontinued in 1987.

| | $1,675 | $1,475 | $1,230 | $1,075 | $900 | $780 | $640 |

Last Mfg.'s Sug. Retail was $1,965.

501 GRAND EUROPEAN—Trap or Skeet, 12 or 20 ga., 20 ga. is Skeet only, 27, 30, or 32 in. barrels, extra select hand checkered walnut with oil finish, Schnabel forearm, extensive scroll engraving on satin-finished receiver, vent barrels and rib, mfg. 1981-86.

| | $1,520 | $1,385 | $1,200 | $1,050 | $900 | $780 | $640 |

Last Mfg.'s Sug. Retail was $1,720.

Grand European Featherweight—20 ga. only, straight grip stock, 25½ in. vent rib barrels, 5¾ lbs. Disc. in 1986.

| | $1,520 | $1,385 | $1,200 | $1,050 | $900 | $780 | $640 |

Last Mfg.'s Sug. Retail was $1,720.

PRESENTATION GRADE—12 ga. only, available in both Trap and Skeet models, blued action-extensively engraved with gold inlays, special crotch walnut, 27 (Skeet) or 30 in. vent barrels, hand checkered, gold lining on perimeter of receiver. Imported 1984-1987 only.

| | $3,475 | $2,850 | $2,510 | $2,280 | $1,950 | $1,800 | $1,600 |

Last Mfg.'s Sug. Retail was $3,840.

SHOTGUN/RIFLE COMBINATION—combination 12 ga./.30-06 O/U, 25 in. barrels, top barrel is Winchoked, Grand European engraving and finish, 8½ lbs. Mfg. 1983-1985.

| | $2,245 | $2,040 | $1,800 | $1,650 | $1,450 | $1,300 | $1,200 |

Also available in limited quantities in .222 Rem., .223 Rem., and 9.3 x 74R cal.'s. Last Mfg.'s Sug. Retail was $2,550.

DOUBLE EXPRESS RIFLE—.30-06, .270 Win., .257 Roberts, 9.3 x 74R, and 7.7 x 65R cal.'s, O/U configuration, ejectors, 23½ in. barrels, game scene engraved, satin finish receiver, 8½ lbs. Mfg. 1984 - 1985 only.

| | $1,750 | $1,495 | $1,250 | $1,125 | $1,000 | $875 | $750 |

Last Mfg.'s Sug. Retail was $2,995.

Grading	100%	98%	95%	90%	80%	70%	60%

MODEL 91 O & U—12 ga. only, manufactured by Laurona in Spain for international sales including Europe, SST, ejectors optional, vent rib, distinguishable by black chrome finish on metal parts. Discontinued.

Prices hard to evaluate because of limited importation domestically. In some regions they are bought as medium priced field guns, while in others they are sold as a rare Winchester O&U.

MODEL 96 XPERT O&U FIELD GRADE—similar action to Model 101, 12 and 20 ga., auto ejectors, SST, various barrel lengths and chokes, action similar to 101, no engraving, checkered pistol grip stock and forearm, made 1976-1982.

	$650	$575	$500	$450	$410	$370	$330

MODEL 96 XPERT SKEET GRADE—same as Field Grade, with 27 in. skeet barrels, skeet style stock, made 1976-1982.

	$665	$575	$500	$450	$410	$370	$330

MODEL 96 XPERT TRAP GRADE—same as Field, in 12 ga. only, 30 in. imp. mod. and full or full and full choke, trap style stock, made 1976-1982.

	$625	$530	$470	$430	$395	$360	$315

Note: Model 101 and Model 96 Xpert guns are made by Olin Kodensha located in Tochigi, Japan.

SHOTGUNS: CURRENT MANUFACTURE SIDE-BY-SIDE

MODEL 21—boxlock, custom order only, choice of gauges, (12, 16, and 20 ga.) and barrel lengths, chokes, style of stocks. Manufactured by custom order only since 1960.

Standard Custom guns (12 ga.) are currently trading in the $5,750 range if NIB.

Custom Built—standard model with no engraving.
Mfg.'s Sug. Retail $8,100 $8,100 $5,000 $3,750

Custom Grade—includes No. 6 engraved receiver and vent rib.
Mfg.'s Sug. Retail $11,080 $11,080 $7,250 $5,500

Grand American Grade—includes 2 sets of barrels with forearms, No. 6 engraved with gold inlays, cased.
Mfg.'s Sug. Retail $22,745 $22,745 $15,000 $11,500

Grand American Small Gauge—28 or .410 ga.
Mfg.'s Sug. Retail $34,460 $34,460 $25,000 $17,500
   Add 10% for 28/.410 ga. combo.

Grand American "1 of 8" set—includes 20, 28, and .410 ga. VR barrels. Only 8 sets produced.
Mfg.'s Sug. Retail $55,000 $55,000 $39,500 $27,500

Note: See Model 21 listing also under Pre-64 shotguns.

MODEL 22—12 ga. only, manufactured by Laurona in Spain for international sales including Europe, SST, ejectors optional, vent rib, distinguishable by black chrome finish on metal parts, introduced 1975-discontinued.

Prices hard to evaluate because of limited importation domestically. In some regions they are bought as medium priced field guns, while in others they are sold as a rare Winchester SXS.

MODEL 23 XTR—12 and 20 ga.'s, 3 in. chambers, 25½, 26, 28, and 30 in. barrels, various chokes, single trigger, vent rib, auto ejectors, scroll engraved, silver grey satin finish, blued barrel, checkered select walnut stock and forearm, first commercial gun to employ interchangeable chokes, made 1978-present.

Grade 1 (disc.)	$915	$820	$750	$650	$575	$500	$440

Pigeon Grade—standard weight model, 6½ - 7 lbs, coin finished receiver with scroll engraving. Winchoke option became standard in 1986. Subtract $150 without Winchokes. Disc. in 1986.

	$995	$875	$750	$675	$600	$550	$495

Last Mfg.'s Sug. Retail was $1,460.

Pigeon Grade Lightweight—25½ in. barrels only, 6¼ - 6¾ lbs., coin finished receiver with scroll engraving. English stock, Winchoke not available. Disc. in 1986.

	$1,265	$1,150	$995	$880	$760	$730	$680

Last Mfg.'s Sug. Retail was $1,420.

Grading	100%	98%	95%	90%	80%	70%	60%

Pigeon Grade Ducks Unlimited—only 500 manufactured in 1981, "SPO" serial no. suffix, cased.

| | $1,450 | $1,200 | $995 | $880 | $760 | $730 | $680 |

Golden Quail Model Series—12 ga. (1986), 20 ga. (1984), 28 ga. (1985), or .410 ga. (1987), 25½ in. barrels bored IC/M, beavertail forearm, straight grip English stock with recoil pad, only 500 manufactured each year per gauge. Discontinued in 1987.

| | $1,450 | $1,150 | $995 | $875 | $780 | $700 | $640 |

Add $165 for .410 and earlier ga.'s.

This limited production series is now complete with the release of the .410 ga. in 1987.

Last Mfg.'s Sug. Retail was $1,950.

Model 23 Light Duck—limited edition, 500 manufactured, introduced in 1985, blued receiver and barrels, select walnut, 20 ga., 28 in.- F&F, 8½ lbs.

| | $1,475 | $1,225 | $995 | $900 | $825 | $775 | $725 |

Last Mfg.'s Sug. Retail was $1,660.

Model 23 Heavy Duck—limited edition, 500 manufactured in 1984 only, blued receiver and barrels, select walnut, 12 ga., 30 in.- F&F, 8½ lbs.

| | $1,500 | $1,265 | $1,025 | $920 | $840 | $785 | $730 |

Custom 2 Barrel Set—interchangeable 20 and 28 ga. barrels (25½ in.), blue engraved receiver with gold inlays, "B" checkering on stock and forearm, leather cased with accessories, only 500 sets mfg. in 1986. Discontinued in 1987.

| | $3,700 | $3,300 | $2,995 | $2,750 | $2,500 | $2,150 | $1,920 |

Last Mfg.'s Sug. Retail was $4,625.

MODEL 23 CUSTOM—12 ga. only, 25½ in. Winchoke barrels, high lustre bluing, no engraving, SST, ejectors, solid red rubber recoil pad, 7 lbs. Imported in 1987 only.

| | $1,300 | $1,175 | $995 | $925 | $875 | $780 | $640 |

Last Mfg.'s Sug. Retail was $1,975.

MODEL 23 CLASSIC—12, 20, 28, and .410 ga.'s, 26 in. VR barrels, single trigger, deluxe hand checkered walnut stock and beavertail forearm, solid recoil pad, brass name plate, gold inlay on bottom of receiver, ebony inlay in forearm, 5¾ - 7 lbs. Imported 1986-1987 only.

| | $1,300 | $1,175 | $995 | $925 | $875 | $780 | $640 |

Add $150 for 28 or .410 ga.

The 28 and .410 ga.'s in this model feature a smaller frame.

Last Mfg.'s Sug. Retail was $1,975.

COMMEMORATIVES: U.S. PRODUCTION

In recent years commemoratives in general have experienced poor liquidity and an overall reduction of prices. Commemorative production in some trademarks has totalled well over 250,000 units, and some collectors are weighing the "limited production" factor on each model before paying a premium over the standard production model of that particular commemorative. Below values reflect maximum purchase prices made in various areas of the U.S. In some regions it is possible to purchase a Winchester 94 commemorative made in substantial quantity for almost no premium over a standard production Winchester 94. Because of this, prices could fluctuate over 25% depending on the geographic location of purchase or sale. It is also important to remember that N.I.B. becomes especially important with commemoratives. Values below assume boxes, informational material, and warranty cards - subtract $75-$100 if without box and literature. Commemoratives having been shot as little as 3 times can only be classified as fancy hunting guns with little premium if any over the standard hunting model from which they were derived.

Many "special interest" limited editions have been ordered through outside private contracts with Winchester (including General Motors, Dodge, Coca-Cola, etc.). These variations do not have the special suffix serialization and many times the embellishments were subcontracted outside of the factory. While these guns do have special interest, they do not have the collectibility or desirability of the below listed factory models. Typically, these limited editions sell in the $195-$350 range.

Grading	100%	Issue price	Qty made

A FINAL NOTE ON COMMEMORATIVE: AS A RULE, WHAT DETERMINES THE BOTTOM OF THE MARKET IN COMMEMMORATIVES IS THE TOP OF THE MARKET FOR THEIR STANDARD MODEL PRODUCTION RELATIVES. A PROBLEM WITH LIMITED EDITIONS IS THAT OVER THE YEARS OF OWNERSHIP, MOST OF THE ORIGINAL AMOUNT MANUFACTURED STAYS IN THE SAME N.I.B. CONDITION. THUS, IF SUPPLY ALWAYS IS CONSTANT AND IN ONE CONDITION (NIB), DEMAND HAS TO INCREASE BEFORE PRICE APPRECIATION CAN OCCUR. TAKING INTO CONSIDERATION THE INFLATION FACTOR DURING THE PAST 2 DECADES, MANY OLDER, HIGH MANUFACTURE COMMEMORATIVES/LIMITED EDITIONS HAVE NOT PERFORMED VERY WELL AS INVESTMENTS. YET, OTHERS HAVE. AFTER 26 YEARS OF SPECIAL EDITION PRODUCTION, MANY MODELS' PERFORMANCE RECORD CAN BE ACCURATELY ANALYZED AND ANY APPRECIATION (OR DEPRECIATION) CAN BE COMPARED AGAINST OTHER PURCHASES OF EQUAL VINTAGE. YOU BE THE JUDGE.

Since U.S. Repeating Arms has announced that they will no longer manufacture commemoratives, this specialized market has improved. Almost all distributors and dealers are sold out on older models (i.e. the dumping is over) and collectors are currently having to purchase these guns from other sources which are more expensive. There is no longer the glut of excess supply in this commemorative marketplace.

1964 WYOMING DIAMOND JUBILEE 94 CARBINE
	$1,850	$100	1,500

1966 CENTENNIAL '66 RIFLE
	$395	$125	unknown

1966 CENTENNIAL '66 CARBINE—total manufacture of both the rifle and carbine was 102,309.
	$395	$125	102,309

Add $50-$75 over individual prices for consecutively serial numbered rifle and carbine set.

1966 NEBRASKA CENTENNIAL 94 RIFLE
	$1,500	$100	2,500

1967 CANADIAN '67 CENTENNIAL RIFLE
	$375	$125	unknown

1967 CANADIAN '67 CENTENNIAL CARBINE—total manufacture of both the rifle and carbine was 90,301.
	$375	$125	90,301

Add $50-$75 over individual prices for consecutively serial numbered rifle and carbine set.

1967 ALASKAN PURCHASE CENTENNIAL CARBINE
	$1,850	$125	1,500

1968 ILLINOIS SESQUICENTENNIAL 94 CARBINE
	$395	$110	37,648

1968 BUFFALO BILL RIFLE "1 OF 300" PRES.
	$2,995	$1,000	300

1968 BUFFALO BILL RIFLE
	$400	$130	unknown

BUFFALO BILL CARBINE—total manufacture of both the rifle and carbine was 112,923.
	$400	$130	112,923

Add $50-$75 over individual prices for consecutively serial numbered rifle and carbine set.

1969 GOLDEN SPIKE CARBINE
	$395	$120	69,996

1969 THEO. ROOSEVELT RIFLE
	$395	$135	

1969 THEO. ROOSEVELT CARBINE—total manufacture of both the rifle and carbine was 52,386.
	$385	$135	52,386

1970 COWBOY COMMEMORATIVE CARBINE
	$425	$125	27,549

1970 COWBOY CARBINE "1 OF 300"
	$3,495	$1,000	300

Grading	100%	Issue price	Qty made
1970 LONE STAR RIFLE			
	$425	$140	
1970 LONE STAR CARBINE—total manufacture of both the rifle and carbine was 38,385.			
	$425	$140	38,385
1971 NRA CENTENNIAL MUSKET			
	$395	$150	23,400
1971 NRA CENTENNIAL RIFLE			
	$395	$150	21,000
1974 TEXAS RANGER CARBINE			
	$625	$135	4,850
1974 TEXAS RANGER PRESENTATION			
	$3,500	$1,000	150
1976 U.S. BICENTENNIAL CARBINE			
	$650	$325	19,999
1977 WELLS FARGO			
	$425	$350	19,999
1977 "LIMITED EDITION I"			
	$1,700	$1,500	1,500
1977 LEGENDARY LAWMEN			
	$425	$375	19,999
1978 ANTLERED GAME CARBINE			
	$425	$375	19,999
1979 LEGENDARY FRONTIERSMAN RIFLE			
	$425	$425	19,999
1979 "LIMITED EDITION II"			
	$1,600	$1,500	1,500
1979 MATCHED SET OF 1000			
	$2,800	$3,000	1,000
1980 "OLIVER WINCHESTER"			
	$575	$375	19,999
1981 U.S. BORDER PATROL			
	$895	$1,195	1,000
1981 U.S. BORDER PATROL — MEMBERS MODEL			
	$1,095	$695	800
1982 GREAT WESTERN ARTIST I			
	$1,395	$2,200	999
1982 GREAT WESTERN ARTIST II			
	$1,395	$2,200	999
1982 JOHN WAYNE			
	$750	$600	49,000
1982 "DUKE"			
	$3,200	$2,250	1,000
1982 JOHN WAYNE "1 OF 300" SET			
	$7,995	$10,000	300
1982 ANNIE OAKLEY			
	$595	$699	6,000
1983 CHIEF CRAZY HORSE			
	$495	$600	19,999
1983 OKLAHOMA DIAMOND JUBILEE			
	$1,800	$2,250	1,001
1983 AMERICAN BALD EAGLE			
	$895	$895	2,800
1983 AMERICAN BALD EAGLE - DELUXE			
	$2,995	$2,995	200

Grading	100%	Issue price	Qty made

1984 WINCHESTER-COLT COMMEMORATIVE SET—1 each of the Model
1894 Carbine and Colt Peacemaker, serial numbered 1 WC-4440 WC. .44-40 cal., elaborate gold etching, cased.

	$2,600	$3,995	2,300

Approx. 2,300 sets were actually put together in this combination. These sets have been split up with individual prices being discounted (Colt SAA's have been trading in the $700-$800 range).

1985 BOY SCOUTS 75TH ANNIVERSARY—Model 9422 action, .22 cal., rifle
configuration, 6¼ lbs.

Eagle Scout—1,000 manufactured, serial numbered Eagle 1 - Eagle 1,000, receiver has triple level gold etching, select American walnut stock and forearm, gold plated lever, hammer, and forearm cap.

	$2,150	$2,140	1,000

Boy Scout—15,000 manufactured, serial numbered BSA 1 - BSA 15,000, roll engraved, antique pewter receiver, hooded front sight.

	$495	$615	15,000

MODEL 94 TEXAS SESQUICENTENNIAL—.38-55 cal., available in carbine or rifle.

Model 94 Rifle—24 in. round barrel, elaborate gold etching, includes Bowie knife, oak cased, 586 manufactured.

	$2,995	$2,995	1,500

Model 94 Carbine—18½ in. round barrel, gold finished receiver and barrel bands, roll engraved receiver, 2,600 manufactured, serial numbered TEX 1 and up.

	$695	$695	15,000

Rifle/Carbine Set—includes one each of the Model 94 rifle and carbine, Bowie knife, 150 manufactured.

	$7,995	$7,995	150

1986 120TH ANNIVERSARY MODEL 94 CARBINE—.44-40 cal. only, 20 in.
barrel, hoop-type finger lever, crescent butt plate, deluxe checkered walnut stock and forearm, extensive gold etching on barrel and framesides, 1,000 mfg. ser. no. WRA001-WRA1000.

	$995	$995	1,000

1986 STATUE OF LIBERTY MODEL 94—Model 94 rifle in .30-30 cal. with octagon
barrel, extensive C. Giovanelli scroll engraving with multiple 22Kt. gold inlays, deluxe walnut with fine checkering, also includes 29 in. hand carved wooden statue of the Statue of Liberty, serial numbered SL1-SL100.

	$7,500	$6,500	100

MODEL 94 DU (1986)—.30-30 cal., approx. 2,800 rifles were mfg. in the U.S. Since each
Model 94 DU was bid on for ownership, prices will vary from points of origin. An average bid price seems to be in the $700-$995 range with lower and completing set ser. no.'s selling at premiums. Serial numbered DU-86 0001 on up.

WINCHESTER COMMEMORATIVES: NON-DOMESTIC — 1970 TO DATE

1970 NORTH WEST TERRITORIES (CANADIAN)

	$800	$150	2,500

1970 NORTHWEST TERRITORIES DELUXE (CANADIAN)

	$1,395	$250	500

1972 YELLOW BOY (SOLD IN EUROPE ONLY)

	$1,495	$150	5,500

1973 M.P.X. (MADE ESPECIALLY FOR A MOVIE)

	$8,500	$ 78	32

1973 R.C.M.P. (CANADIAN)

	$695	$190	9,500

1973 M.P. (MOUNTED POLICE) - (CANADIAN)

	$1,275	$190	5,100

Grading	100%	Issue price	Qty made
1974 APACHE (CANADIAN)			
	$650	$150	8,600
1975 KLONDIKE GOLD RUSH			
	$650	$240	10,500
1975 K.G.R. (DAWSON CITY ISSUE) - (CANADIAN)			
	$8,500	N/A	25
1975 COMMANCHE (CANADIAN)			
	$650	$230	11,500
1976 SIOUX (CANADIAN)			
	$650	$280	10,000
1976 LITTLE BIG HORN (CANADIAN)			
	$650	$230	11,000
1977 CHEYENNE—.44-40 (Canadian)			
	$600	$300	11,225
1977 CHEYENNE—.22 Cal. (Canadian)			
	$675	$320	5,000
1978 CHEROKEE—.30/30 (Canadian)			
	$625	$385	9,000
1978 CHEROKEE—.22 Cal. (Canadian)			
	$675	$385	3,950
1978 ONE OF ONE THOUSAND (SOLD IN EUROPE ONLY)			
	$7,995	$5,000	250
This model was not advertised in the U.S.			
1979 BAT MASTERSON (CANADIAN)			
	$650	$650	8,000
1980 ALBERTA DIAMOND JUBILEE (CANADIAN)			
	$850	$650	2,700
1980 A.D.J. DELUXE PRESENTATION (CANADIAN)			
	$2,400	$1,900	300
1980 SASKATCHEWAN DIAMOND JUBILEE (CANADIAN)			
	$650	$695	2,700
1980 S.D.J. DELUXE PRESENTATION (CANADIAN)			
	$2,100	$1,995	300
1981 CALGARY STAMPEDE (CANADIAN)			
	$2,000	$2,200	1,000
1981 CANADIAN PACIFIC CENTENNIAL (CANADIAN)			
	$550	$800	2,700
1981 CANADIAN PACIFIC CENTENNIAL PRESENTATION (CANADIAN)			
	$2,200	$2,200	300
1981 CANADIAN PACIFIC (EMPL.) - (CANADIAN)			
	$650	$800	2,000
1981 JOHN WAYNE (CANADIAN)			
	$950	$995	1,000
1986 SECOND SERIES EUROPEAN 1 OF 1,000—mfg. for European sales only in 1986.			
	$6,500	$6,000	150

WINSLOW ARMS COMPANY

CAMDEN, SOUTH CAROLINA.

WINSLOW BOLT ACTION SPORTING RIFLE—offered with various actions, FN Supreme, Mark X Mauser, Rem. 700 and 788, Sako and Win. 70, offered in all popular calibers from .17 Rem. to .458 Mag., standard calibers have 24 in. barrels and 3 shot magazines, magnum calibers have 26 in. barrels and 2 shot magazines, two style stocks, "Bushmaster Conventional", slender pistol grip and beavertail forearm, "Plainsmaster", full curl, hooked pistol grip and flat wide forearm, both are Monte Carlo with cheekpieces, recoil pads and swivels, walnut, maple, and myrtle are used with rosewood forend tip and pistol grip cap, rifle comes in 8 basic grades, custom embellishments can increase values greatly, discretion must be used, values are for basic models.

	100%	98%	95%	90%	80%	70%	60%
COMMANDER GRADE	$495	$475	$440	$385	$360	$330	$305
REGAL GRADE	$605	$590	$560	$525	$470	$440	$415
REGENT GRADE	$725	$700	$670	$640	$605	$550	$495
REGIMENTAL GRADE	$935	$890	$855	$800	$745	$660	$605
CROWN GRADE	$1,375	$1,265	$1,155	$990	$910	$825	$715
ROYAL GRADE	$1,540	$1,375	$1,210	$1,100	$1,020	$965	$825
IMPERIAL GRADE	$3,520	$3,080	$2,860	$2,475	$2,200	$1,925	$1,320
EMPEROR GRADE	$6,215	$5,500	$4,950	$4,400	$3,300	$2,750	$2,200

WISEMAN, BILL AND CO.

MANUFACTURER LOCATED IN BRYAN, TX.

RIFLES

HUNTER MODEL—available in various cal.'s, sako action, stainless steel barrel by Wiseman/McMillan, laminate stock, teflon finished metal parts, Pachmayr decelerator pad, sling swivels, glass bedded action.

Please contact the manufacturer for prices on this model.

HUNDER DELUXE—similar to Hunter Model except has custom checkering.

Please contact the manufacturer for prices on this model.

MAVERICK—similar to Hunter but with black fiberglass stock.

Please contact the manufacturer for prices on this model.

VARMENTER—similar to Hunter but with thumb hole stock.

	100%	98%	95%	90%	80%	70%	60%
Mfg.'s Sug. Retail	$1,500	$1,500	$1,200	$995	$875	$800	$750	$700

SILHOUETTE PISTOL

SILHOUETTE PISTOL—various cal.'s, Sako action, 14 in. Wiseman/McMillan fluted stainless barrel, 5 or 7 shot magazine, laminate pistol grip stock, no sights, 4½-5½ lbs. New in 1989.

	100%	98%	95%	90%	80%	70%	60%
Mfg.'s Sug. Retail	$1,295	$1,295	$1,000	$900	$800	$750	$700	$650

WOODWARD, JAMES AND SONS

PREVIOUSLY MFG. IN LONDON, ENGLAND. ACQUIRED BY JAMES PURDEY & SON APPROX. 1935.

SHOTGUNS: DOUBLE AND SINGLE BARREL

Woodward made one of the world's finest shotguns. Prior to WWII, they were acquired by Purdey and Sons. Many of the weapons they made were custom built and grading and pricing should be done individually. We will list some of the general models with approximate values, but strongly urge competent professional appraisal when contemplating purchase or sale.

BEST QUALITY DOUBLE BARREL SHOTGUN—custom built in all gauges, barrel lengths and chokes, sidelock, auto ejectors, stocked to specifications, pre-WWII.

$16,500 $13,500 $12,500 $10,000 $9,000 $8,000 $7,000

20 gauge — add 20%.
28 gauge — add 40%.
.410 gauge — add 60%.
SST — add $1,000.

BEST QUALITY O/U SHOTGUN—custom built in all gauges, barrel lengths, and chokes, vent rib, sidelock, auto ejectors, stocked to customer specifications, pre-WWII.

$20,000 $18,500 $16,000 $14,500 $12,750 $11,000 $10,000

20 gauge — add 35%.
28 gauge — add 75%.
.410 gauge — too rare to accurately predict.
Single trigger — add $1,000.

BEST QUALITY SINGLE BARREL TRAP GUN—12 ga. only, same features as O/U pre-WWII.

$12,750 $10,000 $8,950 $7,725 $6,500 $5,750 $4,900

Z

Z-B RIFLE
BRNO, CZECHOSLOVAKIA.

Grading	100%	98%	95%	90%	80%	70%	60%

Z-B MAUSER VARMINT RIFLE—small Mauser bolt action, .22 Hornet, 23 in. barrel, double set triggers, 3 leaf sight, checkered pistol grip stock, (also known as Brno Hornet).

$825	$745	$690	$605	$550	$470	$415

ZANARDINI

MANUFACTURED AND DISTRIBUTED IN BRESCIA, ITALY SINCE 1946. LIMITED IMPORTATION INTO THE U.S. BY MORTON'S LTD. LOCATED IN LEXINGTON, KY. AND NAVY ARMS CO. INC. LOCATED IN RIDGEFIELD, NJ.

For further information regarding Zanardini rifles and shotguns, Morton's Limited should be contacted directly regarding availability and prices. Oxford rifles are imported by both Navy Arms Co. Inc. and Armes de Chasse. Please contact directly for further information.

Prices could change rapidly on this trademark because of the fluctuating U.S. dollar.

Zanardini exports high quality rifles (single shot, side by side, or over and under), combination guns (O/U only), and shotguns (O/U and side by side). Currently, this manufacturer is exporting firearms into the U.S. on a very limited, basis. Rather than list the models individually, the current retail price range for shotguns varies between $2,400-$8,750. Tip-up rifles range between $1,550-$3,850. O/U combination guns vary between $1,200-$4,900. O/U express rifles vary between $1,775-$5,250. Side by side rifles are priced starting at $3,400 to $11,000 (depending on individual specifications and special orders). Further information can be obtained by writing the factory.

ZANOTTI, FABIO

MANUFACTURED IN BRESCIA, ITALY SINCE 1625. CURRENTLY IMPORTED AND DISTRIBUTED BY NEW ENGLAND ARMS, CO. LOCATED IN KITTERY POINT, ME. ZANOTTI, FABIO IS NOW PART OF THE RENATO GAMBA GROUP AS OF 1985.

Fabio Zanotti is one of the world's oldest quality shotgun manufacturers. Current domestic importation is often times done on a custom order only basis. For more information on Zanotti models and their values, contact New England Arms Co.

SHOTGUNS: OVER/UNDER

MODEL 725—28 or .410 ga. only, scalloped case hardened shallow frame, DT or ST, ejectors, game scene and scroll engraving, custom built to individual specifications. Prices start at $2,995 and go up per special orders.

CASSIANO—12, 20, 28, or .410 ga., Boss style shallow action, best quality gun built to individual specifications. Prices start at $12,500 and go up accordingly.

SHOTGUNS: SIDE BY SIDE
Add $200 for ST.
Add $150 for beavertail forearm.
Add $395 for leather case.

617

Grading	100%	98%	95%	90%	80%	70%	60%

MODEL 625 BOXLOCK
Mfg.'s Sug. Retail — $2,950 $2,650 $2,200 $1,825 $1,430 $1,235 $1,050 $950

MODEL 626 BOXLOCK—scroll, game scene, or combination engraving.
Mfg.'s Sug. Retail — $3,650 $3,175 $2,650 $2,200 $1,825 $1,430 $1,235 $1,050

MODEL GIACINTO—hammer gun.
Mfg.'s Sug. Retail — $4,950 $4,600 $3,850 $3,175 $2,450 $2,000 $1,825 $1,430

MODEL MAXIM SIDELOCK
Mfg.'s Sug. Retail — $7,500 $6,000 $5,250 $4,600 $3,850 $3,175 $2,450 $2,000

MODEL EDWARD SIDELOCK
Mfg.'s Sug. Retail — $9,500 $7,950 $6,500 $5,900 $5,250 $4,600 $3,850 $3,175

MODEL CASSIANO I SIDELOCK
Mfg.'s Sug. Retail — $10,750 $8,950 $7,950 $6,500 $5,900 $5,250 $4,600 $3,850

MODEL CASSIANO II
Mfg.'s Sug. Retail — $12,000 $11,000 $9,750 $8,950 $7,950 $6,500 $5,900 $5,250

CASSIANO EXECUTIVE—prices vary per individual order, top-of-the-line model. Prices start at $12,000 and go up.

ZEPHYR

MADE IN SPAIN, IMPORTED BY STOEGERS 1930's-1972.

SHOTGUNS: SxS OR SINGLE SHOT

WOODLANDER II DOUBLE BARREL SHOTGUN—12 and 20 ga.'s, various chokes, boxlock, double triggers, extractors, engraved, checkered pistol grip stock.
$495 $440 $385 $360 $305 $275 $250

UPLANDER (4E) SXS—12, 16, 20, 28, and .410 ga.'s, sidelock action, double triggers, ejectors, engraved.
$585 $570 $480 $440 $400 $370 $340

UPLAND KING SXS—12 or 16 ga., sidelock, single trigger, vent rib, ejectors, fully engraved.
$780 $720 $650 $590 $540 $490 $475

THUNDERBIRD SXS—10 ga. Mag, 32 in. barrels, double triggers, French walnut, engraved. Add $175 for ejectors.
$850 $750 $625 $550 $510 $490 $475

HONKER—10 ga. Mag, single shot, 36 in. vent rib barrel, lightly engraved.
$500 $460 $420 $350 $310 $290 $270

VANDALIA—12 ga. Trap Model, 32 in. barrel, engraved.
$700 $620 $575 $525 $475 $425 $390

STERLINGWORTH II DOUBLE BARREL SHOTGUN—similar to Woodlander, with sidelock action.
$715 $660 $605 $580 $525 $495 $470

VICTOR SPECIAL DOUBLE BARREL SHOTGUN—12 ga., 25, 28, and 30 in. barrels, various chokes, double triggers, extractors, checkered pistol grip stock.
$440 $385 $330 $305 $250 $220 $195

ZOLI USA, ANGELO

MANUFACTURED IN BRESCIA, ITALY. IMPORTED AND DISTRIBUTED EXCLUSIVELY BY ANGELO ZOLI USA LOCATED IN ADDISON, IL. NEW IN 1985.

Grading	100%	98%	95%	90%	80%	70%	60%

Prices could differ from values shown below because of the fluctuating U.S. dollar.

SHOTGUNS: OVER AND UNDER

SNIPE—.410 ga., 3 in. chambers, 26 or 28 in. barrels, single trigger.
    Mfg.'s Sug. Retail $265 $230 $200 $185 $170 $155 $145 $135

TEXAS—all ga.'s, 26 or 28 in. barrels, double triggers, folding design, lever action.
    Mfg.'s Sug. Retail $291 $250 $220 $200 $185 $170 $155 $145

DOVE—.410 ga. only, 3 in. chambers, 26 or 28 in. barrels, single trigger.
    Mfg.'s Sug. Retail $306 $260 $230 $200 $185 $170 $155 $145

FIELD SPECIAL—12 or 20 ga., 3 in. chambers, various barrel lengths and chokings, single trigger.
    Mfg.'s Sug. Retail $322 $270 $235 $200 $185 $170 $155 $145

PIGEON MODEL—12 or 20 ga., 3 in. chambers, various barrel lengths, single trigger. Add $60 for 20 ga.
    Mfg.'s Sug. Retail $394 $350 $295 $270 $250 $220 $195 $175

STANDARD MODEL—12 or 20 ga., 3 in. chambers, various barrel lengths and chokings, single trigger.
    Mfg.'s Sug. Retail $459 $395 $345 $320 $300 $280 $260 $245

SPECIAL MODEL—12 ga. only, 3 in. chambers, various barrel lengths and chokings, SST. Add $120 for multi-chokes.
    Mfg.'s Sug. Retail $528 $465 $395 $355 $325 $290 $270 $250

DELUXE MODEL—similar to Special Model, except better wood and engraving. Add $80 for multi-chokes.
    Mfg.'s Sug. Retail $730 $645 $550 $495 $450 $400 $360 $320

PRESENTATION MODEL—12 ga. only, includes sideplates. Add $42 for multi-chokes.
    Mfg.'s Sug. Retail $842 $740 $630 $575 $495 $450 $395 $350

ST. GEORGE'S TARGET—12 ga. only, trap or skeet gun, SST, fixed choke.
    Mfg.'s Sug. Retail $1,024 $900 $730 $645 $550 $495 $450 $400

    St. George's Competition—12 ga. only, includes 30 in. O/U barrels and single barrel multi-choke.
    Mfg.'s Sug. Retail $1,627 $1,430 $1,235 $1,050 $950 $895 $820 $740

PATRICIA MODEL—.410 ga. only, 3 in. chambers, 28 in. barrels, SST. Add $121 for case.
    Mfg.'s Sug. Retail $1,345 $1,175 $1,010 $900 $895 $820 $740 $650

SHOTGUNS: SIDE-BY-SIDE

QUAIL SPECIAL—.410 ga., 3 in. chambers, single trigger, 28 in. barrels.
    Mfg.'s Sug. Retail $243 $205 $185 $170 $150 $125 $110 $100

FALCON II—.410 ga., 3 in. chambers, 26 or 28 in. barrels, double triggers.
    Mfg.'s Sug. Retail $246 $205 $185 $170 $150 $125 $110 $100

PHEASANT—12 ga. only, 3 in. chambers, 28 in. barrels only, single trigger.
    Mfg.'s Sug. Retail $428 $370 $320 $300 $280 $260 $240 $220

ALLEY CLEANER—12 or 20 ga., 3 in. chambers, 20 in. barrels, riot configuration, SST. Add $65 for multi-chokes.
    Mfg.'s Sug. Retail $649 $575 $495 $460 $420 $390 $350 $310

CLASSIC—12 ga. only, 3 in. chambers, 26-30 in. barrels, SST. Add $80 for multi-chokes.
    Mfg.'s Sug. Retail $706 $620 $530 $480 $440 $400 $360 $320

SHOTGUNS: SINGLE BARREL AND LEVER ACTION

DIANO I—12, 20, or .410 ga., 3 in. chambers, top lever single barrel action, folding configuration, vent rib.
    Mfg.'s Sug. Retail $129 $115 $95 $85 $80 $75 $70 $65

DIANO II—similar to Diano I, except has bottom lever opening.
    Mfg.'s Sug. Retail $129 $115 $95 $85 $80 $75 $70 $65

LONER I—similar to Diano I.
    Mfg.'s Sug. Retail $109 $95 $80 $75 $65 $55 $45 $35

Grading	100%	98%	95%	90%	80%	70%	60%

LONER II—similar to Diano II.
    Mfg.'s Sug. Retail $109 $95 $80 $75 $65 $55 $45 $35

APACHE—12 ga. only, lever action, 3 in. chambers, 20 in. barrel, SST. Add $80 for multi-chokes.
    Mfg.'s Sug. Retail $473 $410 $355 $325 $300 $280 $260 $245

SHOTGUNS: SLIDE ACTION

PUMP ACTION—12 ga. only, available in riot, field, or deer (slug) barrel configurations, 3 in. chamber, hunter model has multi-chokes standard.
    Mfg.'s Sug. Retail $329 $290 $245 $205 $185 $170 $150 $125

COMBINATION GUNS

AIRONE—12 ga./.30-06 or .308 Win. cal.'s, boxlock with false sideplates, double triggers, checkered walnut stock and forearm, swivels.
    Mfg.'s Sug. Retail $793 $695 $595 $550 $500 $460 $420 $385

CONDOR—similar to Airone, except does not have false sideplates.
    Mfg.'s Sug. Retail $725 $650 $545 $500 $460 $420 $385 $350

DOUBLE RIFLES

LEOPARD EXPRESS—.30-06, .308 Win., .375 H&H, and 7 x 65R cal.'s, boxlock action, double triggers, checkered walnut stock and forearm.
    Mfg.'s Sug. Retail $1,529 $1,325 $1,150 $975 $900 $840 $775 $725

ZOLI, ANTONIO

MANUFACTURED IN BRESCIA, ITALY. IMPORTED AND DISTRIBUTED EXCLUSIVELY BY ANTONIO ZOLI U.S.A. INC., LOCATED IN FORT WAYNE, IN, PREVIOUSLY IMPORTED AND DISTRIBUTED BY FIOCCHI OF AMERICA, INC. LOCATED IN OZARK, MO. AND BY MANDALL SHOOTING SUPPLIES, INC. LOCATED IN SCOTTSDALE, AZ.

All models within this heading are distributed by Fiocchi of America, Inc. unless otherwise noted.

RIFLES: O/U

The rifles listed below (including O/U, side by side, and bolt action) are imported exclusively by Euroarms of America.

EXPRESS—7 x 65R, .30-06, or 9.3 x 74R cal., ejectors, add $146 for Express EM Model.
    Mfg.'s Sug. Retail $3,800 $3,400 $3,000 $2,600 $2,200 $1,950 $1,650 $1,450
    Add $800 for E Model.

EXPRESS EM—7 x 65R, .30-06, or 9.3 x 74R cal., ejectors, add $1,912 for Express ES Deluxe Model.
    Mfg.'s Sug. Retail $4,500 $4,100 $3,600 $3,200 $2,900 $2,600 $2,200 $1,900
    Add $1,700 for Deluxe Model.
    Add $4,200 for E3 Deluxe Model.

RIFLES: S X S

SAVANA E—7 x 65R, .30-06, or 9.3 x 74R cal., boxlock action, ejectors, add $134 for Savana EM Model.
    Mfg.'s Sug. Retail $5,700 $5,000 $4,500 $3,750 $3,000 $2,600 $2,200 $1,950

    Savana Deluxe—similar to Savana E, except has elaborate game scene engraving.
    Mfg.'s Sug. Retail $7,950 $7,250 $6,500 $6,000 $5,500 $5,000 $4,600 $4,200

RIFLES: BOLT ACTION

AZ 1900—.243 Win., .270 Win., 6.5 x 55, .30-06, or .308 cal., checkered walnut stock with sling swivels, iron sights, 7.4 lbs.
    Mfg.'s Sug. Retail $496 $445 $375 $325 $295 $280 $265 $250

    AZ 1900 Deluxe—similar to AZ 1900, except has better grade walnut.
    Mfg.'s Sug. Retail $547 $460 $385 $330 $295 $280 $265 $250

Grading	100%	98%	95%	90%	80%	70%	60%

AZ 1900 Super Deluxe—similar to AZ 1900 Deluxe, except has moderate engraving and select checkered walnut stock.

Mfg.'s Sug. Retail	$796	$720	$595	$525	$460	$420	$385	$350

SHOTGUNS: O/U

SILVER SNIPE—12 or 20 ga., various barrel lengths, vent rib, single trigger, engraved.

	$485	$440	$400	$360	$330	$300	$280

GOLDEN SNIPE—12 or 20 ga, various barrel lengths, vent rib, single trigger, ejectors, engraved.

	$560	$520	$475	$430	$395	$360	$330

DELFINO—12 or 20 ga., 3 in. chambers, 26 or 28 in. barrels, ejectors, vent rib, single non-selective trigger, blued frame with delicate engraving, walnut pistol grip stock and forearm.

Mfg.'s Sug. Retail	$425	$375	$325	$295	$280	$265	$250	$235

RITMO HUNTING—12 ga. only, 3 in. chambers, 26 or 28 in. vent barrels and rib, SST, ejectors, select checkered walnut, blued frame and barrels with moderate engraving, recoil pad, 7¼ lbs.

Mfg.'s Sug. Retail	$590	$510	$465	$410	$370	$350	$335	$310

SILVER SNIPE—12 or 20 ga., 3 in. chambers on the 20 ga., single trigger, ejectors, light engraving.

Mfg.'s Sug. Retail	$739	$675	$585	$530	$485	$440	$400	$375

Add $50 for multi-chokes (12 ga. only).

This model is distributed by Euroarms of America, Inc.

CONDOR MODEL—12 ga. skeet model, 28 in. barrels, SST, ejectors, wide vent rib, engraved silver finished receiver, recoil pad.

Mfg.'s Sug. Retail	$895	$795	$700	$640	$585	$530	$485	$440

This model is distributed by Mandall Shooting Supplies, Inc.

ANGEL MODEL—12 ga. only, field grade, SST, ejectors, wide vent rib, engraved receiver, recoil pad.

Mfg.'s Sug. Retail	$895	$795	$700	$640	$585	$530	$485	$440

This model is distributed by Mandall Shooting Supplies, Inc.

RITMO PIGEON GRADE IV—12 ga. only, live pigeon gun, 28 in. barrels, SST, ejectors, superbly engraved silver finished receiver, extra fine checkering on deluxe walnut, vent barrels and rib, cased, 7½ lbs.

Mfg.'s Sug. Retail	$1,785	$1,495	$1,200	$1,000	$875	$795	$725	$650

M85 RITMO TRAP OR SKEET—12 ga. only, 28 in. (Skeet only), 30, or 32 in. barrels, ejectors, SST, special stock dimensions, engraved blue receiver, select checkered walnut stock and forearm, cased, 7¾ lbs.

Mfg.'s Sug. Retail	$690	$620	$500	$465	$440	$415	$395	$370

This model is also available in a single barrel trap model at no extra charge.

M85 Ritmo Trap Combination—12 ga. only, supplied with O/U and single barrel sets, various barrel lengths, cased.

Mfg.'s Sug. Retail	$1,100	$975	$900	$800	$700	$620	$575	$500

TARGET MODEL 208—12 ga. only, available in either Trap, Skeet, or Monotrap configuration.

Mfg.'s Sug. Retail	$996	$895	$775	$695	$620	$575	$500	$450

Add $494 for Monotrap II 208 Model.

TARGET MODEL 308—12 ga. only, available in either Trap, Skeet, or Monotrap configuration.

Mfg.'s Sug. Retail	$1,581	$1,375	$1,125	$950	$875	$795	$725	$650

Add $76 for multi-chokes.
Add $824 for Monotrap II 308 Model.

Grading	100%	98%	95%	90%	80%	70%	60%

SHOTGUNS: SIDE-BY-SIDE

SILVER HAWK—12 or 20 ga., double trigger, engraved.

	$420	$395	$360	$330	$300	$280	$260

ARIETE M3—12 ga. only, 26 or 28 in. barrels, matted rib, single non-selective trigger, ejectors, blued receiver with fine scroll engraving, cased.

Mfg.'s Sug. Retail	$590	$495	$400	$360	$330	$310	$285	$260

EMPIRE—12 or 20 ga. Mag., 27 or 28 in. barrels, moderate engraving, coin finished receiver.

Mfg.'s Sug. Retail	$1,660	$1,425	$1,175	$975	$875	$795	$725	$650

Add $96 for 3 in. Mag. chambers.

This model is distributed by Euroarms of America, Inc.

VOLCANO RECORD—12 ga. only, 28 in. barrels, H&H type sidelocks, ejectors, SST, treble Purdey locks, silver finished receiver with elaborate engraving, best quality fine checkered walnut, special order only.

Mfg.'s Sug. Retail	$5,994	$5,300	$4,475	$3,950	$3,400	$2,950	$2,650	$2,300

Volcano Record ELM—12 ga. only, built to individual customer specifications, best quality H&H style sidelock.

Mfg.'s Sug. Retail	$14,649	$13,250	$11,000	$9,750	$8,600	$7,400	$6,300	$5,450

This model is distributed by Euroarms of America, Inc.

CUSTOM SERIES—s x s, individual custom order only, every refinement is used in the construction of these extremely rare and expensive shotguns. These guns have to be appraised individually since their numbers are so few.

COMBINATION GUNS

COMBINATO—12 or 20 ga. over .243 or .222 cal.'s, boxlock action, game scene engraved receiver with silver finish, double triggers, folding rear sight, skipline checkering, with sling swivels.

Mfg.'s Sug. Retail	$690	$620	$500	$465	$440	$415	$395	$370

Combinato Set—includes one set of either 20 or 12 ga. barrels and an additional rifle/shotgun barrel set, same cal.'s as Combinato, cased.

Mfg.'s Sug. Retail	$965	$800	$745	$685	$630	$600	$575	$550

SAFARI DELUXE—similar to Combinato, except has sideplates with elaborate game scene engraving.

Mfg.'s Sug. Retail	$2,790	$2,455	$2,100	$1,800	$1,600	$1,425	$1,275	$1,050

Safari Deluxe 2—includes two sets of barrels (12 ga. and 20 ga. Mag. with choice of cal.'s).

Mfg.'s Sug. Retail	$4,166	$3,800	$3,100	$2,775	$2,400	$2,100	$1,850	$1,650

The Safari Deluxe (including Deluxe 2) is imported by Euroarms of America.

EXPRESS E3 SET—includes one set of .30-06 O/U barrels, one set of 20 ga./.243 cal. barrels, one set of 20 ga./20 ga. barrels, special order, elaborate game scene engraving, includes German claw mount 4X scope and case.

Mfg.'s Sug. Retail	$2,700	$2,325	$1,850	$1,600	$1,425	$1,275	$1,050	$950

BLACK POWDER

MODERN BLACK POWDER GUNS

Editors Note: Even though United States' arms manufacturing firms have made some increases in the production of Black Powder arms, the majority of these companies were until recently making only specialty items, beautiful in detail and craftsmanship, but very limited in production. Today, most of the leading technology in Black Powder design is coming from America. Even though the majority of our Black Powder arms are still being imported from abroad, US firms are making inroads in changing the overall proportion of foreign importation. Italy is still the major supplier of old style replicas with Germany and Switzerland following suit with the precision craftsmanship of old world tradition.

1989 should be an interesting year for Black Powder shooting enthusiasts. After 2 relatively soft years of sales due to dramatic price increases caused in part by the falling value of U.S. currency on the international market, Black Powder sales and creativity are once again on the rise. As we have mentioned in years past, Black Powder shooting clubs, shooting teams, special hunting seasons, and continued legislation against firearms continue to increase public awareness of the Black Powder target/sporting shooting potential. Special Black Powder hunting seasons have really been the reason for the comeback after the past several years.

Most of the innovation in the field of Black Powder design has come in development of special hunting guns which are designed to eliminate many of the problems that have made Black Powder hunting difficult in the past. New designs such as those sold by Gonic Arms, Michigan Arms, and Modern Muzzleloaders have gone a long way to eliminate the problems associated with Black Powder shooting in the past.

The guns listed in this section are factory assembled, kit guns are also possible from many of the below listed manufacturers at substantial savings. They are not included in this section, however. Also, most Black Powder guns under $100 in value are not listed.

One final note about pricing in this section. Due to the decreased value of the U.S. dollar on European and Asian markets, many imported Black Powder models have increased substantially in cost over the last two years. Because some dealers may still have stock remaining that was purchased pre-1987, their lower cost structure normally reflects a lower price to the consumer (and lower prices than listed in this section). Newer inventory purchases will follow values established below.

ALL ADD ON'S FOR PRICING LISTED IN THIS SECTION ARE RETAIL WITHOUT DEALER DISCOUNTING.

ALLEN FIREARMS

PREVIOUS IMPORTER LOCATED IN SANTA FE, NM IMPORTING A. UBERTI FIREARMS UNTIL EARLY IN 1987. AFTER ALLEN FIREARMS CLOSED, OLD-WEST GUN CO. (NOW CALLED CIMARRON ARMS) LOCATED IN HOUSTON, TX PURCHASED THE REMAINING INVENTORY AND IS CURRENTLY SELLING THE BALANCE OF ALLEN FIREARMS (IN ADDITION TO ORDERING NEW PRODUCTS UNDER THEIR NAME). VALUES BELOW HAVE INTENTIONALLY NOT BEEN DISCONTINUED AS THEY WILL APPROXIMATE VALUES FOR OLD-WEST GUN CO. UBERTI FIREARMS.

Grading	100%	98%	95%	90%

REVOLVERS: PERCUSSION

1847 WALKER—.44 cal., percussion, charcoal finish, color case hardened frame, hammer, and load lever, brass trim, engraved cylinder, 4.4 lbs.

$230 $190 $135

Grading	100%	98%	95%	90%

1848 BABY DRAGOON—.31 cal., percussion, 3, 4, or 5 in. barrel, 5 shot, color case hardened frame, hammer, no load lever, engraved cylinder, 1.4 lbs. Add $15 for silver straps and trigger guard.

| | $180 | $150 | $105 | |

DRAGOON (1ST, 2ND, OR 3RD)—.44 cal., percussion, 6 shot, brass grip straps, color case hardened frame, hammer, and load lever, brass trim, 3.9 lbs. Add $15 for silver-plated straps, or cut for stock on 3rd Dragoon Model.

| | $185 | $160 | $110 | |

1849 WELLS FARGO—.31 cal., percussion, 3, 4, or 5 in. octagonal barrel, 5 shot, color case hardened frame, hammer, no load lever, brass trim, 1½ lbs. Add $15 for silver straps.

| | $180 | $145 | $105 | |

1849 POCKET—.31 cal., percussion, with loading lever, 3, 4, or 5 in. barrel, 5 shot, color case hardened frame, hammer, and load lever, brass trim, 1½ lbs. Add $15 for silver straps and trigger guard.

| | $180 | $145 | $110 | |

1851 NAVY—.36 cal., percussion, many styles, loading lever, 6 shot engraved cylinder, 2.8 lbs. Add $95 for stock, $30 for stainless steel, $15 for silver plated strap and trigger guard, or steel strap and trigger guard.

| | $180 | $145 | $105 | |

1860 ARMY—.44 cal., percussion, 8 in. barrel, 6 shot, loading lever, color case hardened frame, hammer, and load lever, all brass back strap and trigger guard, or steel backstrap and brass trigger guard on fluted cylinder model, 2.6 lbs. Add $95 for stock, $10 for silver plated strap and trigger guard, $25 for stainless steel.

| | $175 | $145 | $115 | |

1861 NAVY—.36 cal., percussion, 5 in. barrel, many styles, brass back strap or trigger guard, color case hardened frame, hammer, and load lever, 2½ lbs. Add $15 for silver plated strap and trigger guard, $15 for fluted military cylinder, $25 for stainless steel.

| | $185 | $145 | $105 | |

1862 POLICE—.36 cal., percussion, 4½, 5½, or 6½ in. barrel, color case hardened frame, hammer, and load lever, cylinder, semi-fluted or engraved, 1.6 lbs. Add $15 for silver plated straps and trigger guard, $25 for stainless steel.

| | $160 | $130 | $105 | |

AUGUSTA CONFEDERATE—.36 cal., percussion, 7½ in. octagonal barrel, color case hardened hammer and trigger, all brass frame, engraved cylinder, 2½-2¾ lbs.

| | $130 | $105 | $75 | |

GRISWOLD CONFEDERATE—.36 and .44 cal., percussion, same as above except round barrel, forward of lug, does not have engraved cylinder.

| | $130 | $105 | $75 | |

LEECH AND RIGDON CONFEDERATE—.36 cal., percussion, same as above except all steel frame.

| | $180 | $150 | $105 | |

TEXAS CONFEDERATE DRAGOON—.44 cal., percussion, 7½ in. round barrel, color case hardened frame, hammer, and load lever, brass trim, "Tucker, Sherrard, & Co.", 4 lbs. Add $35 for stainless steel.

| | $190 | $155 | $110 | |

1858 REMINGTON—.44 cal., percussion, 7½ in. barrel, 6 shot, blued steel, brass trigger guard, 2.6 lbs. Add $15 for adj. sights.

| | $155 | $130 | $90 | |

1858 REMINGTON STAINLESS—same as above, has brass strap and trigger guard. Add $15 for adj. sights.

| | $215 | $180 | $125 | |

1858 REMINGTON NEW NAVY—.36 cal., percussion, 6½ in. octagonal barrel, 6 shot, blue frame, 2½ lbs. Add $15 for adj. sights.

| | $155 | $130 | $90 | |

1866 REVOLVING CARBINE—.44 cal., percussion, 18 in. barrel, 6 shot, blued steel, brass trigger guard, walnut stock, 4.6 lbs.

| | $295 | $250 | $150 | |

Grading	100%	98%	95%	90%

RIFLES

HAWKEN SANTA FE—.53 cal., percussion, single shot, 32 in. oct. barrel, damascened finish, double set triggers, 9½ lbs., walnut stock.

| | $295 | $250 | $150 |

ST. LOUIS RIFLE—.45, .50, .54, or .58 cal., flintlock and percussion, color case hardened hammer lock and trigger guard, octagonal barrel. Add $15 for .54 or .58 cal., percussion, $15 for flint lock, $30 for 50 cal. flint lock.

| | $195 | $165 | $125 |

SQUIRREL RIFLE—.32 cal., percussion or flintlock, color case hardened hammer and lock, brass trigger guard, 28 in. octagonal barrel. Add $15 for flint lock.

| | $170 | $140 | $105 |

ARMI SAN MARCO

MFG. IN ITALY, CURRENTLY IMPORTED BY DENVER ARMS (FORMERLY HOUSE OF MUSKETS) LOCATED IN PAGOSA SPRINGS, CO. AND MUZZLE LOADERS INC LOCATED IN BURKE, VA.

REVOLVERS: PERCUSSION

WALKER MODEL 1847—.44 cal., percussion, 9 in. barrel, color case hardened frame, loading lever and hammer, brass trigger guard and steel backstrap, 4½ lbs.

| *Mfg.'s Sug. Retail* | $200 | $175 | $150 | $100 |

BABY DRAGOON—.31 cal., percussion, 5 in. octagonal barrel, 5 shot cylinder, color case hardened frame, hammer and load lever, silver plated brass backstrap and trigger guard.

| *Mfg.'s Sug. Retail* | $145 | $135 | $110 | $80 |

1ST MODEL DRAGOON—.44 cal., percussion, 8 in. barrel, color case hardened fram loading lever and hammer, silver plated brass backstrap and trigger guard.

| *Mfg.'s Sug. Retail* | $160 | $140 | $120 | $85 |

2ND MODEL DRAGOON—same as 1st Model Dragoon, except 7½ in. barrel.

| *Mfg.'s Sug. Retail* | $160 | $140 | $120 | $85 |

3RD MODEL DRAGOON—.44 cal., percussion, 7½ in. barrel, Western Model has silver plated brass backstrap, Military Model has steel backstrap - cut for stock, Texas Model has brass backstrap. Add $15 for Western Model.

| *Mfg.'s Sug. Retail* | $160 | $140 | $120 | $85 |

1851 NAVY—.36 or .44 cal., percussion, 7½ in. octagonal barrel, engraved (roll) cylinder, color case hardened frame and load lever, silver plated brass backstrap and square back trigger guard. Sheriff's Model has 5 in. barrel, brass trigger guard and backstrap. Deduct $20 for brass back strap and trigger guard, $25 for brass frame.

| *Mfg.'s Sug. Retail* | $125 | $115 | $95 | $75 |

1860 ARMY—.44 cal., percussion 8 in. round barrel, color case hardened frame, hammer and load lever, Sheriff's Model has 5 in. barrel, 2¾ lbs. Add $5 for Sheriff's Model. Deduct $25 for brass frame or fluted cylinder model.

| *Mfg.'s Sug. Retail* | $135 | $120 | $100 | $60 |

1861 NAVY—.36 cal., percussion, 7½ in. round barrel, color case hardened frame, hammer and load lever, silver plated brass backstrap and trigger guard (very similar to 1860 Army, except cal. and shorter Navy grips).

| *Mfg.'s Sug. Retail* | $145 | $130 | $110 | $80 |

RIFLES

HAWKENS—.50 cal., percussion, 30 in. octagonal chrome lined barrel, brass patchbox, target sights, double set triggers, 8 lbs.

| *Mfg.'s Sug. Retail* | $200 | $180 | $150 | $110 |

ST. LOUIS HAWKEN—.50, .54, or .58 cal., percussion, color case hardened hammer and lock, 28 in. octagonal barrel, brass trim, 7 lbs. 15 oz. Add $65 for curly maple stock.

| *Mfg.'s Sug. Retail* | $155 | $140 | $115 | $100 |

ROCKY MOUNTAIN SHORT RIFLE—.50 cal., percussion, 24 in. octagonal barrel, brass furniture.

| *Mfg.'s Sug. Retail* | $150 | $140 | $120 | $100 |

ARMI SAN PAOLO

MFG. IN ITALY. ARMI SAN PAOLO IS A WHOLLY OWNED SUBSIDIARY OF EUROARMS OF EUROPE WHICH ALSO OWNS EUROARMS OF AMERICA. SEE EUROARMS SECTION FOR PRICING. PREVIOUSLY IMPORTED BY KENDALL INTERNATIONAL LOCATED IN PARIS, KY AND MUZZLE LOADERS, INC. LOCATED IN BURKE, VA).

ARMSPORT

IMPORTERS LOCATED IN MIAMI, FL.

PISTOLS

CORSAIR PISTOL—.44 cal., percussion, double barrel, blued finish, color case hardened hammer and lock, brass trim.

$95 $80 $65

DUELING PISTOL—.45 cal., percussion, blued finish, color case hardened hammer and lock, brass trim.

$105 $90 $75

KENTUCKY PISTOL—.45 or .50 cal., percussion or flintlock, blued finish, color case hardened hammer and lock, brass trim. Add $10 for flint lock.

$75 $65 $55

MODEL 1847 COLT WALKER REVOLVER—.44 cal., percussion, color case hardened frame, hammer, and load lever, brass trigger guard, steel backstrap, 6 shot, 4½ lbs.

Mfg.'s Sug. Retail $220 $190 $165 $120

MODEL 1851 COLT NAVY—.36 or .44 cal., percussion, brass or color case hardened frame, brass trigger guard and backstrap, 6 shot. Add $40 for color case hardened steel with engraved cylinders. Add $110 for engraved gold and silver.

Mfg.'s Sug. Retail $105 $95 $80 $65

MODEL 1860 COLT ARMY—.44 cal., percussion, brass frame, trigger guard, and backstrap, color case hardened hammer and load lever, 6 shot. Add $40 for color case hardened steel, $130 for stainless steel, $95 for engraved gold and silver.

Mfg.'s Sug. Retail $115 $100 $85 $70

MODEL 1858 REMINGTON ARMY—.44 cal., percussion, blued frame, brass trigger guard, steel backstrap, 6 shot. Add $90 for stainless steel, $75 for engraved gold and silver. Deduct $40 for brass frame.

Mfg.'s Sug. Retail $155 $135 $115 $100

REMINGTON BUFFALO TARGET—.44 cal., percussion, 12 in. octagonal barrel, brass frame and trigger guard, adj. sights, based on 1858 Navy frame, 38 oz.

Mfg.'s Sug. Retail $175 $150 $130 $105

RIFLES

BRISTOL KID RIFLE—.32 or .36 cal., percussion. Add $15 for standard version, $25 for deluxe. Discontinued in 1984.

$115 $95 $75

HAWKEN RIFLE—.45, .50, .54 or .58 cal., percussion or flintlock, color case hardened hammer and lock, percussion cap holder in stock, chrome lined barrels. Add $25 for flintlock.

$225 $195 $140

HAWKENTUCKY RIFLE—.36, or .50 cal., percussion or flintlock, color case hardened hammer and lock, percussion cap holder in stock, chrome lined barrels. Add $10 for flintlock.

$180 $150 $120

KENTUCKY RIFLE—.36, .45, or .50, cal., percussion or flintlock, color case hardened hammer and lock, percussion cap holder in stock, chrome lined barrels, brass trim. Add $10 for flintlock, $55 for deluxe with engraved white steel hammer and lock.

$225 $200 $135

TRYON TRAILBLAZER—.50, .53, or .54 cal., percussion, color case hardened hammer and lock, cap holder in stock. Add $45 for deluxe engraved.

$370 $310 $235

Grading	100%	98%	95%	90%

SHOTGUNS

KENTUCKY RIFLE/SHOTGUN COMBO—.45 or .50 cal., 20 ga., percussion only, same as above.

	$300	$245	$160	

DOUBLE BARREL SHOTGUN—12 or 10 ga., percussion only, blued finish, color case hardened hammer and lock. Add $50 for 10 ga.

	$390	$315	$250	

ASSOCIATION FOR THE PRESERVATION OF WESTERN ANTIQUITY

DISTRIBUTED BY WILLIAM BENJAMIN LTD. IN ASHVILLE, NC.

1862 COLT NAVY—.36 cal., percussion, standard construction, roll engraved cylinder with 24Kt. gold inlay, only 100 revolvers made, sold in custom cameo art presentation case depicting a miner panning for gold, some sets may come with the addition of a seated Liberty silver dollar and a Double Eagle gold piece, coins value should be based on current numismatic value, present retail for entire set including gold pieces is $2,395.

Mfg.'s Sug. Retail	$995	$895	$795	$695

BENSON FIREARMS, LTD.

PREVIOUS IMPORTER/DISTRIBUTOR OF A. UBERTI FIREARMS MFG. IN ITALY. BENSON FIREARMS WAS LOCATED IN SEATTLE, WA.

Benson Firearms was a recent importer (1987-1988) and imported A. Uberti firearms that were marked "Benson Firearms Seattle, WA". In 1989 Benson Firearms, Ltd. combined with Uberti USA, Inc. located in New Milford, CT.

All guns were manufactured to the same exact specifications as the originals. Crafted with an unmistakable fire blue finish. A. Uberti is one of the largest manufacturers of black powder firearms.

To the price of each pistol, add $70 for display case, $180 for type "A" engraving, $265 for type "B" engraving, $345 for type "C" engraving (except for Walker & Dragoon Models add $650 for type "C" engraving and 1858 New Army, New Navy or 1858 Carbine add $525), $565 for type "C/O" engraving all models (except 1858 New Army, New Navy or 1858 Carbine add $800).

REVOLVERS

1847 WALKER—.44 cal., percussion, charcoal finish, color case hardened frame, hammer, and load lever, brass trim, engraved cylinder, 4.4 lbs.

	$240	$200	$135	

1848 BABY DRAGOON—.31 cal., percussion, 3, 4, or 5 in. barrel, 5 shot, color case hardened frame, hammer, no load lever, engraved cylinder, 1.4 lbs. Add $15 for silver straps and trigger guard.

	$185	$155	$105	

DRAGOON (1ST, 2ND, OR 3RD)—.44 cal., percussion, 6 shot, brass grip straps, color case hardened frame, hammer, and load lever, brass trim, 3.9 lbs. Add $15 for silver-plated straps, or cut for stock on 3rd Dragoon Model.

	$195	$165	$110	

1849 WELLS FARGO—.31 cal., percussion, 3, 4, or 5 in. octagonal barrel, 5 shot, color case hardened frame, hammer, no load lever, brass trim, 1½ lbs. Add $15 for silver straps.

	$190	$155	$105	

1849 POCKET—.31 cal., percussion, with loading lever, 3, 4, or 5 in. barrel, 5 shot, color casehardened frame, hammer, and load lever, brass trim, 1½ lbs. Add $15 for silver straps and trigger guard.

	$190	$160	$110	

Grading	100%	98%	95%	90%

1851 NAVY—.36 cal., percussion, many styles, loading lever, 6 shot engraved cylinder, 2.8 lbs. Add $100 for stock, $50 for stainless steel, $15 for silver plated strap and trigger guard, or steel strap and trigger guard. Add $125 for shoulder stock.

$190 $160 $105

1860 ARMY—.44 cal., percussion, 8 in. barrel, 6 shot, loading lever, color case hardened frame, hammer, and load lever, all brass back strap and trigger guard, or steel backstrap and brass trigger guard on fluted cylinder model, 2.6 lbs. Add $125 for stock, $15 for silver plated strap and trigger guard, $60 for stainless steel.

$195 $165 $115

1861 NAVY—.36 cal., percussion, 5 in. barrel, many styles, brass back strap or trigger guard, color casehardened frame, hammer, and load lever, 2½ lbs. Add $15 for silver plated strap and trigger guard, $15 for fluted military cylinder, $50 for stainless steel, $125 for shoulder stock.

$195 $160 $105

1862 POCKET NAVY—.36 cal., percussion, 4½, 5½, or 6½ in. barrel, color case hardened frame, hammer, and load lever, cylinder, semi-fluted or engraved, 1.6 lbs. Add $15 for silver plated straps and trigger guard, $50 for stainless steel.

$170 $145 $105

1862 POLICE—.36 cal., percussion, 4½, 5½, or 6½ in. barrel, color case hardened frame, hammer, and load lever, cylinder, semi-fluted or engraved, 1.6 lbs. Add $15 for silver plated straps and trigger guard, $50 for stainless steel.

$170 $140 $105

AUGUSTA CONFEDERATE—.36 cal., percussion, 7½ in. octagonal barrel, color case hardened hammer and trigger, all brass frame, engraved cylinder, 2½-2¾ lbs.

$140 $115 $75

GRISWOLD CONFEDERATE—.36 or .44 cal., percussion, same as above except round barrel, forward of lug, does not have engraved cylinder.

$140 $115 $75

LEECH AND RIGDON CONFEDERATE—.36 cal., percussion, same as above except all steel frame.

$190 $160 $105

TEXAS CONFEDERATE DRAGOON—.44 cal., percussion, 7½ in. round barrel, color case hardened frame, hammer, and load lever, brass trim, "Tucker, Sherrard, & Co.", 4 lbs. Add $35 for stainless steel.

$200 $170 $110

1858 REMINGTON—.44 cal., percussion, 7½ in. barrel, 6 shot, blued steel, brass trigger guard, 2.6 lbs. Add $30 for adj. sights.

$165 $140 $90

1858 REMINGTON STAINLESS—same as above, has brass strap and trigger guard. Add $35 for adj. sights.

$225 $190 $125

1858 REMINGTON NEW NAVY—.36 cal., percussion, 6½ in. octagonal barrel, 6 shot, blue frame, 2½ lbs. Add $30 for adj. sights.

$165 $145 $90

1866 REVOLVING CARBINE—.44 cal., percussion, 18 in. barrel, 6 shot, blued steel, brass trigger guard, walnut stock, 4.6 lbs.

$310 $270 $150

RIFLES: PERCUSSION

HAWKEN SANTA FE—.53 cal., single shot, 32 in. oct. barrel, damascened finish, double set triggers, 9½ lbs., walnut stock.

$310 $270 $150

BERETTA

MANUFACTURER LOCATED IN BRESCIA, ITALY. 1680-PRESENT.

SHOTGUNS

COMMEMORATIVE O/U MODEL M1000—12 ga., percussion, 30 in. barrel, limited production.

	$350	$280	$220

Last Mfg.'s Sug. Retail was $840.

BONDINI

MFG. IN ITALY. IMPORTED BY HELMUT HOFMAN, INC. LOCATED IN PLACITAS, NH. PREVIOUSLY IMPORTED BY HOUSE OF MUSKETS LOCATED IN PAGOSA LAKES, CO.

PISTOLS

ASHABELLA COOK UNDERHAMMER—.45 cal., unique underhammer design uses trigger guard as mainspring. Very accurate.

Mfg.'s Sug. Retail	$80	$65	$55	$45

WM. PARKER PISTOL—.45 cal., flintlock or percussion, 11 in. octagonal browned barrel, silver plated furniture, double set triggers. Add $10 for flintlock.

Mfg.'s Sug. Retail	$250	$225	$185	$145

F. ROCHATTE—.45 cal., percussion, round barrel, single set triggers, hand checkered stock.

Mfg.'s Sug. Retail	$265	$240	$200	$160

RIFLES

SANFTL SCHUETZEN RIFLE—.45 cal., percussion, 31 in. octagonal barrel, unique backward lock, both peep and open iron sights, Schuetzen style butt plate and trigger guard, brass furniture.

Mfg.'s Sug. Retail	$530	$440	$380	$320

SHOTGUNS

GALLYON SHOTGUN—12 ga., percussion, blued barrel, single shot.

Mfg.'s Sug. Retail	$350	$295	$255	$210

BROWNING

HEADQUARTERS LOCATED IN MORGAN, UT.

RIFLES

JONATHAN BROWNING MOUNTAIN RIFLE—50 cal., percussion, 30 in. octagon barrel, single set trigger, engraved lock plate, select walnut stock, cased with medallion, 1,000 produced in 1978. Issue price — $650.

	$650	$500	$440

MOUNTAIN RIFLE—same as Jonathan Browning Mountain Rifle, without Centennial embellishments, not cased. Also in .45 or .54 cal.

	$225	$200	$170

CHARLES DALY

SEE DALY, CHARLES.

CIMARRON ARMS COMPANY

IMPORTER/DISTRIBUTOR OF CUSTOM CRAFTED A. UBERTI MODERN AND BLACKPOWDER FIREARMS. CIMARRON ARMS IS LOCATED IN HOUSTON, TX.

Grading	100%	98%	95%	90%

Cimarron Arms was previously named Old-West Gun Company.

After years of research, Cimarron Arms Co. has contracted A. Uberti to manufacture the most authentic western firearms reproductions to date, including such exact modifications as changing the taper of the cylinder face to exactly match the original Colt's. Also, serial number location, cylinder scenes, stock configuration, etc. have all been carefully manufactured to duplicate the original.

Add the following amounts for engraving on handguns:
Add $280 for "A" style engraving (30% coverage).
Add $425 for "B" style engraving (50% coverage).
Add $750 for "C" style engraving (100% coverage).
Add $825 for "Texas Cattlebrands" engraving pattern.

REVOLVERS

1847 WALKER—.44 cal., percussion, charcoal finish, color case hardened frame, hammer, and load lever, brass trim, engraved cylinder, 4.4 lbs.
Mfg.'s Sug. Retail **$295** **$240** **$200** **$165**

1848 BABY DRAGOON—.31 cal., percussion, 3, 4, or 5 in. barrel, 5 shot, color case hardened frame, hammer, no load lever, engraved cylinder, 1.4 lbs. Add $15 for silver straps and trigger guard.
Mfg.'s Sug. Retail **$250** **$190** **$160** **$130**

DRAGOON (1ST, 2ND, OR 3RD)—.44 cal., percussion, 6 shot, brass grip straps, color case hardened frame, hammer, and load lever, brass trim, 3.9 lbs. Add $15 for silver-plated straps, or cut for stock on 3rd Dragoon Model.
Mfg.'s Sug. Retail **$265** **$210** **$170** **$130**

1849 WELLS FARGO—.31 cal., percussion, 3, 4, or 5 in. octagonal barrel, 5 shot, color case hardened frame, hammer, no load lever, brass trim, 1½ lbs. Add $15 for silver straps.
Mfg.'s Sug. Retail **$250** **$190** **$160** **$130**

1849 POCKET—.31 cal., percussion, with loading lever, 3, 4, or 5 in. barrel, 5 shot, color case hardened frame, hammer, and load lever, brass trim, 1½ lbs. Add $15 for silver straps and trigger guard.
Mfg.'s Sug. Retail **$250** **$190** **$160** **$130**

1851 NAVY—.36 cal., percussion, many styles, loading lever, 6 shot engraved cylinder, 2.8 lbs. Add $100 for stock, $50 for stainless steel, $15 for silver plated strap and trigger guard, or steel strap and trigger guard.
Mfg.'s Sug. Retail **$250** **$190** **$160** **$130**

1860 ARMY—.44 cal., percussion, 8 in. barrel, 6 shot, loading lever, color case hardened frame, hammer, and load lever, all brass back strap and trigger guard, or steel backstrap and brass trigger guard on fluted cylinder model, 2.6 lbs. Add $100 for stock, $15 for silver plated strap and trigger guard, $50 for stainless steel.
Mfg.'s Sug. Retail **$250** **$195** **$165** **$135**

1861 NAVY—.36 cal., percussion, 5 in. barrel, many styles, brass back strap or trigger guard, color case hardened frame, hammer, and load lever, 2½ lbs. Add $15 for silver plated strap and trigger guard, $15 for fluted military cylinder, $50 for stainless steel, $100 for shoulder stock.
Mfg.'s Sug. Retail **$250** **$195** **$165** **$135**

1862 POLICE—.36 cal., percussion, 4½, 5½, or 6½ in. barrel, color case hardened frame, hammer, and load lever, cylinder, semi-fluted or engraved, 1.6 lbs. Add $15 for silver plated straps and trigger guard, $50 for stainless steel.
Mfg.'s Sug. Retail **$250** **$190** **$160** **$130**

1862 POCKET NAVY—.36 cal., percussion, 4½, 5½, or 6½ in. barrel, color case hardened frame, hammer, and load lever, cylinder, semi-fluted or engraved, 1.6 lbs. Add $15 for silver plated straps and trigger guard, $50 for stainless steel.
Mfg.'s Sug. Retail **$250** **$190** **$160** **$130**

AUGUSTA CONFEDERATE—.36 cal., percussion, 7½ in. octagonal barrel, color case hardened hammer and trigger, all brass frame, engraved cylinder, 2½-2¾ lbs.
Mfg.'s Sug. Retail **$190** **$145** **$120** **$90**

Grading	100%	98%	95%	90%

GRISWOLD CONFEDERATE—.36 or .44 cal., percussion, same as above except round barrel, forward of lug, does not have engraved cylinder.
Mfg.'s Sug. Retail **$190** **$145** **$120** **$90**

LEECH AND RIGDON CONFEDERATE—.36 cal., percussion, same as above except all steel frame.
Mfg.'s Sug. Retail **$250** **$190** **$160** **$130**

TEXAS CONFEDERATE DRAGOON—.44 cal., percussion, 7½ in. round barrel, color case hardened frame, hammer, and load lever, brass trim, "Tucker, Sherrard, & Co.", 4 lbs.
Mfg.'s Sug. Retail **$265** **$210** **$170** **$135**

1858 REMINGTON—.44 cal., percussion, 7½ in. barrel, 6 shot, blued steel, brass trigger guard, 2.6 lbs. Add $30 for adj. sights.
Mfg.'s Sug. Retail **$250** **$180** **$150** **$120**

1858 REMINGTON STAINLESS—same as above, has brass strap and trigger guard. Add $45 for adj. sights.
Mfg.'s Sug. Retail **$295** **$240** **$200** **$160**

1858 REMINGTON NEW NAVY—.36 cal., percussion, 6½ in. octagonal barrel, 6 shot, blue frame, 2½ lbs. Add $30 for adj. sights.
Mfg.'s Sug. Retail **$250** **$180** **$150** **$120**

1866 REVOLVING CARBINE—44 cal., percussion, 18 in. barrel, 6 shot, blued steel, brass trigger guard, walnut stock, 4.6 lbs.
Mfg.'s Sug. Retail **$360** **$310** **$260** **$200**

RIFLES: PERCUSSION

HAWKEN SANTA FE—.53 cal., single shot, 32 in. oct. barrel, damascened finish, double set triggers, 9½ lbs., walnut stock.
Mfg.'s Sug. Retail **$350** **$310** **$260** **$200**

ST. LOUIS RIFLE—.45, .50, .54, or .58 cal., flintlock and percussion, color case hardened hammer lock and trigger guard, octagonal barrel. Add $15 for .54 and .58 cal. percussion, $15 for flintlock, $30 for 50 cal. flintlock.
Mfg.'s Sug. Retail **$280** **$250** **$210** **$170**

COLT'S FIREARMS

HARTFORD, CT. COLT SUBCONTRACTED MFR. OF THESE BLACK POWDER PISTOLS TO ALDO UBERTI IN ITALY. PARTS WERE SHIPPED INTO THE U.S. AND ASSEMBLED STATESIDE.

WALKER MODEL—.44 cal., 9 in. barrel, color case hardened frame, hammer, and loading lever, 73 oz., mfg. 1979-1981. Add $100 for cased Heritage Walker Commemorative Model.
$700 **$550** **$450**

Last Mfg.'s Sug. Retail was $500.

BABY DRAGOON—.31 cal., 4 in. barrel, unfluted straight cylinder, color case hardened frame, short frame. Discontinued.
$300 **$240** **$200**

Last Mfg.'s Sug. Retail was $500.
"1 of 500" cased set
$600 **$450** **$350**

Last Mfg.'s Sug. Retail was $900.

1ST MODEL DRAGOON—.44 cal., 7½ in. barrel, oval bolt cuts in cylinder, color case hardened frame, loading lever, plunger, and hammer, one piece stocks, 66 oz. Discontinued in 1981.
$350 **$250** **$195**

Last Mfg.'s Sug. Retail was $300.

Grading	100%	98%	95%	90%

2ND MODEL DRAGOON—.44 cal., 7½ in. barrel, rectangular bolt cuts in cylinder, color case hardened frame, loading lever, plunger, and hammer, one piece stocks, 66 oz. Discontinued in 1981.

| | $350 | $250 | $195 | |

Last Mfg.'s Sug. Retail was $300.

3RD MODEL DRAGOON—.44 cal., 7½ in. barrel, rectangular bolt cuts in cylinder, color case hardened frame, loading lever, plunger, and hammer, round trigger guard, one piece stocks, 66 oz. Discontinued in 1981. Add $400 for cased Giuseppe Garibaldi Commemorative Model.

| | $350 | $250 | $195 | |

Last Mfg.'s Sug. Retail was $300.

1851 NAVY—.36 cal., 7½ in. octagonal barrel, color case hardened frame, loading lever, plunger, and hammer, square trigger guard, one piece stocks, 42 oz. Discontinued in 1981.

| | $350 | $225 | $180 | |

Last Mfg.'s Sug. Retail was $350.

1851 Stainless Navy—stainless steel, only 498 mfg.

| | $695 | $500 | $395 | |

1860 ARMY—.44 cal., 8 in. round barrel, color case hardened frame, loading lever, plunger, and hammer, round trigger guard, one piece stocks, 42 oz. Discontinued in 1981. Two versions made, one has an engraved rebated cylinder and the other has a blued fluted cylinder. Add $125 (over Fluted Cylinder Model) for 1982 Stainless Steel version.

| Fluted Cylinder | $375 | $300 | $200 | |
| Rebated Cylinder | $500 | $400 | $300 | |

Last Mfg.'s Sug. Retail was $350.

1861 NAVY—.36 cal., 7½ in. round barrel, color case hardened frame, loading lever, plunger, and hammer, round trigger guard, one piece stocks, 42 oz. Discontinued in 1981. Add $125 for 1982 Stainless Steel version.

| | $350 | $250 | $200 | |

Last Mfg.'s Sug. Retail was $300.

1862 POCKET NAVY—.36 cal., 5½ in. octagonal barrel, color case hardened frame, loading lever, plunger, and hammer, round trigger guard, one piece stocks, 27 oz. Discontinued in 1981. Add $200 for 1982 Stainless Steel version.

| | $375 | $275 | $225 | |

Last Mfg.'s Sug. Retail was $300.

"1 of 500" cased set

| | $525 | $440 | $320 | |

Last Mfg.'s Sug. Retail was $500.

1862 POCKET POLICE—.36 cal., 5½ in. round barrel, color case hardened frame, loading lever, plunger, and hammer, round trigger guard, fluted cylinder, one piece stocks, 25 oz. Discontinued in 1981. Add $175 for 1982 Stainless Steel version.

| | $325 | $225 | $200 | |

Last Mfg.'s Sug. Retail was $300.

"1 of 500" cased

| | $500 | $400 | $320 | |

Last Mfg.'s Sug. Retail was $500.

CONNECTICUT VALLEY ARMS

DISTRIBUTED IN NORCROSS, GA.

All pistols have color case hardened finishes with solid brass trim.

Grading	100%	98%	95%	90%

PISTOLS

ENGLISH BELT PISTOL—percussion. Discontinued in 1983.

	$60	$50	$40	

COLONIAL PISTOL—.45 cal., percussion, 6¾ in. octagonal barrel, 31 oz. New in 1989.

Mfg.'s Sug. Retail $105 $80 $70 $60

CVA "HAWKINS" PISTOL—.50 cal., percussion or flintlock, 9¾ in. octagonal barrel, 50 oz. Add $10 for flintlock.

Mfg.'s Sug. Retail $145 $110 $95 $75

STANDARD KENTUCKY PISTOL—.45 or .50 cal., percussion, 10¼ in. octagonal barrel, brass blade front sight, 40 oz.

Mfg.'s Sug. Retail $140 $110 $95 $80

MOUNTAIN PISTOL—.45 or .50 cal., percussion, 9 in. octagonal barrel, German silver wedge plate with pewter cap, 40 oz.

$120 $100 $80

PHILADELPHIA DERRINGER—.45 cal., percussion, 3¼ in. octagonal barrel, 16 oz.

Mfg.'s Sug. Retail $75 $60 $55 $45

SIBER PISTOL—.45 cal., percussion, 10½ in. octagonal, white steel engraved barrel, lock also engraved white steel, checkered walnut grip, 38 oz.

Mfg.'s Sug. Retail $395 $295 $255 $190

TOWER PISTOL—.45 cal., percussion, 9 in. octagonal barrel at breach tapers to round, antique brass trigger, 36 oz.

$95 $80 $65

REVOLVERS

All revolvers have solid brass trim and walnut grips.

COLT WALKER MODEL—.44 cal., percussion, 9 in. barrel, color case hardened frame, hammer, and loading lever, 72 oz.

Mfg.'s Sug. Retail $260 $195 $170 $120

3RD MODEL DRAGOON—.44 cal., 7½ in. barrel, rectangular bolt cuts in cylinder, color case hardened frame, loading lever, plunger, and hammer, round trigger guard, one piece stocks, 66 oz.

Mfg.'s Sug. Retail $225 $165 $145 $110

WELLS FARGO—.31 cal., percussion, 3, 4, or 5 in. octagonal barrel, 5 shot, color case hardened frame, hammer, no load lever, brass trim, 1½ lbs. Add $45 for steel frame.

Mfg.'s Sug. Retail $120 $95 $75 $60

1851 NAVY—.36 cal., percussion, 7½ in. octagonal barrel, brass frame, 38 oz. Add $60 for steel frame.

Mfg.'s Sug. Retail $130 $100 $85 $65

CVA COLT POCKET POLICE—.36 cal., 5½ in. round barrel, color case hardened frame, loading lever, plunger, and hammer, round trigger guard, fluted cylinder, one piece stocks, 25 oz. Add $35 for steel frame.

Mfg.'s Sug. Retail $130 $100 $85 $65

1860 ARMY—.44 cal., percussion, 8 in. round barrel, 6 shot engraved cylinder, color case hardened frame, trigger, and load lever, 44 oz.

Mfg.'s Sug. Retail $215 $165 $140 $100

1861 NAVY—.36 or .44 cal., percussion, 7½ in. round barrel, 6 shot engraved cylinder, color case hardened frame, trigger, and load lever, or brass frame (.44 cal. only), 44 oz. Add $55 for color case hardened steel frame, $60 for presentation grade Sheriff's Model (new in 1986).

Mfg.'s Sug. Retail $140 $105 $90 $70

    Add $5 for brass frame on Sheriff Model.

    Add $25 for steel frame on Standard Model.

WAR AND PEACE—.36 cal., 1851 Navy or 1851 Sheriff's Model, heavily engraved in rosewood presentation case.

Mfg.'s Sug. Retail $630 $500 $420 $335

Grading	100%	98%	95%	90%

1858 REMINGTON ARMY—.44 cal., percussion, 8 in. octagonal barrel, color case hardened hammer, steel or brass frame, 38 oz. Add $45 for steel.
    Mfg.'s Sug. Retail $160 $125 $105 $85

REMINGTON BISON—.44 cal., percussion, 1858 Remington Army frame brass, 10¼ in. octagonal barrel, adj. sights, 3 lbs.
    Mfg.'s Sug. Retail $250 $185 $160 $130

REMINGTON POCKET—.31 cal., percussion, 5 shot, 4 in. octagonal barrel, brass frame, 15 oz. New in 1989.
    Mfg.'s Sug. Retail $120 $90 $75 $60

REMINGTON TARGET—.44 cal., percussion, 12 in. octagonal barrel, brass frame and trigger guard, adj. sights, based on 1858 Navy frame, 38 oz.
    Mfg.'s Sug. Retail $230 $175 $150 $120

OFFICER AND THE GENTLEMAN—matched set .44 cal., 1858 Rem. Army and .31 cal. Pocket Rem., heavily engraved in rosewood presentation case.
    Mfg.'s Sug. Retail $650 $525 $435 $350

RIFLES

BLAZER RIFLE—.50 cal., percussion, straight ignition (like Percussion Revolver), 28 in. octagonal barrel, stainless steel nipple, brass tipped ramrod, 6 lbs, 12 oz. Deduct $10 for Blazer II.
    Mfg.'s Sug. Retail $150 $120 $100 $75

EXPRESS RIFLE—.50 or .54 cal., percussion, double barrel, 28 in. tapered round barrel, color case hardened plate, hammers and trim, adj. sights. Add $375 for presentation grade (new in 1986).
    Mfg.'s Sug. Retail $520 $390 $340 $250
    Add $160 for extra set of 12 ga. barrels.

KENTUCKY RIFLE—.45 or .50 cal., percussion or flintlock, 33½ in. octagonal barrel, color case hardened hammer and plate, antique brass trigger, 7 lbs. 4 oz. Add $10 for flintlock.
    Mfg.'s Sug. Retail $260 $215 $175 $125

MOUNTAIN RIFLE—.50 cal., percussion or flintlock, 32 in. octagonal barrel, German silver wedge plate and patch box, pewter or German silver nose cap, 7 lbs. 14 oz.
    Mfg.'s Sug. Retail $290 $205 $175 $150
    Add $80 for premier grade (chrome bore and German silver trim).

HAWKEN RIFLE/CARBINE—.50 or .54 cal., percussion or flintlock, 28 in. octagonal chrome bore barrel, brass trim, beaver tail select walnut stock, 7 lbs. 15 oz. Add $10 for flintlock, $200 for presentation grade (new in 1986).
    Mfg.'s Sug. Retail $390 $240 $180 $140
    Deduct $120 for Hunter Hawken rifle or Carbine.

FRONTIER RIFLE—.45 or .50 cal., percussion or flintlock, 28 in. octagonal barrel, brass trim, right or left hand, 7 lbs. 15 oz. Add $10 for flintlock, $10 for left-hand, deduct $40 for carbine model.
    Mfg.'s Sug. Retail $215 $165 $140 $110

MISSOURI RANGER—.50 cal., percussion, 28 in. octagonal barrel, color case hardened trim, right or left hand, 7 lb. 8 oz.
     $155 $130 $100

OVER/UNDER DOUBLE BARREL CARBINE—.50 cal., percussion, O/U 26 in. octagonal tapering to round barrels, color case hardened lock, hammers, and triggers, checkered walnut stock, 8½ lbs.
    Mfg.'s Sug. Retail $580 $440 $375 $285

PENNSYLVANIA LONG RIFLE—.50 cal., percussion or flintlock, 40 in. octagonal barrel, color case hardened hammers and plate, brass trim, 8 lbs. 3 oz. Add $10 for flintlock.
    Mfg.'s Sug. Retail $475 $355 $310 $250

Grading	100%	98%	95%	90%

ST. LOUIS HAWKEN—.50, .54, or .58 cal., percussion or flintlock, 28 in. octagonal barrel, brass trim, 7 lbs. 13 oz. Add $10 for flintlock, $70 for 12 ga. combo. barrel, $75 for 1-48 twist extra .50 cal. barrel, $10 for left hand.

Mfg.'s Sug. Retail	$255	$180	$165	$115

SQUIRREL RIFLE—.32 cal., percussion or flintlock, 25 in. octagonal barrel, color case hardened hammer and plate, brass trim, stainless steel nipple, 5 lbs. 12 oz. Add $10 for flintlock, $10 for left-hand.

Mfg.'s Sug. Retail	$250	$180	$150	$115

ZOUAVE RIFLE—.58 cal., percussion, 32½ in. tapered barrel with bayonet mount, brass trim and lands, adj. sight, 9¾ lbs. New in 1989.

Mfg.'s Sug. Retail	$380	$300	$245	$200

BLUNDERBUSS—.69 cal., flintlock, 16 in. tapered to flared muzzle barrel, brass trim, available right or left-hand, 5 lbs. 5 oz.

Mfg.'s Sug. Retail	$255	$220	$185	$150

SHOTGUNS

TRAPPER SHOTGUN—12 ga., 28 in. single barrrel, color case hardened hammer and lock, blued barrel, 3 chokes, 5 lbs. 10 oz.

Mfg.'s Sug. Retail	$285	$220	$185	$140

Add $95 for extra 1-66 twist .50 cal. barrel combo.

BRITTANY SHOTGUN—12 ga., 28 in. double barrel, 7 lbs. 7 oz.

Mfg.'s Sug. Retail	$295	$265	$220	$175

BRITTANY SHOTGUN II—.410 ga., 24 in. double barrel, 6 lbs. 4 oz.

Mfg.'s Sug. Retail	$210	$160	$135	$100

SHOTGUN—12 or .410 ga., percussion, 28 in. (24 in. on .410) double barrel, 6 lbs. 10 oz (6 lbs. 4 oz. on .410). Deduct $85 for .410 ga. New in 1987. Presentation grade side by side add $350.

Mfg.'s Sug. Retail	$275	$245	$205	$155

D.P. (DAVIDE PEDERSOLI & CO.)

IMPORTED BY NAVY, E.M.F., ALLEN FIREARMS, HOUSE OF MUSKETS, AND MUZZLE LOADERS INC.

PISTOLS

HARPERS FERRY 1806—.58 cal., flintlock, 10 in. barrel, color case hardened lock, brass furniture.

Mfg.'s Sug. Retail	$270	$210	$150	$100

KENTUCKY PISTOL—.44 cal., flintlock or percussion, available engraved or with brass barrel. Add $25 for flintlock, $35 for brass barrel, or $25 for engraved percussion.

Mfg.'s Sug. Retail	$175	$140	$110	$90

LEPAGE PISTOL—.45 cal., flintlock or percussion, 10½ in. browned octagonal barrel, white steel hammer, and lock, adj. triggers, 2 lbs. (cased set, gold trim, consecutive serial number). Deduct $30 for percussion.

Mfg.'s Sug. Retail	$320	$290	$240	$150

Cased set—custom order only.

Mfg.'s Sug. Retail	$850	$750	$650	$475

RIFLES

ALAMO—.38, .45. or .50 cal., percussion or flintlock, with double set triggers. Add $30 for flintlock.

Mfg.'s Sug. Retail	$295	$275	$235	$190

BROWN BESS MUSKET—.75 cal., flintlock, 31½ or 42 in. smooth bore barrel. Deduct $20 for carbine.

Mfg.'s Sug. Retail	$750	$620	$435	$340

Add $65 for bayonet.

D.P. (DAVIDE PEDERSOLI & CO.), cont.

CHARLEVILLE MUSKET—.69 cal., flintlock, 44⅝ in. white steel barrel, hammer, and lock, brass trim, 8¾ lbs. New in 1989.

Mfg.'s Sug. Retail $550 $490 $425 $310

FREDERICKSBURG MUSKET—.75 cal., flintlock.

Mfg.'s Sug. Retail $675 $480 $400 $300

KENTUCKY—.38, .45. or .50 cal., percussion or flintlock, 35½ in. barrel. Add $5 for flintlock, $20 for luxury version, $110 for Silver Star.

Mfg.'s Sug. Retail $225 $175 $150 $90

PENNSYLVANIA RIFLE—.50 cal., percussion, brass trim, color case hardened lock, hammer, and trigger. New in 1989.

Mfg.'s Sug. Retail $440 $335 $240 $200

PLAINSMAN RIFLE—.38, .45. or .50 cal., percussion. Add $20 for luxury version.

Mfg.'s Sug. Retail $450 $300 $250 $175

TRYON RIFLE—.45, .50, or .54 cal., percussion, 34½ in. octagonal barrel. Add $10 for luxury version.

Mfg.'s Sug. Retail $385 $360 $295 $200

SHOTGUNS

SXS SHOTGUN—12 ga., percussion. Add $20 for cavalry model.

Mfg.'s Sug. Retail $535 $425 $300 $210

KODIAK SXS SHOTGUN/EXPRESS/COMBO.—10 or 12 ga. x .50, .12 x .58, or .50 x .58 cal., percussion. Add $10 for .10 ga., $150 for rifle or comb. barrels.

Mfg.'s Sug. Retail $395 $335 $290 $200

DALY, CHARLES

DISTRIBUTED BY OUTDOOR SPORTS, HDQTRS., INC., DAYTON, OH.

All rifles feature adj. sights, investment cast brass trim, patch boxes, color case hardened hammer and locks, octagonal, rifle barrels, adj. double set triggers, and European hard wood stocks.

HAWKEN RIFLE—.45 cal., percussion, 28 in. barrel, right-hand only.

     $195 $160 $130

Last Mfg.'s Sug. Retail was $240.

HAWKEN RIFLE—.50 cal., percussion, 28 in. barrel, right and left-hand. Add $20 for left-hand.

     $195 $160 $130

Last Mfg.'s Sug. Retail was $240.

HAWKEN RIFLE—.50 cal., flintlock, 28 in. barrel, right and left-hand. Add $20 for left-hand.

     $215 $180 $145

Last Mfg.'s Sug. Retail was $280.

HAWKEN CARBINE—.50 cal., flintlock, 22 in. barrel.

     $195 $160 $130

Last Mfg.'s Sug. Retail was $240.

DIXIE GUN WORKS

UNION CITY, TN — MANUFACTURER AND DISTRIBUTOR.

Short descriptions are for models of standard construction. Also, new for 1986, many models are imported from Uberti (to eliminate duplications see Uberti, Aldo & Co.).

Grading	100%	98%	95%	90%

REVOLVERS: PERCUSSION

WALKER—.44 cal., percussion, 9 in. barrel, 6 shot, color case hardened frame, hammer, and load lever, brass trim, 4½ lbs. Add $90 for Deluxe version.

Mfg.'s Sug. Retail	**$185**	**$175**	**$150**	**$125**

1ST MODEL DRAGOON—.44 cal., percussion, 6 shot, brass grip straps, color case hardened frame, hammer, and load lever, brass trim, 3.9 lbs. Add $15 for silver-plated straps.

Mfg.'s Sug. Retail	**$230**	**$200**	**$170**	**$140**

2ND MODEL DRAGOON—.44 cal., percussion, 6 shot, brass grip straps, color case hardened frame, hammer, and load lever, brass trim, 3.9 lbs. Add $15 for silver-plated straps.

Mfg.'s Sug. Retail	**$230**	**$200**	**$170**	**$140**

3RD MODEL DRAGOON—.45 cal., percussion, 7⅜ in. barrel, color case hardened frame, hammer, and load lever, brass trigger guard and back strap. Add $65 for Deluxe version.

Mfg.'s Sug. Retail	**$190**	**$175**	**$155**	**$125**

BABY DRAGOON—.31 cal., 6 in. barrel, color case hardened frame. Add $80 for Deluxe version.

Mfg.'s Sug. Retail	**$155**	**$145**	**$125**	**$95**

MODEL 1849 POCKET—.31 cal., percussion, with loading lever, 3, 4, or 5 in. barrel, 5 shot, color case hardened frame, hammer, and load lever, brass trim, 1½ lbs. Add $15 for silver straps and trigger guard.

Mfg.'s Sug. Retail	**$235**	**$200**	**$185**	**$150**

1851 NAVY—.36 cal., color case hardened frame. Add $30 for engraved model, $150 for Deluxe or London marked version, or $35 for steel frame.

Mfg.'s Sug. Retail	**$95**	**$75**	**$65**	**$50**

TEXAS PATERSON HOLSTER PISTOL—.36 cal., percussion, has hidden trigger and no loading lever.

Mfg.'s Sug. Retail	**$310**	**$280**	**$250**	**$200**

1858 REMINGTON—.44 cal., percussion, 8 in. octagonal barrel, blue finish. Add $65 for Deluxe version.

Mfg.'s Sug. Retail	**$135**	**$125**	**$110**	**$80**

REMINGTON NAVY—.36 cal., percussion, 6¼ in. octagonal barrel, .36 cal. variation of the 1858 Remington, 2½ lbs. New in 1989.

Mfg.'s Sug. Retail	**$200**	**$175**	**$150**	**$120**

1860 ARMY—.44 cal., percussion, half-fluted cylinder, 8 in. barrel, color case hardened hammer, frame, and load lever, and brass trigger guard. Add $75 for Deluxe version, $20 for silver plated backstrap and trigger guard.

Mfg.'s Sug. Retail	**$150**	**$135**	**$115**	**$90**

MODEL 1861 NAVY REVOLVER—.36 cal., percussion, 5 in. barrel, many styles, brass back strap or trigger guard, color case hardened frame, hammer, and load lever, 2½ lbs. Add $15 for silver plated strap and trigger guard, $15 for fluted military cylinder, $50 for stainless steel. Add $100 for shoulder stock.

Mfg.'s Sug. Retail	**$245**	**$220**	**$180**	**$140**

MODEL 1862 POLICE—.36 cal., percussion, 4½, 5½, or 6½ in. barrel, color case hardened frame, hammer, and load lever, cylinder, semi-fluted or engraved, 1.6 lbs. Add $15 for silver plated straps and trigger guard, $50 for stainless steel.

Mfg.'s Sug. Retail	**$220**	**$200**	**$175**	**$140**

LEECH & RIGDON—.36 cal., percussion, 7 in. round barrel, Confederate copy of the Colt Navy, 2¾ lbs. New in 1989.

Mfg.'s Sug. Retail	**$220**	**$190**	**$165**	**$130**

DIXIE NAVY—.36 cal., percussion, copy of Colt Navy 1851, brass frame. Add $10 for engraving.

Mfg.'s Sug. Retail	**$85**	**$85**	**$70**	**$55**

WYATT EARP—.44 cal., percussion, 6 shot, 12 in. oct. barrel, brass frame.

Mfg.'s Sug. Retail	**$130**	**$105**	**$90**	**$65**

SPILLER & BURR—.36 cal., percussion, octagonal barrel, color case hardened hammer and load lever, brass frame and trigger guard.

Mfg.'s Sug. Retail	**$125**	**$95**	**$80**	**$50**

Grading	100%	98%	95%	90%

PISTOLS

This is an alphabetized listing.

ABILENE DERRINGER—.41 cal., percussion with case.

Mfg.'s Sug. Retail	$80	$60	$55	$40

BLACK WATCH SCOTTISH PISTOL—.577 cal., flintlock, 7 in. smooth bore barrel.

Mfg.'s Sug. Retail	$145	$135	$110	$85

BRASS FRAME DERRINGER—percussion. Add $35 for engraving.

Mfg.'s Sug. Retail	$50	$45	$40	$35

CHARLEVILLE PISTOL—.69 cal., flintlock, 7½ in. white steel barrel.

Mfg.'s Sug. Retail	$145	$135	$110	$85

HARPERS FERRY—.58 cal., flintlock, 10 in. barrel, color case hardened hammer and lock.

Mfg.'s Sug. Retail	$165	$140	$120	$75

KENTUCKY PISTOL—percussion. Discontinued in 1983.

		$95	$80	$65

Last Mfg.'s Sug. Retail was $100.

LEPAGE DELUXE TARGET PISTOL—.45 cal., percussion, 10 in. barrel, adj. sights.

Mfg.'s Sug. Retail	$295	$245	$205	$135

LEPAGE DUELING PISTOL—.45 cal., percussion, 10 in. barrel.

Mfg.'s Sug. Retail	$225	$195	$170	$110

LINCOLN DERRINGER—.41 cal., percussion, 2 in. barrel, with case.

Mfg.'s Sug. Retail	$285	$200	$170	$115

MOUSE KILLER

Mfg.'s Sug. Retail	$20	$20	$15	$12

MOORE AND PATRICK PISTOL—.45 cal., flintlock, 10 in. browned octagonal barrel.

Mfg.'s Sug. Retail	$285	$245	$215	$150

MURDOCK SCOTTISH HIGHLANDERS PISTOL—.52 cal., flintlock, 7¾ in. white steel barrel, hammer, lock, and furniture, 4 lbs. New in 1989.

Mfg.'s Sug. Retail	$300	$260	$225	$190

OVERCOAT DERRINGER

Mfg.'s Sug. Retail	$35	$35	$30	$25

PENNSYLVANIA PISTOL—.44 cal., flintlock or percussion, 10 in. barrel. Add $10 for flintlock.

Mfg.'s Sug. Retail	$120	$105	$90	$70

PHILADELPHIA DERRINGER

Mfg.'s Sug. Retail	$45	$40	$35	$30

QUEEN ANNE PISTOL—.50 cal., flintlock, 7½ in. bronzed steel barrel.

Mfg.'s Sug. Retail	$130	$120	$100	$80

TORNADO TARGET—.44 cal., percussion, 10 in. octagonal barrel. Built on Remington 1860 army frame.

Mfg.'s Sug. Retail	$150	$125	$110	$75

WILLIAM PARKER PISTOL—.45 cal., flintlock, 11 in. barrel.

Mfg.'s Sug. Retail	$270	$245	$205	$160

RIFLES

This is an alphabetized listing.

BROWN BESS MUSKET—.74 cal., flintlock, 41½ in. barrel.

Mfg.'s Sug. Retail	$450	$380	$330	$235

BUFFALO HUNTER—.58 cal., percussion, 26 in. barrel.

		$220	$185	$140

CHARLEVILLE MUSKET—.69 cal., flintlock, 44⅝ in. white steel barrel, hammer, lock, and furniture, 8¾ lbs. New in 1989.

Mfg.'s Sug. Retail	$425	$375	$320	$255

Grading	100%	98%	95%	90%

DELUXE CUB RIFLE—.40 cal., flintlock or percussion, 28 in. octagonal barrel, color case hardened hammer, plate and triggers, brass trim and patch box, double set triggers.
Mfg.'s Sug. Retail $250 $215 $185 $145

HAWKEN RIFLE—.45, .50, .54 or .58 cal., percussion, color case hardened hammer and lock, brass patch box.
Mfg.'s Sug. Retail $225 $200 $175 $130

INDIAN GUN—same as Brown Bess Musket except 31 in. barrel.
Mfg.'s Sug. Retail $375 $360 $300 $240

KENTUCKIAN CARBINE—.45 cal., flintlock or percussion, 27½ in. barrel. Add $15 for flintlock.
Mfg.'s Sug. Retail $210 $195 $160 $120

KENTUCKY RIFLE—.45 cal., flintlock or percussion, 33½ in. barrel, 27½ in. carbine barrel also available. Add $10 for flintlock.
Mfg.'s Sug. Retail $175 $170 $140 $110

LANCASTER COUNTY RIFLE—.45 cal., flintlock or percussion (same as Pennsylvania Rifle above, except less ornate trigger guard and patch box). Add $5 for flintlock.
    $190 $175 $160

MISSISSIPPI RIFLE—U.S. rifle model 1841, .58 cal., percussion.
Mfg.'s Sug. Retail $430 $310 $270 $180

PENNSYLVANIA RIFLE—.45 cal., flintlock or percussion.
Mfg.'s Sug. Retail $295 $260 $225 $180

SANFTL SCHUETZEN TARGET RIFLE—.45 cal., percussion, 29 in. barrel, adj. sights.
Mfg.'s Sug. Retail $595 $570 $475 $385

SHARPS RIFLE/CARBINE—.54 cal., percussion. 28 in. barrel. Deduct $30 for carbine.
    $310 $280 $235

TENNESSEE MOUNTAIN RIFLE—.32 or .50 cal., percussion or flintlock (.32 cal. is a small cal. squirrel rifle), right or left hand.
Mfg.'s Sug. Retail $335 $300 $250 $200

TRYON RIFLE—.50 cal., percussion, 32 in. barrel.
Mfg.'s Sug. Retail $300 $290 $240 $190

WESSON RIFLE—.50 cal., percussion, 28 in. barrel, adj. sights.
Mfg.'s Sug. Retail $395 $375 $315 $255

YORK COUNTY RIFLE—.45 cal., flintlock or percussion, 36 in. barrel. Add $15 for flintlock. Disc. in 1987.
    $205 $170 $135

    Last Mfg.'s Sug. Retail was $210.

ZOUAVE RIFLE—.58 cal., percussion. Deduct $35 for carbine barrel.
Mfg.'s Sug. Retail $275 $240 $200 $155

1858 2-BAND ENFIELD—.58 cal., percussion, 2 barrel bands.
Mfg.'s Sug. Retail $325 $280 $255 $225

1862 3-BAND ENFIELD—.58 cal., percussion, 3 barrel bands.
Mfg.'s Sug. Retail $395 $375 $315 $255

1863 SPRINGFIELD MUSKET—.58 cal., percussion, 41½ in. barrel.
    $370 $310 $240

SHOTGUNS

DOUBLE BARREL: PERCUSSION—10 or 12 ga., 30 in. barrels, brown finish, checkered European walnut. Add $40 for 10 ga.
Mfg.'s Sug. Retail $325 $310 $260 $180

NORTHWEST TRADE RIFLE—20 ga., flintlock, 36 in. octagonal tapering to round barrel, browned barrel and lock assembly, 11 lbs. New in 1989.
Mfg.'s Sug. Retail $495 $425 $370 $295

E.M.F. COMPANY
MANUFACTURED & DISTRIBUTED IN SANTA ANA, CA.

Most percussion revolvers are available in a cased presentation set. Add $130 for cased set.

PISTOLS

1775 BLACK WATCH SCOTTISH PISTOL—.58 cal., flintlock, 7 in. smooth bore white steel barrel, brass frame, ram's horn grips with round ball trigger.
Mfg.'s Sug. Retail $210 $160 $125 $100

1777 CHARLEVILLE PISTOL—.69 cal., flintlock, 7½ in. white steel barrel, brass frame.
Mfg.'s Sug. Retail $250 $190 $150 $100

CORSAIR PISTOL—.36 or .44 cal., percussion, double barrel, color case hardened hammer and lock, brass trim. Disc. in 1987.
                            $150 $125 $100

Last Mfg.'s Sug. Retail was $160.

HARPERS FERRY—.58 cal., flintlock, brass mounted brown barrel.
Mfg.'s Sug. Retail $270 $205 $150 $110

KENTUCKY PISTOL—.44 cal., flintlock or percussion, available engraved or with brass barrel. Add $25 for flintlock. $35 for brass barrel, $25 for engraved percussion.
Mfg.'s Sug. Retail $175 $140 $110 $90

TARGET PISTOL—.44 cal., percussion, 9 in. octagonal barrel, factory engraved, adj. sights (windage only), based on Rem. frame, 43 oz.
Mfg.'s Sug. Retail $235 $175 $120 $80

REVOLVERS

All percussion revolvers are available in cased sets. Add $80 for cased set.

1847 WALKER—.44 cal., percussion, 9 in. barrel, color case hardened frame and load lever, brass trim, 4 lbs. 8 oz. Add $75 for nickel plate, $75 for engraving.
Mfg.'s Sug. Retail $295 $185 $130 $110

1ST MODEL DRAGOON—.44 cal., percussion, 7½ in. barrel, color case hardened frame, brass trim, engraved cylinder, 4 lbs. 2 oz.
Mfg.'s Sug. Retail $275 $180 $140 $100

2ND MODEL DRAGOON—.44 cal., percussion, 7½ in. barrel, color case hardened frame, brass trim, engraved cylinder, 4 lbs.
Mfg.'s Sug. Retail $275 $180 $140 $100

3RD MODEL DRAGOON—.44 cal., percussion, 7½ in. barrel, color case hardened frame and loading lever, brass trim, engraved cylinder, 4 lbs. 2 oz., adj. target sights. Add $20 for buntline model. Texas Dragoon Model (Tucker & Sherrard & Co., Confederate States, Texas Star engraved on cylinder, square brass trigger guard).
Mfg.'s Sug. Retail $275 $180 $140 $100

BABY DRAGOON—.31 cal., percussion, 5 shot, 4 and 6 in. barrel, color case hardened frame and loading lever, brass trim, Add $20 for engraving, $30 for steel frame.
                            $90 $75 $60

WELLS FARGO MODEL 1849—.31 cal., percussion, 5 shot, 5 in. barrel, no loading lever.
                            $110 $90 $70

1851 NAVY—.36 or .44 cal., percussion, 7½ in. barrel, brass frame, color case hardened hammer, and load lever, brass trim, engraved cylinder. Add $30 for engraving, brass, $140 for steel, $40 for steel frame, $60 for nickel plated brass (Mason Dixon Model), $55 for square trigger guard, $55 for silver trimmed steel, $100 for 3 barrel set (.44 cal. only).
Mfg.'s Sug. Retail $125 $90 $65 $55

1851 NAVY BALLISTER—.44 cal., percussion, same as above, except with 12 in. barrel.
                            $110 $90 $70

Grading	100%	98%	95%	90%

1851 NAVY SHERIFF'S MODEL—.36 or .44 cal., percussion, shorter barrel version of 1851 Navy, brass frame - add $30 for steel.
Mfg.'s Sug. Retail $125 $90 $65 $55

The same add on's apply to this model as the 1851 Navy.

1860 ARMY—.44 cal., percussion, 8 in. barrel, brass frame, 2 lbs. 9 oz. Add $35 for engraving, brass, $85 for stainless steel, $45 for steel frame, $55 for fluted cylinder model, $60 for shoulder stock, $125 for deluxe engraving, $50 for premier grade steel.
Mfg.'s Sug. Retail $150 $100 $70 $55

1861 NAVY—.36 cal., percussion, steel frame. Disc. in 1987.
          $110 $90 $70

Last Mfg.'s Sug. Retail was $115.

1862 POLICE—.36 cal., percussion, 5 shot, color case hardened frame. Add $80 for engraved steel.
Mfg.'s Sug. Retail $225 $135 $100 $95

1862 POCKET NAVY—.36 cal., percussion, 5 shot, color case hardened frame.
Mfg.'s Sug. Retail $225 $160 $110 $95

NAVY SQUAREBACK—.36 or .44 cal., percussion, 7½ in. barrel, color case hardened frame and load lever, Dragoon style square back trigger guard.
Mfg.'s Sug. Retail $125 $90 $65 $55

The same add on's apply to this model as the 1851 Navy.

1858 REMINGTON ARMY—.36 and .44 cal., percussion, 8 in. barrel, brass frame, blue finish, 2 lbs. 8 oz. For engraving, add $45 brass, $105 steel. Add $30 for steel frame, $120 for stainless steel, $65 for target sights, $140 for stainless target model.
Mfg.'s Sug. Retail $135 $110 $80 $75

RIFLES

BOSTONIAN—.45 cal., percussion. New in 1989.
Mfg.'s Sug. Retail $295 $205 $170 $130

ALAMO COMMEMORATIVE—.45 cal., percussion, embellished to commemorate the anniversary of the Alamo. New in 1989.
Mfg.'s Sug. Retail $435 $340 $260 $210

DELUXE BROWN BESS MUSKET—.75 cal., flintlock.
Mfg.'s Sug. Retail $750 $620 $480 $360

HAWKEN RIFLE—.50 cal., percussion, brass trim, color case hardened lock and hammer, adj. sights, and stainless steel nipple.
Mfg.'s Sug. Retail $225 $205 $150 $135

KENTUCKY RIFLE—.36, .44, or .45 cal., percussion and flintlock, factory engraved, brass trim, color case hardened lock and hammer. Add $20 for flintlock, $30 for deluxe model, $50 for deluxe engraved.
          $135 $120 $90

"LONDON ARMORY" ENFIELD—.58 cal., percussion. Add $30 for 3 Band Model. Deduct $20 for Musketoon Model. Disc. in 1987.
          $240 $200 $160

Last Mfg.'s Sug. Retail was $285.

MINUTEMAN KENTUCKY RIFLE—.45 cal., flintlock or percussion, 36 in. octagonal barrel, brass blade front sight, brass trim, color case hardened lock, hammer, and trigger. Add $15 for engraving, $15 for flintlock.
          $145 $120 $95

PENNSYLVANIA KENTUCKY RIFLE—.50 cal., percussion, brass trim, color case hardened lock, hammer, and trigger.
Mfg.'s Sug. Retail $440 $335 $240 $200

PLAINSMAN KENTUCKY RIFLE—.44 cal., percussion, shorter forearm than Pennsylvania with more ornate finish.
Mfg.'s Sug. Retail $450 $350 $250 $200

Grading	100%	98%	95%	90%

PURDEY DELUXE—.50 cal., percussion, half stock English style, select checkered walnut, color case hardened nose cap, lock, tang, butt plate and patch box, adj. sights, double set triggers. Carbine or rifles.

| | $310 | $260 | $210 | |

SAN FRANCISCO TO ST. LOUIS COMMEMORATIVE—.45 cal., Kentucky rifle, highly embellished, made to commemorate the 130th anniversary of the stage coach crossing "2,400 miles in 24 days". New in 1989.

Mfg.'s Sug. Retail $395 $280 $230 $190

WESSON BERDAN RIFLE—.45 cal., percussion, engraved brass frame.

| | $145 | $120 | $95 | |

ZOUAVE RIFLE—.58 cal., percussion, brass trim, color case hardened lock and hammer, blue finish, adj. "Sniper Sight". Add $220 for deluxe.

Mfg.'s Sug. Retail $200 $170 $140 $110

SHOTGUNS

SHOTGUN—.12 ga., S X S, percussion, based on early English design, brown barrel, color case hardened lock and hammer, imported from Italy.

Mfg.'s Sug. Retail $535 $420 $300 $210

SHOTGUN O/U—12 ga., percussion, O/U design. New in 1989.

Mfg.'s Sug. Retail $475 $375 $290 $240

EUROARMS OF AMERICA

MANUFACTURER/IMPORTER, WINCHESTER, VA. ALSO IMPORTED BY MUZZLE LOADERS, INC.

REVOLVERS

1851 NAVY "SCHNEIDER & GLASSICK"—.36 or .44 cal., percussion, 5 or 7 in. octagonal barrel, brass frame, 38-40 oz. (Pricing same for Sheriff's Model).

Mfg.'s Sug. Retail $105 $90 $80 $70

1851 NAVY "GRISWOLD & GUNNINSON"—.36 or .44 cal., percussion, 7½ in. octagonal round barrel, brass frame, 39-41 oz. Disc. in 1987.

| | $80 | $70 | $60 | |

Last Mfg.'s Sug. Retail was $90.

1851 NAVY—.36 or .44 cal., percussion, 7½ in. barrel, steel frame, 39-43 oz. Add $10 for square back trigger, $25 for silver strap.

Mfg.'s Sug. Retail $137 $110 $100 $75

1851 NAVY POLICE MODEL—.36 cal., percussion, 5 or 7½ in. octagonal barrel, steel frame, 5 shot fluted cyliinder, 38-41 oz.

| | $115 | $95 | $75 | |

Last Mfg.'s Sug. Retail was $120.

1851 NAVY SHERIFF'S MODEL—.36 or .44 cal., percussion, 5 in. barrel, steel frame, 39 oz.

Mfg.'s Sug. Retail $105 $90 $80 $65

1860 ARMY—.44 cal., percussion, 5 or 8 in. barrel, steel frame, 41 oz. Add $75 for stainless steel, $50 for engraving. Deduct $40 for brass frame.

Mfg.'s Sug. Retail $155 $120 $110 $95

1861 NAVY—.36 cal., percussion, 7½ in. barrel, steel frame, 42 oz.

Mfg.'s Sug. Retail $160 $140 $125 $100

1862 POLICE—.36 cal., percussion, 7½ in. barrel, steel frame, 40 oz. Disc. in 1987.

| | $125 | $115 | $95 | |

Last Mfg.'s Sug. Retail was $130.

Grading	100%	98%	95%	90%

REMINGTON REPLICAS

1858 ARMY—.36 or .44 cal., percussion, 6½ and 8 in. octagonal barrel, 40 oz. Add $90 for engraving, $70 for stainless steel, $40 for target adj. sights, deduct $50 for brass frame.

Mfg.'s Sug. Retail	$165	$135	$120	$90

1858 NAVY—.36 cal., percussion, 6½ in. octagonal barrel, 40 oz.

Mfg.'s Sug. Retail	$165	$135	$120	$90

ROGERS & SPENCER—.44 cal., percussion, 7½ in. octagonal barrel, 47 oz. Add $15 for target sights, $30 for London grey finish, $70 for engraving.

Mfg.'s Sug. Retail	$190	$160	$135	$110

RIFLES

BUFFALO CARBINE—.58 cal., percussion, 26 in round barrel, color case hardened hammer and lock, brass patch box and furniture, 7¾ lbs. New in 1989.

Mfg.'s Sug. Retail	$405	$325	$270	$210

CAPE GUN RIFLE—.50 cal., percussion, 32 in. barrel, engraved with walnut stock. New in 1989.

Mfg.'s Sug. Retail	$380	$320	$275	$215

COOK & BROTHER CARBINE—.58 cal., percussion, 24 in. barrel, adj. front sight (windage only), 2 barrel bands, walnut stock, 7½ lbs.

Mfg.'s Sug. Retail	$365	$300	$265	$220

ENFIELD RIFLE MUSKET (LONDON ARMORY CO.), 1853—.58 cal., percussion, 39 in. barrel, adj. rear sight (windage only), 3 barrel bands, walnut stock, 9½ lbs.

Mfg.'s Sug. Retail	$425	$360	$315	$275

ENFIELD RIFLE MUSKET (LONDON ARMORY CO.), 1858—.58 cal., percussion, 33 in. barrel, adj. rear sight (windage only), 2 barrel bands, walnut stock, 8 lbs.

Mfg.'s Sug. Retail	$380	$340	$295	$250

ENFIELD MUSKETOON (LONDON ARMORY CO.), 1861—.58 cal., percussion, 24 in. barrel, adj. rear sight (windage only), 2 barrel bands, walnut stock, 8 lbs.

Mfg.'s Sug. Retail	$350	$280	$245	$190

HARPER'S FERRY MODEL 1803—.58 cal., flintlock, 35 in. browned barrel, 9 lbs.

Mfg.'s Sug. Retail	$510	$390	$340	$240

HAWKEN RIFLE—.58 cal., percussion, 28 in. octagonal barrel, double set triggers, target model, 9 lbs. 6 oz.

Mfg.'s Sug. Retail	$295	$200	$175	$140

J.P. MURRAY MODEL 1863—.58 cal., percussion, 23 in barrel, 7 lbs. 9 oz.

Mfg.'s Sug. Retail	$360	$280	$240	$180

MISSISSIPPI RIFLE MODEL 1841—.58 cal., percussion, 33 in. barrel, 9 lbs. 8 oz.

Mfg.'s Sug. Retail	$465	$360	$310	$240

PENNSYLVANIA RIFLE—.45 or .50 cal., flintlock or percussion, 36 in. barrel, adj. rear sight (windage only), walnut stock, 7 lbs. Add $30 for flintlock. Disc. in 1987.

	$240	$200	$160

Last Mfg.'s Sug. Retail was $240.

REMINGTON 1862 RIFLE—.58 cal., percussion, 33 in. barrel, 3 leaf folding rear sight, 3 barrel bands, beelia stock, 9½ lbs. Disc. in 1987.

	$240	$200	$160

Last Mfg.'s Sug. Retail was $240.

ZOUAVE RIFLE—.58 cal., percussion, brass trim, color case hardened lock and hammer, blue finish, adj. "Sniper Sight".

Mfg.'s Sug. Retail	$325	$265	$230	$200

Add $65 for "Range" grade.

Grading	100%	98%	95%	90%

SHOTGUNS

MAGNUM CAPE SHOTGUN—12 ga., percussion, 32 in. barrel, engraved with walnut stock, 5½ lbs.

Mfg.'s Sug. Retail	**$400**	**$290**	**$250**	**$195**

DUCK SHOTGUN—8, 10, or 12 ga., percussion, 33 in. round barrel, color case hardened hammer and lock, brass patchbox and furniture, 8½ lbs. New in 1989.

Mfg.'s Sug. Retail	**$405**	**$325**	**$270**	**$210**

DOUBLE BARREL SHOTGUN—12 ga., percussion, 28 in. barrel, engraved with walnut stock, 6 lbs.

	$370	**$325**	**$280**	

Last Mfg.'s Sug. Retail was $405.

F.I.E.

FIREARMS IMPORT & EXPORT - MIAMI, FL.

In 1986, F.I.E. ceased importation of black powder weapons.

PISTOLS

BABY DRAGOON—.31 cal., engraved. Discontinued in 1982.

	$105	**$90**	**$60**	

1851 NAVY—.44 cal., steel frame. Discontinued in 1982.

	$135	**$120**	**$80**	

1858 REMINGTON—.36 or .44 cal., Discontinued in 1982.

	$130	**$110**	**$90**	

1776 KENTUCKY—.44 cal., flintlock, color case hardened hammer and lock.

	$105	**$90**	**$60**	

RIFLES

KENTUCKY RIFLE—.45 cal., percussion or flintlock.

	$135	**$125**	**$90**	

FEDERAL ORDNANCE CORPORATION

MANUFACTURER/IMPORTER LOCATED IN SOUTH EL MONTE, CA.

REVOLVERS

1858 REMINGTON—.44 cal., percussion, 7½ in. octagonal barrel, 6 shot, blued steel, brass trigger guard, 2 lbs. 10 oz.

Mfg.'s Sug. Retail	**$200**	**$145**	**$120**	**$90**

Add $75 for target model.

1860 ARMY—.44 cal., percussion, 8 in. barrel, 6 shot, color case hardened hammer, lock, and load lever, brass backstrap and trigger guard.

Mfg.'s Sug. Retail	**$200**	**$145**	**$120**	**$90**

ROGERS & SPENCER—.44 cal., percussion, 7½ in. octagonal barrel, blued steel, 3 lbs.

Mfg.'s Sug. Retail	**$300**	**$200**	**$170**	**$120**

RIFLES

P-1853 3-BAND ENFIELD—.58 cal., percussion, 39 in. round barrel, color case hardened hammer and lock, brass trim, blued bands, adj. rear sight, 9½ lbs.

Mfg.'s Sug. Retail	**$450**	**$280**	**$240**	**$190**

MODEL 1858 2-BAND ENFIELD—similar to P-1853 3-Band Enfield except has 33 in. round barrel, 10 lbs.

Mfg.'s Sug. Retail	**$480**	**$300**	**$250**	**$200**

HARPERS FERRY—.58 cal., flintlock, 35 in. round barrel, color case hardened hammer and lock, brass trim, 8½ lbs.

Mfg.'s Sug. Retail	**$600**	**$390**	**$330**	**$260**

Grading	100%	98%	95%	90%

HAWKENS RIFLE—.45 or .50 cal., flintlock or percussion, 28½ in. octagonal barrel, color case hardened hammer and lock, double set triggers, 7¾ lbs.

Mfg.'s Sug. Retail	$295	$195	$165	$125

THE J.P. MURRAY CARBINE—.58 cal., percussion, 23½ in. browned round barrel, color case hardened hammer and lock, brass trim and bands, 7½ lbs.

Mfg.'s Sug. Retail	$480	$300	$250	$200

MISSISSIPPI RIFLE—.58 cal., percussion, 33 in. browned round barrel, color case hardened hammer and lock, brass trim and bands, 9½ lbs.

Mfg.'s Sug. Retail	$580	$360	$310	$250

ZOUAVE RIFLE—.58 cal., percussion, 32½ in. round barrel, color case hardened hammer, lock and trigger, brass trim, adj. rear sight, 9 lbs.

Mfg.'s Sug. Retail	$490	$310	$265	$210

FREEDOM ARMS

MANUFACTURED AND DISTRIBUTED IN FREEDOM, WY.

REVOLVERS

STAINLESS MINI-REVOLVER—.22 cal., percussion, 5 shot, 1, 1¾, or 3 in. barrel, stainless steel. Add $15 for 3 in. barrel, $40 for brass buckle.

Mfg.'s Sug. Retail	$205	$185	$155	$115

HATFIELD RIFLE WORKS

MANUFACTURED IN ST. JOSEPH, MO.

SQUIRREL RIFLE—.32, .36, .45, or .50 cal., flintlock or percussion, 39 in. barrel, adj. sights, double set triggers, brass trim, 7½ lbs.

Mfg.'s Sug. Retail	$465	$410	$340	$290

Add $65 for extra fancy maple Grade II.
Add $160 for hand selected fancy Grade III.
Custom guns could easily run 200% over standard.

This gun is a one-of-a-kind model with exceptional craftsmanship in both wood and metal.

GONIC ARMS INC.

MANUFACTURER LOCATED IN GONIC, NH.

Gonic Arms has designed a true hunters Black Powder rifle. Equipped with an ambidextrous safety, it eliminates the noisy "click" often associated with bringing a hammer back from half cock or setting the first of double set triggers. A specially designed firing pin and housing allow spent caps to blow out the bottom of the rifle, thus eliminating the need to "dig out" the spent cap from the breech. This combined with it's modern appearance and newly designed loading system make it a true hunters rifle without the problems associated with most Black Powder arms.

MODEL GA-87 RIFLE/CARBINE—.458 Express, 26 in. round barrel, single stage trigger with left or right safety, cap is placed in breech, hand checkered walnut stock, 6 lbs. New in 1987.

Mfg.'s Sug. Retail	$410	$395	$330	$270

Add $25 for deluxe models with sights and recoil pad.

HEGE

UBERLINGEN, WEST GERMANY (IMPORTED BY BEEMAN).

HEGE-MANTON—.44 cal., flintlock, 6 lbs. Add $100 for engraving.

Mfg.'s Sug. Retail	$1,695	$1,470	$1,270	$900

Grading	100%	98%	95%	90%

HEGE-SIBER PISTOL—.33 or .44 cal., percussion, 10 in. blue octagonal barrel, exceptional finish, world class target model, color case hardened hammer and lock.
Mfg.'s Sug. Retail $1,000 $900 $800 $500

FRENCH STYLE HEGE-SIBER PISTOL—.33 or .44 cal. percussion, 10 in. blue octagonal barrel, exceptional finish, world class target model, London gray finish, 24 Kt. gold inlays, blue trigger guard.
Mfg.'s Sug. Retail $1,795 $1,610 $1,435 $955

Matched set—same serial number.
Mfg.'s Sug. Retail $2,995 $2,750 $2,495 $1,675

KAHNKE GUNWORKS

MANUFACTURER/RETAILER LOCATED IN REDWOOD FALLS, MN.

KAHNKE .54 CAL. MODEL—.54 cal., percussion, single-shot hunting pistol, adj. sights, unusual combination of utilizing both old and new technologies, staight through ignition system, 3½ lbs. New in 1988.
Mfg.'s Sug. Retail $285 $285 $190 $140

This model is available direct from the factory only.

KASSNAR

HARRISBURG, PA.

PISTOLS

1851 NAVY—.44 cal., percussion, 7½ in. barrel, steel frame, 39-43 oz.
Mfg.'s Sug. Retail $130 $100 $85 $80

1860 ARMY—.44 cal., percussion, 5 or 8 in. barrel, steel frame, 41 oz.
Mfg.'s Sug. Retail $175 $155 $135 $110

1858 REMINGTON ARMY—.36 or .44 cal., percussion, 6½ and 8 in. octagonal barrel, 40 oz. Add $40 for steel frame, $140 for stainless steel.
Mfg.'s Sug. Retail $160 $125 $105 $85

HAWKEN RIFLE—.45, .50, .54, or .58 cal., flintlock or percussion, 28 in. octagonal barrel, color case hardened hammer and lock, 9 lbs. Add $20 for flintlock and $20 for left hand.
Mfg.'s Sug. Retail $200 $170 $150 $120

IVER JOHNSON

MANUFACTURED IN JACKSON, AR.

OVER/UNDER DOUBLE RIFLE MODEL BP50HB—.50 cal., percussion, double barrel, separate hammers and triggers, color case hardened hammer and furniture.
$360 $315 $225

LOVEN-PIERSON INC.

APALACHIN ARSENAL - APALACHIN, NY.

RIFLES: PERCUSSION

All rifles have a unique rotating over and under set of barrels to speed a 2nd shot.

LOVEN MODEL 10—.45 cal., percussion swivel breech, 22 in. carbine or 28 in. rifle, octagonal or ½ in. round barrel, blued furniture, maple stock, 7¾ - 8½ lbs.
Mfg.'s Sug. Retail $330 $265 $220 $175

LOVEN MODEL 13—.45, .50 or .54 cal., percussion, same as Loven Model 10, except brass furniture and walnut stock.
Mfg.'s Sug. Retail $440 $360 $300 $240

Grading	100%	98%	95%	90%

LOVEN MODEL 16—.45, .50 or .54 cal., percussion, same as above except color case hardened lock and furniture, browned barrels and curly or bird's-eye maple or figured walnut stock.

Mfg.'s Sug. Retail $880 $720 $600 $480

LYMAN GUNS
MIDDLEFIELD, CT.

Discontinued models still sold by Dixie Gun Works.

PISTOLS
REMINGTON .44 ARMY—.44 cal., 6 shot, percussion. Discontinued.

           $155 $130 $105

Last Mfg.'s Sug. Retail was $170.

1851 NAVY—.36 cal., percussion. Discontinued.

           $150 $125 $100

Last Mfg.'s Sug. Retail was $165.

1860 ARMY—.44 cal., percussion. Discontinued.

           $155 $130 $105

Last Mfg.'s Sug. Retail was $170.

PLAINS PISTOL—.50 or .54 cal., percussion, color case hardened hammer and lock.

Mfg.'s Sug. Retail $175 $155 $130 $105

RIFLES
GREAT PLAINS RIFLE—.50 or .54 cal., flintlock or percussion, color case hardened hammer and lock, blackened steel furniture, 32 in. octagonal barrel, 11 lbs. 6 oz. Add $10 for flintlock.

Mfg.'s Sug. Retail $335 $295 $250 $200

TRADE RIFLE—.50 or .54 cal., percussion or flintlock, color case hardened hammer and lock, 11 lbs. Add $10 for flintlock.

Mfg.'s Sug. Retail $250 $220 $185 $140

MANDALL SHOOTING SUPPLIES, INC.
IMPORTER AND DISTRIBUTOR LOCATED IN SCOTTSDALE, AZ.

FRENCH DUELING PISTOL—.44 cal., percussion, single trigger, classic fluted handle, sold with velvet lined display case and accessories.

Mfg.'s Sug. Retail $295 $240 $200 $160

"NAPOLEON" CANNON—.69 ball, detailed scaled down model of the original used by both the Union and Confederacy during the Cival War, brass furniture, with carriage, 18 lbs.

Mfg.'s Sug. Retail $290 $275 $225 $185

MICHIGAN ARMS CORPORATION
MANUFACTURED IN TROY, MI.

Michigan Arms has made a long needed change for Black Powder enthusiasts. It is now possible with their 3 models — the Wolverine, the Friendship Special Match, and the Silver Wolf — to enjoy Black Powder shooting without the drawbacks commonly associated with it. Rather than using a percussion cap or flint, Michigan Arms has designed an extremely accurate and reliable ignition system using a Model 209 Win. shotgun primer.

WOLVERINE RIFLE—.45, .50 or .54 cal., positive ignition Win. Model 209 centerfire primer, 25¼ in. octagonal barrel, adj. sights, Dayton Traister rifle trigger with adj. pull, 8 lbs.

Mfg.'s Sug. Retail $400 $320 $265 $210

Grading	100%	98%	95%	90%

FRIENDSHIP SPECIAL MATCH—.45, .50 or .54 cal., positive ignition Win. Model 209 centerfire primer, 25¼ in. octagonal barrel, fully adj. target sights with custom Maple stock, Dayton Traister rifle trigger with adj. pull, 8 lbs.

Mfg.'s Sug. Retail	$600	$470	$390	$310

SILVERWOLF—same as Wolverine, only available in stainless steel.

Mfg.'s Sug. Retail	$600	$470	$390	$310

MODERN MUZZLE LOADING, INC.

DISTRIBUTOR LOCATED IN LANCASTER, MO.

The Knight MK Series is the forerunner of the modern Black Powder rifle designed as a true hunting/sporting rifle. These Black Powder rifles feature a unique straight through sure-fire ignition system, double safety, inline bolt assembly, and Timney deluxe trigger system. The Knight rifle is extremely accurate (especially with MMP Sabot bullets) and weighs under 7 lbs. New in 1988.

KNIGHT MK-85 HUNTER—.50 or .54 cal., percussion rifle, straight through ignition system, 24 in. round barrel drilled and tapped for scope, walnut stock, double safety system, under 7 lbs.

Mfg.'s Sug. Retail	$480	$430	$360	$290

KNIGHT MK-85 STALKER—.50 or .54 cal., percussion, 22 in. round barrel, monte carlo stock, double safety system, under 7 lbs.

Mfg.'s Sug. Retail	$520	$460	$390	$310

KNIGHT MK-85 PREDATOR—.50 or .54 cal., percussion, 20 in. round barrel, black synthetic stock, double safety system, under 7 lbs.

Mfg.'s Sug. Retail	$560	$500	$420	$360

MOWREY GUN WORKS, INC.

MANUFACTURED IN SAGINAW, TX.

Mowrey Gun Works has recreated the guns designed by Ethan Allen and marketed under the name Allen & Thurber in the early and mid 1800's. The guns themselves are beautifully hand crafted with "cut rifled" browned barrels (each groove cut individually using as many as 20 passes) and actions using only 5 moving parts creating exceptional accuracy and reliability. The 1 inch in 30 inch rifling was designed specifically to stabilize conical bullets. Each gun is available with a number of features and options (listed below).

Standard: curly maple stocks and forearms, front blade-buckhorn rear and hand rubbed finish.

Options: premium curly maple, cherry or walnut stock and forearm, barrel length from 22-40 in., primative fixed sight, target sights, Scheutzen style butt plate. Add $38 for fancy Grade Curly Maple, $25 for other than standard barrel length or modern sights, $25 for brass forearm on Plains Rifle, $30 for fancy brass or steel Scheutzen butt plate.

RIFLES: PERCUSSION

PLAINS RIFLE—.50 or .54 cal., percussion, 32 in. full octagonal barrel, brass furniture, 10 lbs. Add $25 for brass forearm. Deduct $10 for all steel furniture.

Mfg.'s Sug. Retail	$330	$300	$250	$175

SQUIRREL RIFLE—.32, .36 or .45 cal., percussion, 28 in. full octagonal barrel, brass furniture, 7 lbs., deduct $10 for all steel furniture.

Mfg.'s Sug. Retail	$330	$300	$250	$175

ROCKY MOUNTAIN HUNTER—.50 or .54 cal., percussion, 28 in. full octagonal barrel, all browned steel furniture, 8 lbs.

Mfg.'s Sug. Retail	$330	$300	$250	$175

Grading	100%	98%	95%	90%

SHOTGUNS: PERCUSSION

12 GAUGE SHOTGUN—12 ga., percussion, 32 in. full octagonal barrel, brass or steel furniture, 7½ lbs.

    Mfg.'s Sug. Retail $330 $300 $250 $175

28 GAUGE SHOTGUN—28 ga., percussion, 28 in. full octagonal barrel, brass or steel furniture, built on squirrel frame, 7½ lbs.

    Mfg.'s Sug. Retail $330 $300 $250 $220

MUZZLE LOADERS, INC.

PREVIOUS IMPORTER/DISTRIBUTOR LOCATED IN BURKE, VA.

REVOLVERS

1847 WALKER—.44 cal., percussion, charcoal finish, color case hardened frame, hammer, and load lever, brass trim, engraved cylinder. 4.4 lbs.

     $260 $215 $170

1848 1ST MODEL DRAGOON—.44 cal., percussion, 6 shot, brass grip straps, color case hardened frame, hammer, and load lever, brass trim, 3.9 lbs.

     $215 $180 $145

1850 2ND MODEL DRAGOON—.44 cal., percussion, 6 shot, brass grip straps, color case hardened frame, hammer, and load lever, brass trim, 3.9 lbs.

     $215 $180 $145

1851 3RD MODEL DRAGOON—.44 cal., percussion, 6 shot, brass grip straps, color case hardened frame, hammer, and load lever, brass trim, 3.9 lbs. Add $15 for silver-plated straps, or cut for stock, add $35 for Military Model.

     $215 $180 $145

1851 NAVY—.36 or .44 cal., percussion, 7½ in. octagonal barrel, engraved (roll) cylinder, color case hardened frame and load lever, silver plated brass backstrap and square back trigger guard. Sheriff's Model has 5 in. barrel, brass trigger guard and backstrap. Deduct $10 for Sheriff's Model, $20 for brass backstrap and trigger guard, $50 for brass frame.

     $115 $95 $75

1860 ARMY—.44 cal., percussion, 8 in round barrel, color case hardened frame, hammer and load lever, 2 lbs. 9 oz. Deduct $25 for brass frame.

     $120 $100 $60

1862 POLICE—.36 cal., 5½ in. round barrel, color case hardened frame, loading lever, plunger, and hammer, round trigger guard, fluted cylinder, one piece stocks, 25 oz.

     $130 $110 $90

1858 REMINGTON—.36 or .44 cal., percussion, blued frame, brass trigger guard, steel backstrap, 6 shot, 2 lbs. 7 oz. Add $80 for stainless, deduct $20 for brass frame.

     $130 $115 $95

ROGERS & SPENCER—.44 cal., percussion, 7½ octagonal barrel, 2 lbs. 15 oz. Add $15 for target sights, $25 for engraved London grey finish.

     $155 $130 $105

PISTOLS

DELUXE KENTUCKY PISTOL—.44 cal., percussion or flintlock, 10¼ in. octagonal barrel, brass blade front sight, 40 oz. Add $15 for flintlock.

     $110 $90 $70

RIFLES

1853 ZBAND ENFIELD—.58 cal., percussion, 33 in. barrel, 2 barrel bands.

     $360 $300 $240

DELUXE HAWKEN RIFLE—.45 or .50 cal., percussion or flintlock, color case hardened hammer and lock, percussion cap holder in stock, chrome lined barrels.

     $190 $160 $130

MUZZLE LOADERS, INC., cont.

DELUXE KENTUCKY RIFLE—.45 or .50 cal., percussion or flintlock, color case hardened hammer and lock, percussion cap holder in stock, chrome lined barrels, brass trim. Add $15 for flintlock.

$185 $155 $120

ST. LOUIS HAWKENS—.50 cal., percussion, color case hardened hammer and lock, 28 in. octagonal barrel, brass trim, 7 lbs. 15 oz.

$175 $145 $115

ZOUAVE RIFLE—.58 cal., percussion, brass trim, color case hardened hammer and lock, blue finish.

$250 $210 $170

NAVY ARMS CO.

MANUFACTURER/IMPORTER/DISTRIBUTOR LOCATED IN RIDGEFIELD, NJ.

J.S. HAWKINS PISTOL—.50 or .54 cal., percussion, 9 in. octagonal barrel, German silver trim, blued barrel, adj. trigger, 2 lbs. 9 oz.

$180 $150 $120

Last Mfg.'s Sug. Retail was $200.

LEPAGE PISTOL—.45 cal., flintlock or percussion, 9 in. octagonal white steel barrel and trim, adj. sights, engraved spur type trigger guard, 2 lbs. 2 oz. Deduct $20 for percussion, $70 for percussion cased set, $140 for percussion cased pair.

Mfg.'s Sug. Retail $315 $285 $235 $185

Cased
Mfg.'s Sug. Retail $495 $450 $375 $320

Cased pair
Mfg.'s Sug. Retail $850 $780 $650 $500

1985 cased set—custom order only, gold trim, consecutive serial number.

$1,800 $1,500 $1,200

Last Mfg.'s Sug. Retail was $1,975.

JOHN MANTON MATCH PISTOL—.45 cal., percussion, 10 in. white steel barrel and lock, brass trim, 2 lbs. 4 oz.

$205 $170 $135

Last Mfg.'s Sug. Retail was $225.

NAPOLEON LEPAGE PISTOL—.45 cal., percussion, 10 in. octagonal white steel barrel and lock, brass trim, adj. double set triggers, fluted grip, 2 lbs. 7 oz.

$155 $130 $105

Last Mfg.'s Sug. Retail was $175.

W. PARKER PISTOL—.45 cal., percussion, 10 in. blued octagonal barrel, German silver lock and trim, adj. double set triggers, 2 lbs. 8 oz.

$220 $185 $150

Last Mfg.'s Sug. Retail was $250.

F. ROCHETTE PISTOL—.45 cal., percussion, 10 in. round barrel with flat top, white steel lock and trim, adj. double set triggers, 2 lbs. 8 oz.

$220 $185 $150

Last Mfg.'s Sug. Retail was $250.

PISTOLS: DERRINGER STYLE

ELGIN CUTLAS—.44 cal., percussion, combination knife pistol, white steel hammer and barrel, brass trim, 2 lbs.

Mfg.'s Sug. Retail $80 $70 $60 $50

PHILADELPHIA DERRINGER—.45 cal., percussion, 3 in. barrel, color case hardened lock and hammer, German silver trim, checkered stock, ¾ lb.

$120 $100 $80

Last Mfg.'s Sug. Retail was $130.

Grading	100%	98%	95%	90%

ENGRAVED "SNAKE EYES" PISTOL—.36 cal., percussion, 2⅝ in. brass double barrel, double hammers, 1½ lbs. Deduct $75 if not engraved.

	$145	$120	$95	

PISTOLS: STANDARD

HARPERS FERRY MODEL 1855—.58 cal., flintlock or percussion, 11¾ in. barrel, color case hardened lock and hammer, brass trim, 3 lbs. 14 oz. Add $50 for cased gun. Deduct $25 for percussion.

Mfg.'s Sug. Retail	$165	$150	$130	$105

KENTUCKY PISTOL—.44 cal., flintlock or percussion, 10⅛ in. barrel, color case hardened lock and hammer, brass trim, 2 lbs. Add $16 for brass barrel. Deduct $15 for percussion (each gun).

Mfg.'s Sug. Retail	$120	$110	$90	$75

Cased

Mfg.'s Sug. Retail	$195	$180	$155	$120

Double cased set

Mfg.'s Sug. Retail	$295	$270	$225	$180

MOORE AND PATRICK PISTOL—.45 cal., flintlock or percussion, 10 in. octagonal barrel, white steel hammer and lock, German silver trim, 2 lbs. Disc. in 1987.

	$235	$195	$165	

Last Mfg.'s Sug. Retail was $295.

PISTOLS: FLINTLOCK

BRITISH DRAGOON PISTOL—.614 cal., flintlock, white steel with brass trim, first 240 production models will be used in Governor's palace restoration, Colonial Williamsburg. Add $100 for official Williamsburg crest.

	$360	$300	$240	

Last Mfg.'s Sug. Retail was $395.

DURS EGG SAW HANDLED PISTOL—.45 cal., flintlock, 9½ in. blued octagonal barrel, unique stock, hand checkered, German silver trim, white steel hammer and lock.

	$210	$175	$140	

Last Mfg.'s Sug. Retail was $235.

REVOLVERS

COLT 1851 NAVY - YANK—.36 or .44 cal., percussion, 7½ in. octagonal barrel, color case hardened hammer, frame, and load lever, brass trim. Add $5 for silver plated back strap and trigger guard, $60 for shoulder stock.

Mfg.'s Sug. Retail	$125	$105	$90	$75

Cased set

Mfg.'s Sug. Retail	$200	$175	$150	$120

Double cased set

Mfg.'s Sug. Retail	$325	$290	$240	$190

1861 NAVY—.36 cal., percussion, 7½ in. round barrel, cylinder engraved with navy scene, color case hardened hammer, frame, and load lever, brass trim, 2¾ lbs. Add $60 for shoulder stock. Also available in 5½ in. barrel Sheriff's model.

	$105	$90	$75	

Last Mfg.'s Sug. Retail was $140.

Cased set

	$170	$145	$120	

Last Mfg.'s Sug. Retail was $230.

Double cased set

	$285	$230	$180	

Last Mfg.'s Sug. Retail was $385.

Grading	100%	98%	95%	90%

RIFLES

BROWN BESS MUSKET—.75 cal., flintlock, 42 in. white steel barrel, hammer, and lock, brass trim, 9½ lbs. Add $100 for Colonial Williamsburg seal.
Mfg.'s Sug. Retail $550 $505 $425 $360

BROWN BESS MUSKET COPY—same as above, all brass hardware. Disc. in 1987.
$315 $275 $235

Last Mfg.'s Sug. Retail was $370.

BUFFALO HUNTER—.58 cal., percussion, 26 in. round barrel, color case hardened hammer and lock, brass trim, 8 lbs.
$240 $200 $160

CHARLEVILLE MUSKET—.69 cal., flintlock, 44⅝ in. white steel barrel, hammer, and lock, brass trim, 8¾ lbs.
Mfg.'s Sug. Retail $550 $490 $425 $310

COUNTRY BOY—.32, .36, .45 or .50 cal., percussion, 26 in. octagonal barrel, matte black metal "no glare" finish on all parts, based on mule ear percussion lock, adj. sights, 6 lbs. Add $60 each for extra barrels.
Mfg.'s Sug. Retail $165 $145 $125 $105

CUB RIFLE—.36 cal., percussion, 26 in. octagonal barrel, adj. sights, color case hardened lock, walnut stock, 5 lbs. 12 oz.
Mfg.'s Sug. Retail $185 $165 $140 $120

MODEL 1853 3 BAND ENFIELD—.58 cal., percussion, 39 in. round barrel, color case hardened hammer and lock, brass trim, blued bands, adj. rear sight, 9½ lbs. Add $140 for Parker Hale version.
Mfg.'s Sug. Retail $325 $315 $285 $220

MODEL 1858 2 BAND ENFIELD—.58 cal., percussion, 33 in. round barrel, color case hardened hammer and lock, brass trim, blued bands, adj. rear sight, 10 lbs. Add $140 for Parker Hale version.
Mfg.'s Sug. Retail $325 $315 $285 $220

MODEL 1861 ENFIELD MUSKETOON—.58 cal., percussion, 24 in. round barrel, color case hardened hammer and lock, brass trim, blued bands, adj. rear sight, 7 lbs. Add $180 for Parker Hale version.
Mfg.'s Sug. Retail $295 $285 $245 $190

HAWKEN RIFLE—.50, .54, or .58 cal., flintlock and percussion, 28 in. octagonal barrel, double set triggers, brass trim, 8 lbs. 8 oz. Deduct $20 for percussion.
Mfg.'s Sug. Retail $225 $200 $165 $130

HAWKEN MARK 1 RIFLE—.50 or .54 cal., flintlock or percussion. 26 in. octagonal barrel, adj. double set triggers and sights, brass trim, 9 lbs. Add $15 for flintlock, $140 for commemorative model.
$235 $195 $155

Last Mfg.'s Sug. Retail was $260.

HUNTER RIFLE/CARBINE—.50, .54, or .58 cal., percussion, 28½ in. octagonal barrel, (.22½ carbine), color case hardened hammer and lock, double set triggers, 7 lbs. 12 oz. (6 lbs. 12 oz. carbine).
Mfg.'s Sug. Retail $220 $195 $165 $130

ITHACA-NAVY HAWKENS—.50 or .54 cal., flintlock or percussion. 26 in. octagonal barrel, adj. double set triggers and sights, brass trim, 9 lbs. Add $65 for flintlock. (Left hand version disc. in 1987).
Mfg.'s Sug. Retail $225 $205 $170 $135

HARPERS FERRY 1803 RIFLE—.58 cal., flintlock, 35 in. round barrel, color case hardened hammer and lock, brass trim, 8 lbs. 8 oz.
Mfg.'s Sug. Retail $425 $400 $350 $270

J.P. MURRY ARTILLARY CARBINE—.58 cal., percussion, 23½ in. browned, round barrel, color case hardened hammer and lock, brass trim and bands, 7½ lbs.
Mfg.'s Sug. Retail $295 $285 $245 $1655

Grading	100%	98%	95%	90%

1860 ARMY—.44 cal., percussion, 8 in. round barrel, color case hardened hammer, frame, and load lever, roll engraved or fluted cylinder, 2¾ lbs. Add $60 for shoulder stock. Also available in 5½ in. barrel Sheriff's model.

Mfg.'s Sug. Retail	$150	$135	$115	$95

Cased set

Mfg.'s Sug. Retail	$225	$185	$165	$135

Double cased set

Mfg.'s Sug. Retail	$350	$305	$260	$210

REB MODEL 1860 "GRISWOLD AND GUNNINSON"—.36 or .44 cal., percussion, 7½ in. round barrel, brass frame, color case hardened hammer and load lever, 5½ in. barrel Sheriff's Model, 2 lbs. 12 oz.

Mfg.'s Sug. Retail	$100	$95	$80	$65

Due to overstock, several 1860 Reb revolvers were factory de-activated and cannot be re-activated. These guns can be used only as props — values currently are in the $55 range.

Cased set

Mfg.'s Sug. Retail	$200	$175	$150	$120

Double cased set

Mfg.'s Sug. Retail	$300	$270	$225	$180

1862 POLICE—.36 cal., percussion, 5½ in. round to octagonal barrel, color case hardened hammer, frame, and load lever, brass trim, 1 lb. 10 oz. Add $55 for cased Law & Order set (book style presentation case).

Mfg.'s Sug. Retail	$220	$185	$160	$125

COLT PATERSON—.36 cal., percussion, 7½ in. octagonal barrel, standard "hidden trigger" design, blued steel hardware, no loading lever, 2 lbs. 9 oz. Add $250 for engraved version.

Mfg.'s Sug. Retail	$300	$270	$225	$175

1847 WALKER—.44 cal., percussion, 9 in. round barrel, color case hardened hammer, frame, and load lever, brass trim, engraved barrel and cylinder, 4 lbs. 11 oz. Add $90 for cased set, $170 for deluxe Uberti cased set.

Mfg.'s Sug. Retail	$185	$170	$140	$110

LEECH & RIGDON—.36 cal., percussion, 7½ in. barrel, color case hardened hammer, frame, and load lever, brass trim, 2 lbs. 10 oz.

	$120	$100	$80	

LEMATE REVOLVER—.44 cal., percussion, 9 shot cylinder, plus 1 shot center barrel (maximum fire power for its day), 7⅝ in. octagonal barrel, white steel frame, 3 lbs. 7 oz. Add $400 for engraved Beauregard model, $180 for 18th Georgia engraved model.

Mfg.'s Sug. Retail	$550	$525	$450	$360

Add $85 for single case, $100 for double case.

REMINGTON 1860 ARMY—.36. or .44 cal., percussion, 6½ in. barrel, brass trim. Add $20 for nickel or target model, $75 for stainless steel, $150 for Deluxe Uberti Model. Deduct $10 for brass frame (each gun in a cased set).

Mfg.'s Sug. Retail	$135	$115	$100	$80

Cased set

Mfg.'s Sug. Retail	$205	$175	$150	$120

Double cased set

Mfg.'s Sug. Retail	$330	$290	$245	$195

ROGERS & SPENCER—.44 cal., percussion, 7½ in. octagonal barrel, blued trim, 3 lbs. Add $20 for satin finish.

Mfg.'s Sug. Retail	$160	$140	$120	$100

SPILLER & BURR—.36. cal., percussion, 7 in. barrel, brass frame, color case hardened hammer and load lever, 2 lbs. 8 oz.

Mfg.'s Sug. Retail	$125	$110	$90	$70

Cased set

Mfg.'s Sug. Retail	$200	$175	$150	$120

Double cased set

Mfg.'s Sug. Retail	$325	$285	$240	$190

Grading	100%	98%	95%	90%

KENTUCKY RIFLE—.45 or .50 cal., percussion or flintlock, 35 in. barrel, color case
hardened hammer and lock, brass trim, adj. brass rear sight (windage only), 6 lbs. 14 oz.
Add $125 for .45 cal. deluxe, $20 for flintlock.
Mfg.'s Sug. Retail $235 $205 $180 $155

KODIAK DOUBLE RIFLE—.50, .54, or .58 cal., percussion, 28 in. double barrel, white
steel furniture. New in 1989.
Mfg.'s Sug. Retail $575 $520 $450 $360

MISSISSIPPI RIFLE 1841—.58 cal., percussion, 33 in. browned round barrel, color case
hardened hammer and lock, brass trim and bands, 9½ lbs.
Mfg.'s Sug. Retail $400 $375 $325 $190

MORSE RIFLE—.50 cal., percussion, 26 in. octagonal barrel, brass trim and action, blued
barrel and hammer, adj. rear sight, windage only, 6 lbs.
                        $120 $100 $90

MORTIMER RIFLE—.54 cal., flintlock, 36 in. browned barrel, color case hardened
furniture, waterproof flash pan, chrome lined bore, 9 lbs. New in 1989.
Mfg.'s Sug. Retail $595 $520 $450 $360

MULE EAR MOUNTAIN MAN'S SQUIRREL RIFLE—.32, .36, or .45 cal.,
percussion, 26 in. octagonal barrel, brass trim, blued barrel, hammer, lock, and trigger, 5½
lbs.
                        $160 $135 $110

Last Mfg.'s Sug. Retail was $185.

PARKER HALE VOLUNTEER RIFLE (IMPORTED)—.451 cal., percussion, 32
in. barrel, brass trim, blued band, color case hardened hammer and lock, adj. sights, 9½
lbs.
Mfg.'s Sug. Retail $775 $650 $550 $440

PARKER HALE WHITWORTH VOLUNTEER RIFLE (IMPORTED)—.45
cal., percussion, 36 in. barrel, brass trim, blued barrel and bands, color case hardened
hammer and lock, adj. sights, detented lock hammer, long range accuracy app. 1000 yds.,
comes with accessories, 9¼ lbs.
Mfg.'s Sug. Retail $795 $690 $600 $575

PENNSYLVANIA HALF STOCK HUNTER—.50 cal., percussion, 30 in. octagonal
barrel, white steel hammer and lock, brass patchbox and trim, walnut stock, 6 lbs. 4 oz.
Mfg.'s Sug. Retail $220 $195 $165 $130

PENNSYLVANIA LONG RIFLE—.45 or .50 cal., flintlock or percussion, 40½ in.
octagonal barrel, color case hardened hammer and lock, brass patchbox and trim, walnut
stock, 7 lbs. 8 oz. Deduct $15 for percussion.
Mfg.'s Sug. Retail $340 $305 $255 $205

PIONEER RIFLE—.45 or .50 cal., flintlock, 30 in. octagonal barrel, color case hardened
hammer and lock, walnut stock, 6 lbs. 4 oz.
Mfg.'s Sug. Retail $200 $180 $150 $120

RIGBY STYLE TARGET—.451 cal., 32 in. round blued barrel, color case hardened
hammer and lock, hand checkered walnut stock, very similar to a modern day firearm, adj.
vernier sights, 7 lbs. 12 oz.
Mfg.'s Sug. Retail $500 $460 $400 $325

1808/1835 SPRINGFIELD—.69 cal., flintlock, 44 in. round barrel, all white steel, walnut
stock, 8 lbs. 12 oz.
Mfg.'s Sug. Retail $575 $500 $435 $350

The Model 1835 Springfield is a more refined version of the Model 1808. This was the last
flintlock issued by the U.S. Army.

1863 SPRINGFIELD—.58 cal., percussion, 40 in. barrel, all white steel, 3 barrel bands, 9½
lbs.
Mfg.'s Sug. Retail $475 $420 $360 $280

SMITH ARTILLERY/CAVALRY CARBINE—.54 cal., percussion, 20½ in.
octagonal tapering to round barrel, white steel hammer and receiver. New in 1989.
Mfg.'s Sug. Retail $550 $520 $450 $360

Grading	100%	98%	95%	90%

SWISS FEDERAL TARGET RIFLE—.45 cal., percussion, 32 in. octagonal barrel, color case hardened hammer, lock, and trim, double set triggers, classic Bristlen and Morges design, adj., sights, 13¼ lbs. Add $35 for palm rest. Imported from West Germany by Neumann Co.

| *Mfg.'s Sug. Retail* | $1,200 | $1,050 | $900 | $725 |

TRYON RIFLE—.45 cal., percussion, 34 in octagonal barrel, white steel hammer and engraved lock and patchbox, double set triggers, walnut stock, 9 lbs. 12 oz. Add $25 for target sights.

| *Mfg.'s Sug. Retail* | | $350 | $290 | $240 | $195 |

ZOUAVE RIFLE—.58 cal., percussion, 32½ in. round barrel, color case hardened hammer, lock, and trigger, brass trim, adj. rear sight, 9 lbs. Add $140 for deluxe.

| *Mfg.'s Sug. Retail* | $375 | $350 | $300 | $200 |

RIFLES: BLACK POWDER CARTRIDGE

CREEDMOOR TARGET—45/70 rimfire, 30 in. tapered barrel, color case hardened action, beautiful reproduction, adj. sights, 9 lbs.

| *Mfg.'s Sug. Retail* | $640 | $575 | $480 | $400 |

IRON FRAME HENRY—.44-40, or .44 rimfire, 24 in. barrel, cast iron action, color case hardened lever and hammer, beautiful reproduction, adj. sights, 9¼ lbs.

| *Mfg.'s Sug. Retail* | $770 | $600 | $500 | $425 |

HENRY MILITARY/CARBINE RIFLE—.44-40, or .44 rimfire, 24 in. barrel, brass frame and trim, color case hardened lever and hammer, beautiful reproduction, military version has sling swivels, mounted on left side, adj. sights, 9¼ lbs. Add $850 for engraved brass, $950 for engraved steel frame.

| *Mfg.'s Sug. Retail* | $770 | $660 | $575 | $440 |

HENRY TRAPPER—.44-40, or .44 rimfire, 16½ in. barrel, brass frame and trim, color case hardened lever and hammer, beautiful reproduction, adj. sights, 7¼ lbs.

| *Mfg.'s Sug. Retail* | $770 | $660 | $575 | $440 |

ROLLING BLOCK BUFFALO RIFLE (REMINGTON STYLE)—45/70 rimfire, varying barrel length, round or octagonal, color case hardened action, brass trigger guard, beautiful reproduction, adj. sights, approx. 9 lbs. Add $25 for Creedmoor Model.

| *Mfg.'s Sug. Retail* | $490 | $440 | $365 | $275 |

SHOTGUNS

CLASSIC SXS—12 or 10 ga., percussion, 28 in. barrel, color case hardened hammer, lock, and trim, 7¾ lbs. Add $20 for .10 ga. (10 ga. disc. in 1987).

| *Mfg.'s Sug. Retail* | $395 | $355 | $295 | $240 |

FOWLER SHOTGUN—10 or 12 ga., 28 in. barrel, color case hardened hammer and lock, 7 lbs. 6 oz.

| *Mfg.'s Sug. Retail* | | $300 | $235 | $200 | $165 |

Add $40 for steel shot 10 ga. model.
Add $120 for extra 10 ga. barrel.

HUNTER SHOTGUN—20 ga., 28½ in. barrel, round chrome lined color case hardened hammer and lock, double set triggers, 7 lbs. 12 oz.

| *Mfg.'s Sug. Retail* | $190 | $145 | $120 | $100 |

MORSE SHOTGUN—.12 ga., percussion, 26 in. barrel, brass receiver and trim, blued hammer and butt plate, 5¾ lbs. Disc. in 1987.

| | | $150 | $125 | $100 |

Last Mfg.'s Sug. Retail was $165.

MORTIMER SHOTGUN—12 ga., flintlock, 36 in. browned barrel, color case hardened furniture, walnut stock, waterproof pan and chrome bore. New in 1989.

| *Mfg.'s Sug. Retail* | $595 | $525 | $450 | $360 |

TURKEY AND TRAP—12 ga., percussion s x s, 28 in. blued barrels, color case hardened locks and furniture, walnut stock.

| *Mfg.'s Sug. Retail* | $325 | $295 | $250 | $200 |

OLD-WEST GUN CO.

IMPORTER AND DISTRIBUTOR THAT TOOK OVER THE INVENTORY OF ALLEN FIREARMS AFTER THEY WENT OUT OF BUSINESS IN EARLY 1987. OLD-WEST GUN CO. BECAME CIMARRON ARMS CO. IN 1987. OLDER GUNS MARKED OLD WEST HAVE THE SAME VALUES AS THOSE OF CIMARRON ARMS CO. (PLEASE REFER TO THE CIMARRON HEADING IN THIS TEXT).

RICHLAND ARMS

PREVIOUSLY DISTRIBUTED IN BLISSFIELD, MI.

PISTOLS

ANDREW TARGET—.32, .36. or .45 cal., percussion, 10 in. octagonal barrel, white steel hammer, barrel, frame, and sights, brass trigger guard, adj. trigger and sights, blued and engraved, 2 lbs. 10 oz. Add $55 for deluxe grade.

	$125	$100	$75

Last Mfg.'s Sug. Retail was $150.

REVOLVERS

1860 ARMY—.44 cal., percussion, 8 in. barrel, color case hardened hammer, frame, trigger and load lever, brass trigger guard, engraved cylinder. Deduct $25 for brass frame.

	$160	$130	$90

Last Mfg.'s Sug. Retail was $160.

3rd MODEL DRAGOON—.44 cal., percussion, 7½ in. barrel, color case hardened hammer, frame, trigger and load lever, engraved cylinder, 66 oz.

	$150	$125	$100

Last Mfg.'s Sug. Retail was $165.

1851 NAVY—.36 cal., percussion, 7½ in. octagonal barrel, color case hardened load lever and hammer, brass frame and trigger guard, 44 oz. Add $25 for steel frame.

	$90	$65	$50

Last Mfg.'s Sug. Retail was $100.

WALKER—.44 cal., percussion, 9 in. round barrel, color case hardened hammer, frame, trigger and load lever, engraved cylinder, brass trigger guard, 73 oz.

	$200	$175	$130

Last Mfg.'s Sug. Retail was $185.

REMINGTON REPLICAS

1858 ARMY—.44 cal., percussion, 8 in. octagonal barrel, brass frame and trigger guard, 44 oz. Add $25 for steel frame.

	$110	$80	$70

Last Mfg.'s Sug. Retail was $125.

BUFFALO TARGET—.44 cal., percussion, 12 in. octagonal barrel, brass frame and trigger guard, adj. sights, based on 1858 Navy frame, 38 oz.

	$130	$110	$90

Last Mfg.'s Sug. Retail was $150.

RIFLES

BRISTOL HUNTER—.50 or .54 cal., percussion, 28 in. octagonal barrel, color case hardened hammer and lock, rubber recoil pad, adj. rear sights, chrome plated bore, double set triggers.

	$205	$180	$155

Last Mfg.'s Sug. Retail was $240.

HAWKEN RIFLE—.50 cal., percussion, 28 in. octagonal barrel, color case hardened hammer and lock, brass trim, adj. sights, double set triggers.

	$195	$165	$130

Last Mfg.'s Sug. Retail was $225.

Grading	100%	98%	95%	90%

KODIAK DOUBLE BARREL RIFLE—.50 or .58 cal., percussion, 28 in. octagonal barrel. Add $280 for extra .12 ga. shotgun barrels.

| | $505 | $420 | $335 | |

Last Mfg.'s Sug. Retail was $560.

SHOTGUNS

MUZZLE LOADING SHOTGUNS—.10 or .12 ga., percussion. Add $55 for .10 ga.

| | $290 | $240 | $190 | |

Last Mfg.'s Sug. Retail was $320.

RUGER

MANUFACTURED IN SOUTHPORT, CT.

OLD ARMY—.44 cal., 6 shot, percussion, 7½ in. barrel, adj. rear sight, blue or stainless.

| *Mfg.'s Sug. Retail* | $290 | $230 | $185 | $150 |

Stainless Old Army—stainless steel variation of the Old Army.

| *Mfg.'s Sug. Retail* | $370 | $285 | $225 | $175 |

SILE

IMPORTER NEW YORK, NY.

REVOLVERS

1860 COLT ARMY—.44 cal., percussion, 8 in. blued round barrel, brass or color case hardened steel frame, brass trigger guard and back strap, color case hardened hammer, trigger, and load lever, 2 lbs. 11 oz. Deduct $15 for brass frame.

| | $90 | $80 | $70 | |

1858 REMINGTON ARMY—.44 cal., percussion, 8 in. white octagonal barrel, white steel frame, brass trigger guard, 2 lbs. 9 oz. Add $50 for stainless steel, $75 for stainless steel target.

| | $120 | $105 | $90 | |

RIFLES

BROWN BESS MUSKET—.75 cal., flintlock, 41¾ in. smooth bore barrel, brass furniture, white steel barrel, hammer, and lock, engraved lock, 9 lbs.

| | $375 | $325 | $275 | |

HAWKEN RIFLE—.45, .50 or .54 cal., flintlock or percussion (.50 cal. only in flintlock), 29 in. octagonal barrel, solid brass furniture, color case hardened engraved lock, coil spring mechanism with adj. set triggers, stainless steel nickel, chrome bore, brass patch box, adj. sights, 8 lbs. 10 oz. Add $10 for flintlock.

| *Mfg.'s Sug. Retail* | $210 | $175 | $150 | $120 |

HAWKEN RIFLE CARBINE—.45, .50 or .54 cal., flintlock or percussion (.50 cal. only in flintlock), 22 in. octagonal barrel, solid brass furniture, color case hardened engraved lock, coil spring mechanism with adj. set triggers, stainless steel nickel, chrome bore, brass patch box, adj. sights, 7 lbs. Add $10 for flintlock.

| *Mfg.'s Sug. Retail* | $205 | $175 | $150 | $120 |

HAWKEN HUNTER CARBINE—.45, .50 or .54 cal., flintlock or percussion (.50 cal. only in flintlock), 22 in. octagonal barrel, solid brass furniture, color case hardened engraved lock, coil spring mechanism with adj. set triggers, stainless steel nickel, chrome bore, brass patch box, adj. sights, 7 lbs. Add $10 for flintlock.

| *Mfg.'s Sug. Retail* | $225 | $190 | $160 | $105 |

KENTUCKY RIFLE—.45 or .50 cal., flintlock or percussion, 32 in. blued octagonal barrel, solid brass furniture, color case hardened hammer and engraved lock, brass patch box, adj. rear sight, 7 lbs. 2 oz. Add $10 for flintlock.

| | $130 | $115 | $110 | |

Grading	100%	98%	95%	90%

PENNSYLVANIAN SQUIRREL RIFLE—.32 cal., flintlock, 40½ in. browned octagonal barrel, adj. double set triggers, polished white steel hammer and lock, 9 lbs.

$230 $200 $170

SHOTGUNS

SXS DOUBLE BARREL—10 or 12 ga., percussion, 28 in. double blued barrels, engraved furniture, color case hardened hammer and engraved lock, chrome lined bores, 7 lbs. 12 oz. (8 lbs. 12 oz. for 10 ga.). Add $45 for 10 ga.

$240 $210 $180

SOUTHWEST MUZZLE LOADERS SUPPLY

LOCATED IN ANGLETON, TX.

Importer of Uberti, Italian replicas. See Uberti.

DANCE REVOLVER—.36 or .44 cal., exact reproduction of the original J.H. Dance & Brothers revolver manufactured in Dance, Texas, 500 total production, manufactured by Alto Uberti & Co. from Brescia, Italy, cased. New in 1985.

Mfg.'s Sug. Retail $1,500 $1,150 $750 $500

TAYLOR'S & CO., INC.

IMPORTER/DISTRIBUTOR LOCATED IN WINCHESTER, VA.

PISTOLS: SINGLE SHOT

KENTUCKY PISTOL—.45 cal., percussion, 10¼ in. octagonal barrel, brass blade front sight, 2½ lbs.

Mfg.'s Sug. Retail $165 $150 $125 $95

NAPOLEON LEPAGE PISTOL—.45 cal., percussion, 10 in. barrel, white steel barrel and lock, fixed sights with single barrel wedge, silver plated butt cap and trigger guard, double set triggers, 2 lbs. 7 oz.

Mfg.'s Sug. Retail $310 $270 $230 $190

F. ROCHATTE DUELLING PISTOL—.45 cal., percussion, 10 in. round barrel with flat top, white steel lock and trim, adj. double set triggers, 2½ lbs.

Mfg.'s Sug. Retail $395 $345 $295 $240

REVOLVERS

1847 WALKER—.44 cal., percussion, 9 in. blued barrel, color case hardened frame, hammer, and loading lever, brass trigger guard and steel backstrap, 4 lbs. 6 oz.

Mfg.'s Sug. Retail $200 $175 $150 $120

1851 NAVY—.36 or .44 cal., percussion, 7½ in. octagonal barrel, rolled cylinder scene, color case hardened frame, hammer, and loading lever, brass backstrap and trigger guard. Sheriff's Model has 5 in. barrel.

Mfg.'s Sug. Retail $125 $110 $95 $75
    Deduct $30 for brass frame.

1860 ARMY—.44 cal., percussion, 8 in. round barrel, color case hardened frame, hammer, and loading lever, 2¾ lbs.

Mfg.'s Sug. Retail $135 $120 $100 $80
    Deduct $30 for brass frame.

1858 REMINGTON ARMY—.36 or .44 cal., percussion, 8 in. octagonal barrel, color case hardened hammer, steel or brass frame, 2 lbs. 6 oz.

Mfg.'s Sug. Retail $160 $140 $120 $90
    Deduct $40 for brass frame.

Grading	100%	98%	95%	90%

RIFLES

CHARLEVILLE 1777 MUSKET—.69 cal., flintlock, 44¾ in. smooth bore barrel, white steel lockplate, hammer, and ramrod, brass barrel bands, trigger guard, and buttplate, walnut stock.

Mfg.'s Sug. Retail $635 $560 $475 $380

DELUXE HAWKEN RIFLE—.50 cal., percussion, 30 in. octagonal chrome lined barrel, brass patchbox, target sights, double set triggers, 8 lbs.

Mfg.'s Sug. Retail $200 $180 $150 $110

HAWKEN HUNTER CARBINE—.50 cal., percussion, 24 in. octagonal chrome lined barrel, rubber recoil pad, sling swivels, double set triggers.

Mfg.'s Sug. Retail $200 $185 $160 $115

KENTUCKY RIFLE—.45 cal., percussion, 35 in. octagonal barrel, color case hardened lock, brass buttplate, trigger guard, patchbox, sideplates, thimbles and nose cap, walnut stock with large or small patchbox, rifle weighs 7½ lbs., carbine is 6 lbs.

Mfg.'s Sug. Retail $240 $210 $180 $145

   Add $10 for large patchbox.

   Carbine Model—.50 cal., percussion, chrome lined barrel.

Mfg.'s Sug. Retail $240 $210 $180 $145

   Add $20 for large patchbox.

PENNSYLVANIA RIFLE—.45 cal., percussion, octagonal barrel, color case hardened hammer and lock, small brass patchbox, approx. 7 lbs.

Mfg.'s Sug. Retail $215 $190 $160 $140

1861 SPRINGFIELD—.58 cal., percussion, 40 in. round barrel, white steel barrel, hammer, lock, trigger, and trim, 10¼ lbs.

Mfg.'s Sug. Retail $690 $600 $520 $410

ST. LOUIS HAWKEN RIFLE—.50 cal., percussion, 30 in. octagonal barrel, all steel furniture, adj. rear sight, double set triggers, approx. 8 lbs.

Mfg.'s Sug. Retail $200 $180 $150 $115

1863 ZOUAVE RIFLE—.58 cal., percussion, 32½ in. round barrel, color case hardened hammer, lock, and trigger, brass patchbox, trigger guard, and barrel bands, 9 lbs.

Mfg.'s Sug. Retail $365 $320 $275 $225

THOMPSON/CENTER ARMS

U.S. MANUFACTURER LOCATED IN ROCHESTER, NH.

PISTOLS

PATRIOT—.36 or .45 cal., percussion, 9 in. barrel, double set triggers, target stock, walnut, color case hardened hammer and lock. Disc. 1987.

           $225 $180 $145

   Last Mfg.'s Sug. Retail was $235.

RIFLES

HAWKEN COUGAR—.45 or .50 cal., stainless steel version of Hawken, percussion only, select hardwood stock.

           $350 $290 $230

PENNSYLVANIA HUNTER—.50 cal., flintlock or percussion, 31 in. octagonal barrel, color case hardened hammer and lock, 7 lbs. 9 oz. Add $15 for left hand, $15 for flintlock.

Mfg.'s Sug. Retail $265 $260 $225 $170

RENEGADE—.50 or .54 cal., percussion or flintlock, 26 in. octagonal barrel, color case hardened hammer and lock, double set triggers, 8 lbs. Also in .56 cal. — smooth bore. Add $10 for flintlock, add $105 for 12 ga. barrel. Deduct $20 for single trigger Hunter Model (new in 1987).

Mfg.'s Sug. Retail $285 $270 $235 $175

Grading	100%	98%	95%	90%

SENECA—.36 or .45 cal., percussion, 27 in. octagonal barrel, color case hardened hammer and lock, double set triggers, American walnut, 6 lbs. Disc. in 1987.

		$270	$235	$200

Last Mfg.'s Sug. Retail was $300.

HAWKEN—.45, .50, or .54 cal., percussion or flintlock, 28 in. octagonal barrel, color case hardened hammer and lock, double set triggers, 8½ lbs. Add $15 for flintlock, add $105 for 12 ga. barrel.

Mfg.'s Sug. Retail	$325	$295	$275	$195

CHEROKEE—.32, .36 or .45 cal., percussion, 24 in. octagonal barrel, double set triggers, color case hardened hammer and lock, brass trim, American walnut. Add $115 for extra barrel.

Mfg.'s Sug. Retail	$265	$260	$225	$165

WHITE MOUNTAIN CARBINE—.50 cal., percussion, 21 in. octagonal tapering to a round barrel, color case hardened furniture, single hunting trigger, walnut stock, 6½ lbs. New in 1989.

Mfg.'s Sug. Retail	$275	$270	$235	$190

SHOTGUNS

NEW ENGLANDER SHOTGUN—12 ga., percussion, 28 in. barrel, brass furniture, 5 lbs. 2 oz. Add $85 for extra .50 cal. barrel, $15 for left hand.

Mfg.'s Sug. Retail	$220	$210	$185	$135

TRADITIONS, INC.

DEED RIVER, CT.

PISTOLS

TRAPPER PISTOL—.45 or .50 cal., percussion or 10 in. octagonal barrel, double set triggers, adj. sights, brass trim, 3 lbs. 4 oz.

Mfg.'s Sug. Retail	$130	$110	$95	$65

RIFLES

FRONTIER RIFLE/FRONTIER CARBINE—.45 or .50 cal., percussion or flintlock, 28 in. octagonal barrel (24 in. carbine), double set triggers, adj. sights, brass trim, 6 lbs. 14 oz (6 lbs. 8 oz. carbine). Add $10 for flintlock.

Mfg.'s Sug. Retail	$190	$165	$140	$95

HAWKEN RIFLE—.50, .54, or .58 cal., percussion or flintlock, 32¼ in. octagonal barrel, double set triggers, adj. sights, brass trim, 8 lbs. 2 oz. Add $10 for flintlock (.50 and .54 cal. only).

Mfg.'s Sug. Retail	$315	$250	$235	$130

A fiberglass ramrod and deluxe rear sight were introduced in 1989.

HAWKEN WOODSMAN RIFLE—.50 cal., percussion, 29 in. octagonal barrel, color case hardened hammer and lock, brass trim and patchbox, 7½ lbs.

Mfg.'s Sug. Retail	$205	$180	$155	$110

HUNTER RIFLE—.50 or .54 cal., percussion, 28 in. long octagonal barrel, double set triggers, adj. sights, black chrome brass trim with German silver wedge plates, lock has adj. sear, walnut stock, 8 lbs., 10 oz.

Mfg.'s Sug. Retail	$320	$260	$220	$140

A fiberglass ramrod and deluxe rear sight were introduced in 1989.

KENTUCKY 2-PIECE RIFLE—.45 or .50 cal., percussion, 33½ in. octagonal barrel, color case hardened hammer and lock, unique full length two piece stock is joined with brass plate, 7 lbs. 4 oz.

Mfg.'s Sug. Retail	$145	$110	$95	$80

KENTUCKY SCOUT RIFLE—.45 or .50 cal., percussion or 26 in. octagonal barrel, double set triggers, adj. sights, brass trim, full length stock, lock has adj. sear, 5 lbs. 8 oz. Add $10 for flintlock.

Mfg.'s Sug. Retail	$135	$115	$90	$75

TRADITIONS, INC., cont.

Grading	100%	98%	95%	90%

PENNSYLVANIA RIFLE—.45 or .50 cal., flintlock or percussion, 40½ in. octagonal barrel, double set triggers, adj. sights, brass trim, 9 lbs. 13 oz. Add $10 for flintlock.

Mfg.'s Sug. Retail	$355	$300	$265	$155

PIONEER RIFLE—.50 or .54 cal., percussion, 27¼ in. octagonal barrel, color case hardened hammer, lock and furniture, German silver blade front sight, recoil pad, carbine style stock.

Mfg.'s Sug. Retail	$160	$140	$120	$90

SHENANDOAH RIFLE—.45 or .50 cal., flintlock or percussion, color case hardened hammer and lock, 33½ in. long octagonal barrel, brass furniture, 7 lbs. 4 oz. Add $10 for flintlock.

Mfg.'s Sug. Retail	$185	$160	$140	$100

TRAPPER RIFLE—.36, .45 and .50 cal., percussion, 25 in. octagonal barrel, color case hardened hammer and lock, brass trim, 5 lbs.

Mfg.'s Sug. Retail	$190	$165	$140	$100

TROPHY RIFLE—.50 or .54 cal., percussion, 27½ in. octagonal tapering to round barrel, adj. trigger, fiberglass ramrod, carbine style walnut stock, 7 lbs.

Mfg.'s Sug. Retail	$320	$280	$240	$190

FRONTIER SCOUT RIFLE—.45 or .50 cal., flintlock or percussion, 26 in. octagonal barrel, double set triggers, adj. sights, brass trim, 5 lbs. 8 oz., lock has adj. sear. Add $10 for flintlock, $20 for carbine.

Mfg.'s Sug. Retail	$170	$150	$130	$85

SHOTGUNS

SINGLE BARREL—12 ga., percussion, 32 in. octagonal tapering to round barrel, German silver wedge plate, blued furniture, scroll engraving, and polished steel furniture on Deluxe version, 4 lbs. Add $85 for Deluxe.

Mfg.'s Sug. Retail	$315	$240	$210	$180

TRAIL GUNS ARMORY

LEAGUE CITY, TX.

ALAMO LONG RIFLE—.45 or .50 cal., percussion or flintlock. Add $20 for flintlock.

Mfg.'s Sug. Retail	$295	$270	$235	$170

KODIAK MK-I, MK-II & MK-III DOUBLE RIFLE—.50 and .58 cal., or 12 ga. percussion, 28 in. barrel, adj. sights. Add $295 for spare combo. barrels (.50 cal. x 12 ga.). $185 for 12 ga. barrels.

Mfg.'s Sug. Retail	$550	$500	$445	$320

TRYON PLAINS RIFLE—.50 or .54 cal., percussion, 31 in. browned octagonal barrel, browned furniture, white steel hammer and lock, 9 lbs. 6 oz. Add $60 for deluxe engraved version.

Mfg.'s Sug. Retail	$330	$275	$235	$185

RIFLES: BLACK POWDER CARTRIDGE

CREEDMOOR ROLLING BLOCK—45/70 cal., rimfire, 30 in. tapered barrel, color case hardened action, adj. sights, 9 lbs.

Mfg.'s Sug. Retail	$485	$420	$365	$290

Add $115 for deluxe version.

KODIAK DOUBLE RIFLE—.45-70 cal. rimfire, 24 in. tapered round barrel, color case hardened hammer and lock, 2 piece high gloss walnut hand checkered stock, adj. twin sights, patterned after the very rare Colt Side X Side Double Rifle of the 1870's.

Mfg.'s Sug. Retail	$1,495	$1,375	$1,195	$950

SHOTGUNS

KODIAK 10 DOUBLE BARREL—10 ga., percussion, goose gun barrels. Add $180 for spare barrel.

Mfg.'s Sug. Retail	$395	$335	$290	$225

UBERTI, ALDO & CO

MANUFACTURED IN ITALY BY ALDO UBERTI & CO. UBERTI GUNS ARE IMPORTED AND DISTRIBUTED BY VARIOUS U.S. COMPANIES UNDER BOTH THE UBERTI TRADEMARK AS WELL AS A MULTITUDE OF OTHERS (UBERTI USA, INC., CIMARRON ARMS CO., (FORMERLY OLD-WEST GUN CO.), NAVY ARMS, DIXIE GUN WORKS, ETC.). ALSO PREVIOUSLY IMPORTED BY ALLEN FIREARMS AND BENSON FIREARMS LTD.

All guns are to the exact specifications of the original manufacture. Crafted with an unmistakable fire blue finish. A. Uberti is one of the largest manufacturers of black powder firearms.

To the price of each pistol, add $70 for display case, $180 for type "A" engraving, $265 for type "B" engraving, $345 for type "C" engraving (except for Walker & Dragoon Models add $650 for type "C" engraving and 1858 New Army, New Navy or 1858 Carbine add $525), $565 for type "C/O" engraving all models (except 1858 New Army, New Navy or 1858 Carbine add $800).

Prices may fluctuation due to the recent devaluation of the U.S. dollar in international markets.

REVOLVERS

PATERSON MODEL—.36 cal., 7½ octagon barrel, hidden trigger design, without loading lever, 2 lbs. 9 oz. New in 1988.
Mfg.'s Sug. Retail $300 $270 $225 $175

1847 WALKER—.44 cal., percussion, 9 in. barrel, charcoal finish, color case hardened frame, hammer, and load lever, brass trim, engraved cylinder, 4.4 lbs.
Mfg.'s Sug. Retail $280 $250 $210 $135

1848 BABY DRAGOON—.31 cal., percussion, 3, 4, or 5 in. barrel, 5 shot, color case hardened frame, hammer, no load lever, engraved cylinder, 1.4 lbs. Add $15 for silver straps and trigger guard.
Mfg.'s Sug. Retail $210 $195 $160 $105

DRAGOON (1ST, 2ND, OR 3RD)—.44 cal., percussion, 6 shot, brass grip straps, color case hardened frame, hammer, and load lever, brass trim, 3.9 lbs. Add $15 for silver-plated straps, or cut for stock on 3rd Model Dragoon, $100 for shoulder stock for 3rd Model Dragoon.
Mfg.'s Sug. Retail $225 $205 $170 $110

1849 WELLS FARGO—.31 cal., percussion, 3, 4, or 5 in. octagonal barrel, 5 shot, color case hardened frame, hammer, no load lever, brass trim, 1½ lbs. Add $20 for silver straps.
Mfg.'s Sug. Retail $215 $190 $160 $105

1849 POCKET—.31 cal., percussion, with loading lever, 3, 4, or 5 in. barrel, 5 shot, color case hardened frame, hammer, and load lever, brass trim, 1½ lbs. Add $15 for silver straps and trigger guard.
Mfg.'s Sug. Retail $220 $200 $165 $110

1851 NAVY/NAVY SHERIFF—.36 cal., percussion, 5 (Sheriff's Model) or 7½ in. barrel, many styles, loading lever, 6 shot engraved cylinder, 2.8 lbs. Add $100 for stock, $50 for stainless steel, $15 for silver plated strap and trigger guard, or steel strap and trigger guard, $15 for "London" Model w/steel backstrap and trigger guard or if cut for stock (3rd Model Navy).
Mfg.'s Sug. Retail $220 $200 $165 $105

1860 ARMY—.44 cal., percussion, 8 in. barrel, 6 shot, loading lever, color case hardened frame, hammer, and load lever, all brass back strap and trigger guard, or steel backstrap and brass trigger guard on fluted cylinder model, 2.6 lbs. Add $100 for stock, $15 for silver plated strap and trigger guard, $50 for stainless steel.
Mfg.'s Sug. Retail $220 $200 $165 $115

1861 NAVY—.36 cal., percussion, 5 in. barrel, many styles, brass back strap or trigger guard, color case hardened frame, hammer, and load lever, 2½ lbs. Add $15 for silver plated strap and trigger guard, $15 for fluted military cylinder or cut for stock, $50 for stainless steel, $100 for shoulder stock.
Mfg.'s Sug. Retail $220 $200 $165 $105

Grading	100%	98%	95%	90%

1862 POCKET NAVY—.36 cal., percussion, 4½, 5½, or 6½ in. barrel, color case hardened frame, hammer, and load lever, cylinder, semi-fluted or engraved, 1.6 lbs. Add $15 for silver plated straps and trigger guard, $50 for stainless steel.

Mfg.'s Sug. Retail	$200	$180	$150	$105

1862 POLICE—.36 cal., percussion, 4½, 5½, or 6½ in. barrel, color case hardened frame, hammer, and load lever, cylinder, semi-fluted or engraved, 1.6 lbs. Add $15 for silver plated straps and trigger guard or fluted cylinder model, $50 for stainless steel.

Mfg.'s Sug. Retail	$200	$180	$150	$105

AUGUSTA CONFEDERATE—.36 cal., percussion, 7½ in. octagonal barrel, color case hardened hammer and trigger, all brass frame, engraved cylinder, 2½-2¾ lbs.

Mfg.'s Sug. Retail	$170	$145	$120	$75

GRISWOLD CONFEDERATE—.36 or .44 cal., 5½ or 7½ in. barrel, percussion, same as above except round barrel, forward of lug, does not have engraved cylinder.

Mfg.'s Sug. Retail	$170	$145	$120	$75

LEECH AND RIGDON CONFEDERATE—.36 cal., percussion, same as above except all steel frame.

Mfg.'s Sug. Retail	$220	$200	$165	$105

TEXAS CONFEDERATE DRAGOON—.44 cal., percussion, 7½ in. round barrel, color case hardened frame, hammer, and load lever, brass trim, "Tucker, Sherrard, & Co.", 4 lbs. Add $35 for stainless steel.

Mfg.'s Sug. Retail	$235	$210	$175	$110

1858 REMINGTON—.44 cal., percussion, 7½ in. barrel, 6 shot, blued steel, brass trigger guard, 2.6 lbs. Add $30 for adj. sights.

Mfg.'s Sug. Retail	$200	$175	$145	$90

1858 REMINGTON STAINLESS—same as above, has brass strap and trigger guard. Add $20 for adj. sights.

Mfg.'s Sug. Retail	$260	$235	$195	$125

1858 REMINGTON NEW NAVY—.36 cal., percussion, 6½ in. octagonal barrel, 6 shot, blue frame, 2½ lbs. Add $20 for adj. sights.

Mfg.'s Sug. Retail	$200	$175	$145	$90

1866 REVOLVING CARBINE—.44 cal., percussion, 18 in. barrel, 6 shot, blued steel, brass trigger guard, walnut stock, 4.6 lbs.

Mfg.'s Sug. Retail	$370	$335	$280	$150

RIFLES: PERCUSSION

HAWKEN SANTA FE—.53 cal., percussion, single shot, 32 in. oct. barrel, damascened finish, double set triggers, 9½ lbs., walnut stock.

Mfg.'s Sug. Retail	$370	$335	$280	$150

ST. LOUIS RIFLE—.45, .50, .54, or .58 cal., flintlock and percussion, color case hardened hammer lock and trigger guard, octagonal barrel. Add $25 for .54 and .58 cal. percussion, $15 for flintlock, $30 for 54 cal. flintlock.

Mfg.'s Sug. Retail	$265	$240	$200	$125

SQUIRREL RIFLE—.32 cal., percussion or flintlock, color case hardened hammer and lock, brass trigger guard, 28 in. octagonal barrel. Add $15 for flintlock.

	$200	$165	$105

U.S. HISTORICAL SOCIETY

MARKETING ORGANIZATION WHICH SUBCONTRACTS SPECIAL EDITIONS/ COMMEMORATIVES. LOCATED IN RICHMOND, VA.

Please refer to listing in the Modern Firearms section of this text also.

WESTERN ARMS GUNS

MORE INFORMATION AVAILABLE FROM MANUFACTURER.

COLT 1ST MOD. DRAGOON—.44 cal., 7½ in. barrel, oval bolt cuts in cylinder, color case hardened frame, hammer, and loading lever, one piece stock, 4 lbs. 2 oz.

$160 $135 $110

COLT 2ND MOD. DRAGOON—.44 cal., 7½ in. barrel, oval bolt cuts in cylinder, color case hardened frame, hammer, and loading lever, one piece stock, 4 lbs. 2 oz.

$160 $135 $110

COLT 3RD MOD. DRAGOON—.44 cal., 7½ in. barrel, oval bolt cuts in cylinder, color case hardened frame, hammer, and loading lever, one piece stock, 4 lbs. 2 oz.

$180 $150 $120

1860 ARMY—.44 cal., 8 in. round barrel, color case hardened frame, hammer, and load lever, round trigger guard, one piece stock, 2 lbs. 10 oz.

$155 $130 $105

1851 NAVY—.36 cal., 7½ in. octagonal barrel, color case hardened frame, hammer, and load lever, square trigger guard, one piece stock, 2 lbs. 10 oz.

$155 $130 $105

1861 NAVY—.36 cal., 7½ in. octagonal barrel, color case hardened frame, hammer, and load lever, square trigger guard, one piece stock, 2 lbs. 10 oz.

$180 $150 $120

MODERN AIRGUNS

Modern air gun shooting is still a growing competition sport in America. Since its acceptance as an Olympic sport in 1984, the push to create and market adult air guns (as they are now known) has been staggering. Old well known manufacturers such as Benjamin, Crosman, and Daisy and importers such as Beeman and RWS have all established new models specifically to fill the gap in this field. Even scope manufacturers are developing and marketing scopes capable of focusing down to 10 meters (regulation air rifle distance).

A word about pricing in this section. Even though American companies such as, Marksman, Daisy and Crosman have developed some new lines of adult airguns, all adult airguns currently sold in this country are imported from overseas (with the exception of the Crosman Model 84 and/Skanaker pistol). Due to the decreased value of the U.S. dollar on European and Asian markets, many imported models have increased nearly 100% in cost over the last two years. Unlike Black Powder weapons (where domestic technology is curently superior), almost all of the improvements in airgun refinement have come from Europe and England. Indeed, during the 1988 summer Olympics if you were not looking through the sights of a Feinwerkbau, the chances of winning were greatly decreased.

This has created an interesting situation, it is possible to buy some overstock airguns purchased at pre-1986 prices for less than current dealer cost. It is important to realize this when using this section to buy used or new airguns - there are values out there if you look for them. Most important is the fact that these prices reflect current values issued by non-stocking dealers who have no pre-1986 stock remaining.

As with the section on modern black powder guns, weapons under $100 are not shown in this section.

Models listed in this section have spring-piston operating mechanisms unless otherwise stated. Velocities listed will usually be achieved by using lightweight target pellets.

Grading	100%	98%	95%	90%

ARS/FARCO

MANUFACTURED IN THE PHILIPPINES. IMPORTED BY AIR RIFLE SPECIALISTS LOCATED IN ELMIRA, NY.

AIR SHOTGUNS

FARCO AIR SHOTGUN—28 ga., CO2 powered, 30 in. barrel, 100 FT/LBS. of energy (standard airgun has 12-14 lbs.), charged by refillable (and removeable) 10 oz. cylinder, hardwood stock, 7 lbs. Importation began in 1988.

Mfg.'s Sug. Retail	**$395**	**$360**	**$295**	**$235**

AIR MATCH

PREVIOUSLY IMPORTED BY KENDALL INTERNATIONAL LOCATED IN PARIS, KY.

AIR MATCH MODEL 600 PISTOL—.177 cal., side lever action, adj. trigger, professional target model, 2 lbs.

	$395	**$350**	**$285**

AIR LOGIC

MANUFACTURER/DISTRIBUTOR LOCATED IN FOREST ROW, SUSSEX, ENGLAND.

Air Logic has limited importation into the U.S. More information can be obtained by contacting Air Logic directly at: Air Logic Limited, 3 Medway Bldg.'s, Lower Road Forest Row, East Sussex ENGLAND RH18 5HE.

GENESIS—.22 cal., single stroke pneumatic, 630 FPS, unique bolt action sliding barrel (by L. Walther), recoilless, adj. trigger, side lever action, 9½ lbs. New for 1988.
Mfg.'s Sug. Retail   **$750** **$695** **$525** **$400**

AMERICAN ARMS, INC.

MANUFACTURER/IMPORTER LOCATED IN NORTH KANSAS CITY, MO.

Even though American Arms, Inc. imports Norica airguns, they are listed in this section because of their private label status. Importation began in late 1988.

RIFLES

JET RIFLE—.177 cal., barrel break action, 855 FPS, adj. double set triggers, hardwood stock, 7 lbs.
Mfg.'s Sug. Retail   **$150** **$140** **$120** **$95**
Deduct $65 for Junior Model.

COMMANDO—.177 cal., barrel break action, 540 FPS, adj. sights, 5 lbs.
Mfg.'s Sug. Retail   **$115** **$105** **$90** **$70**

PISTOLS

IDEAL—.177 cal., barrel break action, 400 FPS, adj. sights, 3 lbs.
Mfg.'s Sug. Retail   **$105** **$100** **$85** **$65**

ANSCHUTZ

MANUFACTURED IN ULM, W. GERMANY.

Models 333, 335, and 380 were previously imported by Crossman from 1986-1988. While discontinued, some dealers may still have remaining inventories of these models.

MODEL 333—.177 cal., barrel cocking action, 700 FPS, adj. trigger, 18 in. barrel, 6 lbs. 13 oz.
$160 **$135** **$80**
Last Mfg.'s Sug. Retail was $175.

MODEL 335—.177 cal., barrel cocking, 700 FPS, adj. trigger, 18½ in. barrel, 7 lbs. 10 oz. Add $10 for 335 Mag. (20% higher velocity).
$190 **$160** **$90**
Last Mfg.'s Sug. Retail was $200.

MODEL 380—.177 cal., under lever cocking, 600-640 FPS, professional match model, removable cheekpiece, adj. trigger, stippled walnut grips. Add $30 for left hand, $60 for moving target.
$795 **$700** **$550**
Last Mfg.'s Sug. Retail was $915.

MODEL 2001—.177 cal., single stroke pneumatic, side lever action, exceptional target model, 10 lbs. 8 oz. Add $68 for left hand.
Mfg.'s Sug. Retail   **$1,355** **$1,200** **$995** **$895**
Add $110 for Running Target Model.

Model 2001 imported by Precision Sales, Westfield, Mass.

B S A GUNS, LTD.

PREVIOUSLY MANUFACTURED IN BIRMINGHAM, ENGLAND. BSA GUNS IS IN THE PROCESS OF RESETTLING IN KARACHI, PAKISTAN.

BSA Airguns are not currently imported into the U.S. Small dealer inventories may remain at this time, however.

AIRSPORTER/AIRSPORTER SUPER:—.177 or .22 cal., under lever action, 700-550 FPS/825-600 FPS. (Super), 8 lbs. Add $50 for Super, $25 for Monte Carlo stock Stutzen Model.

| | $175 | $140 | $110 |

CENTENNIAL COMMEMORATIVE—.177 or .22 cal., designed to commemorate BSA's 100th year.

| | $300 | $240 | $190 |

Last Mfg.'s Sug. Retail was $650.

MERCURY/MERCURY SUPER—.177 or .22 cal., barrel cocking action, 700-550 FPS/825-600 FPS (super), 7¼ lbs. Add $35 for Super.

| | $140 | $125 | $90 |

MERCURY CHALLENGER—.177 or .22 cal., barrel cocking action, 850-625 FPS, 7 lbs. 4 oz. Disc. 1988.

| | $180 | $125 | $90 |

Last Mfg.'s Sug. Retail was $205.

METEOR/METEOR SUPER—.177 or .22 cal., barrel cocking action, 650-500 FPS, 6 lbs. Add $15 for Super.

| | $85 | $75 | $50 |

SUPER SPORT/SUPER SPORT CUSTOM—.177 or .22 cal., barrel cocking action, 950-700 FPS, approx. 7 lbs. Add $90 for custom model.

| | $175 | $150 | $100 |

VS 2000—.177 or .22 cal., 9 shot repeater, side lever action, 850-625 FPS, 9 lbs. Add $65 for custom model. Disc. 1988.

| | $240 | $210 | $170 |

Last Mfg.'s Sug. Retail was $330.

SCORPION PISTOL—.177 or .22 cal., barrel-cocking action 510-380 FPS, 3.6 lbs. Add $50 for carbine stock, Shadow Model.

| | $85 | $75 | $50 |

B.S.F. (BAYERISCHE SPORTWAFFENFABRIK)

MANUFACTURED IN W. GERMANY. PREVIOUSLY IMPORTED BY KENDELL INTERNATIONAL LOCATED IN PARIS, KY.

B.S.F. tooling and machinery has been purchased by Weihrauch and is being utilized to manufacture various Weihrauch models. It is not known if B.S.F. will continue to fabricate Air Rifles under their own trademark.

RIFLES

BAVARIA MODEL 35—.177 cal., barrel-cocking action, 500 FPS, 4½ lbs.

| | $105 | $95 | $75 |

Last Mfg.'s Sug. Retail was $125.

BAVARIA MODEL 45—.177 cal., barrel-cocking action, 700 FPS, 6 lbs.

| | $110 | $100 | $75 |

Last Mfg.'s Sug. Retail was $125.

BAVARIA MODEL 50—.177 cal., barrel-cocking action, 700 FPS, 6 lbs.

| | $115 | $105 | $80 |

Grading	100%	98%	95%	90%

BAVARIA MODEL S54—.177 or .22 cal., under barrel-cocking action, 685/500 FPS, 8 lbs. Add $15 for Sport Model (discontinued 1986), $30 for M Model.

	$185	$160	$100	

BAVARIA MODEL 55—.177 or .22 cal., barrel-cocking action, 800/570 FPS, 6½ lbs. Add $15 for Deluxe Model, $30 for Special Model (both discontinued 1986).

	$145	$125	$95	

BAVARIA MODEL S60—.177 or .22 cal., barrel-cocking action, 800/570 FPS, 6½ lbs.

	$150	$130	$80	

BAVARIA MODEL S70—.177 or .22 cal., barrel-cocking action, 800/570 FPS, 7 lbs.

	$155	$135	$100	

BAVARIA MODEL S80—.177 or .22 cal., barrel-cocking action, 800/570 FPS, 8¼ lbs.

	$170	$150	$125	

Last Mfg.'s Sug. Retail was $185.

BEEMAN PRECISION ARMS, INC.

IMPORTERS AND DISTRIBUTORS LOCATED IN SANTA ROSA, CA.

Beeman imported Feinwerkbau and Weihrauch Airguns will appear under their respective headings in this section.

RIFLES

BEEMAN R1—.177, .20, .22 or .25 cal., barrel-cocking action, 940-860 FPS, 8.8 lbs. Add $300 for custom grade, $335 for custom fancy, $400 for X fancy, $40 for left-hand, $10 for .20 or .25 cal.

Mfg.'s Sug. Retail	$380	$335	$280	$235

Add $370 for Laser Model.

BEEMAN R7—.177 cal., barrel-cocking action, 700 FPS, 6.1 lbs.

Mfg.'s Sug. Retail	$220	$185	$155	$110

BEEMAN R8—.177 cal., barrel-cocking action, 720 FPS, 7.2 lbs.

Mfg.'s Sug. Retail	$300	$260	$235	$210

BEEMAN R10—.177, .20, or .22 cal., barrel-cocking action, 1,020-870 FPS, 7.9 lbs. Add $300 for custom grade, $335 for custom fancy, $400 for X fancy, $50 for left-hand, and $50 for deluxe, $10 for .20 cal.

Mfg.'s Sug. Retail	$300	$260	$235	$210

Add $400 for Laser Model.

BEEMAN CARBINE C1—.177 or .22 cal., barrel-cocking action, 830-670 FPS, 6.2-6.3 lbs.

Mfg.'s Sug. Retail	$200	$165	$140	$100

BEEMAN FALCON 1 & 2—.177 cal., barrel-cocking action, 620-680 FPS/560-600 FPS, 6.7/5.9 lbs. Add $30 for Falcon 2. Discontinued in 1984.

	$100	$80	$60	

Last Mfg.'s Sug. Retail was $110.

BEEMAN FX 1 & 2—same as Beeman Falcon 1 & 2. Add $35 for FX 1.

Mfg.'s Sug. Retail	$115	$95	$80	$65

BEEMAN/HARPER AIR CANE—.22 or .25 cal., pneumatic (reuseable gas cartridge), 650 FPS, reproduction of 19th century Walking Cane Gun, 1 lbs. Add $50 for decorative head piece.

Mfg.'s Sug. Retail	$495	$450	$370	$300

BEEMAN/WEBLEY OMEGA—.177 or .22 cal., barrel break action, 830-675 FPS, 7.8 lbs.

Mfg.'s Sug. Retail	$350	$295	$245	$175

BEEMAN/WEBLEY VULCAN II AND VULCAN II DELUXE—.177 or .22 cal., barrel-cocking action, 830-675 FPS, 7.6-7.7 lbs. Add $50 for Deluxe.

Mfg.'s Sug. Retail	$200	$170	$140	$110

Grading	100%	98%	95%	90%

PISTOLS

BEEMAN/FAS 604—.177 cal., top lever spring pneumatic action, 380 FPS, 2.3 lbs. Add $30 for left-hand. Disc. 1988.

	$445	**$370**	**$295**	

Last Mfg.'s Sug. Retail was $495.

BEEMAN/HARPER CLASSIC PISTOL—.22 or .25 cal., similar Harper Air Cane rifle action, 300 FPS, 4 oz. Add $10 for .20 cal., $20 for .25 cal.

Mfg.'s Sug. Retail	**$225**	**$205**	**$170**	**$125**
Cased	**$435**	**$390**	**$325**	**$200**
Cased Pair	**$700**	**$630**	**$525**	**$350**

BEEMAN/HARPER PEPPERBOX PISTOL—.22 cal., pneumatic (like above), 9.8 oz.

Mfg.'s Sug. Retail	**$435**	**$400**	**$335**	**$220**

BEEMAN P1—.177, .20 or.22 cal. Mag., top cocking action, 350-600 FPS, walnut grips, Colt .45 look alike.

Mfg.'s Sug. Retail	**$290**	**$260**	**$200**	**$130**

Add $10 for stainless steel.

Add $295 for gold plating.

BEEMAN/WEBLEY HURRICANE—.177 or .22 cal., barrel-cocking action, 470-400 FPS, 2.4 lbs. Add $30 for M20 scope combo.

Mfg.'s Sug. Retail	**$150**	**$120**	**$105**	**$85**

BEEMAN/WEBLEY TEMPEST—.177 or .22 cal., barrel-cocking action, 470-400 FPS, 2 lbs.

Mfg.'s Sug. Retail	**$130**	**$110**	**$90**	**$65**

BENJAMIN AIR RIFLE COMPANY

MANUFACTURER LOCATED IN RACINE, WI.

CENTENNIAL MODEL 87—.177 or .22 cal., multi-stroke pneumatic, 750/650 FPS, polished brass barrel, all nickel trim, Williams aperature, built to commemorate the 100th anniversary, bronze medallion in stock, 6 lbs, 6,086 mfg.

Mfg.'s Sug. Retail	**$250**	**$235**	**$200**	**$135**

BENJAMIN MODEL 340, 342, AND 347—BB, .177 or .22 cal., pneumatic pump action, 750-650 FPS, 4½ lbs., (340-BB), (342-.22), (347-.177). Add $15 for Williams sight, $30 for 4 x 15 scope.

Mfg.'s Sug. Retail	**$105**	**$85**	**$70**	**$50**

BENJAMIN AIR PISTOL MODEL 130, 132, AND 137—.177 cal., pneumatic pump action, 380 FPS, 2 lbs.

Mfg.'s Sug. Retail	**$85**	**$70**	**$65**	**$45**

CROSMAN AIR GUNS

FAIRPORT, NEW YORK.

Other than the continued sale of the Model 84 and Skanaker, Crosman has dropped adult precision Airguns. The Crosman/Anschutz models listed below should be watched for collectors value due to their limited U.S. distribution using Crosman model numbers.

MODEL 84 AIR RIFLE—.177 cal., CO2 powered, match rifle, 0-720 FPS (fully adj.), adj. sights, walnut stock with adj. cheekplate and butt plate, 11 lbs.

No Mfg.'s Retail	**$1,175**	**$995**	**$845**	**$700**

Crosman Model 84 is the first U.S. made air rifle designed to compete with established European models. Unlike its competitors, it is CO2 powered with a digital gauge mounted on the forearm to show remaining pressure.

Grading	100%	98%	95%	90%

6500 (ANSCHUTZ MODEL 335)—.177 cal., barrel break action, 700 FPS, 18½ in.
barrel, 7 lbs. 10.5 oz. Disc. in 1989.
No Mfg.'s Retail   **$140**   **$125**   **$90**   **$70**

6300 (ANSCHUTZ MODEL 333)—.177 cal., barrel break action, 700 FPS, 18½ in.
barrel, 6 lbs. 13 oz. Disc. in 1989.
No Mfg.'s Retail   **$130**   **$110**   **$80**   **$60**

MODEL 6100 (MADE BY DIANAWERK)—.177 cal., barrel break action, 780/830
FPS, 20½ in. barrel, 8 lbs. 6 oz. Disc. in 1989.
No Mfg.'s Retail   **$235**   **$195**   **$125**   **$95**

PISTOLS

SKANAKER PISTOL (AVAILABLE 1987) MODEL 88—.177 cal., CO2 powered,
550 FPS, professional target model. Add $65 for carrying case.
No Mfg.'s Retail   **$560**   **$485**   **$410**   **$325**

DAISY MANUFACTURING CO., INC.

MANUFACTURED AND DISTRIBUTED IN ROGERS, ARKANSAS.

Even though Daisy is one of the largest airgun manufacturers in the world, only 6 weapons would fall into the category of adult precision airguns - these are the Daisy 126 El Gamo, Model 128 Gamo Olympic, Model 953, Model 753, and their 2 target pistols (Models 747 and 777). The Daisy 126 El Gamo rifle and Model 128 Gamo Olympic are manufactured in Spain and assembled in the U.S. All 6 airguns have barrels made by Lothar Walther.

RIFLES

EL GAMO 126 SUPER MATCH TARGET RIFLE—.177 cal., sidelever action, 590
FPS, adj. sights, hardwood stock, 10 lbs. 9 oz.
Mfg.'s Sug. Retail   **$400**   **$305**   **$265**   **$210**

MODEL 128 GAMO OLYMPIC—same as above except with adj. cheek and butt piece,
high quality European diopter sight.
Mfg.'s Sug. Retail   **$975**   **$700**   **$650**   **$400**

MODEL 753 COMPETITION—.177 cal., single stroke pneumatic, 480 FPS, competition
sights, 6lbs. 8 oz.
Mfg.'s Sug. Retail   **$300**   **$210**   **$175**   **$120**

953 TARGET—.177 cal., single stroke pneumatic, 480 FPS, Lothar Walther barrel, adj. sights,
5 lbs. 8 oz.
Mfg.'s Sug. Retail   **$180**   **$130**   **$110**   **$85**

PISTOLS

MODEL 747 TARGET PISTOL—.177 cal., side lever action, 360 FPS, 3 lbs. 3 oz.
Mfg.'s Sug. Retail   **$130**   **$90**   **$70**   **$40**

MODEL 777 TARGET PISTOL—.177 cal., side lever action, 360 FPS, wood target style
grips, 3 lbs. 3 oz.
Mfg.'s Sug. Retail   **$250**   **$170**   **$145**   **$100**

DIANAWERK, MAYER AND GRAMMELSPACHER

MANUFACTURER LOCATED IN WEST GERMANY.

Dynamit Nobel RWS Inc. is the exclusive Dianawerk importer located in Northvale, NJ.

RIFLES

MODEL 24—.177 or .22 cal., barrel-cocking action, 700/400 FPS, 17¼ in. barrel, 6 lbs.
Deduct $25 for Model 24J. New in 1987.
Mfg.'s Sug. Retail   **$150**   **$130**   **$115**   **$75**

Grading	100%	98%	95%	90%

MODEL 25D—.177 or .22 cal., barrel-cocking action, 525/380 FPS, 15¾ in. barrel, 5¾ lbs. (sport). Disc. in 1987.

	$105	$90	$65

Last Mfg.'s Sug. Retail was $120.

MODEL 26—.177 or .22 cal., barrel-cocking action, 750/500 FPS, 17¼ in. barrel, 6 lbs. 1 oz.

Mfg.'s Sug. Retail	$170	$150	$130	$90

MODEL 27—.177 or .22 cal., barrel-cocking action, 550/415 FPS, 17¼ in. barrel, 6 lbs. (sport). Disc. in 1987.

	$145	$120	$90

Last Mfg.'s Sug. Retail was $150.

MODEL 28—.177 or .22 cal., barrel-cocking action, 750/500 FPS, 15¾ in. barrel, 6 lbs. 12 oz.

Mfg.'s Sug. Retail	$210	$185	$160	$105

MODEL 34—.177 or .22 cal., barrel-cocking action, 950/700 FPS, 19½ in. barrel, 7 lbs. 6 oz.

Mfg.'s Sug. Retail	$225	$165	$140	$110

MODEL 35—.177 or .22 cal., barrel-cocking action, 665/540 FPS, 19 in. barrel, 8 lbs. (sport/target). Disc. in 1987.

	$135	$115	$100

Last Mfg.'s Sug. Retail was $160.

MODEL 36 AND 36 CARBINE—.177 or .22 cal., barrel break action, 1000/700 FPS, 19½ in. barrel, 8 lbs. Add $35 for new S Model, deduct $10 for muzzle break model without factory sights.

Mfg.'s Sug. Retail	$275	$235	$205	$150

MODEL 38—.177 or .22 cal., barrel break action, 1000/700 FPS, 19½ in. barrel, 8 lbs., walnut stock.

Mfg.'s Sug. Retail	$315	$275	$240	$160

Model 38 is the deluxe version of the Model 36 listed above.

MODEL 45 S / 45 DELUXE—.177 or .22 cal., barrel-cocking action, 900/650 FPS, 20½ in. barrel, 7 lbs. 9 oz., S Model equipped w/factory sling and scope. Add $40 for deluxe, $70 for S model with scope.

Mfg.'s Sug. Retail	$240	$215	$185	$130

MODEL 48—.177 or .22 cal., side lever action, 1,100/780 FPS, 17 in. barrel, 8½ lbs.

Mfg.'s Sug. Retail	$325	$290	$200	$170

MODEL 50T/T01—.177 or .22 cal., under lever action, 745/600 FPS, 18½ in. barrel, 8 lbs., (sport/target), parkerized finish. Add $20 for blue finish, $100 for T01 Model. Disc. 1988.

	$190	$170	$140

Last Mfg.'s Sug. Retail was $210.

MODEL 52—.177 or .22 cal., side lever action, 1,100/780 FPS, 17 in. barrel, 8½ lbs.

Mfg.'s Sug. Retail	$355	$315	$275	$200

MODEL 75, 75 HV, 75U, 75K, 75S—.177 cal., side lever action, 580 FPS, 19 in. barrel (professional target), 11 lbs. Add $30 for left-hand, $165 for U, $100 for K, deduct $40 for beech stock. Model 75 HV and Model 75 U were disc. in 1989.

Mfg.'s Sug. Retail	$790	$650	$600	$410

MODEL 100—.177 cal., single stroke pneumatic, 580 FPS, 19 in. barrel, adj. cheekpiece, professional target model, 11 lbs. New in 1989.

Mfg.'s Sug. Retail	$1,000	$965	$840	$670

MODEL 1000—.177 cal., barrel-break action, unique colored plastic stocks (black, red, blue, white, and yellow).

Mfg.'s Sug. Retail	$215	$185	$170	$125

Model 1000 is the sport model of the standard Model 34.

PISTOLS

MODEL 5G/GS—.177 or .22 cal., barrel-cocking action, 450/300 FPS, 7 in. barrel, (sport) 2 lbs. 12 oz. GS Model equipped w/factory scope. Add $60 for GS.

Mfg.'s Sug. Retail	$160	$145	$125	$95

Grading	100%	98%	95%	90%

MODEL 6G/6M/6GS—.177 cal., barrel-cocking action, 450 FPS , 7 in. barrel, (professional target), 3 lbs. GS Model equipped with factory scope. Add $50 for GS model, $15 for left hand.

6G

Mfg.'s Sug. Retail	$275	$245	$210	$135

6M

Mfg.'s Sug. Retail	$340	$315	$275	$195

MODEL 10—.177 cal., barrel-cocking action, 450 FPS, 7 in. barrel, (professional target) 3 lbs. 4 oz. Add $35 for cased model, $40 for left-hand.

Mfg.'s Sug. Retail	$610	$585	$350	$390

ENSIGN ARMS CO., LTD.

PREVIOUS INTERNATIONAL DISTRIBUTORS FOR SAXBY PALMER AIRGUNS LOCATED IN NEWBURY, ENGLAND.

Ensign Arms previously distributed the Saxby Palmer line of airguns into the U.S. Please refer to the Saxby Palmer section for these guns. "Ensign" designated models were trademarked by Ensign Arms Co., Ltd. Marksman Products was the most recent importer located in Huntington Beach, CA.

FEINWERKBAU

MANUFACTURED IN OBERNDORF, WEST GERMANY. IMPORTED AND DISTRIBUTED BY BEEMAN PRECISION ARMS INC. LOCATED IN SANTA ROSA, CA.

The Feinwerkbau trademark is now owned in the U.S. by Beeman Precision Arms, Inc.

Feinwerkbau has been responsible for developing many of the current technical innovations used in fabricating target Air Pistols and Rifles. In 1988, Feinwerkbau Airguns swept the Olympic competition in this newly formed Olympic sport. Feinwerkbau has always been a leader in Airgun technology.

RIFLES

MODEL 124—.177 cal., barrel-cocking action, 780-830 FPS, 7.2 lbs. Add $35 for deluxe, $20 for left-hand deluxe, $400 for custom select, $425 for custom fancy, $475 for custom extra fancy.

Mfg.'s Sug. Retail	$400	$360	$280	$180

MODEL 127—.22 cal., barrel-cocking action, 620-680 FPS, 6-7.1 lbs. Additions same as above.

Mfg.'s Sug. Retail	$400	$360	$280	$180

MODEL 300S—.177 cal., side lever action, 640 FPS, 8.8-10.8 lbs. Add $40 for Running Boar, $50 for left-hand (all styles), $200 for Universal, $30 for barrel sleeve.

Mfg.'s Sug. Retail	$860	$780	$650	$400

Add $50 for Running Boar stock configuration on Universal Model.

MODEL 600—.177 cal., sidelever action, single stroke pneumatic operation, top of the line match rifle with aperture sights, unique hardwood laminate stock, 585 FPS, 10½ lbs. Add $25 for left-hand. Disc. 1988.

	$815	$675	$540	

Last Mfg.'s Sug. Retail was $900.

This model was also available in a Running Boar variation with extra-long barrel that unscrews for transporting.

MODEL 601—.177 cal., side lever action, single stroke, pneumatic operation, replaces Model 600 (see above). 10 lbs. 8 oz. Add $100 for left hand, deduct $50 for running target.

Mfg.'s Sug. Retail	$1,175	$1,000	$890	$660

MODEL C60—.177 cal., CO2 powered, 555 FPS, similar in style to Model 600/601 above, 9.2 to 10.6 lbs. Add $90 for left hand, deduct $40 for running target.

Mfg.'s Sug. Retail	$1,085	$960	$825	$630

Grading	100%	98%	95%	90%

PISTOLS

MODEL 65 MK I AND II—.177 cal., side lever action, 525 FPS, 2.6-2.9 lbs., short barrel Mark II only. Add $45 for Mark II, $50 for left adj., $25 for adj. right.

Mfg.'s Sug. Retail   **$725**   **$500**   **$450**   **$350**

MODEL 80—.177 cal., side lever action, 475-525 FPS, 2.8-3.2 lbs. Discontinued 1983.

     $480   **$400**   **$320**

Last Mfg.'s Sug. Retail was $625.

MODEL 90—same as above. Add $45 for short barrel, $50 for left-hand.

Mfg.'s Sug. Retail   **$880**   **$800**   **$670**   **$425**

MODEL 100—.177 cal., pneumatic action, 460 FPS, 2½ lbs.

Mfg.'s Sug. Retail   **$890**   **$800**   **$675**   **$535**

Add $20 for left hand variation.

MODEL 2—.177 cal., CO_2 cartridge, 425-525 FPS, 2½ lbs. Add $40 for left, deduct $20 for mini.

     $675   **$580**   **$375**

Last Mfg.'s Sug. Retail was $770.

MODEL C 10—.177 cal., CO_2 cartridge, 510 FPS, 2½ lbs.

Mfg.'s Sug. Retail   **$785**   **$710**   **$590**   **$475**

Add $25 for left hand model.

FIOCCHI OF AMERICA, INC.

MANUFACTURER/IMPORTER/DISTRIBUTOR LOCATED IN OZARK, MO.

MODEL P10—.177 cal., underlever action pistol, 7¾ in. barrel, 2 lbs. 3 oz.

Mfg.'s Sug. Retail   **$560**   **$470**   **$400**   **$320**

GAMO

PREVIOUSLY IMPORTED BY STOEGER INDUSTRIES - IMPORTATION DISCONTINUED IN 1986. A FEW MODELS ARE CURRENTLY BEING IMPORTED BY DAISY.

PISTOLS

CENTER—.177 cal., under barrel lever cocking, 400-435 FPS, 14 in. barrel, 2.8 lbs.

     $100   **$85**   **$60**

RIFLES

CADET—.177 cal., barrel cocking, 570 FPS, beechwood stock, 5 lbs.

     $90   **$75**   **$60**

CONTEST—.177 cal., side lever action, 543 FPS, beechwood stock, 10.1 lbs.

     NA   **NA**

EXPO—.177 or .22 cal., barrel cocking, 600 FPS, adj. trigger, special-sights, 5½ lbs.

     $100   **$85**   **$65**

EXPOMATIC—.177 cal., repeating barrel cock action, 600 FPS, adj. trigger

     $130   **$110**   **$90**

GAMO 68—.177 or .22 cal., barrel cocking, 600 FPS, 6½ lbs.

     $130   **$110**   **$90**

MODEL 600—.177 or .22 cal., barrel cocking, 660 FPS, 7 lbs.

     $130   **$110**   **$90**

SUPER—.177 cal., side lever action, 593 FPS, 10½ lbs.

     $160   **$155**   **$125**

MARKSMAN

DIVISION OF S/R INDUSTRIES, HUNTINGTON BEACH, CA.

JUNIOR MODEL 28—.177 cal., barrel break action, 600 FPS, 16¾ in. barrel, 6 lbs. Mfg. for Marksman by Weihrauch.
Mfg.'s Sug. Retail $200 $140 $120 $90

MODEL 29/30—.177 or .22 cal., barrel break action, 800/625 FPS, 18½ in. barrel, 6 lbs. Mfg. for Marksman by BSA.
Mfg.'s Sug. Retail $230 $180 $140 $90

MODEL 40—.177 cal., barrel break action, 720 FPS, 18⅜ in. barrel, 7⅓ lbs.
Mfg.'s Sug. Retail $235 $160 $140 $100

MODEL 55 (RIFLE) & 59 CARBINE—.177 cal., barrel break action, 925 FPS, 19¾ (rifle) or 14 (carbine) in. barrel, 7 lbs. 8 oz. Mfg. for Marksman by Weihrauch.
Mfg.'s Sug. Retail $250 $175 $150 $95

MODEL 56/56K—.177 cal., barrel break action, 925 FPS, 19⅝ in. barrel, adj. cheekpiece and trigger, 8 lbs. 11 oz.
Mfg.'s Sug. Retail $495 $340 $295 $230
  Add $180 for 56K Model with Marksman Model 6941 scope.

  The Model 56/56K is manufactured for Marksman by Weihrauch.

MODEL 58/58K—.177 cal., barrel break action, 925 FPS, 16 in. heavy bull barrel, adj. trigger, designed for silhouette shooting, 8½ lbs.
Mfg.'s Sug. Retail $410 $285 $245 $195
  Add $180 for 58K Model with Marksman Model 6941 scope.

  The Model 58/58K is manufactured for Marksman by Weihrauch.

MODEL 70, 71, 72—.177, .20, or .22 cal., barrel break action, 925/760 FPS, 19¾ in. barrel, 8 lbs. Add $10 for .20 cal. Mfg. for Marksman by Weihrauch.
Mfg.'s Sug. Retail $290 $210 $175 $110

  The Model 72 is a .20 cal.

MAUSER

IMPORTED BY MARKSMAN LOCATED IN HUNTINGTON BEACH, CA.

RIFLES

MATCH 300SL/SLC—.177 cal., under-lever action, 550/450 FPS, adj. sights and hardwood stock, 8.8 lbs. Add $75 for SLC Model with diopter sights.
Mfg.'s Sug. Retail $330 $240 $200 $140

PISTOLS

U90/U91 JUMBO AIR PISTOLS—.177 cal., barrel break action, 260 FPS, 2 lbs.
Mfg.'s Sug. Retail $100 $80 $65 $45
  Add $15 for deluxe model U91 with adj. sights and checkered grips.

NORICA

IMPORTED BY KASSNAR IMPORTS LOCATED IN HARRISBURG, PA AND AMERICAN ARMS, INC. LOCATED IN NORTH KANSAS CITY, MO. PREVIOUSLY IMPORTED BY S.A.E. LOCATED IN MIAMI, FL.

Norica airguns imported by American Arms, Inc. will appear under the American Arms, Inc. heading in this text.

MODEL 47—.177 cal., side lever action, 600 FPS, unique black pistol grip handle, 5½ lbs.
Mfg.'s Sug. Retail $175 $120 $85 $65

MODEL 61C—.177 cal., barrel break action, 600 FPS, 5.8 lbs.
Mfg.'s Sug. Retail $130 $90 $65 $45

Grading	100%	98%	95%	90%

MODEL 73—.177 or .22 cal., barrel break action, 580/525 FPS, 6.4 lbs.
  Mfg.'s Sug. Retail **$155 $105 $75 $50**

MODEL 80G—.177 or .22 cal., barrel break action, 635/570 FPS, 7.2 lbs.
  Mfg.'s Sug. Retail **$200 $135 $100 $70**

MODEL 90—.177 cal., barrel break action, 650 FPS, factory equipped with scope,
  Mfg.'s Sug. Retail **$185 $125 $90 $65**

MODEL 92—.177 cal., side lever action, 650 FPS, 5.75 lbs.
  Mfg.'s Sug. Retail **$175 $120 $85 $65**

NORICA YOUNG—.177 cal., barrel break action, 600 FPS, unique colored stock.
  Mfg.'s Sug. Retail **$120 $80 $60 $40**

BLACK WIDOW—.177 or .22 cal., barrel break action, 500/450 FPS, unique black plastic stock, 5 lbs.
  Mfg.'s Sug. Retail **$150 $115 $75 $50**

S G S (SPORTING GUNS SELECTION)

PREVIOUSLY IMPORTED BY KENDELL INTERNATIONAL.

DUO 300AP—.177 or .22 cal., top cocking action, 455/430 FPS.
  $135 $120 $100

DUO 300AR—.177 or .22 cal., top cocking action, 455/430 FPS, with extra stock and barrel assembly to create a 3-in-1 gun.
  $275 $245 $200

SAXBY PALMER

MANUFACTURED BY SAXBY PALMER LOCATED IN STRATFORD-UPON-AVON, ENGLAND. PREVIOUSLY IMPORTED/DISTRIBUTED BY MARKSMAN PRODUCTS LOCATED IN HUNTINGTON BEACH, CA.

Saxby Palmer has developed the world's first cartridge loading air rifle. This is not a CO2 or other type of compressed gas gun. The cartridges are pressurized (2250 PSI) and reusable facilitating speed of loading and much greater velocities. New rifles are supplied with the table pump (for reloading brass or plastic cartridges) and 10 cartridges. You must have these accessories in order to operate air rifles or pistols. Deduct 50% for used guns without these accessories.

RIFLES: DISCONTINUED

ENSIGN ELITE—.177 or .22 cal., bolt action cartridge, 1000-800 FPS auto safety, price quoted FOB England.
  $120 $100 $80

  Last Mfg.'s Sug. Retail was $175.

ENSIGN ROYAL—.177 or .22 cal., bolt action cartridge, 1000-800 FPS auto safety, walnut stock, price quoted FOB England.
  $195 $150 $115

  Last Mfg.'s Sug. Retail was $275.

RIFLES

GALAXY—.177 or .22 cal., bolt action cartridge, 1,000/800 FPS, auto safety, walnut stain, hardwood stock. 6½ lbs. Current mfg.
  $215 $175 $145

SATURN—.177 or .22 cal., bolt action cartridge, 1,000/800 FPS, auto safety, hi-strength black polymer stock. 6½ lbs. Disc. in 1987.
  $195 $150 $115

  Last Mfg.'s Sug. Retail was $175.

Grading	100%	98%	95%	90%

REVOLVERS

ORION AIR REVOLVER—.38 cal., 30 grain zinc pellets, 6 shot, compressed gas cartridges (reusable), 550 FPS, 6 in. barrel, 2 lbs. 3 oz.

	$315	$240	$175

This model is manufactured by Weihrauch of W. Germany and includes a Slim Jim pump and 12 reuseable cartridges.

MODEL 54—.177 cal., 5 shot, compressed gas cartridges (reusable), 4 in. barrel, 1 lb. 5 oz.

	$190	$150	$100

This model is manufactured by Weihrauch of W. Germany and includes a Slim Jim pump and 12 reuseable cartridges.

SHARP

JAPAN (IMPORTED BY BEEMAN).

SHARP INNOVA—.177 or .22 cal., pneumatic pump action, 920/720 FPS, 4 lbs. 6 oz. Disc. 1988.

	$150	$130	$95

Last Mfg.'s Sug. Retail was $175.

SHARP ACE—.177 or .22 cal., pneumatic pump action, 920/750 FPS, 6 lbs. 4 oz. Disc. 1988.

	$255	$220	$150

Last Mfg.'s Sug. Retail was $295.

R W S

IMPORTERS LOCATED IN NORTHVALE, NJ.

See Dianawerk.

SHERIDAN

MANUFACTURED BY BENJAMIN AIR RIFLE CO. LOCATED IN RACINE, WI.

SHERIDAN BLUE STREAK/SILVER STREAK—20 cal., pneumatic pump or CO2 action, 700 FPS, 6 lbs. Add $5 for Silver Streak, $15 for receiver sight, $30 for 4 x 15 scope, $25 for paint pellet rifle. Deduct $10 for CO2.

Mfg.'s Sug. Retail	$110	$90	$80	$60

SHERIDAN AIR PISTOL

Model E—20 cal., CO2 cartridge, 400 FPS, 2 lbs. 4 oz. Add $40 for paint pellet pistol.

	$50	$45	$30

Model HB—20 cal., pneumatic pump action, 400 FPS, 1 lb. 11 oz.

Mfg.'s Sug. Retail	$90	$75	$65	$40

SIG HAMMERLI

IMPORTED BY MANDALL SHOOTING SUPPLIES, INC. LOCATED IN SCOTTSDALE, AZ.

Prices may increase or decrease based on the value of dollar on international markets.

RIFLES

MODEL 403—.177 cal., side lever action, 700 FPS, adj. sight target model, 9¼ lbs.

Mfg.'s Sug. Retail	$380	$310	$265	$210

MODEL 420—.177 cal., side lever action, 700 FPS, military style plastic stock, 7½ lbs.

Mfg.'s Sug. Retail	$300	$240	$195	$155

STERLING

MANUFACTURED BY BENJAMIN AIR RIFLE COMPANY LOCATED IN RACINE, WI.

RIFLES

HR 81—.177 or .22 cal., under lever cocking action, 700/660 FPS, adj. V type rear sight, 8½ lbs. Add $10 for .22 cal.

Mfg.'s Sug. Retail   **$275**   **$235**   **$195**   **$145**

HR 83—.177 or .22 cal., under lever cocking action, 700/660 FPS, adj. Williams "FP" peep sight, walnut stock, 8½ lbs. Add $5 for .22 cal.

Mfg.'s Sug. Retail   **$385**   **$345**   **$295**   **$230**

STEYR

MANUFACTURED BY STEYR LOCATED IN AUSTRIA. IMPORTED AND DISTRIBUTED BY GUNS SOUTH INC. LOCATED IN TRUSSVILLE, AL.

CO2 RIFLE—.177 cal., CO2 powered match rifle with precision receiver sight and adj. butt plate. New in 1988.

Mfg.'s Sug. Retail   **$1,375**   **$1,250**   **$1,100**   **$750**

THEOBEN ENGINEERING

MANUFACTURER LOCATED IN ENGLAND. IMPORTED BY AIR RIFLE SPECIALISTS LOCATED IN ELMIRA, NY.

SIROCCO COUNTRYMAN—.177 or .22 cal., Anschutz barrel break action, 1,100/800 FPS, unique precharged sealed gas system replaces the springs used in most modern air rifles, not to be confused with a modern gas powered (CO2) air rifle, includes scope rings, barrel weight, walnut stained beech stock, 7½ lbs. Importation disc. in 1987.

   $465   **$350**   **$275**

Last Mfg.'s Sug. Retail was $585.

SIROCCO DELUXE—similar to Countryman, except has hand checkered walnut stock. Importation disc. in 1987.

   $500   **$400**   **$300**

Last Mfg.'s Sug. Retail was $650.

SIROCCO CLASSIC—similar to Sirocco Deluxe, except has updated floating inertia system in piston chamber and auto safety, variable power, 900/1100 FPS. New in 1987.

Mfg.'s Sug. Retail   **$860**   **$815**   **$635**   **$450**

This model is available with either a choked or unchoked Anschutz barrel as standard equipment.

SIROCCO GRAND PRIX—similar specifications to the Sirocco Classic, except has checkered walnut thumbhole stock.

Mfg.'s Sug. Retail   **$940**   **$895**   **$675**   **$500**

In 1987, this model was updated with a floating inertia system in piston chamber and auto safety, variable power.

Subtract 30% for older models without safety and new piston design.

This model is available with either a choked or unchoked Anschutz barrel as standard equipment.

ELIMINATOR—.177 or .22 cal., barrel break action, 1100/1400 FPS, variable power, deluxe checkered thumb hole stock with cheekpiece and pad. 9½ lbs. New in 1987.

Mfg.'s Sug. Retail   **$1,450**   **$1,450**   **$1,000**   **$850**

This model incorporates an improved barrel design featuring pronounced rifling for the higher velocity pellets.

IMPERATOR—.22 cal., underlever action, 750 FPS, variable power, walnut hand checkered stock, auto safety. New in 1989.

Mfg.'s Sug. Retail   **$1,450**   **$1,400**   **$1,100**   **$900**

VENOM ARMS COMPANY

United Kingdom.

Venom Arms specializes in customizing Weihrauch firearms manufactured in Germany. A quick review of their latest pricing scedule for custom guns indicate prices may run nearly 100% over the initial cost of the uncustomized gun (see Weihrauch). Many of their airguns are available through MAC-1 Airgun Distributor, Inglewood, CA.

WALTHER

MANUFACTURED IN WEST GERMANY. IMPORTED BY INTERARMS LOCATED IN ALEXANDRIA, VA.

RIFLES

CG 90—.177 cal., CO2 powered, tilting block action, 18.9 in. barrel, 10 lbs. 2 oz. New in 1989.
Mfg.'s Sug. Retail **$1,225 $1,100 $925 $725**

LGR RIFLE—.177 cal., side lever action, single stroke pneumatic mechanism, 580 FPS (professional target) 10.8 lbs. Add $100 for universal, 10% for left-hand.
Mfg.'s Sug. Retail **$1,050 $950 $790 $630**
Deduct $150 for Match Grade.

Prices based on Running Boar Model.

PISTOLS

CP 2—.177 cal., CO2 powered, 9 in. barrel, 2½ lbs.
Mfg.'s Sug. Retail **$900 $795 $675 $450**

LP 3 AIR PISTOL—.177 cal., single stroke pneumatic action, 405 FPS, 2.8-3.0 lbs. Add $60 for match grade.
$300 $265 $225

LP 53—.177 cal.
$210 $180 $150

WEIHRAUCH

MANUFACTURED IN W. GERMANY. IMPORTED BY BEEMAN PRECISION ARMS INC. LOCATED IN SANTA ROSA, CA.

RIFLES

MODEL 35EB—.177 or .22 cal., barrel-cocking action, 755/660 FPS, 8 lbs. Add $50 for chrome, $10 for .22 cal. Deduct $20 for 35L.
$275 $235 $170

MODEL 55—.177 cal., barrel-cocking action, 660-700 FPS, 7.8 lbs. Add $40 for left-hand, $100 for Match, $140 for Tyrolean.
Mfg.'s Sug. Retail **$390 $350 $290 $240**

MODEL 77/77CARBINE—.177 or .22 cal., under lever cocking action, 830-710 FPS, 8.9 lbs. Add $30 for left-hand, $10 for .20 cal. (5mm), $50 for Deluxe.
Mfg.'s Sug. Retail **$400 $295 $240 $210**

PISTOLS

HW MODEL 70—.177 cal., barrel-cocking action, 410 FPS, 2.4 lbs. Add $45 for chrome.
Mfg.'s Sug. Retail **$145 $120 $105 $70**

WISCHO

PREVIOUSLY IMPORTED BY BEEMAN PRECISON ARMS, INC. LOCATED IN SANTA ROSA, CA.

WISCHO AIR PISTOL MODEL S-20 STANDARD—.177 cal., barrel-cocking action, 450 FPS, 2.8 lbs. Disc. 1988.

$110 $100 $70

Last Mfg.'s Sug. Retail was $130

MODEL CM—same as above but target style. Disc. in 1988.

$110 $100 $70

Last Mfg.'s Sug. Retail was $130

MODEL CM—same as above but target style. Disc. 1988.

$130 $110 $90

Last Mfg.'s Sug. Retail was $160.

NOTES

PROOF MARKINGS

The proof marks shown below will assist in determining nationality of manufacturers when no other markings are evident. Since the U.S. has no federalized proofing houses (as in England, France, Germany and other European countries), most U.S. built guns voluntarily proof their firearms with a specified style of proofmark (i.e.— the interlocked "WP" synonymous with nitro-proofed Winchesters is one example). Remember, only guns with the definitive nitro-proof mark can be fired using modern (smokeless powder) shells. Pre-1850 European firearms oftentimes do not exhibit any commercial proof marks and with the exception of an occasional barrel address, they represent the single hardest bracket of firearms I can research properly. Captured weapons from major wars occasionally show 2 different nationalities of proofmarks. This is acceptable since the gun was proofed in a national proof house after original manufacture and again when the gun was "exported" to a different country as a military acquisition.

BRITISH PROOF MARKS Under 1954 Rules of Proof

A. British rules of proof-1954: (1) London provisional proof, (2) Birmingham provisional proof, (3) Definitive proof for nitro powder (or modern ammo), (4) Definitive London proof for nitro powder (or modern ammo), (5) Definitive Birmingham nitro proof for barrel and action, (6) London proof for black powder only, (7) Birmingham proof for black powder only, (8) Special definitive proof-London, (9) Special definitive proof-Birmingham, (10) Reproof marking for London, (11) Reproofing marking for Birmingham.

B.

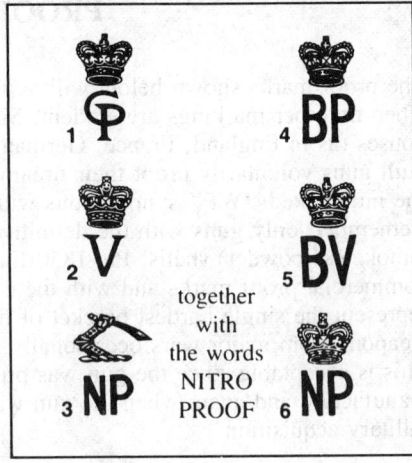

B. England: 1925 Rules of Proof –
(1) London proof, (2) London view,
(3) London nitro proof, (4) Birmingham
proof, (5) Birmingham view, (6)
Birmingham nitro proof.

AUSTRIAN PROOF MARKS

C.

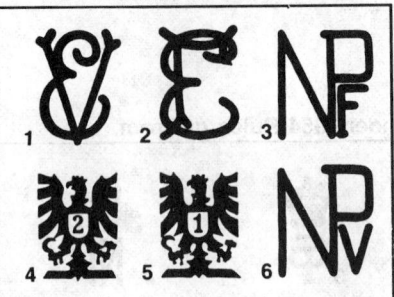

C. Austrian proof marks – (1) Vienna
provisional proof, (2) Ferlach provisional
proof, (3) Vienna black powder proofing,
(4) Ferlach black powder proofing, (5)
Nitro proof-Vienna, (6) Nitro proof-
Ferlach.

BELGIAN PROOF MARKS

D.

D. Belgium liege proof marks – (1) Provisional proof, (2) Double proofed provisional
marking, (3) Triple proofed provisional marking, (4) Definitive proofing, (5) View
proof, (6) Rifled arms definitive proof, (7) Nitro proof, (8) Superior nitro proof.

E.

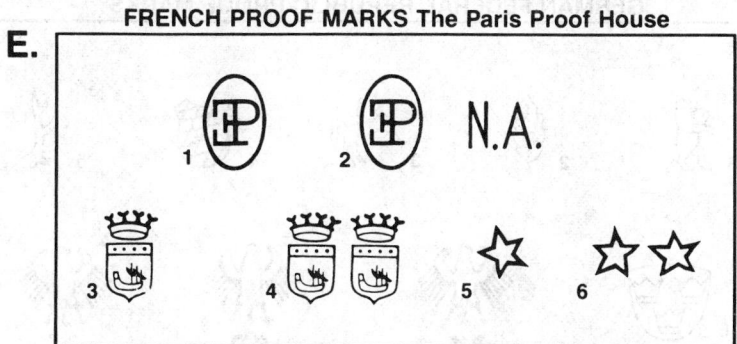

E. French proofings from Paris Proof House – (1) Assembly of tubes, seen in single, double, or tiple configuration, (2) Barrels proofed separately, not assembled, (3) Definitive proof for black powder, (4) Superior proof for black powder, (5) Smokeless powder ordinary proof, (6) Superior proof for smokeless powder.

F.

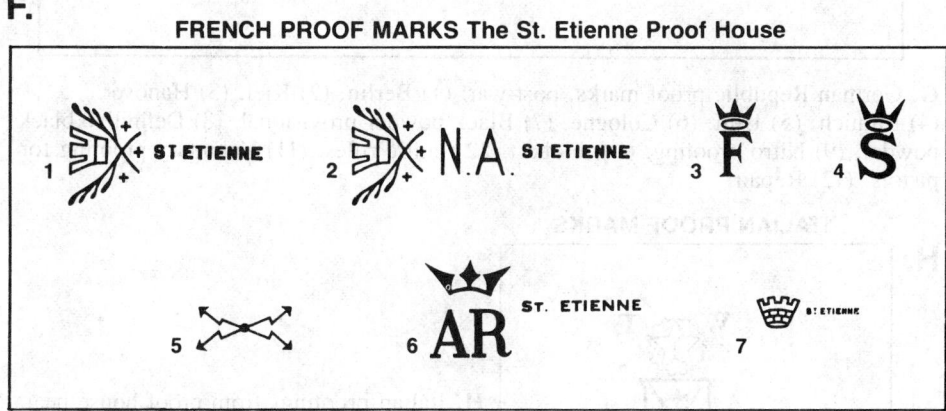

F. French proofs from the St. Etienne Proof House – (1) Ordinary assembled tubes proof—can be single, double, or triple, (2) Separate tube proofing—not assembled, (3) Black powder, (4) Superior black powder, (5) Ordinary smokeless proof, (6) Superior smokeless powder, (7) Short-barreled firearms.

G.

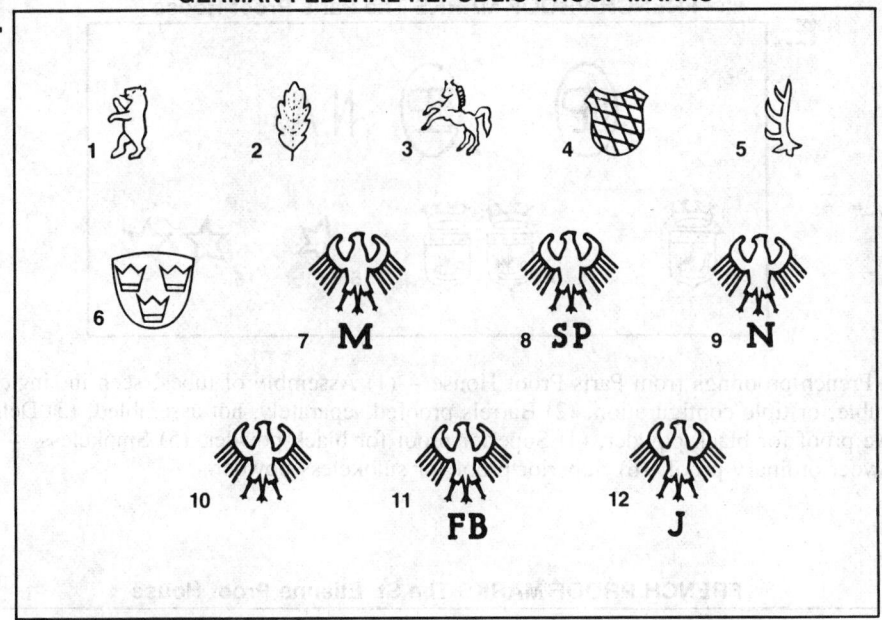

G. German Republic proof marks, post-war: (1) Berlin, (2) Kiel, (3) Hanover, (4) Munich, (5) Ulm, (6) Cologne, (7) Black powder provisional, (8) Definitive black powder, (9) Nitro proofing, (10) Flobert .22 rimfire rifles, (11) Voluntary proofing for pistols, (12) Repair.

ITALIAN PROOF MARKS

H.

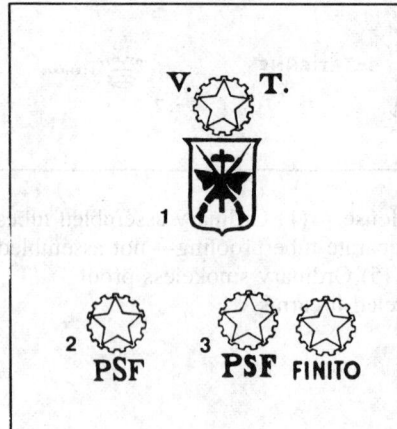

H. Italian proofings from proof house near Brescia – (1) Provisional proof, (2) Definitive proof, (3) Finish proof—firearm is now saleable.

Cartridge Interchangeability

This section is for the shooter whose motto is "If it fits, I'll shoot it". Many apparent "fits" are not adapted for a shorter round, and either immediate or future damage can occur to the firearm by firing ammunition not specifically adapted to the chambering of a particular gun. As an example, many people think that shooting .22 Shorts in a barrel marked for .22 Long Rifle is acceptable. In fact, repeated firing can cause erosion of the chamber to the point that shell extraction can become difficult in addition to experiencing velocity loss in extreme cases. Below is a listing of recommended caliber interchangeability. No other cartridge switching is recommended nor does this chart work vise-versa. For shotguns, there is no interchangeability for gauges. Only shells that are shorter than the specified chamber length in the same gauge may be used (ie. 2¾ in. 12 ga. ammunition may be used in a 12. ga. gun with a 3 in. chamber).

RIMFIRE INTERCHANBEABILITY

Firearm marked for:	Can also be used with:
.22 Short	.22 BB Cap, .22 CB Cap, .22 Short Blank, 22 CB Short
.22 Long	.22 BB Cap, .22 CB Cap, .22 Short Blank, .22 Short, .22 CB Short, .22 CB Long
.22 Long Rifle	.22 BB Cap, .22 CB Cap, .22 Short Blank, .22 CB Short, .22 CB Long, .22 Long, .22 L.R. Shot
.22 Win. Mag. R.F.	.22 Win. R.F., .22 Rem. Spl.
.22 Rem. Spl.	.22 Win. R.F.
.22 Win. R.F.	.22 Rem. Spl.
.25 Stevens	.25 Stevens Short
.32 Long	.32 Short

CENTERFIRE HANDGUN INTERCHANGEABILITY

Firearm marked for:	Can also be used with:
.32 Smith & Wesson Long	.32 Smith & Wesson, .32 Smith & Wesson Blank, .32 Colt New Police
.32 Colt New Police	.32 Smith & Wesson, .32 Smith & Wesson Blank, .32 Smith & Wesson Long
.32 Long Colt	.32 Short Colt
.38 Long Colt	.38 Short Colt
.38 Smith & Wesson	.38 Colt New Police, .38 Smith & Wesson Blank
.38 Colt New Police	.38 Smith & Wesson, .38 Smith & Wesson Blank
.38 Special	.38 Short Colt, .38 Long Colt, .38 Special Blank
.357 Magnum	.38 Short Colt, .38 Long Colt, .38 Special Blank, .38 Special, .38 Special + P
.38-40 Winchester	5 in 1 Blank
.38 Super Auto	.38 Auto Colt
.44 S&W Special	.44 S&W Russian
.44 Remington Magnum	.44 S&W Special

| .44-40 Winchester | 5 in 1 Blank |
| .45 Colt | 5 in 1 Blank |

GUNS ALSO CALLED
CENTERFIRE PISTOLS

Full name:	Also called:
.25 Automatic	.25 Auto, .25 ACP, .25 C.A.P., 6.35mm Auto, 635mm Browning (Auto)
.30 Luger	7.65 Luger, 7.65 Parabellum
.32 Automatic	.32 Auto, .32 ACP, .32 C.A.P., 7.65 Auto, 7.65mm Browning (Auto)
9mm Luger	9mm Parabellum
.380 Automatic	9mm Corto, 9mm Kurtz
.38-40 Winchester	.38-40, .38 W.C.F., .38 Winchester, .38-40 Remington, .38-40 Marlin
.44-40 Winchester	.44-40, .44 W.C.F., .44 Winchester, .44-40 Remington, .44-40 Marlin

CENTERFIRE RIFLES

Full name:	Also called:
6mm Remington	(formerly) .244 Remington
.25-20 Winchester	.25-20, .25 W.C.F., .25-20 Marlin
.30-30 Winchester	.30-30, .30 Winchester, .30 Marlin, .30 Savage, .30 W.C.F.
.32-20 Winchester	.32-20, .32 Winchester, .32 Marlin, .32 Remington, .32 W.C.F., .32 Colt L.M.R.
.38-40 Winchester	.38-40, .38 W.C.F., .38 Winchester, .38-40 Remington, .38-40 Marlin
.44-40 Winchester	.44-40, .44 W.C.F., .44 Winchester, .44-40 Remington, .44-40 Marlin
.45-70 Government	.45-70, .45-70 Marlin, .45-70-405, .45-70-500

Development of Firearms

1247 - FIRST RECORD OF THE FORMULA OF GUNPOWDER

1327 - HANDGUN INVENTED

1440 - MATCHLOCK SYSTSEM OF IGNITION

1475 - SIGHTS WERE DEVELOPED

1500 - MULTI-BARRELED ARMS DEVELOPED

1521 - WHEEL-LOCK SYSTEM OF IGNITION

1543 - ENGLISH FIREARM FABRICATION BEGAN

1547 - RIFLING INVENTED

1580 - SNAPHAUNCE SYSTEM OF IGNITION INVENTED

1630 - FLINTLOCK SYSTEM OF IGNITON INVENTED

1710 - KENTUCKY RIFLE INVENTED

1795 - U.S. FEDERAL ARMORIES ESTABLISHED

1798 - FIREARMS MASS PRODUCTION ACHEIVED THROUGH INTERCHANGEABLE PARTS

1807 - PERCUSSION SYSTEM OF IGNITION INVENTED

1811 - FIRST RIFLE BREECHLOADER INVENTED

1814 - DISCOVERY OF PERCUSSION COPPER CAP

1816 - THE FIRM OF REMINGTON ARMS FOUNDED

1819 - FIRST USE OF INTERCHANGEABLE PARTS IN U.S. ARMORY

1835 - FIRST PRACTICAL REVOLVER FABRICATION

1837 - PEPPERBOX REVOLVER INVENTED

1838 - NEEDLE CARTRIDGE IGNITION SYSTEM INVENTED

1841 - INVENTION OF CONICAL BULLETS

1845 - PERCUSSION TAPE PRIMER SYSTEM INVENTED

1847 - PINFIRE CARTRIDGE INVENTED

1848 - FIRST CONVERSION OF FLINTLOCK ARMS TO PERCUSSION

1850 - INVENTION OF MINIE BULLET

1850 - FIRST PRACTICAL METALLIC CARTRIDGE UTILIZATION

1856 - BREECHLOADING PERCUSSION CARBINE WITH GAS SEALED CARTRIDGE USED

1857 - INVENTION OF THE DERINGER

1860 - FIRST PRACTICAL REPEATING RIFLE

1860 - CENTERFIRE CARTRIDGE INVENTED

1860 - HENRY .44 RIMFIRE REPEATING RIFLE INVENTED

1865 - CONVERSION OF MUZZLE LOADERS TO BREECH LOADERS

1873 - MODEL 1873 WINCHESTER INVENTED

1873 - COLT FRONTIER SINGLE ACTION REVOLVER IN MANUFACTURE

1885 - INVENTION OF SMOKELESS POWDER

1897 - JOHN BROWNING INVENTS AUTOMATIC PISTOL

BROWNING BELGIUM PRODUCTION

A-5 (AUTOMATIC 5) SHOTGUN — approximate recapitulation — 12 ga.

Year	Serial Number Beginning of Year	Serial Number at End of Year
1924	1	3000
1925	3001	18000
1926	18001	33000
1927	33001	48000
1928	48001	63000
1929	63001	78000
1930	78001	93000
1931	93001	108000
1932	108001	123000
1933	123001	138000
1934	138001	153000
1935	153001	168000
1936	168001	183000
1937	183001	198000
1938	198001	213000
1939	213001	229000
1940-1945	No production	
1946	229001	237000
1947	237001	249000
1948	249001	270000
1949	270001	285000
1950	285001	315000
1951	315001	346000
1952	346001	387000
1953	387001	438000
1954	Standard model	
	H1	H39000
	Lightweight model	
	L1	L42000
1955	Standard model	
	H39001	H83000
	Lightweight model	
	L42001	L83000
1956	Standard model	
	H83001	H99000
	M1	M22000
	Lightweight model	
	L83001	L99000
	G1	G23000

Year	Serial Number Beginning of Year	Serial Number at End of Year
1957	Standard model	
	M22001	M85000
	Lightweight model	
	G23001	G85000
1958	Standard model	
	M85001	M99000
	Lightweight model	
	G85001	G99000

1958-1976 Ser. No. sequence changed in include a one or two digit numeral followed by an alpha character. "M" prefix designates standard models, "G" includes lightweight models, and "V" shows magnum models. To illustrate, an A-5 with a Ser. No. of 8G19264 would indicate a lightweight model manufactured in 1958. Ser. No. 71V24690 would specify a 3 inch magnum gun built in 1971.

SUPERPOSED MODEL — O & U — 12 GA.

Year	Serial Number Beginning of Year	Serial Number at End of Year
1931	1	2000
1932	2001	4000
1933	4001	6000
1934	6001	8000
1935	8001	10000
1936	10001	12000
1937	12001	14000
1938	14001	17000
1939-1947	No production	
1948	17001	17200
1949	17201	20000
1950	20001	21000
1951	21001	27000
1952	27001	33000
1953	33001	37000
1954	37001	43000

Year	Serial Number Beginning of Year	Serial Number at End of Year
1955	43001	48000
1956	48001	54000
1957	54001	59000
1958	59001	68500
1959	68501	76500
1960	76501	86500
1961	86501	96500
1962	96501	99999
1963	S3 suffix after Ser. No.	
1964	S4 suffix after Ser. No.	
1965	S5 suffix after Ser. No.	
1966	S6 suffix after Ser. No.	
1967	S7 suffix after Ser. No.	
1968	S8 suffix after Ser. No.	
1969	S69 suffix after Ser. No.	
1970	S70 suffix after Ser. No.	
1971	S71 suffix after Ser. No.	
1972	S72 suffix after Ser. No.	
1973	S73 suffix after Ser. No.	
1974	S74 suffix after Ser. No.	
1975	S75 suffix after Ser. No.	
1976	S76 suffix after Ser. No.	
1976 to date	"P" or Presentation Models only	

LIEGE O & U — Approximately 10,000 produced

1973	73J prefix before Ser. No.	
1974	74J prefix before Ser. No.	
1975	75J prefix before Ser. No.	

DOUBLE AUTOMATIC SHOTGUN

1952-1959	N/A	
1960-1971	1st or both digits indicate last 2 digits in year of manufacture (i.e. — 0A1947 — 1960 mfg., 70A245671 — 1970 mfg.)	

HI-POWER (9 mm) PISTOL

Year	Serial Number Beginning of Year	Serial Number at End of Year
1955-1956	No records available	
1957	70000	80000
1958	80001	85267
1959	85268	89687
1960	89688	93027
1961	93028	109145
1962	109146	113548
1963	113549	115822
1964	115823	T136538
1965	T136569	T146372
1966	T146373	T173285
1967	T173286	T213999
1968	T214000	T258000
1969	69C prefix before Ser. No.	
1970	70C prefix before Ser. No.	
1971	71C prefix before Ser. No.	
1972	72C prefix before Ser. No.	
1973	73C prefix before Ser. No.	
1974	74C prefix before Ser. No.	
1975	75C prefix before Ser. No.	
1976	76C prefix before Ser. No.	
1977 to date	New style serialization	

BROWNING .380

1955-1964	No records exist	
1965	500000	598804
1966	598805	603890
1967	603891	619474
1968	619475	N/A
1969-1970	Discontinued due to GCA of 1968. New model has longer barrel, adj. rear sight, modified grip.	
1971	71N prefix before Ser. No.	
1972	72N prefix before Ser. No.	
1973	73N prefix before Ser. No.	
1974	74N prefix before Ser. No.	
1975	75N prefix before Ser. No.	

.25 CAL. BABY BROWNING PISTOL

Year	Serial Number Beginning of Year	Serial Number at End of Year
1955-		
1958	Records not available	
1959	181000	206349
1960	206350	230999
1961	231000	250999
1962	251000	278999
1963	279000	286099
1964	286100	308499
1965	308500	329999
1966	333000	367443
1967	367444	412999
1968	413000	479000
1969	Discontinued because of GCA of 1968	

.22 CAL. PISTOLS (NOMAD-CHALLENGER-MEDALIST)

One or two digit suffix after single capital letter. "P" designates Nomad, "U" designates Challenger model, "T" designates Medalist model. "P5" suffix would indicate a Nomad built in 1965. "U71" suffix would indicate a Challenger built in 1971. Nomad models were manufactured from 1962 to 1973. Challenger and Medalist models were produced from 1962 to 1974.

BOLT ACTION RIFLES (SAFARI, MEDALLION, & OLYMPIAN MODELS)

1959-	
1962	No prefix (numeral-letter) before Ser. No. (i.e., only digits)
1963	3-single letter prefix or suffix by Ser. No.
1964	4-single letter prefix or suffix by Ser. No.
1965	5-single letter prefix or suffix by Ser. No.
1966	6-single letter prefix or suffix by Ser. No.

Year	
1967	7-single letter prefix or suffix by Ser. No.
1968	8-single letter prefix or suffix by Ser. No.
1969	Single letter (Y, Z, or L) followed by last 2 digits of year of mfg. Prefix only.
1970	"Y70" prefix
1971	"L71" prefix
1972	"Z72" prefix
1973	"Y73" prefix
1974	"Z74" prefix
1975	"L75" prefix

B.A.R

Year	
1967	"M7" suffix after Ser. No.
1968	"M8" suffix after Ser. No.
1969	"M69" suffix after Ser. No.
1970	"M70" suffix after Ser. No.
1971	"M71" suffix after Ser. No.
1972	"M72" suffix after Ser. No.
1973	"M73" suffix after Ser. No.
1974	"M74" suffix after Ser. No.
1975	"M75" suffix after Ser. No.
1976	"M76" suffix after Ser. No.
1977 to date	New sequence with "RT" appearing in middle of Ser. No.

.22 AUTO RIFLE (Grades I, II, and III)

Year	
1956-	
1964	Numeric only — 5 digits or less.
1965	"5T" or "5E" prefix before Ser. No.
1966	"6T" or "6E" prefix before Ser. No.
1967	"7T" or "7E" prefix before Ser. No.
1968	"8T" or "8E" prefix before Ser. No.
1969	"69T" or "69E" prefix before Ser. No.

Year	Serial Number Beginning of Year	Serial Number at End of Year
1970	"70T" or "70E" prefix before Ser. No.	
1971	"71T" or "71E" prefix before Ser. No.	
1972	"72T" or "72E" prefix before Ser. No.	
1973	Japan production	

T-BOLT RIFLE (T1 and T2)

Year		
1965	"X5" suffix after Ser. No.	
1966	"X6" suffix after Ser. No.	
1967	"X7" suffix after Ser. No.	
1968	"X8" suffix after Ser. No.	
1969	"X69" suffix after Ser. No.	
1970	"X70" suffix after Ser. No.	
1971	"X71" suffix after Ser. No.	
1972	"X72" suffix after Ser. No.	
1973	"X73" suffix after Ser. No.	
1974	"X74" suffix after Ser. No.	
1975	"X75" suffix after Ser. No.	

MODEL SERIALIZATION
COLTS FIREARMS

This section is included to identify year of manufacture dates on Brownings, Colt pistols, Mauser broomhandles, Parker shotguns, and Winchester rifles. To use these tables, simply locate the Ser. No. of the above-mentioned trademarks, locate the proper bracket it falls into by model, and refer to the adjacent year to determine the year of manufacture. In several cases, caliber rarity can also be determined.

Year	Serial Number Beginning of Year	Serial Number at End of Year	Total Guns Produced in Year
MODEL 1849 POCKET REVOLVER			
1849	1	11999	11999
1850	12000	15999	3999
1851	16000	24999	8999
1852	25000	54999	29999
1853	55000	84999	29999
1854	85000	99999	14999
1855	100000	109999	9999
1856	110000	129999	19999
1857	130000	139999	9999
1858	140000	149999	9999
1859	150000	159999	9999
1860	160000	183999	23999
1861	184000	196999	12999
1862	197000	222999	25999
1863	223000	249999	26999
1864	250000	269999	16999
1865	270000	279999	9999
1866	280000	289999	9999
1867	290000	299999	9999
1868	300000	309999	9999
1869	310000	319999	9999
1870	320000	324999	4999
1871	325000	329999	4999
1872	330000	330999	999
1873	331000	340000	9000
MODEL 1849 POCKET REVOLVER — LONDON BARREL ADDRESS			
1853	1	999	999
1854	1000	4999	3999

Year	Serial Number Beginning of Year	Serial Number at End of Year	Total Guns Produced in Year
1855	5000	8999	3999
1856	9000	11000	2000
MODEL 1851 NAVY			
1850	1	2499	2499
1851	2500	9999	7499
1852	10000	19999	9999
1853	20000	34999	14999
1854	35000	39999	4999
1855	40000	44999	4999
1856	45000	64999	19999
1857	65000	84999	19999
1858	85000	89999	4999
1859	90000	92999	2999
1860	93000	97999	4999
1861	98000	117999	19999
1862	118000	131999	13999
1863	132000	174999	42999
1864	175000	179999	4999
1865	180000	184999	4999
1866	185000	200000	14999
1867	200000	203999	3999
1868	204000	206999	2999
1869	207000	209999	2999
1870	210000	211999	1999
1871	212000	213999	1999
1872	214000	214999	999
1873	215000	215348	348
MODEL 1851 NAVY — LONDON BARREL ADDRESS			
1853	1	3999	3999
1854	4000	14999	10999
1855	15000	40999	25999
1856	41000	42000	1000
MODEL 1860 ARMY			
1860	1	1999	1999
1861	2000	24999	22999
1862	25000	84999	59999
1863	85000	149999	64999
1864	150000	152999	2999
1865	153000	155999	2999
1866	156000	161999	5999

Year	Serial Number Beginning of Year	Serial Number at End of Year	Total Guns Produced in Year
1867	162000	169999	7999
1868	170000	176999	6999
1869	177000	184999	7999
1870	185000	189999	4999
1871	190000	197999	7999
1872	198000	198999	999
1873	199000	200500	1500

MODEL 1861 NAVY

Year	Serial Number Beginning of Year	Serial Number at End of Year	Total Guns Produced in Year
1861	1	4599	4999
1862	4600	9999	5399
1863	10000	16999	6999
1864	17000	24999	7999
1865	25000	27999	2999
1866	28000	29999	1999
1867	30000	30999	999
1868	31000	32999	1999
1869	33000	33999	999
1870	34000	34999	999
1871	35000	35999	999
1872	36000	36999	999
1873	37000	38843	1843

MODEL 1862 POLICE

Year	Serial Number Beginning of Year	Serial Number at End of Year	Total Guns Produced in Year
1861	1	8499	8499
1862	8500	14999	6499
1863	15000	25999	10999
1864	26000	28999	2999
1865	29000	31999	2999
1866	32000	34999	2999
1867	35000	36999	1999
1868	37000	39999	2999
1869	40000	41999	1999
1870	42000	43999	1999
1871	44000	44999	999
1872	45000	45999	999
1873	46000	47000	1000

MODEL 1873 — SINGLE ACTION ARMY (SAA) — PRE-WAR

Year	Caliber	Serial Number Beginning of Year
1873	.45 Colt Caliber, Standard	1
1874		200
1875	.44 Rimfire series (own serials, 1-1863; made through 1880	15000
1876	.476 Eley introduced	22000
1877		33000
1878	.44-40 introduced in quantity	41000
1879		49000
1880		53000
1881		62000
1882	Sheriff's model introduced	73000
1883	.22 rimfire introduced	85000
1884	.32-20 and .38-40 introduced	102000
1885	.41 Colt introduced	114000
1886	.38 Colt introduced	117000
1887	.32 Colt and .32 S&W introduced	119000
1888	Flattop Target S.A.A. began; no. 126530	125000
1889	.32 rimfire; .32-44 S&W, .38 S&W; and .44 Russian introduced	128000
1890	.44 Smoothbore; .380 and .450 Eley; and .44 S&W introduced	130000
1891	.38-44 introduced	136000
1892	Transverse cylinder latch introduced; screw lock at front of frame dropped	144000
1893		149000

Year	Caliber	Serial Number Beginning of Year	Year	Caliber	Serial Number Beginning of Year
1894	Beginning of Bisley models	154000	1928		351300
			1929		352400
1895		159000	1930	.38 Special introduced	353800
1896		163000			
1897		168000	1931		354100
1898		175000	1932		354500
1899		182000	1933		354800
1900	Revolvers built to handle smokeless powder	192000	1934		355000
			1935	.357 Magnum introduced	355200
1901		203000	1936		355300
1902		220000	1937		355400
1903		238000	1938		356100
1904		250000	1939		356600
1905		261000	1940	A few S.A.A. made during and just after the war	357000 thru 357859
1906		273000			
1907		288000			
1908		304000			
1909		308000			
1910		312000			

Year	Serial Number Beginning of Year	Serial Number at End of Year

Year	Caliber	Serial Number Beginning of Year
1911		316000
1912	Discontinue Bisley model	321000
1913	.44 Russian and S&W Special introduced	325000
1914		328000
1915	Long flute cylinders; range no. 330001 to 331480	329500
1916		332000
1917		335000
1918		337000
1919		337200
1920		338000
1921		341000
1922		343000
1923		344500
1924	.45 ACP introduced, requiring special cylinders	346400
1925		347300
1926		348200
1927		349800

COLT SINGLE ACTION ARMY — POST-WAR PRODUCTION
"SA" suffix from 1956 to 1978. "SA" prefix 1978 to 1981

Year	Serial Number Beginning of Year	Serial Number at End of Year
1956	0001SA	8799SA
1957	8800SA	18499SA
1958	18500SA	23399SA
1959	23400SA	28499SA
1960	28500SA	33599SA
1961	33600SA	35649SA
1962	35650SA	37299SA
1963	37300SA	38499SA
1964	38500SA	39999SA
1965	40000SA	41499SA
1966	41500SA	43799SA
1967	43800SA	46299SA
1968	46300SA	48999SA
1969	49000SA	52599SA
1970	52600SA	59399SA
1971	59400SA	61699SA
1972	61700SA	64399SA
1973	64400SA	69399SA

Year	Serial Number Beginning of Year	Serial Number at End of Year
1974	69400SA	73319SA
1975	None produced	
1976	80000SA	82000SA
	(start of 3rd generation of production)	
1977	82001SA	95999SA
1978	96000SA	99999SA
1978	Start of "SA" prefix on front of Ser. No.	
Mid-1978	SA01000	SA12999
1979	SA13000	discontinuance in 1981

NEW FRONTIER SINGLE ACTION ARMY

Year	Serial Number Beginning of Year	Serial Number at End of Year
1961	3000NF	3005NF
1962	3006NF	3849NF
1963	4325NF	4699NF
1964	4700NF	4974NF
1965	4975NF	5399NF
1966	5400NF	5674NF
1967	5675NF	5699NF
1968	5700NF	
1969	5701NF	5924NF
1970	5925NF	6874NF
1971	6875NF	7049NF
1972	7050NF	7074NF
1973	7075NF	7174NF
1974	7175NF	7264NF
1975	7265NF	7288NF
1978	7501NF	discontinuance in 1981

Caliber	S.A.A.	Flattop Target	Bisley	Bisley Target
COLT SINGLE ACTION ARMY — CALIBER BREAKDOWN				
.22 Rimfire	107	93	0	0
.32 Rimfire	1	0	0	0
.32 Colt	192	24	160	44
.32 S&W	32	30	18	17
.32-44	2	9	14	17
.32-20	29,812	30	13,291	131

Caliber	S.A.A.	Flattop Target	Bisley	Bisley Target
.38 Colt (through 1914)	1,011	122	412	96
.38 Colt (post-1922)	1,365	0	0	0
.38 S&W	9	39	10	5
.38 Colt Special	82	7	0	0
.38 S&W Special	25	0	2	0
.38-44	2	11	6	47
.357 Magnum	525	0	0	0
.380 Eley	1	3	0	0
.38-40	38,240	19	12,163	98
.41	16,402	91	3,159	24
.44 Smoothbore	15	0	1	0
.44 Rimfire	1,863	0	0	0
.44 German	59	0	0	0
.44 Russian	154	51	90	62
.44 S&W	24	51	29	64
.44 S&W Special	506	1	0	0
.44-40	64,489	21	6,803	78
.45	150,683	100	8,005	97
.45 Smoothbore	4	0	2	0
.45 ACP	44	0	0	0
.450 Boxer	729	89	0	0
.450 Eley	2,697	84	5	0
.455 Eley	1,150	37	180	196
.476 Eley	161	2	0	0
Total quantities	310,386	914	44,350	976

Year	Serial Number Beginning of Year	Serial Number at End of Year
MODEL 1911 AND 1911A1 — Commercial production — Capital "C" prefix — .45 cal.		
1912	C1	C1899

Year	Serial Number Beginning of Year	Serial Number at End of Year		Year	Serial Number Beginning of Year	Serial Number at End of Year
1913	C1900	C5399		1956	272550C	276699C
1914	C5400	C16599		1957	276700C	281999C
1915	C16600	C27599		1958	282000C	283799C
1916	C27600	C74999		1959	283800C	285799C
1917	C75000	C98999		1960	285800C	287999C
1918	C99000	C105999		1961	288000C	289849C
1919	C106000	C120999		1962	289850C	291299C
1920	C120000	C126999		1963	291300C	293799C
1921	C127000	C128999		1964	293800C	295999C
1922	C129000	C133999		1965	296000C	300299C
1923	C134000	C134999		1966	300300C	308499C
1924	C135000	C139999		1967	308500C	315599C
1925	C140000	C144999		1968	315600C	324499C
1926	C145000	C150999		1969	324500C	332649C
1927	C151000	C151999		1970	332650C	336169C
1928	C152000	C154999		new		
1929	C155000	C155999		range	70G01001	70G05550
1930	C156000	C158999		1971	70G05551	70G18000
1931	C159000	C160999		1972	70G18001	70G34400
1932	C161000	C164799		1973	70G34401	70G43000
1933	C164800	C174599		1974	70G43001	70G73000
1934	C174600	C177999		1975	70G73001	70G88900
1935	C178000	C179799		1976	70G88901	70G99999
1936	C179800	C183199		new		
1937	C183200	C188699		range	01001G70	13900G70
1938	C188700	C189599		1977	13901G70	45199G70
1939	C189600	C198899		1978		
1940	C198900	C199299		to		
1941	C199300	C208799		date	45200G70	
1942	C208800	C215018				

Year	Serial Number Beginning of Year	Serial Number at End of Year	Manu-facturer

MODEL 1911 AND 1911A1 MILITARY PRODUCTION

Year	Serial Number Beginning of Year	Serial Number at End of Year	Manu-facturer
1912	1	500	Colt
	501	1000	Colt USN
	1001	1500	Colt
	1501	2000	Colt USN
	2001	2500	Colt
	2501	3500	Colt USN
	3501	3800	Colt USMC
	3801	4500	Colt

Left column continuation:

Year	Serial Number Beginning of Year	Serial Number at End of Year
1943-1945:	Commercial production interrupted by WWII	
1946	C221001	C222000
1947	C222001	C231999
1948	C232000	C238500
1949	C238501	C240000
1950	C240000	247701C
	"C" suffix started with Ser. No. 240228	
1951	247701C	253179C
1952	253180C	259549C
1953	259550C	266349C
1954	266350C	270549C
1955	270550C	272549C

Year	Serial Number Beginning of Year	Serial Number at End of Year	Manufacturer	Year	Serial Number Beginning of Year	Serial Number at End of Year	Manufacturer
	4501	5500	Colt USN		151987	185800	Colt
	5501	6500	Colt		185801	186200	Colt USMC
	6501	7500	Colt USN		186201	209586	Colt
	7501	8500	Colt		209587	210386	Colt USMC
	8501	9500	Colt USN		210387	215386	Colt frames
	9501	10500	Colt				(Reserved
	10501	11500	Colt USN				for
	11501	12500	Colt				receivers
	12501	13500	Colt USN		215387	216186	Colt USMC
	13501	17250	Colt		216187	216586	Colt
1913	17251	36400	Colt		216587	216986	Colt USMC
	36401	37650	Colt USMC	1918	216987	217386	Colt USMC
	37651	38000	Colt		217387	232000	Colt
	38001	44000	Colt USN		232001	233600	Colt USN
	44001	60400	Colt		233601	594000	Colt
1914	60401	72570	Colt		1	13152	Rem UMC
	72571	83855	Springfield	1919	13153	21676	Rem UMC
			— (These		594001	629500	Colt
			numbers		629501	700000	Unknown
			reserved	1924	700001	710000	Colt
			Springfield	1937	710001	712349	Colt
	83856	83900	Colt	1938	712350	713645	Colt
	83901	84400	Colt USMC	1939	713646	717281	Colt USN
	84401	96000	Colt	1940	717282	721977	Colt
	96001	97537	Colt	1941	721978	756733	Colt
	97538	102596	Colt	1942	756734	800000	Colt
	102597	107596	Springfield		S800001	S800500	Singer
			—(Reserved		800501	801000	These
			for				numbers
			Springfield				assigned to
1915	107597	109500	Colt				H&R
	109501	11000	Colt USN	1943	801001	958100	Colt
	110001	113496	Colt		958101	1088725	US&S
	113497	120566	Springfield		1088726	1208673	Colt
			—(Reserved		1208674	1279673	Ithaca
			for		1279674	1279698	re no AA
			Springfield		1279699	1441430	Remington-Rand
	120567	125566	Colt		1441431	1471430	Ithaca
	125567	133186	Springfield		1471431	1609528	Remington-Rand
			—(Reserved	1944	1609529	1743846	Colt
			for		1743847	1890503	Ithaca
			Springfield		1890504	2075103	Remington-Rand
1916	133187	137400	Colt				
1917	137401	151186	Colt				
	151187	151986	Colt USMC				

Year	Serial Number Beginning of Year	Serial Number at End of Year	Manu-facturer
1945	2075104	2134403	Ithaca
	2134404	2244803	Remington-Rand
	2244804	2380013	Colt
	2380014	2619013	Remington-Rand
	2619014	2693613	Ithaca

Date	Serial Number
PARKER SHOTGUNS	
1866-1868	0-6,800
1868-1877	9,700
1877-1879	15,700
1880	17,600
1881	22,700
1882	27,300
1883	34,900
1884	36,000
1885	46,450
1886	48,125
1887	56,650
1889	59,500
1890	61,350
1891	66,800
1892	71,600
1893	77,000
1894	80,300
1895	82,400
1896	85,200
1897	86,450
1898	89,350
1899	92,450
1900	97,300
1901	105,750
1902	113,100
1903	121,900
1904	129,200
1905	132,000
1906	138,300
1907	144,250
1908	148,250
1910	153,000

Date	Serial Number
1911	157,050
1912	157,800
1913	165,000
1914	168,200
1915	171,500
first year of Trojan grade	
1916	173,450
1917	175,650
first single barrel trap gun	
1918	180,250
1919	184,900
1920	190,100
1921	195,000
1922	200,500
first Parker single trigger	
1923	205,150
1924	207,600
first beavertail forend	
1925	214,400
1926	218,050
first ventilated rib, first .410	
1927	222,650
1928	228,200
PH grade dropped	
1929	230,700
1930	234,200
1931	235,950
1932	236,100
1933	236,300
1934	236,650
first skeet guns, takeover of factory by Remington	
1935	237,000
1936	239,900
last regular catalog	
1937	240,300
1938-1942	242,385

Serial # Range	Date	Nature of Changes

MAUSER BROOMHANDLES
produced from 1896 to late '30's

before #25	1896	— The cone hammer used in place of spur hammer.
#50	1896	— *"SYSTEM MAUSER"* marked on top of the chamber.
before #200	1897	— The locking system changed from one to two lugs. — The barrel contour at the chamber is tapered instead of stepped.
#390	1897	— *"WAFFENFABRIK MAUSER OBERNDORF A/N"* marked on top of the chamber.
#975	1897	— The center section of the rear panel on the left side of the frame is not milled out (this feature appears earlier on a few 20-shot pistols). This area is sometimes used for special markings on contract pieces such as the Turkish and Persian.
#12,200- #14,999	1898	— The large ring hammer replaces the cone hammer.
#21,000	1899	— There is no panel milling on either side of the frame. — A single lug bayonet type mount adopted for retaining the firing pin instead of the dovetail plate. — The trigger is mounted directly to the frame by two integral lugs rather than attached to a removable block. — The position of the serial number moved from the rear of the frame above the stock slot to the left side of the chamber.
#22,000	1900	— Two integral lugs used to mount the rear sight instead of a pin.
#29,000	1902	— Very shallow panels milled into the frame on both sides.*
#31,200	1903	— *"WAFFENFABRIK MAUSER OBERNDORF A NECKAR"* added to the right rear frame panel.*
#34,000	1904	— The depth of the frame panel milling increased.*
#35,000	1904	— The barrel extension side rails lengthened about a half inch.* — An additional lug for mounting added to the firing pin.* — The hammer changed to the small ring pattern.* — The safety mechanism altered to require that the lever be pushed up to engage it instead of down.* — The center of the safety lever knob is no longer milled out.*
#38,000	1905	— The short extractor with two ribs replaces the long thin extractor.*
#100,000- #130,000	1910 to 1911	— The rifling changed from four groove to six groove.
#270,000	1915	— "NS" *(Neues Sicherung* or New Safety) appears on the back of the hammer. The hammer must be moved back beyond the cocked position to engage the safety.
#440,000	1921	— The lanyard ring stud is rotated 90 degrees.
#501,000	1923	— The Mauser "banner" appears on the left rear frame panel.
#800,000	1930	— The Mauser banner is enlarged. — A step is added to the barrel contour just ahead of the chamber. — The safety is changed to allow the hammer to be dropped from a cocked position, without danger, by pulling the trigger (called Universal Safety).

Serial # Range	Date	Nature of Changes
		— The front of the grip frame widened to equal the rear part where the stock slot is.
#850,000	1932	— *"D.R.P.u.A.P." (Deutsches Reich Patenten und Anderes Patenten)* added below the inscription on the right rear frame panel.
#860,000	1932	— The lettering in the frame inscription is slanted forward.
#900,000	1934	— The serial number is moved to the rear of the barrel extension behind the sight.
		— The two grooves in each side of the barrel extension side rails are eliminated.

*These nine changes appear out of sequence (either early or late) on three small batches of guns (29,000 to 29,900, 40,000 to 41,000, and 42,600 to 43,900). Most of these pistols are of the "bolo" style, that is they have 3.9-inch barrels, small grips, six or 10-shot magazines and fixed or adjustable rear sights. A few of these pistols show non-standard barrel contours, barrel extension milling and hammer safety devices. Apparently the factory withheld these numbers from the regular production series and reissued them at later dates.

REMINGTON FIREARMS SERIAL NUMBER IDENTIFICATION
(CODE LOCATED ON BARREL, LEFT SIDE AT FRAME).

MONTH OF MANUFACTURE
(CODE LETTER CORRESPONDS TO NUMERAL UNDERNEATH)

B	L	A	C	K	P	O	W	D	E	R	X
1	2	3	4	5	6	7	8	9	10	11	12

YEAR OF MANUFACTURE

Year		Year		Year		Year		Year		Year	
1921	M	1931	Z	1941	K	1951	XX	1961	H	1971	U
1922	N	1932	A	1942	L	1952	YY	1962	J	1972	W
1923	P	1933	B	1943	MM	1953	ZZ	1963	K		
1924	R	1934	C	1944	NN	1954	A	1964	L		
1925	S	1935	D	1945	PP	1955	B	1965	M		
1926	T	1936	E	1946	RR	1956	C	1966	N		
1927	U	1937	F	1947	SS	1957	D	1967	P		
1928	W	1938	G	1948	TT	1958	E	1968	R		
1929	X	1939	H	1949	UU	1959	F	1969	S		
1930	Y	1940	J	1950	WW	1960	G	1970	T		

The following Winchester serial numbers appear courtesy of U.S. Repeating Arms, New Haven, CT. I would like to thank U.S. Repeating Arms and Mr. Pardee for making these production figures available (many for the first time).

WINCHESTER RIFLES

Records at the factory indicate the following serial numbers were assigned to guns at the end of the calendar year.

MODEL 1866					
1866 -	12476 to 14813	81 -	81620	78 -	7967
67 -	15578	82 -	109507	79 -	8971
68 -	19768	83 -	145503	80 -	14700
69 -	29516	84 -	175126	81 -	21759
70 -	52527	85 -	196221	82 -	32407
71 -	88184	86 -	222937	83 -	42410
72 -	109784	87 -	225922	84 -	54666
73 -	118401	88 -	284529	85 -	58714
74 -	125038	89 -	323956	86 -	60397
75 -	125965	90 -	363220	87 -	62420
76 -	131907	91 -	405026	88 -	63539
77 -	148207	92 -	441625	89 -	None
78 -	150493	93 -	466641	90 -	None
79 -	152201	94 -	481826	91 -	None
80 -	154379	95 -	499308	92 -	63561
81 -	156107	96 -	507545	93 -	63670
82 -	159513	97 -	513421	94 -	63678
83 -	162376	98 -	525922	95 -	None
84 -	163649	99 -	541328	96 -	63702
85 -	163664	1900 -	554128	97 -	63869
86 -	165071	01 -	557236	98 -	63871
87 -	165912	02 -	564557		
88 -	167155	03 -	573957	**MODEL 1885 —**	
89 -	167401	04 -	588953	**SINGLE SHOT**	
90 -	167702	05 -	602557	1885 -	1 to 375
91 -	169003	06 -	613780	86 -	6841
92 -	None	07 -	None	87 -	18328
93 -	169007	08 -	None	88 -	30571
94 -	169011	09 -	630385	89 -	45019
95 -	None	10 -	656101	90 -	None
96 -	None	11 -	669324	91 -	53700
97 -	169015	12 -	678527	92 -	60371
98 -	170100	13 -	684419	93 -	69534
99 -	Discontinued	14 -	686510	94 -	None
		15 -	688431	95 -	73771
MODEL 1873		16 -	694020	96 -	78253
1873 -	1 to 126	17 -	698617	97 -	78815
74 -	2726	18 -	700734	98 -	84700
75 -	11325	19 -	702042	99 -	85086
76 -	23151	No last # available —		1900 -	88501
77 -	23628	20, 21, 22, 23,	720609	01 -	90424
78 -	27501			02 -	92031
79 -	41525	**MODEL 1876**		03 -	92359
80 -	63537	1876 -	1 to 1429	04 -	92785
		77 -	3579	05 -	93611

06 -	94208
07 -	95743
08 -	96819
09 -	98097
10 -	98506
11 -	99012
12 -	None
13 -	100352

No further serial numbers were recorded until the end of 1923. The last number recorded was: 139700

MODEL 1886

1886 -	1 to 3211
87 -	14728
88 -	28577
89 -	38401
90 -	49723
91 -	63601
92 -	73816
93 -	83261
94 -	94543
95 -	103708
96 -	109670
97 -	113997
98 -	119192
99 -	120571
1900 -	122834
01 -	125630
02 -	128942
03 -	132213
04 -	135524
05 -	138838
06 -	142249
07 -	145119
08 -	147322
09 -	148237
10 -	150129
11 -	151622
12 -	152943
13 -	152947
14 -	153859
15 -	154452
16 -	154979
17 -	155387
18 -	156219
19 -	156930
20 -	158716
21 -	159108
22 -	159337

No further serial numbers were recorded until the discontinuance of the model which was in 1935 - at - 159994

MODEL 1887

1887 -	1 to 7431
88 -	22408
89 -	25673
90 -	29105
91 -	38541
92 -	49763
93 -	54367
94 -	56849
95 -	58289
96 -	60175
97 -	63952
98 -	64855

According to these records no guns were produced during the last few years of this model and it was therefore discontinued in 1901.

Records on the Model 1890 are somewhat incomplete. Our records indicate the following serial numbers were assigned to guns at the end of the calendar year beginning with 1908. Actual records on the firearms which were manufactured between 1890 and 1907 will be available from the "Winchester Museum", located at The "Buffalo Bill Historical Center" P.O. Box 1020, Cody, Wy. 82414

MODEL 1890

1908 -	330000 to 363850
09 -	393427
10 -	423567
11 -	451264
12 -	478595
13 -	506936
14 -	531019
15 -	551290
16 -	570497
17 -	589204
18 -	603438
19 -	630801
20 -	None

21 -	634783
22 -	643304
23 -	654837
24 -	664613
25 -	675774
26 -	687049
27 -	698987
28 -	711354
29 -	722125
30 -	729015
31 -	733178
32 -	734454

The Model 1890 was discontinued in 1932, however, a clean up of the production run lasted another 8+ years and included another 14 to 15000 guns. Our figures indicate approximately 749,000 guns were made.

MODEL 1892

1892 -	1 to 23701
93 -	35987
94 -	73508
95 -	106721
96 -	144935
97 -	159312
98 -	165431
99 -	171820
1900 -	183411
01 -	191787
02 -	208871
03 -	253935
04 -	278546
05 -	315425
06 -	376496
07 -	437919
08 -	476540
09 -	522162
10 -	586996
11 -	643483
12 -	694752
13 -	742675
14 -	771444
15 -	804622
16 -	830031
17 -	853819
18 -	870942
19 -	903649
20 -	906754
21 -	910476
22 -	917300

23 -	926329	27 -	990883	30 -	999730
24 -	938641	28 -	996517	31 -	1000727
25 -	954997	29 -	999238	32 -	1001324
26 -	973896				

Records at the factory, and in some years, estimates, indicate the following serial numbers were assigned to guns at the end of the calendar year.

MODEL 94

1894 -	1 to 14579	1924 -	953198	1954 -	2071100
95 -	44359	25 -	978523	55 -	2145296
96 -	76464	26 -	997603	56 -	2225000
97 -	111453	27 -	1027571	57 -	2290296
98 -	147684	28 -	1054465	58 -	2365887
99 -	183371	29 -	1077097	59 -	2410555
1900 -	204427	30 -	1081755	60 -	2469821
01 -	233975	31 -	1084156	61 -	2500000
02 -	273854	32 -	1087836	62 -	2551921
03 -	291506	33 -	1089270	63 -	2586000
04 -	311363	34 -	1091190	*1964 - 2700000 -	2797428
05 -	337557	35 -	1099605	65 -	2894428
06 -	378878	36 -	1100065	66 -	2991927
07 -	430985	37 -	1100679	67 -	3088458
08 -	474241	38 -	1100915	68 -	3185691
09 -	505831	39 -	1101051	69 -	3284570
10 -	553062	40 -	1142423	70 -	3381299
11 -	599263	41 -	1191307	71 -	3557385
12 -	646114	42 -	1221289	72 -	3806499
13 -	703701	43 -	No Record Avail.	73 -	3929364
14 -	756066	44 -	No Record Avail.	74 -	4111426
15 -	784052	45 -	No Record Avail.	75 -	4277926
16 -	807741	46 -	No Record Avail.	76 -	4463553
17 -	821972	47 -	No Record Avail.	77 -	4565925
18 -	838175	48 -	1500000	78 -	4662210
19 -	870762	49 -	1626100	79 -	4826596
20 -	880627	50 -	1724295	80 -	4892951
21 -	908318	51 -	1819800	81 -	5024957
22 -	919583	52 -	1910000	82 -	5103248
23 -	938539	53 -	2000000		

*The post-64 Model 94 began with serial number 2,700,000.

Serial number 1,000,000 was presented to President Calvin Coolidge in 1927.
Serial number 1,500,000 was presented to President Harry S. Truman in 1948.
Serial numbers 2,500,000 and 3,000,000 were presented to the Winchester Gun Museum, now located in Cody, Wyoming.
Serial number 3,500,000 was not constructed until 1979 and was sold at auction in Las Vegas, Nevada.
Serial number 4,000,000 — whereabouts unknown at this time.
Serial number 4,500,000 — shipped to Italy by Olin in 1978. Whereabouts unknown.
Serial number 5,000,000 — in New Haven, not constructed as of March 1983.

Records at the factory indicate the following serial numbers were assigned to guns at the end of the calendar year.

MODEL 1895

Year	Serial
1895 -	1 to 287
96 -	5715
97 -	7814
98 -	19871
99 -	26434
1900 -	29817
01 -	31584
02 -	35601
03 -	42514
04 -	47805
05 -	54783
06 -	55011
07 -	57351
08 -	60002
09 -	60951
10 -	63771
11 -	65017
12 -	67331
13 -	70823
14 -	72082
15 -	174233
16 -	377411
17 -	389106
18 -	392731
19 -	397250
20 -	400463
21 -	404075
22 -	407200
23 -	410289
24 -	413276
25 -	417402
26 -	419533
27 -	421584
28 -	422676
29 -	423680
30 -	424181
31 -	425132
32 -	425825

MODEL 1903

Year	Serial
1903 -	# Not Available ..
04 -	6944
05 -	14865
06 -	23097
07 -	31852
08 -	39105
09 -	46496
10 -	54298
11 -	61679

Year	Serial
12 -	69586
13 -	76732
14 -	81776
15 -	84563
16 -	87148
17 -	89501
18 -	92617
19 -	96565
20 -	# Not Available ..
21 -	97650
22 -	99011
23 -	100452
24 -	101688
25 -	103075
26 -	104230
27 -	105537
28 -	107157
29 -	109414
30 -	111276
31 -	112533
32 -	112992

This model was discontinued in 1932, however, a clean up of parts was used for further production of approximately 2000 guns. Total production was stopped at serial number ...... 114962 ... in 1936.

MODEL 1905

Year	Serial
1905 -	1 to 5659
06 -	15288
07 -	19194
08 -	20385
09 -	21280
10 -	22423
11 -	23503
12 -	24602
13 -	25559
14 -	26110
15 -	26561
16 -	26910
17 -	27297
18 -	27585
19 -	28287
20 -	29113

MODEL 1906

Year	Serial
1906 -	1 to 52278
07 -	89147
08 -	114138
09 -	165068
10 -	221189
11 -	273355
12 -	327955
13 -	381922
14 -	422734
15 -	453880
16 -	483805
17 -	517743
18 -	535540
19 -	593917
20 -	None
21 -	598691
22 -	608011
23 -	622601
24 -	636163
25 -	649952
26 -	665484
27 -	679892
28 -	695915
29 -	711202
30 -	720116
31 -	725978
32 -	727353

A clean up of production took place for the next few years with a record of production reaching approximately 729305.

MODEL 1907

Year	Serial
1907 -	1 to 8657
08 -	14486
09 -	19707
10 -	23230
11 -	25523
12 -	27724
13 -	29607
14 -	30872
15 -	32272
16 -	36215
17 -	38235
18 -	39172
19 -	40448
20 -	No # Available
21 -	40784
22 -	41289

23 -	41658	14 -	12311	**MODEL 52**	
24 -	42029	15 -	13233	1920 -	None indicated
25 -	42360	16 -	13788	21 -	397
26 -	42688	17 -	14255	22 -	745
27 -	43226	18 -	14625	23 -	1394
28 -	43685	19 -	15665	24 -	2361
29 -	44046	20 -	No # Available.	25 -	3513
30 -	44357	21 -	15845	26 -	6383
31 -	44572	22 -	16347	27 -	9436
32 -	44683	23 -	16637	28 -	12082
33 -	44806	24 -	17030	29 -	14594
34 -	44990	25 -	17281	30 -	17253
35 -	45203	26 -	17696	31 -	21954
36 -	45482	27 -	18182	32 -	24951
37 -	45920	28 -	18469	33 -	26725
38 -	46419	29 -	18893	34 -	29030
39 -	46758	30 -	19065	35 -	32448
40 -	47296	31 -	19172	36 -	36632
1941 -	47957	32 -	19232	37 -	40419
42 -	48275	33 -	19281	38 -	43632
43 -	None	34 -	19338	39 -	45460
44 -	None	35 -	19388	40 -	47519
45 -	48281	36 -	19445	41 -	50317

A cleanup of production continued into 1937 when the total of the guns was completed at approximately 20786 …

42 -	52129
43 -	52553
44 -	52560
45 -	52718
46 -	56080
47 -	60158
48 -	64265
1949 -	68149

46 -	48395
47 -	48996
48 -	49684
**49 -	50662
**50 -	51640
**51 -	52618
**52 -	53596
**53 -	54574
**54 -	55552
**55 -	56530
**56 -	57508
**57 -	58486

MODEL 1911 S.L.

1911 -	1 to 3819
12 -	27659
13 -	36677
14 -	40105
15 -	43284
16 -	45391
17 -	49893
18 -	52895
19 -	57337
20 -	60719
21 -	64109
22 -	69132
23 -	73186
24 -	76199
25 -	78611

50 -	70766
51 -	73385
52 -	76000
53 -	79500
54 -	80693
55 -	81831
56 -	96869
57 -	97869
58 -	98599
59 -	98899
60 -	102200
61 -	106986
62 -	108718
63 -	113583
64 -	118447
65 -	120992
66 -	123537
67 -	123727
68 -	123917
69 -	E 124107
70 -	E 124297
71 -	E 124489

**Actual records on serial numbers stops in 1948. The serial numbers ending each year from 1948 to 1957 were derived at by taking the last serial number recorded (58486) and the last number from 1948, (49684) and dividing the years of production (9), which relates to 978 guns each year for the nine year period.

MODEL 1910

1910 -	1 to 4766
11 -	7695
12 -	9712
13 -	11487

The Model 1911 was discontinued in 1925. However, guns were produced for three years after that date to clean up production and excess parts. When this practice ceased there were approximately 82774 guns produced.

72 -	E 124574		
73 -	E 124659		
74 -	E 124744		
75 -	E 124828		
76 -	E 125019		
77 -	E 125211		
78 -	E 125315		

This Model was discontinued in 1978. A small clean up of production was completed in 1979 with a total of - 125419.

MODEL 53

In the case of the Model 53 the following list pertains to the amount of guns produced each year rather than a serial number list.
The Model 53 was serially numbered concurrently with the MODEL 92.

MODEL 53s PRODUCED

1924 -	1488
25 -	2861

26 -	2531
27 -	2297
28 -	1958
29 -	1733
30 -	920
31 -	621
32 -	206

This Model was discontinued in 1932, however, a clean up of production continued for 9 more years with an additional 486 guns.
TOTAL PRODUCTION APPROXIMATELY — 15100

Records at the factory indicate the following serial numbers were assigned to guns at the end of the calendar year.

MODEL 54

1925 -	1 to 3140
26 -	8051
27 -	14176
28 -	19587
29 -	29104
30 -	32499
31 -	36731
32 -	38543
33 -	40722
34 -	43466
35 -	47125
36 -	50145

MODEL 55 CENTERFIRE

1924 -	1 to 836
25 -	2783
26 -	4957
27 -	8021
28 -	10467
29 -	12258
30 -	17393
31 -	18198
32 -	19204
33 -	Clean - up 20580

MODEL 61

1932 -	1 to 3532
33 -	6008
34 -	8554
35 -	12379
36 -	20615
37 -	30334
38 -	36326

39 -	42610
40 -	49270
41 -	57493
42 -	59871
43 -	59872
44 -	59879
45 -	60512
46 -	71629
47 -	92297
48 -	115281
49 -	125461
50 -	135641
51 -	145821
52 -	156000
53 -	171000
54 -	186000
55 -	200962
56 -	215923
57 -	229457
58 -	242992
59 -	262793
60 -	282594
61 -	302395
62 -	322196
63 -	342001

This Model was discontinued in 1963. For some unknown reason there are no actual records available from 1949 through 1963. The serial number figures for these years are arrived at by taking the total production figure of

342001, subtracting the last known # of 115281, and dividing the difference equally by the amount of remaining years available, (15).

MODEL 62

1932 -	1 to 7643
33 -	10695
34 -	14090
35 -	23924
36 -	42759
37 -	66059
38 -	80205
39 -	96534
40 -	116393
41 -	137379
42 -	155152
43 -	155422
44 -	155425
45 -	156073
46 -	183756
47 -	219085
48 -	252298
49 -	262473
50 -	272648
51 -	282823
52 -	293000
53 -	310500
54 -	328000
55 -	342776
56 -	357551
57 -	383513
58 -	409475

MODEL 63

Year	Serial
1933 -	1 to 2667
34 -	5361
35 -	9830
36 -	16781
37 -	25435
38 -	30934
39 -	36055
40 -	41456
41 -	47708
42 -	51258
43 -	51631
44 -	51656
45 -	53853
46 -	61607
47 -	71714
48 -	80519
49 -	88889
50 -	97259
51 -	105629
52 -	114000
53 -	120500
54 -	127000
55 -	138000
56 -	150000
57 -	162345
58 -	174692

MODEL 70

Year	Serial
1935 -	1 to 19
36 -	2238
37 -	11573
38 -	17844
39 -	23991
40 -	31675
41 -	41753
42 -	49206
43 -	49983
44 -	49997
45 -	50921
46 -	58382
47 -	75675
48 -	101680
49 -	131580
50 -	173150
51 -	206625
52 -	238820
53 -	282735
54 -	323530
55 -	361025
56 -	393595
57 -	425283
58 -	440792

Year	Serial
59 -	465040
60 -	504257
61 -	545446
62 -	565592
63 -	581471

All post - 64 Model 70s began with the serial number 700,000

Year	Serial
64 -	740599
65 -	809177
66 -	833795
67 -	869000
68 -	925908
69 -	G941900
70 -	G957995
71 -	G1018991
72 -	G1099257
73 -	G1128731
74 -	G1175000
75 -	G1218700
76 -	G1266000
77 -	G1350000
78 -	G1410000
79 -	G1447000
80 -	G1490709
81 -	G1537134

MODEL 71

Year	Serial
1935 -	1 to 4
36 -	7821
37 -	12988
38 -	14690
39 -	16155
40 -	18267
41 -	20810
42 -	21959
43 -	22048
44 -	22051
45 -	22224
46 -	23534
47 -	25728
48 -	27900
49 -	29675
50 -	31450
51 -	33225
52 -	35000
53 -	37500
54 -	40770
55 -	43306
56 -	45843
57 -	47254

MODEL 74

Year	Serial
1939 -	1 to 30890

Year	Serial
40 -	67085
41 -	114355
42 -	128293
43 -	None
44 -	128295
45 -	128878
46 -	145168
47 -	173524
48 -	223788
49 -	249900
50 -	276012
51 -	302124
52 -	328236
53 -	354348
54 -	380460
55 -	406574

MODEL 88

Year	Serial
1955 -	1 to 18378
56 -	36756
57 -	55134
58 -	73512
59 -	91890
60 -	110268
61 -	128651
62 -	139838
63 -	148858
64 -	160307
65 -	162699
66 -	192595
67 -	212416
68 -	230199
69 -	H239899
70 -	H258229
71 -	H266784
72 -	H279014
73 -	H283718

MODEL 100

Year	Serial
1961 -	1 to 32189
62 -	60760
63 -	78863
64 -	92016
65 -	135388
66 -	145239
67 -	209498
68 -	210053
69 -	A210999
70 -	A229995
71 -	A242999
72 -	A258001
73 -	A262833

WINCHESTER SHOTGUNS

Records at the factory indicate the following serial numbers were assigned to guns at the end of the calendar year.

MODEL 1897

Year	Serial
1897 -	1 to 32335
98 -	64668
99 -	96999
1900 -	129332
01 -	161665
02 -	193998
03 -	226331
04 -	258664
05 -	296037
06 -	334059
07 -	377999
08 -	413618
09 -	446888
10 -	481062
11 -	512632
12 -	544313
13 -	575213
14 -	592732
15 -	607673
16 -	624537
17 -	646124
18 -	668383
19 -	691943
20 -	696183
21 -	700428
22 -	715902
23 -	732060
24 -	744942
25 -	757629
26 -	770527
27 -	783574
1928 -	796806
29 -	807321
30 -	812729
31 -	830721
32 -	833926
33 -	835637
34 -	837364
35 -	839728
36 -	848684
37 -	856729
38 -	860725
39 -	866938
40 -	875945
41 -	891190
42 -	910072
43 -	912265
44 -	912327
45 -	916472
46 -	926409
47 -	936682
48 -	944085
49 -	953042
50 -	961999
51 -	970956
52 -	979913
53 -	988860
54 -	997827
55 -	1006784
56 -	1015741
57 -	1024700

Records on this Model are incomplete. The above serial numbers are estimated from 1897 thru 1903 and again from 1949 thru 1957. The actual records are in existence from 1904 through 1949.

MODEL 1901 SHOTGUN

Year	Serial
1904 -	64,856 to 64,860
05 -	66453
06 -	67486
07 -	68424
08 -	69197
09 -	70009
10 -	70753
11 -	71441
12 -	72167
13 -	72764
14 -	73202
15 -	73509
16 -	73770
17 -	74027
18 -	74311
19 -	74872
20 -	77000

MODEL 12

Year	Serial
1912 -	5308
13 -	32418
14 -	79765
15 -	109515
16 -	136412
17 -	159391
18 -	183461
19 -	219457
20 -	247458
21 -	267253
22 -	304314
23 -	346319
24 -	385196
25 -	423056
26 -	464564
27 -	510693
28 -	557850
29 -	600834
30 -	626996
31 -	651255
32 -	660110
33 -	664544
34 -	673994
35 -	686978
36 -	720316
37 -	754250
38 -	779455
39 -	814121
40 -	856499
41 -	907431
42 -	958303
43 -	975640
44 -	975727
45 -	990004
1946 -	1029152
47 -	1102371
48 -	1176055
49 -	1214041
50 -	1252028
51 -	1290015
52 -	1328002
53 -	1399996
54 -	1471990
55 -	1541929
56 -	1611868
57 -	1651435
58 -	1690999
59 -	1795500
60 -	1800000
61 -	1930029
62 -	1956990
63 -	1962001

A clean up of production took place from 64 through 66 with the ending serial # 1970875

New Style M/12

Year	Serial
1972 -	Y200 0100 -
	Y2006396
73 -	Y2015662
74 -	Y2022061
75 -	Y2024478
76 -	Y2025482
77 -	Y2025874
78 -	Y2026156
79 -	Y2026399

MODEL 24

Year	Serial
1939 -	1 to 8118
40 -	21382
41 -	27045
42 -	33670
43 -	None recorded
44 -	33683
45 -	34965
46 -	45250
47 -	58940
48 -	64417

There were no records kept on this model from 1949 until its discontinuance in 1958. The total production was approximately 116280.

MODEL 42

Year	Serial
1933 -	1 to 9398
34 -	13963
35 -	17728
36 -	24849
37 -	30900
38 -	34659
39 -	38967
40 -	43348
41 -	48203
42 -	50818
43 -	50822
44 -	50828
45 -	51168
46 -	54256
47 -	64853
48 -	75142
49 -	81107
50 -	87071
51 -	93038
52 -	99000
53 -	108201
54 -	117200
55 -	121883
56 -	126566
57 -	131249
58 -	135932
59 -	140615
60 -	145298
61 -	149981
62 -	154664
63 -	159353

MODEL 50

Year	Serial
1954 -	1 to 24550
55 -	49100
56 -	73650
57 -	98200
58 -	122750
59 -	147300
60 -	171850
61 -	196400

Firearms Associations

Alaska Gun Collectors Association
    c/o Wayne Anthony Ross, President
    P.O. Box 101522
    Anchorage, Alaska 99510

Arkansas Gun and Cartridge Collectors Club
    No Current Address

Ark - La - Tex - Gun Collectors Association
    Charlie Harris, President
    919 Hamilton Road
    Bossier City, LA 71111

Bay Colony Weapons Collectors, Inc.
    Ronald B. Santurjian
    47 Homer Road
    Belmont, MA 02178

Bayou Gun Club, The
    No Current Address

Boardman Valley Collectors Guild
    Secretary Jack Johnson
    County Road 600
    Manton, MI 49663

Browning Collectors Assn.
    c/o Col. W. R. Betz
    1306 Walcott Drive
    Ogden, UT 84403

C.A.D.A. (Collector Arms Dealer Association)
    P.O. Box 427
    Thomson, IL 61285

California Rifle & Pistol Association, Inc.
    Executive Director
    12062 Valley View St.
    Garden Grove, CA 92645

Central Illinois Gun Collectors Assn. Inc.
    Russ Gardner Sec.-Treas.
    Box 875
    Jacksonville, IL 62651-0875

Central Penn Antique Arms Association
    John E. Holman Jr.
    978 Thistle Road
    Elizabethtown, PA 17022

Chisholm Trail Antique Gun Association
    E.D. Stone
    1906 Richmond
    Wichita, KS 67203

Civil War Round Table of North New Jersey
    James F. Elliott
    124 Conover Lane
    Red Bank, NJ 07701

Colt Collectors Association
    Carol Wilkerson, Secretary
    17694 Isleton Court
    Lakeville, MN 55044
    Annual Membership $20

The Corpus Christi Antique Gun Collectors Association
    Corpus Christi Antique Gun Collectors
    P.O. Box 9392
    Corpus Christi, TX 78410

Dallas Arms Collectors Assoc., Inc.
    Richard Shea
    RT 1 Box 282-B
    DeSoto, TX 75115

Delaware Antique Arms Collectors Assoc.
    No Current Address

Denver Muzzle Loading Gun Club, Inc.
    Bill Rutherford
    P.O. Box 888
    Englewood, CO 80151

Forks of the Delaware W.A.
    No Current Address

Fort Lee Arms Collectors
    P.O. Box 1716
    South Hackensack, NJ 07606

Georgia Arms Collectors Association
    No Current Address

Hawaii Historic Arms Association
    Box 1733
    Honolulu, HI 96806

Houston Gun Collectors Association
    P.O. Box 53435
    Houston, TX 77052

Indianhead Firearms Assn.
    R#9 Box 186
    Chippewa Falls, WI 54729

Indian Territory Gun Collectors Association
    Box 4491
    Tulsa, OK 74159

Iroquois Arms Collectors Association
    Kenneth Keller-sec.
    Susann Keller-show sec.
    214 70th St.
    Niagara Falls, NY 14304

Jefferson State Arms Collectors
    Al Perry
    521 South Grape
    Medford, OR 97501

Jersey Shore Antique Arms Collectors
    Joe Sisia
    P.O. Box 100
    Bayville, NJ 08721

Kansas Cartridge Collectors Association
    Vic Suetter
    Route 1
    Lincoln, KS 67455

Kentuckiana Arms Collectors Assoc.
    Wanda Jones, Secretary
    P.O. Box 1776
    Louisville, KY 40201

Kentucky Gun Collectors Association
    Ruth Johnson, Exec. Sec.
    P.O. Box 64
    Owensboro, KY 42376

Lancaster Muzzle Loading Rifle Association
    James H. Frederick, Jr.
    R.D. #2 Box 402
    Columbia, PA 17512

Lehigh Valley Military Collectors Association
    Jay Solomon, Secretary
    P.O. Box 72
    Whitehall, PA 18052

Long Island Antique Gun Collectors Assoc.
    Frederick R. Wilkens
    35 Beach Street
    Farmingdale, L.I., NY 11735

Louisiana Gun Collectors Association, Inc.
    No Current Address

Manlicher Schoenauer Collectors Association
    No Current Address

Maryland Arms Collectors Assoc. (MACA)
    P.O. Box 20388
    Baltimore, MD 21284-0388

Memphis Antique Weapons Association
    Nelson Powers
    4672 Barfield Road
    Memphis, TN 38117

Minnesota Weapons Collectors Association
    Gail Foster, Executive Secretary
    P.O. Box 662
    Hopkins, MN 55343

Missouri Valley Arms Collectors Association
    P.O. Box 33033
    Kansas City, MO 64114

Montana Arms Collectors Association
    Lewis E. Yearout
    308 Riverview Drive
    East Great Falls, MT 59404

N.A.P.C.A. (National Automatic Pistol Collectors Assn.)
    AutoMag
    Box 15738-TOGS
    St. Louis, MO 63163

National Rifle Association
    1600 Rhode Island Avenue N.W.
    Washington, D.C. 20036

New Hampshire Arms Collectors, Inc.
    Warren Thayer
    P.O. Box 6
    Harrisville, N.H. 03450

North Eastern Arms Collectors Assoc., Inc.
    Bob Cole
    P.O. Box 185
    Amityville, NY 11701

Ohio Gun Collectors Association
    P.O. Box 24F
    Cincinnati, OH 45224

Oregon Arms
    Ted Dowd
    P.O. Box 25103
    Portland, OR 97225

Old Fort Gun Collectors Association
    No Current Address

Oregon Arms Collectors
    Ted Dowd
    P.O. Box 25103
    Portland, OR 97225

Pelican Arms Collectors Association
    Bob Thompson
    P.P. Box 747
    Clinton, LA 70722

Pennsylvania Antique Gun Collectors Assoc.
    Mrs. Kathleen Beyer Secy./Treas.
    28 Fulmer Avenue
    Havertown, PA 19083

Pikes Peak Gun Collectors Guild
    Charles Cell
    406 E. Uintah
    Colorado Springs, CO 80903

Potomac Arms Collectors Association
    Bruce D. Feinberg
    P.O. Box 2676
    Laurel, MD 20811

Remington Society of America
    Joe Poyer Secretary-Treasurer
    380 S. Tustin Avenue
    Orange, CA 92666
    Annual Membership $15

Ruger Collectors Association, Inc.
    P.O. Box 1778
    Chino Valley, AZ 86323

Sako Collectors Association, Inc.
    Mims C. Reed
    1725 Woodhill Lane
    Bedford, TX 76021

Santa Barbara Antique Arms Coll. Assoc.
    Alan Herboldsheimer
    P.O. Box 6291
    Santa Barbara, CA 93160-6291

San Bernardino Valley Arms Collectors
    Harold R.F. Thrasher
    1970 Mesa Street
    San Bernardino, CA 92405

Santa Fe Gun Collectors Association
    Ernie Lang
    1085 Nugget
    Los Alamos, NM 87544

San Fernando Valley Arms Coll. Assoc.
    Harold Ball
    P.O. Box 65
    North Hollywood, CA 91603

San Gabriel Valley Arms Collectors
    No Current Address

Shasta Arms Collectors Association
    Bob Fay
    P.O. Box 3292
    Redding, CA 96049

Smith & Wesson Collectors Association
    R. & M. Kolesar, Secretaries
    P.O. Box 321
    Bellevue, WA 98009

The Stark Gun Collectors, Inc.
    Pat F. McDonald
    602 Summerdale N.W.
    Massillon, OH 44646

Tampa Bay Arms Collectors Association
    John J. Tuvell, Secretary
    2461-67th Avenue South
    St. Petersburg, FL 33712

Washington Arms Collectors, Inc.
    J. Dennis Cook
    P.O. Box 7335
    Tacoma, WA 98407

Weapons Collectors Society of Montana
    3100 Bancroft
    Missoula, MT 59801

Weatherby Collectors Association, Inc.
    P.O. Box 128
    Moira, NY 12957

Williamette Valley Arms Collectors Association, Inc.
    Murry Brooks, Executive Secretary
    P.O. Box 5191
    Eugene, OR 97405

Winchester Arms Collectors Association
    Lewis E. Yearout
    308 Riverview Drive East
    Great Falls, MT 59404

Ye Connecticut Gun Guild
    Robert L. Harris
    U.S. Route 7-Kent Road
    Cornwall Bridge, CT 06754

Zumbro Valley Arms Collectors, Inc.
    Box 6621
    Rochester, MN 55901

References

Bady, Donald B., *Colt Automatic Pistols*. Los Angeles, CA: Borden Publishing Co., 1973.

Baer, Larry L., *The Parker Book*. North Hollywood, CA: Beinfeld Publishing Co., 1974.

Belford, James N. and Dunlap, Jack, *Mauser Self Loading Pistol*. Alhambia, CA: Borden Publishing Co., 1969.

Bender, Roy G. III, *Mauser*. Houston, TX: Collector's Press, 1971.

Breathed and Schroeder, *System Mauser*. Chicago, IL: Handgun Press, 1967.

Brophy, William S. *L. C. Smith Shotguns*. North Hollywood, CA: Beinfeld Publishing Co., 1977.

Butzer, David F., *The American Shotgun*. Middlefield, CT: Lyman Publications, 1973.

Buxton, *the P-38 Pistol: Volume I*. Los Alamos, NM: U.C. Ross Books, 1978.

Costanza, Sam, *World of Lugers; Volume I*. Mayfield Heights, OH: World of Lugers, 1977.

Hill and Anthony, *Confederate Long Arms and Pistols*. Charlotte, NC: Confederate Arms, 1978.

Jinks, Roy G., *History of Smith & Wesson*. North Hollywood, CA: Beinfeld Publishing Co., 1977.

Karr and Karr, Jr., *Remington Handgun*. Stackpole Co., Second Edition, 1951.

Kenyon, Charles Jr., *Lugers at Random*. Chicago, IL: Handgun Press, 1969.

Kopel, Graham, and Moore, *A Study of the Colt Single Action Army Revolver*. La Puente, Ca: Kopel, Graham, and Moore Publishers, 1978.

Leithe, Frederick, *Japanese Handguns*. California: Borden Publishing Co., 1968.

Madis, George, *The Winchester Book*. Lancaster, TX: Privately Published by Author, 1975.

Madis, George, *The Model 12*, Lancaster, TX: Published by Author, 1981.

Maxwell, Samuel L., Sr., *Lever Action Magazine Rifles*. Published by Author, 1978.

Olson, Ludwig, *Mauser Bolt Action Rifles*. Montezuma, Ia: F. Brownell & Son Publishers, Inc., 1976.

Rankin, James L., *Walther,* Vol.'s I, II, III — Coral Gabels, FL: Published by Author, 1976.

Sellers, Frank, *Sharp's Firearms*. North Hollywood, CA: Beinfeld Publishing Co., 1978.

Sharpe, Phillip B., *The Rifle in America*. Funk and Wagnals, 1947.

Serven, editor. *The Collecting of Guns.* Bonanza Book, 1964.

Tanner, Hans. *Guns of the World.* Bonanza Books, 1972, 1977.

West, Bill, *Browning Arms & History.* Santa Fe Springs, CA: Stockton Trade Press, Inc., 1972.

West, Bill, *Marlin and Ballard Firearms & History.* Norwalk, CA: Stockton Trade Press, Inc., 1977.

West, Bill, *Remington Arms & History.* Whittier, CA: Stockton Trade Press, Inc., 1970.

West, Bill, *Savage and Stevens Arms & History.* Whittier, CA: Stockton Trade Press, Inc., 1971.

Whitaker, Dean H., *Model 70 Winchester 1937-1964.* Dallas, TX: Taylor Publishing Co., 1978.

Wilkerson, Don, *Post War Colt Single Action Army.* Published by Author, 1978.

Wilson, R. L., *Colt Commemorative Firearms.* Geneseo, IL: Robert E. P. Cherry Publishing Co., 1973.

Wilson, R. L., *The Colt Heritage,* New York, New York: Simon and Schuster.

Periodicals

American Rifleman: Published monthly by the National Rifle Association of America, 1600 Rhode Island Ave., NW, Wash., DC 20036, as a benefit of membership. Dues are $20 per year.

Gun Report: Published monthly by World Wide Gun Report, Inc., P.O. Box 111, Aledo, IL 61231. Annual subscription rate is $20.

Gun Week: Published weekly by Hawkeye Publishing, Inc., P.O. Box 411, Station C, Buffalo, NY 14209. Annual subscription rate is $20.

Gun List: Published monthly at 700 E. State St., Iola, WI 54990. The annual rate is $14.95.

Man at Arms: Published bimonthly at 222 W. Exchange St., Providence, RI 02903. Subscription rate is $18 per year.

Shotgun News: Published three times a month at Box 669, Hastings, NE 68901. The annual rate is $18.

NOTES

Periodicals

Restoration of Firearms

This section deals with firearms restoration done at a professional level. With only so many "mint" original guns to go around, more and more professional restorations are being done on guns in short supply. Insight in this complicated process has been afforded by Mr. John Kaufield, president of Small Arms Engineering. The following question and answer session will explain many questions you might have in this rapidly growing field. Any additional questions should be directed to me at the BLUE BOOK OF GUN VALUES.

Q. John, where do you start when you restore a gun?

A. The first step in restoring a firearm is to determine what the original finish was. If there is original finish, one must determine what type of finish it should be. Also, careful notes must be taken on different types of polishing, any tool marks, inspector's markings, barrel address markings, and any other proof marks. This is done to refer back to once the metal has been polished, and/or wood being refinished. Guns in very poor condition need enlarged copies made of any markings that may have to be replaced. This assumes that the gun is valuable enough to have marking dies made to replace barrel addresses and other proof marks. Once the notes are made, total disassembly of the firearm, including the removal of barrel is the next step. This may require removing any riveted or assembled parts, and strip the gun down to the way the manufacturer originally constructed it.

After these steps, major pitted or damaged areas are repaired. This might require welding to build up metal surfaces suitable for polishing. In short, get the worst out of the way first. Heli-ark welding is a precision die welding capable of laying on a small dot of metal without overheating adjacent areas. This weld is very pure, since the shielding gas is argon which eliminates any oxidation that could form around the weld.

Polishing of the metal is next — a fallacy is to think that hand polishing will produce an original-looking gun. This might be true on pre1850 firearms, but Colonel Colt revolutionized firearms manufacturing by using machine tools. During the resulting industrial revolution, virtually all guns were made primarily with machined operations. This machining included the polishing as well. In order to restore a gun of more recent vintage (post-1875), machinery should be used that is similar to when the gun was made. This machinery includes a large polishing lathe. Prior to WWII, the Colt Firearms polishing room was known as the room of wheels because shaped wheels in all sizes were available to polish every nook and cranny on a Colt. This was all off hand polishing which is machine polishing taking a degree of skill not easily found today. This can be proven by the finishes available from manufacturers today as opposed to fifty years ago.

Correct polishing requires each part getting polished in a manner similar to the way it was done originally. Rough grinding is done first to remove machine and cutter marks. Depending on the gun, final finishing with greased wheels and small smounts of abrasive is next. This highlights the metal and brings the luster up. Most Lugers, for instance, were blued directly after the rough grinding. Pre-war Colts and their translucent mirror finish required quite a bit of extra polishing to get that high luster polish and depth.

When the polishing has been completed (this is 75% of a professional restoration), any restamping or remarking that is needed is done now. For the more popular guns, marking dies are made up to restamp proof marks and other metal markings. Sometimes a roll-die has to be made for a specific model. Roll dies require less pressure in application since only one or two letters are being applied at a time. Flat dies require much more pressure because many characters are being pressed in simultaneously.

Wood is next — any sanding and rough finishing is done now. Sometimes refitting is required for proper metal positioning. After final sanding comes recheckering — this is always necessary, even if the wood is in good condition. Original guns always were checkered after finishing. Winchester rifles had two coats of finish applied to the wood before checkering was performed. After a stain was applied to the new checkering, the gun west back to the finishing department for one final coat of lacquer. This process, of course, sealed the raw checkering.

Once these steps have been completed, metal coloring comes next. This involves applying the same finish or type of finish as was originally put on the gun. An exception would be an owner who wants a different type of finish other than what was original. An individual gun could have over four different types of finishes applied. Case hardening, rust blue, carbona blue, and temper blue all require different methods in application. "Straw" colors on Lugers represent a form of temper blue. Correct wood color and finish is now performed on stock, forend, grips, etc.

Finally reassembly occurs in a very careful fashion with inspection being made to guarantee the functionability of all reassembled parts. This completes the professional restoration process.

Q. What is done to engraving on a restored firearm?

A. The original engraving is recut before the blueing is applied. Or, for that matter, before any special finishes would be applied. Engraving should never be put on after the metal finish has been completed. This will result in the engraving appearing white and subsequently more susceptible to oxidation.

Q. Are popular discontinued firearms appropriate for sporterizing or making custom actions?

A. There are many more suitable firearms available from which to make a custom firearm. These newer, modern designed actions are more adaptable to custom application than a pre-64 Model 70 Winchester in mint condition.

Q. What made or type of firearm(s) is suitable for restoration?

A. Colts, Winchesters, Lugers, Parkers, S&Ws, and other major trademarks that are collectible are among the most popular for restoration. Off brands that enjoy no collector base are very rarely restored professionally.

Q. How can I select the best gunsmith to handle the restoration of my firearm(s)?

A. Recommendations from fellow collectors that are satisfied provide good sources for professional work. It seems that people who have many firearms restored are reluctant to divulge their source. This aura of secrecy has always gone with this territory — some collectors have to be approached several times before they will share the name of their restoration expert.

Q. Is it ethical to restore firearms?

A. If a gun is in fair to poor condition, there is nothing wrong with restoring it back to 100% original condition. All other collectibles have been restored, including cars, paintings, furniture and others. It is only natural that people are attracted to fine condition firearms rather than specimens of lower quality. there is nothing wrong with restoring a firearm if it is done properly, originality is kept in mind, and the potential buyer is informed of the restoration work.

Q. Is the restoration of firearms expensive?

A. Because of the extensive nature of restorations, this process is much more expensive than refinishing or reblueing. Normal refinishing or reblueing will probably decrease the value of a fine gun by as much as 50%. Proper restoration should increase the value of a collectible firearm. This increase happens both intrinsically and monetarily.

Q. Are there any guns that shouldn't be restored?

A. Suicide and/or cheap guns, because the value and the interest are just not there. Guns with a historical provenance should be left in the condition they are found, unless alterations were performed at a known later date. Jessee James' Colt is certainly worth more in poor original condition than if restored to 100%.

Q. Can mismatched or altered parts be replaced or repaired?

A. On guns that have mismatched parts such as Lugers, normally during the restoration process these parts are rematched to the overall serial number of the firearm. Altered parts are then either repaired or replaced.

Q. What is restoration as opposed to merely refinishing?

A. A restoration is the careful refurbishing of a firearm, with originality of finish as the only objective. Refinishing is merely placing a new and usually incorrect finish that is applied merely for looks.

Q. What constitutes a correctly restored gun?

A. Of prime importance is the finishing of metal parts. Correct direction and grit of polish make the all-important difference in a professional restoration. Also, any milling marks, trademarks must be present that were present on the original piece. This area will account for 75% of a quality restoration. The balance being the correctness of the finish or finishes applied (i.e., case hardening, rust blueing, etc.).

Q. Can a bore of a firearm be restored as well as the exterior?

A. Most collectors do not pay that much attention to the condition of the bore. If it is necessary, a new barrel can be made or the old one relined. A liner if properly installed shouldn't be visible from the breach or muzzle. Lapping is not a practical process to undertake on a pitted bore. Too much metal has to be removed and it is not cost efficient.

Q. Can the markings be restored on a badly reblued or pitted firearm?

A. Usually the original marks are retained on the weapon. In deeply pitted areas or previously reblued portions, dies sometimes have to be made to duplicate the original markings. Re-engraved markings such as proofs will always look different from rolled die applied stamps.

Q. If the wood is in poor condition, what can be done?

A. Sometimes on long guns the wood will make the determination if the gun is worth restoring or not. Very poor conditioned wood many times results in restocking the firearm — a very expensive alternative. Less can be done with wood than metal, since no building up of the surface can be performed.

Q. Can deep pitting be repaired?

A. Light pitting can be polished out. However, deep pit must be filled by heli-ark welding. This precision weld can be applied without excessive heating of the base metal. Welding the side of a deeply pitted receiver can be a very expensive proposition. Warpage sometimes results due to the addition of heat when applying the extra metal.

Q. Can a firearm that has had its barrel shortened be returned to its original condition?

A. Barrel-stretching as it is termed can be done relatively easily if rifling in the new section is not considered. New rifling in the added section gets to be quite hard, plus equally expensive. A special liner spanning the entire length of the added-on barrel must be fabricated. Usually only rare firearms are reserved for this process.

Q. What is the hardest type of damage to repair?

A. Badly buffed or poorly blued guns are the hardest to restore. Topping the list are those that have been chrome plated.

Q. Can color case hardening be restored?

A. Color case hardening as applied to older guns was always packhardened. Only a limited amount of craftsmen can restore case hardening and the process is elaborate. True bone dust-charcoal case colors require baking in a vessel at extended high temperatures, after which the parts are quenched in water. Cyanide or flame case colors are done with a torch and are not representative of the original mottled colors, nor are they indicative of a professional restoration.

Q. What types of finishes are found on firearms?

A. Metal finishes are comprised of rust blueing or a satin color blue, color case hardening which is a mottled colored heat treatment, salt blueing, carbona blueing or the translucent blue found on pre-war Colts, different platings are next and are usually brightly polished. On older firearms nickel, silver, and gold are sometimes encountered. Chrome plating never existed at this time. Plating is an electrolytic process involving suspending a firearm in a solution in which the plating metal has been suspended. Current is applied to the anode and the gun, resulting in the base metal flowing through the solution depositing itself on the metal surfaces. Plating in a proper bath usually requires thirty minutes. Plating requires better than normal polishing since any pit or flaw will only be amplified during the plating process. On older guns silver plating was many times applied first, since this base coat could more easily be overplated with gold or other metals. Again, engraving must be recut before the final plating is put on.

Wood finishes on late 1800-WWII items will occasionally be encountered with oil finishes. Most factory guns will be finished in a lacquer because of ease of application. Also, many different effects were achieved using different types of lacquer. Early guns sometimes had shellac.

Q. Why is the restoration of firearms frowned on by some collectors?

A. Usually it depends on whether they are buying or selling. In the mid 50's when salt blueing became popular, many guns were "butchered" by excessive buffing and quick dunk "tank blueing". People involved in collecting quickly recognized these inferior, reblued specimens and quickly placed a discount on these items. This is one reason more and more people are getting involved in quality restoration — to save some of these "hacked up" models.

Q. What is the future of firearms restoration?

A. There appears to be nothing but a rosy future for firearms restoration. As the quantity of mint collectibles dries up, the market will be comprised of original guns in lesser condition, and those that have been restored correctly.

Q. How can it be determined if a gun has been restored or not?

A. A giveaway area is in the corners where the metal is hard to polish. Pitting which has been blued over and appears to be a different color also usually appears questionable. Barrel markings, proof marks, inspector cartouches if checked carefully can usually determine a firearm's original status also. The additional money of a restoration should cover getting pitting removed from hard to get areas. Another telltale area is if the wrong polishing or finishing process is applied to the gun. An example would be if you found salt blue on a Martial Colt or 1900 Luger. It would be obvious at that point that the gun had been reblued since those finishes are not authentic to that time period. Blurry factory markings are certainly another indication that the gun was previously poorly restored.

Q. How many sources are there for restoration services?

A. 10-20 full time restoration experts are currently refurbishing just about all types of firearms. Most of these specialize in different areas. Specialists in flintlocks normally would not touch a Luger.

NOTES

BUSINESS LISTINGS WITH ADDRESSES
FOR INDIVIDUAL TRADEMARKS

The directory provided on the following pages has been provided to assist you when trying to learn more about individual trademarks and their respective manufacturer/importer/distributor. Each trademark/brand name listed on the following pages is followed by the company/individual who is currently manufacturing, importing, distributing, or servicing that specific product. Both addresses and FAX numbers (for facsimile transmissions only — not for telephone conversations) have been provided to assist you when contacting these firms.

If you have a firearm that needs service work of some kind, *DO NOT* automatically write to that company regarding this request. Check with the local dealers in your area to initially find out where the firearm should be taken for repair. If you are not able to find out any information using this approach, then write/FAX the company listed and have patience. Most of the companies listed do not have extra personnel to service these types of requests individually, so give them some courtesy.

If you are requesting more information about a specific model or need other data involving an older discontinued model you may or may not obtain that knowledge from those companies listed in this directory. Remember, firms like Winchester, Colt's, and others have a customer charge for conducting this research — please find their headings in the main part of this publication to find the amount. Also, many firms do not have individuals with enough company longevity to remember the past histories of discontinued models within that trademark.

If you should have any further questions requesting additional data for these (or other) trademarks, please contact me for further assistance. I will help you as much as I can. Send requests or FAX to me at:

Blue Book of Gun Values
Attn: Mr. Steven P. Fjestad
One Appletree Square
Minneapolis, MN 55425

FAX NUMBER: 612-853-1GUN (1867)
TOLL-FREE TEL. NO. (outside MN): 1-800-877-4867
MN Residents call 612-853-1320

Again, please have patience.

TRADEMARK INDEX, cont.

A-Square

A-Square Company, Inc.
Attn: Customer Service
Rt. 4 Simmons Road
Madison, IN   47250

AKS

B-West Inc.
Attn: Customer Service
5146 E. Pima Road
Tucson, AZ   85712
FAX NUMBER: 602-322-5704

Pacific International Mer
Attn: Customer Service
2215 J Street
Sacramento, CA   95816
FAX NUMBER: 916-446-0722

AMAC

AMAC, Inc.
Attn: Customer Service
2202 Redmond Road
Jacksonville, AR   72076
FAX NUMBER: 501-982-4954

AMT

Arcadia Machine & Tool
Attn: Customer Service
6226 Santos Diaz Street
Irwindale, CA   91706
FAX NUMBER: 818-969-5247

Action Arms

Action Arms Ltd.
Attn: Customer Service
P.O. Box 9573
Philadelphia, PA   19124-0573
FAX NUMBER: 215-533-2188

American Arms Inc.

American Arms, Inc.
Attn: Customer Service
715 E. Armour Road
N. Kansas City, MO   64116
FAX NUMBER: 816-474-1225

American Derringer Corporation

American Derringer Corp.
Attn: Customer Service
127 N. Lacy Dr.
Waco, TX   76705

American Historical Foundation, The

Attn: Customer Service
1142 W. Grace St., #C175
Richmond, VA   23220
FAX NUMBER: 804-353-0689

Anschutz

Precision Sales Int'l,Inc
Attn: Customer Service
P.O. Box 1776
Westfield, MA   01086
FAX NUMBER: 413-562-5056

Armes De Chasse

Armes De Chasse
Attn: Customer Service
P.O. Box No. 827
Chadds Ford, PA   19317

Arms Corporation of the Philippines

Armscor Precision Inc.
Attn: Customer Service
1175 Chess Dr., Suite 204
Foster City, CA   94404
FAX NUMBER: 415-349-0259

Arms Research Associates

Arms Research Associates
Attn: Customer Service
1800 Mannheim Rd.
Stone Park, IL   60165

Armscorp of America, Inc.

Armscorp of America
Attn: Customer Service
4424 John Avenue
Baltimore, MD   21227
FAX NUMBER: 301-247-6205

Armsport

Armsport, Inc.
Attn: Customer Service
3590 NW 49th St.
Miami, FL   33142
FAX NUMBER: 305-633-2877

Arrieta, S.L.

Morton's, Ltd.
Attn: Customer Service
156 Trade Street
Lexington, KY   40510
FAX NUMBER: 606-252-1399

Arrizablaga

Morton's, Ltd.
Attn: Customer Service
156 Trade Street
Lexington, KY   40510
FAX NUMBER: 606-252-1399

Astra

Interarms
Attn: Customer Service
Number 10 Prince Street
Alexandria, VA   22313
FAX NUMBER: 703-549-7826

Australian Automatic Arms Pty. Ltd.

N.A.S.I.
Attn: Customer Service
P.O. Box 90
Midland, TX   79702
FAX NUMBER: 915-687-3341

Auto-Mag

Gibbons Sporting Arms
Attn: Customer Service
P.O. Box 751
Torrance, CA   90508

Auto-Ordnance Corp.

Auto-Ordnance Corporation
Attn: Customer Service
Williams Lane
West Hurley, NY   12491
FAX NUMBER: 914-679-5849

BSA Guns Ltd.

Samco Global Arms Inc.
Attn: Customer Service
6995 N.W. 43rd Street
Miami, FL   33166
FAX NUMBER: 305-477-1232

Bailons Gunmakers Ltd.

Bailons Gunmakers Ltd.
Attn: Customer Service
94-95 Bath Street
Birmingham   ENGLAND B4
6HG

Barrett Firearms Manufacturing, Inc.

Barrett Firearms Mfg, Inc
Attn: Customer Service
8211 Manchester Highway
Murfreesboro, TN   37133
FAX NUMBER: 615-896-7313

Beeman Arms, Inc.

Beeman Precision Arms
Attn: Customer Service
3440 Airway Drive
Santa Rosa, CA 95401
FAX NUMBER: 707-578-4751

Benelli

Heckler & Koch, Inc.
Attn: Customer Service
14601 Lee Road
Chantilly, VA 22021
FAX NUMBER: 703-450-8160

Beretta, Dr. Franco

Double M Shooting Supplies
Attn: Customer Service
462 South Hoop Pole Road
Guilford, CT 06437

Beretta, Pietro

Beretta U.S.A. Corp
Attn: Customer Service
17601 Indian Head Hwy.
Accokeek, MD 20607
FAX NUMBER: 301-375-7677

Bernardelli

Aspen Outfitting Co.
Attn: Customer Service
520 E. Cooper
Aspen, CO 81611

Bersa

Eagle Imports Inc.
Attn: Customer Service
1907 Hwy #35
Ocean, NJ 07712
FAX NUMBER: 201-531-1520

Bertuzzi

New England Arms Co.
Attn: Customer Service
Kittery Point, ME 03905

Blaser

Autumn Sales Inc.
Attn: Customer Service
1320 Lake
Fort Worth, TX 76102
FAX NUMBER: 817-246-0301

Boswell, Charles

Charles Boswell Gunmakers
Attn: Customer Service
212 E. Morehead Street
Charlotte, NC 28202

Bretton

Mandall Shooting Supplies
Attn: Customer Service
3616 N. Scottsdale Rd.
Scottsdale, AZ 85251

Quality Arms
Attn: Customer Service
Box 19477
Houston, TX 77224

Brno Arms

T.D. Arms
Attn: Customer Service
30464 #2 23 Mile Road
New Baltimore, MI 48047

Brown Precision Co.

Brown Precision Inc.
Attn: Customer Service
7786 Molinos Avenue
Los Molinos, CA 96055

Browning Arms

Attn: Customer Service
Route One
Morgan, UT 84050

Bruchet

Attn: Customer Service
8139 San Benito Way
Dallas, TX   75218

Bushmaster Firearms Inc.

Bushmaster Firearms Inc.
Attn: Customer Service
999 Roosevelt Tr. Bldg. 3
North Windham, ME   04062
FAX NUMBER: 207-892-8068

Cabanas

Mandall Shooting Supplies
Attn: Customer Service
3616 N. Scottsdale Road
Scottsdale, AZ   85251

Cabela's Inc.

Cabela's
Attn: Customer Service
812 13th Ave.
Sidney, NE   69160

Calico

Calico
Attn: Customer Service
405 East 19th Street
Bakersfield, CA   93305
FAX NUMBER: 805-323-7844

Casartelli, Carlo

New England Arms Co.
Attn: Customer Service
Kittery Point, ME   03905

Caspian Arms

Caspian Arms Ltd.
Attn: Customer Service
14 N. Main St.
Hardwick, VT   05843

Century Gun Dist., Inc.

Century Gun Dist., Inc.
Attn: Customer Service
1467 Jason Road
Greenfield, IN   46140

Century International Arms, Inc.

Century Int'l Arms Inc.
Attn: Customer Service
5 Federal St./PO Box 714
St. Albans, VT   05478
FAX NUMBER: 802-524-5631

Chapuis

Armes De Chasse
Attn: Customer Service
P.O. Box No. 827
Chadds Ford, PA   19317

Charter Arms

Charter Arms Corporation
Attn: Customer Service
430 Sniffens Lane
Stratford, CT   06497
FAX NUMBER: 203-378-2846

Chipmunk Manufacturing Inc.

Chipmunk Mfg., Inc.
Attn: Customer Service
114 East Jackson
Medford, OR   97501

Churchill

Ellett Brothers
Attn: Customer Service
P.O. Drawer G
Chapin, SC   29036
FAX NUMBER: 803-345-1820

Churchill, E.J., (Gunmakers) Ltd.

E.J. Churchill Ltd.
Attn: Customer Service
Ockley Road, Dorking
Surrey   ENGLAND RH5 4PU

Cimarron, F.A. Mfg. Co.

Cimarron F.A. Mfg. Co.
Attn: Customer Service
9439 Katy Freeway
Houston, TX   77024

Classic Doubles

Classic Doubles
Attn: Customer Service
1982 Innerbelt Business
St. Louis, MO   63114

Clifton Arms

Clifton Arms, Inc.
Attn: Customer Service
P.O. Box 531258
Grand Prairie, TX   75053

Colt's Firearms

Colt Industries
Attn: Customer Service
P.O. Box 1868, Talcott Rd
Hartford, CT   06101
FAX NUMBER: 203-244-1442

Connecticut Valley Arms, Inc.

Connecticut Valley Arms
Attn: Customer Service
5988 Peachtree Corners E.
Norcross, GA   40071
FAX NUMBER: 404-242-8546

Coonan Arms, Inc.

Coonan Arms, Inc.
Attn: Customer Service
830 Hampden Ave.
St. Paul, MN   55114
FAX NUMBER: 612-646-8237

Cosmi, Americo & Figlio

New England Arms Co.
Attn: Customer Service
Kittery Point, ME   03905

Daisy

Daisy, Inc.
Attn: Customer Service
P.O. Box 220
Rodgers, AR   72756
FAX NUMBER: 501-636-1601

Dakota Arms Inc.

Dakota Arms, Inc.
Attn: Customer Service
HC55 Box 326
Sturgis, SD   57785

Dakota Single Action Revolvers

EMF Company
Attn: Customer Service
1900 E. Warner Ave. 1-D
Santa Ana, CA   92705

Daly, Charles: Modern Mfg.

Outdoor Sports Hdqtrs.
Attn: Customer Service
967 Watertower Lane
Dayton, OH   45449
FAX NUMBER: 513-865-5962

Davis Industries

Davis Industries
Attn: Customer Service
15150 Sierra Bonita Lane
Chino, CA 91710
FAX NUMBER: 714-393-9771

Detonics Manufacturing Corp.

Detonics Mfg. Corp., New
Attn: Customer Service
13456 S.E. 27th Place
Bellevue, WA 98005
FAX NUMBER: 206-747-2127

Domino

Mandall Shooting Supplies
Attn: Customer Service
3616 N. Scottsdale Rd.
Scottsdale, AZ 85251

DuBiel Arms Company

DuBiel Arms Co.
Attn: Customer Service
1724 Baker Rd.
Sherman, TX 75090

Dumoulin

Midwest Gun Sport
Attn: Customer Service
1108 Herbert Drive
Zebulon, NC 27597

E.M.F. Co., Inc.

EMF Company
Attn: Customer Service
1900 E. Warner Ave. 1-D
Santa Ana, CA 92705
FAX NUMBER: 714-756-0133

Erma-Werke

Beeman Precision Arms
Attn: Customer Service
3440 Airway Drive
Santa Rosa, CA 95401
FAX NUMBER: 707-578-4751

Mandall Shooting Supplies
Attn: Customer Service
3616 N. Scottsdale Rd.
Scottsdale, AZ 85251

Excam

Excam, Inc.
Attn: Customer Service
4480 E. 11th Ave.
Hialeah, FL 33013
FAX NUMBER: 305-681-3774

F.I.E.

FIE Corporation
Attn: Customer Service
4530 NW 135th St.
Opa-Locka, FL 33054
FAX NUMBER: 305-687-6721

FAS

Beeman Precision Arms
Attn: Customer Service
3440 Airway Drive
Santa Rosa, CA 95401
FAX NUMBER: 707-578-4751

Osborne's Distributors
Attn: Customer Service
P.O. Box 408
Cheboygan, MI 49721

Fabarm

St. Lawrence Sales, Inc.
Attn: Customer Service
12 W. Flint Street
Lake Orion, MI 48035

Fabbri, Armi

New England Arms Co.
Attn: Customer Service
Kittery Point, ME   03905

Fabrique Nationale

FN Manufacturing, Inc.
Attn: Customer Service
P.O. Box 104
Columbia, SC   29202

Falcon Firearms

Falcon Firearms Mfg.Corp.
Attn: Customer Service
P.O. Box 3748
Granada Hills, CA   91344

Feather Industries

Feather Enterprises
Attn: Customer Service
2300 Central Ave. Unit K
Boulder, CO   80301
FAX NUMBER: 303-447-0944

Federal Ordnance Inc.

Federal Ordnance, Inc.
Attn: Customer Service
1443 Petrero Avenue So.
South El Monte, CA   91733
FAX NUMBER: 818-350-1538

Feinwerkbau

Beeman Precision Arms
Attn: Customer Service
3440 Airway Drive
Santa Rosa, CA   95401
FAX NUMBER: 707-578-4751

Ferlach Guns

Attn: Customer Service
Waagplatz, 6
Ferlach   AUSTRIA A-9170

Ferlib

New England Arms Co.
Attn: Customer Service
Kittery Point, ME   03905

Quality Arms
Attn: Customer Service
Box 19477
Houston, TX   77224

Fiocchi

Fiocchi of America, Inc.
Attn: Customer Service
Rt. 2, Box 90-8
Ozark, MO   65721
FAX NUMBER: 417-725-1039

Fox, A.H.

Attn: Customer Service
P.O. Box 116
Two Harbors, MN   55616

Franchi, Luigi

American Arms, Inc.
Attn: Customer Service
715 E. Armour Road
N. Kansas City, MO   64116
FAX NUMBER: 816-474-1225

FIE Corporation
Attn: Customer Service
4530 NW 135th St.
Opa-Locka, FL   33054
FAX NUMBER: 305-687-6721

Francotte, Auguste & Cie. S.A.

Armes De Chasse
Attn: Customer Service
P.O. Box No. 827
Chadds Ford, PA   19317

Royal Arms International
Attn: Customer Service
22458 Ventura Blvd. Ste.E
Woodland Hills, CA   91364
FAX NUMBER: 818-887-2059

Fraser Firearms Corp.

Fraser Firearms Corp.
Attn: Customer Service
34575 Commerce
Fraser, MI   48026

Fraser, Danl. & Co.

Sporting Arms Int.'l Inc.
Attn: Customer Service
P.O. Box 1458
Indianola, MS   38751

Freedom Arms

Freedom Arms
Attn: Customer Service
P.O. Box 1776
Freedom, WY   83120
FAX NUMBER: 307-883-2005

Frigon

Frigon Guns
Attn: Customer Service
627 West Crawford
Clay Center, KS   67432

Galil

Action Arms Ltd.
Attn: Customer Service
P.O. Box 9573
Philadelphia, PA   19124-0573
FAX NUMBER: 215-533-2188

Gamba, Renato

Gamba Renato
Attn: Customer Service
Via Michelangelo, 64
Gardone   ITALY 1-25063
FAX NUMBER: 030-837180

Garbi

Wlm. Larkin Moore & Co.
Attn: Customer Service
31360 Via Colinas, Se 109
Westlake Village, CA   91361

Gatling Gun Company

Furr Arms
Attn: Customer Service
76 East 350 North
Orem, UT   84057

J & G Sales, Inc.
Attn: Customer Service
440 Miller Valley
Prescott, AZ   86301

Gibbs Guns, Inc.

Gibbs Guns, Inc.
Attn: Customer Service
Rt. 2, 411 Highway
Green Back, TN   37742

Glock

Glock Inc.
Attn: Customer Service
5000 Highlands, Suite 190
Smyrna, GA   30080
FAX NUMBER: 404-433-8719

Goncz Company

Goncz Company
Attn: Customer Service
10641 Aspen Avenue
California City, CA   93505

Granger

Attn: Customer Service
8139 San Benito Way
Dallas, TX   75218

TRADEMARK INDEX, cont.

Grendel, Inc.

Grendel, Inc.
Attn: Customer Service
P.O. Box 903
Rockledge, FL 32955
FAX NUMBER: 407-633-6710

HWP Industries

Attn: Customer Service
9730 N. Granville Rd. 107 W.
Mequon, WI 53092

Hammerli

Beeman Precision Arms
Attn: Customer Service
3440 Airway Drive
Santa Rosa, CA 95401
FAX NUMBER: 707-578-4751

Mandall Shooting Supplies
Attn: Customer Service
3616 N. Scottsdale Rd.
Scottsdale, AZ 85251

Hatfield Rifle Company

Hatfield Corp.
Attn: Customer Service
2028 Frederick
St. Joseph, MO 64501

Heckler & Koch

Heckler & Koch, Inc.
Attn: Customer Service
14601 Lee Road
Chantilly, VA 22021
FAX NUMBER: 703-450-8160

Heym, Friedrich Wilh.

Heym America, Inc.
Attn: Customer Service
1426 E. Tillman Road
Fort Wayne, IN 46816

Hofer-Jagdwaffen, Peter

Peter Hofer-Jagdwaffen
Attn: Customer Service
Franz-Lang-StraBe 13
Ferlach   AUSTRIA A-9170
FAX NUMBER: 4227/3683

Holland & Holland Ltd.

New England Arms Co.
Attn: Customer Service
Kittery Point, ME 03905

IGA

Stoeger Industries
Attn: Customer Service
55 Ruta Court
S. Hackensack, NJ 07606
FAX NUMBER: 201-440-2707

Interarms firearms

Interarms
Attn: Customer Service
Number Ten Prince Street
Alexandria, VA 22313
FAX NUMBER: 703-549-7826

Intratec

Intratec
Attn: Customer Service
12405 SW 130th St.
Miami, FL 33186
FAX NUMBER: 305-253-7207

Irwindale Arms, Inc.

Irwindale Arms Inc.
Attn: Customer Service
6226 Santos Diaz St.
Irwindale, CA 91702
FAX NUMBER: 818-969-5247

Ithaca Gun Co.

Ithaca Gun
Attn: Customer Service
123 Lake Street
Ithaca, NY   14850
FAX NUMBER: 607-272-5721

Jennings Firearms, Inc.

Jennings Firearms, Inc.
Attn: Customer Service
3680 Research Way, Ste.#1
Carson City, NV   89706

Jericho

K.B.I. Inc.
Attn: Customer Service
P.O. Box 11933
Harrisburg, PA   17108
FAX NUMBER: 717-540-8567

Iver Johnson

AMAC
Attn: Customer Service
2202 Redmond Road
Jacksonville, AR   72076
FAX NUMBER: 501-982-4954

K.B.I., Inc.

Attn: Customer Service
P.O. Box 11933
Harrisburg, PA   17108
FAX NUMBER: 717-540-8567

KDF Inc.

K.D.F., Inc.
Attn: Customer Service
2485 Highway 46 North
Seguin, TX   78155
FAX NUMBER: 512-379-5420

Kassnar Imports

Kassnar Imports, Inc.
Attn: Customer Service
P.O. Box 6097
Harrisburg, PA   17112
FAX NUMBER: 717-652-5514

Kimber of Oregon

Kimber of Oregon, Inc.
Attn: Customer Service
9039 Southeast Jannsen Rd
Clackamos, OR   97015
FAX NUMBER: 503-824-4997

Korriphila

Osborne's Distributors
Attn: Customer Service
P.O. Box 408
Cheboygan, MI   49721

Korth

Beeman Precision Arms
Attn: Customer Service
3440 Airway Drive
Santa Rosa, CA   95401
FAX NUMBER: 707-578-4751

Krieghoff, H., Gun Co.

Krieghoff Intl., Inc.
Attn: Customer Service
P.O. Box 549
Ottsville, PA   18942

L.A.R. Manufacturing, Inc.

L.A.R. Manufacturing, Inc
Attn: Customer Service
4133 West Farm Road
West Jordan, UT   84088

Lanber

Lanber Armas, S.A.
Attn: Customer Service
Zubiaurre, 5
Zaldibar, Vizcaya   SPAIN 48250
FAX NUMBER: 34-43-450794

Laurona

Galaxy Imports Ltd.
Attn: Customer Service
P.O. Box 3361
Victoria, TX   77903

Law Enforcement Ordnance Corp.

Law Enforcement Ord. Corp
Attn: Customer Service
P.O. Box 336
Ridgway, PA   15853
FAX NUMBER: 814-772-2329

Lebeau-Courally

Midwest Gun Sport
Attn: Customer Service
1108 Herbert Drive
Zebulon, NC   27597

Leforgeron

Midwest Gun Sport
Attn: Customer Service
1108 Herbert Drive
Zebulon, NC   27597

Ljutic Industries, Inc.

Attn: Customer Service
P.O. Box 2117
Yakima, WA   98907

Llama Pistols

Stoeger Industries
Attn: Customer Service
55 Ruta Court
S. Hackensack, NJ   07606
FAX NUMBER: 201-440-2707

Lorcin

Lorcin Eng. Co., Inc.
Attn: Customer Service
6471 Mission Blvd.
Riverside, CA   92509
FAX NUMBER: 714-683-8029

Luger

K.D.F., Inc.
Attn: Customer Service
2485 Highway 46 North
Seguin, TX   78155
FAX NUMBER: 512-379-5420

M.O.A. Corporation

M.O.A. Corporation
Attn: Customer Service
P.O. Box 185
Dayton, OH   45404

MK Arms Inc.

MK Arms, Inc.
Attn: Customer Service
P.O. Box 16411
Irvine, CA   92713

MKE

Mandall Shooting Supplies
Attn: Customer Service
3616 N. Scottsdale Rd.
Scottsdale, AZ   85251

Magnum Research Inc.

Magnum Research Inc.
Attn: Customer Service
P.O. Box 32221
Minneapolis, MN   55432
FAX NUMBER: 612-574-0109

Malin, F.E.

Cape Horn Outfitters
Attn: Customer Service
212 E. Morehead Street
Charlotte, NC   28202

Manurhin Handguns

Atlantic Bus. Org., Inc.
Attn: Customer Service
845 Third Ave. Suite 1400
New York, NY   10022
FAX NUMBER: 212-593-1318

Marlin firearms

Marlin Firearms Co.
Attn: Customer Service
100 Kenna Drive
North Haven, CT   06473
FAX NUMBER: 203-234-7991

Marocchi

Marocchi U.S.A.
Attn: Customer Service
5939 W. 66th St.
Chicago, IL   60638

Sile Distributors, Inc.
Attn: Customer Service
7 Centre Market Place
New York, NY   10013
FAX NUMBER: 212-925-3149

Mauser-Werke

K.D.F., Inc.
Attn: Customer Service
2485 Highway 46 North
Seguin, TX   78155
FAX NUMBER: 512-379-5420

Mauser-Werke USA
Attn: Customer Service
242 Hilltop Drive
Sequin, TX   78155

Maverick

Maverick Arms, Inc.
Attn: Customer Service
P.O. Box 586
Eagle Pass, TX   78853
FAX NUMBER: 512-773-8862

McMillan & Co. Inc.

G. McMillan & Co., Inc.
Attn: Customer Service
21438 N. 7th Ave. Suite E
Phoenix, AZ   85027

McMillan/Wiseman

McMillan/Wiseman
Attn: Customer Service
P.O. Box 3427
Bryan, TX   77805
FAX NUMBER: 409-822-3396

Merkel & Gebruder

Armes De Chasse
Attn: Customer Service
P.O. Box No. 827
Chadds Ford, PA   19317

Mitchell

Mitchell Arms, Inc.
Attn: Customer Service
3411 Lake Center Drive
Santa Ana, CA   92704
FAX NUMBER: 714-957-5732

Morini

Osborne's Distributors
Attn: Customer Service
P.O. Box 408
Cheboygan, MI   49721

Mossberg

O.F. Mossberg & Sons, Inc
Attn: Customer Service
7 Grasso Ave.
North Haven, CT   06473
FAX NUMBER: 203-288-2404

TRADEMARK INDEX, cont.

Musgrave Mfg. & Dist. (Pty) Ltd.

Attn: Customer Service
P.O. Box 183 Bloemfontein 9300
Jagersfontein Road
Republic of SOUTH AFRICA

Navy Arms Co.

Navy Arms Company
Attn: Customer Service
689 Bergen Blvd.
Ridgefield, NJ   07657
FAX NUMBER: 201-945-6859

New England Firearms Co., Inc.

New England Firearms Co.
Attn: Customer Service
Industrial Rowe
Gardner, MA   01440
FAX NUMBER: 508-632-2300

Norinco

China Sports, Inc.
Attn: Customer Service
4403 Westgrove
Dallas, TX   75248

North American Arms

North American Arms
Attn: Customer Service
P.O. Box 707   .
Spanish Fork, UT   84660
FAX NUMBER: 801-798-9418

Olympic Arms, Inc.

Olympic Arms, Inc.
Attn: Customer Service
624 Old Pacific Hwy. S.E.
Olympia, WA   98503
FAX NUMBER: 206-491-3447

Omega - Geneseo, Il.

Springfield Armory, Inc.
Attn: Customer Service
420 W. Main St.
Geneseo, IL   61254

Omega - Harrisburg, Pa.

Kassnar Imports, Inc.
Attn: Customer Service
P.O. Box 6097
Harrisburg, PA   17112
FAX NUMBER: 717-652-5514

Orvis

Attn: Customer Service
5848 Westheimer
Houston, TX   77057

P.S.M.G. Gun Co.

P.S.M.G. Gun Company
Attn: Customer Service
10 Park Avenue
Arlington, MA   02174
FAX NUMBER: 617-648-7482

Para-Ordnance

Para-Ordnance Mfg., Inc.
Attn: Customer Service
3411 McNicoll Avenue #14
Scarborough, Ontario
CANADA M1V 2V6
FAX NUMBER: 416-297-1289

Pardini

Fiocchi of America, Inc.
Attn: Customer Service
Rt. 2, Box 90-8
Ozark, MO   65721
FAX NUMBER: 417-725-1039

Parker Reproductions

Parker Reproduction Div.
Attn: Customer Service
17th & S. Hall Street
Webb City, MO   64870
FAX NUMBER: 201-469-9692

Parker-Hale Ltd.

Precision Sports
Attn: Customer Service
P.O. Box 708,
Cortland, NY   13045
FAX NUMBER: 607-753-8835

Perazzi

Perazzi USA, Inc.
Attn: Customer Service
1207 South Shamrock
Monrovia, CA   91016
FAX NUMBER: 818-303-2081

Piotti

Wlm. Larkin Moore & Co.
Attn: Customer Service
31360 Via Colinas, Se 109
Westlake Village, CA   91361

Poly Technologies, Inc.

PTK International, Inc.
Attn: Customer Service
2814 New Spring Rd., 340
Atlanta, GA   30339
FAX NUMBER: 404-438-7839

Prinz

Helmut Hofmann Inc.
Attn: Customer Service
P.O. Box 285
Placitas, NM   87043

RWS

Dynamit Nobel of America
Attn: Customer Service
105 Stonehurst Ct.
Northvale, NJ   07647

Ravell

Ravell
Attn: Customer Service
Diputacion, 289
Barcelona   SPAIN 08009

Raven Arms

Raven Arms
Attn: Customer Service
1300 Bixby Drive
Industry, CA   91745

Remington

Remington Arms Co., Inc.
Attn: Customer Service
1007 Market St.
Wilmington, DE   19898
FAX NUMBER: 302-744-7179

Renette, Gastine

Attn: Customer Service
39 Avenue Franklin D. Roosevelt
Paris   FRANCE 75008

Ripamonti Rifles

Morton's, Ltd.
Attn: Customer Service
156 Trade Street
Lexington, KY   40510
FAX NUMBER: 606-252-1399

Ripamonti Shotguns

Attn: Customer Service
8139 San Benito Way
Dallas, TX   75218

Rizzini

Wlm. Larkin Moore & Co.
Attn: Customer Service
31360 Via Colinas, SE 109
Westlake Village, CA   91361

Rossi

Interarms
Attn: Customer Service
Number Ten Prince Street
Alexandria, VA   22313
FAX NUMBER: 703-549-7826

SKB Arms Co.

The New SKB Co., U.S.A.
Attn: Customer Service
Rd. #8, Box 145
Manhein, PA   17545
FAX NUMBER: 717-664-3733

SSK Industries

Attn: Customer Service
Rt. 1 Della Drive
Bloomingdale, OH   43910

S.W.D., Inc.

Attn: Customer Service
1872 Marietta Blvd.
Atlanta, GA   30318
FAX NUMBER: 404-432-6536

Sako

Stoeger Industries
Attn: Customer Service
55 Ruth Court
S. Hackensack, NJ   07606
FAX NUMBER: 201-440-2707

Sam Inc.

Sam Incorporated
Attn: Customer Service
P.O. Box 7087
Reston, VA   22091

Sardius

Armscorp of America
Attn: Customer Service
4424 John Avenue
Baltimore, MD   21227
FAX NUMBER: 301-247-6205

Sauer, J.P.

Sigarms, Inc.
Attn: Customer Service
470 Spring Park Place Unit 900
Herndon, VA   22070
FAX NUMBER: 703-481-6572

Savage

Savage Industries, Inc.
Attn: Customer Service
Springdale Road
Westfield, MA   01085
FAX NUMBER: 413-562-1145

Scott, W.C.

Holland & Holland Ltd.
Attn: Customer Service
33 Bruton Street
London   ENGLAND W1X 8J

Sedco

Sedco Industries, Inc.
Attn: Customer Service
506 N. Spring St., Unit E
Lake Elsinore, CA   92330

Seecamp, L.W.C.

Attn: Customer Service
301 Brewster Road
Milford, CT   06460

Semmerling

American Derringer Corp.
Attn: Customer Service
127 N. Lacy Drive
Waco, TX   76705

Shiloh Rifle Mfg. Co., Inc.

Attn: Customer Service
P.O. Box 279, Ind. Park
Big Timber, MT   59011

Sig Sauer

Sigarms, Inc.
Attn: Customer Service
470 Spring Park Place Unit 900
Herndon, VA   22070
FAX NUMBER: 703-481-6572

Smith & Wesson

Smith & Wesson
Attn: Customer Service
P.O. Box 2208
Springfield, MA   01102-2208
FAX NUMBER: 413-781-5304

Snake Charmer

Sporting Arms Mfg. Inc.
Attn: Customer Service
P.O. Box 191
Littlefield, TX   79339

Springfield Armory, Inc.

Attn: Customer Service
420 W. Main Street
Geneseo, IL   61254

Star

Interarms
Attn: Customer Service
Number Ten Prince Street
Alexandria, VA   22313
FAX NUMBER: 703-549-7826

Steel City Arms, Inc.
Attn: Customer Service
1883 Main Street
Pittsburgh, PA   15215

Sterling Armament, Ltd.

Cassi Inc.
Attn: Customer Service
4320 N. Parkdrive
Colorado Springs, CO   80907

Stevens, J., Arms Company

Savage Industries, Inc.
Attn: Customer Service
Springdale Road
Westfield, MA   01085
FAX NUMBER: 413-562-1145

Steyr Mannlicher

Guns South, Inc.
Attn: Customer Service
P.O. Box 129
Trussville, AL   35173

Street Sweeper

Sales of Georgia
Attn: Customer Service
P.O. Box 94168
Atlanta, GA   30318
FAX NUMBER: 404-350-9714

Sturm, Ruger & Co.

Attn: Customer Service
35 Lacey Place
Southport, CT   06490
FAX NUMBER: 203-254-2195

Sundance Industries

Attn: Customer Service
8216 Lankershim Blvd. #12-1/2
North Hollywood, CA   91605

Taurus Int'l. Mfg., Inc.

Attn: Customer Service
4563 S.W. 71st Avenue
Miami, FL   33155
FAX NUMBER: 305-661-8187

TRADEMARK INDEX, cont.

Texas Longhorn Arms, Inc.

Attn: Customer Service
P.O. Box 703
Richmond, TX 77469

Thompson/Center Arms

Attn: Customer Service
P.O. Box 5002
Rochester, NH 03867
FAX NUMBER: 603-332-5133

Tikka

Stoeger Industries
Attn: Customer Service
55 Ruta Court
S. Hackensack, NJ 07606
FAX NUMBER: 201-440-2707

U.S.A.S.

Gilbert Equipment Co., Inc.
Attn: Customer Service
P.O. Box 11047
Chickasaw, AL 36611

Uberti

Attn: Customer Service
41 Church Street
New Milford, CT 06776

Ultra Light Arms

Attn: Customer Service
P.O. Box 1270
Granville, WV 26534

U.S. Historical Society

Attn: Customer Service
First & Main Streets
Richmond, VA 23219

Uzi

Action Arms Ltd.
Attn: Customer Service
P.O. Box 9573
Philadelphia, PA 19124-0573
FAX NUMBER: 215-533-2188

Valmet

Stoeger Industries
Attn: Customer Service
55 Ruta Court
S. Hackensack, NJ 07606
FAX NUMBER: 201-440-2707

Varner Sporting Arms, Co.

Attn: Customer Service
1004F Cobb Parkway N.E.
Marietta, GA 30062

Victory Arms Co. Ltd.

Magnum Research Inc.
Attn: Customer Service
P.O. Box 32221
Minneapolis, MN 55432
FAX NUMBER: 612-574-0109

Walther

Interarms
Attn: Customer Service
Number Ten Prince Street
Alexandria, VA 22313
FAX NUMBER: 703-549-7826

Weatherby Inc.

Attn: Customer Service
2781 Firestone Blvd.
South Gate, CA 90280
FAX NUMBER: 213-569-5025

Weaver Arms Corp.

Attn: Customer Service
Monarch Court
6265 Greenwich Drive
Suite 201
San Diego, CA   92122
FAX NUMBER: 619-452-2064

Weihrauch, Hans-Hermann

Beeman Precision Arms
Attn: Customer Service
3440 Airway Drive
Santa Rosa, CA   95401
FAX NUMBER: 707-578-4751

Wesson, Dan, Arms

Attn: Customer Service
293 Main Street
Monson, MA   01057
FAX NUMBER: 413-267-3601

Westley Richards & Co. Ltd.

Attn: Customer Service
40 Grange Road Bournbrook
Birmingham   ENGLAND B29 6A

Wichita Arms, Inc.

Attn: Customer Service
P.O. Box 11371
Wichita, KS   67211

Wildey Inc.

Attn: Customer Service
P.O. Box 475
Brookfield, CT   06804
FAX NUMBER: 203-354-7759

Winchester

U.S. Repeating Arms Co.
Attn: Customer Service
275 Winchester Ave.
New Haven, CT   06511
FAX NUMBER: 203-789-5512

Winchester/Olin Models 101 & 23 only

Attn: Customer Service
Shamrock Street
East Alton, IL   62024
FAX NUMBER: 618-258-3393

Zanardini

Morton's, Ltd.
Attn: Customer Service
156 Trade Street
Lexington, KY   40510
FAX NUMBER: 606-252-1399

Zanotti, Fabio

New England Arms Co.
Attn: Customer Service
Kittery Point, ME   03905

Zoli, Antonio

Antonio Zoli, U.S.A., Inc.
Attn: Customer Service
P.O. Box 9160
Fort Wayne, IN   46896
FAX NUMBER: 219-447-5772

NOTES

Firearms Inventory Record

1. Type of firearm: Pistol _____ Rifle _____ Shotgun _____ Antique _____

   Manufacturer _____ Model _____

   Ser. No. _____ Cal./ga. _____ Barrel length _____ in./cm.

   Overall condition _____ Remarks _____

   _____

   Date purchased _____ Purchase price $ _____ Purchased from _____

   Sell date _____ Sell price $ _____ Sold to _____

2. Type of firearm: Pistol _____ Rifle _____ Shotgun _____ Antique _____

   Manufacturer _____ Model _____

   Ser. No. _____ Cal./ga. _____ Barrel length _____ in./cm.

   Overall condition _____ Remarks _____

   _____

   Date purchased _____ Purchase price $ _____ Purchased from _____

   Sell date _____ Sell price $ _____ Sold to _____

3. Type of firearm: Pistol _____ Rifle _____ Shotgun _____ Antique _____

   Manufacturer _____ Model _____

   Ser. No. _____ Cal./ga. _____ Barrel length _____ in./cm.

   Overall condition _____ Remarks _____

   _____

   Date purchased _____ Purchase price $ _____ Purchased from _____

   Sell date _____ Sell price $ _____ Sold to _____

4. Type of firearm: Pistol _____ Rifle _____ Shotgun _____ Antique _____

   Manufacturer _____ Model _____

   Ser. No. _____ Cal./ga. _____ Barrel length _____ in./cm.

   Overall condition _____ Remarks _____

   _____

   Date purchased _____ Purchase price $ _____ Purchased from _____

   Sell date _____ Sell price $ _____ Sold to _____

5. Type of firearm: Pistol _____ Rifle _____ Shotgun _____ Antique _____

Manufacturer _____ Model _____

Ser. No. _____ Cal./ga. _____ Barrel length _____ in./cm.

Overall condition _____ Remarks _____

_____

Date purchased _____ Purchase price $ _____ Purchased from _____

Sell date _____ Sell price $ _____ Sold to _____

6. Type of firearm: Pistol _____ Rifle _____ Shotgun _____ Antique _____

Manufacturer _____ Model _____

Ser. No. _____ Cal./ga. _____ Barrel length _____ in./cm.

Overall condition _____ Remarks _____

_____

Date purchased _____ Purchase price $ _____ Purchased from _____

Sell date _____ Sell price $ _____ Sold to _____

7. Type of firearm: Pistol _____ Rifle _____ Shotgun _____ Antique _____

Manufacturer _____ Model _____

Ser. No. _____ Cal./ga. _____ Barrel length _____ in./cm.

Overall condition _____ Remarks _____

_____

Date purchased _____ Purchase price $ _____ Purchased from _____

Sell date _____ Sell price $ _____ Sold to _____

8. Type of firearm: Pistol _____ Rifle _____ Shotgun _____ Antique _____

Manufacturer _____ Model _____

Ser. No. _____ Cal./ga. _____ Barrel length _____ in./cm.

Overall condition _____ Remarks _____

_____

Date purchased _____ Purchase price $ _____ Purchased from _____

Sell date _____ Sell price $ _____ Sold to _____

9. Type of firearm: Pistol _____ Rifle _____ Shotgun _____ Antique _____

   Manufacturer _____ Model _____

   Ser. No. _____ Cal./ga. _____ Barrel length _____ in./cm.

   Overall condition _____ Remarks _____

   _____

   Date purchased _____ Purchase price $ _____ Purchased from _____

   Sell date _____ Sell price $ _____ Sold to _____

10. Type of firearm: Pistol _____ Rifle _____ Shotgun _____ Antique _____

    Manufacturer _____ Model _____

    Ser. No. _____ Cal./ga. _____ Barrel length _____ in./cm.

    Overall condition _____ Remarks _____

    _____

    Date purchased _____ Purchase price $ _____ Purchased from _____

    Sell date _____ Sell price $ _____ Sold to _____

11. Type of firearm: Pistol _____ Rifle _____ Shotgun _____ Antique _____

    Manufacturer _____ Model _____

    Ser. No. _____ Cal./ga. _____ Barrel length _____ in./cm.

    Overall condition _____ Remarks _____

    _____

    Date purchased _____ Purchase price $ _____ Purchased from _____

    Sell date _____ Sell price $ _____ Sold to _____

12. Type of firearm: Pistol _____ Rifle _____ Shotgun _____ Antique _____

    Manufacturer _____ Model _____

    Ser. No. _____ Cal./ga. _____ Barrel length _____ in./cm.

    Overall condition _____ Remarks _____

    _____

    Date purchased _____ Purchase price $ _____ Purchased from _____

    Sell date _____ Sell price $ _____ Sold to _____

13. Type of firearm: Pistol _____ Rifle _____ Shotgun _____ Antique _____

Manufacturer _____ Model _____

Ser. No. _____ Cal./ga. _____ Barrel length _____ in./cm.

Overall condition _____ Remarks _____

_____

Date purchased _____ Purchase price $ _____ Purchased from _____

Sell date _____ Sell price $ _____ Sold to _____

14. Type of firearm: Pistol _____ Rifle _____ Shotgun _____ Antique _____

Manufacturer _____ Model _____

Ser. No. _____ Cal./ga. _____ Barrel length _____ in./cm.

Overall condition _____ Remarks _____

_____

Date purchased _____ Purchase price $ _____ Purchased from _____

Sell date _____ Sell price $ _____ Sold to _____

15. Type of firearm: Pistol _____ Rifle _____ Shotgun _____ Antique _____

Manufacturer _____ Model _____

Ser. No. _____ Cal./ga. _____ Barrel length _____ in./cm.

Overall condition _____ Remarks _____

_____

Date purchased _____ Purchase price $ _____ Purchased from _____

Sell date _____ Sell price $ _____ Sold to _____

16. Type of firearm: Pistol _____ Rifle _____ Shotgun _____ Antique _____

Manufacturer _____ Model _____

Ser. No. _____ Cal./ga. _____ Barrel length _____ in./cm.

Overall condition _____ Remarks _____

_____

Date purchased _____ Purchase price $ _____ Purchased from _____

Sell date _____ Sell price $ _____ Sold to _____

17. Type of firearm: Pistol _____ Rifle _____ Shotgun _____ Antique _____

Manufacturer _____ Model _____

Ser. No. _____ Cal./ga. _____ Barrel length _____ in./cm.

Overall condition _____ Remarks _____

_____

Date purchased _____ Purchase price $ _____ Purchased from _____

Sell date _____ Sell price $ _____ Sold to _____

18. Type of firearm: Pistol _____ Rifle _____ Shotgun _____ Antique _____

Manufacturer _____ Model _____

Ser. No. _____ Cal./ga. _____ Barrel length _____ in./cm.

Overall condition _____ Remarks _____

_____

Date purchased _____ Purchase price $ _____ Purchased from _____

Sell date _____ Sell price $ _____ Sold to _____

19. Type of firearm: Pistol _____ Rifle _____ Shotgun _____ Antique _____

Manufacturer _____ Model _____

Ser. No. _____ Cal./ga. _____ Barrel length _____ in./cm.

Overall condition _____ Remarks _____

_____

Date purchased _____ Purchase price $ _____ Purchased from _____

Sell date _____ Sell price $ _____ Sold to _____

20. Type of firearm: Pistol _____ Rifle _____ Shotgun _____ Antique _____

Manufacturer _____ Model _____

Ser. No. _____ Cal./ga. _____ Barrel length _____ in./cm.

Overall condition _____ Remarks _____

_____

Date purchased _____ Purchase price $ _____ Purchased from _____

Sell date _____ Sell price $ _____ Sold to _____

21. Type of firearm: Pistol _____ Rifle _____ Shotgun _____ Antique _____

Manufacturer _____ Model _____

Ser. No. _____ Cal./ga. _____ Barrel length _____ in./cm.

Overall condition _____ Remarks _____

_____

Date purchased _____ Purchase price $ _____ Purchased from _____

Sell date _____ Sell price $ _____ Sold to _____

22. Type of firearm: Pistol _____ Rifle _____ Shotgun _____ Antique _____

Manufacturer _____ Model _____

Ser. No. _____ Cal./ga. _____ Barrel length _____ in./cm.

Overall condition _____ Remarks _____

_____

Date purchased _____ Purchase price $ _____ Purchased from _____

Sell date _____ Sell price $ _____ Sold to _____

23. Type of firearm: Pistol _____ Rifle _____ Shotgun _____ Antique _____

Manufacturer _____ Model _____

Ser. No. _____ Cal./ga. _____ Barrel length _____ in./cm.

Overall condition _____ Remarks _____

_____

Date purchased _____ Purchase price $ _____ Purchased from _____

Sell date _____ Sell price $ _____ Sold to _____

24. Type of firearm: Pistol _____ Rifle _____ Shotgun _____ Antique _____

Manufacturer _____ Model _____

Ser. No. _____ Cal./ga. _____ Barrel length _____ in./cm.

Overall condition _____ Remarks _____

_____

Date purchased _____ Purchase price $ _____ Purchased from _____

Sell date _____ Sell price $ _____ Sold to _____

25. Type of firearm: Pistol _____ Rifle _____ Shotgun _____ Antique _____

Manufacturer _____ Model _____

Ser. No. _____ Cal./ga. _____ Barrel length _____ in./cm.

Overall condition _____ Remarks _____

_____

Date purchased _____ Purchase price $ _____ Purchased from _____

Sell date _____ Sell price $ _____ Sold to _____

26. Type of firearm: Pistol _____ Rifle _____ Shotgun _____ Antique _____

Manufacturer _____ Model _____

Ser. No. _____ Cal./ga. _____ Barrel length _____ in./cm.

Overall condition _____ Remarks _____

_____

Date purchased _____ Purchase price $ _____ Purchased from _____

Sell date _____ Sell price $ _____ Sold to _____

27. Type of firearm: Pistol _____ Rifle _____ Shotgun _____ Antique _____

Manufacturer _____ Model _____

Ser. No. _____ Cal./ga. _____ Barrel length _____ in./cm.

Overall condition _____ Remarks _____

_____

Date purchased _____ Purchase price $ _____ Purchased from _____

Sell date _____ Sell price $ _____ Sold to _____

28. Type of firearm: Pistol _____ Rifle _____ Shotgun _____ Antique _____

Manufacturer _____ Model _____

Ser. No. _____ Cal./ga. _____ Barrel length _____ in./cm.

Overall condition _____ Remarks _____

_____

Date purchased _____ Purchase price $ _____ Purchased from _____

Sell date _____ Sell price $ _____ Sold to _____

29. Type of firearm: Pistol _____ Rifle _____ Shotgun _____ Antique _____

Manufacturer _____ Model _____

Ser. No. _____ Cal./ga. _____ Barrel length _____ in./cm.

Overall condition _____ Remarks _____

_____

Date purchased _____ Purchase price $ _____ Purchased from _____

Sell date _____ Sell price $ _____ Sold to _____

30. Type of firearm: Pistol _____ Rifle _____ Shotgun _____ Antique _____

Manufacturer _____ Model _____

Ser. No. _____ Cal./ga. _____ Barrel length _____ in./cm.

Overall condition _____ Remarks _____

_____

Date purchased _____ Purchase price $ _____ Purchased from _____

Sell date _____ Sell price $ _____ Sold to _____

31. Type of firearm: Pistol _____ Rifle _____ Shotgun _____ Antique _____

Manufacturer _____ Model _____

Ser. No. _____ Cal./ga. _____ Barrel length _____ in./cm.

Overall condition _____ Remarks _____

_____

Date purchased _____ Purchase price $ _____ Purchased from _____

Sell date _____ Sell price $ _____ Sold to _____

32. Type of firearm: Pistol _____ Rifle _____ Shotgun _____ Antique _____

Manufacturer _____ Model _____

Ser. No. _____ Cal./ga. _____ Barrel length _____ in./cm.

Overall condition _____ Remarks _____

_____

Date purchased _____ Purchase price $ _____ Purchased from _____

Sell date _____ Sell price $ _____ Sold to _____

33. Type of firearm: Pistol _____ Rifle _____ Shotgun _____ Antique _____

Manufacturer _____ Model _____

Ser. No. _____ Cal./ga. _____ Barrel length _____ in./cm.

Overall condition _____ Remarks _____

_____

Date purchased _____ Purchase price $ _____ Purchased from _____

Sell date _____ Sell price $ _____ Sold to _____

34. Type of firearm: Pistol _____ Rifle _____ Shotgun _____ Antique _____

Manufacturer _____ Model _____

Ser. No. _____ Cal./ga. _____ Barrel length _____ in./cm.

Overall condition _____ Remarks _____

_____

Date purchased _____ Purchase price $ _____ Purchased from _____

Sell date _____ Sell price $ _____ Sold to _____

35. Type of firearm: Pistol _____ Rifle _____ Shotgun _____ Antique _____

Manufacturer _____ Model _____

Ser. No. _____ Cal./ga. _____ Barrel length _____ in./cm.

Overall condition _____ Remarks _____

_____

Date purchased _____ Purchase price $ _____ Purchased from _____

Sell date _____ Sell price $ _____ Sold to _____

36. Type of firearm: Pistol _____ Rifle _____ Shotgun _____ Antique _____

Manufacturer _____ Model _____

Ser. No. _____ Cal./ga. _____ Barrel length _____ in./cm.

Overall condition _____ Remarks _____

_____

Date purchased _____ Purchase price $ _____ Purchased from _____

Sell date _____ Sell price $ _____ Sold to _____

37. Type of firearm: Pistol _____ Rifle _____ Shotgun _____ Antique _____

Manufacturer _____ Model _____

Ser. No. _____ Cal./ga. _____ Barrel length _____ in./cm.

Overall condition _____ Remarks _____

_____

Date purchased _____ Purchase price $ _____ Purchased from _____

Sell date _____ Sell price $ _____ Sold to _____

38. Type of firearm: Pistol _____ Rifle _____ Shotgun _____ Antique _____

Manufacturer _____ Model _____

Ser. No. _____ Cal./ga. _____ Barrel length _____ in./cm.

Overall condition _____ Remarks _____

_____

Date purchased _____ Purchase price $ _____ Purchased from _____

Sell date _____ Sell price $ _____ Sold to _____

39. Type of firearm: Pistol _____ Rifle _____ Shotgun _____ Antique _____

Manufacturer _____ Model _____

Ser. No. _____ Cal./ga. _____ Barrel length _____ in./cm.

Overall condition _____ Remarks _____

_____

Date purchased _____ Purchase price $ _____ Purchased from _____

Sell date _____ Sell price $ _____ Sold to _____

40. Type of firearm: Pistol _____ Rifle _____ Shotgun _____ Antique _____

Manufacturer _____ Model _____

Ser. No. _____ Cal./ga. _____ Barrel length _____ in./cm.

Overall condition _____ Remarks _____

_____

Date purchased _____ Purchase price $ _____ Purchased from _____

Sell date _____ Sell price $ _____ Sold to _____

41. Type of firearm: Pistol _____ Rifle _____ Shotgun _____ Antique _____

Manufacturer _____ Model _____

Ser. No. _____ Cal./ga. _____ Barrel length _____ in./cm.

Overall condition _____ Remarks _____

_____

Date purchased _____ Purchase price $ _____ Purchased from _____

Sell date _____ Sell price $ _____ Sold to _____

42. Type of firearm: Pistol _____ Rifle _____ Shotgun _____ Antique _____

Manufacturer _____ Model _____

Ser. No. _____ Cal./ga. _____ Barrel length _____ in./cm.

Overall condition _____ Remarks _____

_____

Date purchased _____ Purchase price $ _____ Purchased from _____

Sell date _____ Sell price $ _____ Sold to _____

43. Type of firearm: Pistol _____ Rifle _____ Shotgun _____ Antique _____

Manufacturer _____ Model _____

Ser. No. _____ Cal./ga. _____ Barrel length _____ in./cm.

Overall condition _____ Remarks _____

_____

Date purchased _____ Purchase price $ _____ Purchased from _____

Sell date _____ Sell price $ _____ Sold to _____

44. Type of firearm: Pistol _____ Rifle _____ Shotgun _____ Antique _____

Manufacturer _____ Model _____

Ser. No. _____ Cal./ga. _____ Barrel length _____ in./cm.

Overall condition _____ Remarks _____

_____

Date purchased _____ Purchase price $ _____ Purchased from _____

Sell date _____ Sell price $ _____ Sold to _____

45. Type of firearm: Pistol _____ Rifle _____ Shotgun _____ Antique _____

Manufacturer _____ Model _____

Ser. No. _____ Cal./ga. _____ Barrel length _____ in./cm.

Overall condition _____ Remarks _____

_____

Date purchased _____ Purchase price $ _____ Purchased from _____

Sell date _____ Sell price $ _____ Sold to _____

46. Type of firearm: Pistol _____ Rifle _____ Shotgun _____ Antique _____

Manufacturer _____ Model _____

Ser. No. _____ Cal./ga. _____ Barrel length _____ in./cm.

Overall condition _____ Remarks _____

_____

Date purchased _____ Purchase price $ _____ Purchased from _____

Sell date _____ Sell price $ _____ Sold to _____

47. Type of firearm: Pistol _____ Rifle _____ Shotgun _____ Antique _____

Manufacturer _____ Model _____

Ser. No. _____ Cal./ga. _____ Barrel length _____ in./cm.

Overall condition _____ Remarks _____

_____

Date purchased _____ Purchase price $ _____ Purchased from _____

Sell date _____ Sell price $ _____ Sold to _____

48. Type of firearm: Pistol _____ Rifle _____ Shotgun _____ Antique _____

Manufacturer _____ Model _____

Ser. No. _____ Cal./ga. _____ Barrel length _____ in./cm.

Overall condition _____ Remarks _____

_____

Date purchased _____ Purchase price $ _____ Purchased from _____

Sell date _____ Sell price $ _____ Sold to _____

49. Type of firearm: Pistol _____ Rifle _____ Shotgun _____ Antique _____

Manufacturer _____ Model _____

Ser. No. _____ Cal./ga. _____ Barrel length _____ in./cm.

Overall condition _____ Remarks _____

_____

Date purchased _____ Purchase price $ _____ Purchased from _____

Sell date _____ Sell price $ _____ Sold to _____

50. Type of firearm: Pistol _____ Rifle _____ Shotgun _____ Antique _____

Manufacturer _____ Model _____

Ser. No. _____ Cal./ga. _____ Barrel length _____ in./cm.

Overall condition _____ Remarks _____

_____

Date purchased _____ Purchase price $ _____ Purchased from _____

Sell date _____ Sell price $ _____ Sold to _____

51. Type of firearm: Pistol _____ Rifle _____ Shotgun _____ Antique _____

Manufacturer _____ Model _____

Ser. No. _____ Cal./ga. _____ Barrel length _____ in./cm.

Overall condition _____ Remarks _____

_____

Date purchased _____ Purchase price $ _____ Purchased from _____

Sell date _____ Sell price $ _____ Sold to _____

52. Type of firearm: Pistol _____ Rifle _____ Shotgun _____ Antique _____

Manufacturer _____ Model _____

Ser. No. _____ Cal./ga. _____ Barrel length _____ in./cm.

Overall condition _____ Remarks _____

_____

Date purchased _____ Purchase price $ _____ Purchased from _____

Sell date _____ Sell price $ _____ Sold to _____

NOTES

Index of Manufacturers

Index of Manufacturers

Index of Manufacturers

Index of Manufacturers

Index of Manufacturers

Index of Manufacturers